MR. MAUGHAM HIMSELF

MR.
MAUGHAM
HIMSELF

by

W. SOMERSET
MAUGHAM

Selected by John Beecroft

DOUBLEDAY & COMPANY, INC.
Garden City, New York

Library of Congress Catalog Card Number: 54–11156

Contents

Introduction

WHY MR. MAUGHAM HIMSELF?

A FEW DAYS after Somerset Maugham's eightieth birthday I was lunching with Milton Runyon of Doubleday. We talked about the tributes Mr. Maugham had received on his anniversary, how well deserved they were and what pleasure that acclaim must have given him. I said it was time a collection of Maugham's writings should be made which would represent him at his best. Mr. Runyon asked what I thought should be included in a definitive Maugham anthology. Because I have been an admirer of Maugham's writing ever since I was able to read, I knew what I would like to see in such a book: two or three novels, several short stories, maybe a play, the autobiographical pieces, some essays and parts of his famous introductions. About a week after that luncheon, Ken McCormick, Mr. Maugham's editor, phoned me. He liked the idea and asked me to give him my proposed list of contents.

We discussed the titles I wanted to include and everything seemed to be settled most satisfactorily. But we found our enthusiasm had been so great that we had forgotten to be practical. A volume with that much material would be too heavy to lift.

Some titles would have to be eliminated. There were very few I wanted to drop from my original list and there seemed little point in compiling such a volume within such mechanical limitations. Mr. Maugham had already made a fine anthology of his work in *The Maugham Reader;* another could only prove to be a needless repetition —with some variations. Regretfully, I gave up the project of an anthology representing what I considered the best of Maugham's work.

Mr. Maugham's books have been on my bedside table for years. One night, shortly after making this reluctant decision, I found this question in his admirable introduction to *Tellers of Tales:* "For what in the long run has the writer to give you?" Mr. Maugham's answer was: "Himself." This gave me a new plan for another kind of book and, incidentally, its title. The new book was not designed to be representative of Maugham's writings; instead, it would represent Somerset Maugham, himself, in the way he has revealed his personality and his life through his writings. Certainly to be included would be *Of Human Bondage*—a novel which Mr. Maugham describes as being not autobiography, but autobiographical; *The Summing Up*

ix

was, of course, on my list, for in that he speaks with utter frankness about his innermost thoughts. The play I had intended to include, I was content to omit; but there would be shorter pieces representing him in different moods. The whole was to be a kind of composite autobiography, since Mr. Maugham has not yet written one himself.

Mr. Maugham has always been a superb storyteller. He has repeatedly stated that the purpose of a story is to entertain. He has prided himself, not on the art of his writing, but on his craftsmanship; and, in being the best craftsman he could, he became a great artist. His oft-repeated formula that a story should have "a beginning, a middle and an end" together with his belief that art should communicate, has won for him hundreds of thousands of devoted readers all over the world.

Anyone who has not read Maugham's short stories, now collected in the two volumes *East and West* and *The World Over*, has missed a pleasure that can be savored again and again. Though *Of Human Bondage* is generally regarded as his best novel, Mr. Maugham himself votes for *Cakes and Ale*. Three of my favorites are *The Moon and Sixpence, Christmas Holiday* and *The Painted Veil*.

It makes me happy to remember the hours I spent helping to refinish the desk on which Mr. Maugham wrote *The Razor's Edge*, a novel which was a huge success and was made into an absorbing movie. Anyone who liked *The Summing Up* should read *A Writer's Notebook*; I have included a portion of this because it reveals the author's thoughts which are haunting in their intensity, and we know that Mr. Maugham would not have allowed them to be published if they did not reflect his true feelings.

It is pointless to write more about Mr. Maugham when he is so well able to speak for himself. Included in this volume are the writings which bring him close to his readers. In choosing the autobiographical writings, I feel I have been able to present a better book than was originally planned and, at the same time, the purpose of the proposed volume has been accomplished. Mr. Maugham is still represented at his best.

JOHN BEECROFT

June 10, 1954
Glen Cove, Long Island
New York

Of Human Bondage

FOREWORD

THIS is a very long novel and I am ashamed to make it longer by writing a preface to it. An author is probably the last person who can write fitly about his own work. In this connection an instructive story is told by Roger Martin du Gard, a distinguished French novelist, about Marcel Proust. Proust wanted a certain French periodical to publish an important article on his great novel and thinking that no one could write it better than he, sat down and wrote it himself. Then he asked a young friend of his, a man of letters, to put his name to it and take it to the editor. This the young man did, but after a few days the editor sent for him. "I must refuse your article," he told him. "Marcel Proust would never forgive me if I printed a criticism of his work that was so perfunctory and so unsympathetic." Though authors are touchy about their productions and inclined to resent unfavourable criticism they are seldom self-satisfied. They are miserably conscious how far the work on which they have spent much time and trouble comes short of their conception and when they consider it they are much more vexed with their failure to express this in its completeness

than pleased with the passages here and there that they can regard with complacency. Their aim is perfection and they are wretchedly aware that they have not attained it.

I will say nothing then about my book itself, but will content myself with telling the reader of these lines how a novel that has now had a fairly long life, as novels go, came to be written; and if it does not interest him I ask him to forgive me. I wrote it first when, at the age of twenty-three, having taken my medical degrees after five years at St. Thomas's Hospital, I went to Seville determined to earn my living as a writer. The manuscript of the book I wrote then still exists, but I have not looked at it since I corrected the typescript and I have no doubt that it is very immature. I sent it to Fisher Unwin, who had published my first book (while still a medical student I had published a novel called *Liza of Lambeth*, which had had something of a success), but he refused to give me the hundred pounds I wanted for it and none of the other publishers to whom I afterwards submitted it would have it at any price. This distressed me at the time, but now I know that I was very fortunate;

for if one of them had taken my book (it was called *The Artistic Temperament of Stephen Carey*) I should have lost a subject which I was too young to make proper use of. I was not far enough away from the events I described to use them properly and I had not had a number of experiences which later went to enrich the book I finally wrote. Nor had I learnt that it is easier to write of what you know than of what you don't. For instance, I sent my hero to Rouen (which I knew only as an occasional visitor) to learn French, instead of to Heidelberg (where I had been myself) to learn German.

Thus rebuffed I put the manuscript away. I wrote other novels, which were published, and I wrote plays. I became a very successful playwright and determined to devote the rest of my life to the drama. But I reckoned without a force within me that made my resolutions vain. I was happy, I was prosperous, I was busy. My head was full of the plays I wanted to write. I do not know whether it was that success did not bring me all I had expected or whether it was a natural reaction from it, but I was but just firmly established as the most popular dramatist of the day when I began once more to be obsessed by the teeming memories of my past life. They came back to me so pressingly, in my sleep, on my walks, at rehearsals, at parties, they became such a burden to me, that I made up my mind there was only one way to be free of them and that was to write them all down in a book. After submitting myself for some years to the exigencies of the drama I hankered after the wide liberty of the novel. I knew the book I had in mind would be a long one and I wanted to be undisturbed, so I refused the contracts that managers were eagerly offering

me and temporarily retired from the stage. I was then thirty-seven.

For long after I became a writer by profession I spent much time on learning how to write and subjected myself to very tiresome training in the endeavour to improve my style. But these efforts I abandoned when my plays began to be produced and when I started to write again it was with different aims. I no longer sought a jewelled prose and a rich texture, on unavailing attempts to achieve which I had formerly wasted much labour; I sought on the contrary plainness and simplicity. With so much that I wanted to say within reasonable limits I felt that I could not afford to waste words and I set out now with the notion of using only such as were necessary to make my meaning clear. I had no space for ornament. My experience in the theatre had taught me the value of succinctness and the danger of beating about the bush. I worked unremittingly for two years. I did not know what to call my book and after looking about a great deal hit upon *Beauty from Ashes,* a quotation from Isaiah which seemed to me apposite; but learning that this title had been recently used was obliged to search for another. I chose finally the name of one of the books in Spinoza's *Ethics* and called it *Of Human Bondage.* I have a notion I was once more lucky in finding that I could not use the first title I had thought of.

Of Human Bondage is not an autobiography, but an autobiographical novel; fact and fiction are inextricably mingled; the emotions are my own, but not all the incidents are related as they happened and some of them are transferred to my hero not from my own life but from that of persons with whom I was intimate. The book did for me what I wanted and when it was issued to the world (a world in the throes of a dreadful war and too much concerned with its own sufferings and fears to bother with the adventures of a creature of fiction) I found myself free forever from the pains and unhappy recollections that had tormented me. It was very well reviewed; Theodore Dreiser wrote for *The New Republic* a long criticism in which he dealt with it with the intelligence and sympathy which distinguish everything he has ever written; but it looked very much as though it would go the way of the vast majority of novels and be forgotten forever a few months after its appearance. But, I do not know through what accident, it happened after some years that it attracted the attention of a number of distinguished writers in the United States and the references they continued to make to it in the press gradually brought it to the notice of the public. To these writers is due the new lease of life that the book was thus given and them must I thank for the success it has continued increasingly to have as the years go by.

W. S. M.

I

THE day broke gray and dull. The clouds hung heavily, and there was a rawness in the air that suggested snow. A woman servant came into a room in which a child was sleeping and drew the curtains. She glanced mechanically at the house opposite, a stucco house with a portico, and went to the child's bed.

"Wake up, Philip," she said.

She pulled down the bed-clothes, took him in her arms, and carried him downstairs. He was only half awake.

"Your mother wants you," she said.

She opened the door of a room on the floor below and took the child over to a bed in which a woman was lying. It was his mother. She stretched out her arms, and the child nestled by her side. He did not ask why he had been awakened. The woman kissed his eyes, and with thin, small hands felt the warm body through his white flannel nightgown. She pressed him closer to herself.

"Are you sleepy, darling?" she said.

Her voice was so weak that it seemed to come already from a great distance. The child did not answer, but smiled comfortably. He was very happy in the large, warm bed, with those soft arms about him. He tried to make himself smaller still as he cuddled up against his mother, and he kissed her sleepily. In a moment he closed his eyes and was fast asleep. The doctor came forwards and stood by the bed-side.

"Oh, don't take him away yet," she moaned.

The doctor, without answering, looked at her gravely. Knowing she would not be allowed to keep the child much longer, the woman kissed him again; and she passed her hand down his body till she came to his feet; she held the right foot in her hand and felt the five small toes; and then slowly passed her hand over the left one. She gave a sob.

"What's the matter?" said the doctor. "You're tired."

She shook her head, unable to speak, and the tears rolled down her cheeks. The doctor bent down.

"Let me take him."

She was too weak to resist his wish, and she gave the child up. The doctor handed him back to his nurse.

"You'd better put him back in his own bed."

"Very well, sir."

The little boy, still sleeping, was taken away. His mother sobbed now broken-heartedly.

"What will happen to him, poor child?"

The monthly nurse tried to quiet her, and presently, from exhaustion, the crying ceased. The doctor walked to a table on the other side of the room upon which, under a towel, lay the body of a still-born child. He lifted the towel and looked. He was hidden from the bed by a screen, but the woman guessed what he was doing. "Was it a girl or a boy?" she whispered to the nurse.

"Another boy."

The woman did not answer. In a moment the child's nurse came back. She approached the bed.

"Master Philip never woke up," she said.

There was a pause. Then the doctor felt his patient's pulse once more.

"I don't think there's anything I can do just now," he said. "I'll call again after breakfast."

"I'll show you out, sir," said the child's nurse.

They walked downstairs in silence. In the hall the doctor stopped.

"You've sent for Mrs. Carey's brother-in-law, haven't you?"

"Yes, sir."

"D'you know at what time he'll be here?"

"No, sir, I'm expecting a telegram."

"What about the little boy? I should think he'd be better out of the way."

"Miss Watkin said she'd take him, sir."

"Who's she?"

"She's his godmother, sir. D'you think Mrs. Carey will get over it, sir?"

The doctor shook his head.

II

IT WAS a week later. Philip was sitting on the floor in the drawing-room at Miss Watkin's house in Onslow Gardens. He was an only child and used to amusing himself. The room was filled with massive furniture, and on each of the sofas were three big cushions. There was a cushion too in each arm-chair. All these he had taken and, with the help of the gilt rout chairs, light and easy to move, had made an elaborate cave in which he could hide himself from the Red Indians who were lurking behind the curtains. He put his ear to the floor and listened to the herd of buffaloes that raced across the prairie. Presently, hearing the door open, he held his breath so that he might not be discovered; but a violent hand pulled away a chair and the cushions fell down.

"You naughty boy, Miss Watkin will be cross with you."

"Hulloa, Emma!" he said.

The nurse bent down and kissed him, then began to shake out the cushions, and put them back in their places.

"Am I to come home?" he asked.

"Yes, I've come to fetch you."

"You've got a new dress on."

It was in eighteen-eighty-five, and she wore a bustle. Her gown was of black velvet, with tight sleeves and sloping shoulders, and the skirt had three large flounces. She wore a black bonnet with velvet strings. She hesitated. The question she had expected did not come, and so she could not give the answer she had prepared.

"Aren't you going to ask how your mamma is?" she said at length.

"Oh, I forgot. How is mamma?" Now she was ready.

"Your mamma is quite well and happy."

"Oh, I am glad."

"Your mamma's gone away. You won't ever see her any more."

Philip did not know what she meant.

"Why not?"

"Your mamma's in heaven."

She began to cry, and Philip, though he did not quite understand, cried too. Emma was a tall, big-boned woman, with fair hair and large features. She came from Devonshire and, notwithstanding her many years of service in London, had never lost the breadth of her accent. Her tears increased her emotion, and she pressed the little boy to her heart. She felt vaguely the pity of that child deprived of the only love in the world that is quite unselfish. It seemed dreadful that he must be handed over to strangers. But in a little while she pulled herself together.

"Your Uncle William is waiting in to see you," she said. "Go and say good-bye to Miss Watkin, and we'll go home."

"I don't want to say good-bye," he answered, instinctively anxious to hide his tears.

"Very well, run upstairs and get your hat."

He fetched it, and when he came down Emma was waiting for him in the hall. He heard the sound of voices in the study behind the dining-room. He paused. He knew that Miss Watkin and her sister were talking to friends, and it seemed to him—he was nine years old—that if he went in they would be sorry for him.

"I think I'll go and say good-bye to Miss Watkin."

"I think you'd better," said Emma.

"Go in and tell them I'm coming," he said.

He wished to make the most of his opportunity. Emma knocked at the door and walked in. He heard her speak.

"Master Philip wants to say good-bye to you, miss."

There was a sudden hush of the conversation, and Philip limped in. Henrietta Watkin was a stout woman, with a red face and dyed hair. In those days to dye the hair excited comment, and Philip had heard much gossip at home when his godmother's changed colour. She lived with an elder sister, who had resigned herself contentedly to old age. Two ladies, whom Philip did not know, were calling, and they looked at him curiously.

"My poor child," said Miss Watkin, opening her arms.

She began to cry. Philip understood now why she had not been in to luncheon and why she wore a black dress. She could not speak.

"I've got to go home," said Philip, at last.

He disengaged himself from Miss Watkin's arms, and she kissed him again. Then he went to her sister and bade her good-bye too. One of the strange ladies asked if she might kiss him, and he gravely gave her permission. Though crying, he keenly enjoyed the sensation he was causing; he would have been glad to stay a little longer to be made much of, but felt they expected him to go, so he said that Emma was waiting for him. He went out of the room. Emma had gone downstairs to speak with a friend in the basement, and he waited for her on the landing. He heard Henrietta Watkin's voice.

"His mother was my greatest friend. I can't bear to think that she's dead."

"You oughtn't to have gone to the funeral, Henrietta," said her sister. "I knew it would upset you."

Then one of the strangers spoke.

"Poor little boy, it's dreadful to think of him quite alone in the world. I see he limps."

"Yes, he's got a club-foot. It was such a grief to his mother."

Then Emma came back. They called a hansom, and she told the driver where to go.

III

When they reached the house Mrs. Carey had died in—it was in a dreary, respectable street between Notting Hill Gate and High Street, Kensington— Emma led Philip into the drawing-room. His uncle was writing letters of thanks for the wreaths which had been sent. One of them, which had arrived too late for the funeral, lay in its cardboard box on the hall-table.

"Here's Master Philip," said Emma.

Mr. Carey stood up slowly and shook hands with the little boy. Then on second thoughts he bent down and kissed his forehead. He was a man of somewhat less than average height, inclined to corpulence, with his hair, worn long, arranged over the scalp so as to conceal his baldness. He was clean-shaven. His features were regular, and it was possible to imagine that in his youth he had been good-looking. On his watch-chain he wore a gold cross.

"You're going to live with me now, Philip," said Mr. Carey. "Shall you like that?"

Two years before Philip had been sent down to stay at the vicarage after an attack of chicken-pox; but there remained with him a recollection of an attic and a large garden rather than of his uncle and aunt.

"Yes."

"You must look upon me and your Aunt Louisa as your father and mother."

The child's mouth trembled a little, he reddened, but did not answer.

"Your dear mother left you in my charge."

Mr. Carey had no great ease in expressing himself. When the news came that his sister-in-law was dying, he set off at once for London, but on the way thought of nothing but the disturbance in his life that would be caused if her death forced him to undertake the care of her son. He was well over fifty, and his wife, to whom he had been married for thirty years, was childless; he did not look forward with any pleasure to the presence of a small boy who might be noisy and rough. He had never much liked his sister-in-law.

"I'm going to take you down to Blackstable tomorrow," he said.

"With Emma?"

The child put his hand in hers, and she pressed it.

"I'm afraid Emma must go away," said Mr. Carey.

"But I want Emma to come with me."

Philip began to cry, and the nurse could not help crying too. Mr. Carey looked at them helplessly.

"I think you'd better leave me alone with Master Philip for a moment."

"Very good, sir."

Though Philip clung to her, she released herself gently. Mr. Carey took the boy on his knee and put his arm around him.

"You mustn't cry," he said. "You're too old to have a nurse now. We must see about sending you to school."

"I want Emma to come with me," the child repeated.

"It costs too much money, Philip. Your father didn't leave very much, and I don't know what's become of it. You must look at every penny you spend."

Mr. Carey had called the day before on the family solicitor. Philip's father was a surgeon in good practice, and his hospital appointments suggested an established position; so that it was a surprise on his sudden death from blood-poisoning to find that he had left his widow little more than his life insurance and what could be got for the lease of their house in Bruton Street. This was six months ago; and Mrs. Carey, already in delicate health, finding herself with child, had lost her head and accepted for the lease the first offer that was made. She stored her furniture, and, at a rent which the parson thought outrageous, took a furnished house for a year, so that she might suffer from no inconvenience till her child was born. But she had never been used to the management of money, and was unable to adapt her expenditure to her altered circumstances. The little she had slipped through her fingers in one way and

another, so that now, when all expenses were paid, not much more than two thousand pounds remained to support the boy till he was able to earn his own living. It was impossible to explain all this to Philip and he was sobbing still.

"You'd better go to Emma," Mr. Carey said, feeling that she could console the child better than anyone.

Without a word Philip slipped off his uncle's knee, but Mr. Carey stopped him.

"We must go tomorrow, because on Saturday I've got to prepare my sermon, and you must tell Emma to get your things ready today. You can bring all your toys. And if you want anything to remember your father and mother by you can take one thing for each of them. Everything else is going to be sold."

The boy slipped out of the room. Mr. Carey was unused to work, and he turned to his correspondence with resentment. On one side of the desk was a bundle of bills, and these filled him with irritation. One especially seemed preposterous. Immediately after Mrs. Carey's death Emma had ordered from the florist masses of white flowers for the room in which the dead woman lay. It was sheer waste of money. Emma took far too much upon herself. Even if there had been no financial necessity, he would have dismissed her.

But Philip went to her, and hid his face in her bosom, and wept as though his heart would break. And she, feeling that he was almost her own son—she had taken him when he was a month old—consoled him with soft words. She promised that she would come and see him sometimes, and that she would never forget him; and she told him about the country he was going to and about her own home in Devonshire—her father kept a turnpike on the highroad that led to Exeter, and there were pigs in the sty, and there was a cow, and the cow had just had a calf—till Philip forgot his tears and grew excited at the thought of his approaching journey. Presently she put him down, for there was much to be done, and he helped her to lay out his clothes on the bed. She sent him into the nursery to gather up his toys, and in a little while he was playing happily.

But at last he grew tired of being alone and went back to the bed-room, in which Emma was now putting his things into a big tin box; he remembered then that his uncle had said he might take something to remember his father and mother by. He told Emma and asked her what he should take.

"You'd better go into the drawing-room and see what you fancy."

"Uncle William's there."

"Never mind that. They're your own things now."

Philip went downstairs slowly and found the door open. Mr. Carey had left the room. Philip walked slowly round. They had been in the house so short a time that there was little in it that had a particular interest to him. It was a stranger's room, and Philip saw nothing that struck his fancy. But he knew which were his mother's things and which belonged to the landlord, and presently fixed on a little clock that he had once heard his mother say she liked. With this he walked again rather disconsolately upstairs. Outside the door of his mother's bed-room he stopped and listened. Though no one had told him not to go in, he had a feeling that it would be wrong to do so; he was a little frightened, and his heart beat uncomfortably; but at the same time some-

thing impelled him to turn the handle. He turned it very gently, as if to prevent anyone within from hearing, and then slowly pushed the door open. He stood on the threshold for a moment before he had the courage to enter. He was not frightened now, but it seemed strange. He closed the door behind him. The blinds were drawn, and the room, in the cold light of a January afternoon, was dark. On the dressing-table were Mrs. Carey's brushes and the hand mirror. In a little tray were hairpins. There was a photograph of himself on the chimney-piece and one of his father. He had often been in the room when his mother was not in it, but now it seemed different. There was something curious in the look of the chairs. The bed was made as though someone were going to sleep in it that night, and in a case on the pillow was a night-dress.

Philip opened a large cupboard filled with dresses and stepping in, took as many of them as he could in his arms and buried his face in them. They smelt of the scent his mother used. Then he pulled open the drawers, filled with his mother's things, and looked at them: there were lavender bags among the linen, and their scent was fresh and pleasant. The strangeness of the room left it, and it seemed to him that his mother had just gone out for a walk. She would be in presently and would come upstairs to have nursery tea with him. And he seemed to feel her kiss on his lips.

It was not true that he would never see her again. It was not true simply because it was impossible. He climbed up on the bed and put his head on the pillow. He lay there quite still.

IV

PHILIP parted from Emma with tears, but the journey to Blackstable amused him, and, when they arrived, he was resigned and cheerful. Blackstable was sixty miles from London. Giving their luggage to a porter, Mr. Carey set out to walk with Philip to the vicarage; it took them little more than five minutes, and, when they reached it, Philip suddenly remembered the gate. It was red and five-barred: it swung both ways on easy hinges; and it was possible, though forbidden, to swing backwards and forwards on it. They walked through the garden to the front-door. This was only used by visitors and on Sundays, and on special occasions, as when the Vicar went up to London or came back. The traffic of the house took place through a side-door, and there was a back door as well for the gardener and for beggars and tramps. It was a fairly large house of yellow brick, with a red roof, built about five and twenty years before in an ecclesiastical style. The front-door was like a church porch, and the drawing-room windows were gothic.

Mrs. Carey, knowing by what train they were coming, waited in the drawing-room and listened for the click of the gate. When she heard it she went to the door.

"There's Aunt Louisa," said Mr. Carey, when he saw her. "Run and give her a kiss."

Philip started to run, awkwardly, trailing his club-foot, and then stopped. Mrs. Carey was a little, shrivelled woman of the same age as her husband, with a face extraordinarily filled with deep wrinkles, and pale blue eyes. Her gray hair was arranged in ringlets according to the fashion of her youth. She wore a black dress, and her only ornament was a gold chain, from which hung a cross. She had a shy manner and a gentle voice.

"Did you walk, William?" she said, almost reproachfully, as she kissed her husband.

"I didn't think of it," he answered, with a glance at his nephew.

"It didn't hurt you to walk, Philip, did it?" she asked the child.

"No. I always walk."

He was a little surprised at their conversation. Aunt Louisa told him to come in, and they entered the hall. It was paved with red and yellow tiles, on which alternately were a Greek Cross and the Lamb of God. An imposing staircase led out of the hall. It was of polished pine, with a peculiar smell, and had been put in because fortunately, when the church was re-seated, enough wood remained over. The balusters were decorated with emblems of the Four Evangelists.

"I've had the stove lighted as I thought you'd be cold after your journey," said Mrs. Carey.

It was a large black stove that stood in the hall and was only lighted if the weather was very bad and the Vicar had a cold. It was not lighted if Mrs. Carey had a cold. Coal was expensive. Besides, Mary Ann, the maid, didn't like fires all over the place. If they wanted all them fires they must keep a second girl. In the winter Mr. and Mrs. Carey lived in the dining-room so that one fire should do, and in the summer they could not get out of the habit, so the drawing-room was used only by Mr. Carey on Sunday afternoons for his nap. But every Saturday he had a fire in the study so that he could write his sermon.

Aunt Louisa took Philip upstairs and showed him into a tiny bed-room that looked out on the drive. Immediately in front of the window was a large tree, which Philip remembered now because the branches were so low that it was possible to climb quite high up it.

"A small room for a small boy," said Mrs. Carey. "You won't be frightened at sleeping alone?"

"Oh, no."

On his first visit to the vicarage he had come with his nurse, and Mrs. Carey had had little to do with him. She looked at him now with some uncertainty.

"Can you wash your own hands, or shall I wash them for you?"

"I can wash myself," he answered firmly.

"Well, I shall look at them when you come down to tea," said Mrs. Carey.

She knew nothing about children. After it was settled that Philip should come down to Blackstable, Mrs. Carey had thought much how she should treat him; she was anxious to do her duty; but now he was there she found herself just as shy of him as he was of her. She hoped he would not be noisy and rough, because her husband did not like rough and noisy boys. Mrs. Carey made an excuse to leave Philip alone, but in a moment came back and knocked at the door; she asked him, without coming in, if he could pour out the water himself. Then she went downstairs and rang the bell for tea.

The dining-room, large and well-proportioned, had windows on two sides of it, with heavy curtains of red rep; there was a big table in the middle; and at one end an imposing mahogany sideboard with a looking-glass in it. In one corner stood a harmonium. On each side of the fireplace were chairs covered in stamped leather, each with an antimacassar; one had arms and was called the husband, and the other had none and was called the wife. Mrs. Carey never sat in the armchair: she said she preferred a chair that was not too comfortable; there was always a lot to do, and if her chair had had arms she might not be so ready to leave it.

Mr. Carey was making up the fire when Philip came in, and he pointed out to his nephew that there were two pokers. One was large and bright and polished and unused, and was called the Vicar; and the other, which was much smaller and had evidently passed through many fires, was called the Curate.

"What are we waiting for?" said Mr. Carey.

"I told Mary Ann to make you an egg. I thought you'd be hungry after your journey."

Mrs. Carey thought the journey from London to Blackstable very tiring. She seldom travelled herself, for the living was only three hundred a year, and, when her husband wanted a holiday, since there was not money for two, he went by himself. He was very fond of Church Congresses and usually managed to go up to London once a year; and once he had been to Paris for the exhibition, and two or three times to Switzerland. Mary Ann brought in the egg, and they sat down. The chair was much too low for Philip, and for a moment neither Mr. Carey nor his wife knew what to do.

"I'll put some books under him," said Mary Ann.

She took from the top of the harmonium the large Bible and the prayer-book from which the Vicar was accustomed to read prayers, and put them on Philip's chair.

"Oh, William, he can't sit on the Bible," said Mrs. Carey, in a shocked tone. "Couldn't you get him some books out of the study?"

Mr. Carey considered the question for an instant.

"I don't think it matters this once if you put the prayerbook on the top, Mary Ann," he said. "The book of Common Prayer is the composition of men like ourselves. It has no claim to divine authorship."

"I hadn't thought of that, William," said Aunt Louisa.

Philip perched himself on the books, and the Vicar, having said grace, cut the top off his egg.

"There," he said, handing it to Philip, "you can eat my top if you like."

Philip would have liked an egg to himself, but he was not offered one, so took what he could.

"How have the chickens been laying since I went away?" asked the Vicar.

"Oh, they've been dreadful, only one or two a day."

"How did you like that top, Philip?" asked his uncle.

"Very much, thank you."

"You shall have another one on Sunday afternoon."

Mr. Carey always had a boiled egg at tea on Sunday, so that he might be fortified for the evening service.

V

PHILIP came gradually to know the people he was to live with, and by fragments of conversation, some of it not meant for his ears, learned a good deal both about himself and about his dead parents. Philip's father had been much younger than the Vicar of Blackstable. After a brilliant career at St. Luke's Hospital he was put on the staff, and presently began to earn money in considerable sums. He spent it freely. When the parson set about restoring his church and asked his brother for a subscription, he was surprised by receiving a couple of hundred pounds: Mr. Carey, thrifty by inclination and economical by necessity, accepted it with mingled feelings; he was envious of his brother because he could afford to give so much, pleased for the sake of his church, and vaguely irritated by a generosity which seemed almost ostentatious. Then Henry Carey married a patient, a beautiful girl but penniless, an orphan with no near relations, but of good family; and there was an array of fine friends at the wedding. The parson, on his visits to her when he came to London, held himself with reserve. He felt shy with her and in his heart he resented her great beauty: she dressed more magnificently than became the wife of a hardworking surgeon; and the charming furniture of her house, the flowers among which she lived even in winter, suggested an extravagance which he deplored. He heard her talk of entertainments she was going to; and, as he told his wife on getting home again, it was impossible to accept hospitality without making some return. He had seen grapes in the dining-room that must have cost at least eight shillings a pound; and at luncheon he had been given asparagus two months before it was ready in the vicarage garden.

Now all he had anticipated was come to pass: the Vicar felt the satisfaction of the prophet who saw fire and brimstone consume the city which would not mend its way to his warning. Poor Philip was practically penniless, and what was the good of his mother's fine friends now? He heard that his father's extravagance was really criminal, and it was a mercy that Providence had seen fit to take his dear mother to itself: she had no more idea of money than a child.

When Philip had been a week at Blackstable an incident happened which seemed to irritate his uncle very much. One morning he found on the breakfast table a small packet which had been sent on by post from the late Mrs. Carey's house in London. It was addressed to her. When the parson opened it he found a dozen photographs of Mrs. Carey. They showed the head and shoulders only, and her hair was more plainly done than usual, low on the forehead, which gave her an unusual look; the face was thin and worn, but no illness could impair the beauty of her features. There was in the large dark eyes a sadness which Philip did not remember. The first sight of the dead woman gave Mr. Carey a little shock, but this was quickly followed by perplexity. The photographs seemed quite recent, and he could not imagine who had ordered them. "D'you know anything about these, Philip?" he asked.

"I remember mamma said she'd been taken," he answered. "Miss Watkin scolded her. . . . She said: I wanted the boy to have something to remember me by when he grows up."

Mr. Carey looked at Philip for an instant. The child spoke in a clear treble. He recalled the words, but they meant nothing to him.

"You'd better take one of the photographs and keep it in your room," said Mr. Carey. "I'll put the others away."

He sent one to Miss Watkin, and she wrote and explained how they came to be taken.

One day Mrs. Carey was lying in bed, but she was feeling a little better than usual, and the doctor in the morning had seemed hopeful; Emma had taken the child out, and the maids were downstairs in the basement; suddenly Mrs. Carey felt desperately alone in the world. A great fear seized her that she would not recover from the confinement which she was expecting in a fortnight. Her son was nine years old. How could he be expected to remember her? She could not bear to think that he would grow up and forget, forget her utterly; and she had loved him so passionately, because he was weakly and deformed, and because he was her child. She had no photographs of herself taken since her marriage, and that was ten years before. She wanted her son to know what she looked like at the end. He could not forget her then, not forget utterly. She knew that if she called her maid and told her she wanted to get up, the maid would prevent her, and perhaps send for the doctor, and she had not the strength now to struggle or argue. She got out of bed and began to dress herself. She had been on her back so long that her legs gave way beneath her, and then the soles of her feet tingled so that she could hardly bear to put them to the ground. But she went on. She was unused to doing her own hair and, when she raised her arms and began to brush it, she felt faint. She could never do it as her maid did. It was beautiful hair, very fine, and of a deep rich gold. Her eyebrows were straight and dark. She put on a black skirt, but chose the bodice of the evening dress which she liked best: it was of a white damask which was fashionable in those days. She looked at herself in the glass. Her face was very pale, but her skin was clear: she had never had much colour, and this had always made the redness of her beautiful mouth emphatic. She could not restrain a sob. But she could not afford to be sorry for herself; she was feeling already desperately tired; and she put on the furs which Henry had given her the Christmas before—she had been so proud of them and so happy then—and slipped downstairs with beating heart. She got safely out of the house and drove to a photographer. She paid for a dozen photographs. She was obliged to ask for a glass of water in the middle of the sitting; and the assistant, seeing she was ill, suggested that she should come another day, but she insisted on staying till the end. At last it was finished, and she drove back again to the dingy little house in Kensington which she hated with all her heart. It was a horrible house to die in.

She found the front-door open, and when she drove up the maid and Emma ran down the steps to help her.

They had been frightened when they found her room empty. At first they thought she must have gone to Miss Watkin, and the cook was sent round. Miss Watkin came back with her and was waiting anxiously in the drawing-room. She came downstairs now full of anxiety and reproaches; but the exertion had been more than Mrs. Carey was fit for, and when the occasion for firmness no longer existed she gave way. She fell heavily into Emma's arms and was carried upstairs. She remained unconscious for a time that seemed incredibly long to those that watched her, and the doctor, hurriedly sent for, did not come. It was next day, when she was a little better, that Miss Watkin got some explanation out of her. Philip was playing on the floor of his mother's bed-room, and neither of the ladies paid attention to him. He only understood vaguely what they were talking about, and he could not have said why those words remained in his memory.

"I wanted the boy to have something to remember me by when he grows up."

"I can't make out why she ordered a dozen," said Mr. Carey. "Two would have done."

VI

O n e day was very like another at the vicarage.

Soon after breakfast Mary Ann brought in The Times. Mr. Carey shared it with two neighbours. He had it from ten till one, when the gardener took it over to Mr. Ellis at the Limes, with whom it remained till seven; then it was taken to Miss Brooks at the Manor House, who,

since she got it late, had the advantage of keeping it. In summer Mrs. Carey, when she was making jam, often asked her for a copy to cover the pots with. When the Vicar settled down to his paper his wife put on her bonnet and went out to do the shopping. Philip accompanied her. Blackstable was a fishing village. It consisted of a high street in which were the shops, the bank, the doctor's house, and the houses of two or three coal-ship owners; round the little harbour were shabby streets in which lived fishermen and poor people; but since they went to chapel they were of no account. When Mrs. Carey passed the dissenting ministers in the street she stepped over to the other side to avoid meeting them but if there was not time for this fixed her eyes on the pavement. It was a scandal to which the Vicar had never resigned himself that there were three chapels in the High Street: he could not help feeling that the law should have stepped in to prevent their erection. Shopping in Blackstable was not a simple matter; for dissent, helped by the fact that the parish church was two miles from the town, was very common; and it was necessary to deal only with churchgoers; Mrs. Carey knew perfectly that the vicarage custom might make all the difference to a tradesman's faith. There were two butchers who went to church, and they would not understand that the Vicar could not deal with both of them at once; nor were they satisfied with his simple plan of going for six months to one and for six months to the other. The butcher who was not sending meat to the vicarage constantly threatened not to come to church, and the Vicar was sometimes obliged to make a threat: it was very wrong of him not to come to church, but if he carried iniquity further and actually went to chapel, then of course, excellent as his meat was, Mr. Carey would be forced to leave him for ever. Mrs. Carey often stopped at the bank to deliver a message to Josiah Graves, the manager, who was choir-master, treasurer, and churchwarden. He was a tall, thin man with a sallow face and a long nose; his hair was very white, and to Philip he seemed ex-

tremely old. He kept the parish accounts, arranged the treats for the choir and the schools; though there was no organ in the parish church, it was generally considered (in Blackstable) that the choir he led was the best in Kent; and when there was any ceremony, such as a visit from the Bishop for confirmation or from the Rural Dean to preach at the Harvest Thanksgiving, he made the necessary preparations. But he had no hesitation in doing all manner of things without more than a perfunctory consultation with the Vicar, and the Vicar, though always ready to be saved trouble, much resented the churchwarden's managing ways. He really seemed to look upon himself as the most important person in the parish. Mr. Carey constantly told his wife that if Josiah Graves did not take care he would give him a good rap over the knuckles one day; but Mrs. Carey advised him to bear with Josiah Graves: he meant well, and it was not his fault if he was not quite a gentleman. The Vicar, finding his comfort in the practice of a Christian virtue, exercised forbearance; but he revenged himself by calling the churchwarden Bismarck behind his back.

Once there had been a serious quarrel between the pair, and Mrs. Carey still thought of that anxious time with dismay. The Conservative candidate had announced his intention of addressing a meeting at Blackstable; and Josiah Graves, having arranged that it should take place in the Mission Hall, went to Mr. Carey and told him that he hoped he would say a few words. It appeared that the candidate had asked Josiah Graves to take the chair. This was more than Mr. Carey could put up with. He had firm views upon the respect which was due to the cloth, and it was ridiculous for a churchwarden to take the chair at a meeting when the Vicar was there. He reminded Josiah Graves that parson meant person, that is, the vicar was the person of the parish. Josiah Graves answered that he was the first to recognise the dignity of the church, but this was a matter of politics, and in his turn he reminded the Vicar that their Blessed Saviour had enjoined upon them to render unto Cæsar the things that were Cæsar's. To this Mr. Carey replied that the devil could quote scripture to his purpose, himself had sole authority over the Mission Hall, and if he were not asked to be chairman he would refuse the use of it for a political meeting. Josiah Graves told Mr. Carey that he might do as he chose, and for his part he thought the Wesleyan Chapel would be an equally suitable place. Then Mr. Carey said that if Josiah Graves set foot in what was little better than a heathen temple he was not fit to be churchwarden in a Christian parish. Josiah Graves thereupon resigned all his offices, and that very evening sent to the church for his cassock and surplice. His sister, Miss Graves, who kept house for him, gave up her secretaryship of the Maternity Club, which provided the pregnant poor with flannel, baby linen, coals, and five shillings. Mr. Carey said he was at last master in his own house. But soon he found that he was obliged to see to all sorts of things that he knew nothing about; and Josiah Graves, after the first moment of irritation, discovered that he had lost his chief interest in life. Mrs. Carey and Miss Graves were much distressed by the quarrel; they met after a discreet exchange of letters, and made up their minds to put the matter right: they talked, one to her husband, the other to her brother, from morning till night; and since they were persuading these gentlemen to do what in their hearts they wanted, after three weeks of anxiety a reconciliation was effected. It was to both their interests, but they ascribed it to a common love for their Redeemer. The meeting was held at the Mission Hall, and the doctor was asked to be chairman. Mr. Carey and Josiah Graves both made speeches.

When Mrs. Carey had finished her business with the banker, she generally went upstairs to have a little chat with his sister; and while the ladies talked of parish matters, the curate or the new bonnet of Mrs. Wilson—Mr. Wilson was the richest man in Blackstable, he was thought to have at least five hundred a year, and he had married his cook—Philip sat demurely in the stiff parlour, used only to receive visitors, and busied himself with the restless movements of goldfish in a bowl. The windows were never opened except to air the room for a few minutes in the morning, and it had a stuffy smell which seemed to Philip to have a mysterious connection with banking.

Then Mrs. Carey remembered that she had to go to the grocer, and they continued their way. When the shopping was done they often went down a side street of little houses, mostly of wood, in which fishermen dwelt (and here and there a fisherman sat on his doorstep mending his nets, and nets hung to dry upon the doors), till they came to a small beach, shut in on each side by warehouses, but with a view of the sea. Mrs. Carey stood for a few minutes and looked at it, it was turbid and yellow, [and who knows what thoughts passed through her mind?] while Philip searched for flat stones to play ducks and drakes. Then they walked slowly back. They looked into the post office to get the right time, nodded to Mrs. Wigram the doctor's wife, who sat at her window sewing, and so got home.

Dinner was at one o'clock; and on Monday, Tuesday, and Wednesday it consisted of beef, roast, hashed, and minced, and on Thursday, Friday, and Saturday of mutton. On Sunday they ate one of their own chickens. In the afternoon Philip did his lessons. He was taught Latin and mathematics by his uncle who knew neither, and French and the piano by his aunt. Of French she was ignorant, but she knew the piano well enough to accompany the old-fashioned songs she had sung for thirty years. Uncle William used to tell Philip that when he was a curate his wife had known twelve songs by heart, which she could sing at a moment's notice whenever she was asked. She often sang still when there was a tea-party at the vicarage. There were few people whom the Careys cared to ask there, and their parties consisted always of the curate, Josiah Graves with his sister, Dr. Wigram and his wife. After tea Miss Graves played one or two of Mendelssohn's *Songs without Words,* and Mrs. Carey sang *When the Swallows Homeward Fly,* or *Trot, Trot, My Pony.*

But the Careys did not give tea-parties often; the preparations upset them, and when their guests were gone they felt themselves exhausted. They preferred to have tea by themselves, and after tea they played backgammon. Mrs. Carey arranged that her husband should win, because he did not like losing. They had cold supper at eight. It was a scrappy meal because Mary Ann resented getting anything ready after tea, and Mrs. Carey helped to clear away. Mrs. Carey seldom ate more than bread and butter, with a little stewed fruit to follow, but the Vicar had a slice of cold meat. Immediately after supper Mrs. Carey rang the bell for prayers,

and then Philip went to bed. He rebelled against being undressed by Mary Ann and after a while succeeded in establishing his right to dress and undress himself. At nine o'clock Mary Ann brought in the eggs and the plate. Mrs. Carey wrote the date on each egg and put the number down in a book. She then took the plate-basket on her arm and went upstairs. Mr. Carey continued to read one of his old books, but as the clock struck ten he got up, put out the lamps, and followed his wife to bed.

When Philip arrived there was some difficulty in deciding on which evening he should have his bath. It was never easy to get plenty of hot water, since the kitchen boiler did not work, and it was impossible for two persons to have a bath on the same day. The only man who had a bathroom in Blackstable was Mr. Wilson, and it was thought ostentatious of him. Mary Ann had her bath in the kitchen on Monday night, because she liked to begin the week clean. Uncle William could not have his on Saturday, because he had a heavy day before him and he was always a little tired after a bath, so he had it on Friday. Mrs. Carey had hers on Thursday for the same reason. It looked as though Saturday were naturally indicated for Philip, but Mary Ann said she couldn't keep the fire up on Saturday night: what with all the cooking on Sunday, having to make pastry and she didn't know what all, she did not feel up to giving the boy his bath on Saturday night; and it was quite clear that he could not bath himself. Mrs. Carey was shy about bathing a boy, and of course the Vicar had his sermon. But the Vicar insisted that Philip should be clean and sweet for the Lord's Day. Mary Ann said she would rather go than be put upon—and after eighteen years she didn't expect to have more work given her, and they might show some consideration—and Philip said he didn't want anyone to bath him, but could very well bath himself. This settled it. Mary Ann said she was quite sure he wouldn't bath himself properly, and rather than he should go dirty—and not because he was going into the presence of the Lord, but because she couldn't abide a boy who wasn't properly washed—she'd work herself to the bone even if it was Saturday night.

•

VII

SUNDAY was a day crowded with incident. Mr. Carey was accustomed to say that he was the only man in his parish who worked seven days a week.

The household got up half an hour earlier than usual. No lying abed for a poor parson on the day of rest, Mr. Carey remarked as Mary Ann knocked at the door punctually at eight. It took Mrs. Carey longer to dress, and she got down to breakfast at nine, a little breathless, only just before her husband. Mr. Carey's boots stood in front of the fire to warm. Prayers were longer than usual, and the breakfast more substantial. After breakfast the Vicar cut thin slices of bread for the communion, and Philip was privileged to cut off the crust. He was sent to the study to fetch a marble paperweight, with which Mr. Carey pressed the bread till it was thin and pulpy, and then it was cut into small squares. The amount was regulated by the weather. On a very bad day few people came to church, and on a very fine one, though many came, few stayed for communion. There were most when it was dry enough to make the walk to church pleasant, but not so fine that people wanted to hurry away.

Then Mrs. Carey brought the communion plate out of the safe, which stood in the pantry, and the Vicar polished it with a chamois leather.

At ten the fly drove up, and Mr. Carey got into his boots. Mrs. Carey took several minutes to put on her bonnet, during which the Vicar, in a voluminous cloak, stood in the hall with just such an expression on his face as would have become an early Christian about to be led into the arena. It was extraordinary that after thirty years of marriage his wife could not be ready in time on Sunday morning. At last she came, in black satin; the Vicar did not like colours in a clergyman's wife at any time, but on Sundays he was determined that she should wear black; now and then, in conspiracy with Miss Graves, she ventured a white feather or a pink rose in her bonnet, but the Vicar insisted that it should disappear; he said he would not go to church with the scarlet woman: Mrs. Carey sighed as a woman but obeyed as a wife. They were about to step into the carriage when the Vicar remembered that no one had given him his egg. They knew that he must have an egg for his voice, there were two women in the house, and no one had the least regard for his comfort. Mrs. Carey scolded Mary Ann, and Mary Ann answered that she could not think of everything. She hurried away to fetch an egg, and Mrs. Carey beat it up in a glass of sherry. The Vicar swallowed it at a gulp. The communion plate was stowed in the carriage, and they set off.

The fly came from *The Red Lion* and had a peculiar smell of stale straw. They drove with both windows closed so that the Vicar should not catch cold. The sexton was waiting at the porch to take the communion plate, and while the Vicar went to the vestry Mrs. Carey and Philip settled themselves in the vicarage pew. Mrs. Carey placed in front of her the sixpenny bit she was accustomed to put in the plate, and gave Philip threepence for the same purpose. The church filled up gradually and the service began.

Philip grew bored during the sermon, but if he fidgeted Mrs. Carey put a gentle hand on his arm and looked at him reproachfully. He regained interest when the final hymn was sung and Mr. Graves passed round with the plate.

When everyone had gone Mrs. Carey went into Miss Graves' pew to have a few words with her while they were waiting for the gentlemen, and Philip went to the vestry. His uncle, the curate, and Mr. Graves were still in their surplices. Mr. Carey gave him the remains of the consecrated bread and told him he might eat it. He had been accustomed to eat it himself, as it seemed blasphemous to throw it away, but Philip's keen appetite relieved him from the duty. Then they counted the money. It consisted of pennies, sixpences and threepenny bits. There were always two single shillings, one put in the plate by the Vicar and the other by Mr. Graves; and sometimes there was a florin. Mr. Graves told the Vicar who had given this. It was always a stranger to Blackstable, and Mr. Carey wondered who he was. But Miss Graves had observed the rash act and was able to tell Mrs. Carey that the stranger came from London, was married and had children. During the drive home Mrs. Carey passed the information on, and the Vicar made up his mind to call on him and ask for a subscription to the Additional Curates Society. Mr. Carey asked if Philip had behaved properly; and Mrs. Carey remarked that Mrs. Wigram had a new mantle, Mr. Cox was not in church, and somebody thought that Miss Phillips was engaged. When they reached the vicarage they all felt that they deserved a substantial dinner.

When this was over Mrs. Carey went to her room to rest, and Mr. Carey lay down on the sofa in the drawing-room for forty winks.

They had tea at five, and the Vicar ate an egg to support himself for evensong. Mrs. Carey did not go to this so that Mary Ann might, but she read the service through and the hymns. Mr. Carey walked to church in the evening, and Philip limped along by his side. The walk through the darkness along the country road strangely impressed him, and the church with all its lights in the distance, coming gradually nearer, seemed very friendly. At first he was shy with his uncle, but little by little grew used to him, and he would slip his hand in his uncle's and walk more easily for the feeling of protection.

They had supper when they got home. Mr. Carey's slippers were waiting for him on a footstool in front of the fire and by their side Philip's, one the shoe of a small boy, the other misshapen and odd. He was dreadfully tired when he went up to bed, and he did not resist when Mary Ann undressed him. She kissed him after she tucked him up, and he began to love her.

VIII

PHILIP had led always the solitary life of an only child, and his loneliness at the vicarage was no greater than it had been when his mother lived. He made friends with Mary Ann. She was a chubby little person of thirty-five, the daughter of a fisherman, and had come to the vicarage at eighteen; it was her first place and she had no intention of leaving it; but she held a possible marriage as a rod over the timid heads of her master and mistress. Her father and mother lived in a little house off Harbour Street, and she went to see them on her evenings out. Her stories of the sea touched Philip's imagination, and the narrow alleys round the harbour grew rich with the romance which his young fancy lent them. One evening he asked whether he might go home with her; but his aunt was afraid that he might catch something, and his uncle said that evil communications corrupted good manners. He disliked the fisher folk, who were rough, uncouth, and went to chapel. But Philip was more comfortable in the kitchen than in the dining-room, and, whenever he could, he took his toys and played there. His aunt was not sorry. She did not like disorder, and though she recognised that boys must be expected to be untidy she preferred that he should make a mess in the kitchen. If he fidgetted his uncle was apt to grow restless and say it was high time he went to school. Mrs. Carey thought Philip very young for this, and her heart went out to the motherless child; but her attempts to gain his affection were awkward, and the boy, feeling shy, received her demonstrations with so much sullenness that she was mortified. Sometimes she heard his shrill voice raised in laughter in the kitchen, but when she went in, he grew suddenly silent, and he flushed darkly when Mary Ann explained the joke. Mrs. Carey could not see anything amusing in what she heard, and she smiled with constraint.

"He seems happier with Mary Ann than with us, William," she said, when she returned to her sewing.

"One can see he's been very badly brought up. He wants licking into shape."

On the second Sunday after Philip arrived an unlucky incident occurred. Mr. Carey had retired as usual after dinner for a little snooze in the drawing-room, but he was in an irritable mood and could not sleep. Josiah Graves that morning had objected strongly to some candlesticks with which the Vicar had adorned the altar. He had bought them second-hand in Tercanbury, and he thought they looked very well. But Josiah Graves said they were popish. This was a taunt that always aroused the Vicar. He had been at Oxford during the movement which ended in the secession from the Established Church of Edward Manning, and he felt a certain sympathy for the Church of Rome. He would willingly have made the service more ornate than had been usual in the low-church parish of Blackstable, and in his secret soul he yearned for processions and lighted candles. He drew the line at incense. He hated the word protestant. He called himself a Catholic. He was accustomed to say that Papists required an epithet, they were Roman Catholic; but the Church of England was Catholic in the best, the fullest, and the noblest sense of the term. He was pleased to think that his shaven face gave him the look of a priest, and in his youth he had possessed an ascetic air which added to the impression. He often related that on one of his holidays in Boulogne, one of those holidays upon which his wife for economy's sake did not accompany him, when he was sitting in a church, the *curé* had come up to him and invited him to preach a sermon. He dismissed his curates when they married, having decided views on the celibacy of the unbeneficed clergy. But when at an election the Liberals had written on his garden fence in large blue letters: This way to Rome, he had been very angry, and threatened to prosecute the leaders of the Liberal party in Blackstable. He made up his mind now that nothing Josiah Graves said would induce him to remove the candlesticks from the altar, and he muttered Bismarck to himself once or twice irritably.

Suddenly he heard an unexpected noise. He pulled the handkerchief off his face, got up from the sofa on which he was lying, and went into the dining-room. Philip was seated on the table with all his bricks around him. He had built a monstrous castle, and some defect in the foundation had just brought the structure down in noisy ruin.

"What are you doing with those bricks, Philip? You know you're not allowed to play games on Sunday."

Philip stared at him for a moment with frightened eyes, and, as his habit was, flushed deeply.

"I always used to play at home," he answered.

"I'm sure your dear mamma never allowed you to do such a wicked thing as that."

Philip did not know it was wicked; but if it was, he did not wish it to be supposed that his mother had consented to it. He hung his head and did not answer.

"Don't you know it's very, very wicked to play on Sunday? What d'you suppose it's called the day of rest for? You're going to church tonight, and how can you face your Maker when you've been breaking one of His laws in the afternoon?"

Mr. Carey told him to put the bricks away at once, and stood over him while Philip did so.

"You're a very naughty boy," he repeated. "Think of the grief you're causing your poor mother in heaven."

Philip felt inclined to cry, but he had an instinctive disinclination to letting other people see his tears, and he clenched his teeth to prevent the sobs from escaping. Mr. Carey sat down in his arm-chair and began to turn over the pages of a book. Philip stood at the window. The vicarage was set back from the highroad to Tercanbury, and from the dining-room one saw a semicircular strip of lawn and then as far as the horizon green fields. Sheep were grazing in them. The sky was forlorn and gray. Philip felt infinitely unhappy.

Presently Mary Ann came in to lay the tea, and Aunt Louisa descended the stairs.

"Have you had a nice little nap, William?" she asked.

"No," he answered. "Philip made so much noise that I couldn't sleep a wink."

This was not quite accurate, for he had been kept awake by his own thoughts; and Philip, listening sullenly, reflected that he had only made a noise once, and there was no reason why his uncle should not have slept before or after. When Mrs. Carey asked for an explanation the Vicar narrated the facts.

"He hasn't even said he was sorry," he finished.

"Oh, Philip, I'm sure you're sorry," said Mrs. Carey, anxious that the child should not seem wickeder to his uncle than need be.

Philip did not reply. He went on munching his bread and butter. He did not know what power it was in him that prevented him from making any expression of regret. He felt his ears tingling, he was a little inclined to cry, but no word would issue from his lips.

"You needn't make it worse by sulking," said Mr. Carey.

Tea was finished in silence. Mrs. Carey looked at Philip surreptitiously now and then, but the Vicar elaborately ignored him. When Philip saw his uncle go upstairs to get ready for church he went into the hall and got his hat and coat, but when the Vicar came downstairs and saw him, he said:

"I don't wish you to go to church tonight, Philip. I don't think you're in a proper frame of mind to enter the House of God."

Philip did not say a word. He felt it was a deep humiliation that was placed upon him, and his cheeks reddened. He stood silently watching his uncle put on his broad hat and his voluminous cloak. Mrs. Carey as usual went to the door to see him off. Then she turned to Philip.

"Never mind, Philip, you won't be a naughty boy next Sunday, will you, and then your uncle will take you to church with him in the evening."

She took off his hat and coat, and led him into the dining-room.

"Shall you and I read the service together, Philip, and we'll sing the hymns at the harmonium. Would

you like that?"

Philip shook his head decidedly. Mrs. Carey was taken aback. If he would not read the evening service with her she did not know what to do with him.

"Then what would you like to do until your uncle comes back?" she asked helplessly.

Philip broke his silence at last.

"I want to be left alone," he said.

"Philip, how can you say anything so unkind? Don't you know that your uncle and I only want your good? Don't you love me at all?"

"I hate you. I wish you was dead."

Mrs. Carey gasped. He said the words so savagely that it gave her quite a start. She had nothing to say. She sat down in her husband's chair; and as she thought of her desire to love the friendless, crippled boy and her eager wish that he should love her—she was a barren woman and, even though it was clearly God's will that she should be childless, she could scarcely bear to look at little children sometimes, her heart ached so—the tears rose to her eyes and one by one, slowly, rolled down her cheeks. Philip watched her in amazement. She took out her handkerchief, and now she cried without restraint. Suddenly Philip realised that she was crying because of what he had said, and he was sorry. He went up to her silently and kissed her. It was the first kiss he had ever given her without being asked. And the poor lady, so small in her black satin, shrivelled up and sallow, with her funny corkscrew curls, took the little boy on her lap and put her arms around him and wept as though her heart would break. But her tears were partly tears of happiness, for she felt that the strangeness between them was gone. She loved him now with a new love because he had made her suffer.

IX

ON THE following Sunday, when the Vicar was making his preparations to go into the drawing-room for his nap —all the actions of his life were conducted with ceremony—and Mrs. Carey was about to go upstairs, Philip asked:

"What shall I do if I'm not allowed to play?"

"Can't you sit still for once and be quiet?"

"I can't sit still till tea-time."

Mr. Carey looked out of the window, but it was cold and raw, and he could not suggest that Philip should go into the garden.

"I know what you can do. You can learn by heart the collect for the day."

He took the prayer-book which was used for prayers from the harmonium, and turned the pages till he came to the place he wanted.

"It's not a long one. If you can say it without a mistake when I come in to tea you shall have the top of my egg."

Mrs. Carey drew up Philip's chair to the dining-room table—they had bought him a high chair by now—and placed the book in front of him.

"The devil finds work for idle hands to do," said Mr. Carey.

He put some more coals on the fire so that there should be a cheerful blaze when he came in to tea, and went into the drawing-room. He loosened his collar, arranged the cushions, and settled himself comfortably on the sofa. But thinking the drawing-room a little chilly, Mrs. Carey brought him a rug from the hall; she put it over his legs and tucked it round his feet. She drew the blinds so that the light should not offend his eyes, and since he had closed them already went out of the room on tiptoe. The Vicar was at peace with himself today, and in ten minutes he was asleep. He snored softly.

It was the Sixth Sunday after Epiphany, and the collect began with the words: *O God, whose blessed Son was manifested that he might destroy the works of the devil, and make us the sons of God, and heirs of Eternal life.* Philip read it through. He could make no sense of it. He began saying the words aloud to himself, but many of them were unknown to him, and the construction of the sentences was strange. He could not get more than two lines in his head. And his attention was constantly wandering: there were fruit trees trained on the walls of the vicarage, and a long twig beat now and then against the windowpane; sheep grazed stolidly in the field beyond the garden. It seemed as though there were knots inside his brain. Then panic seized him that he would not know the words by tea-time, and he kept on whispering them to himself quickly; he did not try to understand, but merely to get them parrot-like into his memory.

Mrs. Carey could not sleep that afternoon, and by four o'clock she was so wide awake that she came downstairs. She thought she would hear Philip say his collect so that he should make no mistakes when he said it to his uncle. His uncle then would be pleased; he would see that the boy's heart was in the right place. But when Mrs. Carey came to the dining-room and was about to go in, she heard a sound that made her stop suddenly. Her heart gave a little jump. She turned away and quietly slipped out of the front-door. She walked round the house till she came to the dining-room window and then cautiously looked in. Philip was still sitting on the chair she had put him in, but his head was on the table buried in his arms, and he was sobbing desperately. She saw the convulsive movement of his shoulders. Mrs. Carey was frightened. A thing that had always struck her about the child was that he seemed so collected. She had never seen him cry. And now she realised that his calmness was some instinctive shame of showing his feelings: he hid himself to weep.

Without thinking that her husband disliked being awakened suddenly, she burst into the drawing-room.

"William, William," she said. "The boy's crying as though his heart would break."

Mr. Carey sat up and disentangled himself from the rug about his legs.

"What's he got to cry about?"

"I don't know. . . . Oh, William, we can't let the boy be unhappy. D'you think it's our fault? If we'd had children we'd have known what to do."

Mr. Carey looked at her in perplexity. He felt extraordinarily helpless.

"He can't be crying because I gave him the collect to learn. It's not more than ten lines."

"Don't you think I might take him some picture books to look at, William? There are some of the Holy Land. There couldn't be anything wrong in that."

"Very well, I don't mind."

Mrs. Carey went into the study. To collect books was Mr. Carey's only passion, and he never went into Tercanbury without spending an hour or two in the second-hand shop; he always brought back four or five musty volumes. He never read them, for he had long lost the habit of reading, but he liked to turn the pages, look at the illustrations if they were illustrated, and mend the bindings. He welcomed wet days because on them he could stay at home without pangs of conscience and spend the afternoon with white of egg and a glue-pot, patching up the Russia leather of some battered quarto. He had many volumes of old travels, with steel engravings, and Mrs. Carey quickly found two which described Palestine. She coughed elaborately at the door so that Philip should have time to compose himself, she felt that he would be humiliated if she came upon him in the midst of his tears, then she rattled the door handle. When she went in Philip was poring over the prayer-book, hiding his eyes with his hands so that she might not see he had been crying.

"Do you know the collect yet?" she said.

He did not answer for a moment, and she felt that he did not trust his voice. She was oddly embarrassed.

"I can't learn it by heart," he said at last, with a gasp.

"Oh, well, never mind," she said. "You needn't. I've got some picture books for you to look at. Come and sit on my lap, and we'll look at them together."

Philip slipped off his chair and limped over to her. He looked down so that she should not see his eyes. She put her arms round him.

"Look," she said, "that's the place where our Blessed Lord was born."

She showed him an Eastern town with flat roofs and cupolas and minarets. In the foreground was a group of palm-trees, and under them were resting two Arabs and some camels. Philip passed his hand over the picture as if he wanted to feel the houses and the loose habiliments of the nomads.

"Read what it says," he asked.

Mrs. Carey in her even voice read the opposite page. It was a romantic narrative of some Eastern traveller of the thirties, pompous maybe, but fragrant with the emotion with which the East came to the generation that followed Byron and Chateaubriand. In a moment or two Philip interrupted her.

"I want to see another picture."

When Mary Ann came in and Mrs. Carey rose to help her lay the cloth, Philip took the book in his hands and hurried through the illustrations. It was with difficulty that his aunt induced him to put the book down for tea. He had forgotten his horrible struggle to get the collect by heart; he had forgotten his tears. Next day it was raining, and he asked for the book again. Mrs. Carey gave it him joyfully. Talking over his future with her husband she had found that both desired him to take orders, and this eagerness for the book which described places hallowed by the presence of Jesus seemed a good sign. It looked as though the boy's mind addressed itself naturally to holy things. But in a day or two he asked for more books. Mr. Carey took him into his study, showed him the shelf in which he kept illustrated works, and chose for him one that dealt with Rome. Philip took it greedily. The pictures led him to a new amusement. He began to read the page before and the page after each engraving to find out what it was about, and soon he lost all interest in his toys.

Then, when no one was near, he took out books for himself; and per-haps because the first impression on his mind was made by an Eastern town, he found his chief amusement in those which described the Levant. His heart beat with excitement at the pictures of mosques and rich palaces; but there was one, in a book on Constantinople, which peculiarly stirred his imagination. It was called the Hall of the Thousand Columns. It was a Byzantine cistern, which the popular fancy had endowed with fantastic vastness; and the legend which he read told that a boat was always moored at the entrance to tempt the unwary, but no traveller venturing into the darkness had ever been seen again. And Philip wondered whether the boat went on for ever through one pillared alley after another or came at last to some strange mansion.

One day a good fortune befell him, for he hit upon Lane's translation of *The Thousand Nights and a Night*. He was captured first by the illustrations, and then he began to read, to start with, the stories that dealt with magic, and then the others; and those he liked he read again and again. He could think of nothing else. He forgot the life about him. He had to be called two or three times before he would come to his dinner. Insensibly he formed the most delightful habit in the world, the habit of reading: he did not know that thus he was providing himself with a refuge from all the distress of life; he did not know either that he was creating for himself an unreal world which would make the real world of every day a source of bitter disappointment. Presently he began to read other things. His brain was precocious. His uncle and aunt, seeing that he occupied himself and neither worried nor made a noise, ceased to trouble themselves about him. Mr. Carey had so many books that he did not know them, and as he read little he forgot the odd lots he had bought at one time and another because they were cheap. Haphazard among the sermons and homilies, the travels, the lives of the Saints, the Fathers, the histories of the church, were old-fashioned novels; and these Philip at last discovered. He chose them by their titles, and the first he read was *The Lancashire Witches*, and then he read *The Admirable Crichton*, and then many more. Whenever he started a book with two solitary travellers riding along the brink of a desperate ravine he knew he was safe.

The summer was come now, and the gardener, an old sailor, made him a hammock and fixed it up for him in the branches of a weeping willow. And here for long hours he lay, hidden from anyone who might come to the vicarage, reading, reading passionately. Time passed and it was July; August came: on Sundays the church was crowded with strangers, and the collection at the offertory often amounted to two pounds. Neither the Vicar nor Mrs. Carey went out of the garden much during this period; for they disliked strange faces, and they looked upon the visitors from London with aversion. The house opposite was taken for six weeks by a gentleman who had two little boys, and he sent in to ask if Philip would like to go and play with them; but Mrs. Carey returned a polite refusal. She was afraid that Philip would be corrupted by little boys from London. He was going to be a clergyman, and it was necessary that he should be preserved from contamination. She liked to see in him an infant Samuel.

X

THE Careys made up their minds to send Philip to King's School at Tercanbury. The neighbouring clergy sent their sons there. It was united by long tradition to the Cathedral: its headmaster was an honorary Canon, and a past headmaster was the Archdeacon. Boys were encouraged there to aspire to Holy Orders, and the education was such as might prepare an honest lad to spend his life in God's service. A preparatory school was attached to it, and to this it was arranged that Philip should go. Mr. Carey took him into Tercanbury one Thursday afternoon towards the end of September. All day Philip had been excited and rather frightened. He knew little of school life but what he had read in the stories of *The Boy's Own Paper*. He had also read *Eric, or Little by Little*.

When they got out of the train at Tercanbury, Philip felt sick with apprehension, and during the drive in to the town sat pale and silent. The high brick wall in front of the school gave it the look of a prison. There was a little door in it, which opened on their ringing; and a clumsy, untidy man came out and fetched Philip's tin trunk and his play-box. They were shown into the drawing-room; it was filled with massive, ugly furniture, and the chairs of the suite were placed round the walls with a forbidding rigidity. They waited for the headmaster.

"What's Mr. Watson like?" asked Philip, after a while.

"You'll see for yourself."

There was another pause. Mr. Carey wondered why the headmaster did not come. Presently Philip made an effort and spoke again.

"Tell him I've got a club-foot," he said.

Before Mr. Carey could speak the door burst open and Mr. Watson swept into the room. To Philip he seemed gigantic. He was a man of over six feet high, and broad, with enormous hands and a great red beard; he talked loudly in a jovial manner; but his aggressive cheerfulness struck terror in Philip's heart. He shook hands with Mr. Carey, and then took Philip's small hand in his.

"Well, young fellow, are you glad to come to school?" he shouted.

Philip reddened and found no word to answer.

"How old are you?"

"Nine," said Philip.

"You must say sir," said his uncle.

"I expect you've got a good lot to learn," the headmaster bellowed cheerily.

To give the boy confidence he began to tickle him with rough fingers. Philip, feeling shy and uncomfortable, squirmed under his touch.

"I've put him in the small dormitory for the present. . . . You'll like that, won't you?" he added to Philip. "Only eight of you in there. You won't feel so strange."

Then the door opened, and Mrs. Watson came in. She was a dark woman with black hair, neatly parted in the middle. She had curiously thick lips and a small round nose. Her eyes were large and black. There was a singular coldness in her appearance. She seldom spoke and smiled more seldom still. Her husband introduced Mr. Carey to her, and then gave Philip a friendly push towards her.

"This is a new boy, Helen. His name's Carey."

Without a word she shook hands with Philip and then sat down, not speaking, while the headmaster asked Mr. Carey how much Philip knew and what books he had been working with. The Vicar of Blackstable was a little embarrassed by Mr. Watson's boisterous heartiness, and in a moment or two got up.

"I think I'd better leave Philip with you now."

"That's all right," said Mr. Watson. "He'll be safe with me. He'll get on like a house on fire. Won't you, young fellow?"

Without waiting for an answer from Philip the big man burst into a great bellow of laughter. Mr. Carey kissed Philip on the forehead and went away.

"Come along, young fellow," shouted Mr. Watson. "I'll show you the school-room."

He swept out of the drawing-room with giant strides, and Philip hurriedly limped behind him. He was taken into a long, bare room with two tables that ran along its whole length; on each side of them were wooden forms.

"Nobody much here yet," said Mr. Watson. "I'll just show you the playground, and then I'll leave you to shift for yourself."

Mr. Watson led the way. Philip found himself in a large playground with high brick walls on three sides of it. On the fourth side was an iron railing through which you saw a vast lawn and beyond this some of the buildings of King's School. One small boy was wandering disconsolately, kicking up the gravel as he walked.

"Hulloa, Venning," shouted Mr. Watson. "When did you turn up?"

The small boy came forward and shook hands.

"Here's a new boy. He's older and

bigger than you, so don't you bully him."

The headmaster glared amicably at the two children, filling them with fear by the roar of his voice, and then with a guffaw left them.

"What's your name?"

"Carey."

"What's your father?"

"He's dead."

"Oh! Does your mother wash?"

"My mother's dead, too."

Philip thought this answer would cause the boy a certain awkwardness, but Venning was not to be turned from his facetiousness for so little.

"Well, did she wash?" he went on.

"Yes," said Philip indignantly.

"She was a washerwoman then?"

"No, she wasn't."

"Then she didn't wash."

The little boy crowed with delight at the success of his dialectic. Then he caught sight of Philip's feet.

"What's the matter with your foot?"

Philip instinctively tried to withdraw it from sight. He hid it behind the one which was whole.

"I've got a club-foot," he answered.

"How did you get it?"

"I've always had it."

"Let's have a look."

"No."

"Don't then."

The little boy accompanied the words with a sharp kick on Philip's shin, which Philip did not expect and thus could not guard against. The pain was so great that it made him gasp, but greater than the pain was the surprise. He did not know why Venning kicked him. He had not the presence of mind to give him a black eye. Besides, the boy was smaller than he, and he had read in *The Boy's Own Paper* that it was a mean thing to hit anyone smaller than yourself. While Philip was nursing his shin a third boy appeared, and his tormentor left him. In a little while he noticed that the pair were talking about him, and he felt they were looking at his feet. He grew hot and uncomfortable.

But others arrived, a dozen together, and then more, and they began to talk about their doings during the holidays, where they had been, and what wonderful cricket they had played. A few new boys appeared, and with these presently Philip found himself talking. He was shy and nervous. He was anxious to make himself pleasant, but he could not think of anything to say. He was asked a great many questions and answered them all quite willingly. One boy asked him whether he could play cricket.

"No," answered Philip. "I've got a club-foot."

The boy looked down quickly and reddened. Philip saw that he felt he had asked an unseemly question. He was too shy to apologise and looked at Philip awkwardly.

XI

Next morning when the clanging of a bell awoke Philip he looked round his cubicle in astonishment. Then a voice sang out, and he remembered where he was.

"Are you awake, Singer?"

The partitions of the cubicle were of polished pitch-pine, and there was a green curtain in front. In those days there was little thought of ventilation, and the windows were closed except when the dormitory was aired in the morning.

Philip got up and knelt down to say his prayers. It was a cold morning, and he shivered a little; but he had been taught by his uncle that his prayers were more acceptable to God if he said them in his nightshirt than if he waited till he was dressed. This did not surprise him, for he was beginning to realise that he was the creature of a God who appreciated the discomfort of his worshippers. Then he washed. There were two baths for the fifty boarders, and each boy had a bath once a week. The rest of his washing was done in a small basin on a wash-stand, which, with the bed and a chair, made up the furniture of each cubicle. The boys chatted gaily while they dressed. Philip was all ears. Then another bell sounded, and they ran downstairs. They took their seats on the forms on each side of the two long tables in the school-room; and Mr. Watson, followed by his wife and the servants, came in and sat down. Mr. Watson read prayers in an impressive manner, and the supplications thundered out in his loud voice as though they were threats personally addressed to each boy. Philip listened with anxiety. Then Mr. Watson read a chapter from the Bible, and the servants trooped out. In a moment the untidy youth brought in two large pots of tea and on a second journey immense dishes of bread and butter.

Philip had a squeamish appetite, and the thick slabs of poor butter on the bread turned his stomach, but he saw other boys scraping it off and followed their example. They all had potted meats and such like, which they had brought in their play-boxes; and some had 'extras,' eggs or bacon, upon which Mr. Watson made a profit. When he had asked Mr. Carey whether Philip was to have these, Mr. Carey replied that he did not think boys should be spoilt. Mr. Watson quite agreed with him—he considered nothing was better than bread and butter for growing lads—but some parents, unduly pampering their offspring, insisted on it.

Philip noticed that 'extras' gave boys a certain consideration and made up his mind, when he wrote to Aunt Louisa, to ask for them.

After breakfast the boys wandered out into the playground. Here the day-boys were gradually assembling. They were sons of the local clergy, of the officers at the Depot, and of such manufacturers or men of business as the old town possessed. Presently a bell rang, and they all trooped into school. This consisted of a large, long room at opposite ends of which two under-masters conducted the second and third forms, and of a smaller one, leading out of it, used by Mr. Watson, who taught the first form. To attach the preparatory to the senior school these three classes were known officially, on speech days and in reports, as upper, middle, and lower second. Philip was put in the last. The master, a red-faced man with a pleasant voice, was called Rice; he had a jolly manner with boys, and the time passed quickly. Philip was surprised when it was a quarter to eleven and they were let out for ten minutes' rest.

The whole school rushed noisily into the playground. The new boys were told to go into the middle, while the others stationed themselves along opposite walls. They began to play *Pig in the Middle*. The old boys ran from wall to wall while the new boys tried to catch them: when one was seized and the mystic words said—one, two, three, and a pig for me—he became a prisoner and, turning sides, helped to catch those who were still free. Philip saw a boy running past and tried to catch him, but his limp gave him no chance; and the runners, taking their opportunity, made straight for the ground he covered. Then one of them had the brilliant idea of imitating Philip's clumsy run. Other boys saw it and began to laugh; then they all copied the first; and they ran round Philip, limping grotesquely, screaming in their treble voices with shrill laughter. They lost their heads with the delight of their new amusement, and choked with helpless merriment. One of them tripped Philip up and he fell, heavily as he always fell, and cut his knee. They laughed all the louder when he got up. A boy pushed him from behind, and he would have fallen again if another had not caught him. The game was forgotten in the entertainment of Philip's deformity. One of them invented an odd, rolling limp that struck the rest as supremely ridiculous, and several of the boys lay down on the ground and rolled about in laughter: Philip was completely scared. He could not make out why they were laughing at him. His heart beat so that he could hardly breathe, and he was more frightened than he had ever been in his life. He stood still stupidly while the boys ran round him, mimicking and laughing; they shouted to him to try and catch them; but he did not move. He did not want them to see him run any more. He was using all his strength to prevent himself from crying.

Suddenly the bell rang, and they all trooped back to school. Philip's knee was bleeding, and he was dusty and dishevelled. For some minutes Mr. Rice could not control his form. They were excited still by the strange novelty, and Philip saw one or two of them furtively looking down at his feet. He tucked them under the bench.

In the afternoon they went up to play football, but Mr. Watson stopped Philip on the way out after dinner.

"I suppose you can't play football, Carey?" he asked him.

Philip blushed self-consciously.

"No, sir."

"Very well. You'd better go up to the field. You can walk as far as that, can't you?"

Philip had no idea where the field was, but he answered all the same.

"Yes, sir."

The boys went in charge of Mr. Rice, who glanced at Philip and, seeing he had not changed, asked why he was not going to play.

"Mr. Watson said I needn't, sir," said Philip.

"Why?"

There were boys all round him, looking at him curiously, and a feeling of shame came over Philip. He looked down without answering. Others gave the reply.

"He's got a club-foot, sir."

"Oh, I see."

Mr. Rice was quite young; he had only taken his degree a year before; and he was suddenly embarrassed. His instinct was to beg the boy's pardon, but he was too shy to do so. He made his voice gruff and loud.

"Now then, you boys, what are you waiting about for? Get on with you."

Some of them had already started and those that were left now set off, in groups of two or three.

"You'd better come along with me, Carey," said the master. "You don't know the way, do you?"

Philip guessed the kindness, and a sob came to his throat.

"I can't go very fast, sir."

"Then I'll go very slow," said the master, with a smile.

Philip's heart went out to the red-faced, commonplace young man who said a gentle word to him. He suddenly felt less unhappy.

But at night when they went up to bed and were undressing, the boy who was called Singer came out of his cubicle and put his head in Philip's.

"I say, let's look at your foot," he said.

"No," answered Philip.

He jumped into bed quickly.

"Don't say no to me," said Singer. "Come on, Mason."

The boy in the next cubicle was looking round the corner, and at the words he slipped in. They made for Philip and tried to tear the bed-clothes off him, but he held them tightly.

"Why can't you leave me alone?" he cried.

Singer seized a brush and with the back of it beat Philip's hands clenched on the blanket. Philip cried out.

"Why don't you show us your foot quietly?"

"I won't."

In desperation Philip clenched his fist and hit the boy who tormented him, but he was at a disadvantage, and the boy seized his arm. He began to turn it.

"Oh, don't, don't," said Philip. "You'll break my arm."

"Stop still then and put out your foot."

Philip gave a sob and a gasp. The boy gave the arm another wrench. The pain was unendurable.

"All right. I'll do it," said Philip.

He put out his foot. Singer still kept his hand on Philip's wrist. He looked curiously at the deformity.

"Isn't it beastly?" said Mason.

Another came in and looked too.

"Ugh," he said, in disgust.

"My word, it is rum," said Singer, making a face. "Is it hard?"

He touched it with the tip of his forefinger, cautiously, as though it were something that had a life of its own. Suddenly they heard Mr. Watson's heavy tread on the stairs. They threw the clothes back on Philip and dashed like rabbits into their cubicles. Mr. Watson came into the dormitory. Raising himself on tiptoe he could see over the rod that bore the green curtain, and he looked into two or three of the cubicles. The little boys were safely in bed. He put out the light and went out.

Singer called out to Philip, but he did not answer. He had got his teeth in the pillow so that his sobbing should be inaudible. He was not crying for the pain they had caused him, nor for the humiliation he had suffered when they looked at his foot, but with rage at himself because, unable to stand the torture, he had put out his foot of his own accord.

And then he felt the misery of his life. It seemed to his childish mind that this unhappiness must go on for ever. For no particular reason he remembered that cold morning when Emma had taken him out of bed and put him beside his mother. He had not thought of it once since it happened, but now he seemed to feel the warmth of his mother's body against his and her arms around him. Suddenly it seemed to him that his life was a dream, his mother's death, and the life at the vicarage, and these two wretched days at school, and he would awake in the morning and be back again at home. His tears dried as he thought of it. He was too unhappy, it must be nothing but a dream, and his mother was alive, and Emma would come up presently and go to bed. He fell asleep.

But when he awoke next morning it was to the clanging of a bell, and the first thing his eyes saw was the green curtain of his cubicle.

XII

As TIME went on Philip's deformity ceased to interest. It was accepted like one boy's red hair and another's unreasonable corpulence. But meanwhile he had grown horribly sensitive. He never ran if he could help it, because he knew it made his limp more conspicuous, and he adopted a peculiar walk. He stood still as much as he could, with his club-foot behind the other, so that it should not attract notice, and he was constantly on the look out for any reference to it. Because he could not join in the games which other boys played, their life remained strange to him; he only interested himself from the outside in their doings; and it seemed to him that there was a barrier between them and him. Sometimes they seemed to think that it was his fault if he could not play football, and he was unable to make them understand. He was left a good deal to himself. He had been inclined to talkativeness, but gradually he became silent. He began to think of the difference between himself and others.

The biggest boy in his dormitory, Singer, took a dislike to him, and Philip, small for his age, had to put up with a good deal of hard treatment. About half-way through the term a mania ran through the school for a game called Nibs. It was a game for two, played on a table or a form with steel pens. You had to push your nib with the fingernail so as to get the point of it over your opponent's, while he manœuvred to prevent this and to get the point of his nib over the back of yours; when this result was achieved you breathed on the ball of your thumb, pressed it hard on the two nibs, and if you were able then to lift them without dropping either, both nibs became yours. Soon nothing was seen but boys playing this game, and the more skilful acquired vast stores of nibs. But in a little while Mr. Watson made up his mind that it was a form of gambling, forbade the game, and confiscated all the nibs in the boys' possession. Philip had been very adroit, and it was with a heavy heart that he gave up his winnings; but his fingers itched to play still, and a few days later, on his way to the football field, he went into a shop and bought a pennyworth of J pens. He carried them loose in his pocket and enjoyed feeling them. Presently Singer found out that he had them. Singer had given up his nibs too, but he had kept back a very large one, called a Jumbo, which was almost unconquerable, and he could not resist the opportunity of getting Philip's Js out of him. Though Philip knew that he was at a disadvantage with his small nibs, he had an adventurous disposition and was willing to take the risk; besides, he was aware that Singer would not allow him to refuse. He had not played for a week and sat down to the game now with a thrill of excitement. He lost two of his small nibs quickly, and Singer was jubilant, but the third time by some chance the Jumbo slipped round and Philip was able to push his J across it. He crowed with triumph. At that moment Mr. Watson came in.

"What are you doing?" he asked.

He looked from Singer to Philip, but neither answered.

"Don't you know that I've forbidden you to play that idiotic game?"

Philip's heart beat fast. He knew what was coming and was dreadfully frightened, but in his fright there was a certain exultation. He had never been swished. Of course it would hurt, but it was something to boast about afterwards.

"Come into my study."

The headmaster turned, and they followed him side by side. Singer whispered to Philip:

"We're in for it."

Mr. Watson pointed to Singer.

"Bend over," he said.

Philip, very white, saw the boy quiver at each stroke, and after the third he heard him cry out. Three more followed.

"That'll do. Get up."

Singer stood up. The tears were streaming down his face. Philip stepped forward. Mr. Watson looked at him for a moment.

"I'm not going to cane you. You're a new boy. And I can't hit a cripple. Go away, both of you, and don't be naughty again."

When they got back into the school-room a group of boys, who had learned in some mysterious way what was happening, were waiting for them. They set upon Singer at once with eager questions. Singer faced them, his face red with the pain and marks of tears still on his cheeks. He pointed with his head at Philip, who was standing a little behind him.

"He got off because he's a cripple," he said angrily.

Philip stood silent and flushed. He felt that they looked at him with contempt.

"How many did you get?" one boy asked Singer.

But he did not answer. He was angry because he had been hurt.

"Don't ask me to play Nibs with you again," he said to Philip. "It's jolly nice for you. You don't risk anything."

"I didn't ask you."

"Didn't you!"

He quickly put out his foot and tripped Philip up. Philip was always rather unsteady on his feet, and he fell heavily to the ground.

"Cripple," said Singer.

For the rest of the term he tormented Philip cruelly, and, though Philip tried to keep out of his way, the school was so small that it was impossible; he tried being friendly and jolly with him; he abased himself so far as to buy him a knife; but though Singer took the knife he was not placated. Once or twice, driven beyond endurance, he hit and kicked the bigger boy, but Singer was so much stronger that Philip was helpless, and he was always forced after more or less torture to beg his pardon. It was that which rankled with Philip: he could not bear the humiliation of apologies, which were wrung from him by pain greater than he could bear. And what made it worse was that there seemed no end to his wretchedness; Singer was only eleven and would not go to the upper school till he was thirteen. Philip realized that he must live two years with a tormentor from whom there was no escape. He was only happy while he was working and when he got into bed. And often there recurred to him then that queer feeling that his life with all its misery was nothing but a dream, and that he would awake in the morning in his own little bed in London.

XIII

Two years passed, and Philip was nearly twelve. He was in the first form, within two or three places of the top, and after Christmas when several boys would be leaving for the senior school he would be head boy. He had already quite a collection of prizes, worthless books on bad paper, but in gorgeous bindings decorated with the arms of the school: his position had freed him from bullying, and he was not unhappy. His fellows forgave him his success because of his deformity.

"After all, it's jolly easy for him to get prizes," they said, "there's nothing he *can* do but swat."

He had lost his early terror of Mr. Watson. He had grown used to the loud voice, and when the headmaster's heavy hand was laid on his shoulder Philip discerned vaguely the intention of a caress. He had the good memory which is more useful for scholastic achievements than mental power, and he knew Mr. Watson expected him to leave the preparatory school with a scholarship.

But he had grown very self-conscious. The new-born child does not realise that his body is more a part of himself than surrounding objects, and will play with his toes without any feeling that they belong to him more than the rattle by his side; and it is only by degrees, through pain, that he understands the fact of the body. And experiences of the same kind are necessary for the individual to become conscious of himself; but here there is the difference that, although everyone becomes equally conscious of his body as a separate and complete organism, everyone does not become equally conscious of himself as a complete and separate personality. The feeling of apartness from others comes to most with puberty, but it is not always developed to such a degree as to make the difference between the individual and his fellows noticeable to the individual. It is such as he, as little conscious of himself as the bee in a hive, who are the lucky in life, for they have the best chance of happiness: their activities are shared by all, and their pleasures are only pleasures because they are enjoyed in common; you will see them on Whit-Monday dancing on Hampstead Heath, shouting at a football match, or from club windows in Pall Mall cheering a royal procession. It is because of them that man has been called a social animal.

Philip passed from the innocence of childhood to bitter consciousness of himself by the ridicule which his club-foot had excited. The circumstances of his case were so peculiar that he could not apply to them the ready-made rules which acted well enough in ordinary affairs, and he was forced to think for himself. The many books he had read filled his mind with ideas which, because he only half understood them, gave more scope to his imagination. Beneath his painful shyness something was growing up within him, and obscurely he realised his personality. But at times it gave him odd surprises; he did things, he knew not why, and afterwards when he thought of them found himself all at sea.

There was a boy called Luard between whom and Philip a friendship had arisen, and one day, when they were playing together in the schoolroom, Luard began to perform some trick with an ebony pen-holder of Philip's.

"Don't play the giddy ox," said Philip. "You'll only break it."

"I shan't."

But no sooner were the words out of the boy's mouth than the penholder snapped in two. Luard looked at Philip with dismay.

"Oh, I say, I'm awfully sorry."

The tears rolled down Philip's cheeks, but he did not answer.

"I say, what's the matter?" said Luard, with surprise. "I'll get you another one exactly the same."

"It's not about the pen-holder I care," said Philip, in a trembling voice, "only it was given me by the mater, just before she died."

"I say, I'm awfully sorry, Carey."

"It doesn't matter. It wasn't your fault."

Philip took the two pieces of the pen-holder and looked at them. He tried to restrain his sobs. He felt utterly miserable. And yet he could not tell why, for he knew quite well that he had bought the pen-holder during his last holidays at Blackstable for one and twopence. He did not know in the least what had made him invent that pathetic story, but he was quite as unhappy as though it had

been true. The pious atmosphere of the vicarage and the religious tone of the school had made Philip's conscience very sensitive; he absorbed insensibly the feeling about him that the Tempter was ever on the watch to gain his immortal soul; and though he was not more truthful than most boys he never told a lie without suffering from remorse. When he thought over this incident he was very much distressed, and made up his mind that he must go to Luard and tell him that the story was an invention. Though he dreaded humiliation more than anything in the world, he hugged himself for two or three days at the thought of the agonising joy of humiliating himself to the Glory of God. But he never got any further. He satisfied his conscience by the more comfortable method of expressing his repentance only to the Almighty. But he could not understand why he should have been so genuinely affected by the story he was making up. The tears that flowed down his grubby cheeks were real tears. Then by some accident of association there occurred to him that scene when Emma had told him of his mother's death, and, though he could not speak for crying, he had insisted on going in to say good-bye to the Misses Watkin so that they might see his grief and pity him.

XIV

THEN a wave of religiosity passed through the school. Bad language was no longer heard, and the little nastinesses of small boys were looked upon with hostility; the bigger boys, like

the lords temporal of the Middle Ages, used the strength of their arms to persuade those weaker than themselves to virtuous courses.

Philip, his restless mind avid for

new things, became very devout. He heard soon that it was possible to join a Bible League, and wrote to London for particulars. These consisted in a form to be filled up with the applicant's name, age, and school; a solemn declaration to be signed that he would read a set portion of Holy Scripture every night for a year; and a request for half a crown; this, it was explained, was demanded partly to prove the earnestness of the applicant's desire to become a member of the League, and partly to cover clerical expenses. Philip duly sent the papers and the money, and in return received a calendar worth about a penny, on which was set down the appointed passage to be read each day, and a sheet of paper on one side of which was a picture of the Good Shepherd and a lamb, and on the other, decoratively framed in red lines, a short prayer which had to be said before beginning to read.

Every evening he undressed as quickly as possible in order to have time for his task before the gas was put out. He read industriously, as he read always, without criticism, stories of cruelty, deceit, ingratitude, dishonesty, and low cunning. Actions which would have excited his horror in the life about him, in the reading passed through his mind without comment, because they were committed under direct inspiration of God. The method of the League was to alternate a book of the Old Testament with a book of the New, and one night Philip came across these words of Jesus Christ:

If ye have faith, and doubt not, ye shall not only do this which is done to the fig-tree, but also if ye shall say unto this mountain, Be thou removed, and be thou cast into the sea; it shall

be done.

And all this, whatsoever ye shall ask in prayer, believing, ye shall receive.

They made no particular impression on him, but it happened that two or three days later, being Sunday, the Canon in residence chose them for the text of his sermon. Even if Philip had wanted to hear this it would have been impossible, for the boys of King's School sit in the choir, and the pulpit stands at the corner of the transept so that the preacher's back is almost turned to them. The distance also is so great that it needs a man with a fine voice and a knowledge of elocution to make himself heard in the choir; and according to long usage the Canons of Tercanbury are chosen for their learning rather than for any qualities which might be of use in a cathedral church. But the words of the text, perhaps because he had read them so short a while before, came clearly enough to Philip's ears, and they seemed on a sudden to have a personal application. He thought about them through most of the sermon, and that night, on getting into bed, he turned over the pages of the Gospel and found once more the passage. Though he believed implicitly everything he saw in print, he had learned already that in the Bible things that said one thing quite clearly often mysteriously meant another. There was no one he liked to ask at school, so he kept the question he had in mind till the Christmas holidays, and then one day he made an opportunity. It was after supper and prayers were just finished. Mrs. Carey was counting the eggs that Mary Ann had brought in as usual and writing on each one the date. Philip stood at the table and pretended to turn listlessly the pages of the Bible.

"I say, Uncle William, this passage here, does it really mean that?"

He put his finger against it as though he had come across it accidentally.

Mr. Carey looked up over his spectacles. He was holding *The Blackstable Times* in front of the fire. It had come in that evening damp from the press, and the Vicar always aired it for ten minutes before he began to read.

"What passage is that?" he asked.

"Why, this about if you have faith you can remove mountains."

"If it says so in the Bible it is so, Philip," said Mrs. Carey gently, taking up the plate-basket.

Philip looked at his uncle for an answer.

"It's a matter of faith."

"D'you mean to say that if you really believed you could move mountains you could?"

"By the grace of God," said the Vicar.

"Now, say good-night to your uncle, Philip," said Aunt Louisa. "You're not wanting to move a mountain tonight, are you?"

Philip allowed himself to be kissed on the forehead by his uncle and preceded Mrs. Carey upstairs. He had got the information he wanted. His little room was icy, and he shivered when he put on his nightgown. But he always felt that his prayers were more pleasing to God when he said them under conditions of discomfort. The coldness of his hands and feet were an offering to the Almighty. And tonight he sank on his knees, buried his face in his hands, and prayed to God with all his might that He would make his club-foot whole. It was a very small thing beside the moving of mountains. He knew that God could do it if He wished, and his own faith was complete. Next morning, finishing his prayers with the same request, he fixed a date for the miracle.

"Oh, God, in Thy loving mercy and goodness, if it be Thy will, please make my foot all right on the night before I go back to school."

He was glad to get his petition into a formula, and he repeated it later in the dining-room during the short pause which the Vicar always made after prayers, before he rose from his knees. He said it again in the evening and again, shivering in his nightshirt, before he got into bed. And he believed. For once he looked forward with eagerness to the end of the holidays. He laughed to himself as he thought of his uncle's astonishment when he ran down the stairs three at a time; and after breakfast he and Aunt Louisa would have to hurry out and buy a new pair of boots. At school they would be astounded.

"Hulloa, Carey, what have you done with your foot?"

"Oh, it's all right now," he would answer casually, as though it were the most natural thing in the world.

He would be able to play football. His heart leaped as he saw himself running, running, faster than any of the other boys. At the end of the Easter term there were the sports, and he would be able to go in for the races; he rather fancied himself over the hurdles. It would be splendid to be like everyone else, not to be stared at curiously by new boys who did not know about his deformity, nor at the baths in summer to need incredible precautions, while he was undressing, before he could hide his foot in the water.

He prayed with all the power of his soul. No doubts assailed him. He was confident in the word of God. And the night before he was to go back to school he went up to bed tremulous with excitement. There was snow on the ground, and Aunt Louisa had allowed herself the un- accustomed luxury of a fire in her bed-room; but in Philip's little room it was so cold that his fingers were numb, and he had great difficulty in undoing his collar. His teeth chattered. The idea came to him that he must do something more than usual to attract the attention of God, and he turned back the rug which was in front of his bed so that he could kneel on the bare boards; and then it struck him that his nightshirt was a softness that might displease his Maker, so he took it off and said his prayers naked. When he got into bed he was so cold that for some time he could not sleep, but when he did, it was so soundly that Mary Ann had to shake him when she brought in his hot water next morning. She talked to him while she drew the curtains, but he did not answer; he had remembered at once that this was the morning for the miracle. His heart was filled with joy and gratitude. His first instinct was to put down his hand and feel the foot which was whole now, but to do this seemed to doubt the goodness of God. He knew that his foot was well. But at last he made up his mind, and with the toes of his right foot he just touched his left. Then he passed his hand over it.

He limped downstairs just as Mary Ann was going into the dining-room for prayers, and then he sat down to breakfast.

"You're very quiet this morning, Philip," said Aunt Louisa presently.

"He's thinking of the good break- fast he'll have at school tomorrow," said the Vicar.

When Philip answered, it was in a way that always irritated his uncle, with something that had nothing to do with the matter in hand. He called it a bad habit of wool-gathering.

"Supposing you'd asked God to do something," said Philip, "and really believed it was going to happen, like moving a mountain, I mean, and you had faith, and it didn't happen, what would it mean?"

"What a funny boy you are!" said Aunt Louisa. "You asked about mov- ing mountains two or three weeks ago."

"It would just mean that you hadn't got faith," answered Uncle William.

Philip accepted the explanation. If God had not cured him, it was be- cause he did not really believe. And yet he did not see how he could be- lieve more than he did. But perhaps he had not given God enough time. He had only asked Him for nineteen days. In a day or two he began his prayer again, and this time he fixed upon Easter. That was the day of His Son's glorious resurrection, and God in His happiness might be mercifully inclined. But now Philip added other means of attaining his desire: he be- gan to wish, when he saw a new moon or a dappled horse, and he looked out for shooting stars; during exeat they had a chicken at the vicarage, and he broke the lucky bone with Aunt Louisa and wished again, each time that his foot might be made whole. He was appealing un- consciously to gods older to his race than the God of Israel. And he bom- barded the Almighty with his prayer, at odd times of the day, whenever it occurred to him, in identical words always, for it seemed to him im- portant to make his request in the same terms. But presently the feeling came to him that this time also his faith would not be great enough. He could not resist the doubt that assailed him. He made his own experience into a general rule.

"I suppose no one ever has faith enough," he said.

It was like the salt which his nurse used to tell him about: you could catch any bird by putting salt on his tail; and once he had taken a little bag of it into Kensington Gardens. But he could never get near enough to put the salt on a bird's tail. Before Easter he had given up the struggle. He felt a dull resentment against his uncle for taking him in. The text which spoke of the moving of mountains was just one of those that said one thing and meant another. He thought his uncle had been playing a practical joke on him.

XV

THE King's School at Tercanbury, to which Philip went when he was thirteen, prided itself on its antiquity. It traced its origin to an abbey school, founded before the Conquest, where the rudiments of learning were taught by Augustine monks; and, like many another establishment of this sort, on the destruction of the monasteries it had been reorganised by the officers of King Henry VIII and thus acquired its name. Since then, pursuing its modest course, it had given to the sons of the local gentry and of the professional people of Kent an education sufficient to their needs. One or two men of letters, beginning with a poet, than whom only Shakespeare had a more splendid genius, and ending with a writer of prose whose view of life has affected profoundly the generation of which Philip was a member, had gone forth from its gates to achieve fame; it had produced one or two eminent lawyers, but eminent lawyers are common, and one or two soldiers of distinction; but during the three centuries since its separation from the monastic order it had trained especially men of the church, bishops, deans, canons, and above all country clergymen: there were boys in the school whose fathers, grandfathers, great-grandfathers, had been educated there and had all been rectors of parishes in the diocese of Tercanbury; and they came to it with their minds made up already to be ordained. But there were signs notwithstanding that even there changes were coming; for a few, repeating what they had heard at home, said that the Church was no longer what it used to be. It wasn't so much the money; but the class of people who went in for it weren't the same; and two or three boys knew curates whose fathers were tradesmen: they'd rather go out to the Colonies (in those days the Colonies were still the last hope of those who could get nothing to do in England) than be a curate under some chap who wasn't a gentleman. At King's School, as at Blackstable Vicarage, a tradesman was anyone who was not lucky enough to own land (and here a fine distinction was made between the gentleman farmer and the landowner), or did not follow one of the four professions to which it was possible for a gentleman to belong. Among the day-boys, of whom there were about a hundred and fifty, sons of the local gentry and of the men stationed at the Depot, those whose fathers were engaged in business were made to feel the degradation of their state.

The masters had no patience with modern ideas of education, which they read of sometimes in *The Times* or *The Guardian,* and hoped fervently that King's School would remain true to its old traditions. The dead languages were taught with such thoroughness that an old boy seldom thought of Homer or Virgil in after life without a qualm of boredom; and though in the common room at dinner one or two bolder spirits suggested that mathematics were of increasing importance, the general feeling was that they were a less noble study than the classics. Neither German nor chemistry was taught, and French only by the form-masters; they could keep order better than a foreigner, and, since they knew the grammar as well as any Frenchman, it seemed unimportant that none of them could have got a cup of coffee in the restaurant at Boulogne unless the waiter had known a little English. Geography was taught chiefly by making boys draw maps, and this was a favourite occupation, especially when the country dealt with was mountainous: it was possible to waste a great deal of time in drawing the Andes or the Apennines. The masters, graduates of Oxford or Cambridge, were ordained and unmarried; if by chance they wished to marry they could only do so by accepting one of the smaller livings at the disposal of the Chapter; but for many years none of them had cared to leave the refined society of Tercanbury, which owing to the cavalry Depot had a martial as well as an ecclesiastical tone, for the monotony of life in a country rectory; and they were now all men of middle age.

The headmaster, on the other hand, was obliged to be married, and he conducted the school till age began to tell upon him. When he retired he was rewarded with a much better living than any of the under-masters could hope for, and an honorary Canonry.

But a year before Philip entered the school a great change had come over it. It had been obvious for some time that Dr. Fleming, who had been headmaster for the quarter of a century, was become too deaf to continue his work to the greater glory of God; and when one of the livings on the outskirts of the city fell vacant, with a stipend of six hundred a year, the Chapter offered it to him in such a manner as to imply that they thought it high time for him to retire. He could nurse his ailments comfortably on such an income. Two or three curates who had hoped for preferment told their wives it was scandalous to give a parish that needed a young, strong, and energetic man to an old fellow who knew nothing of parochial work, and had feathered his nest already; but the mutterings of the unbeneficed clergy do not reach the ears of a cathedral Chapter. And as for the parishioners they had nothing to say in the matter, and therefore nobody asked for their opinion. The Wesleyans and the Baptists both had chapels in the village.

When Dr. Fleming was thus disposed of it became necessary to find a successor. It was contrary to the traditions of the school that one of the lower-masters should be chosen. The common-room was unanimous in desiring the election of Mr. Watson, headmaster of the preparatory school; he could hardly be described as already a master of King's School, they had all known him for twenty years, and there was no danger that he would make a nuisance of himself. But the Chapter sprang a surprise on them. It chose a man called Perkins. At first nobody knew who Perkins was, and the name favourably impressed no one; but before the shock of it had passed away, it was realised that Perkins was the son of Perkins the linendraper. Dr. Fleming informed the masters just before dinner, and his manner showed his consternation. Such of them as were dining in, ate their meal almost in silence, and no reference was made to the matter till the servants had left the room. Then they set to. The names of those present on this occasion are unimportant, but they had been known to generations of schoolboys as Sighs, Tar, Winks, Squirts, and Pat.

They all knew Tom Perkins. The first thing about him was that he was not a gentleman. They remembered him quite well. He was a small, dark boy, with untidy black hair and large eyes. He looked like a gipsy. He had come to the school as a day-boy, with the best scholarship on their endowment, so that his education had cost him nothing. Of course he was brilliant. At every Speech-Day he was loaded with prizes. He was their show-boy, and they remembered now bitterly their fear that he would try to get some scholarship at one of the larger public schools and so pass out of their hands. Dr. Fleming had gone to the linendraper his father—they all remembered the shop, Perkins and Cooper, in St. Catherine's Street—and said he hoped Tom would remain with them till he went to Oxford. The school was Perkins and Cooper's best customer, and Mr. Perkins was only too glad to give the required assurance. Tom Perkins continued to triumph, he was the finest classical scholar that Dr. Fleming remembered, and on leaving the school took with

him the most valuable scholarship they had to offer. He got another at Magdalen and settled down to a brilliant career at the University. The school magazine recorded the distinctions he achieved year after year, and when he got his double first Dr. Fleming himself wrote a few words of eulogy on the front page. It was with greater satisfaction that they welcomed his success, since Perkins and Cooper had fallen upon evil days: Cooper drank like a fish, and just before Tom Perkins took his degree the linendrapers filed their petition in bankruptcy.

In due course Tom Perkins took Holy Orders and entered upon the profession for which he was so admirably suited. He had been an assistant master at Wellington and then at Rugby.

But there was quite a difference between welcoming his success at other schools and serving under his leadership in their own. Tar had frequently given him lines, and Squirts had boxed his ears. They could not imagine how the Chapter had made such a mistake. No one could be expected to forget that he was the son of a bankrupt linendraper, and the alcoholism of Cooper seemed to increase the disgrace. It was understood that the Dean had supported his candidature with zeal, so the Dean would probably ask him to dinner; but would the pleasant little dinners in the precincts ever be the same when Tom Perkins sat at the table? And what about the Depot? He really could not expect officers and gentlemen to receive him as one of themselves. It would do the school incalculable harm. Parents would be dissatisfied, and no one could be surprised if there were wholesale withdrawals. And then the indignity of calling him Mr. Perkins! The masters thought by way of protest of sending in their resignations in a body, but the uneasy fear that they would be accepted with equanimity restrained them.

"The only thing is to prepare ourselves for changes," said Sighs, who had conducted the fifth form for five and twenty years with unparalleled incompetence.

And when they saw him they were not reassured. Dr. Fleming invited them to meet him at luncheon. He was now a man of thirty-two, tall and lean, but with the same wild and unkempt look they remembered on him as a boy. His clothes, ill-made and shabby, were put on untidily. His hair was as black and as long as ever, and he had plainly never learned to brush it; it fell over his forehead with every gesture, and he had a quick movement of the hand with which he pushed it back from his eyes. He had a black moustache and a beard which came high up on his face almost to the cheek-bones. He talked to the masters quite easily, as though he had parted from them a week or two before; he was evidently delighted to see them. He seemed unconscious of the strangeness of the position and appeared not to notice any oddness in being addressed as Mr. Perkins.

When he bade them good-bye, one of the masters, for something to say, remarked that he was allowing himself plenty of time to catch his train.

"I want to go round and have a look at the shop," he answered cheerfully.

There was a distinct embarrassment. They wondered that he could be so tactless, and to make it worse Dr. Fleming had not heard what he said. His wife shouted it in his ear.

"He wants to go round and look at his father's old shop."

Only Tom Perkins was unconscious of the humiliation which the whole party felt. He turned to Mrs. Fleming.

"Who's got it now, d'you know?"

She could hardly answer. She was very angry.

"It's still a linendraper's," she said bitterly. "Grove is the name. We don't deal there any more."

"I wonder if he'd let me go over the house."

"I expect he would if you explain who you are."

It was not till the end of dinner that evening that any reference was made in the common-room to the subject that was in all their minds. Then it was Sighs who asked:

"Well, what did you think of our new head?"

They thought of the conversation at luncheon. It was hardly a conversation; it was a monologue. Perkins had talked incessantly. He talked very quickly, with a flow of easy words and in a deep, resonant voice. He had a short, odd little laugh which showed his white teeth. They had followed him with difficulty, for his mind darted from subject to subject with a connection they did not always catch. He talked of pedagogics, and this was natural enough; but he had much to say of modern theories in Germany which they had never heard of and received with misgiving. He talked of the classics, but he had been to Greece, and he discoursed of archæology; he had once spent a winter digging; they could not see how that helped a man to teach boys to pass examinations. He talked of politics. It sounded odd to them to hear him compare Lord Beaconsfield with Alcibiades. He talked of Mr. Gladstone and Home Rule. They realised that he was a Liberal. Their hearts sank. He talked of German philosophy and of French fiction. They could not think a man profound whose interests were so diverse.

It was Winks who summed up the general impression and put it into a form they all felt conclusively damning. Winks was the master of the upper third, a weak-kneed man with drooping eyelids. He was too tall for his strength, and his movements were slow and languid. He gave an impression of lassitude, and his nickname was eminently appropriate.

"He's very enthusiastic," said Winks.

Enthusiasm was ill-bred. Enthusiasm was ungentlemanly. They thought of the Salvation Army with its braying trumpets and its drums. Enthusiasm meant change. They had goose-flesh when they thought of all the pleasant old habits which stood in imminent danger. They hardly dared to look forward to the future.

"He looks more of a gipsy than ever," said one, after a pause.

"I wonder if the Dean and Chapter knew that he was a Radical when they elected him," another observed bitterly.

But conversation halted. They were too much disturbed for words.

When Tar and Sighs were walking together to the Chapter House on Speech-Day a week later, Tar, who had a bitter tongue, remarked to his colleague:

"Well, we've seen a good many Speech-Days here, haven't we? I wonder if we shall see another."

Sighs was more melancholy even than usual.

"If anything worth having comes along in the way of a living I don't mind when I retire."

XVI

A year passed, and when Philip came to the school the old masters were all in their places; but a good many changes had taken place notwithstanding their stubborn resistance, none the less formidable because it was concealed under an apparent desire to fall in with the new head's ideas. Though the form-masters still taught French to the lower school, another master had come, with a degree of doctor of philology from the University of Heidelberg and a record of three years spent in a French lycée, to teach French to the upper forms and German to anyone who cared to take it up instead of Greek. Another master was engaged to teach mathematics more systematically than had been found necessary hitherto. Neither of these was ordained. This was a real revolution, and when the pair arrived the older masters received them with distrust. A laboratory had been fitted up, army classes were instituted; they all said the character of the school was changing. And heaven only knew what further projects Mr. Perkins turned in that untidy head of his. The school was small as public schools go, there were not more than two hundred boarders; and it was difficult for it to grow larger, for it was huddled up against the Cathedral; the precincts, with the exception of a house in which some of the masters lodged, were occupied by the cathedral clergy; and there was no more room for building. But Mr. Perkins devised an elaborate scheme by which he might obtain sufficient space to make the school double its present size. He wanted to attract boys from London. He thought it would be good for them to be thrown in contact with the Kentish lads, and it would sharpen the country wits of these.

"It's against all our traditions," said Sighs, when Mr. Perkins made the suggestion to him. "We've rather gone out of our way to avoid the contamination of boys from London."

"Oh, what nonsense!" said Mr. Perkins.

No one had ever told the formmaster before that he talked nonsense, and he was meditating an acid reply, in which perhaps he might insert a veiled reference to hosiery, when Mr. Perkins in his impetuous way attacked him outrageously.

"That house in the Precincts—if you'd only marry I'd get the Chapter to put another couple of stories on, and we'd make dormitories and studies, and your wife could help you."

The elderly clergyman gasped. Why should he marry? He was fifty-seven, a man couldn't marry at fifty-seven. He couldn't start looking after a house at his time of life. He didn't want to marry. If the choice lay between that and the country living he would much sooner resign. All he wanted now was peace and quietness.

"I'm not thinking of marrying," he said.

Mr. Perkins looked at him with his dark, bright eyes, and if there was a twinkle in them poor Sighs never saw it.

"What a pity! Couldn't you marry to oblige me? It would help me a great deal with the Dean and Chapter when I suggest rebuilding your house."

But Mr. Perkins' most unpopular innovation was his system of taking occasionally another man's form. He asked it as a favour, but after all it was a favour which could not be refused, and as Tar, otherwise Mr. Turner, said, it was undignified for all parties. He gave no warning, but

after morning prayers would say to one of the masters:

"I wonder if you'd mind taking the Sixth today at eleven. We'll change over, shall we?"

They did not know whether this was usual at other schools, but certainly it had never been done at Tercanbury. The results were curious. Mr. Turner, who was the first victim, broke the news to his form that the headmaster would take them for Latin that day, and on the pretence that they might like to ask him a question or two so that they should not make perfect fools of themselves, spent the last quarter of an hour of the history lesson in construing for them the passage of Livy which had been set for the day; but when he rejoined his class and looked at the paper on which Mr. Perkins had written the marks, a surprise awaited him; for the two boys at the top of the form seemed to have done very ill, while others who had never distinguished themselves before were given full marks. When he asked Eldridge, his cleverest boy, what was the meaning of this the answer came sullenly:

"Mr. Perkins never gave us any construing to do. He asked me what I knew about General Gordon."

Mr. Turner looked at him in astonishment. The boys evidently felt they had been hardly used, and he could not help agreeing with their silent dissatisfaction. He could not see either what General Gordon had to do with Livy. He hazarded an enquiry afterwards.

"Eldridge was dreadfully put out because you asked him what he knew about General Gordon," he said to the headmaster, with an attempt at a chuckle.

Mr. Perkins laughed.

"I saw they'd got to the agrarian laws of Caius Gracchus, and I wondered if they knew anything about the agrarian troubles in Ireland. But all they knew about Ireland was that Dublin was on the Liffey. So I wondered if they'd ever heard of General Gordon."

Then the horrid fact was disclosed that the new head had a mania for general information. He had doubts about the utility of examinations on subjects which had been crammed for the occasion. He wanted common sense.

Sighs grew more worried every month; he could not get the thought out of his head that Mr. Perkins would ask him to fix a day for his marriage; and he hated the attitude the head adopted towards classical literature. There was no doubt that he was a fine scholar, and he was engaged on a work which was quite in the right tradition: he was writing a treatise on the trees in Latin literature; but he talked of it flippantly, as though it were a pastime of no great importance, like billiards, which engaged his leisure but was not to be considered with seriousness. And Squirts, the master of the middle-third, grew more ill-tempered every day.

It was in his form that Philip was put on entering the school. The Rev. B. B. Gordon was a man by nature ill-suited to be a schoolmaster: he was impatient and choleric. With no one to call him to account, with only small boys to face him, he had long lost all power of self-control. He began his work in a rage and ended it in a passion. He was a man of middle height and of a corpulent figure; he had sandy hair, worn very short and now growing gray, and a small bristly moustache. His large face, with indistinct features and small blue eyes, was naturally red, but during his frequent attacks of anger it grew dark and purple. His nails were bitten to the quick,

for while some trembling boy was construing he would sit at his desk shaking with the fury that consumed him, and gnaw his fingers. Stories, perhaps exaggerated, were told of his violence, and two years before there had been some excitement in the school when it was heard that one father was threatening a prosecution: he had boxed the ears of a boy named Walters with a book so violently that his hearing was affected and the boy had to be taken away from the school. The boy's father lived in Tercanbury, and there had been much indignation in the city, the local paper had referred to the matter; but Mr. Walters was only a brewer, so the sympathy was divided. The rest of the boys, for reasons best known to themselves, though they loathed the master, took his side in the affair, and, to show their indignation that the school's business had been dealt with outside, made things as uncomfortable as they could for Walters' younger brother, who still remained. But Mr. Gordon had only escaped the country living by the skin of his teeth, and he had never hit a boy since. The right the masters possessed to cane boys on the hand was taken away from them, and Squirts could no longer emphasize his anger by beating his desk with the cane. He never did more now than take a boy by the shoulders and shake him. He still made a naughty or refractory lad stand with one arm stretched out for anything from ten minutes to half an hour, and he was as violent as before with his tongue.

No master could have been more unfitted to teach things to so shy a boy as Philip. He had come to the school with fewer terrors than he had when first he went to Mr. Watson's. He knew a good many boys who had been with him at the preparatory school. He felt more grown-up, and instinctively realised that among the larger numbers his deformity would be less noticeable. But from the first day Mr. Gordon struck terror in his heart; and the master, quick to discern the boys who were frightened of him, seemed on that account to take a peculiar dislike to him. Philip had enjoyed his work, but now he began to look upon the hours passed in school with horror. Rather than risk an answer which might be wrong and excite a storm of abuse from the master, he would sit stupidly silent, and when it came towards his turn to stand up and construe he grew sick and white with apprehension. His happy moments were those when Mr. Perkins took the form. He was able to gratify the passion for general knowledge which beset the head-master; he had read all sorts of strange books beyond his years, and often Mr. Perkins, when a question was going round the room, would stop at Philip with a smile that filled the boy with rapture, and say:

"Now, Carey, you tell them."

The good marks he got on these occasions increased Mr. Gordon's in-dignation. One day it came to Philip's turn to translate, and the master sat there glaring at him and furiously bit-ing his thumb. He was in a ferocious mood. Philip began to speak in a low voice.

"Don't mumble," shouted the mas-ter.

Something seemed to stick in Philip's throat.

"Go on. Go on. Go on."

Each time the words were screamed more loudly. The effect was to drive all he knew out of Philip's head, and he looked at the printed page vacantly. Mr. Gordon began to breathe heavily.

"If you don't know why don't you say so? Do you know it or not? Did you hear all this construed last time

or not? Why don't you speak? Speak, you blockhead, speak!"

The master seized the arms of his chair and grasped them as though to prevent himself from falling upon Philip. They knew that in past days he often used to seize boys by the throat till they almost choked. The veins in his forehead stood out and his face grew dark and threatening. He was a man insane.

Philip had known the passage per-fectly the day before, but now he could remember nothing.

"I don't know it," he gasped.

"Why don't you know it? Let's take the words one by one. We'll soon see if you don't know it."

Philip stood silent, very white, trembling a little, with his head bent down on the book. The master's breathing grew almost stertorous.

"The headmaster says you're clever. I don't know how he sees it. General information." He laughed savagely. "I don't know what they put you in his form for. Blockhead."

He was pleased with the word, and he repeated it at the top of his voice.

"Blockhead! Blockhead! Club-footed blockhead!"

That relieved him a little. He saw Philip redden suddenly. He told him to fetch the Black Book. Philip put down his Cæsar and went silently out. The Black Book was a sombre volume in which the names of boys were written with their misdeeds, and when a name was down three times it meant a caning. Philip went to the head-master's house and knocked at his study-door. Mr. Perkins was seated at his table.

"May I have the Black Book, please, sir."

"There it is," answered Mr. Perkins, indicating its place by a nod of his head. "What have you been doing that you shouldn't?"

"I don't know, sir."

Mr. Perkins gave him a quick look, but without answering went on with his work. Philip took the book and went out. When the hour was up, a few minutes later, he brought it back.

"Let me have a look at it," said the headmaster. "I see Mr. Gordon has black-booked you for 'gross impertinence.' What was it?"

"I don't know, sir. Mr. Gordon said I was a club-footed blockhead."

Mr. Perkins looked at him again. He wondered whether there was sarcasm behind the boy's reply, but he was still much too shaken. His face was white and his eyes had a look of terrified distress. Mr. Perkins got up and put the book down. As he did so he took up some photographs.

"A friend of mine sent me some pictures of Athens this morning," he said casually. "Look here, there's the Acropolis."

He began explaining to Philip what he saw. The ruin grew vivid with his words. He showed him the theatre of Dionysus and explained in what order the people sat, and how beyond they could see the blue Aegean. And then suddenly he said:

"I remember Mr. Gordon used to call me a gipsy counterjumper when I was in his form."

And before Philip, his mind fixed on the photographs, had time to gather the meaning of the remark, Mr. Perkins was showing him a picture of Salamis, and with his finger, a finger of which the nail had a little black edge to it, was pointing out how the Greek ships were placed and how the Persian.

XVII

PHILIP passed the next two years with comfortable monotony. He was not bullied more than other boys of his size; and his deformity, withdrawing him from games, acquired for him an insignificance for which he was grateful. He was not popular, and he was very lonely. He spent a couple of terms with Winks in the Upper Third. Winks, with his weary manner and his drooping eyelids, looked infinitely bored. He did his duty, but he did it with an abstracted mind. He was kind, gentle, and foolish. He had a great belief in the honour of boys; he felt that the first thing to make them truthful was not to let it enter your head for a moment that it was possible for them to lie. "Ask much," he quoted, "and much shall be given to you." Life was easy in the Upper Third. You knew exactly what lines would come to your turn to construe, and with the crib that passed from hand to hand you could find out all you wanted in two minutes; you could hold a Latin Grammar open on your knees while questions were passing round; and Winks never noticed anything odd in the fact that the same incredible mistake was to be found in a dozen different exercises. He had no great faith in examinations, for he noticed that boys never did so well in them as in form: it was disappointing, but not significant. In due course they were moved up, having learned little but a cheerful effrontery in the distortion of truth, which was possibly of greater service to them in after life than an ability to read Latin at sight.

Then they fell into the hands of

Tar. His name was Turner; he was the most vivacious of the old masters, a short man with an immense belly, a black beard turning now to gray, and a swarthy skin. In his clerical dress there was indeed something in him to suggest the tar-barrel; and though on principle he gave five hundred lines to any boy on whose lips he overheard his nickname, at dinner-parties in the precincts he often made little jokes about it. He was the most worldly of the masters; he dined out more frequently than any of the others, and the society he kept was not so exclusively clerical. The boys looked upon him as rather a dog. He left off his clerical attire during the holidays and had been seen in Switzerland in gay tweeds. He liked a bottle of wine and a good dinner, and having once been seen at the Café Royal with a lady who was very probably a near relation, was thenceforward supposed by generations of schoolboys to indulge in orgies the circumstantial details of which pointed to an unbounded belief in human depravity.

Mr. Turner reckoned that it took him a term to lick boys into shape after they had been in the Upper Third; and now and then he let fall a sly hint, which showed that he knew perfectly what went on in his colleague's form. He took it good-humouredly. He looked upon boys as young ruffians who were more apt to be truthful if it was quite certain a lie would be found out, whose sense of honour was peculiar to themselves and did not apply to dealings with masters, and who were least likely to be troublesome when they learned that it did not pay. He was proud of his form and as eager at fifty-five that it should do better in examinations than any of the others as he had been when he first came to the school. He

had the choler of the obese, easily roused and as easily calmed, and his boys soon discovered that there was much kindliness beneath the invective with which he constantly assailed them. He had no patience with fools, but was willing to take much trouble with boys whom he suspected of concealing intelligence behind their wilfulness. He was fond of inviting them to tea; and, though vowing they never got a look in with him at the cakes and muffins, for it was the fashion to believe that his corpulence pointed to a voracious appetite, and his voracious appetite to tapeworms, they accepted his invitations with real pleasure.

Philip was now more comfortable, for space was so limited that there were only studies for boys in the upper school, and till then he had lived in the great hall in which they all ate and in which the lower forms did preparation in a promiscuity which was vaguely distasteful to him. Now and then it made him restless to be with people and he wanted urgently to be alone. He set out for solitary walks into the country. There was a little stream, with pollards on both sides of it, that ran through green fields, and it made him happy, he knew not why, to wander along its banks. When he was tired he lay face-downward on the grass and watched the eager scurrying of minnows and of tadpoles. It gave him a peculiar satisfaction to saunter round the precincts. On the green in the middle they practised at nets in the summer, but during the rest of the year it was quiet: boys used to wander round sometimes arm in arm, or a studious fellow with abstracted gaze walked slowly, repeating to himself something he had to learn by heart. There was a colony of rooks in the great elms, and they filled the air with melancholy cries. Along one side lay the Cathedral with its great central tower, and Philip, who knew as yet nothing of beauty, felt when he looked at it a troubling delight which he could not understand. When he had a study (it was a little square room looking on a slum, and four boys shared it), he bought a photograph of that view of the Cathedral, and pinned it up over his desk. And he found himself taking a new interest in what he saw from the window of the Fourth Form room. It looked on to old lawns, carefully tended, and fine trees with foliage dense and rich. It gave him an odd feeling in his heart, and he did not know if it was pain or pleasure. It was the first dawn of the æsthetic emotion. It accompanied other changes. His voice broke. It was no longer quite under his control, and queer sounds issued from his throat.

Then he began to go to the classes which were held in the headmaster's study, immediately after tea, to prepare boys for confirmation. Philip's piety had not stood the test of time, and he had long since given up his nightly reading of the Bible; but now, under the influence of Mr. Perkins, with this new condition of the body which made him so restless, his old feelings revived, and he reproached himself bitterly for his backsliding. The fires of Hell burned fiercely before his mind's eye. If he had died during that time when he was little better than an infidel he would have been lost; he believed implicitly in pain everlasting, he believed in it much more than in eternal happiness; and he shuddered at the dangers he had run.

Since the day on which Mr. Perkins had spoken kindly to him, when he was smarting under the particular form of abuse which he could least bear, Philip had conceived for his

headmaster a dog-like adoration. He racked his brains vainly for some way to please him. He treasured the smallest word of commendation which by chance fell from his lips. And when he came to the quiet little meetings in his house he was prepared to surrender himself entirely. He kept his eyes fixed on Mr. Perkins' shining eyes, and sat with mouth half open, his head a little thrown forward so as to miss no word. The ordinariness of the surroundings made the matters they dealt with extraordinarily moving. And often the master, seized himself by the wonder of his subject, would push back the book in front of him, and with his hands clasped together over his heart, as though to still the beating, would talk of the mysteries of their religion. Sometimes Philip did not understand, but he did not want to understand, he felt vaguely that it was enough to feel. It seemed to him then that the headmaster, with his black, straggling hair and his pale face, was like those prophets of Israel who feared not to take kings to task; and when he thought of the Redeemer he saw Him only with the same dark eyes and those wan cheeks.

Mr. Perkins took this part of his work with great seriousness. There was never here any of that flashing humour which made the other masters suspect him of flippancy. Finding time for everything in his busy day, he was able at certain intervals to take separately for a quarter of an hour or twenty minutes the boys whom he was preparing for confirmation. He wanted to make them feel that this was the first consciously serious step in their lives; he tried to grope into the depths of their souls; he wanted to instil in them his own vehement devotion. In Philip, notwithstanding his shyness, he felt the possibility of a passion equal to his own. The boy's temperament seemed to him essentially religious. One day he broke off suddenly from the subject on which he had been talking.

"Have you thought at all what you're going to be when you grow up?" he asked.

"My uncle wants me to be ordained," said Philip.

"And you?"

Philip looked away. He was ashamed to answer that he felt himself unworthy.

"I don't know any life that's so full of happiness as ours. I wish I could make you feel what a wonderful privilege it is. One can serve God in every walk, but we stand nearer to Him. I don't want to influence you, but if you made up your mind—oh, at once—you couldn't help feeling that joy and relief which never desert one again."

Philip did not answer, but the headmaster read in his eyes that he realised already something of what he tried to indicate.

"If you go on as you are now you'll find yourself head of the school one of these days, and you ought to be pretty safe for a scholarship when you leave. Have you got anything of your own?"

"My uncle says I shall have a hundred a year when I'm twenty-one."

"You'll be rich. I had nothing."

The headmaster hesitated a moment, and then, idly drawing lines with a pencil on the blotting paper in front of him, went on.

"I'm afraid your choice of professions will be rather limited. You naturally couldn't go in for anything that required physical activity."

Philip reddened to the roots of his hair, as he always did when any reference was made to his club-foot. Mr. Perkins looked at him gravely.

"I wonder if you're not oversensitive about your misfortune. Has it ever struck you to thank God for it?"

Philip looked up quickly. His lips tightened. He remembered how for months, trusting in what they told him, he had implored God to heal him as He had healed the Leper and made the Blind to see.

"As long as you accept it rebelliously it can only cause you shame. But if you looked upon it as a cross that was given you to bear only because your shoulders were strong enough to bear it, a sign of God's favour, then it would be a source of happiness to you instead of misery."

He saw that the boy hated to discuss the matter and he let him go.

But Philip thought over all that the headmaster had said, and presently, his mind taken up entirely with the ceremony that was before him, a mystical rapture seized him. His spirit seemed to free itself from the bonds of the flesh and he seemed to be living a new life. He aspired to perfection with all the passion that was in him. He wanted to surrender himself entirely to the service of God, and he made up his mind definitely that he would be ordained. When the great day arrived, his soul deeply moved by all the preparation, by the books he had studied and above all by the overwhelming influence of the head, he could hardly contain himself for fear and joy. One thought had tormented him. He knew that he would have to walk alone through the chancel, and he dreaded showing his limp thus obviously, not only to the whole school, who were attending the service, but also to the strangers, people from the city or parents who had come to see their sons confirmed. But when the time came he felt suddenly that he could accept the humiliation joyfully; and as he limped up the chancel, very small and insignificant beneath the lofty vaulting of the Cathedral, he offered consciously his deformity as a sacrifice to the God who loved him.

XVIII

B u t Philip could not live long in the rarefied air of the hilltops. What had happened to him when first he was seized by the religious emotion happened to him now. Because he felt so keenly the beauty of faith, because the desire for self-sacrifice burned in his heart with such a gem-like glow, his strength seemed inadequate to his ambition. He was tired out by the violence of his passion. His soul was filled on a sudden with a singular aridity. He began to forget the presence of God which had seemed so surrounding; and his religious exercises, still very punctually performed, grew merely formal. At first he blamed himself for this falling away, and the fear of hell-fire urged him to renewed vehemence; but the passion was dead, and gradually other interests distracted his thoughts.

Philip had few friends. His habit of reading isolated him: it became such a need that after being in company for some time he grew tired and restless; he was vain of the wider knowledge he had acquired from the perusal of so many books, his mind was alert, and he had not the skill to hide his contempt for his companions' stupidity. They complained that he was conceited; and, since he excelled only in matters which to them were unimportant, they asked satirically what he had to be conceited about. He was developing a sense of humour, and found that he had a knack of saying bitter things, which caught people on the raw; he said them because they amused him, hardly

realising how much they hurt, and was much offended when he found that his victims regarded him with active dislike. The humiliations he suffered when first he went to school had caused in him a shrinking from his fellows which he could never entirely overcome; he remained shy and silent. But though he did everything to alienate the sympathy of other boys he longed with all his heart for the popularity which to some was so easily accorded. These from his distance he admired extravagantly; and though he was inclined to be more sarcastic with them than with others, though he made little jokes at their expense, he would have given anything to change places with them. Indeed he would gladly have changed places with the dullest boy in the school who was whole of limb. He took to a singular habit. He would imagine that he was some boy whom he had a particular fancy for; he would throw his soul, as it were, into the other's body, talk with his voice and laugh with his heart; he would imagine himself doing all the things the other did. It was so vivid that he seemed for a moment really to be no longer himself. In this way he enjoyed many intervals of fantastic happiness.

At the beginning of the Christmas term which followed on his confirmation Philip found himself moved into another study. One of the boys who shared it was called Rose. He was in the same form as Philip, and Philip had always looked upon him with envious admiration. He was not good-looking; though his large hands and big bones suggested that he would be a tall man, he was clumsily made; but his eyes were charming, and when he laughed (he was constantly laughing) his face wrinkled all round them in a jolly way. He was neither clever nor stupid, but good enough at his work and better at games. He was a favourite with masters and boys, and he in his turn liked everyone.

When Philip was put in the study he could not help seeing that the others, who had been together for three terms, welcomed him coldly. It made him nervous to feel himself an intruder; but he had learned to hide his feelings, and they found him quiet and unobtrusive. With Rose, because he was as little able as anyone else to resist his charm, Philip was even more than usually shy and abrupt; and whether on account of this, unconsciously bent upon exerting the fascination he knew was his only by the results, or whether from sheer kindness of heart, it was Rose who first took Philip into the circle. One day, quite suddenly, he asked Philip if he would walk to the football field with him. Philip flushed.

"I can't walk fast enough for you," he said.

"Rot. Come on."

And just before they were setting out some boy put his head in the study-door and asked Rose to go with him.

"I can't," he answered. "I've already promised Carey."

"Don't bother about me," said Philip quickly. "I shan't mind."

"Rot," said Rose.

He looked at Philip with those good-natured eyes of his and laughed. Philip felt a curious tremor in his heart.

In a little while, their friendship growing with boyish rapidity, the pair were inseparable. Other fellows wondered at the sudden intimacy, and Rose was asked what he saw in Philip.

"Oh, I don't know," he answered. "He's not half a bad chap really."

Soon they grew accustomed to the two walking into chapel arm in arm or strolling round the precincts in conversation; wherever one was the other could be found also, and, as though acknowledging his proprietorship, boys who wanted Rose would leave messages with Carey. Philip at first was reserved. He would not let himself yield entirely to the proud joy that filled him; but presently his distrust of the fates gave way before a wild happiness. He thought Rose the most wonderful fellow he had ever seen. His books now were insignificant; he could not bother about them when there was something infinitely more important to occupy him. Rose's friends used to come in to tea in the study sometimes or sit about when there was nothing better to do—Rose liked a crowd and the chance of a rag —and they found that Philip was quite a decent fellow. Philip was happy.

When the last day of term came he and Rose arranged by which train they should come back, so that they might meet at the station and have tea in the town before returning to school. Philip went home with a heavy heart. He thought of Rose all through the holidays, and his fancy was active with the things they would do together next term. He was bored at the vicarage, and when on the last day his uncle put him the usual question in the usual facetious tone:

"Well, are you glad to be going back to school?"

Philip answered joyfully:

"Rather."

In order to be sure of meeting Rose at the station he took an earlier train than he usually did, and he waited about the platform for an hour. When the train came in from Faversham, where he knew Rose had to change, he ran along it excitedly. But Rose was not there. He got a porter to tell him when another train was due, and he waited; but again he was disappointed; and he was cold and hungry, so he walked, through side-streets and slums, by a short cut to the school. He found Rose in the study, with his feet on the chimney-piece, talking eighteen to the dozen with half a dozen boys who were sitting on whatever there was to sit on. He shook hands with Philip enthusiastically, but Philip's face fell, for he realised that Rose had forgotten all about their appointment.

"I say, why are you so late?" said Rose. "I thought you were never coming."

"You were at the station at half-past four," said another boy. "I saw you when I came."

Philip blushed a little. He did not want Rose to know that he had been such a fool as to wait for him.

"I had to see about a friend of my people's," he invented readily. "I was asked to see her off."

But his disappointment made him a little sulky. He sat in silence, and when spoken to answered in monosyllables. He was making up his mind to have it out with Rose when they were alone. But when the others had gone Rose at once came over and sat on the arm of the chair in which Philip was lounging.

"I say, I'm jolly glad we're in the same study this term. Ripping, isn't it?"

He seemed so genuinely pleased to see Philip that Philip's annoyance vanished. They began as if they had not been separated for five minutes to talk eagerly of the thousand things that interested them.

XIX

At first Philip had been too grateful for Rose's friendship to make any demands on him. He took things as they came and enjoyed life. But presently he began to resent Rose's universal amiability; he wanted a more exclusive attachment, and he claimed as a right what before he had accepted as a favour. He watched jealously Rose's companionship with others; and though he knew it was unreasonable could not help sometimes saying bitter things to him. If Rose spent an hour playing the fool in another study, Philip would receive him when he returned to his own with a sullen frown. He would sulk for a day, and

he suffered more because Rose either did not notice his ill-humour or deliberately ignored it. Not seldom Philip, knowing all the time how stupid he was, would force a quarrel, and they would not speak to one another for a couple of days. But Philip could not bear to be angry with him long, and even when convinced that he was in the right, would apologise humbly. Then for a week they would be as great friends as ever. But the best was over, and Philip could see that Rose often walked with him merely from old habit or from fear of his anger; they had not so much to say to one another as at first, and Rose was often bored. Philip felt that his lameness began to irritate him.

Towards the end of the term two or three boys caught scarlet fever, and there was much talk of sending them all home in order to escape an epidemic; but the sufferers were isolated, and since no more were attacked it was supposed that the outbreak was stopped. One of the stricken was Philip. He remained in hospital through the Easter holidays, and at the beginning of the summer term was sent home to the vicarage to get a little fresh air. The Vicar, notwithstanding medical assurance that the boy was no longer infectious, received him with suspicion; he thought it very inconsiderate of the doctor to suggest that his nephew's convalescence should be spent by the seaside, and consented to have him in the house only because there was nowhere else he could go.

Philip went back to school at half-term. He had forgotten the quarrels he had had with Rose, but remembered only that he was his greatest friend. He knew that he had been silly. He made up his mind to be more reasonable. During his illness Rose had sent him in a couple of little notes, and he had ended each with the words: "Hurry up and come back." Philip thought Rose must be looking forward as much to his return as he was himself to seeing Rose.

He found that owing to the death from scarlet fever of one of the boys in the Sixth there had been some shifting in the studies and Rose was no longer in his. It was a bitter disappointment. But as soon as he arrived he burst into Rose's study. Rose was sitting at his desk, working with a boy called Hunter, and turned round crossly as Philip came in.

"Who the devil's that?" he cried.

And then, seeing Philip: "Oh, it's you."

Philip stopped in embarrassment.

"I thought I'd come in and see how you were."

"We were just working."

Hunter broke into the conversation.

"When did you get back?"

"Five minutes ago."

They sat and looked at him as though he was disturbing them. They evidently expected him to go quickly. Philip reddened.

"I'll be off. You might look in when you've done," he said to Rose.

"All right."

Philip closed the door behind him and limped back to his own study. He felt frightfully hurt. Rose, far from seeming glad to see him, had looked almost put out. They might never have been more than acquaintances. Though he waited in his study, not leaving it for a moment in case just then Rose should come, his friend never appeared; and next morning when he went into prayers he saw Rose and Hunter swinging along arm in arm. What he could not see for himself others told him. He had forgotten that three months is a long time in a school-boy's life, and though he had passed them in solitude Rose had lived in the world. Hunter had stepped into the vacant place. Philip found that Rose was quietly avoiding him. But he was not the boy to accept a situation without putting it into words; he waited till he was sure Rose was alone in his study and went in.

"May I come in?" he asked.

Rose looked at him with an embarrassment that made him angry with Philip.

"Yes, if you want to."

"It's very kind of you," said Philip sarcastically.

"What d'you want?"

"I say, why have you been so rotten since I came back?"

"Oh, don't be an ass," said Rose.

"I don't know what you see in Hunter."

"That's my business."

Philip looked down. He could not bring himself to say what was in his heart. He was afraid of humiliating himself. Rose got up.

"I've got to go to the Gym," he said.

When he was at the door Philip forced himself to speak.

"I say, Rose, don't be a perfect beast."

"Oh, go to hell."

Rose slammed the door behind him and left Philip alone. Philip shivered with rage. He went back to his study and turned the conversation over in his mind. He hated Rose now, he wanted to hurt him, he thought of biting things he might have said to him. He brooded over the end to their friendship and fancied that others were talking of it. In his sensitiveness he saw sneers and wonderings in other fellows' manner when they were not bothering their heads with him at all. He imagined to himself what they were saying.

"After all, it wasn't likely to last long. I wonder he ever stuck Carey at all. Blighter!"

To show his indifference he struck up a violent friendship with a boy called Sharp whom he hated and despised. He was a London boy, with a loutish air, a heavy fellow with the beginnings of a moustache on his lip and bushy eyebrows that joined one another across the bridge of his nose. He had soft hands and manners too suave for his years. He spoke with the suspicion of a cockney accent. He was one of those boys who are too slack to play games, and he exercised great ingenuity in making excuses to avoid such as were compulsory. He was re-garded by boys and masters with a vague dislike, and it was from arrogance that Philip now sought his society. Sharp in a couple of terms was going to Germany for a year. He hated school, which he looked upon as an indignity to be endured till he was old enough to go out into the world. London was all he cared for, and he had many stories to tell of his doings there during the holidays. From his conversation—he spoke in a soft, deep-toned voice—there emerged the vague rumour of the London streets by night. Philip listened to him at once fascinated and repelled. With his vivid fancy he seemed to see the surging throng round the pit-door of theatres, and the glitter of cheap restaurants, bars where men, half drunk, sat on high stools talking with barmaids; and under the street lamps the mysterious passing of dark crowds bent upon pleasure. Sharp lent him cheap novels from Holywell Row, which Philip read in his cubicle with a sort of wonderful fear.

Once Rose tried to effect a reconciliation. He was a good-natured fellow, who did not like having enemies.

"I say, Carey, why are you being such a silly ass? It doesn't do you any good cutting me and all that."

"I don't know what you mean," answered Philip.

"Well, I don't see why you shouldn't talk."

"You bore me," said Philip.

"Please yourself."

Rose shrugged his shoulders and left him. Philip was very white, as he always became when he was moved, and his heart beat violently. When Rose went away he felt suddenly sick with misery. He did not know why he had answered in that fashion. He would have given anything to be friends with Rose. He hated to have quarrelled with him, and now that he saw he had given him pain he was very sorry. But at the moment he had not been master of himself. It seemed that some devil had seized him, forcing him to say bitter things against his will, even though at the time he wanted to shake hands with Rose and meet him more than half-way. The desire to wound had been too strong for him. He had wanted to revenge himself for the pain and the humiliation he had endured. It was pride: it was folly too, for he knew that Rose would not care at all, while he would suffer bitterly. The thought came to him that he would go to Rose, and say:

"I say, I'm sorry I was such a beast. I couldn't help it. Let's make it up."

But he knew he would never be able to do it. He was afraid that Rose would sneer at him. He was angry with himself, and when Sharp came in a little while afterwards he seized upon the first opportunity to quarrel with him. Philip had a fiendish instinct for discovering other people's raw spots, and was able to say things that rankled because they were true. But Sharp had the last word.

"I heard Rose talking about you to Mellor just now," he said. "Mellor said: why didn't you kick him? It would teach him manners. And Rose said: I didn't like to. Damned cripple."

Philip suddenly became scarlet. He could not answer, for there was a lump in his throat that almost choked him.

XX

PHILIP was moved into the Sixth, but he hated school now with all his heart, and, having lost his ambition, cared nothing whether he did ill or well. He awoke in the morning with a sinking heart because he must go through another day of drudgery. He was tired of having to do things because he was told; and the restrictions irked him, not because they were unreasonable, but because they were restrictions. He yearned for freedom. He was weary of repeating things that he knew already and of the hammering away, for the sake of a thick-witted fellow, at something that he understood from the beginning.

With Mr. Perkins you could work or not as you chose. He was at once eager and abstracted. The Sixth Form room was in a part of the old abbey which had been restored, and it had a gothic window: Philip tried to cheat his boredom by drawing this over and

over again; and sometimes out of his head he drew the great tower of the Cathedral or the gateway that led into the precincts. He had a knack for drawing. Aunt Louisa during her youth had painted in water colours, and she had several albums filled with sketches of churches, old bridges, and picturesque cottages. They were often shown at the vicarage tea-parties. She had once given Philip a paint-box as a Christmas present, and he had started by copying her pictures. He copied them better than anyone could have expected, and presently he did little pictures of his own. Mrs. Carey encouraged him. It was a good way to keep him out of mischief, and later on his sketches would be useful for bazaars. Two or three of them had been framed and hung in his bedroom.

But one day, at the end of the morning's work, Mr. Perkins stopped him as he was lounging out of the form-room.

"I want to speak to you, Carey."

Philip waited. Mr. Perkins ran his lean fingers through his beard and looked at Philip. He seemed to be thinking over what he wanted to say. "What's the matter with you, Carey?" he said abruptly.

Philip, flushing, looked at him quickly. But knowing him well by now, without answering, he waited for him to go on.

"I've been dissatisfied with you lately. You've been slack and inattentive. You seem to take no interest in your work. It's been slovenly and bad."

"I'm very sorry, sir," said Philip.

"Is that all you have to say for yourself?"

Philip looked down sulkily. How could he answer that he was bored to death?

"You know, this term you'll go down instead of up. I shan't give you a very good report."

Philip wondered what he would say if he knew how the report was treated. It arrived at breakfast, Mr. Carey glanced at it indifferently, and passed it over to Philip.

"There's your report. You'd better see what it says," he remarked, as he ran his fingers through the wrapper of a catalogue of second-hand books.

Philip read it.

"Is it good?" asked Aunt Louisa.

"Not so good as I deserve," answered Philip, with a smile, giving it to her.

"I'll read it afterwards when I've got my spectacles," she said.

But after breakfast Mary Ann came in to say the butcher was there, and she generally forgot.

Mr. Perkins went on.

"I'm disappointed with you. And I can't understand. I know you *can* do things if you want to, but you don't seem to want to any more. I was going to make you a monitor next term, but I think I'd better wait a bit."

Philip flushed. He did not like the thought of being passed over. He tightened his lips.

"And there's something else. You must begin thinking of your scholarship now. You won't get anything unless you start working very seriously."

Philip was irritated by the lecture. He was angry with the headmaster, and angry with himself.

"I don't think I'm going up to Oxford," he said.

"Why not? I thought your idea was to be ordained."

"I've changed my mind."

"Why?"

Philip did not answer. Mr. Perkins, holding himself oddly as he always did, like a figure in one of Perugino's pictures, drew his fingers thoughtfully through his beard. He looked at Philip as though he were trying to understand and then abruptly told him he might go.

Apparently he was not satisfied, for one evening, a week later, when Philip had to go into his study with some papers, he resumed the conversation; but this time he adopted a different method: he spoke to Philip not as a schoolmaster with a boy but as one human being with another. He did not seem to care now that Philip's work was poor, that he ran small chance against keen rivals of carrying off the scholarship necessary for him to go to Oxford: the important matter was his changed intention about his life afterwards. Mr. Perkins set himself to revive his eagerness to be ordained. With infinite skill he worked on his feelings, and this was easier since he was himself genuinely moved. Philip's change of mind caused him bitter distress, and he really thought he was throwing away his chance of happiness in life for he knew not what. His voice was very persuasive. And Philip, easily moved by the emotion of others, very emotional himself notwithstanding a placid exterior—his face, partly by nature but also from the habit of all these years at school, seldom except by his quick flushing showed what he felt—Philip was deeply touched by what the master said. He was very grateful to him for the interest he showed, and he was conscience-stricken by the grief which he felt his behaviour caused him. It was subtly flattering to know that with the whole school to think about Mr. Perkins should trouble with him, but at the same time something else in him, like another person standing at his elbow, clung desperately to two words.

"I won't. I won't. I won't."

He felt himself slipping. He was powerless against the weakness that seemed to well up in him; it was like the water that rises up in an empty bottle held over a full basin; and he set his teeth, saying the words over and over to himself.

"I won't. I won't. I won't."

At last Mr. Perkins put his hand on Philip's shoulder.

"I don't want to influence you," he said. "You must decide for yourself. Pray to Almighty God for help and guidance."

When Philip came out of the headmaster's house there was a light rain falling. He went under the archway that led to the precincts, there was not a soul there, and the rooks were silent in the elms. He walked round slowly. He felt hot, and the rain did him good. He thought over all that Mr. Perkins had said, calmly now that he was withdrawn from the fervour of his personality, and he was thankful he had not given way.

In the darkness he could but vaguely see the great mass of the Cathedral: he hated it now because of the irksomeness of the long services which he was forced to attend. The anthem was interminable, and you had to stand drearily while it was being sung; you could not hear the droning sermon, and your body twitched because you had to sit still when you wanted to move about. Then Philip thought of the two services every Sunday at Blackstable. The church was bare and cold, and there was a smell all about one of pomade and starched clothes. The curate preached once and his uncle preached once. As he grew up he had learned to know his uncle; Philip was downright and intolerant, and he could not understand that a man might sincerely say things as a clergyman which he never acted up to as a man. The deception outraged him. His uncle was a weak and selfish man, whose chief desire it was to be saved trouble.

Mr. Perkins had spoken to him of the beauty of a life dedicated to the service of God. Philip knew what sort of lives the clergy led in the corner of East Anglia which was his home. There was the Vicar of Whitestone, a parish a little way from Blackstable: he was a bachelor and to give himself something to do had lately taken up farming: the local paper constantly reported the cases he had in the county court against this one and that, labourers he would not pay their wages to or tradesmen whom he accused of cheating him; scandal said he starved his cows, and there was much talk about some general action which should be taken against him. Then there was the Vicar of Ferne, a bearded, fine figure of a man: his wife had been forced to leave him because of his cruelty, and she had filled the neighbourhood with stories of his immorality. The Vicar of Surle, a tiny hamlet by the sea, was to be seen every evening in the public house a stone's throw from his vicarage; and the churchwardens had been to Mr. Carey to ask his advice. There was not a soul for any of them to talk to except small farmers or fishermen; there were long winter evenings when the wind blew, whistling drearily through the leafless trees, and all around they saw nothing but the bare monotony of ploughed fields; and there was poverty, and there was lack of any work that seemed to matter; every kink in their characters had free play; there was nothing to restrain them; they grew narrow and eccentric: Philip knew all this, but in his young intolerance he did not offer it as an excuse. He shivered at the thought of leading such a life; he wanted to get out into the world.

XXI

MR. PERKINS soon saw that his words had had no effect on Philip, and for the rest of the term ignored him. He wrote a report which was vitriolic. When it arrived and Aunt Louisa asked Philip what it was like, he answered cheerfully:

"Rotten."

"Is it?" said the Vicar. "I must look at it again."

"Do you think there's any use in my staying on at Tercanbury? I should have thought it would be better if I went to Germany for a bit."

"What has put that in your head?" said Aunt Louisa.

"Don't you think it's rather a good idea?"

Sharp had already left King's School and had written to Philip from Hanover. He was really starting life, and it made Philip more restless to think of it. He felt he could not bear another year of restraint.

"But then you wouldn't get a scholarship."

"I haven't a chance of getting one anyhow. And besides, I don't know that I particularly want to go to Oxford."

"But if you're going to be ordained, Philip?" Aunt Louisa exclaimed in dismay.

"I've given up that idea long ago."

Mrs. Carey looked at him with startled eyes, and then, used to self-restraint, she poured out another cup of tea for his uncle. They did not speak. In a moment Philip saw tears slowly falling down her cheeks. His heart was suddenly wrung because he caused her pain. In her tight black dress, made by the dressmaker down the street, with her wrinkled face and pale tired eyes, her gray hair still done in the frivolous ringlets of her youth, she was a ridiculous but strangely pathetic figure. Philip saw it for the first time.

Afterwards, when the Vicar was shut up in his study with the curate, he put his arms round her waist.

"I say, I'm sorry you're upset, Aunt Louisa," he said. "But it's no good my being ordained if I haven't a real vocation, is it?"

"I'm so disappointed, Philip," she moaned. "I'd set my heart on it. I thought you could be your uncle's curate, and then when our time came

—after all, we can't last for ever, can we?—you might have taken his place."

Philip shivered. He was seized with panic. His heart beat like a pigeon in a trap beating with its wings. His aunt wept softly, her head upon his shoulder.

"I wish you'd persuade Uncle William to let me leave Tercanbury. I'm so sick of it."

But the Vicar of Blackstable did not easily alter any arrangements he had made, and it had always been intended that Philip should stay at King's School till he was eighteen, and should then go to Oxford. At all events he would not hear of Philip leaving then, for no notice had been given and the term's fee would have to be paid in any case.

"Then will you give notice for me to leave at Christmas?" said Philip, at the end of a long and often bitter conversation.

"I'll write to Mr. Perkins about it and see what he says."

"Oh, I wish to goodness I were twenty-one. It is awful to be at somebody else's beck and call."

"Philip, you shouldn't speak to your uncle like that," said Mrs. Carey gently.

"But don't you see that Perkins will want me to stay? He gets so much a head for every chap in the school."

"Why don't you want to go to Oxford?"

"What's the good if I'm not going into the Church?"

"You can't go into the Church; you're in the Church already," said the Vicar.

"Ordained then," replied Philip impatiently.

"What are you going to be, Philip?" asked Mrs. Carey.

"I don't know. I've not made up my mind. But whatever I am, it'll be useful to know foreign languages. I shall get far more out of a year in Germany than by staying on at that hole."

He would not say that he felt Oxford would be little better than a continuation of his life at school. He wished immensely to be his own master. Besides he would be known to a certain extent among old schoolfellows, and he wanted to get away from them all. He felt that his life at school had been a failure. He wanted to start fresh.

It happened that his desire to go to Germany fell in with certain ideas which had been of late discussed at Blackstable. Sometimes friends came to stay with the doctor and brought news of the world outside; and the visitors spending August by the sea had their own way of looking at things. The Vicar had heard that there were people who did not think the old-fashioned education so useful nowadays as it had been in the past, and modern languages were gaining an importance which they had not had in his own youth. His own mind was divided, for a younger brother of his had been sent to Germany when he failed in some examination, thus creating a precedent, but since he had there died of typhoid it was impossible to look upon the experiment as other than dangerous. The result of innumerable conversations was that Philip should go back to Tercanbury for another term, and then should leave. With this agreement Philip was not dissatisfied. But when he had been back a few days the headmaster spoke to him.

"I've had a letter from your uncle. It appears you want to go to Germany, and he asks me what I think about it."

Philip was astounded. He was furious with his guardian for going back on his word.

"I thought it was settled, sir," he said.

"Far from it. I've written to say I think it the greatest mistake to take you away."

Philip immediately sat down and wrote a violent letter to his uncle. He did not measure his language. He was so angry that he could not get to sleep till quite late that night, and he awoke in the early morning and began brooding over the way they had treated him. He waited impatiently for an answer. In two or three days it came. It was a mild, pained letter from Aunt Louisa, saying that he should not write such things to his uncle, who was very much distressed. He was unkind and unchristian. He must know they were only trying to do their best for him, and they were so much older than he that they must be better judges of what was good for him. Philip clenched his hands. He had heard that statement so often, and he could not see why it was true; they did not know the conditions as he did, why should they accept it as self-evident that their greater age gave them greater wisdom? The letter ended with the information that Mr. Carey had withdrawn the notice he had given.

Philip nursed his wrath till the next half-holiday. They had them on Tuesdays and Thursdays, since on Saturday afternoons they had to go to a service in the Cathedral. He stopped behind when the rest of the Sixth went out.

"May I go to Blackstable this afternoon, please, sir?" he asked.

"No," said the headmaster briefly.

"I wanted to see my uncle about something very important."

"Didn't you hear me say no?"

Philip did not answer. He went out. He felt almost sick with humiliation, the humiliation of having to ask and the humiliation of the curt refusal. He hated the headmaster now.

Philip writhed under that despotism which never vouchsafed a reason for the most tyrannous act. He was too angry to care what he did, and after dinner walked down to the station, by the back ways he knew so well, just in time to catch the train to Blackstable. He walked into the vicarage and found his uncle and aunt sitting in the dining-room.

"Hulloa, where have you sprung from?" said the Vicar.

It was very clear that he was not pleased to see him. He looked a little uneasy.

"I thought I'd come and see you about my leaving. I want to know what you mean by promising me one thing when I was here, and doing something different a week after."

He was a little frightened at his own boldness, but he had made up his mind exactly what words to use, and, though his heart beat violently, he forced himself to say them.

"Have you got leave to come here this afternoon?"

"No. I asked Perkins and he refused. If you like to write and tell him I've been here you can get me into a really fine old row."

Mrs. Carey sat knitting with trembling hands. She was unused to scenes and they agitated her extremely.

"It would serve you right if I told him," said Mr. Carey.

"If you like to be a perfect sneak you can. After writing to Perkins as you did you're quite capable of it."

It was foolish of Philip to say that, because it gave the Vicar exactly the opportunity he wanted.

"I'm not going to sit still while you say impertinent things to me," he said with dignity.

He got up and walked quickly out of the room into his study. Philip heard him shut the door and lock it.

"Oh, I wish to God I were twenty-one. It is awful to be tied down like this."

Aunt Louisa began to cry quietly.

"Oh, Philip, you oughtn't to have spoken to your uncle like that. Do please go and tell him you're sorry."

"I'm not in the least sorry. He's taking a mean advantage. Of course it's just waste of money keeping me on at school, but what does he care? It's not his money. It was cruel to put me under the guardianship of people who know nothing about things."

"Philip."

Philip in his voluble anger stopped suddenly at the sound of her voice. It was heart-broken. He had not realised what bitter things he was saying.

"Philip, how can you be so unkind? You know we are only trying to do our best for you, and we know that we have no experience; it isn't as if we'd had any children of our own: that's why we consulted Mr. Perkins." Her voice broke. "I've tried to be like a mother to you. I've loved you as if you were my own son."

She was so small and frail, there was something so pathetic in her old-maidish air, that Philip was touched. A great lump came suddenly in his throat and his eyes filled with tears.

"I'm so sorry," he said. "I didn't mean to be beastly."

He knelt down beside her and took her in his arms, and kissed her wet, withered cheeks. She sobbed bitterly, and he seemed to feel on a sudden the pity of that wasted life. She had never surrendered herself before to such a display of emotion.

"I know I've not been what I wanted to be to you, Philip, but I didn't know how. It's been just as dreadful for me to have no children as for you to have no mother."

Philip forgot his anger and his own concerns, but thought only of consoling her, with broken words and clumsy little caresses. Then the clock struck, and he had to bolt off at once to catch the only train that would get him back to Tercanbury in time for call-over. As he sat in the corner of the railway carriage he saw that he had done nothing. He was angry with himself for his weakness. It was despicable to have allowed himself to be turned from his purpose by the pompous airs of the Vicar and the tears of his aunt. But as the result of he knew not what conversations between the couple another letter was written to the headmaster. Mr. Perkins read it with an impatient shrug of the shoulders. He showed it to Philip. It ran:

Dear Mr. Perkins,

Forgive me for troubling you again about my ward, but both his Aunt and I have been uneasy about him. He seems very anxious to leave school, and his Aunt thinks he is unhappy. It is very difficult for us to know what to do as we are not his parents. He does not seem to think he is doing very well and he feels it is wasting his money to stay on. I should be very much obliged if you would have a talk to him, and if he is still of the same mind perhaps it would be better if he left at Christmas as I originally intended.

Yours very truly,
William Carey.

Philip gave him back the letter. He felt a thrill of pride in his triumph. He had got his own way, and he was satisfied. His will had gained a victory over the wills of others.

"It's not much good my spending half an hour writing to your uncle if he changes his mind the next letter he gets from you," said the headmaster irritably.

Philip said nothing, and his face was perfectly placid; but he could not prevent the twinkle in his eyes. Mr. Perkins noticed it and broke into a little laugh.

"You've rather scored, haven't you?" he said.

Then Philip smiled outright. He could not conceal his exultation.

"Is it true that you're very anxious to leave?"

"Yes, sir."

"Are you unhappy here?"

Philip blushed. He hated instinctively any attempt to get into the depths of his feelings.

"Oh, I don't know, sir."

Mr. Perkins, slowly dragging his fingers through his beard, looked at him thoughtfully. He seemed to speak almost to himself.

"Of course schools are made for the average. The holes are all round, and whatever shape the pegs are they must wedge in somehow. One hasn't time to bother about anything but the average." Then suddenly he addressed himself to Philip: "Look here, I've got a suggestion to make to you. It's getting on towards the end of the term now. Another term won't kill you, and if you want to go to Germany you'd better go after Easter than after Christmas. It'll be much pleasanter in the spring than in midwinter. If at the end of the next term you still want to go I'll make no objection. What d'you say to that?"

"Thank you very much, sir."

Philip was so glad to have gained the last three months that he did not mind the extra term. The school seemed less of a prison when he knew that before Easter he would be free from it for ever. His heart danced within him. That evening in chapel he looked round at the boys, standing according to their forms, each in his due place, and he chuckled with satisfaction at the thought that soon he would never see them again. It made

him regard them almost with a friendly feeling. His eyes rested on Rose. Rose took his position as a monitor very seriously: he had quite an idea of being a good influence in the school; it was his turn to read the lesson that evening, and he read it very well. Philip smiled when he thought that he would be rid of him for ever, and it would not matter in six months whether Rose was tall and straight-limbed; and where would the importance be that he was a monitor and captain of the eleven? Philip looked at the masters in their gowns. Gordon was dead, he had died of apoplexy two years before, but all the rest were there. Philip knew now what a poor lot they were, except Turner perhaps, there was something of a man in him; and he writhed at the thought of the subjection in which they had held him. In six months they would not matter either. Their praise would mean nothing to him, and he would shrug his shoulders at their censure.

Philip had learned not to express his emotions by outward signs, and shyness still tormented him, but he had often very high spirits; and then, though he limped about demurely, silent and reserved, it seemed to be hallooing in his heart. He seemed to himself to walk more lightly. All sorts of ideas danced through his head, fancies chased one another so furiously that he could not catch them; but their coming and their going filled him with exhilaration. Now, being happy, he was able to work, and during the remaining weeks of the term set himself to make up for his long neglect. His brain worked easily, and he took a keen pleasure in the activity of his intellect. He did very well in the examinations that closed the term. Mr. Perkins made only one remark: he was talking to him about an essay he had written, and, after the usual criticisms, said:

"So you've made up your mind to stop playing the fool for a bit, have you?"

He smiled at him with his shining teeth, and Philip, looking down, gave an embarrassed smile.

The half dozen boys who expected to divide between them the various prizes which were given at the end of the summer term had ceased to look upon Philip as a serious rival, but now they began to regard him with some uneasiness. He told no one that he was leaving at Easter and so was in no sense a competitor, but left them to their anxieties. He knew that Rose flattered himself on his French, for he had spent two or three holidays in France; and he expected to get the Dean's Prize for English essay; Philip got a good deal of satisfaction in watching his dismay when he saw how much better Philip was doing in these subjects than himself. Another fellow, Norton, could not go to Oxford unless he got one of the scholarships at the disposal of the school. He asked Philip if he was going in for them.

"Have you any objection?" asked Philip.

It entertained him to think that he held someone else's future in his hand. There was something romantic in getting these various rewards actually in his grasp, and then leaving them to others because he disdained them. At last the breaking-up day came, and he went to Mr. Perkins to bid him good-bye.

"You don't mean to say you really want to leave?"

Philip's face fell at the headmaster's evident surprise.

"You said you wouldn't put any objection in the way, sir," he answered.

"I thought it was only a whim that I'd better humour. I know you're obstinate and headstrong. What on earth d'you want to leave for now? You've only got another term in any case. You can get the Magdalen scholarship easily; you'll get half the prizes we've got to give."

Philip looked at him sullenly. He felt that he had been tricked; but he had the promise, and Perkins would have to stand by it.

"You'll have a very pleasant time at Oxford. You needn't decide at once what you're going to do afterwards. I wonder if you realise how delightful the life is up there for anyone who has brains."

"I've made all my arrangements now to go to Germany, sir," said Philip.

"Are they arrangements that couldn't possibly be altered?" asked Mr. Perkins, with his quizzical smile. "I shall be very sorry to lose you. In schools the rather stupid boys who work always do better than the clever boy who's idle, but when the clever boy works—why then, he does what you've done this term."

Philip flushed darkly. He was unused to compliments, and no one had ever told him he was clever. The headmaster put his hand on Philip's shoulder.

"You know, driving things into the heads of thick-witted boys is dull work, but when now and then you have the chance of teaching a boy who comes half-way towards you, who understands almost before you've got the words out of your mouth, why, then teaching is the most exhilarating thing in the world."

Philip was melted by kindness; it had never occurred to him that it mattered really to Mr. Perkins whether he went or stayed. He was touched and immensely flattered. It would be pleasant to end up his school-days with glory and then go to Oxford: in a flash there appeared before him the life which he had heard described from boys who came back to play in the O.K.S. match or in letters from the University read out in one of the studies. But he was ashamed; he would look such a fool in his own eyes if he gave in now; his uncle would chuckle at the success of the headmaster's ruse. It was rather a come-down from the dramatic surrender of all these prizes which were in his reach, because he disdained to take them, to the plain, ordinary winning of them. It only required a little more persuasion, just enough to save his self-respect, and Philip would have done anything that Mr. Perkins wished; but his face showed nothing of his conflicting emotions. It was placid and sullen.

"I think I'd rather go, sir," he said.

Mr. Perkins, like many men who manage things by their personal influence, grew a little impatient when his power was not immediately manifest. He had a great deal of work to do, and could not waste more time on a boy who seemed to him insanely obstinate.

"Very well, I promised to let you if you really wanted it, and I keep my promise. When do you go to Germany?"

Philip's heart beat violently. The battle was won, and he did not know whether he had not rather lost it.

"At the beginning of May, sir," he answered.

"Well, you must come and see us when you get back."

He held out his hand. If he had given him one more chance Philip would have changed his mind, but he seemed to look upon the matter as settled. Philip walked out of the house. His school-days were over, and he was free; but the wild exultation to which he had looked forward at that moment was not there. He walked round the precincts slowly, and a profound depression seized him. He wished now that he had not been foolish. He did not want to go, but he knew he could never bring himself to go to the headmaster and tell him he would stay. That was a humiliation he could never put upon himself. He wondered whether he had done right. He was dissatisfied with himself and with all his circumstances. He asked himself dully whether whenever you got your way you wished afterwards that you hadn't.

XXII

PHILIP'S uncle had an old friend, called Miss Wilkinson, who lived in Berlin. She was the daughter of a clergyman, and it was with her father, the rector of a village in Lincolnshire, that Mr. Carey had spent his last curacy; on his death, forced to earn her living, she had taken various situations as a governess in France and Germany. She had kept up a correspondence with Mrs. Carey, and two or three times had spent her holidays at Blackstable Vicarage, paying as was usual with the Careys' unfrequent guests a small sum for her keep. When it became clear that it was less trouble to yield to Philip's wishes than to resist them, Mrs. Carey wrote to ask her for advice. Miss Wilkinson recommended Heidelberg as an excellent place to learn German in and the house of Frau Professor Erlin as a comfortable home. Philip might live there for thirty marks a week, and the Professor himself, a teacher at the local high school, would instruct him.

Philip arrived in Heidelberg one morning in May. His things were put on a barrow and he followed the porter out of the station. The sky was bright blue, and the trees in the avenue through which they passed were thick with leaves; there was something in the air fresh to Philip, and mingled with the timidity he felt at entering on a new life, among strangers, was a great exhilaration. He was a little disconsolate that no one had come to meet him, and felt very shy when the porter left him at the front door of a big white house. An untidy lad let him in and took him into a drawing-room. It was filled with a large suite covered in green velvet, and in the middle was a round table. On this in water stood a bouquet of flowers tightly packed together in a paper frill like the bone of a mutton chop, and carefully spaced round it were books in leather bindings. There was a musty smell.

Presently, with an odour of cooking, the Frau Professor came in, a short, very stout woman with tightly dressed hair and a red face; she had little eyes, sparkling like beads, and an effusive manner. She took Philip's hands and asked him about Miss Wilkinson, who had twice spent a few weeks with her. She spoke in German and in broken English. Philip could not make her understand that he did not know Miss Wilkinson. Then her two daughters appeared. They seemed hardly young to Philip, but perhaps they were not more than twenty-five: the elder, Thekla, was as short as her mother, with the same, rather shifty air, but with a pretty face and abundant dark hair; Anna, her younger sister, was tall and plain, but since she had a pleasant smile Philip immediately preferred her. After a few minutes of polite conversation the Frau Professor took Philip to his room and left him. It was in a turret, looking over the tops of the trees in the Anlage; and the bed was in an alcove, so that when you sat at the desk it had not the look of a bed-room at all. Philip unpacked his things and set out all his books. He was his own master at last.

A bell summoned him to dinner at one o'clock, and he found the Frau Professor's guests assembled in the drawing-room. He was introduced to her husband, a tall man of middle age with a large fair head, turning now to gray, and mild blue eyes. He spoke to Philip in correct, rather archaic English, having learned it from a study of the English classics, not from conversation; and it was odd to hear him use words colloquially which Philip had only met in the plays of Shakespeare. Frau Professor Erlin called her establishment a family and not a pension; but it would have required the subtlety of a metaphysician to find out exactly where the difference lay. When they sat down to dinner in a long dark apartment that led out of the drawing-room, Philip, feeling very shy, saw that there were sixteen people. The Frau Professor sat at one end and carved. The service was conducted, with a great clattering of plates, by the same clumsy lout who had opened the door for him; and though he was quick, it happened that the first persons to be served had finished before the last had received their appointed portions. The Frau Professor insisted that nothing but German should be spoken, so that Philip, even if his bashfulness had permitted him to be talkative, was forced to hold his tongue. He looked at the people among whom he was to live. By the Frau Professor sat several old ladies, but Philip did not give them much of his attention. There were two young girls, both fair and one of them very pretty, whom Philip heard addressed as Fräulein Hedwig and Fräulein Cäcilie. Fräulein Cäcilie had a long pig-tail hanging down her back. They sat side by side and chattered to one another, with smothered laughter: now and then they glanced at Philip and one of them said something in an undertone; they both giggled, and Philip blushed awkwardly, feeling that they were making fun of him. Near them sat a Chinaman, with a yellow face and an expansive smile, who was studying Western conditions at the University. He spoke so quickly, with a queer accent, that the girls could not always understand him, and then they burst out laughing. He laughed too, good-humouredly, and his almond eyes almost closed as he did so. There were two or three American men, in black coats, rather yellow and dry of skin: they were theological students; Philip heard the twang of their New England accent through their bad German, and he glanced at them with suspicion; for he had been taught to look upon Americans as wild and desperate barbarians.

Afterwards, when they had sat for a little on the stiff green velvet chairs of the drawing-room, Fräulein Anna asked Philip if he would like to go for a walk with them.

Philip accepted the invitation. They were quite a party. There were the two daughters of the Frau Professor, the two other girls, one of the American students, and Philip. Philip walked by the side of Anna and Fräulein Hedwig. He was a little fluttered. He had never known any girls. At Blackstable there were only the farmers' daughters and the girls of the local tradesmen. He knew them by name and by sight, but he was timid, and he thought they laughed at his deformity. He accepted willingly the difference which the Vicar and Mrs. Carey put between their own exalted rank and that of the farmers. The doctor had two daughters, but they were both much older than Philip and had been married to successive assistants while Philip was still a small boy. At school there had been two or three girls of more boldness than modesty whom some of the boys knew; and desperate stories, due in all probability to the masculine imagination, were told of intrigues with them; but Philip had always concealed under a lofty contempt the terror with which they filled him. His imagination and the books he had read had inspired in him a desire for the Byronic attitude; and he was torn between a morbid self-consciousness and a conviction that he owed it to himself to be gallant. He felt now that he should be bright and amusing, but his brain seemed empty and he could not for the life of him think of anything to say. Fräulein Anna, the Frau Professor's daughter, addressed herself to him frequently from a sense of duty, but the other said little: she looked at him now and then with sparkling eyes, and sometimes to his confusion laughed outright. Philip felt that she thought him perfectly ridiculous. They walked along the side of a hill among pine-trees, and their pleasant odour caused Philip a keen delight. The day was warm and cloudless. At last they came to an eminence from which they saw the valley of the Rhine spread out before them under the sun. It was a vast stretch of country, sparkling with golden light, with cities in the distance; and through it meandered the silver ribband of the river. Wide spaces are rare in the corner of Kent which Philip knew, the sea offers the only broad horizon, and the immense distance he saw now gave him a peculiar, an indescribable thrill. He felt suddenly elated. Though he did not know it, it was the first time that he had experienced, quite undiluted with foreign emotions, the sense of beauty. They sat on a bench, the three of them, for the others had gone on, and while the girls talked in rapid German, Philip, indifferent to their proximity, feasted his eyes.

"By Jove, I am happy," he said to himself unconsciously.

XXIII

PHILIP thought occasionally of the King's School at Tercanbury, and laughed to himself as he remembered what at some particular moment of the day they were doing. Now and then he dreamed that he was there still, and it gave him an extraordinary satisfaction, on awaking, to realise that he was in his little room in the turret. From his bed he could see the great cumulus clouds that hung in the blue sky. He revelled in his freedom. He could go to bed when he chose and get up when the fancy took him. There was no one to order him about. It struck him that he need not tell any more lies.

It had been arranged that Professor Erlin should teach him Latin and German; a Frenchman came every day to give him lessons in French; and the Frau Professor had recommended for mathematics an Englishman who was taking a philological degree at the University. This was a man named Wharton. Philip went to him every morning. He lived in one room on the top floor of a shabby house. It was dirty and untidy, and it was filled with a pungent odour made up of many different stinks. He was generally in bed when Philip arrived at ten o'clock, and he jumped out, put on a filthy dressing-gown and felt slippers, and, while he gave instruction, ate his simple breakfast. He was a short man, stout from excessive beer drinking, with a heavy moustache and long, unkempt hair. He had been in Germany for five years and was become very Teutonic. He spoke with scorn of Cambridge where he had taken his degree and with horror of the life which awaited him when, having taken his doctorate in Heidelberg, he must return to England and a pedagogic career. He adored the life of the German University with its happy freedom and its jolly companionships. He was a member of a *Burschenschaft,* and promised to take Philip to a *Kneipe.* He was very poor and made no secret that the lessons he was giving Philip meant the difference between meat for his dinner and bread and cheese. Sometimes after a heavy night he had such a headache that he could not drink his coffee, and he gave his lesson with heaviness of spirit. For these occasions he kept a few bottles of beer under the bed, and one of these and a pipe would help him to bear the burden of life.

"A hair of the dog that bit him," he would say as he poured out the beer, carefully so that the foam should not make him wait too long to drink.

Then he would talk to Philip of the University, the quarrels between rival corps, the duels, and the merits of this and that professor. Philip learnt more of life from him than of mathematics. Sometimes Wharton would sit back with a laugh and say: "Look here, we've not done anything today. You needn't pay me for the lesson."

"Oh, it doesn't matter," said Philip.

This was something new and very interesting, and he felt that it was of greater import than trigonometry, which he never could understand. It was like a window on life that he had a chance of peeping through, and he looked with a wildly beating heart.

"No, you can keep your dirty money," said Wharton.

"But how about your dinner?" said Philip, with a smile, for he knew exactly how his master's finances stood.

Wharton had even asked him to pay him the two shillings which the lesson cost once a week rather than once a month, since it made things less complicated.

"Oh, never mind my dinner. It won't be the first time I've dined off a bottle of beer, and my mind's never clearer than when I do."

He dived under the bed (the sheets were gray with want of washing), and fished out another bottle. Philip, who was young and did not know the good things of life, refused to share it with him, so he drank alone.

"How long are you going to stay here?" asked Wharton.

Both he and Philip had given up with relief the pretence of mathematics.

"Oh, I don't know. I suppose about a year. Then my people want me to go to Oxford."

Wharton gave a contemptuous shrug of the shoulders. It was a new experience for Philip to learn that there were persons who did not look upon that seat of learning with awe.

"What d'you want to go there for? You'll only be a glorified school-boy. Why don't you matriculate here? A year's no good. Spend five years here. You know, there are two good things in life, freedom of thought and freedom of action. In France you get freedom of action: you can do what you like and nobody bothers, but you must think like everybody else. In Germany you must do what everybody else does, but you may think as you choose. They're both very good things. I personally prefer freedom of thought. But in England you get neither: you're ground down by convention. You can't think as you like and you can't act as you like. That's because it's a democratic nation. I expect America's worse."

He leaned back cautiously, for the chair on which he sat had a ricketty leg, and it was disconcerting when a rhetorical flourish was interrupted by a sudden fall to the floor.

"I ought to go back to England this year, but if I can scrape together enough to keep body and soul on speaking terms I shall stay another twelve months. But then I shall have to go. And I must leave all this"—he waved his arm round the dirty garret, with its unmade bed, the clothes lying on the floor, a row of empty beer bottles against the wall, piles of unbound, ragged books in every corner —"for some provincial university where I shall try and get a chair of philology. And I shall play tennis and go to tea-parties." He interrupted himself and gave Philip, very neatly dressed, with a clean collar on and his hair well-brushed, a quizzical look. "And, my God! I shall have to wash."

Philip reddened, feeling his own spruceness an intolerable reproach; for of late he had begun to pay some attention to his toilet, and he had come out from England with a pretty selection of ties.

The summer came upon the country like a conqueror. Each day was beautiful. The sky had an arrogant blue which goaded the nerves like a spur. The green of the trees in the Anlage was violent and crude; and the houses, when the sun caught them, had a dazzling white which stimulated till it hurt. Sometimes on his way back from Wharton Philip would sit in the shade on one of the benches in the Anlage, enjoying the coolness and watching the patterns of light which the sun, shining through the leaves, made on the ground. His soul danced with delight as gaily as the sunbeams. He revelled in those moments of idleness stolen from his work. Sometimes he sauntered through the streets of the old town. He looked with awe at the students of the corps, their cheeks gashed and red, who swaggered about in their coloured caps. In the afternoons he wandered about the hills with the girls in the Frau Professor's house, and sometimes they went up the river and had tea in a leafy beer-garden. In the evenings they walked round and round the Stadtgarten, listening to the band.

Philip soon learned the various interests of the household. Fräulein Thekla, the professor's elder daughter, was engaged to a man in England who had spent twelve months in the house to learn German, and their marriage was to take place at the end of the year. But the young man wrote that his father, an india-rubber merchant who lived in Slough, did not approve of the union, and Fräulein Thekla was often in tears. Sometimes she and her mother might be seen, with stern eyes and determined mouths, looking over the letters of the reluctant lover. Thekla painted in water colour, and occasionally she and Philip, with another of the girls to keep them company, would go out and paint little pictures. The pretty Fräulein Hedwig had amorous troubles too. She was the daughter of a merchant in Berlin and a dashing hussar had fallen in love with her, a *von* if you please: but his parents opposed a marriage with a person of her condition, and she had been sent to Heidelberg to forget him. She could never, never do this, and corresponded with him continually, and he was making every effort to induce an exasperating father to change his mind. She told all this to Philip with pretty sighs and becoming blushes, and showed him the photograph of the gay lieutenant. Philip liked her best of all the girls at the Frau Professor's, and on their walks always tried to get by her side. He blushed a great deal when the others chaffed him for his obvious preference. He made the first declaration in his life to Fräulein Hedwig, but unfortunately it was an accident, and it happened in this manner. In the evenings when they did not go out, the young women sang little songs in the green velvet drawing-room, while Fräulein Anna, who always made herself useful, industriously accompanied. Fräulein Hedwig's favourite song was called *Ich liebe dich*, I love you; and one evening after she had sung this, when Philip was standing with her on the balcony, looking at the stars, it occurred to him to make some remark about it. He began:

"Ich liebe dich."

His German was halting, and he looked about for the word he wanted. The pause was infinitesimal, but before he could go on Fräulein Hedwig said:

"*Ach, Herr Carey, Sie müssen mir nicht du sagen*—you mustn't talk to me in the second person singular."

Philip felt himself grow hot all over, for he would never have dared to do anything so familiar, and he could think of nothing on earth to say. It would be ungallant to explain that he was not making an observation, but merely mentioning the title of a song.

"*Entschuldigen Sie*," he said. "I beg your pardon."

"It does not matter," she whispered. She smiled pleasantly, quietly took his hand and pressed it, then turned back into the drawing-room.

Next day he was so embarrassed that he could not speak to her, and in his shyness did all that was possible to avoid her. When he was asked to go for the usual walk he refused because, he said, he had work to do. But Fräulein Hedwig seized an opportunity to speak to him alone.

"Why are you behaving in this way?" she said kindly. "You know, I'm not angry with you for what you said last night. You can't help it if you love me. I'm flattered. But although I'm not exactly engaged to Hermann I can never love anyone else, and I look upon myself as his bride."

Philip blushed again, but he put on quite the expression of a rejected lover.

"I hope you'll be very happy," he said.

XXIV

PROFESSOR ERLIN gave Philip a lesson every day. He made out a list of books which Philip was to read till he was ready for the final achievement of *Faust,* and meanwhile, ingeniously enough, started him on a German translation of one of the plays by Shakespeare which Philip had studied at school. It was the period in Germany of Goethe's highest fame. Notwithstanding his rather condescending attitude towards patriotism he had been adopted as the national poet, and seemed since the war of seventy to be one of the most significant glories of national unity. The enthusiastic seemed in the wildness of the *Walpurgisnacht* to hear the rattle of artillery at Gravelotte. But one mark of a writer's greatness is that different minds can find in him different in-

spirations; and Professor Erlin, who hated the Prussians, gave his enthusiastic admiration to Goethe because his works, Olympian and sedate, offered the only refuge for a sane mind against the onslaughts of the present generation. There was a dramatist whose name of late had been much heard at Heidelberg, and the winter before one of his plays had been given at the theatre amid the cheers of adherents and the hisses of decent people. Philip heard discussions about it at the Frau Professor's long table, and at these Professor Erlin lost his wonted calm: he beat the table with his fist, and drowned all opposition with the roar of his fine deep voice. It was nonsense and obscene nonsense. He forced himself to sit the play out, but he did not know whether he was more bored or nauseated. If that was what the theatre was coming to, then it was high time the police stepped in and closed the playhouse. He was no prude and could laugh as well as anyone at the witty immorality of a farce at the Palais Royal, but here was nothing but filth. With an emphatic gesture he held his nose and whistled through his teeth. It was the ruin of the family, the uprooting of morals, the destruction of Germany.

"*Aber, Adolf,*" said the Frau Professor from the other end of the table. "Calm yourself."

He shook his fist at her. He was the mildest of creatures and ventured upon no action of his life without consulting her.

"No, Helene, I tell you this," he shouted. "I would sooner my daughters were lying dead at my feet than see them listening to the garbage of that shameless fellow."

The play was *The Doll's House* and the author was Henrik Ibsen.

Professor Erlin classed him with Richard Wagner, but of him he spoke not with anger but with good-humoured laughter. He was a charlatan but a successful charlatan, and in that was always something for the comic spirit to rejoice in.

"*Verrückter Kerl!* A madman!" he said.

He had seen *Lohengrin* and that passed muster. It was dull but no worse. But *Siegfried!* When he mentioned it Professor Erlin leaned his head on his hand and bellowed with laughter. Not a melody in it from beginning to end! He could imagine Richard Wagner sitting in his box and laughing till his sides ached at the sight of all the people who were taking it seriously. It was the greatest hoax of the nineteenth century. He lifted his glass of beer to his lips, threw back his head, and drank till the glass was empty. Then wiping his mouth with the back of his hand, he said:

"I tell you young people that before the nineteenth century is out Wagner will be as dead as mutton. Wagner! I would give all his works for one opera by Donizetti."

XXV

THE oddest of Philip's masters was his teacher of French. Monsieur Ducroz was a citizen of Geneva. He was a tall old man, with a sallow skin and hollow cheeks; his gray hair was thin and long. He wore shabby black clothes, with holes at the elbows of his coat and frayed trousers. His linen was very dirty. Philip had never seen him in a clean collar. He was a man of few words, who gave his lesson conscientiously but without enthusiasm, arriving as the clock struck and leaving on the minute. His charges were very small. He was taciturn, and what Philip learnt about him he learnt from others: it appeared that he had fought with Garibaldi against the Pope, but had left Italy in disgust when it was clear that all his efforts for freedom, by which he meant the establishment of a republic, tended to no more than an exchange of yokes; he had been expelled from Geneva for it was not known what political offences. Philip looked upon him with puzzled surprise; for he was very unlike his idea of the revolutionary:

he spoke in a low voice and was extraordinarily polite; he never sat down till he was asked to; and when on rare occasions he met Philip in the street took off his hat with an elaborate gesture; he never laughed, he never even smiled. A more complete imagination than Philip's might have pictured a youth of splendid hope, for he must have been entering upon manhood in 1848 when kings, remembering their brother of France, went about with an uneasy crick in their necks; and perhaps that passion for liberty which passed through Europe, sweeping before it what of absolutism and tyranny had reared its head during the reaction from the revolution of 1789, filled no breast with a hotter fire. One might fancy him, passionate with theories of human equality and human rights, discussing, arguing, fighting behind barricades in Paris, flying before the Austrian cavalry in Milan, imprisoned here, exiled from there, hoping on and upborne ever with the word which seemed so magical, the word Liberty; till at last, broken with disease and starvation, old, without means to keep body and soul together but by such lessons as he could pick up from poor students, he found himself in that little neat town under the heel of a personal tyranny greater than any in Europe. Perhaps his taciturnity hid a contempt for the human race which had abandoned the great dreams of his youth and now wallowed in sluggish ease; or perhaps these thirty years of revolution had taught him that men are unfit for liberty, and he thought that he had spent his life in the pursuit of that which was not worth the finding. Or maybe he was tired out and waited only with indifference for the release of death.

One day Philip, with the bluntness of his age, asked him if it was true he had been with Garibaldi. The old man did not seem to attach any importance to the question. He answered quite quietly in as low a voice as usual.

"*Oui, monsieur.*"

"They say you were in the Commune?"

"Do they? Shall we get on with our work?"

He held the book open and Philip, intimidated, began to translate the passage he had prepared.

One day Monsieur Ducroz seemed to be in great pain. He had been scarcely able to drag himself up the many stairs to Philip's room: and when he arrived sat down heavily, his sallow face drawn, with beads of sweat on his forehead, trying to recover himself.

"I'm afraid you're ill," said Philip.

"It's of no consequence."

But Philip saw that he was suffering, and at the end of the hour asked whether he would not prefer to give no more lessons till he was better.

"No," said the old man, in his even low voice. "I prefer to go on while I am able."

Philip, morbidly nervous when he had to make any reference to money, reddened.

"But it won't make any difference to you," he said. "I'll pay for the lessons just the same. If you wouldn't mind I'd like to give you the money for next week in advance."

Monsieur Ducroz charged eighteen pence an hour. Philip took a ten-mark piece out of his pocket and shyly put it on the table. He could not bring himself to offer it as if the old man were a beggar.

"In that case I think I won't come again till I'm better." He took the coin and, without anything more than the elaborate bow with which he always took his leave, went out.

"Bonjour, monsieur."

Philip was vaguely disappointed. Thinking he had done a generous thing, he had expected that Monsieur Ducroz would overwhelm him with expressions of gratitude. He was taken aback to find that the old teacher accepted the present as though it were his due. He was so young, he did not realise how much less is the sense of obligation in those who receive favours than in those who grant them. Monsieur Ducroz appeared again five or six days later. He tottered a little more and was very weak, but seemed to have overcome the severity of the attack. He was no more communicative than he had been before. He re-

mained mysterious, aloof, and dirty. He made no reference to his illness till after the lesson: and then, just as he was leaving, at the door, which he held open, he paused. He hesitated, as though to speak were difficult.

"If it hadn't been for the money you gave me I should have starved. It was all I had to live on."

He made his solemn, obsequious bow, and went out. Philip felt a little lump in his throat. He seemed to realise in a fashion the hopeless bitterness of the old man's struggle, and how hard life was for him when to himself it was so pleasant.

XXVI

PHILIP had spent three months in Heidelberg when one morning the Frau Professor told him that an Englishman named Hayward was coming to stay in the house, and the same evening at supper he saw a new face. For some days the family had lived in a state of excitement. First, as the result of heaven knows what scheming, by dint of humble prayers and veiled threats, the parents of the young Englishman to whom Fräulein Thekla was engaged had invited her to visit them in England, and she had set off with an album of water colours to show how accomplished she was and a bundle of letters to prove how deeply the young man had compromised himself. A week later Fräulein Hedwig with radiant smiles announced that the lieutenant of her affections was coming to Heidelberg with his father and mother. Exhausted by the importunity of their son and touched by the dowry which

Fräulein Hedwig's father offered, the lieutenant's parents had consented to pass through Heidelberg to make the young woman's acquaintance. The interview was satisfactory and Fräulein Hedwig had the satisfaction of showing her lover in the Stadtgarten to the whole of Frau Professor Erlin's household. The silent old ladies who sat at the top of the table near the Frau Professor were in a flutter, and when Fräulein Hedwig said she was to go home at once for the formal engagement to take place, the Frau Professor, regardless of expense, said she would give a *Maibowle*. Professor Erlin prided himself on his skill in preparing this mild intoxicant, and after supper the large bowl of hock and soda, with scented herbs floating in it and wild strawberries, was placed with solemnity on the round table in the drawing-room. Fräulein Anna teased Philip about the departure of his lady-love, and he felt very uncomfortable and rather melancholy. Fräulein Hedwig sang several songs, Fräulein Anna played the Wedding March, and the Professor sang *Die Wacht am Rhein*. Amid all this jollification Philip paid little attention to the new arrival. They had sat opposite one another at supper, but Philip was chattering busily with Fräulein Hedwig, and the stranger, knowing no German, had eaten his food in silence. Philip, observing that he wore a pale blue tie, had on that account taken a sudden dislike to him. He was a man of twenty-six, very fair, with long, wavy hair through which he passed his hand frequently with a careless gesture. His eyes were large and blue, but the blue was very pale, and they looked rather tired already. He was clean-shaven, and his mouth, notwithstanding its thin lips, was well-shaped. Fräulein Anna took an interest in physiognomy, and she made Philip notice afterwards how finely shaped was his skull, and how weak was the lower part of his face. The head, she remarked, was the head of a thinker, but the jaw lacked character. Fräulein Anna, foredoomed to a spinster's life, with her high cheekbones and large misshapen nose, laid great stress upon character. While they talked of him he stood a little apart from the others, watching the noisy party with a good-humoured but faintly supercilious expression. He was tall and slim. He held himself with a deliberate grace. Weeks, one of the American students, seeing him alone, went up and began to talk to him. The pair were oddly contrasted: the American very neat in his black coat and pepper-and-salt trousers, thin and dried-up, with something of ecclesiastical unction already in his manner; and the Englishman in his loose tweed suit, large-limbed and slow of gesture.

Philip did not speak to the newcomer till next day. They found themselves alone on the balcony of the drawing-room before dinner. Hayward addressed him.

"You're English, aren't you?"

"Yes."

"Is the food always as bad as it was last night?"

"It's always about the same."

"Beastly, isn't it?"

"Beastly."

Philip had found nothing wrong with the food at all, and in fact had eaten it in large quantities with appetite and enjoyment, but he did not want to show himself a person of so little discrimination as to think a dinner good which another thought execrable.

Fräulein Thekla's visit to England made it necessary for her sister to do more in the house, and she could not often spare the time for long walks; and Fräulein Cäcilie, with her long plait of fair hair and her little snub-nosed face, had of late shown a certain disinclination for society. Fräulein Hedwig was gone, and Weeks, the American who generally accompanied them on their rambles, had set out for a tour of South Germany. Philip was left a good deal to himself. Hayward sought his acquaintance; but Philip had an unfortunate trait: from shyness or from some atavistic inheritance of the cave-dweller, he always disliked people on first acquaintance; and it was not till he became used to them that he got over his first impression. It made him difficult of access. He received Hayward's advances very shyly, and when Hayward asked him one day to go for a walk he accepted only because he could not think of a civil excuse. He made his usual apology, angry with himself for the flushing cheeks he could not control, and trying to carry it off with a laugh.

"I'm afraid I can't walk very fast."

"Good heavens, I don't walk for a wager. I prefer to stroll. Don't you remember the chapter in *Marius* where Pater talks of the gentle exercise of walking as the best incentive to conversation?"

Philip was a good listener; though he often thought of clever things to say, it was seldom till after the opportunity to say them had passed; but Hayward was communicative; anyone more experienced than Philip might have thought he liked to hear himself talk. His supercilious attitude impressed Philip. He could not help admiring, and yet being awed by, a man who faintly despised so many things which Philip had looked upon as almost sacred. He cast down the fetish of exercise, damning with the contemptuous word pot-hunters all those who devoted themselves to its various forms; and Philip did not realise that he was merely putting up in its stead the other fetish of culture.

They wandered up to the castle, and sat on the terrace that overlooked the town. It nestled in the valley along the pleasant Neckar with a comfortable friendliness. The smoke from the chimneys hung over it, a pale blue haze; and the tall roofs, the spires of the churches, gave it a pleasantly mediæval air. There was a homeliness in it which warmed the heart. Hayward talked of *Richard Feverel* and *Madame Bovary*, of Verlaine, Dante, and Matthew Arnold. In those days Fitzgerald's translation of Omar Khayam was known only to the elect, and Hayward repeated it to Philip. He was very fond of reciting poetry, his own and that of others, which he did in a monotonous sing-song. By the time they reached home Philip's distrust of Hayward was changed to enthusiastic admiration.

They made a practice of walking together every afternoon, and Philip learned presently something of Hayward's circumstances. He was the son of a country judge, on whose death some time before he had inherited three hundred a year. His record at Charterhouse was so brilliant that when he went to Cambridge the Master of Trinity Hall went out of his way to express his satisfaction that he was going to that college. He prepared himself for a distinguished career. He moved in the most intellectual circles: he read Browning with enthusiasm and turned up his well-shaped nose at Tennyson; he knew all the details of Shelley's treatment of Harriet; he dabbled in the history of art (on the walls of his rooms were reproductions of pictures by G. F. Watts, Burne-Jones, and Botticelli); and he wrote not without distinction verses of a pessimistic character. His friends told one another that he was a man of excellent gifts, and he listened to them willingly when they prophesied his future eminence. In course of time he became an authority on art and literature. He came under the influence of Newman's *Apologia*; the picturesqueness of the Roman Catholic faith appealed to his æsthetic sensibility; and it was only the fear of his father's wrath (a plain, blunt man of narrow ideas, who read Macaulay) which prevented him from 'going over.' When he only got a pass degree his friends were astonished; but he shrugged his shoulders and delicately insinuated that he was not the dupe of examiners. He made one feel that a first class was ever so slightly vulgar. He described one of the vivas with tolerant humour; some fellow in an outrageous collar was asking him questions in logic; it was infinitely tedious, and suddenly he noticed that he wore elastic-sided boots: it was grotesque and ridiculous; so he withdrew his mind and thought of the gothic beauty of the Chapel at King's. But he had spent some delightful days at Cambridge; he had given better dinners than anyone he knew; and the conversation in his rooms had been often memorable. He quoted to Philip the exquisite epigram:

"*They told me, Herakleitus, they told me you were dead.*"

And now, when he related again the picturesque little anecdote about the examiner and his boots, he laughed.

"Of course it was folly," he said, "but it was a folly in which there was something fine."

Philip, with a little thrill, thought it magnificent.

Then Hayward went to London to read for the bar. He had charming rooms in Clement's Inn, with panelled walls, and he tried to make them look like his old rooms at the Hall. He had ambitions that were vaguely political, he described himself as a Whig, and he was put up for a club which was of Liberal but gentlemanly flavour. His ideal was to practise at the Bar (he chose the Chancery side as less brutal), and get a seat for some pleasant constituency as soon as the various promises made him were carried out; meanwhile he went a great deal to the opera, and made acquaintance with a small number of charming people who admired the things that he admired. He joined a dining-club of which the motto was, The Whole, The Good, and The Beautiful. He formed a platonic friendship with a lady some years older than himself, who lived in Kensington Square; and

nearly every afternoon he drank tea with her by the light of shaded candles, and talked of George Meredith and Walter Pater. It was notorious that any fool could pass the examinations of the Bar Council, and he pursued his studies in a dilatory fashion. When he was ploughed for his final he looked upon it as a personal affront. At the same time the lady in Kensington Square told him that her husband was coming home from India on leave, and was a man, though worthy in every way, of a commonplace mind, who would not understand a young man's frequent visits. Hayward felt that life was full of ugliness, his soul revolted from the thought of affronting again the cynicism of examiners, and he saw something rather splendid in kicking away the ball which lay at his feet. He was also a good deal in debt: it was difficult to live in London like a gentleman on three hundred a year; and his heart yearned for the Venice and Florence which John Ruskin had so magically described. He felt that he was unsuited to the vulgar bustle of the Bar, for he had discovered that it was not sufficient to put your name on a door to get briefs; and modern politics seemed to lack nobility. He felt himself a poet. He disposed of his rooms in Clement's Inn and went to Italy. He had spent a winter in Florence and a winter in Rome, and now was passing his second summer abroad in Germany so that he might read Goethe in the original.

Hayward had one gift which was very precious. He had a real feeling for literature, and he could impart his own passion with an admirable fluency. He could throw himself into sympathy with a writer and see all that was best in him, and then he could talk about him with understanding. Philip had read a great deal, but he had read without discrimination everything that he happened to come across, and it was very good for him now to meet someone who could guide his taste. He borrowed books from the small lending library which the town possessed and began reading all the wonderful things that Hayward spoke of. He did not read always with enjoyment but invariably with perseverance. He was eager for self-improvement. He felt himself very ignorant and very humble. By the end of August, when Weeks returned from South Germany, Philip was completely under Hayward's influence. Hayward did not like Weeks. He deplored the American's black coat and pepper-and-salt trousers, and spoke with a scornful shrug of his New England conscience. Philip listened complacently to the abuse of a man who had gone out of his way to be kind to him, but when Weeks in his turn made disagreeable remarks about Hayward he lost his temper.

"Your new friend looks like a poet," said Weeks, with a thin smile on his careworn, bitter mouth.

"He is a poet."

"Did he tell you so? In America we should call him a pretty fair specimen of a waster."

"Well, we're not in America," said Philip frigidly.

"How old is he? Twenty-five? And he does nothing but stay in pensions and write poetry."

"You don't know him," said Philip hotly.

"Oh yes, I do: I've met a hundred and forty-seven of him."

Weeks' eyes twinkled, but Philip, who did not understand American humour, pursed his lips and looked severe. Weeks to Philip seemed a man of middle-age, but he was in point of fact little more than thirty. He had a long, thin body and the scholar's stoop; his head was large and ugly; he had pale scanty hair and an earthy skin; his thin mouth and thin, long nose, and the great protuberance of his frontal bones, gave him an uncouth look. He was cold and precise in his manner, a bloodless man, without passion; but he had a curious vein of frivolity which disconcerted the serious-minded among whom his instincts naturally threw him. He was studying theology in Heidelberg, but the other theological students of his own nationality looked upon him with suspicion. He was very unorthodox, which frightened them; and his freakish humour excited their disapproval.

"How can you have known a hundred and forty-seven of him?" asked Philip seriously.

"I've met him in the Latin Quarter in Paris, and I've met him in pensions in Berlin and Munich. He lives in small hotels in Perugia and Assisi. He stands by the dozen before the Botticellis in Florence, and he sits on all the benches of the Sistine Chapel in Rome. In Italy he drinks a little too much wine, and in Germany he drinks a great deal too much beer. He always admires the right thing whatever the right thing is, and one of these days he's going to write a great work. Think of it, there are a hundred and forty-seven great works reposing in the bosoms of a hundred and forty-seven great men, and the tragic thing is that not one of those hundred and forty-seven great works will ever be written. And yet the world goes on."

Weeks spoke seriously, but his gray eyes twinkled a little at the end of his long speech, and Philip flushed when he saw that the American was making fun of him.

"You do talk rot," he said crossly.

XXVII

WEEKS had two little rooms at the back of Frau Erlin's house, and one of them, arranged as a parlour, was comfortable enough for him to invite people to sit in. After supper, urged perhaps by the impish humour which was the despair of his friends in Cambridge, Mass., he often asked Philip and Hayward to come in for a chat. He received them with elaborate courtesy and insisted on their sitting in the only two comfortable chairs in the room. Though he did not drink himself, with a politeness of which Philip recognized the irony, he put a couple of bottles of beer at Hayward's elbow, and he insisted on lighting matches whenever in the heat of argument Hayward's pipe went out. At the beginning of their acquaintance Hayward, as a member of so celebrated a university, had adopted a patronising attitude towards Weeks, who was a graduate of Harvard; and when by chance the conversation turned upon the Greek tragedians, a subject upon which Hayward felt he spoke with authority, he had assumed the air that it was his part to give information rather than to exchange ideas. Weeks had listened politely, with smiling modesty, till Hayward finished; then he asked one or two insidious questions, so innocent in appearance that Hayward, not seeing into what a quandary they led him, answered blandly; Weeks made a courteous objection, then a correction of fact, after that a quotation from some little known Latin commentator, then a reference to a German authority; and the fact was disclosed that he

was a scholar. With smiling ease, apologetically, Weeks tore to pieces all that Hayward had said; with elaborate civility he displayed the superficiality of his attainments. He mocked him with gentle irony. Philip could not help seeing that Hayward looked a perfect fool, and Hayward had not the sense to hold his tongue; in his irritation, his self-assurance undaunted, he attempted to argue: he made wild statements and Weeks amicably corrected them; he reasoned falsely and Weeks proved that he was absurd: Weeks confessed that he had taught Greek Literature at Harvard. Hayward gave a laugh of scorn.

"I might have known it. Of course you read Greek like a schoolmaster," he said. "I read it like a poet."

"And do you find it more poetic when you don't quite know what it means? I thought it was only in revealed religion that a mistranslation improved the sense."

At last, having finished the beer, Hayward left Weeks' room hot and dishevelled; with an angry gesture he said to Philip:

"Of course the man's a pedant. He has no real feeling for beauty. Accuracy is the virtue of clerks. It's the spirit of the Greeks that we aim at. Weeks is like that fellow who went to hear Rubenstein and complained that he played false notes. False notes! What did they matter when he played divinely?"

Philip, not knowing how many incompetent people have found solace in these false notes, was much impressed.

Hayward could never resist the opportunity which Weeks offered him of regaining ground lost on a previous occasion, and Weeks was able with the greatest ease to draw him into a discussion. Though he could not help seeing how small his attainments were beside the American's, his British pertinacity, his wounded vanity (perhaps they are the same thing), would not allow him to give up the struggle. Hayward seemed to take a delight in displaying his ignorance, self-satisfaction, and wrongheadedness. Whenever Hayward said something which was illogical, Weeks in a few words would show the falseness of his reasoning, pause for a moment to enjoy his triumph, and then hurry on to another subject as though Christian charity impelled him to spare the vanquished foe. Philip tried sometimes to put in something to help his friend, and Weeks gently crushed him, but so kindly, differently from the way in which he answered Hayward, that even Philip, outrageously sensitive, could not feel hurt. Now and then, losing his calm as he felt himself more and more foolish, Hayward became abusive, and only the American's smiling politeness prevented the argument from degenerating into a quarrel. On these occasions when Hayward left Weeks' room he muttered angrily:

"Damned Yankee!"

That settled it. It was a perfect answer to an argument which had seemed unanswerable.

Though they began by discussing all manner of subjects in Weeks' little room eventually the conversation always turned to religion: the theological student took a professional interest in it, and Hayward welcomed a subject in which hard facts need not disconcert him; when feeling is the gauge you can snap your fingers at logic,

and when your logic is weak that is very agreeable. Hayward found it difficult to explain his beliefs to Philip without a great flow of words; but it was clear (and this fell in with Philip's idea of the natural order of things), that he had been brought up in the church by law established. Though he had now given up all idea of becoming a Roman Catholic, he still looked upon that communion with sympathy. He had much to say in its praise, and he compared favourably its gorgeous ceremonies with the simple services of the Church of England. He gave Philip Newman's *Apologia* to read, and Philip, finding it very dull, nevertheless read it to the end.

"Read it for its style, not for its matter," said Hayward.

He talked enthusiastically of the music at the Oratory, and said charming things about the connection between incense and the devotional spirit. Weeks listened to him with his frigid smile.

"You think it proves the truth of Roman Catholicism that John Henry Newman wrote good English and that Cardinal Manning has a picturesque appearance?"

Hayward hinted that he had gone through much trouble with his soul. For a year he had swum in a sea of darkness. He passed his fingers through his fair, waving hair and told them that he would not for five hundred pounds endure again those agonies of mind. Fortunately he had reached calm waters at last.

"But what *do* you believe?" asked Philip, who was never satisfied with vague statements.

"I believe in the Whole, the Good, and the Beautiful."

Hayward with his loose large limbs and the fine carriage of his head looked very handsome when he said this, and he said it with an air.

"Is that how you would describe your religion in a census paper?" asked Weeks, in mild tones.

"I hate the rigid definition: it's so ugly, so obvious. If you like I will say that I believe in the church of the Duke of Wellington and Mr. Gladstone."

"That's the Church of England," said Philip.

"Oh wise young man!" retorted Hayward, with a smile which made Philip blush, for he felt that in putting into plain words what the other had expressed in a paraphrase, he had been guilty of vulgarity. "I belong to the Church of England. But I love the gold and the silk which clothe the priest of Rome, and his celibacy, and the confessional, and purgatory: and in the darkness of an Italian cathedral, incense-laden and mysterious, I believe with all my heart in the miracle of the Mass. In Venice I have seen a fisherwoman come in, barefoot, throw down her basket of fish by her side, fall on her knees, and pray to the Madonna; and that I felt was the real faith, and I prayed and believed with her. But I believe also in Aphrodite and Apollo and the Great God Pan."

He had a charming voice, and he chose his words as he spoke; he uttered them almost rhythmically. He would have gone on, but Weeks opened a second bottle of beer.

"Let me give you something to drink."

Hayward turned to Philip with the slightly condescending gesture which so impressed the youth.

"Now are you satisfied?" he asked.

Philip, somewhat bewildered, confessed that he was.

"I'm disappointed that you didn't add a little Buddhism," said Weeks.

"And I confess I have a sort of sympathy for Mahomet; I regret that you should have left him out in the cold."

Hayward laughed, for he was in a good humour with himself that evening, and the ring of his sentences still sounded pleasant in his ears. He emptied his glass.

"I didn't expect you to understand me," he answered. "With your cold American intelligence you can only adopt the critical attitude. Emerson and all that sort of thing. But what is criticism? Criticism is purely destructive; anyone can destroy, but not everyone can build up. You are a pedant, my dear fellow. The important thing is to construct: I am constructive; I am a poet."

Weeks looked at him with eyes which seemed at the same time to be quite grave and yet to be smiling brightly.

"I think, if you don't mind my saying so, you're a little drunk."

"Nothing to speak of," answered Hayward cheerfully. "And not enough for me to be unable to overwhelm you in argument. But come, I have unbosomed my soul; now tell us what your religion is."

Weeks put his head on one side so that he looked like a sparrow on a perch.

"I've been trying to find that out for years. I think I'm a Unitarian."

"But that's a dissenter," said Philip.

He could not imagine why they both burst into laughter, Hayward uproariously, and Weeks with a funny chuckle.

"And in England dissenters aren't gentlemen, are they?" asked Weeks.

"Well, if you ask me point-blank, they're not," replied Philip rather crossly.

He hated being laughed at, and they laughed again.

"And will you tell me what a gentleman is?" asked Weeks.

"Oh, I don't know; everyone knows what it is."

"Are you a gentleman?"

No doubt had ever crossed Philip's mind on the subject, but he knew it was not a thing to state of oneself.

"If a man tells you he's a gentleman you can bet your boots he isn't," he retorted.

"Am I a gentleman?"

Philip's truthfulness made it difficult for him to answer, but he was naturally polite.

"Oh, well, you're different," he said. "You're American, aren't you?"

"I suppose we may take it that only Englishmen are gentlemen," said Weeks gravely.

Philip did not contradict him.

"Couldn't you give me a few more particulars?" asked Weeks.

Philip reddened, but, growing angry, did not care if he made himself ridiculous.

"I can give you plenty." He remembered his uncle's saying that it took three generations to make a gentleman: it was a companion proverb to the silk purse and the sow's ear. "First of all he's the son of a gentleman, and he's been to a public school, and to Oxford or Cambridge."

"Edinburgh wouldn't do, I suppose?" asked Weeks.

"And he talks English like a gentleman, and he wears the right sort of things, and if he's a gentleman he can always tell if another chap's a gentleman."

It seemed rather lame to Philip as he went on, but there it was: that was what he meant by the word, and everyone he had ever known had meant that too.

"It is evident to me that I am not a gentleman," said Weeks. "I don't see why you should have been so surprised because I was a dissenter."

"I don't quite know what a Unitarian is," said Philip.

Weeks in his odd way again put his head on one side: you almost expected him to twitter.

"A Unitarian very earnestly disbelieves in almost everything that anybody else believes, and he has a very lively sustaining faith in he doesn't quite know what."

"I don't see why you should make fun of me," said Philip. "I really want to know."

"My dear friend, I'm not making fun of you. I have arrived at that definition after years of great labour and the most anxious, nerve-racking study."

When Philip and Hayward got up to go, Weeks handed Philip a little book in a paper cover.

"I suppose you can read French pretty well by now. I wonder if this would amuse you."

Philip thanked him and, taking the book, looked at the title. It was Renan's *Vie de Jésus*.

XXVIII

It occurred neither to Hayward nor to Weeks that the conversations which helped them to pass an idle evening were being turned over afterwards in Philip's active brain. It had never struck him before that religion was a matter upon which discussion was possible. To him it meant the Church of England, and not to believe in its tenets was a sign of wilfulness which could not fail of punishment here or hereafter. There was some doubt in his mind about the chastisement of unbelievers. It was possible that a merciful judge, reserving the flames of hell for the heathen—Mahommedans, Buddhists, and the rest—would spare Dissenters and Roman Catholics (though at the cost of how much humiliation when they were made to realise their error!), and it was also possible that He would be pitiful to those who had had no chance of learning the truth,—this was reasonable enough, though such were the activities of the Missionary Society there could not be many in this condition—but if the chance had been theirs and they had neglected it (in which category were obviously Roman Catholics and Dissenters), the punishment was sure and merited. It was clear that the miscreant was in a parlous state. Perhaps Philip had not been taught it in so many words, but certainly the impression had been given him that only members of the Church of England had any real hope of eternal happiness.

One of the things that Philip had heard definitely stated was that the unbeliever was a wicked and a vicious man; but Weeks, though he believed in hardly anything that Philip believed, led a life of Christian purity. Philip had received little kindness in his life, and he was touched by the American's desire to help him: once when a cold kept him in bed for three days, Weeks nursed him like a mother. There was neither vice nor wickedness in him, but only sincerity and lovingkindness. It was evidently possible to be virtuous and unbelieving.

Also Philip had been given to understand that people adhered to other faiths only from obstinacy or self-interest: in their hearts they knew they were false; they deliberately sought to deceive others. Now, for the sake of his German he had been accustomed on Sunday mornings to attend the Lutheran service, but when Hayward arrived he began instead to go with him to Mass. He noticed that, whereas the protestant church was nearly empty and the congregation had a listless air, the Jesuit on the other hand was crowded and the worshippers seemed to pray with all their hearts. They had not the look of hypocrites. He was surprised at the contrast; for he knew of course that the Lutherans, whose faith was closer to that of the Church of England, on that account were nearer the truth than the Roman Catholics. Most of the men—it was largely a masculine congregation—were South Germans; and he could not help saying to himself that if he had been born in South Germany he would certainly have been a Roman Catholic. He might just as well have been born in a Roman Catholic country as in England; and in England as well in a Wesleyan, Baptist, or Methodist family as in one that fortunately belonged to the church by law established. He was a little breathless at the danger he had run. Philip was on friendly terms with the little Chinaman who sat at table with him twice each day. His name was Sung. He was always smiling, affable, and polite. It seemed strange that he should frizzle in hell merely because he was a Chinaman; but if salvation was possible whatever a man's faith was, there did not seem to be any particular advantage in belonging to the Church of England.

Philip, more puzzled than he had ever been in his life, sounded Weeks. He had to be careful, for he was very sensitive to ridicule; and the acidulous humour with which the American treated the Church of England disconcerted him. Weeks only puzzled him more. He made Philip acknowledge that those South Germans whom he saw in the Jesuit church were every bit as firmly convinced of the truth of Roman Catholicism as he was of that of the Church of England, and from that he led him to admit that the Mahommedan and the Buddhist were convinced also of the truth of· their respective religions. It looked as though knowing that you were right meant nothing; they all knew they were right. Weeks had no intention of undermining the boy's faith, but he was deeply interested in religion, and found it an absorbing topic of conversation. He had described his own views accurately when he said that he very earnestly disbelieved in almost everything that other people believed. Once Philip asked him a question, which he had heard his uncle put when the conversation at the vicarage had fallen upon some mildly rationalistic work which was then exciting discussion in the newspapers.

"But why should you be right and all those fellows like St. Anselm and St. Augustine be wrong?"

"You mean that they were very clever and learned men, while you have grave doubts whether I am either?" asked Weeks.

"Yes," answered Philip uncertainly, for put in that way his question seemed impertinent.

"St. Augustine believed that the earth was flat and that the sun turned round it."

"I don't know what that proves."

"Why, it proves that you believe with your generation. Your saints lived in an age of faith, when it was practically impossible to disbelieve what to us is positively incredible."

"Then how d'you know that we

have the truth now?"

"I don't."

Philip thought this over for a moment, then he said:

"I don't see why the things we believe absolutely now shouldn't be just as wrong as what they believed in the past."

"Neither do I."

"Then how can you believe anything at all?"

"I don't know."

Philip asked Weeks what he thought of Hayward's religion.

"Men have always formed gods in their own image," said Weeks. "He believes in the picturesque."

Philip paused for a little while, then he said:

"I don't see why one should believe in God at all."

The words were no sooner out of his mouth than he realised that he had ceased to do so. It took his breath away like a plunge into cold water. He looked at Weeks with startled eyes. Suddenly he felt afraid. He left Weeks as quickly as he could. He wanted to be alone. It was the most startling experience that he had ever had. He tried to think it all out; it was very exciting, since his whole life seemed concerned (he thought his decision on this matter must profoundly affect its course) and a mistake might lead to eternal damnation; but the more he reflected the more convinced he was; and though during the next few weeks he read books, aids to scepticism, with eager interest it was only to confirm him in what he felt instinctively. The fact was that he had ceased to believe not for this reason or the other, but because he had not the religious temperament. Faith had been forced upon him from the outside. It was a matter of environment and example. A new environment and a new example gave him the opportunity to find himself. He put off the faith of his childhood quite simply, like a cloak that he no longer needed. At first life seemed strange and lonely without the belief which, though he never realised it, had been an unfailing support. He felt like a man who has leaned on a stick and finds himself forced suddenly to walk without assistance. It really seemed as though the days were colder and the nights more solitary. But he was upheld by the excitement; it seemed to make life a more thrilling adventure; and in a little while the stick which he had thrown aside, the cloak which had fallen from his shoulders, seemed an intolerable burden of which he had been eased. The religious exercises which for so many years had been forced upon him were part and parcel of religion to him. He thought of the collects and epistles which he had been made to learn by heart, and the long services at the Cathedral through which he had sat when every limb itched with the desire for movement; and he remembered those walks at night through muddy roads to the parish church at Blackstable, and the coldness of that bleak building; he sat with his feet like ice, his fingers numb and heavy, and all around was the sickly odour of pomatum. Oh, he had been so bored! His heart leaped when he saw he was free from all that.

He was surprised at himself because he ceased to believe so easily, and, not knowing that he felt as he did on account of the subtle workings of his inmost nature, he ascribed the certainty he had reached to his own cleverness. He was unduly pleased with himself. With youth's lack of sympathy for an attitude other than its own he despised not a little Weeks and Hayward because they were content with the vague emotion which they called God and would not take the further step which to himself seemed so obvious. One day he went alone up a certain hill so that he might see a view which, he knew not why, filled him always with wild exhilaration. It was autumn now, but often the days were cloudless still, and then the sky seemed to glow with a more splendid light: it was as though nature consciously sought to put a fuller vehemence into the remaining days of fair weather. He looked down upon the plain, a-quiver with the sun, stretching vastly before him: in the distance were the roofs of Mannheim and ever so far away the dimness of Worms. Here and there a more piercing glitter was the Rhine. The tremendous spaciousness of it was glowing with rich gold. Philip, as he stood there, his heart beating with sheer joy, thought how the tempter had stood with Jesus on a high mountain and shown him the kingdoms of the earth. To Philip, intoxicated with the beauty of the scene, it seemed that it was the whole world which was spread before him, and he was eager to step down and enjoy it. He was free from degrading fears and free from prejudice. He could go his way without the intolerable dread of hell-fire. Suddenly he realised that he had lost also that burden of responsibility which made every action of his life a matter of urgent consequence. He could breathe more freely in a lighter air. He was responsible only to himself for the things he did. Freedom! He was his own master at last. From old habit, unconsciously he thanked God that he no longer believed in Him.

Drunk with pride in his intelligence and in his fearlessness, Philip entered deliberately upon a new life. But his loss of faith made less difference in his behaviour than he expected.

Though he had thrown on one side the Christian dogmas it never occurred to him to criticise the Christian ethics; he accepted the Christian virtues, and indeed thought it fine to practise them for their own sake, without a thought of reward or punishment. There was small occasion for heroism in the Frau Professor's house, but he was a little more exactly truthful than he had been, and he forced himself to be more than commonly attentive to the dull, elderly ladies who sometimes engaged him in conversation. The gentle oath, the violent adjective, which are typical of our language and which he had cultivated before as a sign of manliness, he now elaborately eschewed.

Having settled the whole matter to his satisfaction he sought to put it out of his mind, but that was more easily said than done; and he could not prevent the regrets nor stifle the misgivings which sometimes tormented him. He was so young and had so few friends that immortality had no particular attractions for him, and he was able without trouble to give up belief in it; but there was one thing which made him wretched; he told himself that he was unreasonable, he tried to laugh himself out of such pathos; but the tears really came to his eyes when he thought that he would never see again the beautiful mother whose love for him had grown more precious as the years since her death passed on. And sometimes, as though the influence of innumerable ancestors, God-fearing and devout, were working in him unconsciously, there seized him a panic fear that perhaps after all it was all true, and there was, up there behind the blue sky, a jealous God who would punish in everlasting flames the atheist. At these times his reason could offer him no help, he imagined the anguish of a physical torment which would last endlessly, he felt quite sick with fear and burst into a violent sweat. At last he would say to himself desperately:

"After all, it's not my fault. I can't force myself to believe. If there is a God after all and he punishes me because I honestly don't believe in Him I can't help it."

XXIX

WINTER set in. Weeks went to Berlin to attend the lectures of Paulssen, and Hayward began to think of going South. The local theatre opened its doors. Philip and Hayward went to it two or three times a week with the praiseworthy intention of improving their German, and Philip found it a more diverting manner of perfecting himself in the language than listening to sermons. They found themselves in the midst of a revival of the drama. Several of Ibsen's plays were on the repertory for the winter; Sudermann's *Die Ehre* was then a new play, and on its production in the quiet university town caused the greatest excitement; it was extravagantly praised and bitterly attacked; other dramatists followed with plays written under the modern influence, and Philip witnessed a series of works in which the vileness of mankind was displayed before him. He had never been to a play in his life till then (poor touring companies sometimes came to the Assembly Rooms at Blackstable, but the Vicar, partly on account of his profession, partly because he thought it would be vulgar, never went to see them; and the passion of the stage seized him. He felt a thrill the moment he got into the little, shabby, ill-lit theatre. Soon he came to know the peculiarities of the small company, and by the casting could tell at once what were the characteristics of the persons in the drama; but this made no difference to him. To him it was real life. It was a strange life, dark and tortured, in which men and women showed to remorseless eyes the evil that was in their hearts: a fair face concealed a depraved mind; the virtuous used virtue as a mask to hide their secret vice, the seeming-strong fainted within with their weakness; the honest were corrupt, the chaste were lewd. You seemed to dwell in a room where the night before an orgy had taken place: the windows had not been opened in the morning; the air was foul with the dregs of beer, and stale smoke, and flaring gas. There was no laughter. At most you sniggered at the hypocrite or the fool: the characters expressed themselves in cruel words that seemed wrung out of their hearts by shame and anguish.

Philip was carried away by the sordid intensity of it. He seemed to see the world again in another fashion, and this world too he was anxious to know. After the play was over he went to a tavern and sat in the bright warmth with Hayward to eat a sandwich and drink a glass of beer. All round were little groups of students, talking and laughing; and here and there was a family, father and mother, a couple of sons and a girl; and sometimes the girl said a sharp thing, and the father leaned back in his chair and laughed, laughed heartily. It was very friendly and innocent. There

was a pleasant homeliness in the scene, but for this Philip had no eyes. His thoughts ran on the play he had just come from.

"You do feel it's life, don't you?" he said excitedly. "You know, I don't think I can stay here much longer. I want to get to London so that I can really begin. I want to have experiences. I'm so tired of preparing for life: I want to live it now."

Sometimes Hayward left Philip to go home by himself. He would never exactly reply to Philip's eager questioning, but with a merry, rather stupid laugh, hinted at a romantic amour; he quoted a few lines of Rossetti, and once showed Philip a sonnet in which passion and purple, pessimism and pathos, were packed together on the subject of a young lady called Trude. Hayward surrounded his sordid and vulgar little adventures with a glow of poetry, and thought he touched hands with Pericles and Pheidias because to describe the object of his attentions he used the word *hetaira* instead of one of those, more blunt and apt, provided by the English language. Philip in the daytime had been led by curiosity to pass through the little street near the old bridge, with its neat white houses and green shutters, in which according to Hayward the Fräulein Trude lived; but the women, with brutal faces and painted cheeks, who came out of their doors and cried out to him, filled him with fear; and he fled in horror from the rough hands that sought to detain him. He yearned above all things for experience and felt himself ridiculous because at his age he had not enjoyed that which all fiction taught him was the most important thing in life; but he had the unfortunate gift of seeing things as they were, and the reality which was offered him differed too terribly from the ideal of his dreams.

He did not know how wide a country, arid and precipitous, must be crossed before the traveller through life comes to an acceptance of reality. It is an illusion that youth is happy, an illusion of those who have lost it; but the young know they are wretched, for they are full of the truthless ideals which have been instilled into them, and each time they come in contact with the real they are bruised and wounded. It looks as if they were victims of a conspiracy; for the books they read, ideal by the necessity of selection, and the conversation of their elders, who look back upon the past through a rosy haze of forgetfulness, prepare them for an unreal life. They must discover for themselves that all they have read and all they have been told are lies, lies, lies; and each discovery is another nail driven into the body on the cross of life. The strange thing is that each one who has gone through that bitter disillusionment adds to it in his turn, unconsciously, by the power within him which is stronger than himself. The companionship of Hayward was the worst possible thing for Philip. He was a man who saw nothing for himself, but only through a literary atmosphere, and he was dangerous because he had deceived himself into sincerity. He honestly mistook his sensuality for romantic emotion, his vacillation for the artistic temperament, and his idleness for philosophic calm. His mind, vulgar in its effort at refinement, saw everything a little larger than life size, with the outlines blurred, in a golden mist of sentimentality. He lied and never knew that he lied, and when it was pointed out to him said that lies were beautiful. He was an idealist.

XXX

PHILIP was restless and dissatisfied. Hayward's poetic allusions troubled his imagination, and his soul yearned for romance. At least that was how he put it to himself.

And it happened that an incident was taking place in Frau Erlin's house which increased Philip's preoccupation with the matter of sex. Two or three times on his walks among the hills he had met Fräulein Cäcilie wandering by herself. He had passed her with a bow, and a few yards further on had seen the Chinaman. He thought nothing of it; but one evening on his way home, when night had already fallen, he passed two people walking very close together. Hearing his footstep, they separated quickly, and though he could not see well in the darkness he was almost certain they were Cäcilie and Herr Sung. Their rapid movement apart suggested that they had been walking arm in arm. Philip was puzzled and surprised. He had never paid much attention to Fräulein Cäcilie. She was a plain girl, with a square face and blunt features. She could not have been more than sixteen, since she still wore her long fair hair in a plait. That evening at supper he looked at her curiously; and, though of late she had talked little at meals, she addressed him.

"Where did you go for your walk today, Herr Carey?" she asked.

"Oh, I walked up towards the Königstuhl."

"I didn't go out," she volunteered. "I had a headache."

The Chinaman, who sat next to her, turned round.

"I'm so sorry," he said. "I hope it's better now."

Fräulein Cäcilie was evidently uneasy, for she spoke again to Philip.

"Did you meet many people on the way?"

Philip could not help reddening when he told a downright lie.

"No. I don't think I saw a living soul."

He fancied that a look of relief passed across her eyes.

Soon, however, there could be no doubt that there was something between the pair, and other people in the Frau Professor's house saw them lurking in dark places. The elderly ladies who sat at the head of the table began to discuss what was now a scandal. The Frau Professor was angry and harassed. She had done her best to see nothing. The winter was at hand, and it was not as easy a matter then as in the summer to keep her house full. Herr Sung was a good customer: he had two rooms on the ground floor, and he drank a bottle of Moselle at each meal. The Frau Professor charged him three marks a bottle and made a good profit. None of her other guests drank wine, and some of them did not even drink beer. Neither did she wish to lose Fräulein Cäcilie, whose parents were in business in South America and paid well for the Frau Professor's motherly care; and she knew that if she wrote to the girl's uncle, who lived in Berlin, he would immediately take her away. The Frau Professor contented herself with giving them both severe looks at table and, though she dared not be rude to the Chinaman, got a certain satisfaction out of incivility to Cäcilie. But the three elderly ladies were not content. Two were widows, and one, a Dutchwoman, was a spinster of masculine appearance; they paid the smallest possible sum for their pension, and gave a good deal of trouble, but they were permanent and therefore had to be put up with. They went to the Frau Professor and said that something must be done; it was disgraceful, and the house was ceasing to be respectable. The Frau Professor tried obstinacy, anger, tears, but the three old ladies routed her, and with a sudden assumption of virtuous indignation she said that she would put a stop to the whole thing.

After luncheon she took Cäcilie into her bed-room and began to talk very seriously to her; but to her amazement the girl adopted a brazen attitude; she proposed to go about as she liked; and if she chose to walk with the Chinaman she could not see it was anybody's business but her own. The Frau Professor threatened to write to her uncle.

"Then Onkel Heinrich will put me in a family in Berlin for the winter, and that will be much nicer for me. And Herr Sung will come to Berlin too."

The Frau Professor began to cry. The tears rolled down her coarse, red, fat cheeks; and Cäcilie laughed at her.

"That will mean three rooms empty all through the winter," she said.

Then the Frau Professor tried another plan. She appealed to Fräulein Cäcilie's better nature: she was kind, sensible, tolerant; she treated her no longer as a child, but as a grown woman. She said that it wouldn't be so dreadful, but a Chinaman, with his yellow skin and flat nose, and his little pig's eyes! That's what made it so horrible. It filled one with disgust to think of it.

"Bitte, bitte," said Cäcilie, with a rapid intake of the breath. "I won't listen to anything against him."

"But it's not serious?" gasped Frau Erlin.

"I love him. I love him. I love him."

"*Gott im Himmel!*"

The Frau Professor stared at her with horrified surprise; she had thought it was no more than naughtiness on the child's part, and innocent folly; but the passion in her voice revealed everything. Cäcilie looked at her for a moment with flaming eyes, and then with a shrug of her shoulders went out of the room.

Frau Erlin kept the details of the interview to herself, and a day or two later altered the arrangement of the table. She asked Herr Sung if he would not come and sit at her end, and he with his unfailing politeness accepted with alacrity. Cäcilie took the change indifferently. But as if the discovery that the relations between them were known to the whole household made them more shameless, they made no secret now of their walks together, and every afternoon quite openly set out to wander about the hills. It was plain that they did not care what was said of them. At last even the placidity of Professor Erlin was moved, and he insisted that his wife should speak to the Chinaman. She took him aside in his turn and expostulated; he was ruining the girl's reputation, he was doing harm to the house, he must see how wrong and wicked his conduct was; but she was met with smiling denials; Herr Sung did not know what she was talking about, he was not paying any attention to Fräulein Cäcilie, he never walked with her; it was all untrue, every word of it.

"*Ach,* Herr Sung, how can you say such things? You've been seen again and again."

"No, you're mistaken. It's untrue."

He looked at her with an unceasing smile, which showed his even, little white teeth. He was quite calm. He denied everything. He denied with bland effrontery. At last the Frau Professor lost her temper and said the girl had confessed she loved him. He was not moved. He continued to smile.

"Nonsense! Nonsense! It's all untrue."

She could get nothing out of him. The weather grew very bad; there was snow and frost, and then a thaw with a long succession of cheerless days, on which walking was a poor amusement. One evening when Philip had just finished his German lesson with the Herr Professor and was standing for a moment in the drawing-room, talking to Frau Erlin, Anna came quickly in.

"Mamma, where is Cäcilie?" she said.

"I suppose she's in her room."

"There's no light in it."

The Frau Professor gave an exclamation, and she looked at her daughter in dismay. The thought which was in Anna's head had flashed across hers.

"Ring for Emil," she said hoarsely.

This was the stupid lout who waited at table and did most of the housework. He came in.

"Emil, go down to Herr Sung's room and enter without knocking. If anyone is there say you came in to see about the stove."

No sign of astonishment appeared on Emil's phlegmatic face.

He went slowly downstairs. The Frau Professor and Anna left the door open and listened. Presently they heard Emil come up again, and they called him.

"Was any one there?" asked the Frau Professor.

"Yes, Herr Sung was there."

"Was he alone?"

The beginning of a cunning smile narrowed his mouth.

"No, Fräulein Cäcilie was there."

"Oh, it's disgraceful," cried the Frau Professor.

Now he smiled broadly.

"Fräulein Cäcilie is there every evening. She spends hours at a time there."

Frau Professor began to wring her hands.

"Oh, how abominable! But why didn't you tell me?"

"It was no business of mine," he answered, slowly shrugging his shoulders.

"I suppose they paid you well. Go away. Go."

He lurched clumsily to the door.

"They must go away, mamma," said Anna.

"And who is going to pay the rent? And the taxes are falling due. It's all very well for you to say they must go away. If they go away I can't pay the bills." She turned to Philip, with tears streaming down her face. "*Ach,* Herr Carey, you will not say what you have heard. If Fräulein Förster—" this was the Dutch spinster—"if Fräulein Förster knew she would leave at once. And if they all go we must close the house. I cannot afford to keep it."

"Of course I won't say anything."

"If she stays, I will not speak to her," said Anna.

That evening at supper Fräulein Cäcilie, redder than usual, with a look of obstinacy on her face, took her place punctually; but Herr Sung did not appear, and for a while Philip thought he was going to shirk the ordeal. At last he came, very smiling, his little eyes dancing with the apologies he made for his late arrival. He insisted as usual on pouring out the Frau Professor a glass of his Moselle, and he offered a glass to Fräulein Förster. The room was very hot, for the stove had been alight all day and the win-dows were seldom opened. Emil blundered about, but succeeded somehow in serving everyone quickly and with order. The three old ladies sat in silence, visibly disapproving: the Frau Professor had scarcely recovered from her tears; her husband was silent and oppressed. Conversation languished. It seemed to Philip that there was something dreadful in that gathering which he had sat with so often; they looked different under the light of the two hanging lamps from what they had ever looked before; he was vaguely uneasy. Once he caught Cäcilie's eye, and he thought she looked at him with hatred and contempt. The room was stifling. It was as though the beastly passion of that pair troubled them all; there was a feeling of Oriental depravity; a faint savour of joss-sticks, a mystery of hidden vices, seemed to make their breath heavy. Philip could feel the beating of the arteries in his forehead. He could not understand what strange emotion distracted him; he seemed to feel something infinitely attractive, and yet he was repelled and horrified.

For several days things went on. The air was sickly with the unnatural passion which all felt about them, and the nerves of the little household seemed to grow exasperated. Only Herr Sung remained unaffected; he was no less smiling, affable, and polite than he had been before: one could not tell whether his manner was a triumph of civilisation or an expression of contempt on the part of the Oriental for the vanquished West. Cäcilie was flaunting and cynical. At last even the Frau Professor could bear the position no longer. Suddenly panic seized her; for Professor Erlin with brutal frankness had suggested the possible consequences of an intrigue which was now manifest to everyone, and she saw her good name in Heidelberg and the repute of her house ruined by a scandal which could not possibly be hidden. For some reason, blinded perhaps by her interests, this possibility had never occurred to her; and now, her wits muddled by a terrible fear, she could hardly be prevented from turning the girl out of the house at once. It was due to Anna's good sense that a cautious letter was written to the uncle in Berlin suggesting that Cäcilie should be taken away.

But having made up her mind to lose the two lodgers, the Frau Professor could not resist the satisfaction of giving rein to the ill-temper she had curbed so long. She was free now to say anything she liked to Cäcilie. "I have written to your uncle, Cäcilie, to take you away. I cannot have you in my house any longer."

Her little round eyes sparkled when she noticed the sudden whiteness of the girl's face.

"You're shameless. Shameless," she went on.

She called her foul names.

"What did you say to my uncle Heinrich, Frau Professor?" the girl asked, suddenly falling from her attitude of flaunting independence.

"Oh, he'll tell you himself. I expect to get a letter from him tomorrow."

Next day, in order to make the humiliation more public, at supper she called down the table to Cäcilie.

"I have had a letter from your uncle, Cäcilie. You are to pack your things tonight, and we will put you in the train tomorrow morning. He

will meet you himself in Berlin at the Central Bahnhof."

"Very good, Frau Professor."

Herr Sung smiled in the Frau Professor's eyes, and notwithstanding her protests insisted on pouring out a glass of wine for her. The Frau Professor ate her supper with a good appetite. But she had triumphed unwisely. Just before going to bed she called the servant.

"Emil, if Fräulein Cäcilie's box is ready you had better take it downstairs tonight. The porter will fetch it before breakfast."

The servant went away and in a moment came back.

"Fräulein Cäcilie is not in her room, and her bag has gone."

With a cry the Frau Professor hurried along: the box was on the floor, strapped and locked; but there was no bag, and neither hat nor cloak. The dressing-table was empty. Breathing heavily, the Frau Professor ran downstairs to the Chinaman's rooms, she had not moved so quickly for twenty years, and Emil called out after her to be beware she did not fall; she did not trouble to knock, but burst in. The rooms were empty. The luggage had gone, and the door into the garden, still open, showed how it had been got away. In an envelope on the table were notes for the money due on the month's board and an approximate sum for extras. Groaning, suddenly overcome by her haste, the Frau Professor sank obesely on to a sofa. There could be no doubt. The pair had gone off together. Emil remained stolid and unmoved.

XXXI

HAYWARD, after saying for a month that he was going South next day delaying from week to week out of inability to make up his mind to the bother of packing and the tedium of a journey, had at last been driven off just before Christmas by the preparations for that festival. He could not support the thought of a Teutonic merry-making. It gave him goose-flesh to think of the season's aggressive cheerfulness, and in his desire to avoid the obvious he determined to travel on Christmas Eve.

Philip was not sorry to see him off, for he was a downright person and it irritated him that anybody should not know his own mind. Though much under Hayward's influence, he would not grant that indecision pointed to a charming sensitiveness; and he resented the shadow of a sneer with which Hayward looked upon his straight ways. They corresponded. Hayward was an admirable letter-writer, and knowing his talent took pains with his letters. His temperament was receptive to the beautiful influences with which he came in contact, and he was able in his letters from Rome to put a subtle fragrance of Italy. He thought the city of the ancient Romans a little vulgar, finding distinction only in the decadence of the Empire; but the Rome of the Popes appealed to his sympathy, and in his chosen words, quite exquisitely, there appeared a Rococo beauty. He wrote of old church music and the Alban Hills, and of the languor of incense and the charm of the streets by night, in the rain, when the pavements shone and the light of the street lamps was mysterious. Perhaps he repeated these admirable letters to various friends. He did not know what a troubling effect they had upon Philip; they seemed to make his life very humdrum. With the spring Hayward grew dithyrambic. He proposed that Philip should come down to Italy. He was wasting his time at Heidelberg. The Germans were gross and life there was common; how could the soul come to her own in that prim landscape? In Tuscany the spring was scattering flowers through the land, and Philip was nineteen; let him come and they could wander through the mountain towns of Umbria. Their names sang in Philip's heart. And Cäcilie too, with her lover, had gone to Italy. When he thought of them Philip was seized with a restlessness he could not account for. He cursed his fate because he had no money to travel, and he knew his uncle would not send him more than the fifteen pounds a month which had been agreed upon. He had not managed his allowance very well. His pension and the price of his lessons left him very little over, and he had found going about with Hayward expensive. Hayward had often suggested excursions, a visit to the play, or a bottle of wine, when Philip had come to the end of his month's money; and with the folly of his age he had been unwilling to confess he could not afford an extravagance.

Luckily Hayward's letters came seldom, and in the intervals Philip settled down again to his industrious life. He had matriculated at the university and attended one or two courses of lectures. Kuno Fischer was then at the height of his fame and during the winter had been lecturing brilliantly on Schopenhauer. It was Philip's introduction to philosophy. He had a practical mind and moved uneasily amid the abstract; but he found an unexpected fascination in listening to metaphysical disquisitions; they made him breathless; it was a little like watching a tight-rope dancer doing perilous feats over an abyss; but it was very exciting. The pessimism of the subject attracted his youth; and he believed that the world he was about to enter was a place of pitiless woe and of darkness. That made him none the less eager to enter it; and when, in due course, Mrs. Carey, acting as the correspondent for his guardian's views, suggested that it was time for him to come back to England, he agreed with enthusiasm. He must make up his mind now what he meant to do. If he left Heidelberg at the end of July they could talk things over during August, and it would be a good time to make arrangements.

The date of his departure was settled, and Mrs. Carey wrote to him again. She reminded him of Miss Wilkinson, through whose kindness he had gone to Frau Erlin's house at Heidelberg, and told him that she had arranged to spend a few weeks with them at Blackstable. She would be crossing from Flushing on such and such a day, and if he travelled at the same time he could look after her and come on to Blackstable in her company. Philip's shyness immediately made him write to say that he could not leave till a day or two afterwards. He pictured himself looking out for Miss Wilkinson, the embarrassment of going up to her and asking if it were she (and he might so easily address the wrong person and be snubbed), and then the difficulty of knowing whether in the train he ought to talk to her or whether he could ignore her and read his book.

At last he left Heidelberg. For three months he had been thinking of nothing but the future; and he went without regret. He never knew that he had been happy there. Fräulein Anna gave him a copy of *Der Trompeter von Säckingen* and in return he presented her with a volume of William Morris. Very wisely neither of them ever read the other's present.

XXXII

PHILIP was surprised when he saw his uncle and aunt. He had never noticed before that they were quite old people. The Vicar received him with his usual, not unamiable indifference. He was a little stouter, a little balder, a little grayer. Philip saw how insignificant he was. His face was weak and self-indulgent. Aunt Louisa took him in her arms and kissed him; and tears of happiness flowed down her cheeks. Philip was touched and embarrassed; he had not known with what a hungry love she cared for him.

"Oh, the time has seemed long since you've been away, Philip," she cried.

She stroked his hands and looked into his face with glad eyes.

"You've grown. You're quite a man now."

There was a very small moustache on his upper lip. He had bought a razor and now and then with infinite care shaved the down off his smooth chin.

"We've been so lonely without you." And then shyly, with a little break in her voice, she asked: "You are glad to come back to your home, aren't you?"

"Yes, rather."

She was so thin that she seemed almost transparent, the arms she put round his neck were frail bones that reminded you of chicken bones, and her faded face was oh! so wrinkled. The gray curls which she still wore in the fashion of her youth gave her a queer, pathetic look; and her little withered body was like an autumn leaf, you felt it might be blown away by the first sharp wind. Philip realised that they had done with life, these two quiet little people: they belonged to a past generation, and they were waiting there patiently, rather stupidly, for death; and he, in his vigour and his youth, thirsting for excitement and adventure, was appalled at the waste. They had done nothing, and when they went it would be just as if they had never been. He felt a great pity for Aunt Louisa, and he loved her suddenly because she loved him.

Then Miss Wilkinson, who had kept discreetly out of the way till the Careys had had a chance of welcoming their nephew, came into the room.

"This is Miss Wilkinson, Philip," said Mrs. Carey.

"The prodigal has returned," she said, holding out her hand. "I have brought a rose for the prodigal's buttonhole."

With a gay smile she pinned to Philip's coat the flower she had just picked in the garden. He blushed and felt foolish. He knew that Miss Wilkinson was the daughter of his Uncle William's last rector, and he had a wide acquaintance with the daughters of clergymen. They wore ill-cut clothes and stout boots. They were generally dressed in black, for in Philip's early years at Blackstable homespuns had not reached East Anglia, and the ladies of the clergy did not favour colours. Their hair was done very untidily, and they smelt aggressively of starched linen. They considered the feminine graces unbecoming and looked the same whether they were old or young. They bore their religion arrogantly. The closeness of their connection with the church made them adopt a slightly dictatorial attitude to the rest of mankind.

Miss Wilkinson was very different. She wore a white muslin gown stamped with gray little bunches of flowers, and pointed, high-heeled shoes, with open-work stockings. To Philip's inexperience it seemed that she was wonderfully dressed; he did not see that her frock was cheap and showy. Her hair was elaborately dressed, with a neat curl in the middle of the forehead: it was very black, shiny and hard, and it looked as though it could never be in the least disarranged. She had large black eyes and her nose was slightly aquiline; in profile she had somewhat the look of a bird of prey, but full face she was prepossessing. She smiled a great deal, but her mouth was large and when she smiled she tried to hide her teeth, which were big and rather yellow. But what embarrassed Philip most was that she was heavily powdered: he had very strict views on feminine behaviour and did not think a lady ever powdered; but of course Miss Wilkinson was a lady because she was a clergyman's daughter, and a clergyman was a gentleman.

Philip made up his mind to dislike her thoroughly. She spoke with a slight French accent; and he did not know why she should, since she had been born and bred in the heart of England. He thought her smile affected, and the coy sprightliness of her manner irritated him. For two or three days he remained silent and hostile, but Miss Wilkinson apparently did not notice it. She was very affable. She addressed her conversation almost exclusively to him, and there was something flattering in the way she appealed constantly to his sane judgment. She made him laugh too, and Philip could never resist people who amused him: he had a gift now and then of saying neat things; and it was pleasant to have an appreciative listener. Neither the Vicar nor Mrs. Carey had a sense of humour, and they never laughed at anything he said. As he grew used to Miss Wilkinson, and his shyness left him, he began to like her better; he found the French accent picturesque; and at a garden party which the doctor gave she was very much better dressed than anyone else. She wore a blue foulard with large white spots, and Philip was tickled at the sensation it caused.

"I'm certain they think you're no better than you should be," he told her, laughing.

"It's the dream of my life to be taken for an abandoned hussy," she answered.

One day when Miss Wilkinson was in her room he asked Aunt Louisa how old she was.

"Oh, my dear, you should never ask a lady's age; but she's certainly too old for you to marry."

The Vicar gave his slow, obese smile.

"She's no chicken, Louisa," he said. "She was nearly grown up when we were in Lincolnshire, and that was twenty years ago. She wore a pigtail hanging down her back."

"She may not have been more than ten," said Philip.

"She was older than that," said Aunt Louisa.

"I think she was near twenty," said the Vicar.

"Oh no, William. Sixteen or seventeen at the outside."

"That would make her well over thirty," said Philip.

At that moment Miss Wilkinson tripped downstairs, singing a song by Benjamin Goddard. She had put her hat on, for she and Philip were going for a walk, and she held out her hand for him to button her glove. He did it awkwardly. He felt embarrassed but gallant. Conversation went easily between them now, and as they strolled along they talked of all manner of things. She told Philip about Berlin, and he told her of his year in Heidelberg. As he spoke, things which had appeared of no importance gained a new interest: he described the people at Frau Erlin's house; and to the conversations between Hayward and Weeks, which at the time seemed so significant, he gave a little twist, so that they looked absurd. He was flattered at Miss Wilkinson's laughter.

"I'm quite frightened of you," she said. "You're so sarcastic."

Then she asked him playfully whether he had not had any love affairs at Heidelberg. Without thinking, he frankly answered that he had not; but she refused to believe him.

"How secretive you are!" she said. "At your age is it likely?"

He blushed and laughed.

"You want to know too much," he said.

"Ah, I thought so," she laughed triumphantly. "Look at him blushing."

He was pleased that she should think he had been a sad dog, and he changed the conversation so as to make her believe he had all sorts of romantic things to conceal. He was angry with himself that he had not. There had been no opportunity.

Miss Wilkinson was dissatisfied with her lot. She resented having to earn her living and told Philip a long story of an uncle of her mother's, who had been expected to leave her a fortune but had married his cook and changed his will. She hinted at the luxury of her home and compared her life in Lincolnshire, with horses to ride and carriages to drive in, with the mean dependence of her present state. Philip was a little puzzled when he mentioned this afterwards to Aunt Louisa, and she told him that when she knew the Wilkinsons they had never had anything more than a pony and a dog-cart; Aunt Louisa had heard of the rich uncle, but as he was married and had children before Emily was born she could never have had much hope of inheriting his fortune. Miss Wilkinson had little good to say of Berlin, where she was now in a situation. She complained of the vulgarity of German life, and compared it bitterly with the brilliance of Paris, where she had spent a number of years. She did not say how many. She had been governess in the family of a fashionable portrait-painter, who had married a Jewish wife of means, and in their house she had met many distinguished people. She dazzled Philip with their names. Actors from the Comédie Française had come to the house frequently, and Coquelin, sitting next her at dinner, had told her he had never met a foreigner who spoke such perfect French. Alphonse Daudet had come also, and he had given her a copy of *Sapho:* he had promised to write her name in it, but she had forgotten to remind him. She treasured the volume none the less and she would lend it to Philip. Then there was Maupassant. Miss Wilkinson with a rippling laugh looked at

Philip knowingly. What a man, but what a writer! Hayward had talked of Maupassant, and his reputation was not unknown to Philip.

"Did he make love to you?" he asked.

The words seemed to stick funnily in his throat, but he asked them nevertheless. He liked Miss Wilkinson very much now, and was thrilled by her conversation, but he could not imagine anyone making love to her.

"What a question!" she cried. "Poor Guy, he made love to every woman he met. It was a habit that he could not break himself of."

She sighed a little, and seemed to look back tenderly on the past.

"He was a charming man," she murmured.

A greater experience than Philip's would have guessed from these words the probabilities of the encounter: the distinguished writer invited to luncheon *en famille,* the governess coming in sedately with the two tall girls she was teaching; the introduction:

"*Notre Miss Anglaise.*"

"*Mademoiselle.*"

And the luncheon during which the *Miss Anglaise* sat silent while the distinguished writer talked to his host and hostess.

But to Philip her words called up much more romantic fancies.

"Do tell me all about him," he said excitedly.

"There's nothing to tell," she said truthfully, but in such a manner as to convey that three volumes would scarcely have contained the lurid facts. "You mustn't be curious."

She began to talk of Paris. She loved the boulevards and the Bois. There was grace in every street, and the trees in the Champs Elysées had a distinction which trees had not elsewhere. They were sitting on a stile now by the high-road, and Miss Wilkinson looked with disdain upon the stately elms in front of them. And the theatres; the plays were brilliant, and the acting was incomparable. She often went with Madame Foyot, the mother of the girls she was educating, when she was trying on clothes.

"Oh, what a misery to be poor!" she cried. "These beautiful things, it's only in Paris they know how to dress, and not to be able to afford them! Poor Madame Foyot, she had no figure. Sometimes the dressmaker used to whisper to me: 'Ah, Mademoiselle, if she only had your figure.'"

Philip noticed then that Miss Wilkinson had a robust form, and was proud of it.

"Men are so stupid in England. They only think of the face. The French, who are a nation of lovers, know how much more important the figure is."

Philip had never thought of such things before, but he observed now that Miss Wilkinson's ankles were thick and ungainly. He withdrew his eyes quickly.

"You should go to France. Why don't you go to Paris for a year? You would learn French, and it would—*déniaiser* you."

"What is that?" asked Philip.

She laughed slyly.

"You must look it out in the dictionary. Englishmen do not know how to treat women. They are so shy. Shyness is ridiculous in a man. They don't know how to make love. They can't even tell a woman she is charming without looking foolish."

Philip felt himself absurd. Miss Wilkinson evidently expected him to behave very differently; and he would have been delighted to say gallant and witty things, but they never occurred to him; and when they did he was too much afraid of making a fool of himself to say them.

"Oh, I love Paris," sighed Miss Wilkinson. "But I had to go to Berlin. I was with the Foyots till the girls married, and then I could get nothing to do, and I had the chance of this post in Berlin. They're relations of Madame Foyot, and I accepted. I had a tiny apartment in the Rue Bréda, on the *cinquième:* it wasn't at all respectable. You know about the Rue Bréda —*ces dames,* you know."

Philip nodded, not knowing at all what she meant, but vaguely suspecting, and anxious she should not think him too ignorant.

"But I didn't care. *Je suis libre, n'est-ce-pas?*" She was very fond of speaking French, which indeed she spoke well. "Once I had such a curious adventure there."

She paused a little and Philip pressed her to tell it.

"You wouldn't tell me yours in Heidelberg," she said.

"They were so unadventurous," he retorted.

"I don't know what Mrs. Carey would say if she knew the sort of things we talk about together."

"You don't imagine I shall tell her."

"Will you promise?"

When he had done this, she told him how an art-student who had a room on the floor above her—but she interrupted herself.

"Why don't you go in for art? You paint so prettily."

"Not well enough for that."

"That is for others to judge. *Je m'y connais,* and I believe you have the making of a great artist."

"Can't you see Uncle William's face if I suddenly told him I wanted to go to Paris and study art?"

"You're your own master, aren't you?"

"You're trying to put me off. Please go on with the story."

Miss Wilkinson, with a little laugh,

went on. The art-student had passed her several times on the stairs, and she had paid no particular attention. She saw that he had fine eyes, and he took off his hat very politely. And one day she found a letter slipped under her door. It was from him. He told her that he had adored her for months, and that he waited about the stairs for her to pass. Oh, it was a charming letter! Of course she did not reply, but what woman could help being flattered? And next day there was another letter! It was wonderful, passionate, and touching. When next she met him on the stairs she did not know which way to look. And every day the letters came, and now he begged her to see him. He said he would come in the evening, *vers neuf heures,* and she did not know what to do. Of course it was impossible, and he might ring and ring, but she would never open the door; and then while she was waiting for the tinkling of the bell, all nerves, suddenly he stood before her. She had forgotten to shut the door when she came in.

"C'était une fatalité."

"And what happened then?" asked Philip.

"That is the end of the story," she replied, with a ripple of laughter.

Philip was silent for a moment. His heart beat quickly, and strange emotions seemed to be hustling one another in his heart. He saw the dark staircase and the chance meetings, and he admired the boldness of the letters —oh, he would never have dared to do that—and then the silent, almost mysterious entrance. It seemed to him the very soul of romance.

"What was he like?"

"Oh, he was handsome. *Charmant garçon.*"

"Do you know him still?"

Philip felt a slight feeling of irritation as he asked this.

"He treated me abominably. Men are always the same. You're heartless, all of you."

"I don't know about that," said Philip, not without embarrassment.

"Let us go home," said Miss Wilkinson.

XXXIII

PHILIP could not get Miss Wilkinson's story out of his head. It was clear enough what she meant even though she cut it short, and he was a little shocked. That sort of thing was all very well for married women, he had read enough French novels to know that in France it was indeed the rule, but Miss Wilkinson was English and unmarried; her father was a clergyman. Then it struck him that the art-student probably was neither the first nor the last of her lovers, and he gasped: he had never looked upon Miss Wilkinson like

that; it seemed incredible that anyone should make love to her. In his ingenuousness he doubted her story as little as he doubted what he read in books, and he was angry that such wonderful things never happened to him. It was humiliating that if Miss Wilkinson insisted upon his telling her of his adventures in Heidelberg he would have nothing to tell. It was true that he had some power of invention, but he was not sure whether he could persuade her that he was steeped in vice; women were full of intuition, he had read that, and she might easily discover that he was fibbing. He blushed scarlet as he thought of her laughing up her sleeve.

Miss Wilkinson played the piano and sang in a rather tired voice; but her songs, Massenet, Benjamin Goddard, and Augusta Holmès, were new to Philip; and together they spent many hours at the piano. One day she wondered if he had a voice and insisted on trying it. She told him he had a pleasant baritone and offered to give him lessons. At first with his usual bashfulness he refused, but she insisted, and then every morning at a convenient time after breakfast she gave him an hour's lesson. She had a natural gift for teaching, and it was clear that she was an excellent governess. She had method and firmness. Though her French accent was so much part of her that it remained, all the mellifluousness of her manner left her when she was engaged in teaching. She put up with no nonsense. Her voice became a little peremptory, and instinctively she suppressed inattention and corrected slovenliness. She knew what she was about and put Philip to scales and exercises.

When the lesson was over she resumed without effort her seductive smiles, her voice became again soft and winning, but Philip could not so easily put away the pupil as she the pedagogue; and this impression conflicted with the feelings her stories had aroused in him. He looked at her more narrowly. He liked her much better in the evening than in the morning. In the morning she was rather lined and the skin of her neck was just a little rough. He wished she would hide it, but the weather was very warm just then and she wore blouses which were cut low. She was very fond of white; in the morning it did not suit her. At night she often

looked very attractive, she put on a gown which was almost a dinner dress, and she wore a chain of garnets round her neck; the lace about her bosom and at her elbows gave her a pleasant softness, and the scent she wore (at Blackstable no one used anything but *Eau de Cologne,* and that only on Sundays or when suffering from a sick headache) was troubling and exotic. She really looked very young then.

Philip was much exercised over her age. He added twenty and seventeen together, and could not bring them to a satisfactory total. He asked Aunt Louisa more than once why she thought Miss Wilkinson was thirty-seven: she didn't look more than thirty, and everyone knew that foreigners aged more rapidly than English women; Miss Wilkinson had lived so long abroad that she might almost be called a foreigner. He personally wouldn't have thought her more than twenty-six.

"She's more than that," said Aunt Louisa.

Philip did not believe in the accuracy of the Careys' statements. All they distinctly remembered was that Miss Wilkinson had not got her hair up the last time they saw her in Lincolnshire. Well, she might have been twelve then: it was so long ago and the Vicar was always so unreliable. They said it was twenty years ago, but people used round figures, and it was just as likely to be eighteen years, or seventeen. Seventeen and twelve were only twenty-nine, and hang it all, that wasn't old, was it? Cleopatra was forty-eight when Antony threw away the world for her sake.

It was a fine summer. Day after day was hot and cloudless; but the heat was tempered by the neighbourhood of the sea, and there was a pleasant exhilaration in the air, so that one was excited and not oppressed by the August sunshine. There was a pond in the garden in which a fountain played; water lilies grew in it and gold fish sunned themselves on the surface. Philip and Miss Wilkinson used to take rugs and cushions there after dinner and lie on the lawn in the shade of a tall hedge of roses. They talked and read all the afternoon. They smoked cigarettes, which the Vicar did not allow in the house; he thought smoking a disgusting habit, and used frequently to say that it was disgraceful for anyone to grow a slave to a habit. He forgot that he was himself a slave to afternoon tea.

One day Miss Wilkinson gave Philip *La Vie de Bohème*. She had found it by accident when she was rummaging among the books in the Vicar's study. It had been bought in a lot with something Mr. Carey wanted and had remained undiscovered for ten years.

Philip began to read Murger's fascinating, ill-written, absurd masterpiece, and fell at once under its spell. His soul danced with joy at that picture of starvation which is so good-humoured, of squalor which is so picturesque, of sordid love which is so romantic, of bathos which is so moving. Rodolphe and Mimi, Musette and Schaunard! They wander through the gray streets of the Latin Quarter, finding refuge now in one attic, now in another, in their quaint costumes of Louis Philippe, with their tears and their smiles, happy-go-lucky and reckless. Who can resist them? It is only when you return to the book with a sounder judgment that you find how gross their pleasures were, how vulgar their minds; and you feel the utter worthlessness, as artists and as human beings, of that gay procession. Philip was enraptured.

"Don't you wish you were going to Paris instead of London?" asked Miss Wilkinson, smiling at his enthusiasm.

"It's too late now even if I did," he answered.

During the fortnight he had been back from Germany there had been much discussion between himself and his uncle about his future. He had refused definitely to go to Oxford, and now that there was no chance of his getting scholarships even Mr. Carey came to the conclusion that he could not afford it. His entire fortune had consisted of only two thousand pounds, and though it had been invested in mortgages at five per cent, he had not been able to live on the interest. It was now a little reduced. It would be absurd to spend two hundred a year, the least he could live on at a university, for three years at Oxford which would lead him no nearer to earning his living. He was anxious to go straight to London. Mrs. Carey thought there were only four professions for a gentleman, the Army, the Navy, the Law, and the Church. She had added medicine because her brother-in-law practised it, but did not forget that in her young days no one ever considered the doctor a gentleman. The first two were out of the question, and Philip was firm in his refusal to be ordained. Only the law remained. The local doctor had suggested that many gentlemen now went in for engineering, but Mrs. Carey opposed the idea at once.

"I shouldn't like Philip to go into trade," she said.

"No, he must have a profession," answered the Vicar.

"Why not make him a doctor like his father?"

"I should hate it," said Philip.

Mrs. Carey was not sorry. The Bar seemed out of the question, since he was not going to Oxford, for the Careys were under the impression that a degree was still necessary for success in that calling; and finally it was suggested that he should become articled to a solicitor. They wrote to the family lawyer, Albert Nixon, who was co-executor with the Vicar of Blackstable for the late Henry Carey's estate, and asked him whether he would take Philip. In a day or two the answer came back that he had not a vacancy, and was very much opposed to the whole scheme; the profession was greatly overcrowded, and without capital or connections a man had small chance of becoming more than a managing clerk; he suggested, however, that Philip should become a chartered accountant. Neither the Vicar nor his wife knew in the least what this was, and Philip had never heard of anyone being a chartered accountant; but another letter from the solicitor explained that the growth of modern businesses and the increase of companies had led to the formation of many firms of accountants to examine the books and put into the financial affairs of their clients an order which old-fashioned methods had lacked. Some years before a Royal Charter had been obtained, and the profession was becoming every year more respectable, lucrative, and important. The chartered accountants whom Albert Nixon had employed for thirty years happened to have a vacancy for an articled pupil, and would take Philip for a fee of three hundred pounds. Half of this would be returned during the five years the articles lasted in the form of salary. The prospect was not exciting, but Philip felt that he must decide on something, and the thought of living in London over-balanced the slight shrinking he felt. The Vicar of Blackstable wrote to ask Mr. Nixon

whether it was a profession suited to a gentleman; and Mr. Nixon replied that, since the Charter, men were going into it who had been to public schools and a university; moreover, if Philip disliked the work and after a year wished to leave, Herbert Carter, for that was the accountant's name, would return half the money paid for the articles. This settled it, and it was arranged that Philip should start work on the fifteenth of September.

"I have a full month before me," said Philip.

"And then you go to freedom and I to bondage," returned Miss Wilkinson.

Her holidays were to last six weeks, and she would be leaving Blackstable only a day or two before Philip.

"I wonder if we shall ever meet again," she said.

"I don't know why not."

"Oh, don't speak in that practical way. I never knew anyone so unsentimental."

Philip reddened. He was afraid that Miss Wilkinson would think him a milksop: after all she was a young woman, sometimes quite pretty, and he was getting on for twenty; it was absurd that they should talk of nothing but art and literature. He ought to make love to her. They had talked a good deal of love. There was the art-student in the Rue Bréda, and then there was the painter in whose family she had lived so long in Paris: he had asked her to sit for him, and had started to make love to her so violently that she was forced to invent excuses not to sit to him again. It was clear enough that Miss Wilkinson was used to attentions of that sort. She looked very nice now in a large straw hat: it was hot that afternoon, the hottest day they had had, and beads of sweat stood in a line on her upper lip. He called to mind

Fräulein Cäcilie and Herr Sung. He had never thought of Cäcilie in an amorous way, she was exceedingly plain; but now, looking back, the affair seemed very romantic. He had a chance of romance too. Miss Wilkinson was practically French, and that added zest to a possible adventure. When he thought of it at night in bed, or when he sat by himself in the garden reading a book, he was thrilled by it; but when he saw Miss Wilkinson it seemed less picturesque.

At all events, after what she had told him, she would not be surprised if he made love to her. He had a feeling that she must think it odd of him to make no sign: perhaps it was only his fancy, but once or twice in the last day or two he had imagined that there was a suspicion of contempt in her eyes.

"A penny for your thoughts," said Miss Wilkinson, looking at him with a smile.

"I'm not going to tell you," he answered.

He was thinking that he ought to kiss her there and then. He wondered if she expected him to do it; but after all he didn't see how he could without any preliminary business at all. She would just think him mad, or she might slap his face; and perhaps she would complain to his uncle. He wondered how Herr Sung had started with Fräulein Cäcilie. It would be beastly if she told his uncle: he knew what his uncle was, he would tell the doctor and Josiah Graves; and he would look a perfect fool. Aunt Louisa kept on saying that Miss Wilkinson was thirty-seven if she was a day; he shuddered at the thought of the ridicule he would be exposed to; they would say she was old enough to be his mother.

"Twopence for your thoughts," smiled Miss Wilkinson.

"I was thinking about you," he answered boldly.

That at all events committed him to nothing.

"What were you thinking?"

"Ah, now you want to know too much."

"Naughty boy!" said Miss Wilkinson.

There it was again! Whenever he had succeeded in working himself up she said something which reminded him of the governess. She called him playfully a naughty boy when he did not sing his exercises to her satisfaction. This time he grew quite sulky.

"I wish you wouldn't treat me as if I were a child."

"Are you cross?"

"Very."

"I didn't mean to."

She put out her hand and he took it. Once or twice lately when they shook hands at night he had fancied she slightly pressed his hand, but this time there was no doubt about it.

He did not quite know what he ought to say next. Here at last was his chance of an adventure, and he would be a fool not to take it; but it was a little ordinary, and he had expected more glamour. He had read many descriptions of love, and he felt in himself none of that uprush of emotion which novelists described; he was not carried off his feet in wave upon wave of passion; nor was Miss Wilkinson the ideal: he had often pictured to himself the great violet eyes and the alabaster skin of some lovely girl, and he had thought of himself burying his face in the rippling masses of her auburn hair. He could not imagine himself burying his face in Miss Wilkinson's hair, it always struck him as a little sticky. All the same it would be very satisfactory to have an intrigue, and he thrilled with the legitimate pride he would enjoy in his conquest. He owed it to himself to seduce her. He made up his mind to kiss Miss Wilkinson; not then, but in the evening; it would be easier in the dark, and after he had kissed her the rest would follow. He would kiss her that very evening. He swore an oath to that effect.

He laid his plans. After supper he suggested that they should take a stroll in the garden. Miss Wilkinson accepted, and they sauntered side by side. Philip was very nervous. He did not know why, but the conversation would not lead in the right direction; he had decided that the first thing to do was to put his arm round her waist; but he could not suddenly put his arm round her waist when she was talking of the regatta which was to be held next week. He led her artfully into the darkest parts of the garden, but having arrived there his courage failed him. They sat on a bench, and he had really made up his mind that here was his opportunity when Miss Wilkinson said she was sure there were earwigs and insisted on moving. They walked round the garden once more, and Philip promised himself he would take the plunge before they arrived at that bench again; but as they passed the house, they saw Mrs. Carey standing at the door.

"Hadn't you young people better come in? I'm sure the night air isn't good for you."

"Perhaps we had better go in," said Philip. "I don't want you to catch cold."

He said it with a sigh of relief. He could attempt nothing more that night. But afterwards, when he was alone in his room, he was furious with himself. He had been a perfect fool. He was certain that Miss Wilkinson expected him to kiss her, otherwise she wouldn't have come into the garden. She was always saying that only Frenchmen knew how to treat women. Philip had read French novels. If he had been a Frenchman he would have seized her in his arms and told her passionately that he adored her; he would have pressed his lips on her *nuque*. He did not know why Frenchmen always kissed ladies on the *nuque*. He did not himself see anything so very attractive in the nape of the neck. Of course it was much easier for Frenchmen to do these things; the language was such an aid; Philip could never help feeling that to say passionate things in English sounded a little absurd. He wished now that he had never undertaken the siege of Miss Wilkinson's virtue; the first fortnight had been so jolly, and now he was wretched; but he was determined not to give in, he would never respect himself again if he did, and he made up his mind irrevocably that the next night he would kiss her without fail.

Next day when he got up he saw it was raining, and his first thought was that they would not be able to go into the garden that evening. He was in high spirits at breakfast. Miss Wilkinson sent Mary Ann in to say that she had a headache and would remain in bed. She did not come down till teatime, when she appeared in a becoming wrapper and a pale face; but she was quite recovered by supper, and the meal was very cheerful. After prayers she said she would go straight to bed, and she kissed Mrs. Carey. Then she turned to Philip.

"Good gracious!" she cried. "I was just going to kiss you too."

"Why don't you?" he said.

She laughed and held out her hand. She distinctly pressed his.

The following day there was not a cloud in the sky, and the garden was sweet and fresh after the rain. Philip went down to the beach to bathe and when he came home ate a magnificent dinner. They were having a tennis party at the vicarage in the afternoon and Miss Wilkinson put on her best dress. She certainly knew how to wear her clothes, and Philip could not help noticing how elegant she looked beside the curate's wife and the doctor's married daughter. There were two roses in her waistband. She sat in a garden chair by the side of the lawn, holding a red parasol over herself, and the light on her face was very becoming. Philip was fond of tennis. He served well and as he ran clumsily played close to the net: notwithstanding his club-foot he was quick, and it was difficult to get a ball past him. He was pleased because he won all his sets. At tea he lay down at Miss Wilkinson's feet, hot and panting.

"Flannels suit you," she said. "You look very nice this afternoon."

He blushed with delight.

"I can honestly return the compliment. You look perfectly ravishing."

She smiled and gave him a long look with her black eyes.

After supper he insisted that she should come out.

"Haven't you had enough exercise for one day?"

"It'll be lovely in the garden to-night. The stars are all out."

He was in high spirits.

"D'you know, Mrs. Carey has been scolding me on your account?" said Miss Wilkinson, when they were sauntering through the kitchen garden. "She says I mustn't flirt with you."

"Have you been flirting with me? I hadn't noticed it."

"She was only joking."

"It was very unkind of you to refuse to kiss me last night."

"If you saw the look your uncle gave me when I said what I did!"

"Was that all that prevented you?"

"I prefer to kiss people without witnesses."

"There are no witnesses now."

Philip put his arm round her waist and kissed her lips. She only laughed a little and made no attempt to withdraw. It had come quite naturally. Philip was very proud of himself. He said he would, and he had. It was the easiest thing in the world. He wished he had done it before. He did it again.

"Oh, you mustn't," she said.

"Why not?"

"Because I like it," she laughed.

XXXIV

NEXT day after dinner they took their rugs and cushions to the fountain, and their books; but they did not read. Miss Wilkinson made herself comfortable and she opened the red sun-shade. Philip was not at all shy now, but at first she would not let him kiss her.

"It was very wrong of me last night," she said. "I couldn't sleep, I felt I'd done so wrong."

"What nonsense!" he cried. "I'm sure you slept like a top."

"What do you think your uncle would say if he knew?"

"There's no reason why he should know."

He leaned over her, and his heart went pit-a-pat.

"Why d'you want to kiss me?"

He knew he ought to reply: "Because I love you." But he could not bring himself to say it.

"Why do you think?" he asked instead.

She looked at him with smiling eyes and touched his face with the tips of her fingers.

"How smooth your face is," she murmured.

"I want shaving awfully," he said.

It was astonishing how difficult he found it to make romantic speeches. He found that silence helped him much more than words. He could look inexpressible things. Miss Wilkinson sighed.

"Do you like me at all?"

"Yes, awfully."

When he tried to kiss her again she did not resist. He pretended to be much more passionate than he really was, and he succeeded in playing a part which looked very well in his own eyes.

"I'm beginning to be rather frightened of you," said Miss Wilkinson.

"You'll come out after supper, won't you?" he begged.

"Not unless you promise to behave yourself."

"I'll promise anything."

He was catching fire from the flame he was partly simulating, and at teatime he was obstreperously merry. Miss Wilkinson looked at him nervously.

"You mustn't have those shining eyes," she said to him afterwards. "What will your Aunt Louisa think?"

"I don't care what she thinks."

Miss Wilkinson gave a little laugh of pleasure. They had no sooner finished supper than he said to her:

"Are you going to keep me company while I smoke a cigarette?"

"Why don't you let Miss Wilkinson rest?" said Mrs. Carey. "You must remember she's not as young as you."

"Oh, I'd like to go out, Mrs. Carey," she said, rather acidly.

"After dinner walk a mile, after supper rest a while," said the Vicar.

"Your aunt is very nice, but she gets on my nerves sometimes," said Miss Wilkinson, as soon as they closed the side-door behind them.

Philip threw away the cigarette he had just lighted, and flung his arms round her. She tried to push him away.

"You promised you'd be good, Philip."

"You didn't think I was going to keep a promise like that?"

"Not so near the house, Philip," she said. "Supposing someone should come out suddenly?"

He led her to the kitchen garden where no one was likely to come, and this time Miss Wilkinson did not think of earwigs. He kissed her passionately. It was one of the things that puzzled him that he did not like her at all in the morning, and only moderately in the afternoon, but at night the touch of her hand thrilled him. He said things that he would never have thought himself capable of saying; he could certainly never have said them in the broad light of day; and he listened to himself with wonder and satisfaction.

"How beautifully you make love," she said.

That was what he thought himself.

"Oh, if I could only say all the things that burn my heart!" he murmured passionately.

It was splendid. It was the most thrilling game he had ever played; and the wonderful thing was that he felt almost all he said. It was only that he exaggerated a little. He was tremendously interested and excited in the effect he could see it had on her. It was obviously with an effort that at last she suggested going in.

"Oh, don't go yet," he cried.

"I must," she muttered. "I'm frightened."

He had a sudden intuition what was the right thing to do then.

"I can't go in yet. I shall stay here and think. My cheeks are burning. I want the night-air. Good-night."

He held out his hand seriously, and she took it in silence. He thought she stifled a sob. Oh, it was magnificent! When, after a decent interval during which he had been rather bored in the dark garden by himself, he went in he found that Miss Wilkinson had already gone to bed.

After that things were different between them. The next day and the day after Philip showed himself an eager lover. He was deliciously flattered to discover that Miss Wilkinson was in love with him: she told him so in English, and she told him so in French. She paid him compliments. No one had ever informed him before that his eyes were charming and that he had a sensual mouth. He had never bothered much about his personal appearance, but now, when occasion presented, he looked at himself in the glass with satisfaction. When he kissed her it was wonderful to feel the passion that seemed to thrill her soul. He kissed her a good deal, for he found it easier to do that than to say the things he instinctively felt she expected of him. It still made him feel a fool to say he worshipped her. He wished there were someone to whom he could boast a little, and he would willingly have discussed minute points of his conduct. Sometimes she said things that were enigmatic, and he was puzzled. He wished Hayward had been there so that he could ask him what he thought she meant, and what he had better do next. He could

not make up his mind whether he ought to rush things or let them take their time. There were only three weeks more.

"I can't bear to think of that," she said. "It breaks my heart. And then perhaps we shall never see one another again."

"If you cared for me at all, you wouldn't be so unkind to me," he whispered.

"Oh, why can't you be content to let it go on as it is? Men are always the same. They're never satisfied."

And when he pressed her, she said:

"But don't you see it's impossible. How can we here?"

He proposed all sorts of schemes, but she would not have anything to do with them.

"I daren't take the risk. It would be too dreadful if your aunt found out."

A day or two later he had an idea which seemed brilliant.

"Look here, if you had a headache on Sunday evening and offered to stay at home and look after the house, Aunt Louisa would go to church."

Generally Mrs. Carey remained in on Sunday evening in order to allow Mary Ann to go to church, but she would welcome the opportunity of attending evensong.

Philip had not found it necessary to impart to his relations the change in his views on Christianity which had occurred in Germany; they could not be expected to understand; and it seemed less trouble to go to church quietly. But he only went in the morning. He regarded this as a graceful concession to the prejudices of society and his refusal to go a second time as an adequate assertion of free thought.

When he made the suggestion, Miss Wilkinson did not speak for a moment, then shook her head.

"No, I won't," she said.

But on Sunday at tea-time she surprised Philip.

"I don't think I'll come to church this evening," she said suddenly. "I've really got a dreadful headache."

Mrs. Carey, much concerned, insisted on giving her some 'drops' which she was herself in the habit of using. Miss Wilkinson thanked her, and immediately after tea announced that she would go to her room and lie down.

"Are you sure there's nothing you'll want?" asked Mrs. Carey anxiously.

"Quite sure, thank you."

"Because, if there isn't, I think I'll go to church. I don't often have the chance of going in the evening."

"Oh yes, do go."

"I shall be in," said Philip. "If Miss Wilkinson wants anything, she can always call me."

"You'd better leave the drawing-room door open, Philip, so that if Miss Wilkinson rings, you'll hear."

"Certainly," said Philip.

So after six o'clock Philip was left alone in the house with Miss Wilkinson. He felt sick with apprehension. He wished with all his heart that he had not suggested the plan; but it was too late now; he must take the opportunity which he had made. What would Miss Wilkinson think of him if he did not! He went into the hall and listened. There was not a sound. He wondered if Miss Wilkinson really had a headache. Perhaps she had forgotten his suggestion. His heart beat painfully. He crept up the stairs as softly as he could, and he stopped with a start when they creaked. He stood outside Miss Wilkinson's room and listened; he put his hand on the knob of the door-handle. He waited. It seemed to him that he waited for at least five minutes, trying to make up his mind; and his hand trembled. He would willingly have bolted, but he was afraid of the remorse which he knew would seize him. It was like getting on the highest diving-board in a swimming-bath; it looked nothing from below, but when you got up there and stared down at the water your heart sank; and the only thing that forced you to dive was the shame of coming down meekly by the steps you had climbed up. Philip screwed up his courage. He turned the handle softly and walked in. He seemed to himself to be trembling like a leaf.

Miss Wilkinson was standing at the dressing-table with her back to the door, and she turned round quickly when she heard it open.

"Oh, it's you. What d'you want?"

She had taken off her skirt and blouse, and was standing in her petticoat. It was short and only came down to the top of her boots; the upper part of it was black, of some shiny material, and there was a red flounce. She wore a camisole of white calico with short arms. She looked grotesque. Philip's heart sank as he stared at her; she had never seemed so unattractive; but it was too late now. He closed the door behind him and locked it.

XXXV

PHILIP woke early next morning. His sleep had been restless; but when he stretched his legs and looked at the sunshine that slid through the Venetian blinds, making patterns on the floor, he sighed with satisfaction. He was delighted with himself. He began to think of Miss Wilkinson. She had asked him to call her Emily, but, he knew not why, he could not; he always thought of her as Miss Wilkinson. Since she chid him for so addressing her, he avoided using her name at all. During his childhood he had often heard a sister of Aunt Louisa, the widow of a naval officer, spoken of as Aunt Emily. It made him uncomfortable to call Miss Wilkinson by that name, nor could he think of any that would have suited her better. She had begun as Miss Wilkinson, and it seemed inseparable from his impression of her. He frowned a little: somehow or other he saw her now at her worst; he could not forget his dismay when she turned round and he saw her in her camisole and the short petticoat; he remembered the slight roughness of her skin and the sharp, long lines on the side of the neck. His triumph was shortlived. He reckoned out her age again, and he did not see how she could be less than forty. It made the affair ridiculous. She was plain and old. His quick fancy showed her to him, wrinkled, haggard, made-up, in those frocks which were too showy for her position and too young for her years. He shuddered; he felt suddenly that he never wanted to see her again; he could not bear the thought of kissing her. He was horrified with himself. Was that love?

He took as long as he could over dressing in order to put back the moment of seeing her, and when at last he went into the dining-room it was with a sinking heart. Prayers were over, and they were sitting down at breakfast.

"Lazy bones," Miss Wilkinson cried gaily.

He looked at her and gave a little gasp of relief. She was sitting with her back to the window. She was really quite nice. He wondered why he had thought such things about her. His self-satisfaction returned to him.

He was taken aback by the change in her. She told him in a voice thrilling with emotion immediately after breakfast that she loved him; and when a little later they went into the drawing-room for his singing lesson and she sat down on the music-stool she put up her face in the middle of a scale and said:

"*Embrasse-moi.*"

When he bent down she flung her arms round his neck. It was slightly uncomfortable, for she held him in such a position that he felt rather choked.

"*Ah, je t'aime. Je t'aime. Je t'aime,*" she cried, with her extravagantly French accent.

Philip wished she would speak English.

"I say, I don't know if it's struck you that the gardener's quite likely to pass the window any minute."

"*Ah, je m'en fiche du jardinier. Je m'en refiche, et je m'en contrefiche.*"

Philip thought it was very like a French novel, and he did not know why it slightly irritated him.

At last he said:

"Well, I think I'll tootle along to the beach and have a dip."

"Oh, you're not going to leave me this morning—of all mornings?"

Philip did not quite know why he should not, but it did not matter.

"Would you like me to stay?" he smiled.

"Oh, you darling! But no, go. Go. I want to think of you mastering the salt sea waves, bathing your limbs in the broad ocean."

He got his hat and sauntered off.

"What rot women talk!" he thought to himself.

But he was pleased and happy and flattered. She was evidently frightfully gone on him. As he limped along the high street of Blackstable he looked with a tinge of superciliousness at the people he passed. He knew a good many to nod to, and as he gave them a smile of recognition he thought to himself, if they only knew! He did want someone to know very badly. He thought he would write to Hayward, and in his mind composed the letter. He would talk of the garden and the roses, and the little French governess, like an exotic flower amongst them, scented and perverse: he would say she was French, because—well, she had lived in France so long that she almost was, and besides it would be shabby to give the whole thing away too exactly, don't you know; and he would tell Hayward how he had seen her first in her pretty muslin dress and of the flower she had given him. He made a delicate idyl of it: the sunshine and the sea gave it passion and magic, and the stars added poetry, and the old vicarage garden was a fit and exquisite setting. There was something Meredithian about it: it was not quite Lucy Feverel and not quite Clara Middleton; but it was inexpressibly charming. Philip's heart beat quickly. He was so delighted with his fancies that he began thinking of them again as soon as he crawled back, dripping and cold, into his bathing-machine. He thought of the object of his affections. She had the most adorable little nose and large brown eyes—he would describe her to Hayward—and masses of soft brown hair, the sort of hair it was delicious to bury your face in, and a skin which was like ivory and sunshine, and her cheek was like a red, red rose. How old was she?

Eighteen perhaps, and he called her Musette. Her laughter was like a rippling brook, and her voice was so soft, so low, it was the sweetest music he had ever heard.

"What *are* you thinking about?"

Philip stopped suddenly. He was walking slowly home.

"I've been waving at you for the last quarter of a mile. You *are* absent-minded."

Miss Wilkinson was standing in front of him, laughing at his surprise.

"I thought I'd come and meet you."

"That's awfully nice of you," he said.

"Did I startle you?"

"You did a bit," he admitted.

He wrote his letter to Hayward all the same. There were eight pages of it.

The fortnight that remained passed quickly, and though each evening, when they went into the garden after supper, Miss Wilkinson remarked that one day more had gone, Philip was in too cheerful spirits to let the thought depress him. One night Miss Wilkinson suggested that it would be delightful if she could exchange her situation in Berlin for one in London. Then they could see one another constantly. Philip said it would be very jolly, but the prospect aroused no enthusiasm in him; he was looking forward to a wonderful life in London, and he preferred not to be hampered. He spoke a little too freely of all he meant to do, and allowed Miss Wilkinson to see that already he was longing to be off.

"You wouldn't talk like that if you loved me," she cried.

He was taken aback and remained silent.

"What a fool I've been," she muttered.

To his surprise he saw that she was

crying. He had a tender heart, and hated to see anyone miserable.

"Oh, I'm awfully sorry. What have I done? Don't cry."

"Oh, Philip, don't leave me. You don't know what you mean to me. I have such a wretched life, and you've made me so happy."

He kissed her silently. There really was anguish in her tone, and he was frightened. It had never occurred to him that she meant what she said quite, quite seriously.

"I'm awfully sorry. You know I'm frightfully fond of you. I wish you would come to London."

"You know I can't. Places are almost impossible to get, and I hate English life."

Almost unconscious that he was acting a part, moved by her distress, he pressed her more and more. Her tears vaguely flattered him, and he kissed her with real passion.

But a day or two later she made a real scene. There was a tennis-party at the vicarage, and two girls came, daughters of a retired major in an Indian regiment who had lately settled in Blackstable. They were very pretty, one was Philip's age and the other was a year or two younger. Being used to the society of young men (they were full of stories of hill-stations in India, and at that time the stories of Rudyard Kipling were in every hand) they began to chaff Philip gaily; and he, pleased with the novelty—the young ladies at Blackstable treated the Vicar's nephew with a certain seriousness—was gay and jolly. Some devil within him prompted him to start a violent flirtation with them both, and as he was the only young man there, they were quite willing to meet him half-way. It happened that they played tennis quite well and Philip was tired of

pat-ball with Miss Wilkinson (she had only begun to play when she came to Blackstable), so when he arranged the sets after tea he suggested that Miss Wilkinson should play against the curate's wife, with the curate as her partner; and he would play later with the newcomers. He sat down by the elder Miss O'Connor and said to her in an undertone:

"We'll get the duffers out of the way first, and then we'll have a jolly set afterwards."

Apparently Miss Wilkinson overheard him, for she threw down her racket, and, saying she had a headache, went away. It was plain to everyone that she was offended. Philip was annoyed that she should make the fact public. The set was arranged without her, but presently Mrs. Carey called him.

"Philip, you've hurt Emily's feelings. She's gone to her room and she's crying."

"What about?"

"Oh, something about a duffer's set. Do go to her, and say you didn't mean to be unkind, there's a good boy."

"All right."

He knocked at Miss Wilkinson's door, but receiving no answer went in. He found her lying face downwards on her bed, weeping. He touched her on the shoulder.

"I say, what on earth's the matter?"

"Leave me alone. I never want to speak to you again."

"What have I done? I'm awfully sorry if I've hurt your feelings. I didn't mean to. I say, do get up."

"Oh, I'm so unhappy. How could you be cruel to me? You know I hate that stupid game. I only play because I want to play with you."

She got up and walked towards the dressing-table, but after a quick look in the glass sank into a chair. She made her handkerchief into a ball and dabbed her eyes with it.

"I've given you the greatest thing a woman can give a man—oh, what a fool I was—and you have no gratitude. You must be quite heartless. How could you be so cruel as to torment me by flirting with those vulgar girls. We've only got just over a week. Can't you even give me that?"

Philip stood over her rather sulkily. He thought her behaviour childish. He was vexed with her for having shown her ill-temper before strangers.

"But you know I don't care twopence about either of the O'Connors. Why on earth should you think I do?"

Miss Wilkinson put away her handkerchief. Her tears had made marks on her powdered face, and her hair was somewhat disarranged. Her white dress did not suit her very well just then. She looked at Philip with hungry, passionate eyes.

"Because you're twenty and so's she," she said hoarsely. "And I'm old."

Philip reddened and looked away. The anguish of her tone made him feel strangely uneasy. He wished with all his heart that he had never had anything to do with Miss Wilkinson.

"I don't want to make you unhappy," he said awkwardly. "You'd better go down and look after your friends. They'll wonder what has become of you."

"All right."

He was glad to leave her.

The quarrel was quickly followed by a reconciliation, but the few days that remained were sometimes irksome to Philip. He wanted to talk of nothing but the future, and the future invariably reduced Miss Wilkinson to tears. At first her weeping affected him, and feeling himself a beast he

redoubled his protestations of undying passion; but now it irritated him: it would have been all very well if she had been a girl, but it was silly of a grown-up woman to cry so much. She never ceased reminding him that he was under a debt of gratitude to her which he could never repay. He was willing to acknowledge this since she made a point of it, but he did not really know why he should be any more grateful to her than she to him. He was expected to show his sense of obligation in ways which were rather a nuisance: he had been a good deal used to solitude, and it was a necessity to him sometimes; but Miss Wilkinson looked upon it as an unkindness if he was not always at her beck and call. The Miss O'Connors asked them both to tea, and Philip would have liked to go, but Miss Wilkinson said she only had five days more and wanted him entirely to herself. It was flattering, but a bore. Miss Wilkinson told him stories of the exquisite delicacy of Frenchmen when they stood in the same relation to fair ladies as he to Miss Wilkinson. She praised their courtesy, their passion for self-sacrifice, their perfect tact. Miss Wilkinson seemed to want a great deal.

Philip listened to her enumeration of the qualities which must be possessed by the perfect lover, and he could not help feeling a certain satisfaction that she lived in Berlin.

"You will write to me, won't you? Write to me every day. I want to know everything you're doing. You must keep nothing from me."

"I shall be awfully busy," he answered. "I'll write as often as I can."

She flung her arms passionately round his neck. He was embarrassed sometimes by the demonstrations of her affection. He would have preferred her to be more passive. It shocked him a little that she should give him so marked a lead: it did not tally altogether with his prepossessions about the modesty of the feminine temperament.

At length the day came on which Miss Wilkinson was to go, and she came down to breakfast, pale and subdued, in a serviceable travelling dress of black and white check. She looked a very competent governess. Philip was silent too, for he did not quite know what to say that would fit the circumstance; and he was terribly afraid that, if he said something flippant, Miss Wilkinson would break down before his uncle and make a scene. They had said their last goodbye to one another in the garden the night before, and Philip was relieved that there was now no opportunity for them to be alone. He remained in the dining-room after breakfast in case Miss Wilkinson should insist on kissing him on the stairs. He did not want Mary Ann, now a woman hard upon middle age with a sharp tongue, to catch them in a compromising position. Mary Ann did not like Miss Wilkinson and called her an old cat. Aunt Louisa was not very well and could not come to the station, but the Vicar and Philip saw her off. Just as the train was leaving she leaned out and kissed Mr. Carey.

"I must kiss you too, Philip," she said.

"All right," he said, blushing.

He stood up on the step and she kissed him quickly. The train started, and Miss Wilkinson sank into the corner of her carriage and wept disconsolately. Philip as he walked back to the vicarage felt a distinct sensation of relief.

"Well, did you see her safely off?" asked Aunt Louisa, when they got in.

"Yes, she seemed rather weepy. She insisted on kissing me and Philip."

"Oh, well, at her age it's not dangerous." Mrs. Carey pointed to the sideboard. "There's a letter for you, Philip. It came by the second post."

It was from Hayward and ran as follows:

My dear boy,

I answer your letter at once. I ventured to read it to a great friend of mine, a charming woman whose help and sympathy have been very precious to me, a woman withal with a real feeling for art and literature; and we agreed that it was charming. You wrote from your heart and you do not know the delightful naïveté which is in every line. And because you love you write like a poet. Ah, dear boy, that is the real thing: I felt the glow of your young passion, and your prose was musical from the sincerity of your emotion. You must be happy! I wish I could have been present unseen in that enchanted garden while you wandered hand in hand, like Daphnis and Chloe, amid the flowers. I can see you, my Daphnis, with the light of young love in your eyes, tender, enraptured, and ardent; while Chloe in your arms, so young and soft and fresh, vowing she would ne'er consent—consented. Roses and violets and honeysuckle! Oh, my friend, I envy you. It is so good to think that your first love should have been pure poetry. Treasure the moments, for the immortal gods have given you the Greatest Gift of All, and it will be a sweet, sad memory till your dying day. You will never again enjoy that careless rapture. First love is best love; and she is beautiful and you are young, and all the world is yours. I felt my pulse go faster when with your adorable simplicity you told me that you buried your face in her long hair. I am sure that it is that exquisite chestnut which seems just touched with gold. I would have you sit under a leafy tree side by side, and read together Romeo and Juliet; *and then I would have you fall on your knees and on my behalf kiss the ground on which her foot has left its imprint; then tell her it is the homage of a poet to her radiant youth and to your love for her.*

Yours always,
G. Etheridge Hayward.

"What damned rot!" said Philip, when he finished the letter.

Miss Wilkinson oddly enough had suggested that they should read *Romeo and Juliet* together; but Philip had firmly declined. Then, as he put the letter in his pocket, he felt a queer little pang of bitterness because reality seemed so different from the ideal.

XXXVI

A few days later Philip went to London. The curate had recommended rooms in Barnes, and these Philip engaged by letter at fourteen shillings a week. He reached them in the evening; and the landlady, a funny little old woman with a shrivelled body and a deeply wrinkled face, had prepared high tea for him. Most of the sitting-room was taken up by the sideboard and a square table; against one wall was a sofa covered with horsehair, and by the fireplace an arm-chair to match: there was a white antimacassar over the back of it, and on the seat, because the springs were broken, a hard cushion.

After having his tea he unpacked and arranged his books, then he sat down and tried to read; but he was depressed. The silence in the street made him slightly uncomfortable, and he felt very much alone.

Next day he got up early. He put on his tail-coat and the tall hat which he had worn at school; but it was very shabby, and he made up his mind to stop at the Stores on his way to the office and buy a new one.

When he had done this he found himself in plenty of time and so walked along the Strand. The office of Messrs. Herbert Carter & Co. was in a little street off Chancery Lane, and he had to ask his way two or three times. He felt that people were staring at him a great deal, and once he took off his hat to see whether by chance the label had been left on. When he arrived he knocked at the door; but no one answered, and looking at his watch he found it was barely half past nine; he supposed he was too early. He went away and ten minutes later returned to find an office-boy, with a long nose, pimply face, and a Scotch accent, opening the door. Philip asked for Mr. Herbert Carter. He had not come yet.

"When will he be here?"

"Between ten and half past."

"I'd better wait," said Philip.

"What are you wanting?" asked the office-boy.

Philip was nervous, but tried to hide the fact by a jocose manner.

"Well, I'm going to work here if you have no objection."

"Oh, you're the new articled clerk? You'd better come in. Mr. Goodworthy'll be here in a while."

Philip walked in, and as he did so saw the office-boy—he was about the same age as Philip and called himself a junior clerk—look at his foot. He flushed and, sitting down, hid it behind the other. He looked round the room. It was dark and very dingy. It was lit by a skylight. There were three rows of desks in it and against them high stools. Over the chimney-piece was a dirty engraving of a prize-fight. Presently a clerk came in and then another; they glanced at Philip and in an undertone asked the office-boy (Philip found his name was Macdougal) who he was. A whistle blew, and Macdougal got up.

"Mr. Goodworthy's come. He's the managing clerk. Shall I tell him you're here?"

"Yes, please," said Philip.

The office-boy went out and in a moment returned.

"Will you come this way?"

Philip followed him across the passage and was shown into a room, small and barely furnished, in which a little, thin man was standing with his back to the fireplace. He was much below the middle height, but his large head, which seemed to hang loosely on his body, gave him an odd ungainliness. His features were wide and flattened, and he had prominent, pale eyes; his thin hair was sandy; he wore whiskers that grew unevenly on his face, and in places where you would have expected the hair to grow thickly there was no hair at all. His skin was pasty and yellow. He held out his hand to Philip, and when he smiled showed badly decayed teeth. He spoke with a patronising and at the same time a timid air, as though he sought to assume an importance which he did not feel. He said he

hoped Philip would like the work; there was a good deal of drudgery about it, but when you got used to it, it was interesting; and one made money, that was the chief thing, wasn't it? He laughed with his odd mixture of superiority and shyness.

"Mr. Carter will be here presently," he said. "He's a little late on Monday mornings sometimes. I'll call you when he comes. In the meantime I must give you something to do. Do you know anything about book-keeping or accounts?"

"I'm afraid not," answered Philip.

"I didn't suppose you would. They don't teach you things at school that are much use in business, I'm afraid." He considered for a moment. "I think I can find you something to do."

He went into the next room and after a little while came out with a large cardboard box. It contained a vast number of letters in great disorder, and he told Philip to sort them out and arrange them alphabetically according to the names of the writers.

"I'll take you to the room in which the articled clerk generally sits. There's a very nice fellow in it. His name is Watson. He's a son of Watson, Crag, and Thompson—you know —the brewers. He's spending a year with us to learn business."

Mr. Goodworthy led Philip through the dingy office, where now six or eight clerks were working, into a narrow room behind. It had been made into a separate apartment by a glass partition, and here they found Watson sitting back in a chair, reading *The Sportsman*. He was a large, stout young man, elegantly dressed, and he looked up as Mr. Goodworthy entered. He asserted his position by calling the managing clerk Goodworthy. The managing clerk objected to the familiarity, and pointedly called him Mr. Watson, but Watson, instead of seeing that it was a rebuke, accepted the title as a tribute to his gentlemanliness.

"I see they've scratched Rigoletto," he said to Philip, as soon as they were left alone.

"Have they?" said Philip, who knew nothing about horse racing.

He looked with awe upon Watson's beautiful clothes. His tail-coat fitted him perfectly, and there was a valuable pin artfully stuck in the middle of an enormous tie. On the chimney-piece rested his tall hat; it was saucy and bell-shaped and shiny. Philip felt himself very shabby. Watson began to talk of hunting—it was such an infernal bore having to waste one's time in an infernal office, he would only be able to hunt on Saturdays—and shooting: he had ripping invitations all over the country and of course he had to refuse them. It was infernal luck, but he wasn't going to put up with it long; he was only in this infernal hole for a year, and then he was going into the business, and he would hunt four days a week and get all the shooting there was.

"You've got five years of it, haven't you?" he said, waving his arm round the tiny room.

"I suppose so," said Philip.

"I daresay I shall see something of you. Carter does our accounts, you know."

Philip was somewhat overpowered by the young gentleman's condescension. At Blackstable they had always looked upon brewing with civil contempt, the Vicar made little jokes about the beerage, and it was a surprising experience for Philip to discover that Watson was such an important and magnificent fellow. He had been to Winchester and to Oxford, and his conversation impressed the fact upon one with frequency. When he discovered the details of Philip's education his manner became more patronising still.

"Of course, if one doesn't go to a public school those sort of schools are the next best thing, aren't they?"

Philip asked about the other men in the office.

"Oh, I don't bother about them much, you know," said Watson. "Carter's not a bad sort. We have him to dine now and then. All the rest are awful bounders."

Presently Watson applied himself to some work he had in hand, and Philip set about sorting his letters. Then Mr. Goodworthy came in to say that Mr. Carter had arrived. He took Philip into a large room next door to his own. There was a big desk in it, and a couple of big arm-chairs; a Turkey carpet adorned the floor, and the walls were decorated with sporting prints. Mr. Carter was sitting at the desk and got up to shake hands with Philip. He was dressed in a long frock coat. He looked like a military man; his moustache was waxed, his gray hair was short and neat, he held himself upright, he talked in a breezy way, he lived at Enfield. He was very keen on games and the good of the country. He was an officer in the Hertfordshire Yeomanry and chairman of the Conservative Association. When he was told that a local magnate had said no one would take him for a City man, he felt that he had not lived in vain. He talked to Philip in a pleasant, off-hand fashion. Mr. Goodworthy would look after him. Watson was a nice fellow, perfect gentleman, good sportsman—did Philip hunt? Pity, *the* sport for gentlemen. Didn't have much chance of hunting now, had to leave that to his son. His son was at Cambridge, he'd sent him to Rugby, fine school Rugby, nice class of boys there, in a couple of years his son would be articled, that would be nice for Philip, he'd like his son, thorough sportsman. He hoped Philip would get on well and like the work, he mustn't miss his lectures, they were getting up the tone of the profession, they wanted gentlemen in it. Well, well, Mr. Goodworthy was there. If he wanted to know anything Mr. Goodworthy would tell him. What was his handwriting like? Ah well, Mr. Goodworthy would see about that.

Philip was overwhelmed by so much gentlemanliness: in East Anglia they knew who were gentlemen and who weren't, but the gentlemen didn't talk about it.

XXXVII

AT FIRST the novelty of the work kept Philip interested. Mr. Carter dictated letters to him, and he had to make fair copies of statements of accounts.

Mr. Carter preferred to conduct the office on gentlemanly lines; he would have nothing to do with typewriting and looked upon shorthand with disfavour: the office-boy knew shorthand, but it was only Mr. Goodworthy who made use of his accomplishment. Now and then Philip with one of the more experienced clerks went out to audit the accounts of some firm: he came to know which of the clients must be treated with respect and which were in low water. Now and then long lists of figures were given him to add up. He attended lectures for his first examination. Mr. Goodworthy repeated to him that the work was dull at first, but he would grow used to it. Philip left the office at six and walked across the river to Waterloo. His supper was waiting for him when he reached his lodgings and he spent the evening reading. On Saturday afternoons he went to the National Gallery. Hayward had recommended to him a guide which had been compiled out of Ruskin's works, and with this in hand he went industriously through room after room: he read carefully what the critic had said about a picture and then in a determined fashion set himself to see the same things in it. His Sundays were difficult to get through. He knew no one in London and spent them by himself. Mr. Nixon, the solicitor, asked him to spend a Sunday at Hampstead, and Philip passed a happy day with a set of exuberant strangers; he ate and drank a great deal, took a walk on the heath, and came away with a general invitation to come again whenever he liked; but he was morbidly afraid of being in the way, so waited for a formal invitation. Naturally enough it never came, for with numbers of friends of their own the Nixons did not think of the lonely, silent boy whose claim upon their hospitality was so small. So on Sundays he got up late and took a walk along the towpath. At Barnes the river is muddy, dingy, and tidal; it has neither the graceful charm of the Thames above the locks nor the romance of the crowded stream below London Bridge. In the afternoon he walked about the common; and that is gray and dingy too; it is neither country nor town; the gorse is stunted; and all about is the litter of civilisation. He went to a play every Saturday night and stood cheerfully for an hour or more at the gallery-door. It was not worth while to go back to Barnes for the interval between the closing of the Museum and his meal in an A. B. C. shop, and the time hung heavily on his hands. He strolled up Bond Street or through the Burlington Arcade, and when he was tired went and sat down in the Park or in wet weather in the public library in St. Martin's Lane. He looked at the people walking about and envied them because they had friends; sometimes his envy turned to hatred because they were happy and he was miserable. He had never imagined that it was possible to be so lonely in a great city. Sometimes when he was standing at the gallery-door the man next to him would attempt a conversation; but Philip had the country boy's suspicion of strangers and answered in such a way as to prevent any further acquaintance. After the play was over, obliged to keep to himself all he thought about it, he hurried across the bridge to Waterloo. When he got back to his rooms, in which for economy no fire had been lit, his heart sank. It was horribly cheerless. He began to loathe his lodgings and the long solitary evenings he spent in them. Sometimes he felt so lonely that he could not read, and then he sat looking into the fire hour after hour in bitter wretchedness.

He had spent three months in London now, and except for that one Sunday at Hampstead had never talked to anyone but his fellow-clerks. One evening Watson asked him to dinner at a restaurant and they went to a music-hall together; but he felt shy and uncomfortable. Watson talked all the time of things he did not care about, and while he looked upon Watson as a Philistine he could not help admiring him. He was angry because Watson obviously set no store on his culture, and with his way of taking himself at the estimate at which he saw others held him he began to despise the acquirements which till then had seemed to him not unimportant. He felt for the first time the humiliation of poverty. His uncle sent him fourteen pounds a month and he had had to buy a good many clothes. His evening suit cost him five guineas. He had not dared tell Watson that it was bought in the Strand. Watson said there was only one tailor in London.

"I suppose you don't dance," said Watson, one day, with a glance at Philip's club-foot.

"No," said Philip.

"Pity. I've been asked to bring some dancing men to a ball. I could have introduced you to some jolly girls."

Once or twice, hating the thought of going back to Barnes, Philip had remained in town, and late in the evening wandered through the West End till he found some house at which there was a party. He stood among the little group of shabby people, behind the footmen, watching the guests arrive, and he listened to the music that floated through the window. Sometimes, notwithstanding the cold, a couple came on to the balcony and stood for a moment to get some fresh air; and Philip, imagining that they were in love with one another, turned away and limped along the street with a heavy heart. He would never be able to stand in that man's place. He felt that no woman could ever really look upon him without distaste for his deformity.

That reminded him of Miss Wilkinson. He thought of her without satisfaction. Before parting they had made an arrangement that she should write to Charing Cross Post Office till he was able to send her an address, and when he went there he found three letters from her. She wrote on blue paper with violet ink, and she wrote in French. Philip wondered why she could not write in English like a sensible woman, and her passionate expressions, because they reminded him of a French novel, left him cold. She upbraided him for not having written, and when he answered he excused himself by saying that he had been busy. He did not quite know how to start the letter. He could not bring himself to use *dearest* or *darling*, and he hated to address her as Emily, so finally he began with the word *dear*. It looked odd, standing by itself, and rather silly, but he made it do. It was the first love letter he had ever written, and he was conscious of its tameness; he felt that he should say all sorts of vehement things, how he thought of her every minute of the day and how he longed to kiss her beautiful hands and how he trembled at the thought of her red lips, but some inexplicable modesty prevented him; and instead he told her of his new rooms and his office. The answer came by return of post, angry, heart-broken, reproachful: how could he be so cold? Did he not know that she hung on his letters? She had given him all that a woman could give, and this was her reward. Was he tired of her already? Then, because he did not reply for several days, Miss Wilkinson bombarded him with letters. She could not bear his unkindness, she waited for the post, and it never brought her his letter, she cried herself to sleep night after night, she was looking so ill that everyone remarked on it: if he did not love her why did he not say so? She added that she could not live without him, and the only thing was for her to commit suicide. She told him he was cold and selfish and ungrateful. It was all in French, and Philip knew that she wrote in that language to show off, but he was worried all the

same. He did not want to make her unhappy. In a little while she wrote that she could not bear the separation any longer, she would arrange to come over to London for Christmas. Philip wrote back that he would like nothing better, only he had already an engagement to spend Christmas with friends in the country, and he did not see how he could break it. She answered that she did not wish to force herself on him, it was quite evident that he did not wish to see her; she was deeply hurt, and she never thought he would repay with such cruelty all her kindness. Her letter was touching, and Philip thought he saw marks of her tears on the paper; he wrote an impulsive reply saying that he was dreadfully sorry and imploring her to come; but it was with relief that he received her answer in which she said that she found it would be impossible for her to get away. Presently when her letters came his heart sank: he delayed opening them, for he knew what they would contain, angry reproaches and pathetic appeals; they would make him feel a perfect beast, and yet he did not see with what he had to blame himself. He put off his answer from day to day, and then another letter would come, saying she was ill and lonely and miserable.

"I wish to God I'd never had anything to do with her," he said.

He admired Watson because he arranged these things so easily. The young man had been engaged in an intrigue with a girl who played in touring companies, and his account of the affair filled Philip with envious amazement. But after a time Watson's young affections changed, and one day he described the rupture to Philip.

"I thought it was no good making any bones about it so I just told her I'd had enough of her," he said.

"Didn't she make an awful scene?" asked Philip.

"The usual thing, you know, but I told her it was no good trying on that sort of thing with me."

"Did she cry?"

"She began to, but I can't stand women when they cry, so I said she'd better hook it."

Philip's sense of humour was growing keener with advancing years.

"And did she hook it?" he asked smiling.

"Well, there wasn't anything else for her to do, was there?"

Meanwhile the Christmas holidays approached. Mrs. Carey had been ill all through November, and the doctor suggested that she and the Vicar should go to Cornwall for a couple of weeks round Christmas so that she should get back her strength. The result was that Philip had nowhere to go, and he spent Christmas Day in his lodgings. Under Hayward's influence he had persuaded himself that the festivities that attend this season were vulgar and barbaric, and he made up his mind that he would take no notice of the day; but when it came, the jollity of all around affected him strangely. His landlady and her husband were spending the day with a married daughter, and to save trouble Philip announced that he would take his meals out. He went up to London towards mid-day and ate a slice of turkey and some Christmas pudding by himself at Gatti's, and since he had nothing to do afterwards went to Westminster Abbey for the afternoon service. The streets were almost empty, and the people who went along had a preoccupied look; they did not saunter but walked with some definite

goal in view, and hardly anyone was alone. To Philip they all seemed happy. He felt himself more solitary than he had ever done in his life. His intention had been to kill the day somehow in the streets and then dine at a restaurant, but he could not face again the sight of cheerful people, talking, laughing, and making merry; so he went back to Waterloo, and on his way through the Westminster Bridge Road bought some ham and a couple of mince pies and went back to Barnes. He ate his food in his lonely little room and spent the evening with a book. His depression was almost intolerable.

When he was back at the office it made him very sore to listen to Watson's account of the short holiday. They had had some jolly girls staying with them, and after dinner they had cleared out the drawing-room and had a dance.

"I didn't get to bed till three and I don't know how I got there then. By George, I was squiffy."

At last Philip asked desperately:

"How does one get to know people in London?"

Watson looked at him with surprise and with a slightly contemptuous amusement.

"Oh, I don't know, one just knows them. If you go to dances you soon get to know as many people as you can do with."

Philip hated Watson, and yet he would have given anything to change places with him. The old feeling that he had had at school came back to him, and he tried to throw himself into the other's skin, imagining what life would be if he were Watson.

XXXVIII

AT THE end of the year there was a great deal to do. Philip went to various places with a clerk named Thompson and spent the day monotonously calling out items of expenditure, which the other checked; and sometimes he was given long pages of figures to add up. He had never had a head for figures, and he could only do this slowly. Thompson grew irritated at his mistakes. His fellow-clerk was a long, lean man of forty, sallow, with black hair and a ragged moustache; he had hollow cheeks and deep lines on each side of his nose. He took a dislike to Philip because he was an articled clerk. Because he could put down three hundred guineas and keep himself for five years Philip had the chance of a career; while he, with his experience and ability, had no possibility of ever being more than a clerk at thirty-five shillings a week. He was a cross-grained man, oppressed by a large family, and he resented the superciliousness which he fancied he saw in Philip. He sneered at Philip because he was better educated than himself, and he mocked at Philip's pronunciation; he could not forgive him because he spoke without a cockney accent, and when he talked to him sarcastically exaggerated his aitches. At first his manner was merely gruff and repellent, but as he discovered that Philip had no gift for accountancy he took pleasure in humiliating him; his attacks were gross and silly, but they wounded Philip, and in self-defence he assumed an attitude of superiority which he did not feel.

"Had a bath this morning?" Thompson said when Philip came to the office late, for his early punctuality had not lasted.

"Yes, haven't you?"

"No, I'm not a gentleman, I'm only a clerk. I have a bath on Saturday night."

"I suppose that's why you're more than usually disagreeable on Monday."

"Will you condescend to do a few sums in simple addition today? I'm afraid it's asking a great deal from a gentleman who knows Latin and Greek."

"Your attempts at sarcasm are not very happy."

But Philip could not conceal from himself that the other clerks, ill-paid and uncouth, were more useful than himself. Once or twice Mr. Goodworthy grew impatient with him.

"You really ought to be able to do better than this by now," he said. "You're not even as smart as the office-boy."

Philip listened sulkily. He did not like being blamed, and it humiliated him, when, having been given accounts to make fair copies of, Mr. Goodworthy was not satisfied and gave them to another clerk to do. At first the work had been tolerable from its novelty, but now it grew irksome; and when he discovered that he had no aptitude for it, he began to hate it. Often, when he should have been doing something that was given him, he wasted his time drawing little pictures on the office note-paper. He made sketches of Watson in every conceivable attitude, and Watson was impressed by his talent. It occurred to him to take the drawings home, and he came back next day with the praises of his family.

"I wonder you didn't become a painter," he said. "Only of course there's no money in it."

It chanced that Mr. Carter two or three days later was dining with the Watsons, and the sketches were shown him. The following morning he sent for Philip. Philip saw him seldom and stood in some awe of him.

"Look here, young fellow, I don't care what you do out of office-hours, but I've seen those sketches of yours and they're on office-paper, and Mr. Goodworthy tells me you're slack. You won't do any good as a chartered accountant unless you look alive. It's a fine profession, and we're getting a very good class of men in it, but it's a profession in which you have to . . ." he looked for the termination of his phrase, but could not find exactly what he wanted, so finished rather tamely, "in which you have to look alive."

Perhaps Philip would have settled down but for the agreement that if he did not like the work he could leave after a year, and get back half the money paid for his articles. He felt that he was fit for something better than to add up accounts, and it was humiliating that he did so ill something which seemed contemptible. The vulgar scenes with Thompson got on his nerves. In March Watson ended his year at the office and Philip, though he did not care for him, saw him go with regret. The fact that the other clerks disliked them equally, because they belonged to a class a little higher than their own, was a bond of union. When Philip thought that he must spend over four years more with that dreary set of fellows his heart sank. He had expected wonderful things from London and it had given him nothing. He hated it now. He did not know a soul, and he had no idea how he was to get to know anyone. He was tired of going everywhere by himself. He began to feel that he could not stand much more of such a life. He would lie in bed at night and think of the joy of never seeing again that dingy office or any of the men in it, and of getting away from those drab lodgings.

A great disappointment befell him in the spring. Hayward had announced his intention of coming to London for the season, and Philip had looked forward very much to seeing him again. He had read so much lately and thought so much that his mind was full of ideas which he wanted to discuss, and he knew nobody who was willing to interest himself in abstract things. He was quite excited at the thought of talking his fill with someone, and he was wretched when Hayward wrote to say that the spring was lovelier than ever he had known it in Italy, and he could not bear to tear himself away. He went on to ask why Philip did not come. What was the use of squandering the days of his youth in an office when the world was beautiful? The letter proceeded.

I wonder you can bear it. I think of Fleet Street and Lincoln's Inn now with a shudder of disgust. There are only two things in the world that make life worth living, love and art. I cannot imagine you sitting in an office over a ledger, and do you wear a tall hat and an umbrella and a little black bag? My feeling is that one should look upon life as an adventure, one should burn with the hard, gemlike flame, and one should take risks, one should expose oneself to danger. Why do you not go to Paris and study art? I always thought you had talent.

The suggestion fell in with the possibility that Philip for some time had been vaguely turning over in his mind. It startled him at first, but he could not help thinking of it, and in the constant rumination over it he found his only escape from the wretchedness of his present state. They all thought he had talent; at Heidelberg they had admired his water colours, Miss Wilkinson had told him over and over again that they were charming; even strangers like the Watsons had been struck by his sketches. *La Vie de Bohème* had made a deep impression on him. He had brought it to London and when he was most depressed he had only to read a few pages to be transported into those charming attics where Rodolphe and the rest of them danced and loved and sang. He began to think of Paris as before he had thought of London, but he had no fear of a second disillusion; he yearned for romance and beauty and love, and Paris seemed to offer them all. He had a passion for pictures, and why should he not be able to paint as well as anybody else? He wrote to Miss Wilkinson and asked her how much she thought he could live on in Paris. She told him that he could manage easily on eighty pounds a year, and she enthusiastically approved of his project. She told him he was too good to be wasted in an office. Who would be a clerk when he might be a great artist, she asked dramatically, and she besought Philip to believe in himself: that was the great thing. But Philip had a cautious nature. It was all very well for Hayward to talk of taking risks, he had three hundred a year in gilt-edged securities; Philip's entire fortune amounted to no more than eighteen-hundred pounds. He hesitated.

Then it chanced that one day Mr. Goodworthy asked him suddenly if he would like to go to Paris. The firm did the accounts for a hotel in the Faubourg St. Honoré, which was owned by an English company, and twice a year Mr. Goodworthy and a clerk went over. The clerk who generally went happened to be ill, and a press of work prevented any of the others from getting away. Mr. Goodworthy thought of Philip because he could best be spared, and his articles gave him some claim upon a job which was one of the pleasures of the business. Philip was delighted.

"You'll 'ave to work all day," said Mr. Goodworthy, "but we get our evenings to ourselves, and Paris is Paris." He smiled in a knowing way. "They do us very well at the hotel, and they give us all our meals, so it don't cost one anything. That's the way I like going to Paris, at other people's expense."

When they arrived at Calais and Philip saw the crowd of gesticulating porters his heart leaped.

"This is the real thing," he said to himself.

He was all eyes as the train sped through the country; he adored the sand dunes, their colour seemed to him more lovely than anything he had ever seen; and he was enchanted with the canals and the long lines of poplars. When they got out of the Gare du Nord, and trundled along the cobbled streets in a ramshackle, noisy cab, it seemed to him that he was breathing a new air so intoxicating that he could hardly restrain himself from shouting aloud. They were met at the door of the hotel by the manager, a stout, pleasant man, who spoke tolerable English; Mr. Goodworthy was an old friend and he greeted them effusively; they dined in his private room with his wife, and to Philip it seemed that he had never eaten anything so delicious as the *beefsteak aux pommes,* nor drunk such nectar as the *vin ordinaire,* which were set before them.

To Mr. Goodworthy, a respectable householder with excellent principles, the capital of France was a paradise of the joyously obscene. He asked the manager next morning what there was to be seen that was 'thick.' He thoroughly enjoyed these visits of his to Paris; he said they kept you from growing rusty. In the evenings, after their work was over and they had dined, he took Philip to the Moulin Rouge and the Folies Bergères. His little eyes twinkled and his face wore a sly, sensual smile as he sought out the pornographic. He went into all the haunts which were specially arranged for the foreigner, and afterwards said that a nation could come to no good which permitted that sort of thing. He nudged Philip when at some revue a woman appeared with practically nothing on, and pointed out to him the most strapping of the courtesans who walked about the hall. It was a vulgar Paris that he showed Philip, but Philip saw it with eyes blinded with illusion. In the early morning he would rush out of the hotel and go to the Champs Elysées, and stand at the Place de la Concorde. It was June, and Paris was silvery with the delicacy of the air. Philip felt his heart go out to the people. Here he thought at last was romance.

They spent the inside of a week there, leaving on Sunday, and when Philip late at night reached his dingy rooms in Barnes his mind was made up; he would surrender his articles, and go to Paris to study art; but so that no one should think him unreasonable he determined to stay at the office till his year was up. He was to have his holiday during the last fort-

night in August, and when he went away he would tell Herbert Carter that he had no intention of returning. But though Philip could force himself to go to the office every day he could not even pretend to show any interest in the work. His mind was occupied with the future. After the middle of July there was nothing much to do and he escaped a good deal by pretending he had to go to lectures for his first examination. The time he got in this way he spent in the National Gallery. He read books about Paris and books about painting. He was steeped in Ruskin. He read many of Vasari's lives of the painters. He liked that story of Correggio, and he fancied himself standing before some great masterpiece and crying: *Anch' io son' pittore.* His hesitation had left him now, and he was convinced that he had in him the makings of a great painter.

"After all, I can only try," he said to himself. "The great thing in life is to take risks."

At last came the middle of August. Mr. Carter was spending the month in Scotland, and the managing clerk was in charge of the office. Mr. Goodworthy had seemed pleasantly disposed to Philip since their trip to Paris, and now that Philip knew he was so soon to be free, he could look upon the funny little man with tolerance.

"You're going for your holiday tomorrow, Carey?" he said to him in the evening.

All day Philip had been telling himself that this was the last time he would ever sit in that hateful office.

"Yes, this is the end of my year."

"I'm afraid you've not done very well. Mr. Carter's very dissatisfied with you."

"Not nearly so dissatisfied as I am

with Mr. Carter," returned Philip cheerfully.

"I don't think you should speak like that, Carey."

"I'm not coming back. I made the arrangement that if I didn't like accountancy Mr. Carter would return me half the money I paid for my articles and I could chuck it at the end of a year."

"You shouldn't come to such a decision hastily."

"For ten months I've loathed it all, I've loathed the work, I've loathed the office, I loathe London. I'd rather sweep a crossing than spend my days here."

"Well, I must say, I don't think you're very fitted for accountancy."

"Good-bye," said Philip, holding out his hand. "I want to thank you for your kindness to me. I'm sorry if I've been troublesome. I knew almost from the beginning I was no good."

"Well, if you really do make up your mind it is good-bye. I don't know what you're going to do, but if you're in the neighbourhood at any time come in and see us."

Philip gave a little laugh.

"I'm afraid it sounds very rude, but I hope from the bottom of my heart that I shall never set eyes on any of you again."

XXXIX

THE Vicar of Blackstable would have nothing to do with the scheme which Philip laid before him. He had a great idea that one should stick to whatever one had begun. Like all weak men he laid an exaggerated stress on not changing one's mind.

"You chose to be an accountant of your own free will," he said.

"I just took that because it was the only chance I saw of getting up to town. I hate London, I hate the work, and nothing will induce me to go back to it."

Mr. and Mrs. Carey were frankly shocked at Philip's idea of being an artist. He should not forget, they said, that his father and mother were gentlefolk, and painting wasn't a serious profession; it was Bohemian, disreputable, immoral. And then Paris!

"So long as I have anything to say in the matter, I shall not allow you to live in Paris," said the Vicar firmly. It was a sink of iniquity. The scarlet woman and she of Babylon flaunted their vileness there; the cities of the plain were not more wicked.

"You've been brought up like a gentleman and Christian, and I should be false to the trust laid upon me by your dead father and mother if I allowed you to expose yourself to such temptation."

"Well, I know I'm not a Christian and I'm beginning to doubt whether I'm a gentleman," said Philip.

The dispute grew more violent. There was another year before Philip took possession of his small inheritance, and during that time Mr. Carey proposed only to give him an allowance if he remained at the office. It was clear to Philip that if he meant not to continue with accountancy he must leave it while he could still get back half the money that he had been paid for his articles. The Vicar would not listen. Philip, losing all reserve, said things to wound and irritate.

"You've got no right to waste my money," he said at last. "After all it's my money, isn't it? I'm not a child. You can't prevent me from going to Paris if I make up my mind to. You can't force me to go back to London."

"All I can do is to refuse you money unless you do what I think fit."

"Well, I don't care, I've made up my mind to go to Paris. I shall sell my clothes, and my books, and my father's jewellery."

Aunt Louisa sat by in silence, anxious and unhappy: she saw that Philip was beside himself, and anything she said then would but increase his anger. Finally the Vicar announced that he wished to hear nothing more about it and with dignity left the room. For the next three days neither Philip nor he spoke to one another. Philip wrote to Hayward for information about Paris, and made up his mind to set out as soon as he got a reply. Mrs. Carey turned the matter over in her mind incessantly; she felt that Philip included her in the hatred he bore her husband, and the thought tortured her. She loved him with all her heart. At length she spoke to him; she listened attentively while he poured out all his disillusionment of London and his eager ambition for the future.

"I may be no good, but at least let me have a try. I can't be a worse failure than I was in that beastly office. And I feel that I *can* paint. I know I've got it in me."

She was not so sure as her husband that they did right in thwarting so strong an inclination. She had read of great painters whose parents had opposed their wish to study, the event had shown with what folly; and after all it was just as possible for a painter to lead a virtuous life to the glory of God as for a chartered accountant.

"I'm so afraid of your going to Paris," she said piteously. "It wouldn't be so bad if you studied in London."

"If I'm going in for painting I must do it thoroughly, and it's only in Paris that you can get the real thing."

At his suggestion Mrs. Carey wrote to the solicitor, saying that Philip was discontented with his work in London, and asking what he thought of a change. Mr. Nixon answered as follows:

Dear Mrs. Carey,

I have seen Mr. Herbert Carter, and I am afraid I must tell you that Philip has not done so well as one could have wished. If he is very strongly set against the work, perhaps it is better that he should take the opportunity there is now to break his articles. I am naturally very disappointed, but as you know you can take a horse to the water, but you can't make him drink.

Yours very sincerely,
Albert Nixon.

The letter was shown to the Vicar, but served only to increase his obstinacy. He was willing enough that Philip should take up some other profession, he suggested his father's calling, medicine, but nothing would induce him to pay an allowance if Philip went to Paris.

"It's a mere excuse for self-indulgence and sensuality," he said.

"I'm interested to hear you blame self-indulgence in others," retorted Philip acidly.

But by this time an answer had come from Hayward, giving the name of a hotel where Philip could get a room for thirty francs a month and enclosing a note of introduction to the *massière* of a school. Philip read the letter to Mrs. Carey and told her he proposed to start on the first of September.

"But you haven't got any money?" she said.

"I'm going into Tercanbury this afternoon to sell the jewellery."

He had inherited from his father a gold watch and chain, two or three rings, some links, and two pins. One of them was a pearl and might fetch a considerable sum.

"It's a very different thing, what a thing's worth and what it'll fetch," said Aunt Louisa.

Philip smiled, for this was one of his uncle's stock phrases.

"I know, but at the worst I think I can get a hundred pounds on the lot, and that'll keep me till I'm twenty-one."

Mrs. Carey did not answer, but she went upstairs, put on her little black bonnet, and went to the bank. In an hour she came back. She went to Philip, who was reading in the drawing-room, and handed him an envelope.

"What's this?" he asked.

"It's a little present for you," she answered, smiling shyly.

He opened it and found eleven five-pound notes and a little paper sack bulging with sovereigns.

"I couldn't bear to let you sell your father's jewellery. It's the money I had in the bank. It comes to very nearly a hundred pounds."

Philip blushed, and, he knew not why, tears suddenly filled his eyes.

"Oh, my dear, I can't take it," he said. "It's most awfully good of you, but I couldn't bear to take it."

When Mrs. Carey was married she had three hundred pounds, and this money, carefully watched, had been used by her to meet any unforeseen expense, any urgent charity, or to buy Christmas and birthday presents for her husband and for Philip. In the course of years it had diminished sadly, but it was still with the Vicar a subject for jesting. He talked of his wife as a rich woman and he constantly spoke of the 'nest egg.'

"Oh, please take it, Philip. I'm so sorry I've been extravagant, and there's only that left. But it'll make me so happy if you'll accept it."

"But you'll want it," said Philip.

"No, I don't think I shall. I was keeping it in case your uncle died before me. I thought it would be useful to have a little something I could get at immediately if I wanted it, but I don't think I shall live very much longer now."

"Oh, my dear, don't say that. Why, of course you're going to live for ever. I can't possibly spare you."

"Oh, I'm not sorry." Her voice broke and she hid her eyes, but in a moment, drying them, she smiled bravely.

"At first, I used to pray to God that He might not take me first, because I didn't want your uncle to be left alone, I didn't want him to have all the suffering, but now I know that it wouldn't mean so much to your uncle as it would mean to me. He wants to live more than I do, I've never been the wife he wanted, and I daresay he'd marry again if anything happened to me. So I should like to go first. You don't think it's selfish of me, Philip, do you? But I couldn't bear it if he went."

Philip kissed her wrinkled, thin cheek. He did not know why the sight he had of that overwhelming love made him feel strangely ashamed. It was incomprehensible that she should care so much for a man who was so indifferent, so selfish, so grossly self-indulgent; and he divined dimly that in her heart she knew his indifference and his selfishness, knew them and loved him humbly all the same.

"You will take the money, Philip?" she said, gently stroking his hand. "I know you can do without it, but it'll give me so much happiness. I've always wanted to do something for you. You see, I never had a child of my own, and I've loved you as if you were my son. When you were a little boy, though I knew it was wicked, I used to wish almost that you might be ill, so that I could nurse you day and night. But you were only ill once and then it was at school. I should so like to help you. It's the only chance I shall ever have. And perhaps some day when you're a great artist you won't forget me, but you'll remember that I gave you your start."

"It's very good of you," said Philip. "I'm very grateful."

A smile came into her tired eyes, a smile of pure happiness.

"Oh, I'm so glad."

XL

A FEW days later Mrs. Carey went to the station to see Philip off. She stood at the door of the carriage, trying to keep back her tears. Philip was restless and eager. He wanted to be gone.

"Kiss me once more," she said.

He leaned out of the window and kissed her. The train started, and she stood on the wooden platform of the little station, waving her handkerchief till it was out of sight. Her heart was dreadfully heavy, and the few hundred yards to the vicarage seemed very, very long. It was natural enough that he should be eager to go, she thought, he was a boy and the future beckoned to him; but she—she clenched her teeth so that she should not cry. She uttered a little inward prayer that God would guard him, and keep him out of temptation, and give him happiness and good fortune.

But Philip ceased to think of her a moment after he had settled down in his carriage. He thought only of the future. He had written to Mrs. Otter, the *massière* to whom Hayward had given him an introduction, and had in his pocket an invitation to tea on the following day. When he arrived in Paris he had his luggage put on a cab and trundled off slowly through the gay streets, over the bridge, and along the narrow ways of the Latin Quarter. He had taken a room at the Hôtel des Deux Ecoles, which was in a shabby street off the Boulevard du Montparnasse; it was convenient for Amitrano's School at which he was going to work. A waiter took his box up five flights of stairs, and Philip was shown into a tiny room, fusty from unopened windows, the greater part of which was taken up by a large wooden bed with a canopy over it of red rep; there were heavy curtains on the windows of the same dingy material; the chest of drawers served also as a washing-stand; and there was a massive wardrobe of the style which is connected with the good King Louis Philippe. The wall-paper was discoloured with age; it was dark gray, and there could be vaguely seen on it garlands of brown leaves. To Philip the room seemed quaint and charming.

Though it was late he felt too excited to sleep and, going out, made his way into the boulevard and walked towards the light. This led him to the station; and the square in front of it, vivid with arc-lamps, noisy with the yellow trams that seemed to cross it in all directions, made him laugh aloud with joy. There were cafés all round, and by chance, thirsty and eager to get a nearer sight of the crowd, Philip installed himself at a little table outside the Café de Versailles. Every other table was taken, for it was a fine night; and Philip looked curiously at the people, here little family groups, there a knot of men with odd-shaped hats and beards talking loudly and gesticulating; next to him were two men who looked like painters with women who Philip hoped were not their lawful wives; behind him he heard Americans loudly arguing on art. His soul was thrilled. He sat till very late, tired out but too happy to move, and when at last he went to bed he was wide awake; he listened to the manifold noise of Paris.

Next day about tea-time he made his way to the Lion de Belfort, and in a new street that led out of the Boulevard Raspail found Mrs. Otter. She was an insignificant woman of thirty, with a provincial air and a deliberately lady-like manner; she introduced him to her mother. He discovered presently that she had been studying in Paris for three years and later that she was separated from her husband. She had in her small drawing-room one or two portraits which she had painted, and to Philip's inexperience they seemed extremely accomplished.

"I wonder if I shall ever be able to paint as well as that," he said to her.

"Oh, I expect so," she replied, not without self-satisfaction. "You can't expect to do everything all at once, of course."

She was very kind. She gave him the address of a shop where he could get a portfolio, drawing-paper, and charcoal.

"I shall be going to Amitrano's about nine tomorrow, and if you'll be there then I'll see that you get a good place and all that sort of thing."

She asked him what he wanted to do, and Philip felt that he should not let her see how vague he was about the whole matter.

"Well, first I want to learn to draw," he said.

"I'm so glad to hear you say that. People always want to do things in such a hurry. I never touched oils till I'd been here for two years, and look at the result."

She gave a glance at the portrait of her mother, a sticky piece of painting that hung over the piano.

"And if I were you, I would be very careful about the people you get to know. I wouldn't mix myself up with any foreigners. I'm very careful myself."

Philip thanked her for the suggestion, but it seemed to him odd. He did not know that he particularly wanted to be careful.

"We live just as we would if we were in England," said Mrs. Otter's mother, who till then had spoken little. "When we came here we brought all our own furniture over."

Philip looked round the room. It was filled with a massive suite, and at the window were the same sort of white lace curtains which Aunt Louisa put up at the vicarage in summer. The piano was draped in Liberty silk and so was the chimney-piece. Mrs. Otter followed his wandering eye.

"In the evening when we close the shutters one might really feel one was in England."

"And we have our meals just as if we were at home," added her mother. "A meat breakfast in the morning and dinner in the middle of the day."

When he left Mrs. Otter Philip went to buy drawing materials; and next morning at the stroke of nine, trying to seem self-assured, he presented himself at the school. Mrs. Otter was already there, and she came forward with a friendly smile. He had been anxious about the reception he would have as a *nouveau,* for he had read a good deal of the rough joking to which a newcomer was exposed at some of the studios; but Mrs. Otter had reassured him.

"Oh, there's nothing like that here," she said. "You see, about half our students are ladies, and they set a tone to the place."

The studio was large and bare, with gray walls, on which were pinned the studies that had received prizes. A model was sitting in a chair with a loose wrap thrown over her, and about a dozen men and women were standing about, some talking and others still working on their sketch. It was the first rest of the model.

"You'd better not try anything too difficult at first," said Mrs. Otter. "Put your easel here. You'll find that's the easiest pose."

Philip placed an easel where she indicated, and Mrs. Otter introduced him to a young woman who sat next to him.

"Mr. Carey—Miss Price. Mr. Carey's never studied before, you won't mind helping him a little just at first, will you?" Then she turned to the model. "*La Pose.*"

The model threw aside the paper she had been reading, *La Petite République,* and sulkily, throwing off her gown, got on to the stand. She stood, squarely on both feet, with her hands clasped behind her head.

"It's a stupid pose," said Miss Price. "I can't imagine why they chose it."

When Philip entered, the people in the studio had looked at him curiously, and the model gave him an indifferent glance, but now they ceased to pay attention to him. Philip, with his beautiful sheet of paper in front of him, stared awkwardly at the model. He did not know how to begin. He had never seen a naked woman before. She was not young and her breasts were shrivelled. She had colourless, fair hair that fell over her forehead untidily, and her face was covered with large freckles. He glanced at Miss Price's work. She had only been working on it two days, and it looked as though she had had trouble; her paper was in a mess from constant rubbing out, and to Philip's eyes the figure looked strangely distorted.

"I should have thought I could do as well as that," he said to himself.

He began on the head, thinking that he would work slowly downwards, but, he could not understand why, he found it infinitely more difficult to draw a head from the model than to draw one from his imagination. He got into difficulties. He glanced at Miss Price. She was working with vehement gravity. Her brow was wrinkled with eagerness, and there was an anxious look in her eyes. It was hot in the studio, and drops of sweat stood on her forehead. She was a girl of twenty-six, with a great deal of dull gold hair; it was handsome hair, but it was carelessly done, dragged back from her forehead and tied in a hurried knot. She had a large face, with broad, flat features and small eyes; her skin was pasty, with a singular unhealthiness of tone, and there was no colour in the cheeks. She had an unwashed air and you could not help wondering if she slept in her clothes. She was serious and silent. When the next pause came, she stepped back to look at her work.

"I don't know why I'm having so much bother," she said. "But I mean to get it right." She turned to Philip. "How are you getting on?"

"Not at all," he answered, with a rueful smile.

She looked at what he had done. "You can't expect to do anything that way. You must take measurements. And you must square out your paper."

She showed him rapidly how to set about the business. Philip was impressed by her earnestness, but repelled by her want of charm. He was grateful for the hints she gave him and set to work again. Meanwhile other people had come in, mostly men, for the women always arrived first, and the studio for the time of year (it was early yet) was fairly full. Presently there came in a young man with thin, black hair, an enormous nose, and a face so long that it reminded you of a horse. He sat down next to Philip and nodded across him to Miss Price.

"You're very late," she said. "Are you only just up?"

"It was such a splendid day, I thought I'd lie in bed and think how beautiful it was out."

Philip smiled, but Miss Price took the remark seriously.

"That seems a funny thing to do, I should have thought it would be more to the point to get up and enjoy it."

"The way of the humorist is very hard," said the young man gravely.

He did not seem inclined to work. He looked at his canvas; he was working in colour, and had sketched in the day before the model who was posing. He turned to Philip.

"Have you just come out from England?"

"Yes."

"How did you find your way to Amitrano's?"

"It was the only school I knew of."

"I hope you haven't come with the idea that you will learn anything here which will be of the smallest use to you."

"It's the best school in Paris," said Miss Price. "It's the only one where they take art seriously."

"Should art be taken seriously?" the young man asked; and since Miss Price replied only with a scornful shrug, he added: "But the point is, all schools are bad. They are academical, obviously. Why this is less injurious than most is that the teaching is more incompetent than elsewhere. Because you learn nothing. . . ."

"But why d'you come here then?" interrupted Philip.

"I see the better course, but do not follow it. Miss Price, who is cultured, will remember the Latin of that."

"I wish you would leave me out of your conversation, Mr. Clutton," said Miss Price brusquely.

"The only way to learn to paint," he went on, imperturbable, "is to take a studio, hire a model, and just fight it out for yourself."

"That seems a simple thing to do," said Philip.

"It only needs money," replied Clutton.

He began to paint, and Philip looked at him from the corner of his eye. He was long and desperately thin; his huge bones seemed to protrude from his body; his elbows were so sharp that they appeared to jut out through the arms of his shabby coat. His trousers were frayed at the bottom, and on each of his boots was a clumsy patch. Miss Price got up and went over to Philip's easel.

"If Mr. Clutton will hold his tongue for a moment, I'll just help you a little," she said.

"Miss Price dislikes me because I

have humour," said Clutton, looking meditatively at his canvas, "but she detests me because I have genius."

He spoke with solemnity, and his colossal, misshapen nose made what he said very quaint. Philip was obliged to laugh, but Miss Price grew darkly red with anger.

"You're the only person who has ever accused you of genius."

"Also I am the only person whose opinion is of the least value to me."

Miss Price began to criticise what Philip had done. She talked glibly of anatomy and construction, planes and lines, and of much else which Philip did not understand. She had been at the studio a long time and knew the main points which the masters insisted upon, but though she could show what was wrong with Philip's work she could not tell him how to put it right.

"It's awfully kind of you to take so much trouble with me," said Philip.

"Oh, it's nothing," she answered, flushing awkwardly. "People did the same for me when I first came, I'd do it for anyone."

"Miss Price wants to indicate that she is giving you the advantage of her knowledge from a sense of duty rather than on account of any charms of your person," said Clutton.

Miss Price gave him a furious look, and went back to her own drawing. The clock struck twelve, and the model with a cry of relief stepped down from the stand.

Miss Price gathered up her things.

"Some of us go to Gravier's for lunch," she said to Philip, with a look at Clutton. "I always go home myself."

"I'll take you to Gravier's if you like," said Clutton.

Philip thanked him and made ready to go. On his way out Mrs. Otter asked him how he had been getting on.

"Did Fanny Price help you?" she asked. "I put you there because I know she can do it if she likes. She's a disagreeable, ill-natured girl, and she can't draw herself at all, but she knows the ropes, and she can be useful to a newcomer if she cares to take the trouble."

On the way down the street Clutton said to him:

"You've made an impression on Fanny Price. You'd better look out."

Philip laughed. He had never seen anyone on whom he wished less to make an impression. They came to the cheap little restaurant at which several of the students ate, and Clutton sat down at a table at which three or four men were already seated. For a franc, they got an egg, a plate of meat, cheese; and a small bottle of wine. Coffee was extra. They sat on the pavement, and yellow trams passed up and down the boulevard with a ceaseless ringing of bells.

"By the way, what's your name?" said Clutton, as they took their seats.

"Carey."

"Allow me to introduce an old and trusted friend, Carey by name," said Clutton gravely. "Mr. Flanagan, Mr. Lawson."

They laughed and went on with their conversation. They talked of a thousand things, and they all talked at once. No one paid the smallest attention to anyone else. They talked of the places they had been to in the summer, of studios, of the various schools; they mentioned names which were unfamiliar to Philip, Monet, Manet, Renoir, Pizarro, Degas. Philip listened with all his ears, and though he felt a little out of it, his heart leaped with exultation. The time flew. When Clutton got up he said:

"I expect you'll find me here this

evening if you care to come. You'll find this about the best place for get-ting dyspepsia at the lowest cost in the Quarter."

XLI

Philip walked down the Boulevard du Montparnasse. It was not at all like the Paris he had seen in the spring during his visit to do the accounts of the Hôtel St. Georges—he thought already of that part of his life with a shudder—but reminded him of what he thought a provincial town must be. There was an easy-going air about it, and a sunny spaciousness which invited the mind to day-dreaming. The trimness of the trees, the vivid whiteness of the houses, the breadth, were very agreeable; and he felt himself already thoroughly at home. He sauntered along, staring at the people; there seemed an elegance about the most ordinary, workmen with their broad red sashes and their wide trousers, little soldiers in dingy, charming uniforms. He came presently to the Avenue de l'Observatoire, and he gave a sigh of pleasure at the magnificent, yet so graceful, vista. He came to the gardens of the Luxembourg; children were playing, nurses with long ribbons walked slowly two by two, busy men passed through with satchels under their arms, youths strangely dressed. The scene was formal and dainty; nature was arranged and ordered, but so exquisitely, that nature unordered and unarranged seemed barbaric. Philip was enchanted. It excited him to stand on that spot of which he had read so much; it was classic ground to him; and he felt the awe and the delight which some old don might feel when for the first time he looked on the smiling plain of Sparta.

As he wandered he chanced to see Miss Price sitting by herself on a bench. He hesitated, for he did not at that moment want to see anyone, and her uncouth way seemed out of place amid the happiness he felt around him; but he had divined her sensitiveness to affront, and since she had seen him thought it would be polite to speak to her.

"What are you doing here?" she said, as he came up.

"Enjoying myself. Aren't you?"

"Oh, I come here every day from four to five. I don't think one does any good if one works straight through."

"May I sit down for a minute?" he said.

"If you want to."

"That doesn't sound very cordial," he laughed.

"I'm not much of a one for saying pretty things."

Philip, a little disconcerted, was silent as he lit a cigarette.

"Did Clutton say anything about my work?" she asked suddenly.

"No, I don't think he did," said Philip.

"He's no good, you know. He thinks he's a genius, but he isn't. He's too lazy, for one thing. Genius is an infinite capacity for taking pains. The only thing is to peg away. If one only makes up one's mind badly enough to do a thing one can't help doing it."

She spoke with a passionate strenuousness which was rather striking. She wore a sailor hat of black straw, a white blouse which was not quite clean, and a brown skirt. She had no gloves on, and her hands wanted washing. She was so unattractive that Philip wished he had not begun to talk to her. He could not make out whether she wanted him to stay or go.

"I'll do anything I can for you," she said all at once, without reference to anything that had gone before. "I know how hard it is."

"Thank you very much," said Philip, then in a moment: "Won't you come and have tea with me somewhere?"

She looked at him quickly and flushed. When she reddened her pasty skin acquired a curiously mottled look, like strawberries and cream that had gone bad.

"No, thanks. What d'you think I want tea for? I've only just had lunch."

"I thought it would pass the time," said Philip.

"If you find it long you needn't bother about me, you know. I don't mind being left alone."

At that moment two men passed, in brown velveteens, enormous trousers, and basque caps. They were young, but both wore beards.

"I say, are those art-students?" said Philip. "They might have stepped out of the *Vie de Bohème*."

"They're Americans," said Miss Price scornfully. "Frenchmen haven't worn things like that for thirty years, but the Americans from the Far West buy those clothes and have themselves photographed the day after they arrive in Paris. That's about as near to art as they ever get. But it doesn't matter to them, they've all got money."

Philip liked the daring picturesqueness of the Americans' costume; he thought it showed the romantic spirit.

Miss Price asked him the time.

"I must be getting along to the studio," she said. "Are you going to the sketch classes?"

Philip did not know anything about them, and she told him that from five to six every evening a model sat, from whom anyone who liked could go and draw at the cost of fifty centimes. They had a different model every day, and it was very good practice.

"I don't suppose you're good enough yet for that. You'd better wait a bit."

"I don't see why I shouldn't try. I haven't got anything else to do."

They got up and walked to the studio. Philip could not tell from her manner whether Miss Price wished him to walk with her or preferred to walk alone. He remained from sheer embarrassment, not knowing how to leave her; but she would not talk; she answered his questions in an ungracious manner.

A man was standing at the studio door with a large dish into which each person as he went in dropped his half franc. The studio was much fuller than it had been in the morning, and there was not the preponderance of English and Americans; nor were women there in so large a proportion. Philip felt the assemblage was more the sort of thing he had expected. It was very warm, and the air quickly grew fetid. It was an old man who sat this time, with a vast gray beard, and Philip tried to put into practice the little he had learned in the morning; but he made a poor job of it; he realised that he could not draw nearly as well as he thought. He glanced enviously at one or two sketches of men who sat near him, and wondered whether he would ever be able to use the charcoal with that mastery. The hour passed quickly. Not wishing to press himself upon Miss Price he sat down at some distance from her, and at the end, as he passed her on his way out, she asked him brusquely how he had got on.

"Not very well," he smiled.

"If you'd condescended to come and sit near me I could have given you some hints. I suppose you thought yourself too grand."

"No, it wasn't that. I was afraid you'd think me a nuisance."

"When I do that I'll tell you sharp enough."

Philip saw that in her uncouth way she was offering him help.

"Well, tomorrow I'll just force myself upon you."

"I don't mind," she answered.

Philip went out and wondered what he should do with himself till dinner. He was eager to do something characteristic. *Absinthe!* Of course it was indicated, and so, sauntering towards the station, he seated himself outside a café and ordered it. He drank with nausea and satisfaction. He found the taste disgusting, but the moral effect magnificent; he felt every inch an art-student; and since he drank on an empty stomach his spirits presently grew very high. He watched the crowds, and felt all men were his brothers. He was happy. When he reached Gravier's the table at which Clutton sat was full, but as soon as he saw Philip limping along he called out to him. They made room. The dinner was frugal, a plate of soup, a dish of meat, fruit, cheese, and half a bottle of wine; but Philip paid no attention to what he ate. He took note of the men at the table. Flanagan was there again: he was an American, a short, snub-nosed youth with a jolly face and a laughing mouth. He wore a Norfolk jacket of bold pattern, a blue stock round his neck, and a

tweed cap of fantastic shape. At that time impressionism reigned in the Latin Quarter, but its victory over the older schools was still recent; and Carolus-Duran, Bouguereau, and their like were set up against Manet, Monet, and Degas. To appreciate these was still a sign of grace. Whistler was an influence strong with the English and his compatriots, and the discerning collected Japanese prints. The old masters were tested by new standards. The esteem in which Raphael had been for centuries held was a matter of derision to wise young men. They offered to give all his works for Velasquez' head of Philip IV in the National Gallery. Philip found that a discussion on art was raging. Lawson, whom he had met at luncheon, sat opposite to him. He was a thin youth with a freckled face and red hair. He had very bright green eyes. As Philip sat down he fixed them on him and remarked suddenly:

"Raphael was only tolerable when he painted other people's pictures. When he painted Peruginos or Pinturichios he was charming; when he painted Raphaels he was," with a scornful shrug, "Raphael."

Lawson spoke so aggressively that Philip was taken aback, but he was not obliged to answer because Flanagan broke in impatiently.

"Oh, to hell with art!" he cried. "Let's get ginny."

"You were ginny last night, Flanagan," said Lawson.

"Nothing to what I mean to be tonight," he answered. "Fancy being in Pa-ris and thinking of nothing but art all the time." He spoke with a broad Western accent. "My, it is good to be alive." He gathered himself together and then banged his fist on the table. "To hell with art, I say."

"You not only say it, but you say

it with tiresome iteration," said Clutton severely.

There was another American at the table. He was dressed like those fine fellows whom Philip had seen that afternoon in the Luxembourg. He had a handsome face, thin, ascetic, with dark eyes; he wore his fantastic garb with the dashing air of a buccaneer. He had a vast quantity of dark hair which fell constantly over his eyes, and his most frequent gesture was to throw back his head dramatically to get some long wisp out of the way. He began to talk of the *Olympia* by Manet, which then hung in the Luxembourg.

"I stood in front of it for an hour today, and I tell you it's not a good picture."

Lawson put down his knife and fork. His green eyes flashed fire, he gasped with rage; but he could be seen imposing calm upon himself.

"It's very interesting to hear the mind of the untutored savage," he said. "Will you tell us why it isn't a good picture?"

Before the American could answer someone else broke in vehemently.

"D'you mean to say you can look at the painting of that flesh and say it's not good?"

"I don't say that. I think the right breast is very well painted."

"The right breast be damned," shouted Lawson. "The whole thing's a miracle of painting."

He began to describe in detail the beauties of the picture, but at this table at Gravier's they who spoke at length spoke for their own edification. No one listened to him. The American interrupted angrily.

"You don't mean to say you think the head's good?"

Lawson, white with passion now, began to defend the head; but Clutton, who had been sitting in silence with a look on his face of good-humoured scorn, broke in.

"Give him the head. We don't want the head. It doesn't affect the picture."

"All right, I'll give you the head," cried Lawson. "Take the head and be damned to you."

"What about the black line?" cried the American, triumphantly pushing back a wisp of hair which nearly fell in his soup. "You don't see a black line round objects in nature."

"Oh, God, send down fire from heaven to consume the blasphemer," said Lawson. "What has nature got to do with it? No one knows what's in nature and what isn't! The world sees nature through the eyes of the artist. Why, for centuries it saw horses jumping a fence with all their legs extended, and by Heaven, sir, they were extended. It saw shadows black until Monet discovered they were coloured, and by Heaven, sir, they were black. If we choose to surround objects with a black line, the world will see the black line, and there will be a black line; and if we paint grass red and cows blue, it'll see them red and blue, and, by Heaven, they will be red and blue."

"To hell with art," murmured Flanagan. "I want to get ginny."

Lawson took no notice of the interruption.

"Now look here, when *Olympia* was shown at the Salon, Zola—amid the jeers of the Philistines and the hisses of the *pompiers,* the academicians, and the public, Zola said: 'I look forward to the day when Manet's picture will hang in the Louvre opposite the *Odalisque* of Ingres, and it will not be the *Odalisque* which will gain by comparison.' It'll be there. Every day I see the time grow nearer. In ten years the *Olympia* will be in the Louvre."

"Never," shouted the American, using both hands now with a sudden desperate attempt to get his hair once for all out of the way. "In ten years that picture will be dead. It's only a fashion of the moment. No picture can live that hasn't got something which that picture misses by a million miles."

"And what is that?"

"Great art can't exist without a moral element."

"Oh God!" cried Lawson furiously. "I knew it was that. He wants morality." He joined his hands and held them towards heaven in supplication. "Oh, Christopher Columbus, Christopher Columbus, what did you do when you discovered America?"

"Ruskin says . . ."

But before he could add another word, Clutton rapped with the handle of his knife imperiously on the table.

"Gentlemen," he said in a stern voice, and his huge nose positively wrinkled with passion, "a name has been mentioned which I never thought to hear again in decent society. Freedom of speech is all very well, but we must observe the limits of common propriety. You may talk of Bouguereau if you will: there is a cheerful disgustingness in the sound which excites laughter; but let us not sully our chaste lips with the names of J. Ruskin, G. F. Watts, or E. B. Jones."

"Who was Ruskin anyway?" asked Flanagan.

"He was one of the great Victorians. He was a master of English style."

"Ruskin's style—a thing of shreds and purple patches," said Lawson. "Besides, damn the Great Victorians. Whenever I open a paper and see Death of a Great Victorian, I thank Heaven there's one more of them gone. Their only talent was longevity,

and no artist should be allowed to live after he's forty; by then a man has done his best work, all he does after that is repetition. Don't you think it was the greatest luck in the world for them that Keats, Shelley, Bonnington, and Byron died early? What a genius we should think Swinburne if he had perished on the day the first series of *Poems and Ballads* was published!"

The suggestion pleased, for no one at the table was more than twenty-four, and they threw themselves upon it with gusto. They were unanimous for once. They elaborated. Someone proposed a vast bonfire made out of the works of the Forty Academicians into which the Great Victorians might be hurled on their fortieth birthday. The idea was received with acclamation. Carlyle and Ruskin, Tennyson, Browning, G. F. Watts, E. B. Jones, Dickens, Thackeray, they were hurried into the flames; Mr. Gladstone, John Bright, and Cobden; there was a moment's discussion about George Meredith, but Matthew Arnold and Emerson were given up cheerfully. At last came Walter Pater.

"Not Walter Pater," murmured Philip.

Lawson stared at him for a moment with his green eyes and then nodded.

"You're quite right, Walter Pater is the only justification for Monna Lisa. D'you know Cronshaw? He used to know Pater."

"Who's Cronshaw?" asked Philip.

"Cronshaw's a poet. He lives here. Let's go to the Lilas."

La Closerie des Lilas was a café to which they often went in the evening after dinner, and here Cronshaw was invariably to be found between the hours of nine at night and two in the morning. But Flanagan had had enough of intellectual conversation for one evening, and when Lawson made his suggestion, turned to Philip. "Oh gee, let's go where there are girls," he said. "Come to the Gaîté Montparnasse, and we'll get ginny."

"I'd rather go and see Cronshaw and keep sober," laughed Philip.

XLII

THERE was a general disturbance. Flanagan and two or three more went on to the music-hall, while Philip walked slowly with Clutton and Lawson to the Closerie des Lilas.

"You must go to the Gaîté Montparnasse," said Lawson to him. "It's one of the loveliest things in Paris. I'm going to paint it one of these days."

Philip, influenced by Hayward, looked upon music-halls with scornful eyes, but he had reached Paris at a time when their artistic possibilities were just discovered. The peculiarities of lighting, the masses of dingy red and tarnished gold, the heaviness of the shadows and the decorative lines, offered a new theme; and half the studios in the Quarter contained sketches made in one or other of the local theatres. Men of letters, following in the painters' wake, conspired suddenly to find artistic value in the turns; in red-nosed comedians were lauded to the skies for their sense of character; fat female singers, who had bawled obscurely for twenty years, were discovered to possess inimitable drollery; there were those who found an æsthetic delight in performing dogs; while others exhausted their vocabulary to extol the distinction of conjurers and trickcyclists. The crowd too, under another influence, was become an object of sympathetic interest. With Hayward, Philip had disdained humanity in the mass; he adopted the attitude of one who wraps himself in solitariness and watches with disgust the antics of the vulgar; but Clutton and Lawson talked of the multitude with enthusiasm. They described the seething throng that filled the various fairs of Paris, the sea of faces, half seen in the glare of acetylene, half hidden in the darkness, and the blare of trumpets, the hooting of whistles, the hum of voices. What they said was new and strange to Philip. They told him about Cronshaw.

"Have you ever read any of his work?"

"No," said Philip.

"It came out in *The Yellow Book*."

They looked upon him, as painters often do writers, with contempt because he was a layman, with tolerance because he practised an art, and with awe because he used a medium in which themselves felt ill-at-ease.

"He's an extraordinary fellow. You'll find him a bit disappointing at first, he only comes out at his best when he's drunk."

"And the nuisance is," added Clutton, "that it takes him a devil of a time to get drunk."

When they arrived at the café Lawson told Philip that they would have to go in. There was hardly a bite in the autumn air, but Cronshaw had a morbid fear of draughts and even in the warmest weather sat inside.

"He knows everyone worth knowing," Lawson explained. "He knew Pater and Oscar Wilde, and he knows Mallarmé and all those fellows."

The object of their search sat in

the most sheltered corner of the café, with his coat on and the collar turned up. He wore his hat pressed well down on his forehead so that he should avoid cold air. He was a big man, stout but not obese, with a round face, a small moustache, and little, rather stupid eyes. His head did not seem quite big enough for his body. It looked like a pea uneasily poised on an egg. He was playing dominoes with a Frenchman, and greeted the newcomers with a quiet smile; he did not speak, but as if to make room for them pushed away the little pile of saucers on the table which indicated the number of drinks he had already consumed. He nodded to Philip when he was introduced to him, and went on with the game. Philip's knowledge of the language was small, but he knew enough to tell that Cronshaw, although he had lived in Paris for several years, spoke French execrably.

At last he leaned back with a smile of triumph.

"*Je vous ai battu,*" he said, with an abominable accent. "*Garçong!*"

He called the waiter and turned to Philip.

"Just out from England? See any cricket?"

Philip was a little confused at the unexpected question.

"Cronshaw knows the averages of every first-class cricketer for the last twenty years," said Lawson, smiling.

The Frenchman left them for friends at another table, and Cronshaw, with the lazy enunciation which was one of his peculiarities, began to discourse on the relative merits of Kent and Lancashire. He told them of the last test match he had seen and described the course of the game wicket by wicket.

"That's the only thing I miss in Paris," he said, as he finished the

bock which the waiter had brought. "You don't get any cricket."

Philip was disappointed, and Lawson, pardonably anxious to show off one of the celebrities of the Quarter, grew impatient. Cronshaw was taking his time to wake up that evening, though the saucers at his side indicated that he had at least made an honest attempt to get drunk. Clutton watched the scene with amusement. He fancied there was something of affectation in Cronshaw's minute knowledge of cricket; he liked to tantalise people by talking to them of things that obviously bored them; Clutton threw in a question.

"Have you seen Mallarmé lately?"

Cronshaw looked at him slowly, as if he were turning the inquiry over in his mind, and before he answered rapped on the marble table with one of the saucers.

"Bring my bottle of whiskey," he called out. He turned again to Philip. "I keep my own bottle of whiskey. I can't afford to pay fifty centimes for every thimbleful."

The waiter brought the bottle, and Cronshaw held it up to the light.

"They've been drinking it. Waiter, who's been helping himself to my whiskey?"

"*Mais personne, Monsieur Cronshaw.*"

"I made a mark on it last night, and look at it."

"Monsieur made a mark, but he kept on drinking after that. At that rate Monsieur wastes his time in making marks."

The waiter was a jovial fellow and knew Cronshaw intimately. Cronshaw gazed at him.

"If you give me your word of honour as a nobleman and a gentleman that nobody but I has been drinking my whiskey, I'll accept your statement."

This remark, translated literally into the crudest French, sounded very funny, and the lady at the *comptoir* could not help laughing.

"*Il est impayable*," she murmured.

Cronshaw, hearing her, turned a sheepish eye upon her; she was stout, matronly, and middle-aged; and solemnly kissed his hand to her. She shrugged her shoulders.

"Fear not, madam," he said heavily. "I have passed the age when I am tempted by forty-five and gratitude."

He poured himself out some whiskey and water, and slowly drank it. He wiped his mouth with the back of his hand.

"He talked very well."

Lawson and Clutton knew that Cronshaw's remark was an answer to the question about Mallarmé. Cronshaw often went to the gatherings on Tuesday evenings when the poet received men of letters and painters, and discoursed with subtle oratory on any subject that was suggested to him. Cronshaw had evidently been there lately.

"He talked very well, but he talked nonsense. He talked about art as though it were the most important thing in the world."

"If it isn't, what are we here for?" asked Philip.

"What you're here for I don't know. It is no business of mine. But art is a luxury. Men attach importance only to self-preservation and the propagation of their species. It is only when these instincts are satisfied that they consent to occupy themselves with the entertainment which is provided for them by writers, painters, and poets."

Cronshaw stopped for a moment to drink. He had pondered for twenty years the problem whether he loved liquor because it made him talk or whether he loved conversation because it made him thirsty.

Then he said: "I wrote a poem yesterday."

Without being asked he began to recite it, very slowly, marking the rhythm with an extended forefinger. It was possibly a very fine poem, but at that moment a young woman came in. She had scarlet lips, and it was plain that the vivid colour of her cheeks was not due to the vulgarity of nature; she had blackened her eyelashes and eyebrows, and painted both eyelids a bold blue, which was continued to a triangle at the corner of the eyes. It was fantastic and amusing. Her dark hair was done over her ears in the fashion made popular by Mlle. Cléo de Merode. Philip's eyes wandered to her, and Cronshaw, having finished the recitation of his verses, smiled upon him indulgently.

"You were not listening," he said.

"Oh yes, I was."

"I do not blame you, for you have given an apt illustration of the statement I just made. What is art beside love? I respect and applaud your indifference to fine poetry when you contemplate the meretricious charms of this young person."

She passed by the table at which they were sitting, and he took her arm.

"Come and sit by my side, dear child, and let us play the divine comedy of love."

"*Fichez-moi la paix*," she said, and pushing him on one side continued her perambulation.

"Art," he continued, with a wave of the hand, "is merely the refuge which the ingenious have invented, when they were supplied with food and women, to escape the tediousness of life."

Cronshaw filled his glass again, and began to talk at length. He spoke with rotund delivery. He chose his words carefully. He mingled wisdom and nonsense in the most astounding manner, gravely making fun of his hearers at one moment, and at the next playfully giving them sound advice. He talked of art, and literature, and life. He was by turns devout and obscene, merry and lachrymose. He grew remarkably drunk, and then he began to recite poetry, his own and Milton's, his own and Shelley's, his own and Kit Marlowe's.

At last Lawson, exhausted, got up to go home.

"I shall go too," said Philip.

Clutton, the most silent of them all, remained behind listening, with a sardonic smile on his lips, to Cronshaw's maunderings. Lawson accompanied Philip to his hotel and then bade him good-night. But when

Philip got to bed he could not sleep. All these new ideas that had been flung before him carelessly seethed in his brain. He was tremendously excited. He felt in himself great powers. He had never before been so self-confident.

"I know I shall be a great artist," he said to himself. "I feel it in me."

A thrill passed through him as another thought came, but even to himself he would not put it into words:

"By George, I believe I've got genius."

He was in fact very drunk, but as he had not taken more than one glass of beer, it could have been due only to a more dangerous intoxicant than alcohol.

XLIII

ON TUESDAYS and Fridays masters spent the morning at Amitrano's, criticising the work done. In France the painter earns little unless he paints portraits and is patronised by rich Americans; and men of reputation are glad to increase their incomes by spending two or three hours once a week at one of the numerous studios where art is taught. Tuesday was the day upon which Michel Rollin came to Amitrano's. He was an elderly man, with a white beard and a florid complexion, who had painted a number of decorations for the State, but these were an object of derision to the students he instructed: he was a disciple of Ingres, impervious to the progress of art and angrily impatient with that *tas de farceurs* whose names were Manet, Degas, Monet, and Sisley; but he was an excellent teacher, helpful, polite, and encouraging. Foinet, on the other hand, who visited the studio

on Fridays, was a difficult man to get on with. He was a small, shrivelled person, with bad teeth and a bilious air, an untidy gray beard, and savage eyes; his voice was high and his tone sarcastic. He had had pictures bought by the Luxembourg, and at twenty-five looked forward to a great career; but his talent was due to youth rather than to personality, and for twenty years he had done nothing but repeat the landscape which had brought him his early success. When he was reproached with monotony, he answered:

"Corot only painted one thing. Why shouldn't I?"

He was envious of everyone else's success, and had a peculiar, personal loathing of the Impressionists; for he looked upon his own failure as due to the mad fashion which had attracted the public, *sale bête,* to their works. The genial disdain of Michel

Rollin, who called them impostors, was answered by him with vituperation, of which *crapule* and *canaille* were the least violent items; he amused himself with abuse of their private lives, and with sardonic humour, with blasphemous and obscene detail, attacked the legitimacy of their births and the purity of their conjugal relations; he used an Oriental imagery and an Oriental emphasis to accentuate his ribald scorn. Nor did he conceal his contempt for the students whose work he examined. By them he was hated and feared; the women by his brutal sarcasm he reduced often to tears, which again aroused his ridicule; and he remained at the studio, notwithstanding the protests of those who suffered too bitterly from his attacks, because there could be no doubt that he was one of the best masters in Paris. Sometimes the old model who kept the school ventured to remonstrate with him, but his expostulations quickly gave way before the violent insolence of the painter to abject apologies.

It was Foinet with whom Philip first came in contact. He was already in the studio when Philip arrived. He went round from easel to easel, with Mrs. Otter, the *massière*, by his side to interpret his remarks for the benefit of those who could not understand French. Fanny Price, sitting next to Philip, was working feverishly. Her face was sallow with nervousness, and every now and then she stopped to wipe her hands on her blouse; for they were hot with anxiety. Suddenly she turned to Philip with an anxious look, which she tried to hide by a sullen frown.

"D'you think it's good?" she asked, nodding at her drawing.

Philip got up and looked at it. He was astounded; he felt she must have no eye at all; the thing was hopelessly out of drawing.

"I wish I could draw half as well myself," he answered.

"You can't expect to, you've only just come. It's a bit too much to expect that you should draw as well as I do. I've been here two years."

Fanny Price puzzled Philip. Her conceit was stupendous. Philip had already discovered that everyone in the studio cordially disliked her; and it was no wonder, for she seemed to go out of her way to wound people.

"I complained to Mrs. Otter about Foinet," she said now. "The last two weeks he hasn't looked at my drawings. He spends about half an hour on Mrs. Otter because she's the *massière*. After all I pay as much as anybody else, and I suppose my money's as good as theirs. I don't see why I shouldn't get as much attention as anybody else."

She took up her charcoal again, but in a moment put it down with a groan.

"I can't do any more now. I'm so frightfully nervous."

She looked at Foinet, who was coming towards them with Mrs. Otter. Mrs. Otter, meek, mediocre, and self-satisfied, wore an air of importance. Foinet sat down at the easel of an untidy little Englishwoman called Ruth Chalice. She had the fine black eyes, languid but passionate, the thin face, ascetic but sensual, the skin like old ivory, which under the influence of Burne-Jones were cultivated at that time by young ladies in Chelsea. Foinet seemed in a pleasant mood; he did not say much to her, but with quick, determined strokes of her charcoal pointed out her errors. Miss Chalice beamed with pleasure when he rose. He came to Clutton, and by this time Philip was nervous too but Mrs. Otter had promised to make things easy for him. Foinet stood for a moment in front of Clutton's work, biting his thumb silently, then absent-mindedly spat out upon the canvas the little piece of skin which he had bitten off.

"That's a fine line," he said at last, indicating with his thumb what pleased him. "You're beginning to learn to draw."

Clutton did not answer, but looked at the master with his usual air of sardonic indifference to the world's opinion.

"I'm beginning to think you have at least a trace of talent."

Mrs. Otter, who did not like Clutton, pursed her lips. She did not see anything out of the way in his work. Foinet sat down and went into technical details. Mrs. Otter grew rather tired of standing. Clutton did not say anything, but nodded now and then, and Foinet felt with satisfaction that he grasped what he said and the reasons of it; most of them listened to him, but it was clear they never understood. Then Foinet got up and came to Philip.

"He only arrived two days ago," Mrs. Otter hurried to explain. "He's a beginner. He's never studied before."

"*Ça se voit*," the master said. "One sees that."

He passed on, and Mrs. Otter murmured to him:

"This is the young lady I told you about."

He looked at her as though she were some repulsive animal, and his voice grew more rasping.

"It appears that you do not think I pay enough attention to you. You have been complaining to the *massière*. Well, show me this work to which you wish me to give attention."

Fanny Price coloured. The blood under her unhealthy skin seemed to be of a strange purple. Without answering she pointed to the drawing on which she had been at work since the beginning of the week. Foinet sat down.

"Well, what do you wish me to say to you? Do you wish me to tell you it is good? It isn't. Do you wish me to tell you it is well drawn? It isn't. Do you wish me to say it has merit? It hasn't. Do you wish me to show you what is wrong with it? It is all wrong. Do you wish me to tell you what to do with it? Tear it up. Are you satisfied now?"

Miss Price became very white. She was furious because he had said all this before Mrs. Otter. Though she had been in France so long and could understand French well enough, she could hardly speak two words.

"He's got no right to treat me like that. My money's as good as anyone else's. I pay him to teach me. That's not teaching me."

"What does she say? What does she say?" asked Foinet.

Mrs. Otter hesitated to translate, and Miss Price repeated in execrable French.

"*Je vous paye pour m'apprendre.*"

His eyes flashed with rage, he raised his voice and shook his fist.

"*Mais, nom de Dieu,* I can't teach you. I could more easily teach a camel." He turned to Mrs. Otter. "Ask her, does she do this for amusement, or does she expect to earn money by it?"

"I'm going to earn my living as an artist," Miss Price answered.

"Then it is my duty to tell you that you are wasting your time. It would not matter that you have no talent, talent does not run about the streets in these days, but you have not the beginning of an aptitude. How long have you been here? A child of five after two lessons would draw better than you do. I only say one thing to you, give up this hopeless attempt. You're more likely to earn your living as a *bonne à tout faire* than as a painter. Look."

He seized a piece of charcoal, and it broke as he applied it to the paper. He cursed, and with the stump drew great firm lines. He drew rapidly and spoke at the same time, spitting out the words with venom.

"Look, those arms are not the same length. That knee, it's grotesque. I tell you a child of five. You see, she's not standing on her legs. That foot!"

With each word the angry pencil made a mark, and in a moment the drawing upon which Fanny Price had spent so much time and eager trouble was unrecognisable, a confusion of lines and smudges. At last he flung down the charcoal and stood up.

"Take my advice, Mademoiselle, try dressmaking." He looked at his watch. "It's twelve. *A la semaine prochaine, messieurs.*"

Miss Price gathered up her things slowly. Philip waited behind after the others to say to her something consolatory. He could think of nothing but:

"I say, I'm awfully sorry. What a beast that man is!"

She turned on him savagely.

"Is that what you're waiting about for? When I want your sympathy I'll ask for it. Please get out of my way."

She walked past him, out of the studio, and Philip, with a shrug of the shoulders, limped along to Gravier's for luncheon.

"It served her right," said Lawson, when Philip told him what had happened. "Ill-tempered slut."

Lawson was very sensitive to criticism and, in order to avoid it, never went to the studio when Foinet was coming.

"I don't want other people's opinion of my work," he said. "I know myself if it's good or bad."

"You mean you don't want other people's bad opinion of your work," answered Clutton dryly.

In the afternoon Philip thought he would go to the Luxembourg to see the pictures, and walking through the garden he saw Fanny Price sitting in her accustomed seat. He was sore at the rudeness with which she had met his well-meant attempt to say something pleasant, and passed as though he had not caught sight of her. But she got up at once and came towards him.

"Are you trying to cut me?" she said.

"No, of course not. I thought perhaps you didn't want to be spoken to."

"Where are you going?"

"I wanted to have a look at the Manet, I've heard so much about it."

"Would you like me to come with you? I know the Luxembourg rather well. I could show you one or two good things."

He understood that, unable to bring herself to apologise directly, she made this offer as amends.

"It's awfully kind of you. I should like it very much."

"You needn't say yes if you'd rather go alone," she said suspiciously.

"I wouldn't."

They walked towards the gallery. Caillebotte's collection had lately been placed on view, and the student for the first time had the opportunity to examine at his ease the works of the Impressionists. Till then it had been possible to see them only at Durand-Ruel's shop in the Rue Lafitte (and the dealer, unlike his fellows in England, who adopt towards the painter an attitude of superiority, was always pleased to show the shabbiest student whatever he wanted to see), or at his private house, to which it was not difficult to get a card of admission on Tuesdays, and where you might see pictures of world-wide reputation. Miss Price led Philip straight up to Manet's *Olympia*. He looked at it in astonished silence.

"Do you like it?" asked Miss Price.

"I don't know," he answered helplessly.

"You can take it from me that it's the best thing in the gallery except perhaps Whistler's portrait of his mother."

She gave him a certain time to contemplate the masterpiece and then took him to a picture representing a railway-station.

"Look, here's a Monet," she said. "It's the Gare St. Lazare."

"But the railway lines aren't parallel," said Philip.

"What does that matter?" she asked, with a haughty air.

Philip felt ashamed of himself. Fanny Price had picked up the glib chatter of the studios and had no difficulty in impressing Philip with the extent of her knowledge. She proceeded to explain the pictures to him, superciliously but not without insight, and showed him what the painters had attempted and what he must look for. She talked with much gesticulation of the thumb, and Philip, to whom all she said was new, listened with profound but bewildered interest. Till now he had worshipped Watts and Burne-Jones. The pretty colour of the first, the affected drawing of the second, had entirely satisfied his æsthetic sensibilities. Their vague idealism, the suspicion of a philosophical idea which underlay the titles they gave their pictures, accorded very well with the functions of art as from his diligent perusal of Ruskin he understood it; but here was something quite different: here was no moral appeal; and the contemplation of these works could help no one to lead a purer and a higher life. He was puzzled.

At last he said: "You know, I'm simply dead. I don't think I can absorb anything more profitably. Let's go and sit down on one of the benches."

"It's better not to take too much art at a time," Miss Price answered.

When they got outside he thanked her warmly for the trouble she had taken.

"Oh, that's all right," she said, a little ungraciously. "I do it because I enjoy it. We'll go to the Louvre tomorrow if you like, and then I'll take you to Durand-Ruel's."

"You're really awfully good to me."

"You don't think me such a beast as the most of them do."

"I don't," he smiled.

"They think they'll drive me away from the studio; but they won't; I shall stay there just exactly as long as it suits me. All that this morning, it was Lucy Otter's doing, I know it was. She always has hated me. She thought after that I'd take myself off. I daresay she'd like me to go. She's afraid I know too much about her."

Miss Price told him a long, involved story, which made out that Mrs. Otter, a humdrum and respectable little person, had scabrous intrigues. Then she talked of Ruth Chalice, the girl whom Foinet had praised that morning.

"She's been with every one of the fellows at the studio. She's nothing better than a street-walker. And she's dirty. She hasn't had a bath for a month. I know it for a fact."

Philip listened uncomfortably. He had heard already that various rumours were in circulation about Miss Chalice; but it was ridiculous to suppose that Mrs. Otter, living with her mother, was anything but rigidly virtuous. The woman walking by his side with her malignant lying positively horrified him.

"I don't care what they say. I shall go on just the same. I know I've got it in me. I feel I'm an artist. I'd sooner kill myself than give it up. Oh, I shan't be the first they've all laughed at in the schools and then he's turned out the only genius of the lot. Art's the only thing I care for, I'm willing to give my whole life to it. It's only a question of sticking to it and pegging away."

She found discreditable motives for everyone who would not take her at her own estimate of herself. She detested Clutton. She told Philip that his friend had no talent really; it was just flashy and superficial; he couldn't compose a figure to save his life. And Lawson:

"Little beast, with red hair and his freckles. He's so afraid of Foinet that he won't let him see his work. After all, I don't funk it, do I? I don't care what Foinet says to me, I know I'm a real artist."

They reached the street in which she lived, and with a sigh of relief Philip left her.

XLIV

B u t notwithstanding when Miss Price on the following Sunday offered to take him to the Louvre Philip accepted. She showed him Monna Lisa. He looked at it with a slight feeling of disappointment, but he had read till he knew by heart the jewelled words with which Walter Pater has added beauty to the most famous picture in the world; and these now he repeated to Miss Price.

"That's all literature," she said, a little contemptuously. "You must get away from that."

She showed him the Rembrandts, and she said many appropriate things about them. She stood in front of the *Disciples at Emmaus.*

"When you feel the beauty of that," she said, "you'll know something about painting."

She showed him the *Odalisque* and *La Source* of Ingres. Fanny Price was a peremptory guide, she would not let him look at the things he wished, and attempted to force his admiration for all she admired. She was desperately in earnest with her study of art, and when Philip, passing in the Long Gallery a window that looked out on the Tuileries, gay, sunny, and urbane, like a picture by Raffaëlli, exclaimed:

"I say, how jolly! Do let's stop here a minute."

She said, indifferently: "Yes, it's all right. But we've come here to look at pictures."

The autumn air, blithe and vivacious, elated Philip; and when towards mid-day they stood in the great court-yard of the Louvre, he felt inclined to cry like Flanagan: To Hell with art.

"I say, do let's go to one of those restaurants in the Boul' Mich' and have a snack together, shall we?" he suggested.

Miss Price gave him a suspicious look.

"I've got my lunch waiting for me at home," she answered.

"That doesn't matter. You can eat it tomorrow. Do let me stand you a lunch."

"I don't know why you want to."

"It would give me pleasure," he replied, smiling.

They crossed the river, and at the

corner of the Boulevard St. Michel there was a restaurant.

"Let's go in there."

"No, I won't go there, it looks too expensive."

She walked on firmly, and Philip was obliged to follow. A few steps brought them to a smaller restaurant, where a dozen people were already lunching on the pavement under an awning; on the window was announced in large white letters: *Déjeuner 1.25, vin compris.*

"We couldn't have anything cheaper than this, and it looks quite all right."

They sat down at a vacant table and waited for the omelette which was the first article on the bill of fare. Philip gazed with delight upon the passersby. His heart went out to them. He was tired but very happy.

"I say, look at that man in the blouse. Isn't he ripping!"

He glanced at Miss Price, and to his astonishment saw that she was looking down at her plate, regardless of the passing spectacle, and two heavy tears were rolling down her cheeks.

"What on earth's the matter?" he exclaimed.

"If you say anything to me I shall get up and go at once," she answered.

He was entirely puzzled, but fortunately at that moment the omelette came. He divided it in two and they began to eat. Philip did his best to talk of indifferent things, and it seemed as though Miss Price were making an effort on her side to be agreeable; but the luncheon was not altogether a success. Philip was squeamish, and the way in which Miss Price ate took his appetite away. She ate noisily, greedily, a little like a wild beast in a menagerie, and after she had finished each course rubbed the plate with pieces of bread till it was white and shining, as if she did not wish to lose a single drop of gravy. They had Camembert cheese, and it disgusted Philip to see that she ate rind and all of the portion that was given her. She could not have eaten more ravenously if she were starving.

Miss Price was unaccountable, and having parted from her on one day with friendliness he could never tell whether on the next she would not be sulky and uncivil; but he learned a good deal from her: though she could not draw well herself, she knew all that could be taught, and her constant suggestions helped his progress. Mrs. Otter was useful to him too, and sometimes Miss Chalice criticised his work; he learned from the glib loquacity of Lawson and from the example of Clutton. But Fanny Price hated him to take suggestions from anyone but herself, and when he asked her help after someone else had been talking to him she would refuse with brutal rudeness. The other fellows, Lawson, Clutton, Flanagan, chaffed him about her.

"You be careful, my lad," they said, "she's in love with you."

"Oh, what nonsense," he laughed.

The thought that Miss Price could be in love with anyone was preposterous. It made him shudder when he thought of her uncomeliness, the bedraggled hair and the dirty hands, the brown dress she always wore, stained and ragged at the hem: he supposed she was hard up, they were all hard up, but she might at least be clean; and it was surely possible with a needle and thread to make her skirt tidy.

Philip began to sort his impressions of the people he was thrown in contact with. He was not so ingenuous as in those days which now seemed so long ago at Heidelberg, and, beginning to take a more deliberate interest in humanity, he was inclined to examine and to criticise. He found it difficult to know Clutton any better after seeing him every day for three months than on the first day of their acquaintance. The general impression at the studio was that he was able; it was supposed that he would do great things, and he shared the general opinion; but what exactly he was going to do neither he nor anybody else quite knew. He had worked at several studios before Amitrano's, at Julian's, the Beaux Arts, and MacPherson's, and was remaining longer at Amitrano's than anywhere because he found himself more left alone. He was not fond of showing his work, and unlike most of the young men who were studying art neither sought nor gave advice. It was said that in the little studio in the Rue Campagne Première, which served him for work-room and bed-room, he had wonderful pictures which would make his reputation if only he could be induced to exhibit them. He could not afford a model but painted still life, and Lawson constantly talked of a plate of apples which he declared was a masterpiece. He was fastidious, and, aiming at something he did not quite fully grasp, was constantly dissatisfied with his work as a whole: perhaps a part would please him, the forearm or the leg and foot of a figure, a glass or a cup in a still-life; and he would cut this out and keep it, destroying the rest of the canvas; so that when people invited themselves to see his work he could truthfully answer that he had not a single picture to show. In Brittany he had come across a painter whom nobody else had heard of, a queer fellow who had been a stock-broker and taken up painting at middle-age, and he was greatly influenced by his work. He was turning his back on the Impressionists and working out for himself painfully an individual way not only of painting but of seeing. Philip felt in him something strangely original.

At Gravier's where they ate, and in the evening at the Versailles or at the Closerie des Lilas Clutton was inclined to taciturnity. He sat quietly, with a sardonic expression on his gaunt face, and spoke only when the opportunity occurred to throw in a witticism. He liked a butt and was most cheerful when someone was there on whom he could exercise his sarcasm. He seldom talked of anything but painting, and then only with the one or two persons whom he thought worth while. Philip wondered whether there was in him really anything: his reticence, the haggard look of him, the pungent humour, seemed to suggest personality, but might be no more than an effective mask which covered nothing.

With Lawson on the other hand Philip soon grew intimate. He had a variety of interests which made him an agreeable companion. He read more than most of the students and though his income was small, loved to buy books. He lent them willingly; and Philip became acquainted with Flaubert and Balzac, with Verlaine, Heredia, and Villiers de l'Isle Adam. They went to plays together and sometimes to the gallery of the Opéra Comique. There was the Odéon quite near them, and Philip soon shared his friend's passion for the tragedians of Louis XIV and the sonorous Alexandrine. In the Rue Taitbout were the Concerts Rouge, where for seventy-five centimes they could hear excellent music and get into the bargain something which it was quite possible to drink: the seats were uncomfortable, the place was crowded, the air thick with caporal horrible to breathe, but in their young enthusiasm they were indifferent. Sometimes they went to the Bal Bullier. On these occasions Flanagan accompanied them. His excitability and his roisterous enthusiasm made them laugh. He was an excellent dancer, and before they had been ten minutes in the room he was prancing round with some little shop-girl whose acquaintance he had just made.

The desire of all of them was to have a mistress. It was part of the paraphernalia of the art-student in Paris. It gave consideration in the eyes of one's fellows. It was something to boast about. But the difficulty was that they had scarcely enough money to keep themselves, and though they argued that Frenchwomen were so clever it cost no more to keep two than one, they found it difficult to meet young women who were willing to take that view of the circumstances. They had to content themselves for the most part with envying and abusing the ladies who received protection from painters of more settled respectability than their own. It was extraordinary how difficult these things were in Paris. Lawson would become acquainted with some young thing and make an appointment; for twenty-four hours he would be all in a flutter and describe the charmer at length to everyone he met; but she never by any chance turned up at the time fixed. He would come to Gravier's very late, ill-tempered, and exclaim:

"Confound it, another rabbit! I don't know why it is they don't like me. I suppose it's because I don't speak French well, or my red hair. It's too sickening to have spent over a year in Paris without getting hold of anyone."

"You don't go the right way to work," said Flanagan.

He had a long and enviable list of triumphs to narrate, and though they took leave not to believe all he said, evidence forced them to acknowledge that he did not altogether lie.

But he sought no permanent arrangement. He only had two years in Paris: he had persuaded his people to let him come and study art instead of going to college; but at the end of that period he was to return to Seattle and go into his father's business. He had made up his mind to get as much fun as possible into the time, and demanded variety rather than duration in his love affairs.

"I don't know how you get hold of them," said Lawson furiously.

"There's no difficulty about that, sonny," answered Flanagan. "You just go right in. The difficulty is to get rid of them. That's where you want tact."

Philip was too much occupied with his work, the books he was reading, the plays he saw, the conversation he listened to, to trouble himself with the desire for female society. He thought there would be plenty of time for that when he could speak French more glibly.

It was more than a year now since he had seen Miss Wilkinson, and during his first weeks in Paris he had been too busy to answer a letter she had written to him just before he left Blackstable. When another came, knowing it would be full of reproaches and not being just then in the mood for them, he put it aside, intending to open it later; but he forgot and did not run across it till a month afterwards, when he was turning out a drawer to find some socks that had no holes in them. He looked at the unopened letter with dismay. He was afraid that Miss Wilkinson had suffered a good deal, and it made him feel a brute; but she had probably got over the suffering by now, at all events the worst of it. It suggested itself to him that women were often very emphatic in their expressions. These did not mean so much as when men used them. He had quite made up his mind that nothing would induce him ever to see her again. He had not written for so long that it seemed hardly worth while to write now. He made up his mind not to read the letter.

"I daresay she won't write again," he said to himself. "She can't help seeing the thing's over. After all, she was old enough to be my mother; she ought to have known better."

For an hour or two he felt a little uncomfortable. His attitude was obviously the right one, but he could not help a feeling of dissatisfaction with the whole business. Miss Wilkinson, however, did not write again; nor did she, as he absurdly feared, suddenly appear in Paris to make him ridiculous before his friends. In a little while he clean forgot her.

Meanwhile he definitely forsook his old gods. The amazement with which at first he had looked upon the works of the Impressionists, changed to admiration; and presently he found himself talking as emphatically as the rest on the merits of Manet, Monet, and Degas. He bought a photograph of a drawing by Ingres of the *Odalisque* and a photograph of the *Olympia*.

They were pinned side by side over his washing-stand so that he could contemplate their beauty while he shaved. He knew now quite positively that there had been no painting of landscape before Monet; and he felt a real thrill when he stood in front of Rembrandt's *Disciples at Emmaus* or Velasquez' *Lady with the Fleabitten Nose*. That was not her real name, but by that she was distinguished at Gravier's to emphasise the picture's beauty notwithstanding the somewhat revolting peculiarity of the sitter's appearance. With Ruskin, Burne-Jones, and Watts, he had put aside his bowler hat and the neat blue tie with white spots which he had worn on coming to Paris; and now disported himself in a soft, broad-brimmed hat, a flowing black cravat, and a cape of romantic cut. He walked along the Boulevard du Montparnasse as though he had known it all his life, and by virtuous perseverance he had learnt to drink absinthe without distaste. He was letting his hair grow, and it was only because Nature is unkind and has no regard for the immortal longings of youth that he did not attempt a beard.

XLV

PHILIP soon realised that the spirit which informed his friends was Cronshaw's. It was from him that Lawson got his paradoxes; and even Clutton, who strained after individuality, expressed himself in the terms he had insensibly acquired from the older man. It was his ideas that they bandied about at table, and on his authority they formed their judgments. They made up for the respect with which unconsciously they treated him by

laughing at his foibles and lamenting his vices.

"Of course, poor old Cronshaw will never do any good," they said. "He's quite hopeless."

They prided themselves on being alone in appreciating his genius; and though, with the contempt of youth for the follies of middle-age, they patronised him among themselves, they did not fail to look upon it as a feather in their caps if he had chosen a time when only one was there to be particularly wonderful. Cronshaw never came to Gravier's. For the last four years he had lived in squalid conditions with a woman whom only Lawson had once seen, in a tiny apartment on the sixth floor of one of the most dilapidated houses on the Quai des Grands Augustins: Lawson described with gusto the filth, the untidiness, the litter.

"And the stink nearly blew your head off."

"Not at dinner, Lawson," expostulated one of the others.

But he would not deny himself the pleasure of giving picturesque details of the odours which met his nostril. With a fierce delight in his own realism he described the woman who had opened the door for him. She was dark, small, and fat, quite young, with black hair that seemed always on the point of coming down. She wore a slatternly blouse and no corsets. With her red cheeks, large sensual mouth, and shining, lewd eyes, she reminded you of the *Bohémienne* in the Louvre by Franz Hals. She had a flaunting vulgarity which amused and yet horrified. A scrubby, unwashed baby was playing on the floor. It was known that the slut deceived Cronshaw with the most worthless ragamuffins of the Quarter, and it was a mystery to the ingenuous youths who absorbed his wisdom over a café table that Cronshaw with his keen intellect and his passion for beauty could ally himself to such a creature. But he seemed to revel in the coarseness of her language and would often report some phrase which reeked of the gutter. He referred to her ironically as *la fille de mon concierge*. Cronshaw was very poor. He earned a bare subsistence by writing on the exhibitions of pictures for one or two English papers, and he did a certain amount of translating.

He had been on the staff of an English paper in Paris; but had been dismissed for drunkenness; he still however did odd jobs for it, describing sales at the Hôtel Drouot or the revues at music-halls. The life of Paris had got into his bones, and he would not change it, notwithstanding its squalor, drudgery, and hardship, for any other in the world. He remained there all through the year, even in summer when everyone he knew was away, and felt himself only at ease within a mile of the Boulevard St. Michel. But the curious thing was that he had never learnt to speak French passably, and he kept in his shabby clothes bought at *La Belle Jardinière* an ineradicably English appearance.

He was a man who would have made a success of life a century and a half ago when conversation was a passport to good company and inebriety no bar.

"I ought to have lived in the eighteen hundreds," he said himself. "What I want is a patron. I should have published my poems by subscription and dedicated them to a nobleman. I long to compose rhymed couplets upon the poodle of a countess. My soul yearns for the love of chambermaids and the conversation of bishops."

He quoted the romantic Rolla,

"Je suis venu trop tard dans un monde trop vieux."

He liked new faces, and he took a fancy to Philip, who seemed to achieve the difficult feat of talking just enough to suggest conversation and not too much to prevent monologue. Philip was captivated. He did not realise that little that Cronshaw said was new. His personality in conversation had a curious power. He had a beautiful and a sonorous voice, and a manner of putting things which was irresistible to youth. All he said seemed to excite thought, and often on the way home Lawson and Philip would walk to and from one another's hotels, discussing some point which a chance word of Cronshaw had suggested. It was disconcerting to Philip, who had a youthful eagerness for results, that Cronshaw's poetry hardly came up to expectation. It had never been published in a volume, but most of it had appeared in periodicals; and after a good deal of persuasion Cronshaw brought down a bundle of pages torn out of *The Yellow Book, The Saturday Review,* and other journals, on each of which was a poem. Philip was taken aback to find that most of them reminded him either of Henley or of Swinburne. It needed the splendour of Cronshaw's delivery to make them personal. He expressed his disappointment to Lawson, who carelessly repeated his words; and next time Philip went to the Closerie des Lilas the poet turned to him with his sleek smile:

"I hear you don't think much of my verses."

Philip was embarrassed.

"I don't know about that," he answered. "I enjoyed reading them very much."

"Do not attempt to spare my feelings," returned Cronshaw, with a wave of his fat hand. "I do not attach any exaggerated importance to my poetical works. Life is there to be lived rather than to be written about. My aim is to search out the manifold experience that it offers, wringing from each moment what of emotion it presents. I look upon my writing as a graceful accomplishment which does not absorb but rather adds pleasure to existence. And as for posterity—damn posterity."

Philip smiled, for it leaped to one's eyes that the artist in life had produced no more than a wretched daub. Cronshaw looked at him meditatively

and filled his glass. He sent the waiter for a packet of cigarettes.

"You are amused because I talk in this fashion and you know that I am poor and live in an attic with a vulgar trollop who deceives me with hairdressers and *garçons de café;* I translate wretched books for the British public, and write articles upon contemptible pictures which deserve not even to be abused. But pray tell me what is the meaning of life?"

"I say, that's rather a difficult question. Won't you give the answer yourself?"

"No, because it's worthless unless you yourself discover it. But what do you suppose you are in the world for?"

Philip had never asked himself, and he thought for a moment before replying.

"Oh, I don't know: I suppose to do one's duty, and make the best possible use of one's faculties, and avoid hurting other people."

"In short, to do unto others as you would they should do unto you?"

"I suppose so."

"Christianity."

"No, it isn't," said Philip indignantly. "It has nothing to do with Christianity. It's just abstract morality."

"But there's no such thing as abstract morality."

"In that case, supposing under the influence of liquor you left your purse behind when you leave here and I picked it up, why do you imagine that I should return it to you? It's not the fear of the police."

"It's the dread of hell if you sin and the hope of Heaven if you are virtuous."

"But I believe in neither."

"That may be. Neither did Kant when he devised the Categorical Imperative. You have thrown aside a creed, but you have preserved the ethic which was based upon it. To all intents you are a Christian still, and if there is a God in Heaven you will undoubtedly receive your reward. The Almighty can hardly be such a fool as the churches make out. If you keep His laws I don't think He can care a packet of pins whether you believe in Him or not."

"But if I left my purse behind you would certainly return it to me," said Philip.

"Not from motives of abstract morality, but only from fear of the police."

"It's a thousand to one that the police would never find out."

"My ancestors have lived in a civilised state so long that the fear of the police has eaten into my bones. The daughter of my *concierge* would not hesitate for a moment. You answer that she belongs to the criminal classes; not at all, she is merely devoid of vulgar prejudice."

"But then that does away with honour and virtue and goodness and decency and everything," said Philip.

"Have you ever committed a sin?"

"I don't know, I suppose so," answered Philip.

"You speak with the lips of a dissenting minister. I have never committed a sin."

Cronshaw in his shabby great-coat, with the collar turned up, and his hat well down on his head, with his red fat face and his little gleaming eyes, looked extraordinarily comic; but Philip was too much in earnest to laugh.

"Have you never done anything you regret?"

"How can I regret when what I did was inevitable?" asked Cronshaw in return.

"But that's fatalism."

"The illusion which man has that his will is free is so deeply rooted that I am ready to accept it. I act as though I were a free agent. But when an action is performed it is clear that all the forces of the universe from all eternity conspired to cause it, and nothing I could do could have prevented it. It was inevitable. If it was good I can claim no merit; if it was bad I can accept no censure."

"My brain reels," said Philip.

"Have some whiskey," returned Cronshaw, passing over the bottle. "There's nothing like it for clearing the head. You must expect to be thick-witted if you insist upon drinking beer."

Philip shook his head, and Cronshaw proceeded:

"You're not a bad fellow, but you won't drink. Sobriety disturbs conversation. But when I speak of good and bad . . ." Philip saw he was taking up the thread of his discourse, "I speak conventionally. I attach no meaning to those words. I refuse to make a hierarchy of human actions and ascribe worthiness to some and ill-repute to others. The terms vice and virtue have no signification for me. I do not confer praise or blame: I accept. I am the measure of all things. I am the centre of the world."

"But there are one or two other people in the world," objected Philip.

"I speak only for myself. I know them only as they limit my activities. Round each of them too the world turns, and each one for himself is the centre of the universe. My right over them extends only as far as my power. What I can do is the only limit of what I may do. Because we are gregarious we live in society, and society holds together by means of force, force of arms (that is the policeman) and force of public opinion (that is Mrs. Grundy). You have society on one hand and the individual on the other: each is an organism striving for self-perservation. It is might against might. I stand alone, bound to accept society and not unwilling, since in return for the taxes I pay it protects me, a weakling, against the tyranny of another stronger than I am; but I submit to its laws because I must; I do not acknowledge their justice: I do not know justice, I only know power. And when I have paid for the policeman who protects me and, if I live in a country where conscription is in force, served in the army which guards my house and land from the invader, I am quits with society: for the rest I counter its might with my wiliness. It makes laws for its self-preservation, and if I break them it imprisons or kills me: it has the might to do so and therefore the right. If I break the laws I will accept the vengeance of the state, but I will not regard it as punishment nor shall I feel myself convicted of wrong-doing. Society tempts me to its service by honours and riches and the good opinion of my fellows; but I am indifferent to their good opinion, I despise honours and I can do very well without riches."

"But if everyone thought like you things would go to pieces at once."

"I have nothing to do with others, I am only concerned with myself. I take advantage of the fact that the majority of mankind are led by certain rewards to do things which directly or indirectly tend to my convenience."

"It seems to me an awfully selfish way of looking at things," said Philip.

"But are you under the impression that men ever do anything except for selfish reasons?"

"Yes."

"It is impossible that they should. You will find as you grow older that the first thing needful to make the world a tolerable place to live in is to recognise the inevitable selfishness of humanity. You demand unselfishness from others, which is a prepos-terous claim that they should sacrifice their desires to yours. Why should they? When you are reconciled to the fact that each is for himself in the world you will ask less from your fellows. They will not disappoint you, and you will look upon them more charitably. Men seek but one thing in life—their pleasure."

"No, no, no!" cried Philip.

Cronshaw chuckled.

"You rear like a frightened colt, because I use a word to which your Christianity ascribes a deprecatory meaning. You have a hierarchy of values; pleasure is at the bottom of the ladder, and you speak with a little thrill of self-satisfaction, of duty, charity, and truthfulness. You think pleasure is only of the senses; the wretched slaves who manufactured your morality despised a satisfaction which they had small means of enjoying. You would not be so frightened if I had spoken of happiness instead of pleasure: it sounds less shocking, and your mind wanders from the sty of Epicurus to his garden. But I will speak of pleasure, for I see that men aim at that, and I do not know that they aim at happiness. It is pleasure that lurks in the practice of every one of your virtues. Man performs actions because they are good for him, and when they are good for other people as well they are thought virtuous: if he finds pleasure in giving alms he is charitable; if he finds pleasure in helping others he is benevolent; if he finds pleasure in working for society he is public-spirited; but it is for your private pleasure that you give two-pence to a beggar as much as it is for my private pleasure that I drink another whiskey and soda. I, less of a humbug than you, neither applaud myself for my pleasure nor demand your admiration."

"But have you never known people

do things they didn't want to instead of things they did?"

"No. You put your question foolishly. What you mean is that people accept an immediate pain rather than an immediate pleasure. The objection is as foolish as your manner of putting it. It is clear that men accept an immediate pain rather than an immediate pleasure, but only because they expect a greater pleasure in the future. Often the pleasure is illusory, but their error in calculation is no refutation of the rule. You are puzzled because you cannot get over the idea that pleasures are only of the senses; but, child, a man who dies for his country dies because he likes it as surely as a man eats pickled cabbage because he likes it. It is a law of creation. If it were possible for men to prefer pain to pleasure the human race would have long since become extinct."

"But if all that is true," cried Philip, "what is the use of anything? If you take away duty and goodness and beauty why are we brought into the world?"

"Here comes the gorgeous East to suggest an answer," smiled Cronshaw.

He pointed to two persons who at that moment opened the door of the café, and, with a blast of cold air, entered. They were Levantines, itinerant vendors of cheap rugs, and each bore on his arm a bundle. It was Sunday evening, and the café was very full. They passed among the tables, and in that atmosphere heavy and discoloured with tobacco smoke, rank with humanity, they seemed to bring an air of mystery. They were clad in European, shabby clothes, their thin great-coats were threadbare, but each wore a tarbouch. Their faces were gray with cold. One was of middle age, with a black beard, but the other was a youth of eighteen, with a face deeply scarred by smallpox and with one eye only. They passed by Cronshaw and Philip.

"Allah is great, and Mahomet is his prophet," said Cronshaw impressively.

The elder advanced with a cringing smile, like a mongrel used to blows. With a sidelong glance at the door and a quick surreptitious movement he showed a pornographic picture.

"Are you Masr-ed-Deen, the merchant of Alexandria, or is it from far Bagdad that you bring your goods, O, my uncle; and yonder one-eyed youth, do I see in him one of the three kings of whom Scheherazade told stories to her lord?"

The pedlar's smile grew more ingratiating, though he understood no word of what Cronshaw said, and like a conjurer he produced a sandal-wood box.

"Nay, show us the priceless web of Eastern looms," quoth Cronshaw. "For I would point a moral and adorn a tale."

The Levantine unfolded a tablecloth, red and yellow, vulgar, hideous, and grotesque.

"Thirty-five francs," he said.

"O, my uncle, this cloth knew not the weavers of Samarkand, and those colours were never made in the vats of Bokhara."

"Twenty-five francs," smiled the pedlar obsequiously.

"Ultima Thule was the place of its manufacture, even Birmingham the place of my birth."

"Fifteen francs," cringed the bearded man.

"Get thee gone, fellow," said Cronshaw. "May wild asses defile the grave of thy maternal grandmother."

Imperturbably, but smiling no more, the Levantine passed with his wares to another table. Cronshaw turned to Philip.

"Have you ever been to the Cluny, the museum? There you will see Persian carpets of the most exquisite hue and of a pattern the beautiful intricacy of which delights and amazes the eye. In them you will see the mystery and the sensual beauty of the East, the roses of Hafiz and the wine-cup of Omar; but presently you will see more. You were asking just now what was the meaning of life. Go and look at those Persian carpets, and one of these days the answer will come to you."

"You are cryptic," said Philip.

"I am drunk," answered Cronshaw.

XLVI

P H I L I P did not find living in Paris as cheap as he had been led to believe and by February had spent most of the money with which he started. He was too proud to appeal to his guardian, nor did he wish Aunt Louisa to know that his circumstances were straitened, since he was certain she would make an effort to send him something from her own pocket, and he knew how little she could afford to. In three months he would attain his majority and come into possession of his small fortune. He tided over the interval by selling the few trinkets which he had inherited from his father.

At about this time Lawson suggested that they should take a small studio which was vacant in one of the streets that led out of the Boulevard Raspail. It was very cheap. It had a room attached, which they could use as a bed-room; and since Philip was at the school every morning Lawson could have the undisturbed use of the studio then; Lawson, after wandering from school to school, had come to the conclusion that he could work best alone, and proposed to get a model in three or four days a week. At first Philip hesitated on account of the expense, but they reckoned it out; and it seemed (they were so anxious to have a studio of their own that they calculated pragmatically) that the cost would not be much greater than that of living in a hotel. Though the rent and the cleaning by the *concierge* would come to a little more, they would save on the *petit déjeuner*, which they could make themselves. A year or two earlier Philip would have refused to share a room with anyone, since he was so sensitive about his deformed foot, but his morbid way of looking at it was growing less marked: in Paris it did not seem to matter so much, and, though he never by any chance forgot it himself, he ceased to feel that other people were constantly noticing it.

They moved in, bought a couple of beds, a washing-stand, a few chairs, and felt for the first time the thrill of possession. They were so excited that the first night they went to bed in what they could call a home they lay awake talking till three in the morning; and next day found lighting the fire and making their own coffee, which they had in pyjamas, such a jolly business that Philip did not get to Amitrano's till nearly eleven. He was in excellent spirits. He nodded to Fanny Price.

"How are you getting on?" he asked cheerily.

"What does that matter to you?" she asked in reply.

Philip could not help laughing. "Don't jump down my throat. I was only trying to make myself polite."

"I don't want your politeness."

"D'you think it's worth while quarrelling with me too?" asked Philip mildly. "There are so few people you're on speaking terms with, as it is."

"That's my business, isn't it?"

"Quite."

He began to work, vaguely wondering why Fanny Price made herself so disagreeable. He had come to the conclusion that he thoroughly disliked her. Everyone did. People were only civil to her at all from fear of the malice of her tongue; for to their faces and behind their backs she said abominable things. But Philip was feeling so happy that he did not want even Miss Price to bear ill-feeling towards him. He used the artifice which had often before succeeded in banishing her ill-humour.

"I say, I wish you'd come and look at my drawing. I've got in an awful mess."

"Thank you very much, but I've got something better to do with my time."

Philip stared at her in surprise, for the one thing she could be counted upon to do with alacrity was to give advice. She went on quickly in a low voice, savage with fury.

"Now that Lawson's gone you think you'll put up with me. Thank you very much. Go and find somebody else to help you. I don't want anybody else's leavings."

Lawson had the pedagogic instinct; whenever he found anything out he was eager to impart it; and because he taught with delight he talked with profit. Philip, without thinking anything about it, had got into the habit of sitting by his side; it never occurred to him that Fanny Price was consumed with jealousy, and watched his acceptance of someone else's tuition with ever-increasing anger.

"You were very glad to put up with me when you knew nobody here," she said bitterly, "and as soon as you made friends with other people you threw me aside, like an old glove"—she repeated the stale metaphor with satisfaction—"like an old glove. All right, I don't care, but I'm not going to be made a fool of another time."

There was a suspicion of truth in what she said, and it made Philip angry enough to answer what first came into his head.

"Hang it all, I only asked your advice because I saw it pleased you."

She gave a gasp and threw him a sudden look of anguish. Then two tears rolled down her cheeks. She looked frowsy and grotesque. Philip, not knowing what on earth this new attitude implied, went back to his work. He was uneasy and conscience-stricken; but he would not go to her and say he was sorry if he had caused her pain, because he was afraid she would take the opportunity to snub him. For two or three weeks she did not speak to him, and, after Philip had got over the discomfort of being cut by her, he was somewhat relieved to be free from so difficult a friendship. He had been a little disconcerted by the air of proprietorship she assumed over him. She was an extraordinary woman. She came every day to the studio at eight o'clock, and was ready to start working when the model was in position; she worked steadily, talking to no one, struggling hour after hour with difficulties she could not overcome, and remained till the clock struck twelve. Her work was hopeless. There was not in it the smallest approach even to the mediocre achievement at which most of the young persons were able after some months to arrive. She wore every day the same ugly brown dress, with the mud of the last wet day still caked on the hem and with the raggedness, which Philip had noticed the first time he saw her, still unmended.

But one day she came up to him, and with a scarlet face asked whether she might speak to him afterwards.

"Of course, as much as you like," smiled Philip. "I'll wait behind at twelve."

He went to her when the day's work was over.

"Will you walk a little bit with me?" she said, looking away from him with embarrassment.

"Certainly."

They walked for two or three minutes in silence.

"D'you remember what you said to me the other day?" she asked then on a sudden.

"Oh, I say, don't let's quarrel," said Philip. "It really isn't worth while."

She gave a quick, painful inspiration.

"I don't want to quarrel with you. You're the only friend I had in Paris. I thought you rather liked me. I felt there was something between us. I was drawn towards you—you know what I mean, your club-foot."

Philip reddened and instinctively tried to walk without a limp. He did not like anyone to mention the deformity. He knew what Fanny Price meant. She was ugly and uncouth, and because he was deformed there was between them a certain sympathy.

He was very angry with her, but he forced himself not to speak.

"You said you only asked my advice to please me. Don't you think my work's any good?"

"I've only seen your drawing at Amitrano's. It's awfully hard to judge from that."

"I was wondering if you'd come and look at my other work. I've never asked anyone else to look at it. I should like to show it to you."

"It's awfully kind of you. I'd like to see it very much."

"I live quite near here," she said apologetically. "It'll only take you ten minutes."

"Oh, that's all right," he said.

They were walking along the boulevard, and she turned down a side street, then led him into another, poorer still, with cheap shops on the ground floor, and at last stopped. They climbed flight after flight of stairs. She unlocked a door, and they went into a tiny attic with a sloping roof and a small window. This was closed and the room had a musty smell. Though it was very cold there was no fire and no sign that there had been one. The bed was unmade. A chair, a chest of drawers which served also as a wash-stand, and a cheap easel, were all the furniture. The place would have been squalid enough in any case, but the litter, the untidiness, made the impression revolting. On the chimneypiece, scattered over with paints and brushes, were a cup, a dirty plate, and a tea-pot.

"If you'll stand over there I'll put them on the chair so that you can see them better."

She showed him twenty small canvases, about eighteen by twelve. She placed them on the chair, one after the other, watching his face; he nodded as he looked at each one.

"You do like them, don't you?" she said anxiously, after a bit.

"I just want to look at them all first," he answered. "I'll talk afterwards."

He was collecting himself. He was panic-stricken. He did not know what to say. It was not only that they were ill-drawn, or that the colour was put on amateurishly by someone who had no eye for it; but there was no attempt at getting the values, and the perspective was grotesque. It looked like the work of a child of five, but a child would have had some naïveté and might at least have made an attempt to put down what he saw; but here was the work of a vulgar mind chock full of recollections of vulgar pictures. Philip remembered that she had talked enthusiastically about Monet and the Impressionists, but here were only the worst traditions of the Royal Academy.

"There," she said at last, "that's the lot."

Philip was no more truthful than anybody else, but he had a great difficulty in telling a thundering, deliberate lie, and he blushed furiously when he answered:

"I think they're most awfully good."

A faint colour came into her unhealthy cheeks, and she smiled a little.

"You needn't say so if you don't think so, you know. I want the truth."

"But I do think so."

"Haven't you got any criticism to offer? There must be some you don't like as well as others."

Philip looked round helplessly. He saw a landscape, the typical picturesque 'bit' of the amateur, an old bridge, a creeper-clad cottage, and a leafy bank.

"Of course I don't pretend to know anything about it," he said. "But I wasn't quite sure about the values of that."

She flushed darkly and taking up the picture quickly turned its back to him.

"I don't know why you should have chosen that one to sneer at. It's the best thing I've ever done. I'm sure my values are all right. That's a thing you can't teach anyone, you either understand values or you don't."

"I think they're all most awfully good," repeated Philip.

She looked at them with an air of self-satisfaction.

"I don't think they're anything to be ashamed of."

Philip looked at his watch.

"I say, it's getting late. Won't you let me give you a little lunch?"

"I've got my lunch waiting for me here."

Philip saw no sign of it, but supposed perhaps the *concierge* would bring it up when he was gone. He was in a hurry to get away. The mustiness of the room made his head ache.

XLVII

IN MARCH there was all the excitement of sending in to the Salon. Clutton, characteristically, had nothing ready, and he was very scornful of the two heads that Lawson sent; they were obviously the work of a student, straight-forward portraits of models, but they had a certain force; Clutton, aiming at perfection, had no patience with efforts which betrayed hesitancy, and with a shrug of the shoulders told Lawson it was an impertinence to exhibit stuff which should never have been allowed out of his studio; he was not less contemptuous when the two heads were accepted. Flanagan tried his luck too, but his picture was refused. Mrs. Otter sent a blameless *Portrait de ma Mère,* accomplished and second-rate; and was hung in a very good place.

Hayward, whom Philip had not seen since he left Heidelberg, arrived in Paris to spend a few days in time to come to the party which Lawson and Philip were giving in their studio to celebrate the hanging of Lawson's pictures. Philip had been eager to see Hayward again, but when at last they met, he experienced some disappointment. Hayward had altered a little in appearance: his fine hair was thinner, and with the rapid wilting of the very fair, he was becoming wizened and colourless; his blue eyes were paler than they had been, and there was a muzziness about his features. On the other hand, in mind he did not seem to have changed at all, and the culture which had impressed Philip at eighteen aroused somewhat the contempt of Philip at twenty-one. He had altered a good deal himself, and regarding with scorn all his old opinions of art, life, and letters, had no patience with anyone who still held them. He was scarcely conscious of the fact that he wanted to show off before Hayward, but when he took him round the galleries he poured out to him all the revolutionary opinions which himself had so recently adopted. He took him to Manet's *Olympia* and said dramatically:

"I would give all the old masters except Velasquez, Rembrandt, and Vermeer for that one picture."

"Who was Vermeer?" asked Hayward.

"Oh, my dear fellow, don't you know Vermeer? You're not civilised. You mustn't live a moment longer without making his acquaintance. He's the one old master who painted like a modern."

He dragged Hayward out of the Luxembourg and hurried him off to the Louvre.

"But aren't there any more pictures here?" asked Hayward, with the tourist's passion for thoroughness.

"Nothing of the least consequence. You can come and look at them by yourself with your Baedeker."

When they arrived at the Louvre Philip led his friend down the Long Gallery.

"I should like to see *The Gioconda,*" said Hayward.

"Oh, my dear fellow, it's only literature," answered Philip.

At last, in a small room, Philip stopped before *The Lacemaker* of Vermeer van Delft.

"There, that's the best picture in the Louvre. It's exactly like a Manet."

With an expressive, eloquent thumb Philip expatiated on the charming work. He used the jargon of the studios with overpowering effect.

"I don't know that I see anything so wonderful as all that in it," said Hayward.

"Of course it's a painter's picture," said Philip. "I can quite believe the layman would see nothing much in it."

"The what?" said Hayward.

"The layman."

Like most people who cultivate an interest in the arts, Hayward was extremely anxious to be right. He was dogmatic with those who did not venture to assert themselves, but with the self-assertive he was very modest. He was impressed by Philip's assurance, and accepted meekly Philip's implied suggestion that the painter's arrogant claim to be the sole possible judge of painting has anything but its impertinence to recommend it.

A day or two later Philip and Lawson gave their party. Cronshaw, making an exception in their favour, agreed to eat their food; and Miss Chalice offered to come and cook for them. She took no interest in her own sex and declined the suggestion that other girls should be asked for her sake. Clutton, Flanagan, Potter, and two others made up the party. Furniture was scarce, so the model stand was used as a table, and the guests were to sit on portmanteaux if they liked, and if they didn't on the floor. The feast consisted of a *pot-au-feu*, which Miss Chalice had made, of a leg of mutton roasted round the corner and brought round hot and savoury (Miss Chalice had cooked the potatoes, and the studio was redolent of the carrots she had fried; fried carrots were her specialty); and this was to be followed by *poires flambées*, pears with burning brandy, which Cronshaw had volunteered to make. The meal was to finish with an enormous *fromage de Brie*, which stood near the window and added fragrant odours to all the others which filled the studio. Cronshaw sat in the place of honour on a Gladstone bag, with his legs curled under him like a Turkish bashaw, beaming good-naturedly on the young people who surrounded him. From force of habit, though the small studio with the stove lit was very hot, he kept on his great-coat, with the collar turned up, and his bowler hat: he looked with satisfaction on the four large *fiaschi* of Chianti which stood in front of him in a row, two on each side of a bottle of whiskey; he said it reminded him of a slim fair Circassian guarded by four corpulent eunuchs. Hayward in order to put the rest of them at their ease had clothed himself in a tweed suit and a Trinity Hall tie. He looked grotesquely British. The others were elaborately polite to him, and during the soup they talked of the weather and the political situation. There was a pause while they waited for the leg of mutton, and Miss Chalice lit a cigarette.

"Rampunzel, Rampunzel, let down your hair," she said suddenly.

With an elegant gesture she untied a ribbon so that her tresses fell over her shoulders. She shook her head. "I always feel more comfortable with my hair down."

With her large brown eyes, thin, ascetic face, her pale skin, and broad forehead, she might have stepped out of a picture by Burne-Jones. She had long, beautiful hands, with fingers deeply stained by nicotine. She wore sweeping draperies, mauve and green. There was about her the romantic air of High Street, Kensington. She was wantonly æsthetic; but she was an excellent creature, kind and good natured; and her affectations were but skin-deep. There was a knock at the door, and they all gave a shout of exultation. Miss Chalice rose and opened. She took the leg of mutton and held it high above her, as though it were the head of John the Baptist on a platter; and, the cigarette still in her mouth, advanced with solemn, hieratic steps.

"Hail, daughter of Herodias," cried Cronshaw.

The mutton was eaten with gusto, and it did one good to see what a hearty appetite the pale-faced lady had. Clutton and Potter sat on each side of her, and everyone knew that neither had found her unduly coy. She grew tired of most people in six weeks, but she knew exactly how to treat afterwards the gentlemen who had laid their young hearts at her feet. She bore them no ill-will, though having loved them she had ceased to do so, and treated them with friendliness but without familiarity. Now and then she looked at Lawson with melancholy eyes. The *poires flambées* were a great success, partly because of the brandy, and partly because Miss Chalice insisted that they should be eaten with the cheese.

"I don't know whether it's perfectly delicious, or whether I'm just going to vomit," she said, after she had thoroughly tried the mixture.

Coffee and cognac followed with sufficient speed to prevent any untoward consequence, and they settled down to smoke in comfort. Ruth Chalice, who could do nothing that was not deliberately artistic, arranged herself in a graceful attitude by Cronshaw and just rested her exquisite head on his shoulder. She looked into the dark abyss of time with brooding eyes, and now and then with a long meditative glance at Lawson she sighed deeply.

Then came the summer, and restlessness seized these young people. The blue skies lured them to the sea, and the pleasant breeze sighing through the leaves of the plane-trees on the boulevard drew them towards the country. Everyone made plans for leaving Paris; they discussed what was the most suitable size for the canvases they meant to take; they laid in stores of panels for sketching; they argued about the merits of various places in Brittany. Flanagan and Potter went to Concarneau; Mrs. Otter and her mother, with a natural instinct for the obvious, went to Pont-Aven; Philip and Lawson made up their minds to go to the forest of Fontainebleau, and Miss Chalice knew of a very good hotel at Moret where there was lots of stuff to paint; it was near Paris, and neither Philip nor

Lawson was indifferent to the railway fare. Ruth Chalice would be there, and Lawson had an idea for a portrait of her in the open air. Just then the Salon was full of portraits of people in gardens, in sunlight, with blinking eyes and green reflections of sunlit leaves on their faces. They asked Clutton to go with them, but he preferred spending the summer by himself. He had just discovered Cézanne, and was eager to go to Provence; he wanted heavy skies from which the hot blue seemed to drip like beads of sweat, and broad white dusty roads, and pale roofs out of which the sun had burnt the colour, and olive trees gray with heat.

The day before they were to start, after the morning class, Philip, putting his things together, spoke to Fanny Price.

"I'm off tomorrow," he said cheerfully.

"Off where?" she said quickly. "You're not going away?" Her face fell.

"I'm going away for the summer. Aren't you?"

"No, I'm staying in Paris. I thought you were going to stay too. I was looking forward. . . ."

She stopped and shrugged her shoulders.

"But won't it be frightfully hot here? It's awfully bad for you."

"Much you care if it's bad for me. Where are you going?"

"Moret."

"Chalice is going there. You're not going with her?"

"Lawson and I are going. And she's going there too. I don't know that we're actually going together."

She gave a low guttural sound, and her large face grew dark and red.

"How filthy! I thought you were a decent fellow. You were about the only one here. She's been with Clutton and Potter and Flanagan, even with old Foinet—that's why he takes so much trouble about her—and now two of you, you and Lawson. It makes me sick."

"Oh, what nonsense! She's a very decent sort. One treats her just as if she were a man."

"Oh, don't speak to me, don't speak to me."

"But what can it matter to you?" asked Philip. "It's really no business of yours where I spend my summer."

"I was looking forward to it so much," she gasped, speaking it seemed almost to herself. "I didn't think you had the money to go away, and there wouldn't have been anyone else here, and we could have worked together, and we'd have gone to see things." Then her thoughts flung back to Ruth Chalice. "The filthy beast," she cried. "She isn't fit to speak to."

Philip looked at her with a sinking heart. He was not a man to think girls were in love with him; he was too conscious of his deformity, and he felt awkward and clumsy with women; but he did not know what else this outburst could mean. Fanny Price, in the dirty brown dress, with her hair falling over her face, sloppy, untidy, stood before him; and tears of anger rolled down her cheeks. She was repellent. Philip glanced at the door, instinctively hoping that someone would come in and put an end to the scene.

"I'm awfully sorry," he said.

"You're just the same as all of them. You take all you can get, and you don't even say thank you. I've taught you everything you know. No one else would take any trouble with you. Has Foinet ever bothered about you? And I can tell you this—you can work here for a thousand years and you'll never do any good. You haven't got any talent. You haven't got any originality.

And it's not only me—they all say it. You'll never be a painter as long as you live."

"That is no business of yours either, is it?" said Philip, flushing.

"Oh, you think it's only my temper. Ask Clutton, ask Lawson, ask Chalice. Never, never, never. You haven't got it in you."

Philip shrugged his shoulders and walked out. She shouted after him. "Never, never, never."

Moret was in those days an old-fashioned town of one street at the edge of the forest of Fontainebleau, and the *Ecu d'Or* was a hotel which still had about it the decrepit air of the *Ancien Régime*. It faced the winding river, the Loing; and Miss Chalice had a room with a little terrace overlooking it, with a charming view of the old bridge and its fortified gateway. They sat here in the evenings after dinner, drinking coffee, smoking, and discussing art. There ran into the river, a little way off, a narrow canal bordered by poplars, and along the banks of this after their day's work they often wandered. They spent all day painting. Like most of their generation they were obsessed by the fear of the picturesque, and they turned their backs on the obvious beauty of the town to seek subjects which were devoid of a prettiness they despised. Sisley and Monet had painted the canal with its poplars, and they felt a desire to try their hands at what was so typical of France; but they were frightened of its formal beauty, and set themselves deliberately to avoid it. Miss Chalice, who had a clever dexterity which impressed Lawson notwithstanding his contempt for feminine art, started a picture in which she tried to circumvent the commonplace by leaving out the tops of the trees; and Lawson had the brilliant idea of putting in his foreground a large blue advertisement of *chocolat Menier* in order to emphasise his abhorrence of the chocolate box.

Philip began now to paint in oils. He experienced a thrill of delight when first he used that grateful medium. He went out with Lawson in the morning with his little box and sat by him painting a panel; it gave him so much satisfaction that he did not realise he was doing no more than copy; he was so much under his friend's influence that he saw only with his eyes. Lawson painted very low in tone, and they both saw the emerald of the grass like dark velvet, while the brilliance of the sky turned in their hands to a brooding ultramarine. Through July they had one fine day after another; it was very hot; and the heat, searing Philip's heart, filled him with languor; he could not work; his mind was eager with a thousand thoughts. Often he spent the mornings by the side of the canal in the shade of the poplars, reading a few lines and then dreaming for half an hour. Sometimes he hired a rickety bicycle and rode along the dusty road that led to the forest, and then lay down in a clearing. His head was full of romantic fancies. The ladies of Watteau, gay and insouciant, seemed to wander with their cavaliers among the great trees, whispering to one another careless, charming things, and yet somehow oppressed by a nameless fear.

They were alone in the hotel but for a fat Frenchwoman of middle age, a Rabelaisian figure with a broad, obscene laugh. She spent the day by the river patiently fishing for fish she never caught, and Philip sometimes went down and talked to her. He found out that she had belonged to a profession whose most notorious member for our generation was Mrs. War-ren, and having made a competence she now lived the quiet life of the *bourgeoise*. She told Philip lewd stories.

"You must go to Seville," she said—she spoke a little broken English. "The most beautiful women in the world."

She leered and nodded her head. Her triple chin, her large belly, shook with inward laughter.

It grew so hot that it was almost impossible to sleep at night. The heat seemed to linger under the trees as though it were a material thing. They did not wish to leave the starlit night, and the three of them would sit on the terrace of Ruth Chalice's room, silent, hour after hour, too tired to talk any more, but in voluptuous enjoyment of the stillness. They listened to the murmur of the river. The church clock struck one and two and sometimes three before they could drag themselves to bed. Suddenly Philip became aware that Ruth Chalice and Lawson were lovers. He divined it in the way the girl looked at the young painter, and in his air of possession; and as Philip sat with them he felt a kind of effluence surrounding them, as though the air were heavy with something strange. The revelation was a shock. He had looked upon Miss Chalice as a very good fellow and he liked to talk to her, but it had never seemed to him possible to enter into a closer relationship. One Sunday they had all gone with a tea-basket into the forest, and when they came to a glade which was suitably sylvan, Miss Chalice, because it was idyllic, insisted on taking off her shoes and stockings. It would have been very charming only her feet were rather large and she had on both a large corn on the third toe. Philip felt it made her proceeding a little ridiculous. But now he looked upon her quite differently; there was something softly feminine in her large eyes and her olive skin; he felt himself a fool not to have seen that she was attractive. He thought he detected in her a touch of contempt for him, because he had not had the sense to see that she was there, in his way, and in Lawson a suspicion of superiority. He was envious of Lawson, and he was jealous, not of the individual concerned, but of his love. He wished that he was standing in his shoes and feeling with his heart. He was troubled, and the fear seized him that love would pass him by. He wanted a passion to seize him, he wanted to be swept off his feet and borne powerless in a mighty rush he cared not whither. Miss Chalice and Lawson seemed to him now somehow different, and the constant companionship with them made him restless. He was dissatisfied with himself. Life was not giving him what he wanted, and he had an uneasy feeling that he was losing his time.

The stout Frenchwoman soon guessed what the relations were between the couple, and talked of the matter to Philip with the utmost frankness.

"And you," she said, with the tolerant smile of one who had fattened on the lust of her fellows, "have you got a *petite amie?*"

"No," said Philip, blushing.

"And why not? *C'est de votre âge.*"

He shrugged his shoulders. He had a volume of Verlaine in his hands, and he wandered off. He tried to read, but his passion was too strong. He thought of the stray amours to which he had been introduced by Flanagan, the sly visits to houses in a *cul-de-sac*, with the drawing-room in Utrecht velvet, and the mercenary graces of painted women. He shuddered. He threw himself on the grass, stretching his limbs like a young animal freshly awaked from sleep; and the rippling water, the poplars gently tremulous in the faint breeze, the blue sky, were almost more than he could bear. He was in love with love. In his fancy he felt the kiss of warm lips on his, and around his neck the touch of soft hands. He imagined himself in the arms of Ruth Chalice, he thought of her dark eyes and the wonderful texture of her skin; he was mad to have let such a wonderful adventure slip through his fingers. And if Lawson had done it why should not he? But this was only when he did not see her, when he lay awake at night or dreamed idly by the side of the canal; when he saw her he felt suddenly quite different; he had no desire to take her in his arms, and he could not imagine himself kissing her. It was very curious. Away from her he thought her beautiful, remembering only her magnificent eyes and the creamy pallor of her face; but when he was with her he saw only that she was flatchested and that her teeth were slightly decayed; he could not forget the corns on her toes. He could not understand himself. Would he always love only in absence and be prevented from enjoying anything when he had the chance by that deformity of vision which seemed to exaggerate the revolting?

He was not sorry when a change in the weather, announcing the definite end of the long summer, drove them all back to Paris.

XLVIII

WHEN Philip returned to Amitrano's he found that Fanny Price was no longer working there. She had given up the key of her locker. He asked Mrs. Otter whether she knew what had become of her; and Mrs. Otter, with a shrug of the shoulders, answered that she had probably gone back to England. Philip was relieved. He was profoundly bored by her ill-temper. Moreover she insisted on advising him about his work, looked upon it as a slight when he did not follow her precepts, and would not understand that he felt himself no longer the duffer he had been at first. Soon he forgot all about her. He was working in oils now and he was full of enthusiasm. He hoped to have something done of sufficient importance to send to the following year's Salon. Lawson was painting a portrait of Miss Chalice. She was very paintable, and all the young men who had fallen victims to her charm had made portraits of her. A natural indolence, joined with a passion for picturesque attitude, made her an excellent sitter; and she had enough technical knowledge to offer useful criticisms. Since her passion for art was chiefly a passion to live the life of artists, she was quite content to neglect her own work. She liked the warmth of the studio, and the opportunity to smoke innumerable cigarettes; and she spoke in a low, pleasant voice of the love of art and the art of love. She made no clear distinction between the two.

Lawson was painting with infinite labour, working till he could hardly stand for days and then scraping out all he had done. He would have exhausted the patience of anyone but Ruth Chalice. At last he got into a hopeless muddle.

"The only thing is to take a new canvas and start fresh," he said. "I know exactly what I want now, and it won't take me long."

Philip was present at the time, and Miss Chalice said to him:

"Why don't you paint me too? You'll be able to learn a lot by watching Mr. Lawson."

It was one of Miss Chalice's delicacies that she always addressed her lovers by their surnames.

"I should like it awfully if Lawson wouldn't mind."

"I don't care a damn," said Lawson.

It was the first time that Philip set about a portrait, and he began with trepidation but also with pride. He sat by Lawson and painted as he saw him paint. He profited by the example and by the advice which both Lawson and Miss Chalice freely gave him. At last Lawson finished and invited Clutton in to criticise. Clutton had only just come back to Paris. From Provence he had drifted down to Spain, eager to see Velasquez at Madrid, and thence he had gone to Toledo. He stayed there three months, and he was returned with a name new to the young men: he had wonderful things to say of a painter called El Greco, who it appeared could only be studied in Toledo.

"Oh yes, I know about him," said Lawson, "he's the old master whose distinction it is that he painted as badly as the moderns."

Clutton, more taciturn than ever, did not answer, but he looked at Lawson with a sardonic air.

"Are you going to show us the stuff you've brought back from Spain?" asked Philip.

"I didn't paint in Spain, I was too busy."

"What did you do then?"

"I thought things out. I believe I'm through with the Impressionists; I've got an idea they'll seem very thin and superficial in a few years. I want to make a clean sweep of everything I've learnt and start fresh. When I came back I destroyed everything I'd painted. I've got nothing in my studio now but an easel, my paints, and some clean canvases."

"What are you going to do?"

"I don't know yet. I've only got an inkling of what I want."

He spoke slowly, in a curious manner, as though he were straining to hear something which was only just audible. There seemed to be a mysterious force in him which he himself did not understand, but which was struggling obscurely to find an outlet. His strength impressed you. Lawson dreaded the criticism he asked for and had discounted the blame he thought he might get by affecting a contempt for any opinion of Clutton's; but Philip knew there was nothing which would give him more pleasure than Clutton's praise. Clutton looked at the portrait for some time in silence, then glanced at Philip's picture, which was standing on an easel.

"What's that?" he asked.

"Oh, I had a shot at a portrait too."

"The sedulous ape," he murmured.

He turned away again to Lawson's canvas. Philip reddened but did not speak.

"Well, what d'you think of it?" asked Lawson at length.

"The modelling's jolly good," said Clutton. "And I think it's very well drawn."

"D'you think the values are all right?"

"Quite."

Lawson smiled with delight. He shook himself in his clothes like a wet dog.

"I say, I'm jolly glad you like it."

"I don't. I don't think it's of the smallest importance."

Lawson's face fell, and he stared at Clutton with astonishment: he had no notion what he meant, Clutton had no gift of expression in words, and he spoke as though it were an effort. What he had to say was confused, halting, and verbose; but Philip knew the words which served as the text of his rambling discourse. Clutton, who never read, had heard them first from Cronshaw; and though they had made small impression, they had remained in his memory; and lately, emerging on a sudden, had acquired the character of a revelation: a good painter had two chief objects to paint, namely, man and the intention of his soul. The Impressionists had been occupied with other problems, they had painted man admirably, but they had troubled themselves as little as the English portrait painters of the eighteenth century with the intention of his soul.

"But when you try to get that you become literary," said Lawson, interrupting. "Let me paint the man like Manet, and the intention of his soul can go to the devil."

"That would be all very well if you could beat Manet at his own game, but you can't get anywhere near him. You can't feed yourself on the day before yesterday, it's ground which has been swept dry. You must go back. It's when I saw the Grecos that I felt one could get something more out of portraits than we knew before."

"It's just going back to Ruskin," cried Lawson.

"No—you see, he went for morality: I don't care a damn for morality: teaching doesn't come in, ethics and all that, but passion and emotion. The greatest portrait painters have painted both, man and the intention of his soul; Rembrandt and El Greco; it's only the second-raters who've only painted man. A lily of the valley would be lovely even if it didn't smell, but it's more lovely because it has perfume. That picture"—he pointed to Lawson's portrait—"Well, the drawing's all right and so's the modelling all right, but just conventional; it ought to be drawn and modelled so that you know the girl's a lousy slut. Correctness is all very well: El Greco made his people eight feet high because he wanted to express something he couldn't get any other way."

"Damn El Greco," said Lawson, "what's the good of jawing about a man when we haven't a chance of seeing any of his work?"

Clutton shrugged his shoulders, smoked a cigarette in silence, and went away. Philip and Lawson looked at one another.

"There's something in what he says," said Philip.

Lawson stared ill-temperedly at his picture.

"How the devil is one to get the intention of the soul except by painting exactly what one sees?"

About this time Philip made a new friend. On Monday morning models assembled at the school in order that one might be chosen for the week, and one day a young man was taken who was plainly not a model by profession. Philip's attention was attracted by the manner in which he held himself: when he got on to the stand he stood firmly on both feet, square, with clenched hands, and with his head defiantly thrown forward; the attitude emphasised his fine figure; there was no fat on him, and his muscles stood out as though they were of iron. His head, close-cropped, was well-shaped, and he wore a short beard; he had large, dark eyes and heavy eyebrows. He held the pose hour after hour without appearance of fatigue. There was in his mien a mixture of shame and of determination. His air of passionate energy excited Philip's romantic imagination, and when, the sitting ended, he saw him in his clothes, it seemed to him that he wore them as though he were a king in rags. He was uncommunicative, but in a day or two Mrs. Otter told Philip that the model was a Spaniard and that he had never sat before.

"I suppose he was starving," said Philip.

"Have you noticed his clothes? They're quite neat and decent, aren't they?"

It chanced that Potter, one of the Americans who worked at Amitrano's, was going to Italy for a couple of months, and offered his studio to Philip. Philip was pleased. He was growing a little impatient of Lawson's peremptory advice and wanted to be by himself. At the end of the week he went up to the model and on the pretence that his drawing was not finished asked whether he would come and sit to him one day.

"I'm not a model," the Spaniard answered. "I have other things to do next week."

"Come and have luncheon with me now, and we'll talk about it," said Philip, and as the other hesitated, he added with a smile: "It won't hurt you to lunch with me."

With a shrug of the shoulders the model consented, and they went off to a *crémerie*. The Spaniard spoke broken French, fluent but difficult to follow, and Philip managed to get on well enough with him. He found out that he was a writer. He had come to Paris to write novels and kept himself meanwhile by all the expedients possible to a penniless man: he gave lessons, he did any translations he could get hold of, chiefly business documents, and at last had been driven to make money by his fine figure. Sitting was well paid, and what he had earned during the last week was enough to keep him for two more; he told Philip, amazed, that he could live easily on two francs a day; but it filled him with shame that he was obliged to show his body for money, and he looked upon sitting as a degradation which only hunger could excuse. Philip explained that he did not want him to sit for the figure, but only for the head; he wished to do a portrait of him which he might send to the next Salon.

"But why should you want to paint me?" asked the Spaniard.

Philip answered that the head interested him, he thought he could do a good portrait.

"I can't afford the time. I grudge every minute that I have to rob from my writing."

"But it would only be in the afternoon. I work at the school in the morning. After all, it's better to sit to me than to do translations of legal documents."

There were legends in the Latin Quarter of a time when students of different countries lived together intimately, but this was long since passed, and now the various nations were almost as much separated as in an Oriental city. At Julian's and at the Beaux Arts a French student was looked upon with disfavour by his fellow-countrymen when he consorted with foreigners, and it was difficult for an Englishman to know more than quite superficially any native inhabitants of the city in which he dwelt. Indeed, many of the students after living in Paris for five years knew no more French than served them in shops and lived as English a life as though they were working in South Kensington.

Philip, with his passion for the romantic, welcomed the opportunity to get in touch with a Spaniard; he used all his persuasiveness to overcome the man's reluctance.

"I'll tell you what I'll do," said the Spaniard at last. "I'll sit to you, but not for money, for my own pleasure."

Philip expostulated, but the other was firm, and at length they arranged that he should come on the following Monday at one o'clock. He gave Philip a card on which was printed his name: Miguel Ajuria.

Miguel sat regularly, and though he refused to accept payment he borrowed fifty francs from Philip every now and then: it was a little more expensive than if Philip had paid for the sittings in the usual way; but gave the Spaniard a satisfactory feeling that he was not earning his living in a degrading manner. His nationality made Philip regard him as a representative of romance, and he asked him about Seville and Granada, Velasquez and Calderon. But Miguel had no patience with the grandeur of his country. For him, as for so many of his compatriots, France was the only country for a man of intelligence and Paris the centre of the world.

"Spain is dead," he cried. "It has no writers, it has no art, it has nothing."

Little by little, with the exuberant rhetoric of his race, he revealed his ambitions. He was writing a novel which he hoped would make his name. He was under the influence of

Zola, and he had set his scene in Paris. He told Philip the story at length. To Philip it seemed crude and stupid; the naïve obscenity—*c'est la vie, mon cher, c'est la vie*, he cried—the naïve obscenity served only to emphasise the conventionality of the anecdote. He had written for two years, amid incredible hardships, denying himself all the pleasures of life which had attracted him to Paris, fighting with starvation for art's sake, determined that nothing should hinder his great achievement. The effort was heroic.

"But why don't you write about Spain?" cried Philip. "It would be so much more interesting. You know the life."

"But Paris is the only place worth writing about. Paris is life."

One day he brought part of the manuscript, and in his bad French, translating excitedly as he went along so that Philip could scarcely understand, he read passages. It was lamentable. Philip, puzzled, looked at the picture he was painting: the mind behind that broad brow was trivial; and the flashing, passionate eyes saw nothing in life but the obvious. Philip was not satisfied with his portrait, and at the end of a sitting he nearly always scraped out what he had done. It was all very well to aim at the intention of the soul: who could tell what that was when people seemed a mass of contradictions? He liked Miguel, and it distressed him to realise that his magnificent struggle was futile; he had everything to make a good writer but talent. Philip looked at his own work. How could you tell whether there was anything in it or whether you were wasting your time? It was clear that the will to achieve could not help you and confidence in yourself meant nothing. Philip thought of Fanny Price; she had a vehement be-

lief in her talent; her strength of will was extraordinary.

"If I thought I wasn't going to be really good, I'd rather give up painting," said Philip. "I don't see any use in being a second-rate painter."

Then one morning when he was going out, the *concierge* called out to him that there was a letter. Nobody wrote to him but his Aunt Louisa and sometimes Hayward, and this was a handwriting he did not know. The letter was as follows:

Please come at once when you get this. I couldn't put up with it any more. Please come yourself. I can't bear the thought that anyone else should touch me. I want you to have everything.
                              F. Price.
I have not had anything to eat for three days.

Philip felt on a sudden sick with fear. He hurried to the house in which she lived. He was astonished that she was in Paris at all. He had not seen her for months and imagined she had long since returned to England. When he arrived he asked the *concierge* whether she was in.

"Yes, I've not seen her go out for two days."

Philip ran upstairs and knocked at the door. There was no reply. He called her name. The door was locked, and on bending down he found the key was in the lock.

"Oh, my God, I hope she hasn't done something awful," he cried aloud.

He ran down and told the porter that she was certainly in the room. He had had a letter from her and feared a terrible accident. He suggested breaking open the door. The porter, who had been sullen and disinclined to listen, became alarmed; he could not take the responsibility of breaking into the room; they must go for the *commissaire de police*. They walked together to the *bureau*, and then they fetched a locksmith. Philip found that Miss Price had not paid the last quarter's rent: on New Year's Day she had not given the *concierge* the present which old-established custom led him to regard as a right. The four of them went upstairs, and they knocked again at the door. There was no reply. The locksmith set to work, and at last they entered the room. Philip gave a cry and instinctively covered his eyes with his hands. The wretched woman was hanging with a rope round her neck, which she had tied to a hook in the ceiling fixed by some previous tenant to hold up the curtains of the bed. She had moved her own little bed out of the way and had stood on a chair, which had been kicked away. It was lying on its side on the floor. They cut her down. The body was quite cold.

XLIX

THE story which Philip made out in one way and another was terrible. One of the grievances of the women-students was that Fanny Price would never share their gay meals in restaurants, and the reason was obvious: she had been oppressed by dire poverty. He remembered the luncheon they had eaten together when first he came to Paris and the ghoulish appetite which had disgusted him: he realised now that she ate in that manner because she was ravenous. The *concierge* told him what her food had consisted of. A bottle of milk was left for her every day and she brought in her own loaf of bread; she ate half the loaf and drank half the milk at mid-day when she came back from the school, and consumed the rest in the evening. It was the same day after day. Philip thought with anguish of what she must have endured. She had never given anyone to understand that she was poorer than the rest, but it was clear that her money had been coming to an end, and at last she could not afford to come any more to the studio. The little room was almost bare of furni-ture, and there were no other clothes than the shabby brown dress she had always worn. Philip searched among her things for the address of some friend with whom he could communicate. He found a piece of paper on which his own name was written a score of times. It gave him a peculiar shock. He supposed it was true that she had loved him; he thought of the emaciated body, in the brown dress, hanging from the nail in the ceiling; and he shuddered. But if she had cared for him why did she not let him help her? He would so gladly have done all he could. He felt remorseful because he had refused to see that she looked upon him with any particular feeling, and now these words in her letter were infinitely pathetic: *I can't bear the thought that anyone else should touch me.* She had died of starvation.

Philip found at length a letter signed: *your loving brother, Albert.* It was two or three weeks old, dated from some road in Surbiton, and refused a loan of five pounds. The writer had his wife and family to think of, he didn't feel justified in lending money, and his advice was that Fanny should come back to London and try to get a situation. Philip telegraphed to Albert Price, and in a little while an answer came:

Deeply distressed. Very awkward to leave my business. Is presence essential. Price."

Philip wired a succinct affirmative, and next morning a stranger presented himself at the studio.

"My name's Price," he said, when Philip opened the door.

He was a commonish man in black with a band round his bowler hat; he had something of Fanny's clumsy look; he wore a stubbly moustache, and had a Cockney accent. Philip asked him to come in. He cast sidelong glances round the studio while Philip gave him details of the accident and told him what he had done.

"I needn't see her, need I?" asked Albert Price. "My nerves aren't very strong, and it takes very little to upset me."

He began to talk freely. He was a rubber-merchant, and he had a wife and three children. Fanny was a governess, and he couldn't make out why she hadn't stuck to that instead of coming to Paris.

"Me and Mrs. Price told her Paris was no place for a girl. And there's no money in art—never 'as been."

It was plain enough that he had not been on friendly terms with his sister, and he resented her suicide as a last injury that she had done him. He did not like the idea that she had been forced to it by poverty; that seemed to reflect on the family. The idea struck him that possibly there was a more respectable reason for her act.

"I suppose she 'adn't any trouble with a man, 'ad she? You know what I mean, Paris and all that. She might 'ave done it so as not to disgrace herself."

Philip felt himself reddening and cursed his weakness. Price's keen little eyes seemed to suspect him of an intrigue.

"I believe your sister to have been perfectly virtuous," he answered acidly. "She killed herself because she was starving."

"Well, it's very 'ard on her family, Mr. Carey. She only 'ad to write to me. I wouldn't have let my sister want."

Philip had found the brother's address only by reading the letter in which he refused a loan; but he shrugged his shoulders: there was no use in recrimination. He hated the little man and wanted to have done with him as soon as possible. Albert Price also wished to get through the necessary business quickly so that he could get back to London. They went to the tiny room in which poor Fanny had lived. Albert Price looked at the pictures and the furniture.

"I don't pretend to know much about art," he said. "I suppose these pictures would fetch something, would they?"

"Nothing," said Philip.

"The furniture's not worth ten shillings."

Albert Price knew no French and Philip had to do everything. It seemed that it was an interminable process to get the poor body safely hidden away under ground: papers had to be obtained in one place and signed in another; officials had to be seen. For three days Philip was occupied from morning till night. At last he and Albert Price followed the hearse to the cemetery at Montparnasse.

"I want to do the thing decent," said Albert Price, "but there's no use wasting money."

The short ceremony was infinitely dreadful in the cold gray morning.

Half a dozen people who had worked with Fanny Price at the studio came to the funeral, Mrs. Otter because she was *massière* and thought it her duty, Ruth Chalice because she had a kind heart, Lawson, Clutton, and Flanagan. They had all disliked her during her life. Philip, looking across the cemetery crowded on all sides with monuments, some poor and simple, others vulgar, pretentious, and ugly, shuddered. It was horribly sordid. When they came out Albert Price asked Philip to lunch with him. Philip loathed him now and he was tired; he had not been sleeping well, for he dreamed constantly of Fanny Price in the torn brown dress, hanging from the nail in the ceiling; but he could not think of an excuse.

"You take me somewhere where we can get a regular slap-up lunch. All this is the very worst thing for my nerves."

"Lavenue's is about the best place round here," answered Philip.

Albert Price settled himself on a velvet seat with a sigh of relief. He ordered a substantial luncheon and a bottle of wine.

"Well, I'm glad that's over," he said.

He threw out a few artful questions, and Philip discovered that he was eager to hear about the painter's life in Paris. He represented it to himself as deplorable, but he was anxious for details of the orgies which his fancy suggested to him. With sly winks and discreet sniggering he conveyed that he knew very well that there was a great deal more than Philip confessed. He was a man of the world, and he knew a thing or two. He asked Philip whether he had ever been to any of those places in Montmartre which are celebrated from Temple Bar to the Royal Exchange. He would like to say he had

been to the Moulin Rouge. The luncheon was very good and the wine excellent. Albert Price expanded as the processes of digestion went satisfactorily forwards.

"Let's 'ave a little brandy," he said when the coffee was brought, "and blow the expense."

He rubbed his hands.

"You know, I've got 'alf a mind to stay over tonight and go back tomorrow. What d'you say to spending the evening together?"

"If you mean you want me to take you round Montmartre tonight, I'll see you damned," said Philip.

"I suppose it wouldn't be quite the thing."

The answer was made so seriously that Philip was tickled.

"Besides it would be rotten for your nerves," he said gravely.

Albert Price concluded that he had better go back to London by the four o'clock train, and presently he took leave of Philip.

"Well, good-bye, old man," he said. "I tell you what, I'll try and come over to Paris again one of these days and I'll look you up. And then we won't 'alf go on the razzle."

Philip was too restless to work that afternoon, so he jumped on a bus and crossed the river to see whether there were any pictures on view at Durand-Ruel's. After that he strolled along the boulevard. It was cold and windswept. People hurried by wrapped up in their coats, shrunk together in an effort to keep out of the cold, and their faces were pinched and careworn. It was icy underground in the cemetery at Montparnasse among all those white tombstones. Philip felt lonely in the world and strangely homesick. He wanted company. At that hour Cronshaw would be working, and Clutton never welcomed visitors; Lawson was painting another portrait of Ruth Chalice and would not care to be disturbed. He made up his mind to go and see Flanagan. He found him painting, but delighted to throw up his work and talk. The studio was comfortable, for the American had more money than most of them, and warm; Flanagan set about making tea. Philip looked at the two heads that he was sending to the Salon.

"It's awful cheek my sending anything," said Flanagan, "but I don't care, I'm going to send. D'you think they're rotten?"

"Not so rotten as I should have expected," said Philip.

They showed in fact an astounding cleverness. The difficulties had been avoided with skill, and there was a dash about the way in which the paint was put on which was surprising and even attractive. Flanagan, without knowledge or technique, painted with the loose brush of a man who has spent a lifetime in the practice of the art.

"If one were forbidden to look at any picture for more than thirty seconds you'd be a great master, Flanagan," smiled Philip.

These young people were not in the habit of spoiling one another with excessive flattery.

"We haven't got time in America to spend more than thirty seconds in looking at any picture," laughed the other.

Flanagan, though he was the most scatter-brained person in the world, had a tenderness of heart which was unexpected and charming. Whenever anyone was ill he installed himself as sicknurse. His gaiety was better than any medicine. Like many of his countrymen he had not the English dread of sentimentality which keeps so tight a hold on emotion; and, finding nothing absurd in the show of feeling, could offer an exuberant sympathy which was often grateful to his friends in distress. He saw that Philip was depressed by what he had gone through and with unaffected kindliness set himself boisterously to cheer him up. He exaggerated the Americanisms which he knew always made the Englishmen laugh and poured out a breathless stream of conversation, whimsical, high-spirited, and jolly. In due course they went out to dinner and afterwards to the Gaîté Montparnasse, which was Flanagan's favourite place of amusement. By the end of the evening he was in his most extravagant humour. He had drunk a good deal, but any inebriety from which he suffered was due much more to his own vivacity than to alcohol. He proposed that they should go to the Bal Bullier, and Philip, feeling too tired to go to bed, willingly enough consented. They sat down at a table on the platform at the side, raised a little from the level of the floor so that they could watch the dancing, and drank a bock. Presently Flanagan saw a friend and with a wild shout leaped over the barrier onto the space where they were dancing. Philip watched the people. Bullier was not the resort of fashion. It was Thursday night and the place was crowded. There were a number of students of the various faculties, but most of the men were clerks or assistants in shops; they wore their every-day clothes, ready-made tweeds or queer tail-coats, and their hats, for they had brought them in with them, and when they danced there was no place to put them but their heads. Some of the women looked like servant-girls, and some were painted hussies, but for the most part they were shop-girls. They were poorly-dressed in cheap imitation of the fashions on the other side of the river. The hussies were got up to resemble the music-hall artiste or the dancer who enjoyed notoriety at the moment; their eyes were heavy with black and their cheeks impudently scarlet. The hall was lit by great white lights, low down, which emphasised the shadows on the faces; all the lines seemed to harden under it, and the colours were most crude. It was a sordid scene. Philip leaned over the rail, staring down, and he ceased to hear the music. They danced furiously. They danced round the room, slowly, talking very little, with all their attention given to the dance. The room was hot, and their faces shone with sweat. It seemed to Philip that they had thrown off the guard which people wear on their expression, the homage to convention, and he saw them now as they really were. In that moment of abandon they were strangely animal: some were foxy and some were wolflike; and others had the long, foolish face of sheep. Their skins were sallow from the unhealthy life they led and the poor food they ate. Their features were blunted by mean interests, and their little eyes were shifty and cunning. There was nothing of nobility in their bearing, and you felt that for all of them life was a long succession of petty concerns and sordid thoughts. The air was heavy with the musty smell of humanity. But they danced furiously as though impelled by some strange power within them, and it seemed to Philip that they were driven forward by a rage for enjoyment. They were seeking desperately to escape from a world of horror. The desire for pleasure which Cronshaw said was the only motive of human action urged them blindly on, and the very vehemence of the desire seemed to rob it of all pleasure. They were hurried on by a great wind, helplessly, they knew not why and they knew not whither. Fate seemed to tower above them, and they danced as though everlasting darkness were beneath their feet. Their silence was vaguely alarming. It was as if life terrified them and robbed them of power of speech so that the shriek which was in their hearts died at their throats. Their eyes were haggard and grim; and notwithstanding the beastly lust that disfigured them, and the meanness of their faces, and the cruelty, notwithstanding the stupidness which was worst of all, the anguish of those fixed eyes made all that crowd terrible and pathetic. Philip loathed them, and yet his heart ached with the infinite pity which filled him.

He took his coat from the cloakroom and went out into the bitter coldness of the night.

L

PHILIP could not get the unhappy event out of his head. What troubled him most was the uselessness of Fanny's effort. No one could have worked harder than she, nor with more sincerity; she believed in herself with all her heart; but it was plain that self-confidence meant very little, all his friends had it, Miguel Ajuria among the rest; and Philip was shocked by the contrast between the Spaniard's heroic endeavour and the triviality of the thing he attempted. The unhappiness of Philip's life at school had called up in him the power of self-analysis; and this vice, as subtle as drug-taking, had taken possession of him so that he had now a peculiar keenness in the dissection of his feelings. He could not help seeing that art affected him differently from others. A fine picture gave Lawson an immediate thrill. His appreciation was instinctive. Even Flanagan felt certain things which Philip was obliged to think out. His own appreciation was intellectual. He could not help thinking that if he had in him the artistic temperament (he hated the phrase, but could discover no other) he would feel beauty in the emotional, unreasoning way in which they did. He began to wonder whether he had anything more than a superficial cleverness of the hand which enabled him to copy objects with accuracy. That was nothing. He had learned to despise technical dexterity. The important thing was to feel in terms of paint. Lawson painted in a certain way because it was his nature to, and through the imitativeness of a student sensitive to every influence, there pierced individuality. Philip looked at his own portrait of Ruth Chalice, and now that three months had passed he realised that it was no more than a servile copy of Lawson. He felt himself barren. He painted with the brain, and he could not help knowing that the only painting worth anything was done with the heart.

He had very little money, barely sixteen hundred pounds, and it would be necessary for him to practise the severest economy. He could not count on earning anything for ten years. The history of painting was full of artists who had earned nothing at all. He must resign himself to penury; and it was worth while if he produced work which was immortal; but he had a terrible fear that he would never be more than second-rate. Was it worth while for that to give up one's youth,

and the gaiety of life, and the manifold chances of being? He knew the existence of foreign painters in Paris enough to see that the lives they led were narrowly provincial. He knew some who had dragged along for twenty years in the pursuit of a fame which always escaped them till they sunk into sordidness and alcoholism. Fanny's suicide had aroused memories, and Philip heard ghastly stories of the way in which one person or another had escaped from despair. He remembered the scornful advice which the master had given poor Fanny: it would have been well for her if she had taken it and given up an attempt which was hopeless.

Philip finished his portrait of Miguel Ajuria and made up his mind to send it to the Salon. Flanagan was sending two pictures, and he thought he could paint as well as Flanagan. He had worked so hard on the portrait that he could not help feeling it must have merit. It was true that when he looked at it he felt that there was something wrong, though he could not tell what; but when he was away from it his spirits went up and he was not dissatisfied. He sent it to the Salon and it was refused. He did not mind much, since he had done all he could to persuade himself that there was little chance that it would be taken, till Flanagan a few days later rushed in to tell Lawson and Philip that one of his pictures was accepted. With a blank face Philip offered his congratulations, and Flanagan was so busy congratulating himself that he did not catch the note of irony which Philip could not prevent from coming into his voice. Lawson, quicker-witted, observed it and looked at Philip curiously. His own picture was all right, he knew that a day or two before, and he was vaguely resentful of Philip's attitude. But he was surprised at the sudden question which Philip put him as soon as the American was gone.

"If you were in my place would you chuck the whole thing?"

"What *do* you mean?"

"I wonder if it's worth while being a second-rate painter. You see, in other things, if you're a doctor or if you're in business, it doesn't matter so much if you're mediocre. You make a living and you get along. But what is the good of turning out second-rate pictures?"

Lawson was fond of Philip and, as soon as he thought he was seriously distressed by the refusal of his picture, he set himself to console him. It was notorious that the Salon had refused pictures which were afterwards famous; it was the first time Philip had sent, and he must expect a rebuff; Flanagan's success was explicable, his picture was showy and superficial: it was just the sort of thing a languid jury would see merit in. Philip grew impatient; it was humiliating that Lawson should think him capable of being seriously disturbed by so trivial a calamity and would not realise that his dejection was due to a deep-seated distrust of his powers.

Of late Clutton had withdrawn himself somewhat from the group who took their meals at Gravier's, and lived very much by himself. Flanagan said he was in love with a girl, but Clutton's austere countenance did not suggest passion; and Philip thought it more probable that he separated himself from his friends so that he might grow clear with the new ideas which were in him. But that evening, when the others had left the restaurant to go to a play and Philip was sitting alone, Clutton came in and ordered dinner. They began to talk, and finding Clutton more loquacious and less sardonic than usual, Philip determined to take advantage of his good humour.

"I say I wish you'd come and look at my picture," he said. "I'd like to know what you think of it."

"No, I won't do that."

"Why not?" asked Philip, reddening.

The request was one which they all made of one another, and no one ever thought of refusing. Clutton shrugged his shoulders.

"People ask you for criticism, but they only want praise. Besides, what's the good of criticism? What does it matter if your picture is good or bad?"

"It matters to me."

"No. The only reason that one paints is that one can't help it. It's a function like any of the other functions of the body, only comparatively few people have got it. One paints for oneself: otherwise one would commit suicide. Just think of it, you spend God knows how long trying to get something on to canvas, putting the sweat of your soul into it, and what is the result? Ten to one it will be refused at the Salon; if it's accepted, people glance at it for ten seconds as they pass; if you're lucky some ignorant fool will buy it and put it on his walls and look at it as little as he looks at his dining-room table. Criticism has nothing to do with the artist. It judges objectively, but the objective doesn't concern the artist."

Clutton put his hands over his eyes so that he might concentrate his mind on what he wanted to say.

"The artist gets a peculiar sensation from something he sees, and is impelled to express it and, he doesn't know why, he can only express his feeling by lines and colours. It's like a musician; he'll read a line or two, and a certain combination of notes presents itself to him: he doesn't know why such and such words call forth in him such and such notes; they just do. And I'll tell you another reason why criticism is meaningless: a great painter forces the world to see nature as he sees it; but in the next generation another painter sees the world in another way, and then the public judges him not by himself but by his predecessor. So the Barbizon people taught our fathers to look at trees in a certain manner, and when Monet came along and painted differently, people said: But trees aren't like that. It never struck them that trees are exactly how a painter chooses to see them. We paint from within outwards —if we force our vision on the world it calls us great painters; if we don't it ignores us; but *we* are the same. We don't attach any meaning to greatness or to smallness. What happens to our work afterwards is unimportant; we have got all we could out of it while we were doing it."

There was a pause while Clutton with voracious appetite devoured the food that was set before him. Philip, smoking a cheap cigar, observed him closely. The ruggedness of the head, which looked as though it were carved from a stone refractory to the sculptor's chisel, the rough mane of dark hair, the great nose, and the massive bones of the jaw, suggested a man of strength; and yet Philip wondered whether perhaps the mask concealed a strange weakness. Clutton's refusal to show his work might be sheer vanity: he could not bear the thought of anyone's criticism, and he would not expose himself to the chance of a refusal from the Salon; he wanted to be received as a master and would not risk comparisons with other work which might force him to diminish his own opinion of himself. During the eighteen months Philip had known him Clutton had grown more harsh and bitter; though he would not come out into the open and com-

pete with his fellows, he was indignant with the facile success of those who did. He had no patience with Lawson, and the pair were no longer on the intimate terms upon which they had been when Philip first knew them.

"Lawson's all right," he said contemptuously, "he'll go back to England, become a fashionable portrait painter, earn ten thousand a year and be an A. R. A. before he's forty. Portraits done by hand for the nobility and gentry!"

Philip, too, looked into the future, and he saw Clutton in twenty years, bitter, lonely, savage, and unknown; still in Paris, for the life there had got into his bones, ruling a small *cénacle* with a savage tongue, at war with himself and the world, producing little in his increasing passion for a perfection he could not reach: and perhaps sinking at last into drunkenness. Of late Philip had been captivated by an idea that since one had only one life it was important to make a success of it, but he did not count success by the acquiring of money or the achieving of fame; he did not quite know yet what he meant by it, perhaps variety of experience and the making the most of his abilities. It was plain anyway that the life which Clutton seemed destined to was failure. Its only justification would be the painting of imperishable masterpieces. He recollected Cronshaw's whimsical metaphor of the Persian carpet; he had thought of it often; but Cronshaw with his faun-like humour had refused to make his meaning clear: he repeated that it had none unless one discovered it for oneself. It was this desire to make a success of life which was at the bottom of Philip's uncertainty about continuing his artistic career. But Clutton began to talk again.

"D'you remember my telling you about that chap I met in Brittany? I saw him the other day here. He's just off to Tahiti. He was broke to the world. He was a *brasseur d'affaires,* a stockbroker I suppose you call it in English; and he had a wife and family, and he was earning a large income. He chucked it all to become a painter. He just went off and settled down in Brittany and began to paint. He hadn't got any money and did the next best thing to starving."

"And what about his wife and family?" asked Philip.

"Oh, he dropped them. He left them to starve on their own account."

"It sounds a pretty low-down thing to do."

"Oh, my dear fellow, if you want to be a gentleman you must give up being an artist. They've got nothing to do with one another. You hear of men painting pot-boilers to keep an aged mother—well, it shows they're excellent sons, but it's no excuse for bad work. They're only tradesmen. An artist would let his mother go to the workhouse. There's a writer I know over here who told me that his wife died in childbirth. He was in love with her and he was mad with grief, but as he sat at the bedside watching her die he found himself making mental notes of how she looked and what she said and the things he was feeling. Gentlemanly, wasn't it?"

"But is your friend a good painter?" asked Philip.

"No, not yet, he paints just like Pissarro. He hasn't found himself, but he's got a sense of colour and a sense of decoration. But that isn't the question. It's the feeling, and that he's got. He's behaved like a perfect cad to his wife and children, he's always behaving like a perfect cad; the way he treats the people who've helped him

—and sometimes he's been saved from starvation merely by the kindness of his friends—is simply beastly. He just happens to be a great artist."

Philip pondered over the man who was willing to sacrifice everything, comfort, home, money, love, honour, duty, for the sake of getting on to canvas with paint the emotion which the world gave him. It was magnificent, and yet his courage failed him.

Thinking of Cronshaw recalled to him the fact that he had not seen him for a week, and so, when Clutton left him, he wandered along to the café in which he was certain to find the writer. During the first few months of his stay in Paris Philip had accepted as gospel all that Cronshaw said, but Philip had a practical outlook and he grew impatient with the theories which resulted in no action. Cronshaw's slim bundle of poetry did not seem a substantial result for a life which was sordid. Philip could not wrench out of his nature the instincts of the middle-class from which he came; and the penury, the hack work which Cronshaw did to keep body and soul together, the monotony of existence between the slovenly attic and the café table jarred with his respectability. Cronshaw was astute enough to know that the young man disapproved of him, and he attacked his philistinism with an irony which was sometimes playful but often very keen.

"You're a tradesman," he told Philip, "you want to invest life in console so that it shall bring you in a safe three percent. I'm a spendthrift, I run through my capital. I shall spend my last penny with my last heartbeat."

The metaphor irritated Philip, because it assumed for the speaker a romantic attitude and cast a slur upon the position which Philip instinctively felt had more to say for it than he could think of at the moment.

But this evening Philip, undecided, wanted to talk about himself. Fortunately it was late already and Cronshaw's pile of saucers on the table, each indicating a drink, suggested that he was prepared to take an independent view of things in general.

"I wonder if you'd give me some advice," said Philip suddenly.

"You won't take it, will you?"

Philip shrugged his shoulders impatiently.

"I don't believe I shall ever do much good as a painter. I don't see any use in being second-rate. I'm thinking of chucking it."

"Why shouldn't you?"

Philip hesitated for an instant.

"I suppose I like the life."

A change came over Cronshaw's placid, round face. The corners of the mouth were suddenly depressed, the eyes sunk dully in their orbits; he seemed to become strangely bowed and old.

"This?" he cried, looking round the café in which they sat. His voice really trembled a little.

"If you can get out of it, do while there's time."

Philip stared at him with astonishment, but the sight of emotion always made him feel shy, and he dropped his eyes. He knew that he was looking upon the tragedy of failure. There was silence. Philip thought that Cronshaw was looking upon his own life; and perhaps he considered his youth with its bright hopes and the disappointments which wore out the radiancy; the wretched monotony of pleasure, and the black future. Philip's eyes rested on the little pile of saucers, and he knew that Cronshaw's were on them too.

LI

Two months passed.

It seemed to Philip, brooding over these matters, that in the true painters, writers, musicians, there was a power which drove them to such complete absorption in their work as to make it inevitable for them to subordinate life to art. Succumbing to an influence they never realised, they were merely dupes of the instinct that possessed them, and life slipped through their fingers unlived. But he had a feeling that life was to be lived rather than portrayed, and he wanted to search out the various experiences of it and wring from each moment all the emotion that it offered. He made up his mind at length to take a certain step and abide by the result,

and, having made up his mind, he determined to take the step at once. Luckily enough the next morning was one of Foinet's days, and he resolved to ask him point-blank whether it was worth his while to go on with the study of art. He had never forgotten the master's brutal advice to Fanny Price. It had been sound. Philip could never get Fanny entirely out of his head. The studio seemed strange without her, and now and then the gesture of one of the women working there or the tone of a voice would give him a sudden start, reminding him of her: her presence was more noticeable now she was dead than it had ever been during her life; and he often dreamed of her at night, waking with a cry of terror. It was horrible to think of all the suffering she must have endured.

Philip knew that on the days Foinet came to the studio he lunched at a little restaurant in the Rue d'Odessa, and he hurried his own meal so that he could go and wait outside till the painter came out. Philip walked up and down the crowded street and at last saw Monsieur Foinet walking, with bent head, towards him; Philip was very nervous, but he forced himself to go up to him.

"*Pardon, monsieur,* I should like to speak to you for one moment."

Foinet gave him a rapid glance, recognised him, but did not smile a greeting.

"Speak," he said.

"I've been working here nearly two years now under you. I wanted to ask you to tell me frankly if you think it worth while for me to continue."

Philip's voice was trembling a little. Foinet walked on without looking up. Philip, watching his face, saw no trace of expression upon it.

"I don't understand."

"I'm very poor. If I have no talent I would sooner do something else."

"Don't you know if you have talent?"

"All my friends know they have talent, but I am aware some of them are mistaken."

Foinet's bitter mouth outlined the shadow of a smile, and he asked:

"Do you live near here?"

Philip told him where his studio was. Foinet turned round.

"Let us go there? You shall show me your work."

"Now?" cried Philip.

"Why not?"

Philip had nothing to say. He walked silently by the master's side. He felt horribly sick. It had never struck him that Foinet would wish to see his things there and then; he

meant, so that he might have time to prepare himself, to ask him if he would mind coming at some future date or whether he might bring them to Foinet's studio. He was trembling with anxiety. In his heart he hoped that Foinet would look at his picture, and that rare smile would come into his face, and he would shake Philip's hand and say: "*Pas mal.* Go on, my lad. You have talent, real talent." Philip's heart swelled at the thought. It was such a relief, such a joy! Now he could go on with courage; and what did hardship matter, privation, and disappointment, if he arrived at last? He had worked very hard, it would be too cruel if all that industry were futile. And then with a start he remembered that he had heard Fanny Price say just that. They arrived at the house, and Philip was seized with fear. If he had dared he would have asked Foinet to go away. He did not want to know the truth. They went in and the *concierge* handed him a letter as they passed. He glanced at the envelope and recognised his uncle's handwriting. Foinet followed him up the stairs. Philip could think of nothing to say; Foinet was mute, and the silence got on his nerves. The professor sat down; and Philip without a word placed before him the picture which the Salon had rejected; Foinet nodded but did not speak; then Philip showed him the two portraits he had made of Ruth Chalice, two or three landscapes which he had painted at Moret, and a number of sketches.

"That's all," he said presently, with a nervous laugh.

Monsieur Foinet rolled himself a cigarette and lit it.

"You have very little private means?" he asked at last.

"Very little," answered Philip, with

a sudden feeling of cold at his heart. "Not enough to live on."

"There is nothing so degrading as the constant anxiety about one's means of livelihood. I have nothing but contempt for the people who despise money. They are hypocrites or fools. Money is like a sixth sense without which you cannot make a complete use of the other five. Without an adequate income half the possibilities of life are shut off. The only thing to be careful about is that you do not pay more than a shilling for the shilling you earn. You will hear people say that poverty is the best spur to the artist. They have never felt the iron of it in their flesh. They do not know how mean it makes you. It exposes you to endless humiliation, it cuts your wings, it eats into your soul like a cancer. It is not wealth one asks for, but just enough to preserve one's dignity, to work unhampered, to be generous, frank, and independent. I pity with all my heart the artist, whether he writes or paints, who is entirely dependent for subsistence upon his art."

Philip quietly put away the various things which he had shown.

"I'm afraid that sounds as if you didn't think I had much chance."

Monsieur Foinet slightly shrugged his shoulders.

"You have a certain manual dexterity. With hard work and perseverance there is no reason why you should not become a careful, not incompetent painter. You would find hundreds who painted worse than you, hundreds who painted as well. I see no talent in anything you have shown me. I see industry and intelligence. You will never be anything but mediocre."

Philip obliged himself to answer quite steadily.

"I'm very grateful to you for having taken so much trouble. I can't thank you enough."

Monsieur Foinet got up and made as if to go, but he changed his mind and, stopping, put his hand on Philip's shoulder.

"But if you were to ask me my advice, I should say: take your courage in both hands and try your luck at something else. It sounds very hard, but let me tell you this: I would give all I have in the world if someone had given me that advice when I was your age and I had taken it."

Philip looked up at him with surprise. The master forced his lips into a smile, but his eyes remained grave and sad.

"It is cruel to discover one's mediocrity only when it is too late. It does not improve the temper."

He gave a little laugh as he said the last words and quickly walked out of the room.

Philip mechanically took up the letter from his uncle. The sight of his handwriting made him anxious, for it was his aunt who always wrote to him. She had been ill for the last three months, and he had offered to go over to England and see her; but she, fearing it would interfere with his work, had refused. She did not want him to put himself to inconvenience; she said she would wait till August and then she hoped he would come and stay at the vicarage for two or three weeks. If by any chance she grew worse she would let him know, since she did not wish to die without seeing him again. If his uncle wrote to him it must be because she was too ill to hold a pen. Philip opened the letter. It ran as follows:

My dear Philip,

I regret to inform you that your dear Aunt departed this life early this morning. She died very suddenly, but quite peacefully. The change for the worse was so rapid that we had no time to send for you. She was fully prepared for the end and entered into rest with the complete assurance of a blessed resurrection and with resignation to the divine will of our blessed Lord Jesus Christ. Your Aunt would have liked you to be present at the funeral so I trust you will come as soon as you can. There is naturally a great deal of work thrown upon my shoulders and I am very much upset. I trust that you will be able to do everything for me.

Your affectionate uncle,
William Carey.

LII

NEXT day Philip arrived at Blackstable. Since the death of his mother he had never lost anyone closely connected with him; his aunt's death shocked him and filled him also with a curious fear; he felt for the first time his own mortality. He could not realise what life would be for his uncle without the constant companionship of the woman who had loved and tended him for forty years. He expected to find him broken down with hopeless grief. He dreaded the first meeting; he knew that he could say nothing which would be of use. He rehearsed to himself a number of apposite speeches.

He entered the vicarage by the side-door and went into the dining-room. Uncle William was reading the paper. "Your train was late," he said, looking up.

Philip was prepared to give way to his emotion, but the matter-of-fact reception startled him. His uncle, subdued but calm, handed him the paper. "There's a very nice little paragraph about her in *The Blackstable Times*," he said.

Philip read it mechanically.

"Would you like to come up and see her?"

Philip nodded and together they walked upstairs. Aunt Louisa was lying in the middle of the large bed, with flowers all round her.

"Would you like to say a short prayer?" said the Vicar.

He sank on his knees, and because it was expected of him Philip followed his example. He looked at the little shrivelled face. He was only conscious of one emotion: what a wasted life! In a minute Mr. Carey gave a cough, and stood up. He pointed to a wreath at the foot of the bed.

"That's from the Squire," he said. He spoke in a low voice as though he were in church, but one felt that, as a clergyman, he found himself quite at home. "I expect tea is ready."

They went down again to the dining-room. The drawn blinds gave a lugubrious aspect. The Vicar sat at the end of the table at which his wife had always sat and poured out the tea with ceremony. Philip could not help feeling that neither of them should have been able to eat anything, but when he saw that his uncle's appetite was unimpaired he fell to with his usual heartiness. They did not speak for a while. Philip set himself to eat an excellent cake with the air of grief which he felt was decent.

"Things have changed a great deal since I was a curate," said the Vicar presently. "In my young days the mourners used always to be given a pair of black gloves and a piece of black silk for their hats. Poor Louisa used to make the silk into dresses. She always said that twelve funerals gave her a new dress."

Then he told Philip who had sent wreaths; there were twenty-four of them already; when Mrs. Rawlingson, wife of the Vicar at Ferne, had died she had had thirty-two; but probably a good many more would come the next day; the funeral would start at eleven o'clock from the vicarage, and they should beat Mrs. Rawlingson easily. Louisa never liked Mrs. Rawlingson.

"I shall take the funeral myself. I promised Louisa I would never let anyone else bury her."

Philip looked at his uncle with disapproval when he took a second piece of cake. Under the circumstances he could not help thinking it greedy.

"Mary Ann certainly makes capital cakes. I'm afraid no one else will make such good ones."

"She's not going?" cried Philip, with astonishment.

Mary Ann had been at the vicarage ever since he could remember. She never forgot his birthday, but made a point always of sending him a trifle, absurd but touching. He had a real affection for her.

"Yes," answered Mr. Carey. "I didn't think it would do to have a single woman in the house."

"But, good heavens, she must be over forty."

"Yes, I think she is. But she's been rather troublesome lately, she's been inclined to take too much on herself, and I thought this was a very good opportunity to give her notice."

"It's certainly one which isn't likely to recur," said Philip.

He took out a cigarette, but his uncle prevented him from lighting it.

"Not till after the funeral, Philip," he said gently.

"All right," said Philip.

"It wouldn't be quite respectful to smoke in the house so long as your poor Aunt Louisa is upstairs."

Josiah Graves, churchwarden and manager of the bank, came back to dinner at the vicarage after the funeral. The blinds had been drawn up, and Philip, against his will, felt a curious sensation of relief. The body in the house had made him uncomfortable: in life the poor woman had been all that was kind and gentle; and yet, when she lay upstairs in her bed-room, cold and stark, it seemed as though she cast upon the survivors a baleful influence. The thought horrified Philip.

He found himself alone for a minute or two in the dining-room with the churchwarden.

"I hope you'll be able to stay with your uncle a while," he said. "I don't think he ought to be left alone just yet."

"I haven't made any plans," answered Philip. "If he wants me I shall be very pleased to stay."

By way of cheering the bereaved husband the churchwarden during dinner talked of a recent fire at Blackstable which had partly destroyed the Wesleyan chapel.

"I hear they weren't insured," he said, with a little smile.

"That won't make any difference," said the Vicar. "They'll get as much money as they want to rebuild. Chapel people are always ready to give money."

"I see that Holden sent a wreath."

Holden was the dissenting minister, and, though for Christ's sake who died for both of them, Mr. Carey nodded to him in the street, he did not speak to him.

"I think it was very pushing," he

remarked. "There were forty-one wreaths. Yours was beautiful. Philip and I admired it very much."

"Don't mention it," said the banker. He had noticed with satisfaction that it was larger than any one's else. It had looked very well. They began to discuss the people who attended the funeral. Shops had been closed for it, and the churchwarden took out of his pocket the notice which had been printed: *Owing to the funeral of Mrs. Carey this establishment will not be opened till one o'clock.*"

"It was my idea," he said.

"I think it was very nice of them to close," said the Vicar. "Poor Louisa would have appreciated that."

Philip ate his dinner. Mary Ann had treated the day as Sunday, and they had roast chicken and a gooseberry tart.

"I suppose you haven't thought about a tombstone yet?" said the churchwarden.

"Yes, I have. I thought of a plain stone cross. Louisa was always against ostentation."

"I don't think one can do much better than a cross. If you're thinking of a text, what do you say to: *With Christ, which is far better?*"

The Vicar pursed his lips. It was just like Bismarck to try and settle everything himself. He did not like that text; it seemed to cast an aspersion on himself.

"I don't think I should put that. I much prefer: *The Lord has given and the Lord has taken away.*"

"Oh, do you? That always seems to me a little indifferent."

The Vicar answered with some acidity, and Mr. Graves replied in a tone which the widower thought too authoritative for the occasion. Things were going rather far if he could not choose his own text for his own wife's tombstone. There was a pause, and then the conversation drifted to parish matters. Philip went into the garden to smoke his pipe. He sat on a bench, and suddenly began to laugh hysterically.

A few days later his uncle expressed the hope that he would spend the next few weeks at Blackstable.

"Yes, that will suit me very well," said Philip.

"I suppose it'll do if you go back to Paris in September."

Philip did not reply. He had thought much of what Foinet said to him, but he was still so undecided that he did not wish to speak of the future. There would be something fine in giving up art because he was convinced that he could not excel; but unfortunately it would seem so only to himself: to others it would be an admission of defeat, and he did not want to confess that he was beaten. He was an obstinate fellow, and the suspicion that his talent did not lie in one direction made him inclined to force circumstances and aim notwithstanding precisely in that direction. He could not bear that his friends should laugh at him. This might have prevented him from ever taking the definite step of abandoning the study of painting, but the different environment made him on a sudden see things differently. Like many another he discovered that crossing the Channel makes things which had seemed important singularly futile. The life which had been so charming that he could not bear to leave it now seemed inept; he was seized with a distaste for the cafés, the restaurants with their ill-cooked food, the shabby way in which they all lived. He did not care any more what his friends thought about him: Cronshaw with his rhetoric, Mrs. Otter with her respectability, Ruth Chalice with her affectations, Lawson and Clutton with their quarrels; he felt a revulsion from them all. He wrote to Lawson and asked him to send over all his belongings. A week later they arrived. When he unpacked his canvases he found himself able to examine his work without emotion. He noticed the fact with interest. His uncle was anxious to see his pictures. Though he had so greatly disapproved of Philip's desire to go to Paris, he accepted the situation now with equanimity. He was interested in the life of students and constantly put Philip questions about it. He was in fact a little proud of him because he was a painter, and when people were present made attempts to draw him out. He looked eagerly at the studies of models which Philip showed him. Philip set before him his portrait of Miguel Ajuria.

"Why did you paint him?" asked Mr. Carey.

"Oh, I wanted a model, and his head interested me."

"As you haven't got anything to do here I wonder you don't paint me."

"It would bore you to sit."

"I think I should like it."

"We must see about it."

Philip was amused at his uncle's vanity. It was clear that he was dying to have his portrait painted. To get something for nothing was a chance not to be missed. For two or three days he threw out little hints. He reproached Philip for laziness, asked him when he was going to start work, and finally began telling everyone he met that Philip was going to paint him. At last there came a rainy day, and after breakfast Mr. Carey said to Philip:

"Now, what d'you say to starting on my portrait this morning?" Philip put down the book he was reading and leaned back in his chair.

"I've given up painting," he said.

"Why?" asked his uncle in astonishment.

"I don't think there's much object in being a second-rate painter, and I came to the conclusion that I should never be anything else."

"You surprise me. Before you went to Paris you were quite certain that you were a genius."

"I was mistaken," said Philip.

"I should have thought now you'd taken up a profession you'd have the pride to stick to it. It seems to me that what you lack is perseverance."

Philip was a little annoyed that his uncle did not even see how truly heroic his determination was.

"'A rolling stone gathers no moss,'" proceeded the clergyman. Philip hated that proverb above all, and it seemed to him perfectly meaningless. His uncle had repeated it often during the arguments which had preceded his departure from business. Apparently it recalled that occasion to his guardian.

"You're no longer a boy, you know; you must begin to think of settling down. First you insist on becoming a chartered accountant, and then you get tired of that and you want to become a painter. And now if you please you change your mind again. It points to . . ."

He hesitated for a moment to consider what defects of character exactly it indicated, and Philip finished the sentence.

"Irresolution, incompetence, want of foresight, and lack of determination."

The Vicar looked up at his nephew quickly to see whether he was laughing at him. Philip's face was serious, but there was a twinkle in his eyes which irritated him. Philip should really be getting more serious. He felt it right to give him a rap over the knuckles.

"Your money matters have nothing to do with me now. You're your own master; but I think you should remember that your money won't last for ever, and the unlucky deformity you have doesn't exactly make it easier for you to earn your living."

Philip knew by now that whenever anyone was angry with him his first thought was to say something about his club-foot. His estimate of the human race was determined by the fact that scarcely anyone failed to resist the temptation. But he had trained himself not to show any sign that the reminder wounded him. He had even acquired control over the blushing which in his boyhood had been one of his torments.

"As you justly remark," he answered, "my money matters have nothing to do with you and I am my own master."

"At all events you will do me the justice to acknowledge that I was justified in my opposition when you made up your mind to become an art-student."

"I don't know so much about that. I daresay one profits more by the mistakes one makes off one's own bat than by doing the right thing on somebody's else advice. I've had my fling, and I don't mind settling down now."

"What at?"

Philip was not prepared for the question, since in fact he had not made up his mind. He had thought of a dozen callings.

"The most suitable thing you could do is to enter your father's profession and become a doctor."

"Oddly enough that is precisely what I intend."

He had thought of doctoring among other things, chiefly because it was an occupation which seemed to give a good deal of personal freedom, and his experience of life in an office had made him determine never to have anything more to do with one; his answer to the Vicar slipped out almost unawares, because it was in the nature of a repartee. It amused him to make up his mind in that accidental way, and he resolved then and there to enter his father's old hospital in the autumn.

"Then your two years in Paris may be regarded as so much wasted time?"

"I don't know about that. I had a very jolly two years, and I learned one or two useful things."

"What?"

Philip reflected for an instant, and his answer was not devoid of a gentle desire to annoy.

"I learned to look at hands, which I'd never looked at before. And instead of just looking at houses and trees I learned to look at houses and trees against the sky. And I learned also that shadows are not black but coloured."

"I suppose you think you're very clever. I think your flippancy is quite inane."

LIII

Taking the paper with him Mr. Carey retired to his study. Philip changed his chair for that in which his uncle had been sitting (it was the only comfortable one in the room), and looked out of the window at the pouring rain. Even in that sad weather there was something restful about the green fields that stretched to the horizon. There was an intimate charm in the landscape which he did not remember ever to have noticed before. Two years in France had opened his eyes to the beauty of his own countryside.

He thought with a smile of his uncle's remark. It was lucky that the turn of his mind tended to flippancy. He had begun to realise what a great loss he had sustained in the death of his father and mother. That was one of the differences in his life which prevented him from seeing things in the same way as other people. The love of parents for their children is the only emotion which is quite disinterested. Among strangers he had grown up as best he could, but he had seldom been used with patience or forbearance. He prided himself on his self-control. It had been whipped into him by the mockery of his fellows. Then they called him cynical and callous. He had acquired calmness of demeanour and under most circumstances an unruffled exterior, so that now he could not show his feelings. People told him he was unemotional; but he knew that he was at the mercy of his emotions: an accidental kindness touched him so much that sometimes he did not venture to speak in order not to betray the unsteadiness of his voice. He remembered the bitterness of his life at school, the humiliation which he had endured, the banter which had made him morbidly afraid of making himself ridiculous; and he remembered the loneliness he had felt since, faced with the world, the disillusion and the disappointment caused by the difference between what it promised to his active imagination and what it gave. But notwithstanding he was able to look at himself from the outside and smile with amusement.

"By Jove, if I weren't flippant, I should hang myself," he thought cheerfully.

His mind went back to the answer he had given his uncle when he asked him what he had learnt in Paris. He had learnt a good deal more than he told him. A conversation with Cronshaw had stuck in his memory, and one phrase he had used, a commonplace one enough, had set his brain working.

"My dear fellow," Cronshaw said, "there's no such thing as abstract morality."

When Philip ceased to believe in Christianity he felt that a great weight was taken from his shoulders; casting off the responsibility which weighed down every action, when every action was infinitely important for the welfare of his immortal soul, he experienced a vivid sense of liberty. But he knew now that this was an illusion. When he put away the religion in which he had been brought up, he had kept unimpaired the morality which was part and parcel of it. He made up his mind therefore to think things out for himself. He determined to be swayed by no prejudices. He swept away the virtues and the vices, the established laws of good and evil, with the idea of finding out the rules of life for himself. He did not know whether rules were necessary at all. That was one of the things he wanted to discover. Clearly much that seemed valid seemed so only because he had been taught it from his earliest youth. He had read a number of books, but they did not help him much, for they were based on the morality of Christianity; and even the writers who emphasised the fact that they did not believe in it were never satisfied till they had framed a system of ethics in accordance with that of the Sermon on the Mount. It seemed hardly worth while to read a long volume in order to learn that you ought to behave exactly like everybody else. Philip wanted to find out how he ought to behave, and he thought he could prevent himself from being influenced by the opinions that surrounded him. But meanwhile he had to go on living, and, until he formed a theory of conduct, he made himself a provisional rule.

"Follow your inclinations with due regard to the policeman round the corner."

He thought the best thing he had gained in Paris was a complete liberty of spirit, and he felt himself at last absolutely free. In a desultory way he had read a good deal of philosophy, and he looked forward with delight to the leisure of the next few months. He began to read at haphazard. He entered upon each system with a little thrill of excitement, expecting to find in each some guide by which he could rule his conduct; he felt himself like a traveller in unknown countries and as he pushed forward the enterprise fascinated him; he read emotionally, as other men read pure literature, and his heart leaped as he discovered in noble words what himself had obscurely felt. His mind was concrete and moved with difficulty in regions of the abstract; but, even when he could not follow the reasoning, it gave him a curious pleasure to follow the tortuosities of thoughts that threaded their nimble way on the edge of the incomprehensible. Sometimes great philosophers seemed to have nothing to say to him, but at others he recognised a mind with which he felt himself at home. He was like the explorer in Central Africa who comes suddenly upon wide uplands, with great trees in them and stretches of meadow, so that he might fancy himself in an English park. He delighted in the robust common sense of Thomas Hobbes; Spinoza filled him with awe, he had never before come in contact with a mind so noble, so unapproachable and austere; it reminded him of that statue by Rodin, *L'Age d'Airain,* which he passionately admired; and then there was Hume: the scepticism of that charming philosopher touched a kindred note in Philip; and, revelling in the lucid style which seemed able to put complicated thought into simple words, musical and measured, he read as he might have read a novel, a smile of pleasure on his lips. But in none could he find exactly what he wanted. He had read somewhere that every man was born a Platonist, an Aristotelian, a Stoic, or an Epicurean; and the history of George Henry Lewes (besides telling you that philosophy was all moonshine) was there to show that the thought of each philosopher was inseparably connected with the man he was. When you knew that you could guess to a great extent the philosophy he wrote. It looked as though you did not act in a certain way because you thought in a certain way, but rather that you thought in a certain way because you were made in a certain way. Truth had nothing to do with it. There was no such thing as truth. Each man was his own philosopher, and the elaborate systems which the great men of the past had composed were only valid for the writers.

The thing then was to discover what one was and one's system of philosophy would devise itself. It seemed to Philip that there were three things to find out: man's relation to the world he lives in, man's relation with the men among whom he lives, and finally man's relation to himself. He made an elaborate plan of study.

The advantage of living abroad is that, coming in contact with the manners and customs of the people among whom you live, you observe them from the outside and see that they have not the necessity which those who practise them believe. You cannot fail to discover that the beliefs which to you are self-evident to the foreigner are absurd. The year in Germany, the long stay in Paris, had prepared Philip to receive the sceptical teaching which came to him now with such a feeling of relief. He saw that nothing was good and nothing was evil; things were merely adapted to an end. He read *The Origin of Species*. It seemed to offer an explanation of much that troubled him. He was like an explorer now who has reasoned that certain natural features must present themselves, and, beating up a broad river, finds here the tributary that he expected, there the fertile, populated plains, and further on the mountains. When some great discovery is made the world is surprised afterwards that it was not accepted at once, and even on those who acknowledge its truth the effect is unimportant. The first readers of *The Origin of Species* accepted it with their reason; but their emotions, which are the ground of conduct, were untouched. Philip was born a generation after this great book was published, and much that horrified its contemporaries had passed into the feeling of the time, so that he was able to accept it with a joyful heart. He was intensely moved by the grandeur of the struggle for life, and the ethical rule which it suggested seemed to fit in with his predispositions. He said to himself that might was right. Society stood on one side, an organism with its own laws of growth and self-preservation, while the individual stood on the other.

The actions which were to the advantage of society it termed virtuous and those which were not it called vicious. Good and evil meant nothing more than that. Sin was a prejudice from which the free man should rid himself. Society had three arms in its contest with the individual, laws, public opinion, and conscience: the first two could be met by guile, guile is the only weapon of the weak against the strong: common opinion put the matter well when it stated that sin consisted in being found out; but conscience was the traitor within the gates; it fought in each heart the battle of society, and caused the individual to throw himself, a wanton sacrifice, to the prosperity of his enemy. For it was clear that the two were irreconcilable, the state and the individual conscious of himself. *That* uses the individual for its own ends, trampling upon him if he thwarts it, rewarding him with medals, pensions, honours, when he serves it faithfully; *this,* strong only in his independence, threads his way through the state, for convenience' sake, paying in money or service for certain benefits, but with no sense of obligation; and, indifferent to the rewards, asks only to be left alone. He is the independent traveller, who uses Cook's tickets because they save trouble, but looks with good-humoured contempt on the personally conducted parties. The free man can do no wrong. He does everything he likes—if he can. His power is the only measure of his morality. He recognises the laws of the state and he can break them without sense of sin, but if he is punished he accepts the punishment without rancour. Society has the power.

But if for the individual there was no right and no wrong, then it seemed to Philip that conscience lost its power. It was with a cry of triumph that he seized the knave and flung him from his breast. But he was no nearer to the meaning of life than he had been before. Why the world was there and what men had come into existence for at all was as inexplicable as ever. Surely there must be some reason. He thought of Cronshaw's parable of the Persian carpet. He offered it as a solution of the riddle, and mysteriously he stated that it was no answer at all unless you found it out for yourself.

"I wonder what the devil he meant," Philip smiled.

And so, on the last day of September, eager to put into practice all these new theories of life, Philip, with sixteen hundred pounds and his club-foot, set out for the second time to London to make his third start in life.

LIV

THE examination Philip had passed before he was articled to a chartered accountant was sufficient qualification for him to enter a medical school. He chose St. Luke's because his father had been a student there, and before the end of the summer session had gone up to London for a day in order to see the secretary. He got a list of rooms from him, and took lodgings in a dingy house which had the advantage of being within two minutes' walk of the hospital.

"You'll have to arrange about a part to dissect," the secretary told him. "You'd better start on a leg; they generally do; they seem to think it easier."

Philip found that his first lecture was in anatomy, at eleven, and about half past ten he limped across the road, and a little nervously made his way to the Medical School. Just inside the door a number of notices were pinned up, lists of lectures, football fixtures, and the like; and these he looked at idly, trying to seem at his ease. Young men and boys dribbled in and looked for letters in the rack, chatted with one another, and passed downstairs to the basement, in which was the students' reading-room. Philip saw several fellows with a desultory, timid look dawdling around, and surmised that, like himself, they were there for the first time. When he had exhausted the notices he saw a glass door which led into what was apparently a museum, and having still twenty minutes to spare he walked in. It was a collection of pathological specimens. Presently a boy of about eighteen came up to him.

"I say, are you first year?" he said.

"Yes," answered Philip.

"Where's the lecture room, d'you know? It's getting on for eleven."

"We'd better try to find it."

They walked out of the museum into a long, dark corridor, with the walls painted in two shades of red, and other youths walking along suggested the way to them. They came to a door marked Anatomy Theatre. Philip found that there were a good many people already there. The seats were arranged in tiers, and just as Philip entered an attendant came in, put a glass of water on the table in the well of the lecture-room and then brought in a pelvis and two thigh-bones, right and left. More men entered and took their seats and by eleven the theatre was fairly full. There were about sixty students. For the most part they were a good deal younger than Philip, smooth-faced boys of eighteen, but there were a few who were older than he: he noticed one tall man, with a fierce red moustache, who might have been thirty; another little fellow with black hair, only a year or two younger; and there was one man with spectacles and a beard which was quite gray.

The lecturer came in, Mr. Cameron, a handsome man with white hair and clean-cut features. He called out the long list of names. Then he made a little speech. He spoke in a pleasant voice, with well-chosen words, and he seemed to take a discreet pleasure in their careful arrangement. He suggested one or two books which they might buy and advised the purchase of a skeleton. He spoke of anatomy with enthusiasm: it was essential to the study of Surgery; a knowledge of it added to the appreciation of art. Philip pricked up his ears. He heard later that Mr. Cameron lectured also to the students at the Royal Academy. He had lived many years in Japan, with a post at the University of Tokio, and he flattered himself on his appreciation of the beautiful.

"You will have to learn many tedious things," he finished, with an indulgent smile, "which you will forget the moment you have passed your final examination, but in anatomy it is better to have learned and lost than never to have learned at all."

He took up the pelvis which was lying on the table and began to describe it. He spoke well and clearly.

At the end of the lecture the boy who had spoken to Philip in the pathological museum and sat next to him in the theatre suggested that they should go to the dissecting-room. Philip and he walked along the corridor again, and an attendant told them where it was. As soon as they entered Philip understood what the acrid smell was which he had noticed in the passage. He lit a pipe. The attendant gave a short laugh.

"You'll soon get used to the smell. I don't notice it myself."

He asked Philip's name and looked at a list on the board.

"You've got a leg—number four."

Philip saw that another name was bracketed with his own.

"What's the meaning of that?" he asked.

"We're very short of bodies just now. We've had to put two on each part."

The dissecting-room was a large apartment painted like the corridors, the upper part a rich salmon and the dado a dark terra-cotta. At regular intervals down the long sides of the room, at right angles with the wall, were iron slabs, grooved like meat-dishes; and on each lay a body. Most of them were men. They were very dark from the preservative in which they had been kept, and the skin had almost the look of leather. They were extremely emaciated. The attendant took Philip up to one of the slabs. A youth was standing by it.

"Is your name Carey?" he asked.

"Yes."

"Oh, then we've got this leg together. It's lucky it's a man, isn't it?"

"Why?" asked Philip.

"They generally always like a male better," said the attendant. "A female's liable to have a lot of fat about her."

Philip looked at the body. The arms and legs were so thin that there was no shape in them, and the ribs stood out so that the skin over them was tense. A man of about forty-five with a thin, gray beard, and on his skull scanty, colourless hair: the eyes were closed and the lower jaw sunken.

Philip could not feel that this had ever been a man, and yet in the row of them there was something terrible and ghastly.

"I thought I'd start at two," said the young man who was dissecting with Philip.

"All right, I'll be here then."

He had bought the day before the case of instruments which was needful, and now he was given a locker. He looked at the boy who had accompanied him into the dissecting-room and saw that he was white.

"Make you feel rotten?" Philip asked him.

"I've never seen anyone dead before."

They walked along the corridor till they came to the entrance of the school. Philip remembered Fanny Price. She was the first dead person he had ever seen, and he remembered how strangely it had affected him. There was an immeasurable distance between the quick and the dead: they did not seem to belong to the same species; and it was strange to think that but a little while before they had spoken and moved and eaten and laughed. There was something horrible about the dead, and you could imagine that they might cast an evil influence on the living.

"What d'you say to having something to eat?" said his new friend to Philip.

They went down into the basement, where there was a dark room fitted up as a restaurant, and here the students were able to get the same sort of fare as they might have at an aërated bread shop. While they ate (Philip had a scone and butter and a cup of chocolate), he discovered that his companion was called Dunsford. He was a fresh-complexioned lad, with pleasant blue eyes and curly, dark hair, large-limbed, slow of speech

and movement. He had just come from Clifton.

"Are you taking the Conjoint?" he asked Philip.

"Yes, I want to get qualified as soon as I can."

"I'm taking it too, but I shall take the F. R. C. S. afterwards. I'm going in for surgery."

Most of the students took the curriculum of the Conjoint Board of the College of Surgeons and the College of Physicians; but the more ambitious or the more industrious added to this the longer studies which led to a degree from the University of London. When Philip went to St. Luke's changes had recently been made in the regulations, and the course took five years instead of four as it had done for those who registered before the autumn of 1892. Dunsford was well up in his plans and told Philip the usual course of events. The "first conjoint" examination consisted of Biology, Anatomy, and Chemistry; but it could be taken in sections, and most fellows took their biology three months after entering the school. This science had been recently added to the list of subjects upon which the student was obliged to inform himself, but the amount of knowledge required was very small.

When Philip went back to the dissecting-room, he was a few minutes late, since he had forgotten to buy the loose sleeves which they wore to protect their shirts, and he found a number of men already working. His partner had started on the minute and was busy dissecting out cutaneous nerves. Two others were engaged on the second leg, and more were occupied with the arms.

"You don't mind my having started?"

"That's all right, fire away," said Philip.

He took the book, open at a diagram of the dissected part, and looked at what they had to find.

"You're rather a dab at this," said Philip.

"Oh, I've done a good deal of dissecting before, animals, you know, for the Pre Sci."

There was a certain amount of conversation over the dissecting-table, partly about the work, partly about the prospects of the football season, the demonstrators, and the lectures. Philip felt himself a great deal older than the others. They were raw schoolboys. But age is a matter of knowledge rather than of years; and Newson, the active young man who was dissecting with him, was very much at home with his subject. He was perhaps not sorry to show off, and he explained very fully to Philip what he was about. Philip, notwithstanding his hidden stores of wisdom, listened meekly. Then Philip took up the scalpel and the tweezers and began working while the other looked on.

"Ripping to have him so thin," said Newson, wiping his hands. "The blighter can't have had anything to eat for a month."

"I wonder what he died of," murmured Philip.

"Oh, I don't know, any old thing, starvation chiefly, I suppose. . . . I say, look out, don't cut that artery."

"It's all very fine to say, don't cut that artery," remarked one of the men working on the opposite leg. "Silly old fool's got an artery in the wrong place."

"Arteries always are in the wrong place," said Newson. "The normal's the one thing you practically never get. That's why it's called the normal."

"Don't say things like that," said Philip, "or I shall cut myself."

"If you cut yourself," answered Newson, full of information, "wash it at once with antiseptic. It's the one thing you've got to be careful about. There was a chap here last year who gave himself only a prick, and he didn't bother about it, and he got septicæmia."

"Did he get all right?"

"Oh, no, he died in a week. I went and had a look at him in the P. M. room."

Philip's back ached by the time it was proper to have tea, and his luncheon had been so light that he was quite ready for it. His hands smelt of that peculiar odour which he had first noticed that morning in the corridor. He thought his muffin tasted of it too.

"Oh, you'll get used to that," said Newson. "When you don't have the good old dissecting-room stink about, you feel quite lonely."

"I'm not going to let it spoil my appetite," said Philip, as he followed up the muffin with a piece of cake.

LV

PHILIP'S ideas of the life of medical students, like those of the public at large, were founded on the pictures which Charles Dickens drew in the middle of the nineteenth century. He soon discovered that Bob Sawyer, if he ever existed, was no longer at all like the medical student of the present.

It is a mixed lot which enters upon the medical profession, and naturally there are some who are lazy and reckless. They think it is an easy life, idle away a couple of years; and then, because their funds come to an end or because angry parents refuse any longer to support them, drift away from the hospital. Others find the examinations too hard for them; one failure after another robs them of their nerve; and, panic-stricken, they forget as soon as they come into the forbidding buildings of the Conjoint Board the knowledge which before they had so pat. They remain year after year, objects of good-humoured scorn to younger men: some of them crawl through the examination of the Apothecaries Hall; others become nonqualified assistants, a precarious position in which they are at the mercy of their employer; their lot is poverty, drunkenness, and Heaven only knows their end. But for the most part medical students are industrious young men of the middle-class with a sufficient allowance to live in the respectable fashion they have been used to; many are the sons of doctors who have already something of the professional manner; their career is mapped out: as soon as they are qualified they propose to apply for a hospital appointment, after holding which (and perhaps a trip to the Far East as a ship's doctor), they will join their father and spend the rest of their days in a country practice. One or two are marked out as exceptionally brilliant: they will take the various prizes and scholarships which are open each year to the deserving, get one appointment after another at the hospital, go on the staff, take a consulting-room in Harley Street and, specialising in one subject or another, become prosperous, eminent, and titled.

The medical profession is the only one which a man may enter at any age with some chance of making a living. Among the men of Philip's year were three or four who were past their first youth: one had been in the Navy, from which according to report he had been dismissed for drunkenness; he was a man of thirty, with a red face, a brusque manner, and a loud voice. Another was a married man with two children, who had lost money through a defaulting solicitor; he had a bowed look as if the world were too much for him; he went about his work silently, and it was plain that he found it difficult at his age to commit facts to memory. His mind worked slowly. His effort at application was painful to see.

Philip made himself at home in his tiny rooms. He arranged his books and hung on the walls such pictures and sketches as he possessed. Above him, on the drawing-room floor, lived a fifth-year man called Griffiths; but Philip saw little of him, partly because he was occupied chiefly in the wards and partly because he had been to Oxford. Such of the students as had been to a university kept a good deal together: they used a variety of means natural to the young in order to impress upon the less fortunate a proper sense of their inferiority; the rest of the students found their Olympian serenity rather hard to bear. Griffiths was a tall fellow, with a quantity of curly red hair and blue eyes, a white skin and a very red mouth; he was one of those fortunate people whom everybody liked, for he had high spirits and a constant gaiety. He strummed a little on the piano and sang comic songs with gusto; and evening after evening, while Philip was reading in his solitary room, he heard the shouts and the uproarious laughter of Griffiths' friends above him. He thought of those delightful evenings in Paris when they would sit in the studio, Lawson and he, Flanagan and Clutton, and talk of art and morals, the love-affairs of the present, and the fame of the future. He felt sick at heart. He found that it was easy to make a heroic gesture, but hard to abide by its results. The worst of it was that the work seemed to him very tedious. He had got out of the habit of being asked questions by demonstrators. His attention wandered at lectures. Anatomy was a dreary science, a mere matter of learning by heart an enormous number of facts; dissection bored him; he did not see the use of dissecting out laboriously nerves and arteries when with much less trouble you could see in the diagrams of a book or in the specimens of the pathological museum exactly where they were.

He made friends by chance, but not intimate friends, for he seemed to have nothing in particular to say to his companions. When he tried to interest himself in their concerns, he felt that they found him patronising. He was not of those who can talk of what moves them without caring whether it bores or not the people they talk to. One man, hearing that he had studied art in Paris, and fancying himself on his taste, tried to discuss art with him; but Philip was impatient of views which did not agree with his own; and, finding quickly that the other's ideas were conventional, grew monosyllabic. Philip desired popularity but could bring himself to make no advances to others. A fear of rebuff prevented him from affability, and he concealed his shyness, which was still intense, under a frigid taciturnity. He was going through the same experience as he had done at school, but here the freedom of the medical students' life made it possible for him to live a good deal by himself.

It was through no effort of his that he became friendly with Dunsford, the fresh-complexioned, heavy lad whose acquaintance he had made at the beginning of the session. Dunsford attached himself to Philip merely because he was the first person he had known at St. Luke's. He had no friends in London, and on Saturday nights he and Philip got into the habit of going together to the pit of a music-hall or the gallery of a theatre. He was stupid, but he was good-humoured and never took offence; he always said the obvious thing, but when Philip laughed at him he merely smiled. He had a very sweet smile. Though Philip made him his butt, he liked him; he was amused by his candour and delighted with his agreeable nature: Dunsford had the charm which himself was acutely conscious of not possessing.

They often went to have tea at a shop in Parliament Street, because Dunsford admired one of the young women who waited. Philip did not find anything attractive in her. She was tall and thin, with narrow hips and the chest of a boy.

"No one would look at her in Paris," said Philip scornfully.

"She's got a ripping face," said Dunsford.

"What *does* the face matter?"

She had the small regular features, the blue eyes, and the broad low brow, which the Victorian painters, Lord Leighton, Alma Tadema, and a hundred others, induced the world they lived in to accept as a type of Greek beauty. She seemed to have a great deal of hair: it was arranged with peculiar elaboration and done over the forehead in what she called an Alexandra fringe. She was very anæmic. Her thin lips were pale, and her skin was delicate, of a faint green colour, without a touch of red even in the cheeks. She had very good teeth. She took great pains to prevent her work from spoiling her hands, and they were small, thin, and white. She went about her duties with a bored look.

Dunsford, very shy with women, had never succeeded in getting into conversation with her; and he urged Philip to help him.

"All I want is a lead," he said, "and then I can manage for myself."

Philip, to please him, made one or two remarks, but she answered with monosyllables. She had taken their measure. They were boys, and she surmised they were students. She had no use for them. Dunsford noticed that a man with sandy hair and a bristly moustache, who looked like a German, was favoured with her attention whenever he came into the shop; and then it was only by calling her two or three times that they could induce her to take their order. She used the clients whom she did not know with frigid insolence, and when she was talking to a friend was perfectly indifferent to the calls of the hurried. She had the art of treating women who desired refreshment with just that degree of impertinence which irritated them without affording them an opportunity of complaining to the management. One day Dunsford told him her name was Mildred. He had heard one of the other girls in the shop address her.

"What an odious name," said Philip.

"Why?" asked Dunsford. "I like it."

"It's so pretentious."

It chanced that on this day the German was not there, and, when she brought the tea, Philip, smiling, remarked:

"Your friend's not here today."

"I don't know what you mean," she said coldly.

"I was referring to the nobleman with the sandy moustache. Has he left you for another?"

"Some people would do better to mind their own business," she retorted.

She left them, and, since for a minute or two there was no one to attend to, sat down and looked at the evening paper which a customer had left behind him.

"You are a fool to put her back up," said Dunsford.

"I'm really quite indifferent to the attitude of her vertebræ," replied Philip.

But he was piqued. It irritated him that when he tried to be agreeable with a woman she should take offence. When he asked for the bill, he hazarded a remark which he meant to lead further.

"Are we no longer on speaking terms?" he smiled.

"I'm here to take orders and to wait on customers. I've got nothing to say to them, and I don't want them to say anything to me."

She put down the slip of paper on which she had marked the sum they had to pay, and walked back to the table at which she had been sitting. Philip flushed with anger.

"That's one in the eye for you, Carey," said Dunsford, when they got outside.

"Ill-mannered slut," said Philip. "I shan't go there again."

His influence with Dunsford was strong enough to get him to take their tea elsewhere, and Dunsford soon found another young woman to flirt with. But the snub which the waitress had inflicted on him rankled. If she had treated him with civility he would have been perfectly indifferent to her; but it was obvious that she disliked him rather than otherwise, and his pride was wounded. He could not suppress a desire to be even with her. He was impatient with himself because he had so petty a feeling, but three or four days' firmness, during which he would not go to the shop, did not help him to surmount it; and he came to the conclusion that it would be least trouble to see her. Having done so he would certainly cease to think of her. Pretexting an appointment one afternoon, for he was not a little ashamed of his weakness, he left Dunsford and went straight to the shop which he had vowed never again to enter. He saw the waitress the moment he came in and sat down at one of her tables. He expected her to make some reference to the fact that he had not been there for a week, but when she came up for his order she said nothing. He had heard her say to other customers:

"You're quite a stranger."

She gave no sign that she had ever seen him before. In order to see whether she had really forgotten him, when she brought his tea, he asked:

"Have you seen my friend tonight?"

"No, he's not been in here for some days."

He wanted to use this as the beginning of a conversation, but he was strangely nervous and could think of nothing to say. She gave him no opportunity, but at once went away. He had no chance of saying anything till he asked for his bill.

"Filthy weather, isn't it?" he said.

It was mortifying that he had been forced to prepare such a phrase as that. He could not make out why she filled him with such embarrassment.

"It don't make much difference to me what the weather is, having to be in here all day."

There was an insolence in her tone that peculiarly irritated him. A sarcasm rose to his lips, but he forced himself to be silent.

"I wish to God she'd say something really cheeky," he raged to himself, "so that I could report her and get her sacked. It would serve her damned well right."

LVI

HE COULD not get her out of his mind. He laughed angrily at his own foolishness: it was absurd to care what an anæmic little waitress said to him; but he was strangely humiliated. Though no one knew of the humiliation but Dunsford, and he had certainly forgotten, Philip felt that he could have no peace till he had wiped it out. He thought over what he had better do. He made up his mind that he would go to the shop every day; it was obvious that he had made a disagreeable impression on her, but he thought he had the wits to eradicate it; he would take care not to say anything at which the most susceptible person could be offended. All this he did, but it had no effect. When he went in and said good-evening she answered with the same words, but when once he omitted to say it in order to see whether she would say it first, she said nothing at all. He murmured in his heart an expression which though frequently applicable to members of the female sex is not often used of them in polite society; but with an unmoved face he ordered his tea. He made up his mind not to speak a word, and left the shop without his usual good-night. He promised himself that he would not go any more, but the next day at tea-time he grew restless. He tried to think of other things, but he had no command over his thoughts. At last he said desperately:

"After all there's no reason why I shouldn't go if I want to."

The struggle with himself had taken a long time, and it was getting on for seven when he entered the shop.

"I thought you weren't coming," the girl said to him, when he sat down.

His heart leaped in his bosom and he felt himself reddening. "I was detained. I couldn't come before."

"Cutting up people, I suppose?"

"Not so bad as that."

"You are a stoodent, aren't you?"

"Yes."

But that seemed to satisfy her curiosity. She went away and, since at that late hour there was nobody else at her tables, she immersed herself in a novelette. This was before the time of the sixpenny reprints. There was a regular supply of inexpensive fiction written to order by poor hacks for the consumption of the illiterate. Philip was elated; she had addressed him of her own accord; he saw the time approaching when his turn would come and he would tell her exactly what he thought of her. It would be a great comfort to express the immensity of his contempt. He looked at her. It was true that her profile was beautiful; it was extraordinary how English girls of that class had so often a perfection of outline which took your breath away, but it was as cold as marble; and the faint green of her delicate skin gave an impression of unhealthiness. All the waitresses were dressed alike, in plain black dresses, with a white apron, cuffs, and a small cap. On a half sheet of paper that he had in his pocket Philip made a sketch of her as she sat leaning over her book (she outlined the words with her lips as she read), and left it on the table when he went away. It was an inspiration, for next day, when he came in, she smiled at him.

"I didn't know you could draw," she said.

"I was an art-student in Paris for two years."

"I showed that drawing you left be'ind you last night to the manageress and she *was* struck with it. Was it meant to be me?"

"It was," said Philip.

When she went for his tea, one of the other girls came up to him.

"I saw that picture you done of Miss Rogers. It was the very image of her," she said.

That was the first time he had heard her name, and when he wanted his bill he called her by it.

"I see you know my name," she said, when she came.

"Your friend mentioned it when she said something to me about that drawing."

"She wants you to do one of her. Don't you do it. If you once begin you'll have to go on, and they'll all be wanting you to do them." Then without a pause, with peculiar inconsequence, she said: "Where's that young fellow that used to come with you? Has he gone away?"

"Fancy you remembering him," said Philip.

"He was a nice-looking young fellow."

Philip felt quite a peculiar sensation in his heart. He did not know what it was. Dunsford had jolly curling hair, a fresh complexion, and a beautiful smile. Philip thought of these advantages with envy.

"Oh, he's in love," said he, with a little laugh.

Philip repeated every word of the conversation to himself as he limped home. She was quite friendly with him now. When opportunity arose he would offer to make a more finished sketch of her, he was sure she would like that; her face was interesting, the profile was lovely, and there was something curiously fascinating about the chlorotic colour. He tried to think what it was like; at first he thought of pea soup; but, driving away that idea angrily, he thought of the petals of a yellow rosebud when you tore it to pieces before it had burst. He had no ill-feeling towards her now.

"She's not a bad sort," he murmured.

It was silly of him to take offence at what she had said; it was doubtless his own fault; she had not meant to make herself disagreeable: he ought to be accustomed by now to making at first sight a bad impression on people. He was flattered at the success of his drawing; she looked upon him with more interest now that she was aware of this small talent. He was restless next day. He thought of going to lunch at the tea-shop, but he was certain there would be many people there then, and Mildred would not be able to talk to him. He had managed before this to get out of having tea with Dunsford, and, punctually at half past four (he had looked at his watch a dozen times), he went into the shop.

Mildred had her back turned to him. She was sitting down, talking to the German whom Philip had seen there every day till a fortnight ago and since then had not seen at all. She was laughing at what he said. Philip thought she had a common laugh, and it made him shudder. He called her, but she took no notice; he called her again; then, growing angry, for he was impatient, he rapped the table loudly with his stick. She approached sulkily.

"How d'you do?" he said.

"You seem to be in a great hurry."

She looked down at him with the insolent manner which he knew so well.

"I say, what's the matter with you?" he asked.

"If you'll kindly give your order I'll get what you want. I can't stand talking all night."

"Tea and toasted bun, please," Philip answered briefly.

He was furious with her. He had *The Star* with him and read it elaborately when she brought the tea.

"If you'll give me my bill now I needn't trouble you again," he said icily.

She wrote out the slip, placed it on the table, and went back to the German. Soon she was talking to him with animation. He was a man of middle height, with the round head of his nation and a sallow face; his moustache was large and bristling; he had on a tail-coat and gray trousers, and he wore a massive gold watch-chain. Philip thought the other girls looked from him to the pair at the table and exchanged significant glances. He felt certain they were laughing at him, and his blood boiled. He detested Mildred now with all his heart. He knew that the best thing he could do was to cease coming to the tea-shop, but he could not bear to think that he had been worsted in the affair, and he devised a plan to show her that he despised her. Next day he sat down at another table and ordered his tea from another waitress. Mildred's friend was there again and she was talking to him. She paid no attention to Philip, and so when he went out he chose a moment when she had to cross his path: as he passed he looked at her as though he had never seen her before. He repeated this for three or four days. He expected that presently she would take the opportunity to say something to him; he thought she would ask why he never came to one of her tables now, and he had prepared an answer charged with all the loathing he felt for her. He knew it was absurd to trouble, but he could not help himself. She had beaten him again. The German suddenly disappeared, but Philip still sat at other tables. She paid no attention to him. Suddenly he realised that what he did was a matter of complete indifference to her; he could go on in that way till doomsday, and it would have no effect.

"I've not finished yet," he said to himself.

The day after he sat down in his old seat, and when she came up said good-evening as though he had not ignored her for a week. His face was placid, but he could not prevent the mad beating of his heart. At that time the musical comedy had lately leaped into public favour, and he was sure that Mildred would be delighted to go to one.

"I say," he said suddenly, "I wonder if you'd dine with me one night and come to *The Belle of New York*. I'll get a couple of stalls."

He added the last sentence in order to tempt her. He knew that when the girls went to the play it was either in the pit, or, if some man took them, seldom to more expensive seats than the upper circle. Mildred's pale face showed no change of expression.

"I don't mind," she said.

"When will you come?"

"I get off early on Thursdays."

They made arrangements. Mildred lived with an aunt at Herne Hill. The play began at eight so they must dine at seven. She proposed that he should meet her in the second-class waiting-room at Victoria Station. She showed no pleasure, but accepted the invitation as though she conferred a favour. Philip was vaguely irritated.

LVII

PHILIP arrived at Victoria Station nearly half an hour before the time which Mildred had appointed, and sat down in the second-class waiting-room. He waited and she did not come. He began to grow anxious, and walked into the station watching the incoming suburban trains; the hour which she had fixed passed, and still there was no sign of her. Philip was impatient. He went into the other waiting-rooms and looked at the people sitting in them. Suddenly his heart gave a great thud.

"There you are. I thought you were never coming."

"I like that after keeping me wait-

ing all this time. I had half a mind to go back home again."

"But you said you'd come to the second-class waiting-room."

"I didn't say any such thing. It isn't exactly likely I'd sit in the second-class room when I could sit in the first, is it?"

Though Philip was sure he had not made a mistake, he said nothing, and they got into a cab.

"Where are we dining?" she asked.

"I thought of the Adelphi Restaurant. Will that suit you?"

"I don't mind where we dine."

She spoke ungraciously. She was put out by being kept waiting and answered Philip's attempt at conversation with monosyllables. She wore a long cloak of some rough, dark material and a crochet shawl over her head. They reached the restaurant and sat down at a table. She looked round with satisfaction. The red shades to the candles on the tables, the gold of the decorations, the looking-glasses, lent the room a sumptuous air.

"I've never been here before."

She gave Philip a smile. She had taken off her cloak; and he saw that she wore a pale blue dress, cut square at the neck; and her hair was more elaborately arranged than ever. He had ordered champagne and when it came her eyes sparkled.

"You are going it," she said.

"Because I've ordered fiz?" he asked carelessly, as though he never drank anything else.

"I *was* surprised when you asked me to do a theatre with you."

Conversation did not go very easily, for she did not seem to have much to say; and Philip was nervously conscious that he was not amusing her. She listened carelessly to his remarks, with her eyes on other diners, and made no pretence that she was interested in him. He made one or two little jokes, but she took them quite seriously. The only sign of vivacity he got was when he spoke of the other girls in the shop; she could not bear the manageress and told him all her misdeeds at length.

"I can't stick her at any price and all the air she gives herself. Sometimes I've got more than half a mind to tell her something she doesn't think I know anything about."

"What is that?" asked Philip.

"Well, I happen to know that she's not above going to Eastbourne with a man for the week-end now and again. One of the girls has a married sister who goes there with her husband, and

she's seen her. She was staying at the same boarding-house, and she 'ad a wedding-ring on, and I know for one she's not married."

Philip filled her glass, hoping that champagne would make her more affable; he was anxious that his little jaunt should be a success. He noticed that she held her knife as though it were a pen-holder, and when she drank protruded her little finger. He started several topics of conversation, but he could get little out of her, and he remembered with irritation that he had seen her talking nineteen to the dozen and laughing with the German. They finished dinner and went to the play. Philip was a very cultured young man, and he looked upon musical comedy with scorn. He thought the jokes vulgar and the melodies obvious; it seemed to him that they did these things much better in France; but Mildred enjoyed herself thoroughly; she laughed till her sides ached, looking at Philip now and then when something tickled her to exchange a glance of pleasure; and she applauded rapturously.

"This is the seventh time I've been," she said, after the first act, "and I don't mind if I come seven times more."

She was much interested in the women who surrounded them in the stalls. She pointed out to Philip those who were painted and those who wore false hair.

"It is horrible, these West-end people," she said. "I don't know how they can do it." She put her hand to her hair. "Mine's all my own, every bit of it."

She found no one to admire, and whenever she spoke of anyone it was to say something disagreeable. It made Philip uneasy. He supposed that next day she would tell the girls in the shop that he had taken her out and that he had bored her to death. He disliked her, and yet, he knew not why, he wanted to be with her. On the way home he asked:

"I hope you've enjoyed yourself?"

"Rather."

"Will you come out with me again one evening?"

"I don't mind."

He could never get beyond such expressions as that. Her indifference maddened him.

"That sounds as if you didn't much care if you came or not."

"Oh, if you don't take me out some other fellow will. I need never want for men who'll take me to the theatre."

Philip was silent. They came to the station, and he went to the booking-office.

"I've got my season," she said.

"I thought I'd take you home as it's rather late, if you don't mind."

"Oh, I don't mind if it gives you any pleasure."

He took a single first for her and a return for himself.

"Well, you're not mean, I will say that for you," she said, when he opened the carriage-door.

Philip did not know whether he was pleased or sorry when other people entered and it was impossible to speak. They got out at Herne Hill, and he accompanied her to the corner of the road in which she lived.

"I'll say good-night to you here," she said, holding out her hand. "You'd better not come up to the door. I know what people are, and I don't want to have anybody talking."

She said good-night and walked quickly away. He could see the white shawl in the darkness. He thought she might turn round, but she did not. Philip saw which house she went into, and in a moment he walked along to look at it. It was a trim, common little house of yellow brick, exactly like all the other little houses in the street. He stood outside for a few minutes, and presently the window on the top floor was darkened. Philip strolled slowly back to the station. The evening had been unsatisfactory. He felt irritated, restless, and miserable.

When he lay in bed he seemed still to see her sitting in the corner of the railway carriage, with the white crochet shawl over her head. He did not know how he was to get through the hours that must pass before his eyes rested on her again. He thought drowsily of her thin face, with its delicate features, and the greenish pallor of her skin. He was not happy with her, but he was unhappy away from her. He wanted to sit by her side and look at her, he wanted to touch her, he wanted . . . the thought came to him and he did not finish it, suddenly he grew wide awake . . . he wanted to kiss the thin, pale mouth with its narrow lips. The truth came to him at last. He was in love with her. It was incredible.

He had often thought of falling in love, and there was one scene which he had pictured to himself over and over again. He saw himself coming into a ball-room; his eyes fell on a little group of men and women talking; and one of the women turned round. Her eyes fell upon him, and he knew that the gasp in his throat was in her throat too. He stood quite still. She was tall and dark and beautiful with eyes like the night; she was dressed in white, and in her black hair shone diamonds; they stared at one another, forgetting that people surrounded them. He went straight up to her, and she moved a little towards him. Both felt that the formality of introduction was out of place. He spoke to her.

"I've been looking for you all my life," he said.

"You've come at last," she murmured.

"Will you dance with me?"

She surrendered herself to his outstretched hands and they danced. (Philip always pretended that he was not lame.) She danced divinely.

"I've never danced with anyone who danced like you," she said.

She tore up her programme, and they danced together the whole evening.

"I'm so thankful that I waited for you," he said to her. "I knew that in the end I must meet you."

People in the ball-room stared. They did not care. They did not wish to hide their passion. At last they went into the garden. He flung a light cloak over her shoulders and put her in a waiting cab. They caught the midnight train to Paris; and they sped through the silent, star-lit night into the unknown.

He thought of this old fancy of his, and it seemed impossible that he should be in love with Mildred Rogers. Her name was grotesque. He did not think her pretty; he hated the thinness of her, only that evening he had noticed how the bones of her chest stood out in evening-dress; he went over her features one by one; he did not like her mouth, and the unhealthiness of her colour vaguely repelled him. She was common. Her phrases, so bald and few, constantly repeated, showed the emptiness of her mind; he recalled her vulgar little laugh at the jokes of the musical comedy; and he remembered the little finger carefully extended when she held her glass to her mouth; her manners like her conversation, were odiously genteel. He remembered her insolence; sometimes he had felt inclined to box her ears; and suddenly, he knew not why, perhaps it was the thought of hitting her or the recollection of her tiny, beautiful ears, he was seized by an uprush of emotion. He yearned for her. He thought of taking her in his arms, the thin, fragile body, and kissing her pale mouth: he wanted to pass his fingers down the slightly greenish cheeks. He wanted her.

He had thought of love as a rapture which seized one so that all the world seemed spring-like, he had looked forward to an ecstatic happiness; but this was not happiness; it was a hunger of the soul, it was a painful yearning, it was a bitter anguish he had never known before. He tried to think when it had first come to him. He did not know. He only remembered that each time he had gone into the shop, after the first two or three times, it had been with a little feeling in the heart that was pain; and he remembered that when she spoke to him he felt curiously breathless. When she left him it was wretchedness, and when she came to him again it was despair.

He stretched himself in his bed as a dog stretches himself. He wondered how he was going to endure that ceaseless aching of his soul.

LVIII

Philip woke early next morning, and his first thought was of Mildred. It struck him that he might meet her at Victoria Station and walk with her to the shop. He shaved quickly, scrambled into his clothes, and took a bus to the station. He was there by twenty to eight and watched the incoming trains. Crowds poured out of them, clerks and shop-people at that early hour, and thronged up the platform: they hurried along, sometimes in pairs, here and there a group of girls, but more often alone. They were white, most of them, ugly in the early morning, and they had an abstracted look; the younger ones walked lightly, as though the cement of the platform were pleasant to tread, but the others went as though impelled by a machine: their faces were set in an anxious frown.

At last Philip saw Mildred, and he went up to her eagerly.

"Good-morning," he said. "I thought I'd come and see how you were after last night."

She wore an old brown ulster and a sailor hat. It was very clear that she was not pleased to see him.

"Oh, I'm all right. I haven't got much time to waste."

"D'you mind if I walk down Victoria Street with you?"

"I'm none too early. I shall have to walk fast," she answered, looking down at Philip's club-foot.

He turned scarlet.

"I beg your pardon. I won't detain you."

"You can please yourself."

She went on, and he with a sinking heart made his way home to breakfast. He hated her. He knew he was a fool to bother about her; she was not the sort of woman who would ever care two straws for him, and she must look upon his deformity with distaste. He made up his mind that he would not go in to tea that afternoon, but, hating himself, he went. She nodded to him as he came in and smiled.

"I expect I was rather short with you this morning," she said. "You see, I didn't expect you, and it came like a surprise."

"Oh, it doesn't matter at all."

He felt that a great weight had suddenly been lifted from him. He was infinitely grateful for one word of kindness.

"Why don't you sit down?" he asked. "Nobody's wanting you just now."

"I don't mind if I do."

He looked at her, but could think of nothing to say; he racked his brains anxiously, seeking for a remark which should keep her by him; he wanted to tell her how much she meant to him; but he did not know how to make love now that he loved in earnest.

"Where's your friend with the fair moustache? I haven't seen him lately."

"Oh, he's gone back to Birmingham. He's in business there. He only comes up to London every now and again."

"Is he in love with you?"

"You'd better ask him," she said, with a laugh. "I don't know what it's got to do with you if he is."

A bitter answer leaped to his tongue, but he was learning self-restraint.

"I wonder why you say things like that," was all he permitted himself to say.

She looked at him with those indifferent eyes of hers.

"It looks as if you didn't set much store on me," he added.

"Why should I?"

"No reason at all."

He reached over for his paper.

"You are quick-tempered," she said, when she saw the gesture. "You do take offence easily."

He smiled and looked at her appealingly.

"Will you do something for me?" he asked.

"That depends what it is."

"Let me walk back to the station with you tonight."

"I don't mind."

He went out after tea and went back to his rooms, but at eight o'clock, when the shop closed, he was waiting outside.

"You are a caution," she said, when she came out. "I don't understand you."

"I shouldn't have thought it was very difficult," he answered bitterly.

"Did any of the girls see you waiting for me?"

"I don't know and I don't care."

"They all laugh at you, you know. They say you're spoony on me."

"Much you care," he muttered.

"Now then, quarrelsome."

At the station he took a ticket and said he was going to accompany her home.

"You don't seem to have much to do with your time," she said.

"I suppose I can waste it in my own way."

They seemed to be always on the verge of a quarrel. The fact was that he hated himself for loving her. She seemed to be constantly humiliating him, and for each snub that he endured he owed her a grudge. But she was in a friendly mood that evening, and talkative: she told him that her parents were dead; she gave him to understand that she did not have to earn her living, but worked for amusement.

"My aunt doesn't like my going to business. I can have the best of everything at home. I don't want you to think I work because I need to."

Philip knew that she was not speaking the truth. The gentility of her class made her use this pretence to avoid the stigma attached to earning her living.

"My family's very well-connected," she said.

Philip smiled faintly, and she noticed it.

"What are you laughing at?" she said quickly. "Don't you believe I'm telling you the truth?"

"Of course I do," he answered.

She looked at him suspiciously, but in a moment could not resist the temptation to impress him with the splendour of her early days.

"My father always kept a dog-cart, and we had three servants. We had a cook and a housemaid and an odd man. We used to grow beautiful roses. People used to stop at the gate and ask who the house belonged to, the roses were so beautiful. Of course it isn't very nice for me having to mix with them girls in the shop, it's not the class of person I've been used to, and sometimes I really think I'll give up business on that account. It's not the work I mind, don't think that; but it's the class of people I have to mix with."

They were sitting opposite one another in the train, and Philip, listening sympathetically to what she said, was quite happy. He was amused at her naïveté and slightly touched. There was a very faint colour in her cheeks. He was thinking that it would be delightful to kiss the tip of her chin.

"The moment you come into the shop I saw you was a gentleman in every sense of the word. Was your father a professional man?"

"He was a doctor."

"You can always tell a professional man. There's something about them, I don't know what it is, but I know at once."

They walked along from the station together.

"I say, I want you to come and see another play with me," he said.

"I don't mind," she said.

"You might go so far as to say you'd like to."

"Why?"

"It doesn't matter. Let's fix a day. Would Saturday night suit you?"

"Yes, that'll do."

They made further arrangements, and then found themselves at the corner of the road in which she lived. She gave him her hand, and he held it.

"I say, I do so awfully want to call you Mildred."

"You may if you like, I don't care."

"And you'll call me Philip, won't you?"

"I will if I can think of it. It seems more natural to call you Mr. Carey."

He drew her slightly towards him, but she leaned back.

"What are you doing?"

"Won't you kiss me good-night?" he whispered.

"Impudence!" she said.

She snatched away her hand and hurried towards her house.

Philip bought tickets for Saturday night. It was not one of the days on which she got off early and therefore she would have no time to go home and change; but she meant to bring a frock up with her in the morning and hurry into her clothes at the shop. If the manageress was in a good temper she would let her go at seven. Philip had agreed to wait outside from a quarter past seven onwards. He looked forward to the occasion with painful eagerness, for in the cab on the way from the theatre to the station he thought she would let him kiss her. The vehicle gave every facility for a man to put his arm round a girl's waist, (an advantage which the hansom had over the taxi of the present day,) and the delight of that was worth the cost of the evening's entertainment.

But on Saturday afternoon when he went in to have tea, in order to confirm the arrangements, he met the man with the fair moustache coming out of the shop. He knew by now that he was called Miller. He was a naturalized German, who had anglicised his name, and he had lived many years in England. Philip had heard him speak, and, though his English was fluent and natural, it had not quite the intonation of the native. Philip knew that he was flirting with Mildred, and he was horribly jealous of him; but he took comfort in the coldness of her temperament, which otherwise distressed him; and, thinking her incapable of passion, he looked upon his rival as no better off than himself. But his heart sank now, for his first thought was that Miller's sudden appearance might interfere with the jaunt which he had so looked forward to. He entered, sick with apprehension. The waitress came up to him, took his order for tea, and presently brought it.

"I'm awfully sorry," she said, with an expression on her face of real distress. "I shan't be able to come tonight after all."

"Why?" said Philip.

"Don't look so stern about it," she laughed. "It's not my fault. My aunt was taken ill last night, and it's the girl's night out so I must go and sit with her. She can't be left alone, can she?"

"It doesn't matter. I'll see you home instead."

"But you've got the tickets. It would be a pity to waste them."

He took them out of his pocket and deliberately tore them up.

"What are you doing that for?"

"You don't suppose I want to go and see a rotten musical comedy by myself, do you? I only took seats there for your sake."

"You can't see me home if that's what you mean?"

"You've made other arrangements."

"I don't know what you mean by that. You're just as selfish as all the rest of them. You only think of yourself. It's not my fault if my aunt's queer."

She quickly wrote out his bill and left him. Philip knew very little about women, or he would have been aware that one should accept their most transparent lies. He made up his mind that he would watch the shop and see for certain whether Mildred went out with the German. He had an unhappy passion for certainty. At seven he stationed himself on the opposite pavement. He looked about for Miller, but did not see him. In ten minutes she came out, she had on the cloak and shawl which she had worn when he took her to the Shaftesbury Theatre. It was obvious that she was not going home. She saw him before he had time to move away, started a little, and then came straight up to him.

"What are you doing here?" she said.

"Taking the air," he answered.

"You're spying on me, you dirty little cad. I thought you was a gentleman."

"Did you think a gentleman would be likely to take any interest in you?" he murmured.

There was a devil within him which forced him to make matters worse. He wanted to hurt her as much as she was hurting him.

"I suppose I can change my mind if I like. I'm not obliged to come out with you. I tell you I'm going home, and I won't be followed or spied upon."

"Have you seen Miller today?"

"That's no business of yours. In point of fact I haven't, so you're wrong again."

"I saw him this afternoon. He'd just come out of the shop when I went in."

"Well, what if he did? I can go out with him if I want to, can't I? I don't know what you've got to say to it."

"He's keeping you waiting, isn't he?"

"Well, I'd rather wait for him than have you wait for me. Put that in your pipe and smoke it. And now p'raps you'll go off home and mind your own business in future."

His mood changed suddenly from anger to despair, and his voice trembled when he spoke.

"I say, don't be beastly with me, Mildred. You know I'm awfully fond of you. I think I love you with all my heart. Won't you change your mind? I was looking forward to this evening so awfully. You see, he hasn't come, and he can't care twopence about you really. Won't you dine with me? I'll get some more tickets, and we'll go anywhere you like."

"I tell you I won't. It's no good you talking. I've made up my mind, and when I make up my mind I keep to it."

He looked at her for a moment. His heart was torn with anguish. People were hurrying past them on the pavement, and cabs and omnibuses rolled by noisily. He saw that Mildred's eyes were wandering. She was afraid of missing Miller in the crowd.

"I can't go on like this," groaned Philip. "It's too degrading. If I go now I go for good. Unless you'll come with me tonight you'll never see me again."

"You seem to think that'll be an awful thing for me. All I say is, good riddance to bad rubbish."

"Then good-bye."

He nodded and limped away slowly, for he hoped with all his heart that she would call him back. At the next lamp-post he stopped and looked over his shoulder. He thought she might beckon to him—he was willing to forget everything, he was ready for any humiliation—but she had turned away, and apparently had ceased to trouble about him. He realised that she was glad to be quit of him.

LIX

PHILIP passed the evening wretchedly. He had told his landlady that he would not be in, so there was nothing for him to eat, and he had to go to Gatti's for dinner. Afterwards he went back to his rooms, but Griffiths on the floor above him was having a party, and the noisy merriment made his own misery more hard to bear. He went to a music-hall, but it was Saturday night and there was standing-room only: after half an hour of boredom his legs grew tired and he went home. He tried to read, but he could not fix his attention; and yet it was necessary that he should work hard. His examination in biology was in little more than a fortnight, and, though it was easy, he had neglected his lectures of late and was conscious that he knew nothing. It was only a *viva*, however, and he felt sure that in a fortnight he could find out enough about the subject to scrape through. He had confidence in his intelligence. He threw aside his book and gave himself up to thinking deliberately of the matter which was in his mind all the time.

He reproached himself bitterly for his behaviour that evening. Why had he given her the alternative that she must dine with him or else never see him again? Of course she refused. He should have allowed for her pride. He had burnt his ships behind him. It would not be so hard to bear if he thought that she was suffering now, but he knew her too well: she was perfectly indifferent to him. If he hadn't been a fool he would have pretended to believe her story; he ought to have had the strength to conceal his disappointment and the self-control to master his temper. He could not tell why he loved her. He had read of the idealisation that takes place in love, but he saw her exactly as she was. She was not amusing or clever, her mind was common; she had a vulgar shrewdness which revolted him, she had no gentleness nor softness. As she would have put it herself, she was on the make. What aroused her admiration was a clever trick played on an unsuspecting person; to 'do' somebody always gave her satisfaction. Philip laughed savagely as he thought of her gentility and the refinement with which she ate her food; she could not bear a coarse word, so far as her limited vocabulary reached she had a passion for euphemisms, and she scented indecency everywhere; she never spoke of trousers but referred to them as nether garments; she thought it slightly indelicate to blow her nose and did it in a deprecating way. She was dreadfully anæmic and suffered from the dyspepsia which accompanies that ailing. Philip was repelled by her flat breast and narrow hips, and he hated the vulgar way in which she did her hair. He loathed and despised himself for loving her.

The fact remained that he was helpless. He felt just as he had felt sometimes in the hands of a bigger boy at school. He had struggled against the superior strength till his own strength was gone, and he was rendered quite powerless—he remembered the peculiar languor he had felt in his limbs, almost as though he were paralysed—so that he could not help himself at all. He might have been dead. He felt just that same weakness now. He loved the woman so that he knew he had never loved before. He did not mind her faults of person or of character, he thought he loved them too: at all events they meant nothing to him. It did not seem himself that was concerned; he felt that he had been seized by some strange force that moved him against his will, contrary to his interests; and because he had a passion for freedom he hated the chains which bound him. He laughed at himself when he thought how often he had longed to experience the overwhelming passion. He cursed himself because he had given way to it. He thought of the beginnings; nothing of all this would have happened if he had not gone into the shop with Dunsford. The whole thing was his own fault. Except for his ridiculous vanity he would never have troubled himself with the ill-mannered slut.

At all events the occurrences of that evening had finished the whole affair. Unless he was lost to all sense of shame he could not go back. He wanted passionately to get rid of the love that obsessed him; it was degrading and hateful. He must prevent himself from thinking of her. In a little while the anguish he suffered must grow less. His mind went back to the past. He wondered whether Emily Wilkinson and Fanny Price had endured on his account anything like the torment that he suffered now. He felt a pang of remorse.

"I didn't know then what it was like," he said to himself.

He slept very badly. The next day was Sunday, and he worked at his biology. He sat with the book in front of him, forming the words with his lips in order to fix his attention, but he could remember nothing. He found his thoughts going back to Mildred every minute, and he repeated to himself the exact words of the quarrel they had had. He had to force himself back to his book. He went out for a walk. The streets on the South side of the river were dingy enough on week-days, but there was an energy, a coming and going, which gave them a sordid vivacity; but on Sundays, with no shops open, no carts in the roadway, silent and depressed, they were indescribably dreary. Philip thought that day would never end. But he was so tired that he slept heavily, and when Monday came he entered upon life with determination. Christmas was approaching, and a good many of the students had gone into the country for the short holiday between the two parts of the winter session; but Philip had refused his uncle's invitation to go down to Blackstable. He had given the approaching examination as his excuse, but in point of fact he had been unwilling to leave London and Mildred. He had neglected his work so much that now he had only a fortnight to learn what the curriculum allowed three months for. He set to work seriously. He found it easier each day not to think of Mildred. He congratulated himself on his force of character. The pain he suffered was no longer anguish, but a sort of soreness, like what one might be expected to feel if one had been thrown off a horse and, though no bones were broken, were bruised all over and shaken. Philip found that he was able to observe with curiosity the condition he had been in during the last few weeks. He analysed his feelings with interest. He was a little amused at himself. One thing that struck him was how little under those circumstances it mattered what one thought; the system of personal philosophy, which had given him great satisfaction to devise, had not served him. He was puzzled by this.

But sometimes in the street he would see a girl who looked so like Mildred that his heart seemed to stop beating. Then he could not help himself, he hurried on to catch her up, eager and anxious, only to find that it was a total stranger. Men came back from the country, and he went with Dunsford to have tea at an A. B. C. shop. The well-known uniform made him so miserable that he could not speak. The thought came to him that perhaps she had been transferred to another establishment of the firm for which she worked, and he might suddenly find himself face to face with her. The idea filled him with panic, so that he feared Dunsford would see that something was the matter with him: he could not think of anything to say; he pretended to listen to what Dunsford was talking about; the conversation maddened him; and it was all he could do to prevent himself from crying out to Dunsford for Heaven's sake to hold his tongue.

Then came the day of his examination. Philip, when his turn arrived, went forward to the examiner's table with the utmost confidence. He answered three or four questions. Then they showed him various specimens; he had been to very few lectures and, as soon as he was asked about things which he could not learn from books, he was floored. He did what he could to hide his ignorance, the examiner did not insist, and soon his ten minutes were over. He felt certain he had passed; but next day, when he went up to the examination buildings to see the result posted on the door, he was

astounded not to find his number among those who had satisfied the examiners. In amazement he read the list three times. Dunsford was with him.

"I say, I'm awfully sorry you're ploughed," he said.

He had just inquired Philip's number. Philip turned and saw by his radiant face that Dunsford had passed.

"Oh, it doesn't matter a bit," said Philip. "I'm jolly glad you're all right. I shall go up again in July."

He was very anxious to pretend he did not mind, and on their way back along The Embankment insisted on talking of indifferent things. Dunsford good-naturedly wanted to discuss the causes of Philip's failure, but Philip was obstinately casual. He was horribly mortified; and the fact that Dunsford, whom he looked upon as a very pleasant but quite stupid fellow, had passed made his own rebuff harder to bear. He had always been proud of his intelligence, and now he asked himself desperately whether he was not mistaken in the opinion he held of himself. In the three months of the winter session the students who had joined in October had already shaken down into groups, and it was clear which were brilliant, which were clever or industrious, and which were 'rotters.' Philip was conscious that his failure was a surprise to no one but himself. It was tea-time, and he knew that a lot of men would be having tea in the basement of the Medical School: those who had passed the examination would be exultant, those who disliked him would look at him with satisfaction, and the poor devils who had failed would sympathise with him in order to receive sympathy. His instinct was not to go near the hospital for a week, when the affair would be no more thought of, but, because he hated so much to go just then, he went: he wanted to inflict suffering upon himself. He forgot for the moment his maxim of life to follow his inclinations with due regard for the policeman round the corner; or, if he acted in accordance with it, there must have been some strange morbidity in his nature which made him take a grim pleasure in self-torture.

But later on, when he had endured the ordeal to which he forced himself, going out into the night after the noisy conversation in the smoking-room, he was seized with a feeling of utter loneliness. He seemed to himself absurd and futile. He had an urgent need of consolation, and the temptation to see Mildred was irresistible. He thought bitterly that there was small chance of consolation from her; but he wanted to see her even if he did not speak to her; after all, she was a waitress and would be obliged to serve him. She was the only person in the world he cared for. There was no use in hiding that fact from himself. Of course it would be humiliating to go back to the shop as though nothing had happened, but he had not much self-respect left. Though he would not confess it to himself, he had hoped each day that she would write to him; she knew that a letter addressed to the hospital would find him; but she had not written: it was evident that she cared nothing if she saw him again or not. And he kept on repeating to himself:

"I must see her. I must see her."

The desire was so great that he could not give the time necessary to walk, but jumped in a cab. He was too thrifty to use one when it could possibly be avoided. He stood outside the shop for a minute or two. The thought came to him that perhaps she had left, and in terror he walked in quickly. He saw her at once. He sat down and she came up to him.

"A cup of tea and a muffin, please," he ordered.

He could hardly speak. He was afraid for a moment that he was going to cry.

"I almost thought you was dead," she said.

She was smiling. Smiling! She seemed to have forgotten completely that last scene which Philip had repeated to himself a hundred times.

"I thought if you'd wanted to see me you'd write," he answered.

"I've got too much to do to think about writing letters."

It seemed impossible for her to say a gracious thing. Philip cursed the fate which chained him to such a woman. She went away to fetch his tea.

"Would you like me to sit down for a minute or two?" she said, when she brought it.

"Yes."

"Where have you been all this time?"

"I've been in London."

"I thought you'd gone away for the holidays. Why haven't you been in then?"

Philip looked at her with haggard, passionate eyes.

"Don't you remember that I said I'd never see you again?"

"What are you doing now then?"

She seemed anxious to make him drink up the cup of his humiliation; but he knew her well enough to know that she spoke at random; she hurt him frightfully, and never even tried to. He did not answer.

"It was a nasty trick you played on me, spying on me like that. I always thought you was a gentleman in every sense of the word."

"Don't be beastly to me, Mildred. I can't bear it."

"You are a funny feller. I can't make you out."

"It's very simple. I'm such a blasted

fool as to love you with all my heart and soul, and I know that you don't care twopence for me."

"If you had been a gentleman I think you'd have come next day and begged my pardon."

She had no mercy. He looked at her neck and thought how he would like to jab it with the knife he had for his muffin. He knew enough anatomy to make pretty certain of getting the carotid artery. And at the same time he wanted to cover her pale, thin face with kisses.

"If I could only make you understand how frightfully I'm in love with you."

"You haven't begged my pardon yet."

He grew very white. She felt that she had done nothing wrong on that occasion. She wanted him now to humble himself. He was very proud. For one instant he felt inclined to tell her to go to hell, but he dared not. His passion made him abject. He was willing to submit to anything rather than not see her.

"I'm very sorry, Mildred. I beg your pardon."

He had to force the words out. It was a horrible effort.

"Now you've said that I don't mind telling you that I wish I had come out with you that evening. I thought Miller was a gentleman, but I've discovered my mistake now. I soon sent him about his business."

Philip gave a little gasp.

"Mildred, won't you come out with me tonight? Let's go and dine somewhere."

"Oh, I can't. My aunt'll be expecting me home."

"I'll send her a wire. You can say you've been detained in the shop; she won't know any better. Oh, do come, for God's sake. I haven't seen you for so long, and I want to talk to you."

She looked down at her clothes.

"Never mind about that. We'll go somewhere where it doesn't matter how you're dressed. And we'll go to a music-hall afterwards. Please say yes. It would give me so much pleasure."

She hesitated a moment; he looked at her with pitifully appealing eyes.

"Well, I don't mind if I do. I haven't been out anywhere since I don't know how long."

It was with the greatest difficulty he could prevent himself from seizing her hand there and then to cover it with kisses.

LX

THEY dined in Soho. Philip was tremulous with joy. It was not one of the more crowded of those cheap restaurants where the respectable and needy dine in the belief that it is bohemian and the assurance that it is economical. It was a humble establishment, kept by a good man from Rouen and his wife, that Philip had discovered by accident. He had been attracted by the Gallic look of the window, in which was generally an uncooked steak on one plate and on each side two dishes of raw vegetables. There was one seedy French waiter, who was attempting to learn English in a house where he never heard anything but French; and the customers were a few ladies of easy virtue, a *ménage* or two, who had their own napkins reserved for them, and a few queer men who came in for hurried, scanty meals.

Here Mildred and Philip were able to get a table to themselves. Philip sent the waiter for a bottle of Burgundy from the neighbouring tavern, and they had a *potage aux herbes,* a steak from the window *aux pommes,* and an *omelette au kirsch.* There was really an air of romance in the meal and in the place. Mildred, at first a little reserved in her appreciation—"I never quite trust these foreign places, you never know what there is in these messed up dishes"—was insensibly moved by it.

"I like this place, Philip," she said. "You feel you can put your elbows on the table, don't you?"

A tall fellow came in, with a mane of gray hair and a ragged thin beard. He wore a dilapidated cloak and a wide-awake hat. He nodded to Philip, who had met him there before.

"He looks like an anarchist," said Mildred.

"He is, one of the most dangerous in Europe. He's been in every prison on the Continent and has assassinated more persons than any gentleman unhung. He always goes about with a bomb in his pocket, and of course it makes conversation a little difficult because if you don't agree with him he lays it on the table in a marked manner."

She looked at the man with horror and surprise, and then glanced suspiciously at Philip. She saw that his eyes were laughing. She frowned a little.

"You're getting at me."

He gave a little shout of joy. He was so happy. But Mildred didn't like being laughed at.

"I don't see anything funny in telling lies."

"Don't be cross."

He took her hand, which was lying on the table, and pressed it gently.

"You are lovely, and I could kiss the ground you walk on," he said.

The greenish pallor of her skin intoxicated him, and her thin white lips had an extraordinary fascination. Her anæmia made her rather short of breath, and she held her mouth slightly open. It seemed to add somehow to the attractiveness of her face.

"You do like me a bit, don't you?" he asked.

"Well, if I didn't I suppose I shouldn't be here, should I? You're a gentleman in every sense of the word, I will say that for you."

They had finished their dinner and were drinking coffee. Philip, throwing economy to the winds, smoked a three-penny cigar.

"You can't imagine what a pleasure it is to me just to sit opposite and look at you. I've yearned for you. I was sick for a sight of you."

Mildred smiled a little and faintly flushed. She was not then suffering from the dyspepsia which generally attacked her immediately after a meal. She felt more kindly disposed to Philip than ever before, and the unaccustomed tenderness in her eyes filled him with joy. He knew instinctively that it was madness to give himself into her hands; his only chance was to treat her casually and never allow her to see the untamed passions that seethed in his breast; she would only take advantage of his weakness; but he could not be prudent now: he told her all the agony he had endured during the separation from her; he told her of his struggles with himself, how he had tried to get over his passion, thought he had succeeded,

and how he found out that it was as
strong as ever. He knew that he had
never really wanted to get over it. He
loved her so much that he did not
mind suffering. He bared his heart
to her. He showed her proudly all his
weakness.

Nothing would have pleased him
more than to sit on in the cosy, shabby
restaurant, but he knew that Mildred
wanted entertainment. She was restless and, wherever she was, wanted
after a while to go somewhere else.
He dared not bore her.

"I say, how about going to a music-
hall?" he said.

He thought rapidly that if she cared
for him at all she would say she preferred to stay there.

"I was just thinking we ought to
be going if we are going," she answered.

"Come on then."

Philip waited impatiently for the
end of the performance. He had made
up his mind exactly what to do, and
when they got into the cab he passed
his arm, as though almost by accident,
round her waist. But he drew it back
quickly with a little cry. He had
pricked himself. She laughed.

"There, that comes of putting your
arm where it's got no business to be,"
she said. "I always know when men
try and put their arm round my waist.

That pin always catches them."

"I'll be more careful."

He put his arm round again. She
made no objection.

"I'm so comfortable," he sighed
blissfully.

"So long as you're happy," she retorted.

They drove down St. James' Street
into the Park, and Philip quickly
kissed her. He was strangely afraid of
her, and it required all his courage.
She turned her lips to him without
speaking. She neither seemed to mind
nor to like it.

"If you only knew how long I've
wanted to do that," he murmured.

He tried to kiss her again, but she
turned her head away.

"Once is enough," she said.

On the chance of kissing her a
second time he travelled down to
Herne Hill with her, and at the end
of the road in which she lived he
asked her:

"Won't you give me another kiss?"

She looked at him indifferently and
then glanced up the road to see that
no one was in sight.

"I don't mind."

He seized her in his arms and kissed
her passionately, but she pushed him
away.

"Mind my hat, silly. You are
clumsy," she said.

LXI

H E s A w her then every day. He began going to lunch at the shop, but
Mildred stopped him: she said it made
the girls talk; so he had to content
himself with tea; but he always waited
about to walk with her to the station;
and once or twice a week they dined
together. He gave her little presents,

a gold bangle, gloves, handkerchiefs,
and the like. He was spending more
than he could afford, but he could
not help it: it was only when he
gave her anything that she showed any
affection. She knew the price of everything, and her gratitude was in exact proportion with the value of his

gift. He did not care. He was too happy when she volunteered to kiss him to mind by what means he got her demonstrativeness. He discovered that she found Sundays at home tedious, so he went down to Herne Hill in the morning, met her at the end of the road, and went to church with her.

"I always like to go to church once," she said. "It looks well, doesn't it?"

Then she went back to dinner, he got a scrappy meal at a hotel, and in the afternoon they took a walk in Brockwell Park. They had nothing much to say to one another, and Philip, desperately afraid she was bored, (she was very easily bored,) racked his brain for topics of conversation. He realised that these walks amused neither of them, but he could not bear to leave her, and did all he could to lengthen them till she became tired and out of temper. He knew that she did not care for him, and he tried to force a love which his reason told him was not in her nature: she was cold. He had no claim on her, but he could not help being exacting. Now that they were more intimate he found it less easy to control his temper; he was often irritable and could not help saying bitter things. Often they quarrelled, and she would not speak to him for a while; but this always reduced him to subjection, and he crawled before her. He was angry with himself for showing so little dignity. He grew furiously jealous if he saw her speaking to any other man in the shop, and when he was jealous he seemed to be beside himself. He would deliberately insult her, leave the shop and spend afterwards a sleepless night tossing on his bed, by turns angry and remorseful. Next day he would go to the shop and appeal for forgiveness.

"Don't be angry with me," he said. "I'm so awfully fond of you that I can't help myself."

"One of these days you'll go too far," she answered.

He was anxious to come to her home in order that the greater intimacy should give him an advantage over the stray acquaintances she made during her working-hours; but she would not let him.

"My aunt would think it so funny," she said.

He suspected that her refusal was due only to a disinclination to let him see her aunt. Mildred had represented her as the widow of a professional man, (that was her formula of distinction,) and was uneasily conscious that the good woman could hardly be called distinguished. Philip imagined that she was in point of fact the widow of a small tradesman. He knew that Mildred was a snob. But he found no means by which he could indicate to her that he did not mind how common the aunt was.

Their worst quarrel took place one evening at dinner when she told him that a man had asked her to go to a play with him. Philip turned pale, and his face grew hard and stern.

"You're not going?" he said.

"Why shouldn't I? He's a very nice gentlemanly fellow."

"I'll take you anywhere you like."

"But that isn't the same thing. I can't always go about with you. Besides he's asked me to fix my own day, and I'll just go one evening when I'm not going out with you. It won't make any difference to you."

"If you had any sense of decency, if you had any gratitude, you wouldn't dream of going."

"I don't know what you mean by gratitude. If you're referring to the things you've given me you can have them back. I don't want them."

Her voice had the shrewish tone it sometimes got.

"It's not very lively, always going about with you. It's always do you love me, do you love me, till I just get about sick of it."

(He knew it was madness to go on asking her that, but he could not help himself.

"Oh, I like you all right," she would answer.

"Is that all? I love you with all my heart."

"I'm not that sort, I'm not one to say much."

"If you knew how happy just one word would make me!"

"Well, what I always say is, people must take me as they find me, and if they don't like it they can lump it."

But sometimes she expressed herself more plainly still, and when he asked the question, answered:

"Oh, don't go on at that again."

Then he became sulky and silent. He hated her.)

And now he said:

"Oh, well, if you feel like that about it I wonder you condescend to come out with me at all."

"It's not my seeking, you can be very sure of that, you just force me to."

His pride was bitterly hurt, and he answered madly.

"You think I'm just good enough to stand you dinners and theatres when there's no one else to do it, and when someone else turns up I can go to hell. Thank you, I'm about sick of being made a convenience."

"I'm not going to be talked to like that by anyone. I'll just show you how much I want your dirty dinner."

She got up, put on her jacket, and walked quickly out of the restaurant. Philip sat on. He determined he would not move, but ten minutes aft-

erwards he jumped in a cab and followed her. He guessed that she would take a 'bus to Victoria, so that they would arrive about the same time. He saw her on the platform, escaped her notice, and went down to Herne Hill in the same train. He did not want to speak to her till she was on the way home and could not escape him. As soon as she had turned out of the main street, brightly lit and noisy with traffic, he caught her up.

"Mildred," he called.

She walked on and would neither look at him nor answer. He repeated her name. Then she stopped and faced him.

"What d'you want? I saw you hanging about Victoria. Why don't you leave me alone?"

"I'm awfully sorry. Won't you make it up?"

"No, I'm sick of your temper and your jealousy. I don't care for you, I never have cared for you, and I never shall care for you. I don't want to have anything more to do with you."

She walked on quickly, and he had to hurry to keep up with her.

"You never make allowances for me," he said. "It's all very well to be jolly and amiable when you're indifferent to anyone. It's very hard when you're as much in love as I am. Have mercy on me. I don't mind that you don't care for me. After all you can't help it. I only want you to let me love you."

She walked on, refusing to speak, and Philip saw with agony that they had only a few hundred yards to go before they reached her house. He abased himself. He poured out an incoherent story of love and penitence.

"If you'll only forgive me this time I promise you you'll never have t[e] complain of me in future. You can go out with whomever you choose. I'[l] be only too glad if you'll come with me when you've got nothing better to do."

She stopped again, for they had reached the corner at which he always left her.

"Now you can take yourself off. I won't have you coming up to the door."

"I won't go till you say you'll forgive me."

"I'm sick and tired of the whole thing."

He hesitated a moment, for he had an instinct that he could say something that would move her. It made him feel almost sick to utter the words.

"It is cruel, I have so much to put up with. You don't know what it is to be a cripple. Of course you don't like me. I can't expect you to."

"Philip, I didn't mean that," she answered quickly, with a sudden break of pity in her voice. "You know it's not true."

He was beginning to act now, and his voice was husky and low.

"Oh, I've felt it," he said.

She took his hand and looked at him, and her own eyes were filled with tears.

"I promise you it never made any difference to me. I never thought about it after the first day or two."

He kept a gloomy, tragic silence. He wanted her to think he was overcome with emotion.

"You know I like you awfully, Philip. Only you are so trying sometimes. Let's make it up."

She put up her lips to his, and with a sigh of relief he kissed her.

"Now are you happy again?" she asked.

"Madly."

She bade him good-night and hurried down the road. Next day he took her in a little watch with a brooch to pin on her dress. She had been hankering for it.

But three or four days later, when she brought him his tea, Mildred said to him:

"You remember what you promised the other night? You mean to keep that, don't you?"

"Yes."

He knew exactly what she meant and was prepared for her next words.

"Because I'm going out with that gentleman I told you about tonight."

"All right. I hope you'll enjoy yourself."

"You don't mind, do you?"

He had himself now under excellent control.

"I don't like it," he smiled, "but I'm not going to make myself more disagreeable than I can help."

She was excited over the outing and talked about it willingly. Philip wondered whether she did so in order to pain him or merely because she was callous. He was in the habit of condoning her cruelty by the thought of her stupidity. She had not the brains to see when she was wounding him.

"It's not much fun to be in love with a girl who has no imagination and no sense of humour," he thought, as he listened.

But the want of these things excused her. He felt that if he had not realised this he could never forgive her for the pain she caused him.

"He's got seats for the Tivoli," she said. "He gave me my choice and I chose that. And we're going to dine at the Café Royal. He says it's the most expensive place in London."

"He's a gentleman in every sense of the word," thought Philip, but he clenched his teeth to prevent himself from uttering a syllable.

Philip went to the Tivoli and saw

Mildred with her companion, a smooth-faced young man with sleek hair and the spruce look of a commercial traveller, sitting in the second row of the stalls. Mildred wore a black picture hat with ostrich feathers in it, which became her well. She was listening to her host with that quiet smile which Philip knew; she had no vivacity of expression, and it required broad farce to excite her laughter; but Philip could see that she was interested and amused. He thought to himself bitterly that her companion, flashy and jovial, exactly suited her. Her sluggish temperament made her appreciate noisy people. Philip had a passion for discussion, but no talent for small-talk. He admired the easy drollery of which some of his friends were masters, Lawson for instance, and his sense of inferiority made him shy and awkward. The things which interested him bored Mildred. She expected men to talk about football and racing, and he knew nothing of either. He did not know the catchwords which only need be said to excite a laugh.

Printed matter had always been a fetish to Philip, and now, in order to make himself more interesting, he read industriously *The Sporting Times*.

LXII

PHILIP did not surrender himself willingly to the passion that consumed him. He knew that all things human are transitory and therefore that it must cease one day or another. He looked forward to that day with eager longing. Love was like a parasite in his heart, nourishing a hateful existence on his life's blood; it absorbed his existence so intensely that he could take pleasure in nothing else. He had been used to delight in the grace of St. James' Park, and often he sat and looked at the branches of a tree silhouetted against the sky, it was like a Japanese print; and he found a continual magic in the beautiful Thames with its barges and its wharfs; the changing sky of London had filled his soul with pleasant fancies. But now beauty meant nothing to him. He was bored and restless when he was not with Mildred. Sometimes he thought he would console his sorrow by looking at pictures, but he walked through the National Gallery like a sight-seer; and no picture called up in him a thrill of emotion. He wondered if he could ever care again for all the things he had loved. He had been devoted to reading, but now books were meaningless; and he spent his spare hours in the smoking-room of the hospital club, turning over innumerable periodicals. This love was a torment, and he resented bitterly the subjugation in which it held him; he was a prisoner and he longed for freedom.

Sometimes he awoke in the morning and felt nothing; his soul leaped, for he thought he was free; he loved no longer; but in a little while, as he grew wide awake, the pain settled in his heart, and he knew that he was not cured yet. Though he yearned for Mildred so madly he despised her. He thought to himself that there could be no greater torture in the world than at the same time to love and to contemn.

Philip, burrowing as was his habit into the state of his feelings, discussing with himself continually his condition, came to the conclusion that he could only cure himself of his degrading passion by making Mildred his mistress. It was sexual hunger that he suffered from, and if he could satisfy this he might free himself from the intolerable chains that bound him. He knew that Mildred did not care for him at all in that way. When he kissed her passionately she withdrew herself from him with instinctive distaste. She had no sensuality. Sometimes he had tried to make her jealous by talking of adventures in Paris, but they did not interest her; once or twice he had sat at other tables in the teashop and affected to flirt with the waitress who attended them, but she was entirely indifferent. He could see that it was no pretence on her part.

"You didn't mind my not sitting at one of your tables this afternoon?" he asked once, when he was walking to the station with her. "Yours seemed to be all full."

This was not a fact, but she did not contradict him. Even if his desertion meant nothing to her he would have been grateful if she had pretended it did. A reproach would have been balm to his soul.

"I think it's silly of you to sit at the same table every day. You ought to give the other girls a turn now and again."

But the more he thought of it the more he was convinced that complete surrender on her part was his only way to freedom. He was like a knight of old, metamorphosed by magic spells, who sought the potions which should restore him to his fair and proper form. Philip had only one hope. Mildred greatly desired to go to Paris. To her, as to most English people, it was the centre of gaiety and fashion: she had heard of the Magasin du Louvre, where you could

get the very latest thing for about half the price you had to pay in London; a friend of hers had passed her honeymoon in Paris and had spent all day at the Louvre; and she and her husband, my dear, they never went to bed till six in the morning all the time they were there; the Moulin Rouge and I don't know what all. Philip did not care that if she yielded to his desires it would only be the unwilling price she paid for the gratification of her wish. He did not care upon what terms he satisfied his passion. He had even had a mad, melodramatic idea to drug her. He had plied her with liquor in the hope of exciting her, but she had no taste for wine; and though she liked him to order champagne because it looked well, she never drank more than half a glass. She liked to leave untouched a large glass filled to the brim.

"It shows the waiters who you are," she said.

Philip chose an opportunity when she seemed more than usually friendly. He had an examination in anatomy at the end of March. Easter, which came a week later, would give Mildred three whole days holiday.

"I say, why don't you come over to Paris then?" he suggested. "We'd have such a ripping time."

"How could you? It would cost no end of money."

Philip had thought of that. It would cost at least five-and-twenty pounds. It was a large sum to him. He was willing to spend his last penny on her.

"What does that matter? Say you'll come, darling."

"What next, I should like to know. I can't see myself going away with a man that I wasn't married to. You oughtn't to suggest such a thing."

"What does it matter?"

He enlarged on the glories of the

Rue de la Paix and the garish splendour of the Folies Bergères. He described the Louvre and the Bon Marché. He told her about the Cabaret du Néant, the Abbaye, and the various haunts to which foreigners go. He painted in glowing colours the side of Paris which he despised. He pressed her to come with him.

"You know, you say you love me, but if you really loved me you'd want to marry me. You've never asked me to marry you."

"You know I can't afford it. After all, I'm in my first year, I shan't earn a penny for six years."

"Oh, I'm not blaming you. I wouldn't marry you if you went down on your bended knees to me."

He had thought of marriage more than once, but it was a step from which he shrank. In Paris he had come by the opinion that marriage was a ridiculous institution of the philistines. He knew also that a permanent tie would ruin him. He had middleclass instincts, and it seemed a dreadful thing to him to marry a waitress. A common wife would prevent him from getting a decent practice. Besides, he had only just enough money to last him till he was qualified; he could not keep a wife even if they arranged not to have children. He thought of Cronshaw bound to a vulgar slattern, and he shuddered with dismay. He foresaw what Mildred, with her genteel ideas and her mean mind, would become: it was impossible for him to marry her. But he decided only with his reason; he felt that he must have her whatever happened; and if he could not get her without marrying her he would do that; the future could look after itself. It might end in disaster; he did not care. When he got hold of an idea it obsessed him, he could think of nothing else, and he had a more than common power to persuade himself of the reasonableness of what he wished to do. He found himself overthrowing all the sensible arguments which had occurred to him against marriage. Each day he found that he was more passionately devoted to her; and his unsatisfied love became angry and resentful.

"By George, if I marry her I'll make her pay for all the suffering I've endured," he said to himself.

At last he could bear the agony no longer. After dinner one evening in the little restaurant in Soho, to which now they often went, he spoke to her.

"I say, did you mean it the other day that you wouldn't marry me if I asked you?"

"Yes, why not?"

"Because I can't live without you. I want you with me always. I've tried to get over it and I can't. I never shall now. I want you to marry me."

She had read too many novelettes not to know how to take such an offer.

"I'm sure I'm very grateful to you, Philip. I'm very much flattered at your proposal."

"Oh, don't talk rot. You will marry me, won't you?"

"D'you think we should be happy?"

"No. But what does that matter?"

The words were wrung out of him almost against his will. They surprised her.

"Well, you are a funny chap. Why d'you want to marry me then? The other day you said you couldn't afford it."

"I think I've got about fourteen hundred pounds left. Two can live just as cheaply as one. That'll keep us till I'm qualified and have got through with my hospital appointments, and then I can get an assistantship."

"It means you wouldn't be able to

earn anything for six years. We should have about four pounds a week to live on till then, shouldn't we?"

"Not much more than three. There are all my fees to pay."

"And what would you get as an assistant?"

"Three pounds a week."

"D'you mean to say you have to work all that time and spend a small fortune just to earn three pounds a week at the end of it? I don't see that I should be any better off than I am now."

He was silent for a moment.

"D'you mean to say you won't marry me?" he asked hoarsely. "Does my great love mean nothing to you at all?"

"One has to think of oneself in those things, don't one? I shouldn't mind marrying, but I don't want to marry if I'm going to be no better off than what I am now. I don't see the use of it."

"If you cared for me you wouldn't think of all that."

"P'raps not."

He was silent. He drank a glass of wine in order to get rid of the choking in his throat.

"Look at that girl who's just going out," said Mildred. "She got them furs at the Bon Marché at Brixton. I saw them in the window last time I went down there."

Philip smiled grimly.

"What are you laughing at?" she asked. "It's true. And I said to my aunt at the time, I wouldn't buy anything that had been in the window like that, for everyone to know how much you paid for it."

"I can't understand you. You make me frightfully unhappy, and in the next breath you talk rot that has nothing to do with what we're speaking about."

"You are nasty to me," she answered, aggrieved. "I can't help noticing those furs, because I said to my aunt . . ."

"I don't care a damn what you said to your aunt," he interrupted impatiently.

"I wish you wouldn't use bad language when you speak to me, Philip. You know I don't like it."

Philip smiled a little, but his eyes were wild. He was silent for a while. He looked at her sullenly. He hated, despised, and loved her.

"If I had an ounce of sense I'd never see you again," he said at last. "If you only knew how heartily I despise myself for loving you!"

"That's not a very nice thing to say to me," she replied sulkily.

"It isn't," he laughed. "Let's go to the Pavilion."

"That's what's so funny in you, you start laughing just when one doesn't expect you to. And if I make you that unhappy why d'you want to take me to the Pavilion? I'm quite ready to go home."

"Merely because I'm less unhappy with you than away from you."

"I should like to know what you really think of me."

He laughed outright.

"My dear, if you did you'd never speak to me again."

LXIII

PHILIP did not pass the examination in anatomy at the end of March. He and Dunsford had worked at the subject together on Philip's skeleton, asking each other questions till both knew by heart every attachment and the meaning of every nodule and groove on the human bones; but in the examination room Philip was seized with panic, and failed to give right answers to questions from a sudden fear that they might be wrong. He knew he was ploughed and did not even trouble to go up to the building next day to see whether his number was up. The second failure put him definitely among the incompetent and idle men of his year.

He did not care much. He had other things to think of. He told himself that Mildred must have senses like anybody else, it was only a question of awakening them; he had theories about woman, the rip at heart, and thought that there must come a time with every one when she would yield to persistence. It was a question of watching for the opportunity, keeping his temper, wearing her down with small attentions, taking advantage of the physical exhaustion which opened the heart of tenderness, making himself a refuge from the petty vexations of her work. He talked to her of the relations between his friends in Paris and the fair ladies they admired. The life he described had a charm, an easy gaiety, in which was no grossness. Weaving into his own recollections the adventures of Mimi and Rodolphe, of Musette and the rest of them, he poured into Mildred's ears a story of poverty made picturesque by song and laughter, of lawless love made romantic by beauty and youth. He never attacked her prejudices directly, but sought to combat them by the suggestion that they were suburban. He never let himself be disturbed by her inattention, nor irritated by her indifference. He thought he had bored her. By an effort he made himself affable and entertaining; he never let himself be angry, he never asked for anything, he never complained, he never scolded. When she made engagements and broke them, he met her next day with a smiling face; when she excused herself, he said it did not matter. He never let her see that she pained him. He understood that his passionate grief had wearied her, and he took care to hide every sentiment which could be in the least degree troublesome. He was heroic.

Though she never mentioned the change, for she did not take any conscious notice of it, it affected her nevertheless: she became more confidential with him; she took her little grievances to him, and she always had some grievance against the manageress of the shop, one of her fellow-waitresses, or her aunt; she was talkative enough now, and though she never said anything that was not trivial Philip was never tired of listening to her.

"I like you when you don't want to make love to me," she told him once.

"That's flattering for me," he laughed.

She did not realise how her words

made his heart sink nor what an effort it needed for him to answer so lightly.

"Oh, I don't mind your kissing me now and then. It doesn't hurt me and it gives you pleasure."

Occasionally she went so far as to ask him to take her out to dinner, and the offer, coming from her, filled him with rapture. "I wouldn't do it to anyone else," she said, by way of apology. "But I know I can with you."

"You couldn't give me greater pleasure," he smiled.

She asked him to give her something to eat one evening towards the end of April.

"All right," he said. "Where would you like to go afterwards?"

"Oh, don't let's go anywhere. Let's just sit and talk. You don't mind, do you?"

"Rather not."

He thought she must be beginning to care for him. Three months before the thought of an evening spent in conversation would have bored her to death. It was a fine day, and the spring added to Philip's high spirits. He was content with very little now.

"I say, won't it be ripping when the summer comes along," he said, as they drove along on the top of a 'bus to Soho—she had herself suggested that they should not be so extravagant as to go by cab. "We shall be able to spend every Sunday on the River. We'll take our luncheon in a basket."

She smiled slightly, and he was encouraged to take her hand. She did not withdraw it.

"I really think you're beginning to like me a bit," he smiled.

"You *are* silly, you know I like you, or else I shouldn't be here, should I?"

They were old customers at the little restaurant in Soho by now, and the *patronne* gave them a smile as they came in. The waiter was obsequious.

"Let me order the dinner tonight," said Mildred.

Philip, thinking her more enchanting than ever, gave her the menu, and she chose her favourite dishes. The range was small, and they had eaten many times all that the restaurant could provide. Philip was gay. He looked into her eyes, and he dwelt on every perfection of her pale cheek. When they had finished Mildred by way of exception took a cigarette. She smoked very seldom.

"I don't like to see a lady smoking," she said.

She hesitated a moment and then spoke.

"Were you surprised, my asking you to take me out and give me a bit of dinner tonight?"

"I was delighted."

"I've got something to say to you, Philip."

He looked at her quickly, his heart sank, but he had trained himself well.

"Well, fire away," he said, smiling.

"You're not going to be silly about it, are you? The fact is I'm going to get married."

"Are you?" said Philip.

He could think of nothing else to say. He had considered the possibility often and had imagined to himself what he would do and say. He had suffered angonies when he thought of the despair he would suffer, he had thought of suicide, of the mad passion of anger that would seize him; but perhaps he had too completely anticipated the emotion he would experience, so that now he felt merely exhausted. He felt as one does in a serious illness when the vitality is so low that one is indifferent to the issue and wants only to be left alone.

"You see, I'm getting on," she said. "I'm twenty-four and it's time I settled down."

He was silent. He looked at the *patronne* sitting behind the counter, and his eye dwelt on a red feather one of the diners wore in her hat. Mildred was nettled.

"You might congratulate me," she said.

"I might, mightn't I? I can hardly believe it's true. I've dreamt it so often. It rather tickles me that I should have been so jolly glad that you asked me to take you out to dinner. Whom are you going to marry?"

"Miller," she answered, with a slight blush.

"Miller?" cried Philip, astounded. "But you've not seen him for months."

"He came in to lunch one day last week and asked me then. He's earning very good money. He makes seven pounds a week now and he's got prospects."

Philip was silent again. He remembered that she had always liked Miller; he amused her; there was in his foreign birth an exotic charm which she felt unconsciously.

"I suppose it was inevitable," he said at last. "You were bound to accept the highest bidder. When are you going to marry?"

"On Saturday next. I have given notice."

Philip felt a sudden pang.

"As soon as that?"

"We're going to be married at a registry office. Emil prefers it."

Philip felt dreadfully tired. He wanted to get away from her. He thought he would go straight to bed. He called for the bill.

"I'll put you in a cab and send you down to Victoria. I daresay you won't have to wait long for a train."

"Won't you come with me?"

"I think I'd rather not if you don't mind."

"It's just as you please," she answered haughtily. "I suppose I shall see you at tea-time tomorrow?"

"No, I think we'd better make a full stop now. I don't see why I should go on making myself unhappy. I've paid the cab."

He nodded to her and forced a smile on his lips, then jumped on a 'bus and made his way home. He smoked a pipe before he went to bed, but he could hardly keep his eyes open. He suffered no pain. He fell into a heavy sleep almost as soon as his head touched the pillow.

LXIV

But about three in the morning Philip awoke and could not sleep again. He began to think of Mildred. He tried not to, but could not help himself. He repeated to himself the same thing time after time till his brain reeled. It was inevitable that she should marry: life was hard for a girl who had to earn her own living; and if she found someone who could give her a comfortable home she should not be blamed if she accepted. Philip acknowledged that from her point of view it would have been madness to marry him: only love could have made such poverty bearable, and she did not love him. It was no fault of hers; it was a fact that must be accepted like any other. Philip tried to reason with himself.

He told himself that deep down in his heart was mortified pride; his passion had begun in wounded vanity, and it was this at bottom which caused now great part of his wretchedness. He despised himself as much as he despised her. Then he made plans for the future, the same plans over and over again, interrupted by recollections of kisses on her soft pale cheek and by the sound of her voice with its trailing accent; he had a great deal of work to do, since in the summer he was taking Chemistry as well as the two examinations he had failed in. He had separated himself from his friends at the hospital, but now he wanted companionship. There was one happy occurrence: Hayward a fortnight before had written to say that he was passing through London and had asked him to dinner; but Philip, unwilling to be bothered, had refused. He was coming back for the season, and Philip made up his mind to write to him.

He was thankful when eight o'clock struck and he could get up. He was pale and weary. But when he had bathed, dressed, and had breakfast, he felt himself joined up again with the world at large; and his pain was a little easier to bear. He did not feel like going to lectures that morning, but went instead to the Army and Navy Stores to buy Mildred a wedding-present. After much wavering he settled on a dressing-bag. It cost twenty pounds, which was much more than he could afford, but it was showy and vulgar: he knew she would be aware exactly how much it cost; he got a melancholy satisfaction in choosing a gift which would give her pleasure and at the same time indicate for himself the contempt he had for her.

Philip had looked forward with apprehension to the day on which Mildred was to be married; he was expecting an intolerable anguish; and it was with relief that he got a letter from Hayward on Saturday morning to say that he was coming up early on that very day and would fetch Philip to help him to find rooms. Philip, anxious to be distracted, looked up a time-table and discovered the only train Hayward was likely to come by; he went to meet him, and the reunion of the friends was enthusiastic. They left the luggage at the station, and set off gaily. Hayward characteristically proposed that first of all they should go for an hour to the National Gallery; he had not seen pictures for some time, and he stated that it needed a glimpse to set him in tune with life. Philip for months had had no one with whom he could talk of art and books. Since the Paris days Hayward had immersed himself in the modern French versifiers, and, such a plethora of poets is there in France, he had several new geniuses to tell Philip about. They walked through the gallery pointing out to one another their favourite pictures; one subject led to another; they talked excitedly. The sun was shining and the air was warm.

"Let's go and sit in the Park," said Hayward. "We'll look for rooms after luncheon."

The spring was pleasant there. It was a day upon which one felt it good merely to live. The young green of the trees was exquisite against the sky; and the sky, pale and blue, was dappled with little white clouds. At the end of the ornamental water was the gray mass of the Horse Guards. The ordered elegance of the scene had the charm of an eighteenth-century picture. It reminded you not of Watteau, whose landscapes are so idyllic that they recall only the woodland glens seen in dreams, but of the more prosaic Jean-Baptiste Pater. Philip's heart was filled with lightness. He realised, what he had only read before, that art (for there was art in the manner in which he looked upon nature) might liberate the soul from pain.

They went to an Italian restaurant for luncheon and ordered themselves a *fiaschetto* of Chianti. Lingering over the meal they talked on. They reminded one another of the people they had known at Heidelberg, they spoke of Philip's friends in Paris, they talked of books, pictures, morals, life; and suddenly Philip heard a clock strike three. He remembered that by this time Mildred was married. He felt a sort of stitch in his heart, and for a minute or two he could not hear what Hayward was saying. But he filled his glass with Chianti. He was unaccustomed to alcohol and it had gone to his head. For the time at all events he was free from care. His quick brain had lain idle for so many months that he was intoxicated now with conversation. He was thankful to have someone to talk to who would interest himself in the things that interested him.

"I say don't let's waste this beautiful day in looking for rooms. I'll put you up to-night. You can look for rooms to-morrow or Monday."

"All right. What shall we do?" answered Hayward.

"Let's get on a penny steamboat and go down to Greenwich."

The idea appealed to Hayward, and they jumped into a cab which took them to Westminster Bridge. They got on the steamboat just as she was starting. Presently Philip, a smile on his lips, spoke.

"I remember when first I went to Paris, Clutton, I think it was, gave a long discourse on the subject that beauty is put into things by painters and poets. They create beauty. In themselves there is nothing to choose between the Campanile of Giotto and a factory chimney. And then beautiful things grow rich with the emotion that they have aroused in succeeding generations. That is why old things are more beautiful than modern. The *Ode on a Grecian Urn* is more lovely now than when it was written, because for a hundred years lovers have read it and the sick at heart taken comfort in its lines."

Philip left Hayward to infer what in the passing scene had suggested these words to him, and it was a delight to know that he could safely leave the inference. It was in sudden reaction from the life he had been leading for so long that he was now deeply affected. The delicate iridescence of the London air gave the softness of a pastel to the gray stone of the buildings; and in the wharves and storehouses there was the severity of grace of a Japanese print. They went further down; and the splendid channel, a symbol of the great empire, broadened, and it was crowded with traffic; Philip thought of the painters and the poets who had made all these things so beautiful, and his heart was filled with gratitude. They came to the Pool of London, and who can describe its majesty? The imagination thrills, and Heaven knows what figures people still its broad stream, Doctor Johnson with Boswell by his side, an old Pepys going on board a man-o'-war: the pageant of English history, and romance, and high adventure. Philip turned to Hayward with shining eyes.

"Dear Charles Dickens," he murmured, smiling a little at his own emotion.

"Aren't you rather sorry you chucked painting?" asked Hayward.

"No."

"I suppose you like doctoring?"

"No, I hate it, but there was nothing else to do. The drudgery of the first two years is awful, and unfortunately I haven't got the scientific temperament."

"Well, you can't go on changing professions."

"Oh, no. I'm going to stick to this. I think I shall like it better when I get into the wards. I have an idea that I'm more interested in people than in anything else in the world. And as far as I can see, it's the only profession in which you have your freedom. You carry your knowledge in your head; with a box of instruments and a few drugs you can make your living anywhere."

"Aren't you going to take a practice then?"

"Not for a good long time at any rate," Philip answered. "As soon as I've got through my hospital appointments I shall get a ship; I want to go to the East—the Malay Archipelago, Siam, China, and all that sort of thing—and then I shall take odd jobs. Something always comes along, cholera duty in India and things like that. I want to go from place to place. I want to see the world. The only way a poor man can do that is by going in for the medical."

They came to Greenwich then. The noble building of Inigo Jones faced the river grandly.

"I say, look, that must be the place where Poor Jack dived into the mud for pennies," said Philip.

They wandered in the park. Ragged children were playing in it, and it was noisy with their cries: here and there old seamen were basking in the sun. There was an air of a hundred years ago.

"It seems a pity you wasted two years in Paris," said Hayward.

"Waste? Look at the movement of that child, look at the pattern which the sun makes on the ground, shining through the trees, look at that sky—why, I should never have seen that sky if I hadn't been to Paris."

Hayward thought that Philip choked a sob, and he looked at him with astonishment.

"What's the matter with you?"

"Nothing. I'm sorry to be so damned emotional, but for six months I've been starved for beauty."

"You used to be so matter of fact. It's very interesting to hear you say that."

"Damn it all, I don't want to be interesting," laughed Philip. "Let's go and have a stodgy tea."

LXV

HAYWARD's visit did Philip a great deal of good. Each day his thoughts dwelt less on Mildred. He looked back upon the past with disgust. He could not understand how he had submitted to the dishonour of such a love; and when he thought of Mildred it was with angry hatred, because she had submitted him to so much humiliation. His imagination presented her to him now with her defects of person and manner exaggerated, so that he shuddered at the thought of having been connected with her.

"It just shows how damned weak I am," he said to himself. The adventure was like a blunder that one had committed at a party so horrible that one felt nothing could be done to excuse it: the only remedy was

to forget. His horror at the degradation he had suffered helped him. He
was like a snake casting its skin and
he looked upon the old covering with
nausea. He exulted in the possession
of himself once more; he realised how
much of the delight of the world he
had lost when he was absorbed in that
madness which they called love; he
had had enough of it; he did not want
to be in love any more if love was
that. Philip told Hayward something
of what he had gone through.

"Wasn't it Sophocles," he asked,
"who prayed for the time when he
would be delivered from the wild
beast of passion that devoured his
heart-strings?"

Philip seemed really to be born
again. He breathed the circumambient
air as though he had never breathed
it before, and he took a child's pleasure in all the facts of the world. He
called his period of insanity six
months' hard labour.

Hayward had only been settled in
London a few days when Philip received from Blackstable, where it
had been sent, a card for a private
view at some picture gallery. He took
Hayward, and, on looking at the catalogue, saw that Lawson had a picture
in it.

"I suppose he sent the card," said
Philip. "Let's go and find him, he's
sure to be in front of his picture."

This, a profile of Ruth Chalice,
was tucked away in a corner, and
Lawson was not far from it. He looked
a little lost, in his large soft hat and
loose, pale clothes, amongst the fashionable throng that had gathered for
the private view. He greeted Philip
with enthusiasm, and with his usual
volubility told him that he had come
to live in London, Ruth Chalice was
a hussy, he had taken a studio, Paris
was played out, he had a commission
for a portrait, and they'd better dine

together and have a good old talk.
Philip reminded him of his acquaintance with Hayward, and was
entertained to see that Lawson was
slightly awed by Hayward's elegant
clothes and grand manner. They sat
upon him better than they had done
in the shabby little studio which Lawson and Philip had shared.

At dinner Lawson went on with
his news. Flanagan had gone back to
America. Clutton had disappeared. He
had come to the conclusion that a
man had no chance of doing anything
so long as he was in contact with
art and artists: the only thing was to
get right away. To make the step
easier he had quarrelled with all his
friends in Paris. He developed a talent
for telling them home truths, which
made them bear with fortitude his
declaration that he had done with
that city and was settling in Gerona,
a little town in the north of Spain
which had attracted him when he
saw it from the train on his way to
Barcelona. He was living there now
alone.

"I wonder if he'll ever do any good,"
said Philip.

He was interested in the human
side of that struggle to express something which was so obscure in the
man's mind that he was become morbid and querulous. Philip felt vaguely
that he was himself in the same case,
but with him it was the conduct of
his life as a whole that perplexed him.
That was his means of self-expression,
and what he must do with it was not
clear. But he had no time to continue
with this train of thought, for Lawson poured out a frank recital of his
affair with Ruth Chalice. She had
left him for a young student who had
just come from England, and was behaving in a scandalous fashion. Lawson really thought someone ought to
step in and save the young man. She

would ruin him. Philip gathered that Lawson's chief grievance was that the rupture had come in the middle of a portrait he was painting.

"Women have no real feeling for art," he said. "They only pretend they have." But he finished philosophically enough: "However, I got four portraits out of her, and I'm not sure if the last I was working on would ever have been a success."

Philip envied the easy way in which the painter managed his love-affairs. He had passed eighteen months pleasantly enough, had got an excellent model for nothing, and had parted from her at the end with no great pang.

"And what about Cronshaw?" asked Philip.

"Oh, he's done for," answered Lawson, with the cheerful callousness of his youth. "He'll be dead in six months. He got pneumonia last winter. He was in the English hospital for seven weeks, and when he came out they told him his only chance was to give up liquor."

"Poor devil," smiled the abstemious Philip.

"He kept off for a bit. He used to go to the Lilas all the same, he couldn't keep away from that, but he used to drink hot milk, *avec de la fleur d'oranger,* and he was damned dull."

"I take it you did not conceal the fact from him."

"Oh, he knew it himself. A little while ago he started on whiskey again. He said he was too old to turn over any new leaves. He would rather be happy for six months and die at the end of it than linger on for five years. And then I think he's been awfully

hard up lately. You see, he didn't earn anything while he was ill, and the slut he lives with has been giving him a rotten time."

"I remember, the first time I saw him I admired him awfully," said Philip. "I thought he was wonderful. It is sickening that vulgar, middle-class virtue should pay."

"Of course he was a rotter. He was bound to end in the gutter sooner or later," said Lawson.

Philip was hurt because Lawson would not see the pity of it. Of course it was cause and effect, but in the necessity with which one follows the other lay all tragedy of life.

"Oh, I'd forgotten," said Lawson. "Just after you left he sent round a present for you. I thought you'd be coming back and I didn't bother about it, and then I didn't think it worth sending on; but it'll come over to London with the rest of my things, and you can come to my studio one day and fetch it away if you want it."

"You haven't told me what it is yet."

"Oh, it's only a ragged little bit of carpet. I shouldn't think it's worth anything. I asked him one day what the devil he'd sent the filthy thing for. He told me he'd seen it in a shop in the Rue de Rennes and bought it for fifteen francs. It appears to be a Persian rug. He said you'd asked him the meaning of life and that was the answer. But he was very drunk."

Philip laughed.

"Oh yes, I know. I'll take it. It was a favourite wheeze of his. He said I must find out for myself, or else the answer meant nothing."

LXVI

PHILIP worked well and easily; he had a good deal to do, since he was taking in July the three parts of the First Conjoint examination, two of which he had failed in before; but he found life pleasant. He made a new friend. Lawson, on the look out for models, had discovered a girl who was understudying at one of the theatres, and in order to induce her to sit to him arranged a little luncheon-party one Sunday. She brought a chaperon with her; and to her Philip, asked to make a fourth, was instructed to confine his attentions. He found this easy, since she turned out to be an agreeable chatterbox with an amusing tongue. She asked Philip to go and see her; she had rooms in Vincent Square, and was always in to tea at five o'clock; he went, was delighted with his welcome, and went again. Mrs. Nesbit was not more than twenty-five, very small, with a pleasant, ugly face; she had very bright eyes, high cheek-bones, and a large mouth: the excessive contrasts of her colouring reminded one of a portrait by one of the modern French painters; her skin was very white, her cheeks were very red, her thick eyebrows, her hair, were very black. The effect was odd, a little unnatural, but far from unpleasing. She was separated from her husband and earned her living and her child's by writing penny novelettes. There were one or two publishers who made a specialty of that sort of thing, and she had as much work as she could do. It was ill-paid, she received fifteen pounds for a story of thirty thousand words; but she was satisfied. "After all, it only costs the reader twopence," she said, "and they like the same thing over and over again. I just change the names and that's all. When I'm bored I think of the washing and the rent and clothes for baby, and I go on again."

Besides, she walked on at various theatres where they wanted supers and earned by this when in work from sixteen shillings to a guinea a week. At the end of her day she was so tired that she slept like a top. She made the best of her difficult lot. Her keen sense of humour enabled her to get amusement out of every vexatious circumstance. Sometimes things went wrong, and she found herself with no money at all; then her trifling possessions found their way to a pawnshop in the Vauxhall Bridge Road, and she ate bread and butter till things grew brighter. She never lost her cheerfulness.

Philip was interested in her shiftless life, and she made him laugh with the fantastic narration of her struggles. He asked her why she did not try her hand at literary work of a better sort, but she knew that she had no talent, and the abominable stuff she turned out by the thousand words was not only tolerably paid, but was the best she could do. She had nothing to look forward to but a continuation of the life she led. She seemed to have no relations, and her friends were as poor as herself.

"I don't think of the future," she said. "As long as I have enough money for three weeks' rent and a pound or two over for food I never bother. Life wouldn't be worth living if I worried over the future as well as the present.

When things are at their worst I find something always happens."

Soon Philip grew in the habit of going in to tea with her every day, and so that his visits might not embarrass her he took in a cake or a pound of butter or some tea. They started to call one another by their Christian names. Feminine sympathy was new to him, and he delighted in someone who gave a willing ear to all his troubles. The hours went quickly. He did not hide his admiration for her. She was a delightful companion. He could not help comparing her with Mildred; and he contrasted with the one's obstinate stupidity, which refused interest to everything she did not know, the other's quick appreciation and ready intelligence. His heart sank when he thought that he might have been tied for life to such a woman as Mildred. One evening he told Norah the whole story of his love. It was not one to give him much reason for self-esteem, and it was very pleasant to receive such charming sympathy.

"I think you're well out of it," she said, when he had finished. She had a funny way at times of holding her head on one side like an Aberdeen puppy. She was sitting in an upright chair, sewing, for she had no time to do nothing, and Philip had made himself comfortable at her feet.

"I can't tell you how heartily thankful I am it's all over," he sighed.

"Poor thing, you must have had a rotten time," she murmured, and by way of showing her sympathy put her hand on his shoulder.

He took it and kissed it, but she withdrew it quickly.

"Why did you do that?" she asked, with a blush.

"Have you any objection?"

She looked at him for a moment with twinkling eyes, and she smiled.

"No," she said.

He got up on his knees and faced her. She looked into his eyes steadily, and her large mouth trembled with a smile.

"Well?" she said.

"You know, you are a ripper. I'm so grateful to you for being nice to me. I like you so much."

"Don't be idiotic," she said.

Philip took hold of her elbows and drew her towards him. She made no resistance, but bent forward a little, and he kissed her red lips.

"Why did you do that?" she asked again.

"Because it's comfortable."

She did not answer, but a tender look came into her eyes, and she passed her hand softly over his hair.

"You know, it's awfully silly of you to behave like this. We were such good friends. It would be so jolly to leave it at that."

"If you really want to appeal to my better nature," replied Philip, "you'll do well not to stroke my cheek while you're doing it."

She gave a little chuckle, but she did not stop.

"It's very wrong of me, isn't it?" she said.

Philip, surprised and a little amused, looked into her eyes, and as he looked he saw them soften and grow liquid, and there was an expression in them that enchanted him. His heart was suddenly stirred, and tears came to his eyes.

"Norah, you're not fond of me, are you?" he asked, incredulously.

"You clever boy, you ask such stupid questions."

"Oh, my dear, it never struck me that you could be."

He flung his arms round her and kissed her, while she, laughing, blushing, and crying, surrendered herself willingly to his embrace.

Presently he released her and sitting back on his heels looked at her curiously.

"Well, I'm blowed!" he said.

"Why?"

"I'm so surprised."

"And pleased?"

"Delighted," he cried with all his heart, "and so proud and so happy and so grateful."

He took her hands and covered them with kisses. This was the beginning for Philip of a happiness which seemed both solid and durable. They became lovers but remained friends. There was in Norah a maternal instinct which received satisfaction in her love for Philip; she wanted someone to pet, and scold, and make a fuss of; she had a domestic temperament and found pleasure in looking after his health and his linen. She pitied his deformity, over which he was so sensitive, and her pity expressed itself instinctively in tenderness. She was young, strong, and healthy, and it seemed quite natural for her to give her love. She had high spirits and a merry soul. She liked Philip because he laughed with her at all the amusing things in life that caught her fancy, and above all she liked him because he was he.

When she told him this he answered gaily:

"Nonsense. You like me because I'm a silent person and never want to get a word in."

Philip did not love her at all. He was extremely fond of her, glad to be with her, amused and interested by her conversation. She restored his belief in himself and put healing ointments, as it were, on all the bruises of his soul. He was immensely flattered that she cared for him. He admired her courage, her optimism, her impudent defiance of fate; she had a little philosophy of her own, ingenuous and practical.

"You know, I don't believe in churches and parsons and all that," she said, "but I believe in God, and I don't believe He minds much about what you do as long as you keep your end up and help a lame dog over a stile when you can. And I think people on the whole are very nice, and I'm sorry for those who aren't."

"And what about afterwards?" asked Philip.

"Oh, well, I don't know for certain, you know," she smiled, "but I hope for the best. And anyhow there'll be no rent to pay and no novelettes to write."

She had a feminine gift for delicate flattery. She thought that Philip did a brave thing when he left Paris because he was conscious he could not be a great artist; and he was enchanted when she expressed enthusiastic admiration for him. He had never been quite certain whether this action indicated courage or infirmity of purpose. It was delightful to realise that she considered it heroic. She ventured to tackle him on a subject which his friends instinctively avoided.

"It's very silly of you to be so sensitive about your club-foot," she said. She saw him flush darkly, but went on. "You know, people don't think about it nearly as much as you do. They notice it the first time they see you, and then they forget about it."

He would not answer.

"You're not angry with me, are you?"

"No."

She put her arm round his neck.

"You know, I only speak about it because I love you. I don't want it to make you unhappy."

"I think you can say anything you choose to me," he answered, smiling. "I wish I could do something to show you how grateful I am to you."

She took him in hand in other ways. She would not let him be bearish and laughed at him when he was out of temper. She made him more urbane.

"You can make me do anything you like," he said to her once.

"D'you mind?"

"No, I want to do what you like."

He had the sense to realise his happiness. It seemed to him that she gave him all that a wife could, and he preserved his freedom; she was the most charming friend he had ever had, with a sympathy that he had never found in a man. The sexual relationship was no more than the strongest link in their friendship. It completed it, but was not essential. And because Philip's appetites were satisfied, he became more equable and easier to live with. He felt in complete possession of himself. He thought sometimes of the winter, during which he had been obsessed by a hideous passion, and he was filled with loathing for Mildred and with horror of himself.

His examinations were approaching, and Norah was as interested in them as he. He was flattered and touched by her eagerness. She made him promise to come at once and tell her the results. He passed the three parts this time without mishap, and when he went to tell her she burst into tears.

"Oh, I'm so glad, I was so anxious."

"You silly little thing," he laughed, but he was choking.

No one could help being pleased with the way she took it.

"And what are you going to do now?" she asked.

"I can take a holiday with a clear conscience. I have no work to do till the winter session begins in October."

"I suppose you'll go down to your uncle's at Blackstable?"

"You suppose quite wrong. I'm going to stay in London and play with you."

"I'd rather you went away."

"Why? Are you tired of me?"

She laughed and put her hands on his shoulders.

"Because you've been working hard, and you look utterly washed out. You want some fresh air and a rest. Please go."

He did not answer for a moment. He looked at her with loving eyes.

"You know, I'd never believe it of anyone but you. You're only thinking of my good. I wonder what you see in me."

"Will you give me a good character with my month's notice?" she laughed gaily.

"I'll say that you're thoughtful and kind, and you're not exacting; you never worry, you're not troublesome, and you're easy to please."

"All that's nonsense," she said, "but I'll tell you one thing: I'm one of the few persons I ever met who are able to learn from experience."

LXVII

PHILIP looked forward to his return to London with impatience. During the two months he spent at Blackstable Norah wrote to him frequently, long letters in a bold, large hand, in which with cheerful humour she described the little events of the daily round, the domestic troubles of her landlady, rich food for laughter, the comic vexations of her rehearsals—she was walking on in an important spectacle at one of the London theatres—and her odd adventures with the publishers of novelettes. Philip read a great deal, bathed, played tennis, and sailed. At the beginning of October he settled down in London to work for the Second Conjoint examination. He was eager to pass it, since that ended the drudgery of the curriculum; after it was done with the student became an out-patients' clerk, and was brought in contact with men and women as well as with text-books. Philip saw Norah every day.

Lawson had been spending the summer at Poole, and had a number of sketches to show of the harbour and of the beach. He had a couple of commissions for portraits and proposed to stay in London till the bad light drove him away. Hayward, in London too, intended to spend the winter abroad, but remained week after week from sheer inability to make up his mind to go. Hayward had run to fat during the last two or three years—it was five years since Philip first met him in Heidelberg—and he was prematurely bald. He was very sensitive about it and wore his hair long to conceal the unsightly patch on the crown of his head. His only consolation was that his brow was now very noble. His blue eyes had lost their colour; they had a listless droop; and his mouth, losing the fulness of youth, was weak and pale. He still talked vaguely of the things he was going to do in the future, but with less conviction; and he was conscious that his friends no longer believed in him: when he had drunk two or three glasses of whiskey he was inclined to be elegiac.

"I'm a failure," he murmured, "I'm unfit for the brutality of the struggle of life. All I can do is to stand aside and let the vulgar throng hustle by in their pursuit of the good things."

He gave you the impression that to fail was a more delicate, a more exquisite thing, than to succeed. He insinuated that his aloofness was due to distaste for all that was common and low. He talked beautifully of Plato.

"I should have thought you'd got through with Plato by now," said Philip impatiently.

"Would you?" he asked, raising his eyebrows.

He was not inclined to pursue the subject. He had discovered of late the effective dignity of silence.

"I don't see the use of reading the same thing over and over again," said Philip. "That's only a laborious form of idleness."

"But are you under the impression that you have so great a mind that you can understand the most profound writer at a first reading?"

"I don't want to understand him, I'm not a critic. I'm not interested in him for his sake but for mine."

"Why d'you read then?"

"Partly for pleasure, because it's a habit and I'm just as uncomfortable if I don't read as if I don't smoke, and partly to know myself. When I read a book I seem to read it with my eyes only, but now and then I come across a passage, perhaps only a phrase, which has a meaning for *me,* and it becomes part of me; I've got out of the book all that's any use to me, and I can't get anything more if I read it a dozen times. You see, it seems to me, one's like a closed bud, and most of what one reads and does has no effect at all; but there are certain things that have a peculiar significance for one, and they open a petal; and the petals open one by one; and at last the flower is there."

Philip was not satisfied with his

metaphor, but he did not know how else to explain a thing which he felt and yet was not clear about.

"You want to do things, you want to become things," said Hayward, with a shrug of the shoulders. "It's so vulgar."

Philip knew Hayward very well by now. He was weak and vain, so vain that you had to be on the watch constantly not to hurt his feelings; he mingled idleness and idealism so that he could not separate them. At Lawson's studio one day he met a journalist, who was charmed by his conversation, and a week later the editor of a paper wrote to suggest that he should do some criticism for him. For forty-eight hours Hayward lived in an agony of indecision. He had talked of getting occupation of this sort so long that he had not the face to refuse outright, but the thought of doing anything filled him with panic. At last he declined the offer and breathed freely.

"It would have interfered with my work," he told Philip.

"What work?" asked Philip brutally.

"My inner life," he answered.

Then he went on to say beautiful things about Amiel, the professor of Geneva, whose brilliancy promised achievement which was never fulfilled; till at his death the reason of his failure and the excuse were at once manifest in the minute, wonderful journal which was found among his papers. Hayward smiled enigmatically.

But Hayward could still talk delightfully about books; his taste was exquisite and his discrimination elegant; and he had a constant interest in ideas, which made him an entertaining companion. They meant nothing to him really, since they never had any effect on him; but he treated them as he might have pieces of china

in an auction-room, handling them with pleasure in their shape and their glaze, pricing them in his mind; and then, putting them back into their case, thought of them no more.

And it was Hayward who made a momentous discovery. One evening, after due preparation, he took Philip and Lawson to a tavern situated in Beak Street, remarkable not only in itself and for its history—it had memories of eighteenth-century glories which excited the romantic imagination—but for its snuff, which was the best in London, and above all for its punch. Hayward led them into a large, long room, dingily magnificent, with huge pictures on the walls of nude women: they were vast allegories of the school of Haydon; but smoke, gas, and the London atmosphere had given them a richness which made them look like old masters. The dark panelling, the massive, tarnished gold of the cornice, the mahogany tables, gave the room an air of sumptuous comfort, and the leather-covered seats along the wall were soft and easy. There was a ram's head on a table opposite the door, and this contained the celebrated snuff. They ordered punch. They drank it. It was hot rum punch. The pen falters when it attempts to treat of the excellence thereof; the sober vocabulary, the sparse epithet of this narrative, are inadequate to the task; and pompous terms, jewelled, exotic phrases rise to the excited fancy. It warmed the blood and cleared the head; it filled the soul with well-being; it disposed the mind at once to utter wit and to appreciate the wit of others; it had the vagueness of music and the precision of mathematics. Only one of its qualities was comparable to anything else: it had the warmth of a good heart; but its taste, its smell, its feel, were not to be described in words. Charles Lamb, with his infinite tact, attempting to, might have drawn charming pictures of the life of his day; Lord Byron in a stanza of Don Juan, aiming at the impossible, might have achieved the sublime; Oscar Wilde, heaping jewels of Ispahan upon brocades of Byzantium, might have created a troubling beauty. Considering it, the mind reeled under visions of the feasts of Elagabalus; and the subtle harmonies of Debussy mingled with the musty, fragrant romance of chests in which have been kept old clothes, ruffs, hose, doublets, of a forgotten generation, and the wan odour of lilies of the valley and the savour of Cheddar cheese.

Hayward discovered the tavern at which this priceless beverage was to be obtained by meeting in the street a man called Macalister who had been at Cambridge with him. He was a stockbroker and a philosopher. He was accustomed to go to the tavern once a week; and soon Philip, Lawson, and Hayward got into the habit of meeting there every Tuesday evening: change of manners made it now little frequented, which was an advantage to persons who took pleasure in conversation. Macalister was a big-boned fellow, much too short for his width, with a large, fleshy face and a soft voice. He was a student of Kant and judged everything from the standpoint of pure reason. He was fond of expounding his doctrines. Philip listened with excited interest. He had long come to the conclusion that nothing amused him more than metaphysics, but he was not so sure of their efficacy in the affairs of life. The neat little system which he had formed as the result of his meditations at Blackstable had not been of conspicuous use during his infatuation for Mildred. He could not be positive that reason was much help in the conduct of life.

It seemed to him that life lived itself. He remembered very vividly the violence of the emotion which had possessed him and his inability, as if he were tied down to the ground with ropes, to react against it. He read many wise things in books, but he could only judge from his own experience; (he did not know whether he was different from other people;) he did not calculate the pros and cons of an action, the benefits which must befall him if he did it, the harm which might result from the omission; but his whole being was urged on irresistibly. He did not act with a part of himself but altogether. The power that possessed him seemed to have nothing to do with reason: all that reason did was to point out the methods of obtaining what his whole soul was striving for.

Macalister reminded him of the Categorical Imperative.

"Act so that every action of yours should be capable of becoming a universal rule of action for all men."

"That seems to me perfect nonsense," said Philip.

"You're a bold man to say that of anything stated by Emanuel Kant," retorted Macalister.

"Why? Reverence for what somebody said is a stultifying quality: there's a damned sight too much reverence in the world. Kant thought things not because they were true, but because he was Kant."

"Well, what is your objection to the Categorical Imperative?"

(They talked as though the fate of empires were in the balance.)

"It suggests that one can choose one's course by an effort of will. And it suggests that reason is the surest guide. Why should its dictates be any better than those of passion? They're different. That's all."

"You seem to be a contented slave of your passions."

"A slave because I can't help myself, but not a contented one," laughed Philip.

While he spoke he thought of that hot madness which had driven him in pursuit of Mildred. He remembered how he had chafed against it and how he had felt the degradation of it.

"Thank God, I'm free from all that now," he thought.

And yet even as he said it he was not quite sure whether he spoke sincerely. When he was under the influence of passion he had felt a singular vigour, and his mind had worked with unwonted force. He was more alive, there was an excitement in sheer being, an eager vehemence of soul, which made life now a trifle dull. For all the misery he had endured there was a compensation in that sense of rushing, overwhelming existence.

But Philip's unlucky words engaged him in a discussion on the freedom of the will, and Macalister, with his well-stored memory, brought out argument after argument. He had a mind that delighted in dialectics, and he forced Philip to contradict himself; he pushed him into corners from which he could only escape by damaging concessions; he tripped him up with logic and battered him with authorities.

At last Philip said:

"Well, I can't say anything about other people. I can only speak for myself. The illusion of free will is so strong in my mind that I can't get away from it, but I believe it is only an illusion. But it is an illusion which is one of the strongest motives of my actions. Before I do anything I feel that I have choice, and that influences what I do; but afterwards, when the thing is done, I believe that it was inevitable from all eternity."

"What do you deduce from that?" asked Hayward.

"Why, merely the futility of regret. It's no good crying over spilt milk, because all the forces of the universe were bent on spilling it."

LXVIII

One morning Philip on getting up felt his head swim, and going back to bed suddenly discovered he was ill. All his limbs ached and he shivered with cold. When the landlady brought in his breakfast he called to her through the open door that he was not well, and asked for a cup of tea and a piece of toast. A few minutes later there was a knock at his door, and Griffiths came in. They had lived in the same house for over a year, but had never done more than nod to one another in the passage.

"I say, I hear you're seedy," said Griffiths. "I thought I'd come in and see what was the matter with you."

Philip, blushing he knew not why, made light of the whole thing. He would be all right in an hour or two.

"Well, you'd better let me take your temperature," said Griffiths.

"It's quite unnecessary," answered Philip irritably.

"Come on."

Philip put the thermometer in his mouth. Griffiths sat on the side of the bed and chatted brightly for a moment, then he took it out and looked at it.

"Now, look here, old man, you must stay in bed, and I'll bring old

Deacon in to have a look at you."

"Nonsense," said Philip. "There's nothing the matter. I wish you wouldn't bother about me."

"But it isn't any bother. You've got a temperature and you must stay in bed. You will, won't you?"

There was a peculiar charm in his manner, a mingling of gravity and kindliness, which was infinitely attractive.

"You've got a wonderful bed-side manner," Philip murmured, closing his eyes with a smile.

Griffiths shook out his pillow for him, deftly smoothed down the bedclothes, and tucked him up. He went into Philip's sitting-room to look for a siphon, could not find one, and fetched it from his own room. He drew down the blind.

"Now, go to sleep and I'll bring the old man round as soon as he's done the wards."

It seemed hours before anyone came to Philip. His head felt as if it would split, anguish rent his limbs, and he was afraid he was going to cry. Then there was a knock at the door and Griffiths, healthy, strong, and cheerful, came in.

"Here's Doctor Deacon," he said.

The physician stepped forward, an elderly man with a bland manner, whom Philip knew only by sight. A few questions, a brief examination, and the diagnosis.

"What d'you make it?" he asked Griffiths, smiling.

"Influenza."

"Quite right."

Doctor Deacon looked round the dingy lodging-house room.

"Wouldn't you like to go to the hospital? They'll put you in a private ward, and you can be better looked after than you can here."

"I'd rather stay where I am," said Philip.

He did not want to be disturbed, and he was always shy of new surroundings. He did not fancy nurses fussing about him, and the dreary cleanliness of the hospital.

"I can look after him, sir," said Griffiths at once.

"Oh, very well."

He wrote a prescription, gave instructions, and left.

"Now you've got to do exactly as I tell you," said Griffiths. "I'm day-nurse and night-nurse all in one."

"It's very kind of you, but I shan't want anything," said Philip.

Griffiths put his hand on Philip's forehead, a large cool, dry hand, and the touch seemed to him good.

"I'm just going to take this round to the dispensary to have it made up, and then I'll come back."

In a little while he brought the medicine and gave Philip a dose. Then he went upstairs to fetch his books.

"You won't mind my working in your room this afternoon, will you?" he said, when he came down. "I'll leave the door open so that you can give me a shout if you want anything."

Later in the day Philip, awaking from an uneasy doze, heard voices in his sitting-room. A friend had come in to see Griffiths.

"I say, you'd better not come in tonight," he heard Griffiths saying.

And then a minute or two afterwards someone else entered the room and expressed his surprise at finding Griffiths there. Philip heard him explain.

"I'm looking after a second year's man who's got these rooms. The wretched blighter's down with influenza. No whist tonight, old man."

Presently Griffiths was left alone and Philip called him.

"I say, you're not putting off a party tonight, are you?" he asked.

"Not on your account. I must work at my surgery."

"Don't put it off. I shall be all right. You needn't bother about me."

"That's all right."

Philip grew worse. As the night came on he became slightly delirious, but towards morning he awoke from a restless sleep. He saw Griffiths get out of an arm-chair, go down on his knees, and with his fingers put piece after piece of coal on the fire. He was in pyjamas and a dressing-gown.

"What are you doing here?" he asked.

"Did I wake you up? I tried to make up the fire without making a row."

"Why aren't you in bed? What's the time?"

"About five. I thought I'd better sit up with you tonight. I brought an arm-chair in as I thought if I put a mattress down I should sleep so soundly that I shouldn't hear you if you wanted anything."

"I wish you wouldn't be so good to me," groaned Philip. "Suppose you catch it?"

"Then you shall nurse me, old man," said Griffiths, with a laugh.

In the morning Griffiths drew up the blind. He looked pale and tired after his night's watch, but was full of spirits.

"Now, I'm going to wash you," he said to Philip cheerfully.

"I can wash myself," said Philip, ashamed.

"Nonsense. If you were in the small ward a nurse would wash you, and I can do it just as well as a nurse."

Philip, too weak and wretched to resist, allowed Griffiths to wash his hands and face, his feet, his chest and back. He did it with charming tenderness, carrying on meanwhile a stream of friendly chatter; then he changed the sheet just as they did at the hospital, shook out the pillow, and arranged the bed-clothes.

"I should like Sister Arthur to see me. It would make her sit up. Deacon's coming in to see you early."

"I can't imagine why you should be so good to me," said Philip.

"It's good practice for me. It's rather a lark having a patient."

Griffiths gave him his breakfast and went off to get dressed and have something to eat. A few minutes before ten he came back with a bunch of grapes and a few flowers.

"You are awfully kind," said Philip.

He was in bed for five days.

Norah and Griffiths nursed him between them. Though Griffiths was the same age as Philip he adopted towards him a humorous, motherly attitude. He was a thoughtful fellow, gentle and encouraging; but his greatest quality was a vitality which seemed to give health to everyone with whom he came in contact. Philip was unused to the petting which most people enjoy from mothers or sisters and he was deeply touched by the feminine tenderness of this strong young man. Philip grew better. Then Griffiths, sitting idly in Philip's room, amused him with gay stories of amorous adventure. He was a flirtatious creature, capable of carrying on three or four affairs at a time; and his account of the devices he was forced to in order to keep out of difficulties made excellent hearing. He had a gift for throwing a romantic glamour over everything that happened to him. He was crippled with debts, everything he had of any value was pawned, but he managed always to be cheerful, extravagant, and generous. He was the adventurer by nature. He loved people of doubtful occupations and shifty purposes; and his acquaintance among the riff-raff that frequents the bars of London was enormous. Loose women, treating him as a friend, told him the troubles, difficulties, and successes of their lives; and card-sharpers, respecting his impecuniosity, stood him dinners and lent him five-pound notes. He was ploughed in his examinations time after time; but he bore this cheerfully, and submitted with such a charming grace to the parental expostulations that his father, a doctor in practice at Leeds, had not the heart to be seriously angry with him.

"I'm an awful fool at books," he said cheerfully, "but I *can't* work."

Life was much too jolly. But it was clear that when he had got through the exuberance of his youth, and was at last qualified, he would be a tremendous success in practice. He would cure people by the sheer charm of his manner.

Philip worshipped him as at school he had worshipped boys who were tall and straight and high of spirits. By the time he was well they were fast friends, and it was a peculiar satisfaction to Philip that Griffiths seemed to enjoy sitting in his little parlour, wasting Philip's time with his amusing chatter and smoking innumerable cigarettes. Philip took him sometimes to the tavern off Regent Street. Hayward found him stupid,

but Lawson recognised his charm and was eager to paint him; he was a picturesque figure with his blue eyes, white skin, and curly hair. Often they discussed things he knew nothing about, and then he sat quietly, with a good-natured smile on his handsome face, feeling quite rightly that his presence was sufficient contribution to the entertainment of the company. When he discovered that Macalister was a stockbroker he was eager for tips; and Macalister, with his grave smile, told him what fortunes he could have made if he had bought certain stock at certain times. It made Philip's mouth water, for in one way and another he was spending more than he had expected, and it would have suited him very well to make a little money by the easy method Macalister suggested.

"Next time I hear of a really good thing I'll let you know," said the stockbroker. "They do come along sometimes. It's only a matter of biding one's time."

Philip could not help thinking how delightful it would be to make fifty pounds, so that he could give Norah the furs she so badly needed for the winter. He looked at the shops in Regent Street and picked out the articles he could buy for the money. She deserved everything. She made his life very happy.

LXIX

ONE afternoon, when he went back to his rooms from the hospital to wash and tidy himself before going to tea as usual with Norah, as he let himself in with his latch-key, his landlady opened the door for him.

"There's a lady waiting to see you,"

she said.

"Me?" exclaimed Philip.

He was surprised. It would only be Norah, and he had no idea what had brought her.

"I shouldn't 'ave let her in, only she's been three times, and she seemed that upset at not finding you, so I told her she could wait."

He pushed past the explaining landlady and burst into the room. His heart turned sick. It was Mildred. She was sitting down, but got up hurriedly as he came in. She did not move towards him nor speak. He was so surprised that he did not know what he was saying.

"What the hell d'you want?" he asked.

She did not answer, but began to cry. She did not put her hands to her eyes, but kept them hanging by the side of her body. She looked like a housemaid applying for a situation. There was a dreadful humility in her bearing. Philip did not know what feelings came over him. He had a sudden impulse to turn round and escape from the room.

"I didn't think I'd ever see you again," he said at last.

"I wish I was dead," she moaned.

Philip left her standing where she was. He could only think at the moment of steadying himself. His knees were shaking. He looked at her, and he groaned in despair.

"What's the matter?" he said.

"He's left me—Emil."

Philip's heart bounded. He knew then that he loved her as passionately as ever. He had never ceased to love her. She was standing before him humble and unresisting. He wished to take her in his arms and cover her tear-stained face with kisses. Oh, how long the separation had been! He did not know how he could have endured it.

"You'd better sit down. Let me give you a drink."

He drew the chair near the fire and she sat in it. He mixed her whiskey and soda, and, sobbing still, she drank it. She looked at him with great, mournful eyes. There were large black lines under them. She was thinner and whiter than when last he had seen her.

"I wish I'd married you when you asked me," she said.

Philip did not know why the remark seemed to swell his heart. He could not keep the distance from her which he had forced upon himself. He put his hand on her shoulder.

"I'm awfully sorry you're in trouble."

She leaned her head against his bosom and burst into hysterical crying. Her hat was in the way and she took it off. He had never dreamt that she was capable of crying like that. He kissed her again and again. It seemed to ease her a little.

"You were always good to me, Philip," she said. "That's why I knew I could come to you."

"Tell me what's happened."

"Oh, I can't, I can't," she cried out, breaking away from him.

He sank down on his knees beside her and put his cheek against hers.

"Don't you know that there's nothing you can't tell me? I can never blame you for anything."

She told him the story little by little, and sometimes she sobbed so much that he could hardly understand.

"Last Monday week he went up to Birmingham, and he promised to be back on Thursday, and he never came, and he didn't come on the Friday, so I wrote to ask what was the matter, and he never answered the letter. And I wrote and said that if I didn't hear from him by return I'd go up to Birmingham, and this morning I got a solicitor's letter to say I had no claim on him, and if I molested him he'd seek the protection of the law."

"But it's absurd," cried Philip. "A man can't treat his wife like that. Had you had a row?"

"Oh, yes, we'd had a quarrel on the Sunday, and he said he was sick of me, but he'd said it before, and he'd come back all right. I didn't think he meant it. He was frightened, because I told him a baby was coming. I kept it from him as long as I could. Then I had to tell him. He said it was my fault, and I ought to have known better. If you'd only heard the things he said to me! But I found out precious quick that he wasn't a gentleman. He left me without a penny. He hadn't paid the rent, and I hadn't got the money to pay it, and the woman who kept the house said such things to me—well, I might have been a thief the way she talked."

"I thought you were going to take a flat."

"That's what he said, but we just took furnished apartments in Highbury. He was that mean. He said I was extravagant, he didn't give me anything to be extravagant with."

She had an extraordinary way of mixing the trivial with the important. Philip was puzzled. The whole thing was incomprehensible.

"No man could be such a blackguard."

"You don't know him. I wouldn't go back to him now not if he was to come and ask me on his bended knees. I was a fool ever to think of him. And he wasn't earning the money he said he was. The lies he told me!"

Philip thought for a minute or two. He was so deeply moved by her distress that he could not think of himself.

"Would you like me to go to Birmingham? I could see him and try to make things up."

"Oh, there's no chance of that. He'll never come back now, I know him."

"But he must provide for you. He can't get out of that. I don't know

anything about these things, you'd better go and see a solicitor."

"How can I? I haven't got the money."

"I'll pay all that. I'll write a note to my own solicitor, the sportsman who was my father's executor. Would you like me to come with you now? I expect he'll still be at his office."

"No, give me a letter to him. I'll go alone."

She was a little calmer now. He sat down and wrote a note. Then he remembered that she had no money. He had fortunately changed a cheque the day before and was able to give her five pounds.

"You are good to me, Philip," she said.

"I'm so happy to be able to do something for you."

"Are you fond of me still?"

"Just as fond as ever."

She put up her lips and he kissed her. There was a surrender in the action which he had never seen in her before. It was worth all the agony he had suffered.

She went away and he found that she had been there for two hours. He was extraordinarily happy.

"Poor thing, poor thing," he murmured to himself, his heart glowing with a greater love than he had ever felt before.

He never thought of Norah at all till about eight o'clock a telegram came. He knew before opening it that it was from her.

Is anything the matter? Norah.

He did not know what to do nor what to answer. He could fetch her after the play, in which she was walking on, was over and stroll home with her as he sometimes did; but his whole soul revolted against the idea of seeing her that evening. He thought of writing to her, but he could not bring himself to address her as usual, *dearest Norah*. He made up his mind to telegraph.

Sorry. Could not get away, Philip.

He visualised her. He was slightly repelled by the ugly little face, with its high cheek-bones and the crude colour. There was a coarseness in her skin which gave him goose-flesh. He knew that his telegram must be followed by some action on his part, but at all events it postponed it.

Next day he wired again.

Regret, unable to come. Will write.

Mildred had suggested coming at four in the afternoon, and he would not tell her that the hour was inconvenient. After all she came first. He waited for her impatiently. He watched for her at the window and opened the front-door himself.

"Well? Did you see Nixon?"

"Yes," she answered. "He said it wasn't any good. Nothing's to be done. I must just grin and bear it."

"But that's impossible," cried Philip.

She sat down wearily.

"Did he give any reasons?" he asked.

She gave him a crumpled letter.

"There's your letter, Philip. I never took it. I couldn't tell you yesterday, I really couldn't. Emil didn't marry me. He couldn't. He had a wife already and three children."

Philip felt a sudden pang of jealousy and anguish. It was almost more than he could bear.

"That's why I couldn't go back to my aunt. There's no one I can go to but you."

"What made you go away with him?" Philip asked, in a low voice which he struggled to make firm.

"I don't know. I didn't know he was a married man at first, and when he told me I gave him a piece of my mind. And then I didn't see him for months, and when he came to the shop again and asked me I don't know what came over me. I felt as if I couldn't help it. I had to go with him."

"Were you in love with him?"

"I don't know. I couldn't hardly help laughing at the things he said. And there was something about him —he said I'd never regret it, he promised to give me seven pounds a week —he said he was earning fifteen, and it was all a lie, he wasn't. And then I was sick of going to the shop every morning, and I wasn't getting on very well with my aunt; she wanted to treat me as a servant instead of a relation, said I ought to do my own room, and if I didn't do it nobody was going to do it for me. Oh, I wish I hadn't. But when he came to the shop and asked me I felt I couldn't help it."

Philip moved away from her. He sat down at the table and buried his face in his hands. He felt dreadfully humiliated.

"You're not angry with me, Philip?" she asked piteously.

"No," he answered, looking up but away from her, "only I'm awfully hurt."

"Why?"

"You see, I was so dreadfully in love with you. I did everything I could to make you care for me. I thought you were incapable of loving anyone. It's so horrible to know that you were willing to sacrifice everything for that bounder. I wonder what you saw in him."

"I'm awfully sorry, Philip. I regretted it bitterly afterwards, I promise you that."

He thought of Emil Miller, with his pasty, unhealthy look, his shifty blue eyes, and the vulgar smartness of his appearance; he always wore bright red knitted waistcoats. Philip sighed. She got up and went to him. She put her arm round his neck.

"I shall never forget that you offered to marry me, Philip."

He took her hand and looked up at her. She bent down and kissed him.

"Philip, if you want me still I'll do anything you like now. I know you're a gentleman in every sense of the word."

His heart stood still. Her words made him feel slightly sick.

"It's awfully good of you, but I couldn't."

"Don't you care for me any more?"

"Yes, I love you with all my heart."

"Then why shouldn't we have a good time while we've got the chance? You see, it can't matter now."

He released himself from her.

"You don't understand. I've been sick with love for you ever since I saw you, but now—that man. I've unfortunately got a vivid imagination. The thought of it simply disgusts me."

"You are funny," she said.

He took her hand again and smiled at her.

"You mustn't think I'm not grateful. I can never thank you enough, but you see, it's just stronger than I am."

"You are a good friend, Philip."

They went on talking, and soon they had returned to the familiar companionship of old days. It grew late. Philip suggested that they should dine together and go to a music-hall. She wanted some persuasion, for she had an idea of acting up to her situation, and felt instinctively that it did not accord with her distressed condition to go to a place of entertainment. At last Philip asked her to go simply to please him, and when she could look upon it as an act of self-sacrifice she accepted. She had a new thoughtfulness which delighted Philip. She

asked him to take her to the little restaurant in Soho to which they had so often been; he was infinitely grateful to her, because her suggestion showed that happy memories were attached to it. She grew much more cheerful as dinner proceeded. The Burgundy from the public house at the corner warmed her heart, and she forgot that she ought to preserve a dolorous countenance. Philip thought it safe to speak to her of the future.

"I suppose you haven't got a brass farthing, have you?" he asked, when an opportunity presented itself.

"Only what you gave me yesterday, and I had to give the landlady three pounds of that."

"Well, I'd better give you a tenner to go on with. I'll go and see my solicitor and get him to write to Miller. We can make him pay up something, I'm sure. If we can get a hundred pounds out of him it'll carry you on till after the baby comes."

"I wouldn't take a penny from him. I'd rather starve."

"But it's monstrous that he should leave you in the lurch like this."

"I've got my pride to consider."

It was a little awkward for Philip. He needed rigid economy to make his own money last till he was qualified, and he must have something over to keep him during the year he intended to spend as house physician and house surgeon either at his own or at some other hospital. But Mildred had told him various stories of Emil's meanness, and he was afraid to remonstrate with her in case she accused him too of want of generosity.

"I wouldn't take a penny piece from him. I'd sooner beg my bread. I'd have seen about getting some work to do long before now, only it wouldn't be good for me in the state I'm in. You have to think of your health, don't you?"

"You needn't bother about the present," said Philip. "I can let you have all you want till you're fit to work again."

"I knew I could depend on you. I told Emil he needn't think I hadn't got somebody to go to. I told him you was a gentleman in every sense of the word."

By degrees Philip learned how the separation had come about. It appeared that the fellow's wife had discovered the adventure he was engaged in during his periodical visits to London, and had gone to the head of the firm that employed him. She threatened to divorce him, and they announced that they would dismiss him if she did. He was passionately devoted to his children and could not bear the thought of being separated from them. When he had to choose between his wife and his mistress he chose his wife. He had been always anxious that there should be no child to make the entanglement more complicated; and when Mildred, unable longer to conceal its approach, informed him of the fact, he was seized with panic. He picked a quarrel and left her without more ado.

"When d'you expect to be confined?" asked Philip.

"At the beginning of March."

"Three months."

It was necessary to discuss plans. Mildred declared she would not remain in the rooms at Highbury, and Philip thought it more convenient too that she should be nearer to him. He promised to look for something next day. She suggested the Vauxhall Bridge Road as a likely neighbourhood.

"And it would be near for afterwards," she said.

"What do you mean?"

"Well, I should only be able to stay there about two months or a little more, and then I should have to go into a house. I know a very respectable place, where they have a most superior class of people, and they take you for four guineas a week and no extras. Of course the doctor's extra, but that's all. A friend of mine went there, and the lady who keeps it is a thorough lady. I mean to tell her that my husband's an officer in India and I've come to London for my baby, because it's better for my health."

It seemed extraordinary to Philip to hear her talking in this way. With her delicate little features and her pale face she looked cold and maidenly. When he thought of the passions that burnt within her, so unexpected, his heart was strangely troubled. His pulse beat quickly.

LXX

PHILIP expected to find a letter from Norah when he got back to his rooms, but there was nothing; nor did he receive one the following morning. The silence irritated and at the same time alarmed him. They had seen one another every day he had been in London since the previous June; and it must seem odd to her that he should let two days go by without visiting her or offering a reason for his absence; he wondered whether by an unlucky chance she had seen him with Mildred. He could not bear to think that she was hurt or unhappy, and he made up his mind to call on her that afternoon. He was almost inclined to reproach her because he had allowed himself to get on such intimate terms with her. The thought of continuing them filled him with disgust.

He found two rooms for Mildred on the second floor of a house in the Vauxhall Bridge Road. They were noisy, but he knew that she liked the rattle of traffic under her windows. "I don't like a dead and alive street where you don't see a soul pass all day," she said. "Give me a bit of life."

Then he forced himself to go to Vincent Square. He was sick with apprehension when he rang the bell. He had an uneasy sense that he was treating Norah badly; he dreaded reproaches; he knew she had a quick temper, and he hated scenes: perhaps the best way would be to tell her frankly that Mildred had come back to him and his love for her was as violent as it had ever been; he was very sorry, but he had nothing to offer Norah any more. Then he thought of her anguish, for he knew she loved him; it had flattered him before, and he was immensely grateful; but now it was horrible. She had not deserved that he should inflict pain upon her. He asked himself how she would greet him now, and as he walked up the stairs all possible forms of her behaviour flashed across his mind. He knocked at the door. He felt that he was pale, and wondered how to conceal his nervousness.

She was writing away industriously, but she sprang to her feet as he entered.

"I recognised your step," she cried. "Where have you been hiding yourself, you naughty boy?"

She came towards him joyfully and put her arms round his neck. She was delighted to see him. He kissed her, and then, to give himself countenance, said he was dying for tea. She bustled the fire to make the kettle boil.

"I've been awfully busy," he said lamely.

She began to chatter in her bright way, telling him of a new commission she had to provide a novelette for a firm which had not hitherto employed her. She was to get fifteen guineas for it.

"It's money from the clouds. I'll tell you what we'll do, we'll stand ourselves a little jaunt. Let's go and spend a day at Oxford, shall we? I'd love to see the colleges."

He looked at her to see whether there was any shadow of reproach in her eyes; but they were as frank and merry as ever: she was overjoyed to see him. His heart sank. He could not tell her the brutal truth. She made some toast for him, and cut it into little pieces, and gave it him as though he were a child.

"Is the brute fed?" she asked.

He nodded, smiling; and she lit a cigarette for him. Then, as she loved to do, she came and sat on his knees. She was very light. She leaned back in his arms with a sigh of delicious happiness.

"Say something nice to me," she murmured.

"What shall I say?"

"You might by an effort of imagination say that you rather liked me."

"You know I do that."

He had not the heart to tell her then. He would give her peace at all events for that day, and perhaps he might write to her. That would be easier. He could not bear to think of her crying. She made him kiss her, and as he kissed her he thought of Mildred and Mildred's pale, thin lips. The recollection of Mildred remained with him all the time, like an incorporated form, but more substantial than a shadow; and the sight continually distracted his attention.

"You're very quiet today," Norah said.

Her loquacity was a standing joke between them, and he answered:

"You never let me get a word in, and I've got out of the habit of talking."

"But you're not listening, and that's bad manners."

He reddened a little, wondering whether she had some inkling of his secret; he turned away his eyes uneasily. The weight of her irked him this afternoon, and he did not want her to touch him.

"My foot's gone to sleep," he said.

"I'm so sorry," she cried, jumping up. "I shall have to bant if I can't break myself of this habit of sitting on gentlemen's knees."

He went through an elaborate form of stamping his foot and walking about. Then he stood in front of the fire so that she should not resume her position. While she talked he thought that she was worth ten of Mildred; she amused him much more and was jollier to talk to; she was cleverer, and she had a much nicer nature. She was a good, brave, honest little woman; and Mildred, he thought bitterly, deserved none of these epithets. If he had any sense he would stick to Norah, she would make him much happier than he would ever be with Mildred: after all she loved him, and Mildred was only grateful for his help. But when all was said the important thing was to love rather than to be loved; and he yearned for Mildred with his whole soul. He would sooner have ten minutes with her than a whole afternoon with Norah, he prized one kiss of her cold lips more than all Norah could give him.

"I can't help myself," he thought.

"I've just got her in my bones."

He did not care if she was heartless, vicious and vulgar, stupid and grasping, he loved her. He would rather have misery with the one than happiness with the other.

When he got up to go Norah said casually:

"Well, I shall see you tomorrow, shan't I?"

"Yes," he answered.

He knew that he would not be able to come, since he was going to help Mildred with her moving, but he had not the courage to say so. He made up his mind that he would send a wire. Mildred saw the rooms in the morning, was satisfied with them, and after luncheon Philip went up with her to Highbury. She had a trunk for her clothes and another for the various odds and ends, cushions, lampshades, photograph frames, with which she had tried to give the apartments a home-like air; she had two or three large cardboard boxes besides, but in all there was no more than could be put on the roof of a four-wheeler. As they drove through Victoria Street Philip sat well back in the cab in case Norah should happen to be passing. He had not had an opportunity to telegraph and could not do so from the postoffice in the Vauxhall Bridge Road, since she would wonder what he was doing in that neighbourhood; and if he was there he could have no excuse for not going into the neighbouring square where she lived. He made up his mind that he had better go in and see her for half an hour; but the necessity irritated him: he was angry with Norah, because she forced him to vulgar and degrading shifts. But he was happy to be with Mildred. It amused him to help her with the unpacking; and he experienced a charming sense of possession in installing her in these lodgings which he had found and was paying for. He would not let her exert herself. It was a pleasure to do things for her, and she had no desire to do what somebody else seemed desirous to do for her. He unpacked her clothes and put them away. She was not proposing to go out again, so he got her slippers and took off her boots. It delighted him to perform menial offices.

"You do spoil me," she said, running her fingers affectionately through his hair, while he was on his knees unbuttoning her boots.

He took her hands and kissed them.

"It is nipping to have you here."

He arranged the cushions and the photograph frames. She had several jars of green earthenware.

"I'll get you some flowers for them," he said.

He looked round at his work proudly.

"As I'm not going out any more I think I'll get into a teagown," she said. "Undo me behind, will you?"

She turned round as unconcernedly as though he were a woman. His sex meant nothing to her. But his heart was filled with gratitude for the intimacy her request showed. He undid the hooks and eyes with clumsy fingers.

"That first day I came into the shop I never thought I'd be doing this for you now," he said, with a laugh which he forced.

"Somebody must do it," she answered.

She went into the bed-room and slipped into a pale blue teagown decorated with a great deal of cheap lace. Then Philip settled her on a sofa and made tea for her.

"I'm afraid I can't stay and have it with you," he said regretfully. "I've got a beastly appointment. But I shall be back in half an hour."

He wondered what he should say if she asked him what the appointment was, but she showed no curiosity. He had ordered dinner for the two of them when he took the rooms, and proposed to spend the evening with her quietly. He was in such a hurry to get back that he took a tram along the Vauxhall Bridge Road. He thought he had better break the fact to Norah at once that he could not stay more than a few minutes.

"I say, I've got only just time to say how d'you do," he said, as soon as he got into her rooms. "I'm frightfully busy."

Her face fell.

"Why, what's the matter?"

It exasperated him that she should force him to tell lies, and he knew that he reddened when he answered that there was a demonstration at the hospital which he was bound to go to. He fancied that she looked as though she did not believe him, and this irritated him all the more.

"Oh, well, it doesn't matter," she said. "I shall have you all tomorrow."

He looked at her blankly. It was Sunday, and he had been looking forward to spending the day with Mildred. He told himself that he must do that in common decency; he could not leave her by herself in a strange house.

"I'm awfully sorry, I'm engaged tomorrow."

He knew this was the beginning of a scene which he would have given anything to avoid. The colour on Norah's cheeks grew brighter.

"But I've asked the Gordons to lunch"—they were an actor and his wife who were touring the provinces and in London for Sunday—"I told you about it a week ago."

"I'm awfully sorry, I forgot." He hesitated. "I'm afraid I can't possibly come. Isn't there somebody else you can get?"

"What are you doing tomorrow then?"

"I wish you wouldn't cross-examine me."

"Don't you want to tell me?"

"I don't in the least mind telling you, but it's rather annoying to be forced to account for all one's movements."

Norah suddenly changed. With an effort of self-control she got the better of her temper, and going up to him took his hands.

"Don't disappoint me tomorrow, Philip, I've been looking forward so much to spending the day with you. The Gordons want to see you, and we'll have such a jolly time."

"I'd love to if I could."

"I'm not very exacting, am I? I don't often ask you to do anything that's a bother. Won't you get out of your horrid engagement—just this once?"

"I'm awfully sorry, I don't see how I can," he replied sullenly.

"Tell me what it is," she said coaxingly.

He had had time to invent something.

"Griffiths' two sisters are up for the week-end and we're taking them out."

"Is that all?" she said joyfully. "Griffiths can so easily get another man."

He wished he had thought of something more urgent than that. It was a clumsy lie.

"No, I'm awfully sorry, I can't— I've promised and I mean to keep my promise."

"But you promised me too. Surely I come first."

"I wish you wouldn't persist," he said.

She flared up.

"You won't come because you don't want to. I don't know what you've been doing the last few days, you've

been quite different."

He looked at his watch.

"I'm afraid I'll have to be going," he said.

"You won't come tomorrow?"

"No."

"In that case you needn't trouble to come again," she cried, losing her temper for good.

"That's just as you like," he answered.

"Don't let me detain you any longer," she added ironically.

He shrugged his shoulders and walked out. He was relieved that it had gone no worse. There had been no tears. As he walked along he congratulated himself on getting out of the affair so easily. He went into Victoria Street and bought a few flowers to take in to Mildred.

The little dinner was a great success. Philip had sent in a small pot of caviare, which he knew she was very fond of, and the landlady brought them up some cutlets with vegetables and a sweet. Philip had ordered Burgundy, which was her favourite wine. With the curtains drawn, a bright fire, and one of Mildred's shades on the lamp, the room was cosy.

"It's really just like home," smiled Philip.

"I might be worse off, mightn't I?" she answered.

When they finished, Philip drew two arm-chairs in front of the fire, and they sat down. He smoked his pipe comfortably. He felt happy and generous.

"What would you like to do tomorrow?" he asked.

"Oh, I'm going to Tulse Hill. You remember the manageress at the shop, well, she's married now, and she's asked me to go and spend the day with her. Of course she thinks I'm married too."

Philip's heart sank.

"But I refused an invitation so that I might spend Sunday with you."

He thought that if she loved him she would say that in that case she would stay with him. He knew very well that Norah would not have hesitated.

"Well, you were a silly to do that. I've promised to go for three weeks and more."

"But how can you go alone?"

"Oh, I shall say that Emil's away on business. Her husband's in the glove trade, and he's a very superior fellow."

Philip was silent, and bitter feelings passed through his heart. She gave him a sidelong glance.

"You don't grudge me a little pleasure, Philip? You see, it's the last time

I shall be able to go anywhere for I don't know how long, and I had promised."

He took her hand and smiled.

"No, darling, I want you to have the best time you can. I only want you to be happy."

There was a little book bound in blue paper lying open, face downwards, on the sofa, and Philip idly took it up. It was a two-penny novelette, and the author was Courtenay Paget. That was the name under which Norah wrote.

"I do like his books," said Mildred. "I read them all. They're so refined."

He remembered what Norah had said of herself.

"I have an immense popularity among kitchen-maids. They think me so genteel."

LXXI

PHILIP, in return for Griffiths' confidences, had told him the details of his own complicated amours, and on Sunday morning, after breakfast when they sat by the fire in their dressing-gowns and smoked, he recounted the scene of the previous day. Griffiths congratulated him because he had got out of his difficulties so easily.

"It's the simplest thing in the world to have an affair with a woman," he remarked sententiously, "but it's a devil of a nuisance to get out of it."

Philip felt a little inclined to pat himself on the back for his skill in managing the business. At all events he was immensely relieved. He thought of Mildred enjoying herself in Tulse Hill, and he found in himself a real satisfaction because she was happy. It was an act of self-sacrifice on his part that he did not grudge

her pleasure even though paid for by his own disappointment, and it filled his heart with a comfortable glow.

But on Monday morning he found on his table a letter from Norah. She wrote:

Dearest,

I'm sorry I was cross on Saturday. Forgive me and come to tea in the afternoon as usual. I love you.

Your Norah.

His heart sank, and he did not know what to do. He took the note to Griffiths and showed it to him.

"You'd better leave it unanswered," said he.

"Oh, I can't," cried Philip. "I should be miserable if I thought of her waiting and waiting. You don't know what it is to be sick for the postman's knock. I do, and I can't expose anybody else to that torture."

"My dear fellow, one can't break that sort of affair off without somebody suffering. You must just set your teeth to that. One thing is, it doesn't last very long."

Philip felt that Norah had not deserved that he should make her suffer; and what did Griffiths know about the degrees of anguish she was capable of? He remembered his own pain when Mildred had told him she was going to be married. He did not want anyone to experience what he had experienced then.

"If you're so anxious not to give her pain, go back to her," said Griffiths.

"I can't do that."

He got up and walked up and down the room nervously. He was angry with Norah because she had not let the matter rest. She must have seen that he had no more love to give her. They said women were so quick at seeing those things.

"You might help me," he said to Griffiths.

"My dear fellow, don't make such a fuss about it. People do get over these things, you know. She probably isn't so wrapped up in you as you think, either. One's always rather apt to exaggerate the passion one's inspired other people with."

He paused and looked at Philip with amusement.

"Look here, there's only one thing you can do. Write to her, and tell her the thing's over. Put it so that there can be no mistake about it. It'll hurt her, but it'll hurt her less if you do the thing brutally than if you try half-hearted ways."

Philip sat down and wrote the following letter:

My dear Norah,

I am sorry to make you unhappy, but I think we had better let things remain where we left them on Saturday. I don't think there's any use in letting these things drag on when they've ceased to be amusing. You told me to go and I went. I do not propose to come back. Good-bye.

Philip Carey.

He showed the letter to Griffiths and asked him what he thought of it. Griffiths read it and looked at Philip with twinkling eyes. He did not say what he felt.

"I think that'll do the trick," he said.

Philip went out and posted it. He passed an uncomfortable morning, for he imagined with great detail what Norah would feel when she received his letter. He tortured himself with the thought of her tears. But at the same time he was relieved. Imagined grief was more easy to bear than grief seen, and he was free now to love Mildred with all his soul. His heart leaped at the thought of going to see her that afternoon, when his day's work at the hospital was over.

When as usual he went back to his rooms to tidy himself, he had no sooner put the latch-key in his door than he heard a voice behind him.

"May I come in? I've been waiting for you for half an hour."

It was Norah. He felt himself blush to the roots of his hair. She spoke gaily. There was no trace of resentment in her voice and nothing to indicate that there was a rupture between them. He felt himself cornered. He was sick with fear, but he did his best to smile.

"Yes, do," he said.

He opened the door, and she preceded him into his sitting-room. He was nervous and, to give himself countenance, offered her a cigarette and lit one for himself. She looked at him brightly.

"Why did you write me such a horrid letter, you naughty boy? If I'd taken it seriously it would have made me perfectly wretched."

"It was meant seriously," he answered gravely.

"Don't be so silly. I lost my temper the other day, and I wrote and apologised. You weren't satisfied, so I've come here to apologise again. After all, you're your own master and I have no claims upon you. I don't want you to do anything you don't want to."

She got up from the chair in which she was sitting and went towards him impulsively, with outstretched hands.

"Let's make friends again, Philip. I'm so sorry if I offended you."

He could not prevent her from taking his hands, but he could not look at her.

"I'm afraid it's too late," he said.

She let herself down on the floor by his side and clasped his knees.

"Philip, don't be silly. I'm quick-tempered too and I can understand that I hurt you, but it's so stupid to sulk over it. What's the good of making us both unhappy? It's been so jolly, our friendship." She passed her fingers slowly over his hand. "I love you, Philip."

He got up, disengaging himself from her, and went to the other side of the room.

"I'm awfully sorry, I can't do anything. The whole thing's over."

"D'you mean to say you don't love me any more?"

"I'm afraid so."

"You were just looking for an opportunity to throw me over and you took that one?"

He did not answer. She looked at him steadily for a time which seemed intolerable. She was sitting on the floor where he had left her, leaning against the arm-chair. She began to cry quite silently, without trying to hide her face, and the large tears rolled down her cheeks one after the other. She did not sob. It was horribly painful to see her. Philip turned away.

"I'm awfully sorry to hurt you. It's not my fault if I don't love you."

She did not answer. She merely sat there, as though she were overwhelmed, and the tears flowed down her cheeks. It would have been easier to bear if she had reproached him. He had thought her temper would get the better of her, and he was prepared for that. At the back of his mind was a feeling that a real quarrel, in which each said to the other cruel things, would in some way be a justification of his behaviour. The time passed. At last he grew frightened by her silent crying; he went into his bed-room and got a glass of water; he leaned over her.

"Won't you drink a little? It'll relieve you."

She put her lips listlessly to the glass and drank two or three mouthfuls. Then in an exhausted whisper she asked him for a handkerchief. She dried her eyes.

"Of course I knew you never loved me as much as I loved you," she moaned.

"I'm afraid that's always the case," he said. "There's always one who loves and one who lets himself be loved."

He thought of Mildred, and a bitter pain traversed his heart. Norah did not answer for a long time.

"I'd been so miserably unhappy, and my life was so hateful," she said at last.

She did not speak to him, but to herself. He had never heard her before complain of the life she had led with her husband or of her poverty. He had always admired the bold front she displayed to the world.

"And then you came along and you were so good to me. And I admired you because you were clever and it was so heavenly to have someone I could put my trust in. I loved you. I never thought it could come to an end. And without any fault of mine at all."

Her tears began to flow again, but now she was more mistress of herself, and she hid her face in Philip's handkerchief. She tried hard to control herself.

"Give me some more water," she said.

She wiped her eyes.

"I'm sorry to make such a fool of myself. I was so unprepared."

"I'm awfully sorry, Norah. I want you to know that I'm very grateful for all you've done for me."

He wondered what it was she saw in him.

"Oh, it's always the same," she sighed, "if you want men to behave well to you, you must be beastly to them; if you treat them decently they make you suffer for it."

She got up from the floor and said she must go. She gave Philip a long, steady look. Then she sighed.

"It's so inexplicable. What does it all mean?"

Philip took a sudden determination.

"I think I'd better tell you, I don't want you to think too badly of me, I want you to see that I can't help myself. Mildred's come back."

The colour came to her face.

"Why didn't you tell me at once? I deserved that surely."

"I was afraid to."

She looked at herself in the glass and set her hat straight.

"Will you call me a cab," she said. "I don't feel I *can* walk."

He went to the door and stopped a passing hansom; but when she followed him into the street he was startled to see how white she was. There was a heaviness in her movements as though she had suddenly grown older. She looked so ill that he had not the heart to let her go alone.

"I'll drive back with you if you don't mind."

She did not answer, and he got into the cab. They drove along in silence over the bridge, through shabby streets in which children, with shrill cries, played in the road. When they arrived at her door she did not immediately get out. It seemed as though she could not summon enough strength to her legs to move.

"I hope you'll forgive me, Norah," he said.

She turned her eyes towards him, and he saw that they were bright again with tears, but she forced a smile to her lips.

"Poor fellow, you're quite worried about me. You mustn't bother. I don't blame you. I shall get over it all right."

Lightly and quickly she stroked his face to show him that she bore no ill-feeling, the gesture was scarcely more than suggested; then she jumped out of the cab and let herself into her house.

Philip paid the hansom and walked to Mildred's lodgings. There was a curious heaviness in his heart. He was inclined to reproach himself. But why? He did not know what else he could have done. Passing a fruiterer's, he remembered that Mildred was fond of grapes. He was so grateful that he could show his love for her by recollecting every whim she had.

LXXII

FOR the next three months Philip went every day to see Mildred. He took his books with him and after tea worked, while Mildred lay on the sofa reading novels. Sometimes he would look up and watch her for a minute. A happy smile crossed his lips. She would feel his eyes upon her.

"Don't waste your time looking at me, silly. Go on with your work," she said.

"Tyrant," he answered gaily.

He put aside his book when the landlady came in to lay the cloth for dinner, and in his high spirits he exchanged chaff with her. She was a little cockney, of middle-age, with an amusing humour and a quick tongue. Mildred had become great friends with her and had given her an elaborate but mendacious account of the circumstances which had brought her to the pass she was in. The good-hearted little woman was touched and found no trouble too great to make Mildred comfortable. Mildred's sense of propriety had suggested that Philip should pass himself off as her brother. They dined together, and Philip was delighted when he had ordered something which tempted Mildred's capricious appetite. It enchanted him to see her sitting opposite him, and every now and then from sheer joy he took her hand and pressed it. After dinner she sat in the arm-chair by the fire, and he settled himself down on the floor beside her, leaning against her knees, and smoked. Often they did not talk at all, and sometimes Philip noticed that she had fallen into a doze. He dared not move then in case he

woke her, and he sat very quietly, looking lazily into the fire and enjoying his happiness.

"Had a nice little nap?" he smiled, when she woke.

"I've not been sleeping," she answered. "I only just closed my eyes."

She would never acknowledge that she had been asleep. She had a phlegmatic temperament, and her condition did not seriously inconvenience her. She took a lot of trouble about her health and accepted the advice of anyone who chose to offer it. She went for a 'constitutional' every morning that it was fine and remained out a definite time. When it was not too cold she sat in St. James' Park. But the rest of the day she spent quite happily on her sofa, reading one novel after another or chatting with the landlady; she had an inexhaustible interest in gossip, and told Philip with abundant detail the history of the landlady, of the lodgers on the drawing-room floor, and of the people who lived in the next house on either side. Now and then she was seized with panic; she poured out her fears to Philip about the pain of the confinement and was in terror lest she should die; she gave him a full account of the confinements of the landlady and of the lady on the drawing-room floor (Mildred did not know her; "I'm one to keep myself to myself," she said, "I'm not one to go about with anybody.") and she narrated details with a queer mixture of horror and gusto; but for the most part she looked forward to the occurrence with equanimity.

"After all, I'm not the first one to

have a baby, am I? And the doctor says I shan't have any trouble. You see, it isn't as if I wasn't well made."

Mrs. Owen, the owner of the house she was going to when her time came, had recommended a doctor, and Mildred saw him once a week. He was to charge fifteen guineas.

"Of course I could have got it done cheaper, but Mrs. Owen strongly recommended him, and I thought it wasn't worth while to spoil the ship for a coat of tar."

"If you feel happy and comfortable I don't mind a bit about the expense," said Philip.

She accepted all that Philip did for her as if it were the most natural thing in the world, and on his side he loved to spend money on her: each five-pound note he gave her caused him a little thrill of happiness and pride; he gave her a good many, for she was not economical.

"I don't know where the money goes to," she said herself, "it seems to slip through my fingers like water."

"It doesn't matter," said Philip. "I'm so glad to be able to do anything I can for you."

She could not sew well and so did not make the necessary things for the baby; she told Philip it was much cheaper in the end to buy them. Philip had lately sold one of the mortgages in which his money had been put; and now, with five hundred pounds in the bank waiting to be invested in something that could be more easily realised, he felt himself uncommonly well-to-do. They talked often of the future. Philip was anxious that Mildred should keep the child with her, but she refused: she had her living to earn, and it would be more easy to do this if she had not also to look after a baby. Her plan was to get back into one of the shops of the company for which she

had worked before, and the child could be put with some decent woman in the country.

"I can find someone who'll look after it well for seven and sixpence a week. It'll be better for the baby and better for me."

It seemed callous to Philip, but when he tried to reason with her she pretended to think he was concerned with the expense.

"You needn't worry about that," she said. "I shan't ask *you* to pay for it."

"You know I don't care how much I pay."

At the bottom of her heart was the hope that the child would be still-born. She did no more than hint it, but Philip saw that the thought was there. He was shocked at first; and then, reasoning with himself, he was obliged to confess that for all concerned such an event was to be desired.

"It's all very fine to say this and that," Mildred remarked querulously, "but it's jolly difficult for a girl to earn her living by herself; it doesn't make it any easier when she's got a baby."

"Fortunately you've got me to fall back on," smiled Philip, taking her hand.

"You've been good to me, Philip."

"Oh, what rot!"

"You can't say I didn't offer anything in return for what you've done."

"Good heavens, I don't want a return. If I've done anything for you, I've done it because I love you. You owe me nothing. I don't want you to do anything unless you love me."

He was a little horrified by her feeling that her body was a commodity which she could deliver indifferently as an acknowledgment for services rendered.

"But I do want to, Philip. You've been so good to me."

"Well, it won't hurt for waiting. When you're all right again we'll go for our little honeymoon."

"You are naughty," she said, smiling.

Mildred expected to be confined early in March, and as soon as she was well enough she was to go to the seaside for a fortnight: that would give Philip a chance to work without interruption for his examination; after that came the Easter holidays, and they had arranged to go to Paris together. Philip talked endlessly of the things they would do. Paris was delightful then. They would take a room in a little hotel he knew in the Latin Quarter, and they would eat in all sorts of charming little restaurants; they would go to the play, and he would take her to music-halls. It would amuse her to meet his friends. He had talked to her about Cronshaw, she would see him; and there was Lawson, he had gone to Paris for a couple of months; and they would go to the Bal Bullier; there were excursions; they would make trips to Versailles, Chartres, Fontainebleau.

"It'll cost a lot of money," she said.

"Oh, damn the expense. Think how I've been looking forward to it. Don't you know what it means to me? I've never loved anyone but you. I never shall."

She listened to his enthusiasm with smiling eyes. He thought he saw in them a new tenderness, and he was grateful to her. She was much gentler than she used to be. There was in her no longer the superciliousness which had irritated him. She was so accustomed to him now that she took no pains to keep up before him any pretences. She no longer troubled to do her hair with the old elaboration, but just tied it in a knot; and she left off the vast fringe which she generally wore: the more careless style suited her. Her face was so thin that it made her eyes seem very large; there were heavy lines under them, and the pallor of her cheeks made their colour more profound. She had a wistful look which was infinitely pathetic. There seemed to Philip to be in her something of the Madonna. He wished they could continue in that same way always. He was happier than he had ever been in his life.

He used to leave her at ten o'clock every night, for she liked to go to bed early, and he was obliged to put in another couple of hours' work to make up for the lost evening. He generally brushed her hair for her before he went. He had made a ritual of the kisses he gave her when he bade her good-night; first he kissed the palms of her hands, (how thin the fingers were, the nails were beautiful, for she spent much time in manicuring them,) then he kissed her closed eyes, first the right one and then the left, and at last he kissed her lips. He went home with a heart overflowing with love. He longed for an opportunity to gratify the desire for self-sacrifice which consumed him.

Presently the time came for her to move to the nursing-home where she was to be confined. Philip was then able to visit her only in the afternoons. Mildred changed her story and represented herself as the wife of a soldier who had gone to India to join his regiment, and Philip was introduced to the mistress of the establishment as her brother-in-law.

"I have to be rather careful what I say," she told him, "as there's another lady here whose husband's in the Indian Civil."

"I wouldn't let that disturb me if I were you," said Philip. "I'm convinced that her husband and yours went out on the same boat."

"What boat?" she asked innocently.

"The Flying Dutchman."

Mildred was safely delivered of a daughter, and when Philip was allowed to see her the child was lying by her side. Mildred was very weak, but relieved that everything was over. She showed him the baby, and herself looked at it curiously.

"It's a funny-looking little thing, isn't it? I can't believe it's mine."

It was red and wrinkled and odd. Philip smiled when he looked at it. He did not quite know what to say; and it embarrassed him because the nurse who owned the house was standing by his side; and he felt by the way she was looking at him that, disbelieving Mildred's complicated story, she thought he was the father.

"What are you going to call her?" asked Philip.

"I can't make up my mind if I shall call her Madeleine or Cecilia."

The nurse left them alone for a few minutes, and Philip bent down and kissed Mildred on the mouth.

"I'm so glad it's all over happily, darling."

She put her thin arms round his neck.

"You have been a brick to me, Phil dear."

"Now I feel that you're mine at last. I've waited so long for you, my dear."

They heard the nurse at the door, and Philip hurriedly got up. The nurse entered. There was a slight smile on her lips.

LXXIII

THREE weeks later Philip saw Mildred and her baby off to Brighton. She had made a quick recovery and looked better than he had ever seen her. She was going to a boardinghouse where she had spent a couple of week-ends with Emil Miller, and had written to say that her husband was obliged to go to Germany on business and she was coming down with her baby. She got pleasure out of the stories she invented, and she showed a certain fertility of invention in the working out of the details. Mildred proposed to find in Brighton some woman who would be willing to take charge of the baby. Philip was startled at the callousness with which she insisted on getting rid of it so soon, but she argued with common sense that the poor child had much better be put somewhere before it grew used to her. Philip had expected the maternal instinct to make itself felt when she had had the baby two or three weeks and had counted on this to help him persuade her to keep it; but nothing of the sort occurred. Mildred was not unkind to her baby; she did all that was necessary; it amused her sometimes, and she talked about it a good deal; but at heart she was indifferent to it. She could not look upon it as part of herself. She fancied it resembled its father already. She was continually wondering how she would manage when it grew older; and she was exasperated with herself for being such a fool as to have it at all.

"If I'd only known then all I do now," she said.

She laughed at Philip, because he was anxious about its welfare.

"You couldn't make more fuss if you was the father," she said. "I'd like to see Emil getting into such a stew about it."

Philip's mind was full of the stories he had heard of baby-farming and the ghouls who ill-treat the wretched children that selfish, cruel parents have put in their charge.

"Don't be so silly," said Mildred. "That's when you give a woman a sum down to look after a baby. But when you're going to pay so much a week it's to their interest to look after it well."

Philip insisted that Mildred should place the child with people who had no children of their own and would promise to take no other.

"Don't haggle about the price," he said. "I'd rather pay half a guinea a week than run any risk of the kid being starved or beaten."

"You're a funny old thing, Philip," she laughed.

To him there was something very touching in the child's helplessness. It was small, ugly, and querulous. Its birth had been looked forward to with shame and anguish. Nobody wanted it. It was dependent on him, a stranger, for food, shelter, and clothes to cover its nakedness.

As the train started he kissed Mildred. He would have kissed the baby too, but he was afraid she would laugh at him.

"You will write to me, darling, won't you? And I shall look forward to your coming back with oh! such impatience."

"Mind you get through your exam."

He had been working for it industriously, and now with only ten days before him he made a final effort. He was very anxious to pass, first to save himself time and expense, for money had been slipping through his fingers during the last four months with incredible speed; and then because this examination marked the end of the drudgery: after that the student had to do with medicine, midwifery, and surgery, the interest of which was more vivid than the anatomy and physiology with which he had been hitherto concerned. Philip looked forward with interest to the rest of the curriculum. Nor did he want to have to confess to Mildred that he had failed: though the examination was difficult and the majority of candidates were ploughed at the first attempt, he knew that she would think less well of him if he did not succeed; she had a peculiarly humiliating way of showing what she thought.

Mildred sent him a postcard to announce her safe arrival, and he snatched half an hour every day to write a long letter to her. He had always a certain shyness in expressing himself by word of mouth, but he found he could tell her, pen in hand, all sorts of things which it would have made him feel ridiculous to say. Profiting by the discovery he poured out to her his whole heart. He had never been able to tell her before how his adoration filled every part of him so that all his actions, all his thoughts, were touched with it. He wrote to her of the future, the happiness that lay before him, and the gratitude which he owed her. He asked himself (he had often asked himself before but had never put it into words) what it was in her that filled him with such extravagant delight; he did not know; he knew only that when she was with him he was happy, and when she was away from him the world was on a sudden cold and gray; he knew only that when he thought of her his heart seemed to grow big in his body so that it was difficult to breathe (as if it pressed against his lungs) and it throbbed, so that the delight of her presence was almost pain; his knees shook, and he felt strangely weak as though, not having eaten, he were tremulous from want of food. He looked forward eagerly to her answers. He did not expect her to write often, for he knew that letter-writing came difficultly to her; and he was quite content with the clumsy little note that arrived in reply to four of his. She spoke of the boarding-house in which she had taken a room, of the weather and the baby, told him she had been for a walk on the front with a lady-friend whom she had met in the boarding-house and who had taken such a fancy to baby, she was going to the threatre on Saturday night, and Brighton was filling up. It touched Philip because it was so matter-of-fact. The crabbed style, the formality of the matter, gave him a queer desire to laugh and to take her in his arms and kiss her.

He went into the examination with happy confidence. There was nothing in either of the papers that gave him trouble. He knew that he had done well, and though the second part of the examination was *viva voce* and he was more nervous, he managed to answer the questions adequately. He sent a triumphant telegram to Mildred when the result was announced.

When he got back to his rooms Philip found a letter from her, saying that she thought it would be better for her to stay another week in Brighton. She had found a woman who would be glad to take the baby for seven shillings a week, but she wanted to make inquiries about her, and she was herself benefiting so much by the sea-air that she was sure a few days more would do her no end of good. She hated asking Philip for money, but would he send some by return, as she had had to buy herself a new hat, she couldn't go about with her lady-friend always

in the same hat, and her lady-friend was so dressy. Philip had a moment of bitter disappointment. It took away all his pleasure at getting through his examination.

"If she loved me one quarter as much as I love her she couldn't bear to stay away a day longer than necessary."

He put the thought away from him quickly; it was pure selfishness; of course her health was more important than anything else. But he had nothing to do now; he might spend the week with her in Brighton, and they could be together all day. His heart leaped at the thought. It would be amusing to appear before Mildred suddenly with the information that he had taken a room in the boarding-house. He looked out trains. But he paused. He was not certain that she would be pleased to see him; she had made friends in Brighton; he was quiet, and she liked boisterous joviality; he realised that she amused herself more with other people than with him. It would torture him if he felt for an instant that he was in the way. He was afraid to risk it. He dared not even write and suggest that, with nothing to keep him in town, he would like to spend the week where he could see her every day. She knew he had nothing to do; if she wanted him to come she would have asked him to. He dared not risk the anguish he would suffer if he proposed to come and she made excuses to prevent him.

He wrote to her next day, sent her a five-pound note, and at the end of his letter said that if she were very nice and cared to see him for the week-end he would be glad to run down; but she was by no means to alter any plans she had made. He awaited her answer with impatience. In it she said that if she had only known before she could have arranged it, but she had promised to go to a music-hall on the Saturday night; besides, it would make the people at the boarding-house talk if he stayed there. Why did he not come on Sunday morning and spend the day? They could lunch at the Metropole, and she would take him afterwards to see the very superior lady-like person who was going to take the baby.

Sunday. He blessed the day because it was fine. As the train approached Brighton the sun poured through the carriage window. Mildred was waiting for him on the platform.

"How jolly of you to come and meet me!" he cried, as he seized her hands.

"You expected me, didn't you?"

"I hoped you would. I say, how well you're looking."

"It's done me a rare lot of good, but I think I'm wise to stay here as long as I can. And there are a very nice class of people at the boarding-house. I wanted cheering up after seeing nobody all these months. It was dull sometimes."

She looked very smart in her new hat, a large black straw with a great many inexpensive flowers on it; and round her neck floated a long boa of imitation swansdown. She was still very thin, and she stooped a little when she walked, (she had always done that,) but her eyes did not seem so large; and though she never had any colour, her skin had lost the earthy look it had. They walked down to the sea. Philip, remembering he had not walked with her for months, grew suddenly conscious of his limp and walked stiffly in the attempt to conceal it.

"Are you glad to see me?" he asked, love dancing madly in his heart.

"Of course I am. You needn't ask that."

"By the way, Griffiths sends you his love."

"What cheek!"

He had talked to her a great deal of Griffiths. He had told her how flirtatious he was and had amused her often with the narration of some adventure which Griffiths under the seal of secrecy had imparted to him. Mildred had listened, with some pretence of disgust sometimes, but generally with curiosity; and Philip, admiringly, had enlarged upon his friend's good looks and charm.

"I'm sure you'll like him just as much as I do. He's so jolly and amusing, and he's such an awfully good sort."

Philip told her how, when they were perfect strangers, Griffiths had nursed him through an illness; and in the telling Griffiths' self-sacrifice lost nothing.

"You can't help liking him," said Philip.

"I don't like good-looking men," said Mildred. "They're too conceited for me."

"He wants to know you. I've talked to him about you an awful lot."

"What have you said?" asked Mildred.

Philip had no one but Griffiths to talk to of his love for Mildred, and little by little had told him the whole story of his connection with her. He described her to him fifty times. He dwelt amorously on every detail of her appearance, and Griffiths knew exactly how her thin hands were shaped and how white her face was, and he laughed at Philip when he talked of the charm of her pale, thin lips.

"By Jove, I'm glad I don't take things so badly as that," he said. "Life wouldn't be worth living."

Philip smiled. Griffiths did not know the delight of being so madly in love that it was like meat and wine and the air one breathed and whatever else was essential to existence. Griffiths knew that Philip had looked after the girl while she was having her baby and was now going away with her.

"Well, I must say you've deserved to get something," he remarked. "It must have cost you a pretty penny. It's lucky you can afford it."

"I can't," said Philip. "But what do I care!"

Since it was early for luncheon, Philip and Mildred sat in one of the shelters on the parade, sunning themselves, and watched the people pass. There were the Brighton shop-boys who walked in twos and threes, swinging their canes, and there were the Brighton shop-girls who tripped along in giggling bunches. They could tell the people who had come down from London for the day; the keen air gave a fillip to their weariness. There were many Jews, stout ladies in tight satin dresses and diamonds, little corpulent men with a gesticulative manner. There were middle-aged gentlemen spending a week-end in one of the large hotels, carefully dressed; and they walked industriously after too substantial a breakfast to give themselves an appetite for too substantial a luncheon: they exchanged the time of day with friends and talked of Dr. Brighton or London-by-the-Sea. Here and there a well-known actor passed, elaborately unconscious of the attention he excited: sometimes he wore patent leather boots, a coat with an astrakhan collar, and carried a silver-knobbed stick; and sometimes, looking as though he had come from a day's shooting, he strolled in knickerbockers, and ulster of Harris tweed, and a tweed hat on the back of his head.

The sun shone on the blue sea, and the blue sea was trim and neat.

After luncheon they went to Hove to see the woman who was to take charge of the baby. She lived in a small house in a back street, but it was clean and tidy. Her name was Mrs. Harding. She was an elderly, stout person, with gray hair and a red, fleshy face. She looked motherly in her cap, and Philip thought she seemed kind.

"Won't you find it an awful nuisance to look after a baby?" he asked her.

She explained that her husband was a curate, a good deal older than herself, who had difficulty in getting permanent work since vicars wanted young men to assist them; he earned a little now and then by doing locums when someone took a holiday or fell ill, and a charitable institution gave them a small pension; but her life was lonely, it would be something to do to look after a child, and the few shillings a week paid for it would help her to keep things going. She promised that it should be well fed.

"Quite the lady, isn't she?" said Mildred, when they went away.

They went back to have tea at the Metropole. Mildred liked the crowd and the band. Philip was tired of talking, and he watched her face as she looked with keen eyes at the dresses of the women who came in. She had a peculiar sharpness for reckoning up what things cost, and now and then she leaned over to him and whispered the result of her meditations.

"D'you see that aigrette there? That cost every bit of seven guineas."

Or: "Look at that ermine, Philip. That's rabbit, that is—that's not ermine." She laughed triumphantly. "I'd know it a mile off."

Philip smiled happily. He was glad to see her pleasure, and the ingenuousness of her conversation amused and touched him. The band played sentimental music.

After dinner they walked down to the station, and Philip took her arm. He told her what arrangements he had made for their journey to France. She was to come up to London at the end of the week, but she told him that she could not go away till the Saturday of the week after that. He had already engaged a room in a hotel in Paris. He was looking forward eagerly to taking the tickets.

"You won't mind going second-class, will you? We mustn't be extravagant, and it'll be all the better if we can do ourselves pretty well when we get there."

He had talked to her a hundred times of the Quarter. They would wander through its pleasant old streets, and they would sit idly in the charming gardens of the Luxembourg. If the weather was fine perhaps, when they had had enough of Paris, they might go to Fontainebleau. The trees would be just bursting into leaf. The green of the forest in spring was more beautiful than anything he knew; it was like a song, and it was like the happy pain of love. Mildred listened quietly. He turned to her and tried to look deep into her eyes.

"You do want to come, don't you?" he said.

"Of course I do," she smiled.

"You don't know how I'm looking forward to it. I don't know how I shall get through the next days. I'm so afraid something will happen to prevent it. It maddens me sometimes that I can't tell you how much I love you. And at last, at last . . ."

He broke off. They reached the station, but they had dawdled on the way, and Philip had barely time to say good-night. He kissed her quickly and ran towards the wicket as fast as he could. She stood where he left her. He was strangely grotesque when he ran.

LXXIV

THE following Saturday Mildred returned, and that evening Philip kept her to himself. He took seats for the play, and they drank champagne at dinner. It was her first gaiety in London for so long that she enjoyed everything ingenuously. She cuddled up to Philip when they drove from the theatre to the room he had taken for her in Pimlico.

"I really believe you're quite glad to see me," he said.

She did not answer, but gently pressed his hand. Demonstrations of affection were so rare with her that Philip was enchanted.

"I've asked Griffiths to dine with us tomorrow," he told her.

"Oh, I'm glad you've done that. I wanted to meet him."

There was no place of entertainment to take her to on Sunday night, and Philip was afraid she would be bored if she were alone with him all day. Griffiths was amusing; he would help them to get through the evening; and Philip was so fond of them both that he wanted them to know and to like one another. He left Mildred with the words:

"Only six days more."

They had arranged to dine in the

gallery at Romano's on Sunday, because the dinner was excellent and looked as though it cost a good deal more than it did. Philip and Mildred arrived first and had to wait some time for Griffiths.

"He's an unpunctual devil," said Philip. "He's probably making love to one of his numerous flames."

But presently he appeared. He was a handsome creature, tall and thin; his head was placed well on the body, it gave him a conquering air which was attractive; and his curly hair, his bold, friendly blue eyes, his red mouth, were charming. Philip saw Mildred look at him with appreciation, and he felt a curious satisfaction. Griffiths greeted them with a smile.

"I've heard a great deal about you," he said to Mildred, as he took her hand.

"Not so much as I've heard about you," she answered.

"Nor so bad," said Philip.

"Has he been blackening my character?"

Griffiths laughed, and Philip saw that Mildred noticed how white and regular his teeth were and how pleasant his smile.

"You ought to feel like old friends," said Philip. "I've talked so much about you to one another."

Griffiths was in the best possible humour, for, having at length passed his final examination, he was qualified, and he had just been appointed house-surgeon at a hospital in the North of London. He was taking up his duties at the beginning of May and meanwhile was going home for a holiday; this was his last week in town, and he was determined to get as much enjoyment into it as he could. He began to talk the gay nonsense which Philip admired because he could not copy it. There was nothing much in what he said, but his vivacity gave it point.

There flowed from him a force of life which affected everyone who knew him; it was almost as sensible as bodily warmth. Mildred was more lively than Philip had ever known her, and he was delighted to see that his little party was a success. She was amusing herself enormously. She laughed louder and louder. She quite forgot the genteel reserve which had become second nature to her.

Presently Griffiths said:

"I say, it's dreadfully difficult for me to call you Mrs. Miller. Philip never calls you anything but Mildred."

"I daresay she won't scratch your eyes out if you call her that too," laughed Philip.

"Then she must call me Harry."

Philip sat silent while they chattered away and thought how good it was to see people happy. Now and then Griffiths teased him a little, kindly, because he was always so serious.

"I believe he's quite fond of you, Philip," smiled Mildred.

"He isn't a bad old thing," answered Griffiths, and taking Philip's hand he shook it gaily.

It seemed an added charm in Griffiths that he liked Philip. They were all sober people, and the wine they had drunk went to their heads. Griffiths became more talkative and so boisterous that Philip, amused, had to beg him to be quiet. He had a gift for story-telling, and his adventures lost nothing of their romance and their laughter in his narration. He played in all of them a gallant, humorous part. Mildred, her eyes shining with excitement, urged him on. He poured out anecdote after anecdote. When the lights began to be turned out she was astonished.

"My word, the evening has gone quickly. I thought it wasn't more than half past nine."

They got up to go and when she said good-bye, she added:

"I'm coming to have tea at Philip's room tomorrow. You might look in if you can."

"All right," he smiled.

On the way back to Pimlico Mildred talked of nothing but Griffiths. She was taken with his good looks, his well-cut clothes, his voice, his gaiety.

"I *am* glad you like him," said Philip. "D'you remember you were rather sniffy about meeting him?"

"I think it's so nice of him to be so fond of you, Philip. He is a nice friend for you to have."

She put up her face to Philip for him to kiss her. It was a thing she did rarely.

"I have enjoyed myself this evening, Philip. Thank you so much."

"Don't be so absurd," he laughed, touched by her appreciation so that he felt the moisture come to his eyes.

She opened her door and just before she went in, turned again to Philip.

"Tell Harry I'm madly in love with him," she said.

"All right," he laughed. "Goodnight."

Next day, when they were having tea, Griffiths came in. He sank lazily into an arm-chair. There was something strangely sensual in the slow movements of his large limbs. Philip remained silent, while the others chattered away, but he was enjoying himself. He admired them both so much that it seemed natural enough for them to admire one another. He did not care if Griffiths absorbed Mildred's attention, he would have her to himself during the evening: he had something the attitude of a loving husband, confident in his wife's affection, who looks on with amusement while she flirts harmlessly with a stranger. But

at half past seven he looked at his watch and said:

"It's about time we went out to dinner, Mildred."

There was a moment's pause, and Griffiths seemed to be considering.

"Well, I'll be getting along," he said at last. "I didn't know it was so late."

"Are you doing anything tonight?" asked Mildred.

"No."

There was another silence. Philip felt slightly irritated.

"I'll just go and have a wash," he said, and to Mildred he added: "Would you like to wash your hands?"

She did not answer him.

"Why don't you come and dine with us?" she said to Griffiths.

He looked at Philip and saw him staring at him sombrely.

"I dined with you last night," he laughed. "I should be in the way."

"Oh, that doesn't matter," insisted Mildred. "Make him come, Philip. He won't be in the way, will he?"

"Let him come by all means if he'd like to."

"All right, then," said Griffiths promptly. "I'll just go upstairs and tidy myself."

The moment he left the room Philip turned to Mildred angrily.

"Why on earth did you ask him to dine with us?"

"I couldn't help myself. It would have looked so funny to say nothing when he said he wasn't doing anything."

"Oh, what rot! And why the hell did you ask him if he was doing anything?"

Mildred's pale lips tightened a little.

"I want a little amusement sometimes. I get tired always being alone with you."

They heard Griffiths coming heavily

down the stairs, and Philip went into his bed-room to wash. They dined in the neighbourhood in an Italian restaurant. Philip was cross and silent, but he quickly realised that he was showing to disadvantage in comparison with Griffiths, and he forced himself to hide his annoyance. He drank a good deal of wine to destroy the pain that was gnawing at his heart, and he set himself to talk. Mildred, as though remorseful for what she had said, did all she could to make herself pleasant to him. She was kindly and affectionate. Presently Philip began to think he had been a fool to surrender to a feeling of jealousy. After dinner when they got into a hansom to drive to a music-hall Mildred, sitting between the two men, of her own accord gave him her hand. His anger vanished. Suddenly, he knew not how, he grew conscious that Griffiths was holding her other hand. The pain seized him again violently, it was a real physical pain, and he asked himself, panic-stricken, what he might have asked himself before, whether Mildred and Griffiths were in love with one another. He could not see anything of the performance on account of the mist of suspicion, anger, dismay, and wretchedness which seemed to be before his eyes; but he forced himself to conceal the fact that anything was the matter; he went on talking and laughing. Then a strange desire to torture himself seized him, and he got up, saying he wanted to go and drink something. Mildred and Griffiths had never been alone together for a moment. He wanted to leave them by themselves.

"I'll come too," said Griffiths. "I've got rather a thirst on."

"Oh, nonsense, you stay and talk to Mildred."

Philip did not know why he said that. He was throwing them together now to make the pain he suffered more intolerable. He did not go to the bar, but up into the balcony, from where he could watch them and not be seen. They had ceased to look at the stage and were smiling into one another's eyes. Griffiths was talking with his usual happy fluency and Mildred seemed to hang on his lips. Philip's head began to ache frightfully. He stood there motionless. He knew he would be in the way if he went back. They were enjoying themselves without him, and he was suffering, suffering. Time passed, and now he had an extraordinary shyness about rejoining them. He knew they had not thought of him at all, and he reflected bitterly that he had paid for the dinner and their seats in the music-hall. What a fool they were making of him! He was hot with shame. He could see how happy they were without him. His instinct was to leave them to themselves and go home, but he had not his hat and coat, and it would necessitate endless explanations. He went back. He felt a shadow of annoyance in Mildred's eyes when she saw him, and his heart sank.

"You've been a devil of a time," said Griffiths, with a smile of welcome.

"I met some men I knew. I've been talking to them, and I couldn't get away. I thought you'd be all right together."

"I've been enjoying myself thoroughly," said Griffiths. "I don't know about Mildred."

She gave a little laugh of happy complacency. There was a vulgar sound in the ring of it that horrified Philip. He suggested that they should go.

"Come on," said Griffiths, "we'll both drive you home."

Philip suspected that she had suggested that arrangement so that she might not be left alone with him. In the cab he did not take her hand nor did she offer it, and he knew all the time that she was holding Griffiths'. His chief thought was that it was all so horribly vulgar. As they drove along he asked himself what plans they had made to meet without his knowledge, he cursed himself for having left them alone, he had actually gone out of his way to enable them to arrange things.

"Let's keep the cab," said Philip, when they reached the house in which Mildred was lodging. "I'm too tired to walk home."

On the way back Griffiths talked gaily and seemed indifferent to the fact that Philip answered in monosyllables. Philip felt he must notice that something was the matter. Philip's silence at last grew too significant to struggle against, and Griffiths, suddenly nervous, ceased talking. Philip wanted to say something, but he was so shy he could hardly bring himself to, and yet the time was passing and the opportunity would be lost. It was best to get at the truth at once. He forced himself to speak.

"Are you in love with Mildred?" he asked suddenly.

"I?" Griffiths laughed. "Is that what you've been so funny about this evening? Of course not, my dear old man."

He tried to slip his hand through Philip's arm, but Philip drew himself away. He knew Griffiths was lying. He could not bring himself to force Griffiths to tell him that he had not been holding the girl's hand. He suddenly felt very weak and broken.

"It doesn't matter to you, Harry," he said. "You've got so many women —don't take her away from me. It means my whole life. I've been so awfully wretched."

His voice broke, and he could not prevent the sob that was torn from him. He was horribly ashamed of himself.

"My dear old boy, you know I wouldn't do anything to hurt you. I'm far too fond of you for that. I was only playing the fool. If I'd known you were going to take it like that I'd have been more careful."

"Is that true?" asked Philip.

"I don't care a twopenny damn for her. I give you my word of honour."

Philip gave a sigh of relief. The cab stopped at their door.

LXXV

Next day Philip was in a good temper. He was very anxious not to bore Mildred with too much of his society, and so had arranged that he should not see her till dinner-time. She was ready when he fetched her, and he chaffed her for her unwonted punctuality. She was wearing a new dress he had given her. He remarked on its smartness.

"It'll have to go back and be al-tered," she said. "The skirt hangs all wrong."

"You'll have to make the dressmaker hurry up if you want to take it to Paris with you."

"It'll be ready in time for that."

"Only three more whole days. We'll go over by the eleven o'clock, shall we?"

"If you like."

He would have her for nearly a

month entirely to himself. His eyes rested on her with hungry adoration. He was able to laugh a little at his own passion.

"I wonder what it is I see in you," he smiled.

"That's a nice thing to say," she answered.

Her body was so thin that one could almost see her skeleton. Her chest was as flat as a boy's. Her mouth, with its narrow pale lips, was ugly, and her skin was faintly green.

"I shall give you Blaud's Pills in quantities when we're away," said Philip, laughing. "I'm going to bring you back fat and rosy."

"I don't want to get fat," she said.

She did not speak of Griffiths, and presently while they were dining Philip half in malice, for he felt sure of himself and his power over her, said:

"It seems to me you were having a great flirtation with Harry last night?"

"I told you I was in love with him," she laughed.

"I'm glad to know that he's not in love with you."

"How d'you know?"

"I asked him."

She hesitated a moment, looking at Philip, and a curious gleam came into her eyes.

"Would you like to read a letter I had from him this morning?"

She handed him an envelope and Philip recognised Griffiths' bold, legible writing. There were eight pages. It was well written, frank and charming; it was the letter of a man who was used to making love to women. He told Mildred that he loved her passionately, he had fallen in love with her the first moment he saw her; he did not want to love her, for he knew how fond Philip was of her, but he could not help himself. Philip was such a dear, and he was very

much ashamed of himself, but it was not his fault, he was just carried away. He paid her delightful compliments. Finally he thanked her for consenting to lunch with him next day and said he was dreadfully impatient to see her. Philip noticed that the letter was dated the night before; Griffiths must have written it after leaving Philip, and had taken the trouble to go out and post it when Philip thought he was in bed.

He read it with a sickening palpitation of his heart, but gave no outward sign of surprise. He handed it back to Mildred with a smile, calmly.

"Did you enjoy your lunch?"

"Rather," she said emphatically.

He felt that his hands were trembling, so he put them under the table.

"You mustn't take Griffiths too seriously. He's just a butterfly, you know."

She took the letter and looked at it again.

"I can't help it either," she said, in a voice which she tried to make nonchalant. "I don't know what's come over me."

"It's a little awkward for me, isn't it?" said Philip.

She gave him a quick look.

"You're taking it pretty calmly, I must say."

"What do you expect me to do? Do you want me to tear out my hair in handfuls?"

"I knew you'd be angry with me."

"The funny thing is, I'm not at all. I ought to have known this would happen. I was a fool to bring you together. I know perfectly well that he's got every advantage over me; he's much jollier, and he's very handsome, he's more amusing, he can talk to you about the things that interest you."

"I don't know what you mean by that. If I'm not clever I can't help it, but I'm not the fool you think I am, not by a long way, I can tell you. You're a bit too superior for me, my young friend."

"D'you want to quarrel with me?" he asked mildly.

"No, but I don't see why you should treat me as if I was I don't know what."

"I'm sorry, I didn't mean to offend you. I just wanted to talk things over quietly. We don't want to make a mess of them if we can help it. I saw you were attracted by him and it seemed to me very natural. The only thing that really hurts me is that he should have encouraged you. He knew how awfully keen I was on you. I think it's rather shabby of him to have written that letter to you five minutes after he told me he didn't care twopence about you."

"If you think you're going to make me like him any the less by saying nasty things about him, you're mistaken."

Philip was silent for a moment. He did not know what words he could use to make her see his point of view. He wanted to speak coolly and deliberately, but he was in such a turmoil of emotion that he could not clear his thoughts.

"It's not worth while sacrificing everything for an infatuation that you know can't last. After all, he doesn't care for anyone more than ten days, and you're rather cold; that sort of thing doesn't mean very much to you."

"That's what you think."

She made it more difficult for him by adopting a cantankerous tone.

"If you're in love with him you can't help it. I'll just bear it as best I can. We get on very well together, you and I, and I've not behaved badly to you, have I? I've always known that you're not in love with me, but you like me all right, and when we get over to Paris you'll for-get about Griffiths. If you make up your mind to put him out of your thoughts you won't find it so hard as all that, and I've deserved that you should do something for me."

She did not answer, and they went on eating their dinner. When the silence grew oppressive Philip began to talk of indifferent things. He pretended not to notice that Mildred was inattentive. Her answers were perfunctory, and she volunteered no remarks of her own. At last she interrupted abruptly what he was saying:

"Philip, I'm afraid I shan't be able to go away on Saturday. The doctor says I oughtn't to."

He knew this was not true, but he answered:

"When will you be able to come away?"

She glanced at him, saw that his face was white and rigid, and looked nervously away. She was at that moment a little afraid of him.

"I may as well tell you and have done with it, I can't come away with you at all."

"I thought you were driving at that. It's too late to change your mind now. I've got the tickets and everything."

"You said you didn't wish me to go unless I wanted it too, and I don't."

"I've changed my mind. I'm not going to have any more tricks played with me. You must come."

"I like you very much, Philip, as a friend. But I can't bear to think of anything else. I don't like you that way. I couldn't, Philip."

"You were quite willing to a week ago."

"It was different then."

"You hadn't met Griffiths?"

"You said yourself I couldn't help it if I'm in love with him."

Her face was set into a sulky look, and she kept her eyes fixed on her plate. Philip was white with rage. He would have liked to hit her in the face with his clenched fist, and in fancy he saw how she would look with a black eye. There were two lads of eighteen dining at a table near them, and now and then they looked at Mildred; he wondered if they envied him dining with a pretty girl; perhaps they were wishing they stood in his shoes. It was Mildred who broke the silence.

"What's the good of our going away together? I'd be thinking of him all the time. It wouldn't be much fun for you."

"That's my business," he answered.

She thought over all his reply implicated, and she reddened.

"But that's just beastly."

"What of it?"

"I thought you were a gentleman in every sense of the word."

"You were mistaken."

His reply entertained him, and he laughed as he said it.

"For God's sake don't laugh," she cried. "I can't come away with you, Philip. I'm awfully sorry. I know I haven't behaved well to you, but one can't force themselves."

"Have you forgotten that when you were in trouble I did everything for you? I planked out the money to keep you till your baby was born, I paid for your doctor and everything, I paid for you to go to Brighton, and I'm paying for the keep of your baby, I'm paying for your clothes, I'm paying for every stitch you've got on now."

"If you was a gentleman you wouldn't throw what you've done for me in my face."

"Oh, for goodness' sake, shut up. What d'you suppose I care if I'm a gentleman or not? If I were a gentleman I shouldn't waste my time with a vulgar slut like you. I don't care a damn if you like me or not. I'm sick of being made a blasted fool of. You're jolly well coming to Paris with

me on Saturday or you can take the consequences."

Her cheeks were red with anger, and when she answered her voice had the hard commonness which she concealed generally by a genteel enunciation.

"I never liked you, not from the beginning, but you forced yourself on me, I always hated it when you kissed me. I wouldn't let you touch me now not if I was starving."

Philip tried to swallow the food on his plate, but the muscles of his throat refused to act. He gulped down something to drink and lit a cigarette. He was trembling in every part. He did not speak. He waited for her to move, but she sat in silence, staring at the white tablecloth. If they had been alone he would have flung his arms round her and kissed her passionately; he fancied the throwing back of her long white throat as he pressed upon her mouth with his lips. They passed an hour without speaking, and at last Philip thought the waiter began to stare at them curiously. He called for the bill.

"Shall we go?" he said then, in an even tone.

She did not reply, but gathered together her bag and her gloves. She put on her coat.

"When are you seeing Griffiths again?"

"Tomorrow," she answered indifferently.

"You'd better talk it over with him."

She opened her bag mechanically and saw a piece of paper in it. She took it out.

"Here's the bill for this dress," she said hesitatingly.

"What of it?"

"I promised I'd give her the money tomorrow."

"Did you?"

"Does that mean you won't pay for

it after having told me I could get it?"

"It does."

"I'll ask Harry," she said, flushing quickly.

"He'll be glad to help you. He owes me seven pounds at the moment, and he pawned his microscope last week, because he was so broke."

"You needn't think you can frighten me by that. I'm quite capable of earning my own living."

"It's the best thing you can do. I don't propose to give you a farthing more."

She thought of her rent due on Saturday and the baby's keep, but did not say anything. They left the restaurant, and in the street Philip asked her:

"Shall I call a cab for you? I'm going to take a little stroll."

"I haven't got any money. I had to pay a bill this afternoon."

"It won't hurt you to walk. If you want to see me tomorrow I shall be in about tea-time."

He took off his hat and sauntered away. He looked round in a moment and saw that she was standing helplessly where he had left her, looking at the traffic. He went back and with a laugh pressed a coin into her hand.

"Here's two bob for you to get home with."

Before she could speak he hurried away.

LXXVI

NEXT day, in the afternoon, Philip sat in his room and wondered whether Mildred would come. He had slept badly. He had spent the morning in the club of the Medical School, reading one newspaper after another. It was the vacation and few students he knew were in London, but he found one or two people to talk to, he played a game of chess, and so wore out the tedious hours. After luncheon he felt so tired, his head was aching so, that he went back to his lodgings and lay down; he tried to read a novel. He had not seen Griffiths. He was not in when Philip returned the night before; he heard him come back, but he did not as usual look into Philip's room to see if he was asleep; and in the morning Philip heard him go out early. It was clear that he wanted to avoid him. Suddenly there was a light tap at his door. Philip sprang to his feet and opened it. Mildred stood on the threshold. She did not move.

"Come in," said Philip.

He closed the door after her. She sat down. She hesitated to begin.

"Thank you for giving me that two shillings last night," she said.

"Oh, that's all right."

She gave him a faint smile. It reminded Philip of the timid, ingratiating look of a puppy that has been beaten for naughtiness and wants to reconcile himself with his master.

"I've been lunching with Harry," she said.

"Have you?"

"If you still want me to go away with you on Saturday, Philip, I'll come."

A quick thrill of triumph shot through his heart, but it was a sensation that only lasted an instant; it was followed by a suspicion.

"Because of the money?" he asked.

"Partly," she answered simply. "Harry can't do anything. He owes five weeks here, and he owes you seven pounds, and his tailor's pressing him for money. He'd pawn anything he could, but he's pawned everything already. I had a job to put the woman off about my new dress, and on Saturday there's the book at my lodgings, and I can't get work in five minutes. It always means waiting some little time till there's a vacancy."

She said all this in an even, querulous tone, as though she were recounting the injustices of fate, which had to be borne as part of the natural order of things. Philip did not answer. He knew what she told him well enough.

"You said partly," he observed at last.

"Well, Harry says you've been a brick to both of us. You've been a real good friend to him, he says, and you've done for me what p'raps no other man would have done. We must do the straight thing, he says. And he said what you said about him, that he's fickle by nature, he's not like you, and I should be a fool to throw you away for him. He won't last and you will, he says so himself."

"D'you *want* to come away with me?" asked Philip.

"I don't mind."

He looked at her, and the corners of his mouth turned down in an expression of misery. He had triumphed indeed, and he was going to have his way. He gave a little laugh of derision at his own humiliation. She looked at him quickly, but did not speak.

"I've looked forward with all my soul to going away with you, and I thought at last, after all that wretchedness, I was going to be happy . . ."

He did not finish what he was going to say. And then on a sudden, without warning, Mildred broke into a storm of tears. She was sitting in the chair in which Norah had sat and wept, and like her she hid her face on the back of it, towards the side

where there was a little bump formed by the sagging in the middle, where the head had rested.

"I'm not lucky with women," thought Philip.

Her thin body was shaken with sobs. Philip had never seen a woman cry with such an utter abandonment. It was horribly painful, and his heart was torn. Without realising what he did, he went up to her and put his arms round her; she did not resist, but in her wretchedness surrendered herself to his comforting. He whispered to her little words of solace. He scarcely knew what he was saying, he bent over her and kissed her repeatedly.

"Are you awfully unhappy?" he said at last.

"I wish I was dead," she moaned. "I wish I'd died when the baby come."

Her hat was in her way, and Philip took it off for her. He placed her head more comfortably in the chair, and then he went and sat down at the table and looked at her.

"It is awful, love, isn't it?" he said. "Fancy anyone wanting to be in love."

Presently the violence of her sobbing diminished and she sat in the chair, exhausted, with her head thrown back and her arms hanging by her side. She had the grotesque look of one of those painters' dummies used to hang draperies on.

"I didn't know you loved him so much as all that," said Philip.

He understood Griffiths' love well enough, for he put himself in Griffiths' place and saw with his eyes, touched with his hands; he was able to think himself in Griffiths' body, and he kissed her with his lips, smiled at her with his smiling blue eyes. It was her emotion that surprised him. He had never thought her capable of passion, and this was passion: there was no mistaking it. Something seemed to give way in his heart; it really felt to him as though something were breaking, and he felt strangely weak.

"I don't want to make you unhappy. You needn't come away with me if you don't want to. I'll give you the money all the same."

She shook her head.

"No, I said I'd come, and I'll come."

"What's the good, if you're sick with love for him?"

"Yes, that's the word. I'm sick with love. I know it won't last, just as well as he does, but just now . . ."

She paused and shut her eyes as though she were going to faint. A strange idea came to Philip, and he spoke it as it came, without stopping to think it out.

"Why don't you go away with him?"

"How can I? You know we haven't got the money."

"I'll give you the money."

"You?"

She sat up and looked at him. Her eyes began to shine, and the colour came into her cheeks.

"Perhaps the best thing would be to get it over, and then you'd come back to me."

Now that he had made the suggestion he was sick with anguish, and yet the torture of it gave him a strange, subtle sensation. She stared at him with open eyes.

"Oh, how could we, on your money? Harry wouldn't think of it."

"Oh yes, he would, if you persuaded him."

Her objections made him insist, and yet he wanted her with all his heart to refuse vehemently.

"I'll give you a fiver, and you can go away from Saturday to Monday. You could easily do that. On Monday he's going home till he takes up his appointment at the North London."

"Oh, Philip, do you mean that?" she cried, clasping her hands. "If you could only let us go—I would love you so much afterwards, I'd do anything for you. I'm sure I shall get over it if you'll only do that. Would you really give us the money?"

"Yes," he said.

She was entirely changed now. She began to laugh. He could see that she was insanely happy. She got up and knelt down by Philip's side, taking his hands.

"You are a brick, Philip. You're the best fellow I've ever known. Won't you be angry with me afterwards?"

He shook his head, smiling, but with what agony in his heart!

"May I go and tell Harry now? And can I say to him that you don't mind? He won't consent unless you promise it doesn't matter. Oh, you don't know how I love him! And afterwards I'll do anything you like. I'll come over to Paris with you or anywhere on Monday."

She got up and put on her hat.

"Where are you going?"

"I'm going to ask him if he'll take me."

"Already?"

"D'you want me to stay? I'll stay if you like."

She sat down, but he gave a little laugh.

"No, it doesn't matter, you'd better go at once. There's only one thing: I can't bear to see Griffiths just now, it would hurt me too awfully. Say I have no ill-feeling towards him or anything like that, but ask him to keep out of my way."

"All right." She sprang up and put on her gloves. "I'll let you know what he says."

"You'd better dine with me to-night."

"Very well."

She put up her face for him to kiss

her, and when he pressed his lips to hers she threw her arms round his neck.

"You are a darling, Philip."

She sent him a note a couple of hours later to say that she had a headache and could not dine with him. Philip had almost expected it. He knew that she was dining with Griffiths. He was horribly jealous, but the sudden passion which had seized the pair of them seemed like something that had come from the outside, as though a god had visited them with it, and he felt himself helpless. It seemed so natural that they should love one another. He saw all the advantages that Griffiths had over himself and confessed that in Mildred's place he would have done as Mildred did. What hurt him most was Griffiths' treachery; they had been such good friends, and Griffiths knew how passionately devoted he was to Mildred: he might have spared him.

He did not see Mildred again till Friday; he was sick for a sight of her by then; but when she came and he realised that he had gone out of her thoughts entirely, for they were engrossed in Griffiths, he suddenly hated her. He saw now why she and Griffiths loved one another, Griffiths was stupid, oh so stupid! he had known that all along, but had shut his eyes to it, stupid and empty-headed: that charm of his concealed an utter selfishness; he was willing to sacrifice anyone to his appetites. And how inane was the life he led, lounging about bars and drinking in music-halls, wandering from one light amour to another! He never read a book, he was blind to everything that was not frivolous and vulgar; he had never a thought that was fine: the word most common on his lips was smart; that was his highest praise for man or woman. Smart! It was no wonder he

pleased Mildred. They suited one another.

Philip talked to Mildred of things that mattered to neither of them. He knew she wanted to speak of Griffiths, but he gave her no opportunity. He did not refer to the fact that two evenings before she had put off dining with him on a trivial excuse. He was casual with her, trying to make her think he was suddenly grown indifferent; and he exercised peculiar skill in saying little things which he knew would wound her; but which were so indefinite, so delicately cruel, that she could not take exception to them. At last she got up.

"I think I must be going off now," she said.

"I daresay you've got a lot to do," he answered.

She held out her hand, he took it, said good-bye, and opened the door for her. He knew what she wanted to speak about, and he knew also that his cold, ironical air intimidated her. Often his shyness made him seem so frigid that unintentionally he frightened people, and, having discovered this, he was able when occasion arose to assume the same manner.

"You haven't forgotten what you promised?" she said at last, as he held open the door.

"What is that?"

"About the money."

"How much d'you want?"

He spoke with an icy deliberation which made his words peculiarly offensive. Mildred flushed. He knew she hated him at that moment, and he wondered at the self-control by which she prevented herself from flying out at him. He wanted to make her suffer.

"There's the dress and the book tomorrow. That's all. Harry won't come, so we shan't want money for that."

Philip's heart gave a great thud

against his ribs, and he let the door-handle go. The door swung to.

"Why not?"

"He says we couldn't, not on your money."

A devil seized Philip, a devil of self-torture which was always lurking within him, and, though with all his soul he wished that Griffiths and Mildred should not go away together, he could not help himself; he set himself to persuade Griffiths through her.

"I don't see why not, if I'm willing," he said.

"That's what I told him."

"I should have thought if he really wanted to go he wouldn't hesitate."

"Oh, it's not that, he wants to all right. He'd go at once if he had the money."

"If he's squeamish about it I'll give *you* the money."

"I said you'd lend it if he liked, and we'd pay it back as soon as we could."

"It's rather a change for you going on your knees to get a man to take you away for a week-end."

"It is rather, isn't it?" she said, with a shameless little laugh.

It sent a cold shudder down Philip's spine.

"What are you going to do then?" he asked.

"Nothing. He's going home tomorrow. He must."

That would be Philip's salvation. With Griffiths out of the way he could get Mildred back. She knew no one in London, she would be thrown on to his society, and when they were alone together he could soon make her forget this infatuation. If he said nothing more he was safe. But he had a fiendish desire to break down their scruples, he wanted to know how abominably they could behave towards him; if he tempted them a little more

they would yield, and he took a fierce joy at the thought of their dishonour. Though every word he spoke tortured him, he found in the torture a horrible delight.

"It looks as if it were now or never."

"That's what I told him," she said.

There was a passionate note in her voice which struck Philip. He was biting his nails in his nervousness.

"Where were you thinking of going?"

"Oh, to Oxford. He was at the 'Varsity there, you know. He said he'd show me the colleges."

Philip remembered that once he had suggested going to Oxford for the day, and she had expressed firmly the boredom she felt at the thought of sights.

"And it looks as if you'd have fine weather. It ought to be very jolly there just now."

"I've done all I could to persuade him."

"Why don't you have another try?"

"Shall I say you want us to go?"

"I don't think you must go as far as that," said Philip.

She paused for a minute or two, looking at him. Philip forced himself to look at her in a friendly way. He hated her, he despised her, he loved her with all his heart.

"I'll tell you what I'll do, I'll go and see if he can't arrange it. And then, if he says yes, I'll come and fetch the money tomorrow. When shall you be in?"

"I'll come back here after luncheon and wait."

"All right."

"I'll give you the money for your dress and your room now."

He went to his desk and took out what money he had. The dress was six guineas; there was besides her rent and her food, and the baby's keep for a week. He gave her eight pounds ten.

"Thanks very much," she said. She left him.

LXXVII

AFTER lunching in the basement of the Medical School Philip went back to his rooms. It was Saturday afternoon, and the landlady was cleaning the stairs.

"Is Mr. Griffiths in?" he asked.

"No, sir. He went away this morning, soon after you went out."

"Isn't he coming back?"

"I don't think so, sir. He's taken his luggage."

Philip wondered what this could mean. He took a book and began to read. It was Burton's *Journey to Meccah*, which he had just got out of the Westminster Public Library; and he read the first page, but could make no sense of it, for his mind was elsewhere; he was listening all the time for a ring at the bell. He dared not hope that Griffiths had gone away already, without Mildred, to his home in Cumberland. Mildred would be coming presently for the money. He set his teeth and read on; he tried desperately to concentrate his attention; the sentences etched themselves in his brain by the force of his effort, but they were distorted by the agony he was enduring. He wished with all his heart that he had not made the horrible proposition to give them money; but now that he had made it he lacked the strength to go back on it, not on Mildred's account, but on his own. There was a morbid obstinacy in him which forced him to do the thing he had determined. He discovered that the three pages he had read had made no impression on him

at all; and he went back and started from the beginning: he found himself reading one sentence over and over again; and now it weaved itself in with his thoughts, horribly, like some formula in a nightmare. One thing he could do was to go out and keep away till midnight; they could not go then; and he saw them calling at the house every hour to ask if he was in. He enjoyed the thought of their disappointment. He repeated that sentence to himself mechanically. But he could not do that. Let them come and take the money, and he would know then to what depths of infamy it was possible for men to descend. He could not read any more now. He simply could not see the words. He leaned back in his chair, closing his eyes, and, numb with misery, waited for Mildred.

The landlady came in.

"Will you see Mrs. Miller, sir?"

"Show her in."

Philip pulled himself together to receive her without any sign of what he was feeling. He had an impulse to throw himself on his knees and seize her hands and beg her not to go; but he knew there was no way of moving her; she would tell Griffiths what he had said and how he acted. He was ashamed.

"Well, how about the little jaunt?" he said gaily.

"We're going. Harry's outside. I told him you didn't want to see him, so he's kept out of your way. But he wants to know if he can come in just for a minute to say good-bye to you."

"No, I won't see him," said Philip.

He could see she did not care if he saw Griffiths or not. Now that she was there he wanted her to go quickly.

"Look here, here's the fiver. I'd like you to go now."

She took it and thanked him. She turned to leave the room.

"When are you coming back?" he asked.

"Oh, on Monday. Harry must go home then."

He knew what he was going to say was humiliating, but he was broken down with jealousy and desire.

"Then I shall see you, shan't I?" He could not help the note of appeal in his voice.

"Of course. I'll let you know the moment I'm back."

He shook hands with her. Through the curtains he watched her jump into a four-wheeler that stood at the door. It rolled away. Then he threw himself on his bed and hid his face in his hands. He felt tears coming to his eyes, and he was angry with himself; he clenched his hands and screwed up his body to prevent them; but he could not; and great painful sobs were forced from him.

He got up at last, exhausted and ashamed, and washed his face. He mixed himself a strong whiskey and soda. It made him feel a little better. Then he caught sight of the tickets to Paris, which were on the chimney-piece, and, seizing them, with an impulse of rage he flung them in the fire. He knew he could have got the money back on them, but it relieved him to destroy them. Then he went out in search of someone to be with. The club was empty. He felt he would go mad unless he found some-one to talk to; but Lawson was abroad; he went on to Hayward's rooms: the maid who opened the door told him that he had gone down to Brighton for the week-end. Then Philip went to a gallery and found it was just closing. He did not know what to do. He was distracted. And he thought of Griffiths and Mildred going to Ox-ford, sitting opposite one another in the train, happy. He went back to his rooms, but they filled him with horror, he had been so wretched in them; he tried once more to read Burton's book, but, as he read, he told himself again and again what a fool he had been; it was he who had made the suggestion that they should go away, he had offered the money, he had forced it upon them; he might have known what would happen when he intro-duced Griffiths to Mildred; his own vehement passion was enough to arouse the other's desire. By this time they had reached Oxford. They would put up in one of the lodging-houses in John Street; Philip had never been to Oxford, but Griffiths had talked to him about it so much that he knew exactly where they would go; and they would dine at the Clarendon: Griffiths had been in the habit of dining there when he went on the spree. Philip got himself something to eat in a restaurant near Charing Cross; he had made up his mind to go to a play, and afterwards he fought his way into the pit of a theatre at which one of Oscar Wilde's pieces was being performed. He wondered if Mildred and Griffiths would go to a play that evening: they must kill the evening somehow; they were too stupid, both of them to content them-selves with conversation: he got a fierce delight in reminding himself of the vulgarity of their minds which suited them so exactly to one another. He watched the play with an abstracted mind, trying to give himself gaiety by drinking whiskey in each interval; he was unused to alcohol, and it affected him quickly, but his drunkenness was savage and morose. When the play was over he had another drink. He could not go to bed, he knew he would not sleep, and he dreaded the pictures which his vivid imagination would place before him. He tried not to think of them. He knew he had drunk too much. Now he was seized with a desire to do horrible, sordid things; he wanted to roll himself in gutters; his whole being yearned for beastliness; he wanted to grovel.

He walked up Piccadilly, dragging his club-foot, sombrely drunk, with rage and misery clawing at his heart. He was stopped by a painted harlot, who put her hand on his arm; he pushed her violently away with brutal words. He walked on a few steps and then stopped. She would do as well as another. He was sorry he had spoken so roughly to her. He went up to her.

"I say," he began.

"Go to hell," she said.

Philip laughed.

"I merely wanted to ask if you'd do me the honour of supping with me tonight."

She looked at him with amazement, and hesitated for a while. She saw he was drunk.

"I don't mjnd."

He was amused that she should use a phrase he had heard so often on Mildred's lips. He took her to one of the restaurants he had been in the habit of going to with Mildred. He noticed as they walked along that she looked down at his limb.

"I've got a club-foot," he said. "Have you any objection?"

"You are a cure," she laughed.

When he got home his bones were aching, and in his head there was a hammering that made him nearly scream. He took another whiskey and soda to steady himself, and going to bed sank into a dreamless sleep till mid-day.

LXXVIII

At last Monday came, and Philip thought his long torture was over. Looking out the trains he found that the latest by which Griffiths could reach home that night left Oxford soon after one, and he supposed that Mildred would take one which started a few minutes later to bring her to London. His desire was to go and meet it, but he thought Mildred would like to be left alone for a day; perhaps she would drop him a line in the evening to say she was back, and if not he would call at her lodgings next morning: his spirit was cowed. He felt a bitter hatred for Griffiths, but for Mildred, notwithstanding all that had passed, only a heart-rending desire. He was glad now that Hayward was not in London on Saturday afternoon when, distraught, he went in search of human comfort: he could not have prevented himself from telling him everything, and Hayward would have been astonished at his weakness. He would despise him, and perhaps be shocked or disgusted that he could envisage the possibility of making Mildred his mistress after she had given herself to another man.

What did he care if it was shocking or disgusting? He was ready for any compromise, prepared for more degrading humiliations still, if he could only gratify his desire.

Towards the evening his steps took him against his will to the house in which she lived, and he looked up at her window. It was dark. He did not venture to ask if she was back. He was confident in her promise. But there was no letter from her in the morning, and, when about mid-day he called, the maid told him she had not arrived. He could not understand it. He knew that Griffiths would have been obliged to go home the day before, for he was to be best man at a wedding, and Mildred had no money. He turned over in his mind every possible thing that might have happened. He went again in the afternoon and left a note, asking her to dine with him that evening as calmly as though the events of the last fortnight had not happened. He mentioned the place and time at which they were to meet, and hoping against hope kept the appointment: though he waited for an hour she did not come. On Wednesday morning he was ashamed to ask at the house and sent a messenger-boy with a letter and instructions to bring back a reply; but in an hour the boy came back with Philip's letter unopened and the answer that the lady had not returned from the country. Philip was beside himself. The last deception was more than he could bear. He repeated to himself over and over again that he loathed Mildred, and, ascribing to Griffiths this new disappointment, he hated him so much that he knew what was the delight of murder: he walked about considering what a joy it would be to come upon him on a dark night and stick a knife into his throat, just about the carotid artery,

and leave him to die in the street like a dog. Philip was out of his senses with grief and rage. He did not like whiskey, but he drank to stupefy himself. He went to bed drunk on the Tuesday and on the Wednesday night.

On Thursday morning he got up very late and dragged himself, blear-eyed and sallow, into his sitting-room to see if there were any letters. A curious feeling shot through his heart when he recognised the handwriting of Griffiths.

Dear old man:

I hardly know how to write to you and yet I feel I must write. I hope you're not awfully angry with me. I know I oughtn't to have gone away with Milly, but I simply couldn't help myself. She simply carried me off my feet and I would have done anything to get her. When she told me you had offered us the money to go I simply couldn't resist. And now it's all over I'm awfully ashamed of myself and I wish I hadn't been such a fool. I wish you'd write and say you're not angry with me, and I want you to let me come and see you. I was awfully hurt at your telling Milly you didn't want to see me. Do write me a line, there's a good chap, and tell me you forgive me. It'll ease my conscience. I thought you wouldn't mind or you wouldn't have offered the money. But I know I oughtn't to have taken it. I came home on Monday and Milly wanted to stay a couple of days at Oxford by herself. She's going back to London on Wednesday, so by the time you receive this letter you will have seen her and I hope everything will go off all right. Do write and say you forgive me. Please write at once.

Yours ever,

Harry.

Philip tore up the letter furiously.

He did not mean to answer it. He despised Griffiths for his apologies, he had no patience with his prickings of conscience: one could do a dastardly thing if one chose, but it was contemptible to regret it afterwards. He thought the letter cowardly and hypocritical. He was disgusted at its sentimentality.

"It would be very easy if you could do a beastly thing," he muttered to himself, "and then say you were sorry, and that put it all right again."

He hoped with all his heart he would have the chance one day to do Griffiths a bad turn.

But at all events he knew that Mildred was in town. He dressed hurriedly, not waiting to shave, drank a cup of tea, and took a cab to her room. The cab seemed to crawl. He was painfully anxious to see her, and unconsciously he uttered a prayer to the God he did not believe in to make her receive him kindly. He only wanted to forget. With beating heart he rang the bell. He forgot all his suffering in the passionate desire to enfold her once more in his arms.

"Is Mrs. Miller in?" he asked joyously.

"She's gone," the maid answered.

He looked at her blankly.

"She came about an hour ago and took away her things."

For a moment he did not know what to say.

"Did you give her my letter? Did she say where she was going?"

Then he understood that Mildred had deceived him again. She was not coming back to him. He made an effort to save his face.

"Oh, well, I daresay I shall hear from her. She may have sent a letter to another address."

He turned away and went back hopeless to his rooms. He might have known that she would do this; she had never cared for him, she had made a fool of him from the beginning; she had no pity, she had no kindness, she had no charity. The only thing was to accept the inevitable. The pain he was suffering was horrible, he would sooner be dead than endure it; and the thought came to him that it would be better to finish with the whole thing: he might throw himself in the river or put his neck on a railway line; but he had no sooner set the thought into words than he rebelled against it. His reason told him that he would get over his unhappiness in time; if he tried with all his might he could forget her; and it would be grotesque to kill himself on account of a vulgar slut. He had only one life, and it was madness to fling it away. He *felt* that he would never overcome his passion, but he *knew* that after all it was only a matter of time.

He would not stay in London. There everything reminded him of his unhappiness. He telegraphed to his uncle that he was coming to Blackstable, and, hurrying to pack, took the first train he could. He wanted to get away from the sordid rooms in which he had endured so much suffering. He wanted to breathe clean air. He was disgusted with himself. He felt that he was a little mad.

Since he was grown up Philip had been given the best spare room at the vicarage. It was a corner-room and in front of one window was an old tree which blocked the view, but from the other you saw, beyond the garden and the vicarage field, broad meadows. Philip remembered the wallpaper from his earliest years. On the walls were quaint water colours of the early Victorian period by a friend of the Vicar's youth. They had a faded charm. The dressing-table was surrounded by stiff muslin. There was an old tall-boy to put your clothes in. Philip gave a sigh of pleasure; he had never realised that all those things meant anything to him at all. At the vicarage life went on as it had always done. No piece of furniture had been moved from one place to another; the Vicar ate the same things, said the same things, went for the same walk every day; he had grown a little fatter, a little more silent, a little more narrow. He had become accustomed to living without his wife and missed her very little. He bickered still with Josiah Graves. Philip went to see the churchwarden. He was a little thinner, a little whiter, a little more austere; he was autocratic still and still disapproved of candles on the altar. The shops had still a pleasant quaintness; and Philip stood in front of that in which things useful to seamen were sold, sea-boots and tarpaulins and tackle, and remembered that he had felt there in his childhood the thrill of the sea and the adventurous magic of the unknown.

He could not help his heart beating at each double knock of the postman in case there might be a letter from Mildred sent on by his landlady in London; but he knew that there would be none. Now that he could think it out more calmly he understood that in trying to force Mildred to love him he had been attempting the impossible. He did not know what it was that passed from a man to a woman, from a woman to a man, and made one of them a slave: it was convenient to call it the sexual instinct; but if it was no more than that, he did not understand why it should occasion so vehement an attraction to one person rather than another. It was irresistible: the mind could not battle with it; friendship, gratitude, interest, had no power beside it. Because he had not attracted

Mildred sexually, nothing that he did had any effect upon her. The idea revolted him; it made human nature beastly; and he felt suddenly that the hearts of men were full of dark places. Because Mildred was indifferent to him he had thought her sexless; her anæmic appearance and thin lips, the body with its narrow hips and flat chest, the languor of her manner, carried out his supposition; and yet she was capable of sudden passions which made her willing to risk everything to gratify them. He had never understood her adventure with Emil Miller: it had seemed so unlike her, and she had never been able to explain it; but now that he had seen her with Griffiths he knew that just the same thing had happened then: she had been carried off her feet by an ungovernable desire. He tried to think out what those two men had which so strangely attracted her. They both had a vulgar facetiousness which tickled her simple sense of humour, and a certain coarseness of nature; but what took her perhaps was the blatant sexuality which was their most marked characteristic. She had a genteel refinement which shuddered at the facts of life, she looked upon the bodily functions as indecent, she had all sorts of euphemisms for common objects, she always chose an elaborate word as more becoming than a simple one: the brutality of these men was like a whip on her thin white shoulders, and she shuddered with voluptuous pain.

One thing Philip had made up his mind about. He would not go back to the lodgings in which he had suffered. He wrote to his landlady and gave her notice. He wanted to have his own things about him. He determined to take unfurnished rooms: it would be pleasant and cheaper; and this was an urgent consideration, for during the last year and a half he had spent nearly seven hundred pounds. He must make up for it now by the most rigid economy. Now and then he thought of the future with panic; he had been a fool to spend so much money on Mildred; but he knew that if it were to come again he would act in the same way. It amused him sometimes to consider that his friends, because he had a face which did not express his feelings very vividly and a rather slow way of moving, looked upon him as strong-minded, deliberate, and cool. They thought him reasonable and praised his common sense; but he knew that his placid expression was no more than a mask, assumed unconsciously, which acted like the protective colouring of butterflies; and himself was astonished at the weakness of his will. It seemed to him that he was swayed by every light emotion, as though he were a leaf in the wind, and when passion seized him he was powerless. He had no self-control. He merely seemed to possess it because he was indifferent to many of the things which moved other people.

He considered with some irony the philosopy which he had developed for himself, for it had not been of much use to him in the conjuncture he had passed through; and he wondered whether thought really helped a man in any of the critical affairs of life: it seemed to him rather that he was swayed by some power alien to and yet within himself, which urged him like that great wind of Hell which drove Paolo and Francesca ceaselessly on. He thought of what he was going to do and, when the time came to act, he was powerless in the grasp of instincts, emotions, he knew not what. He acted as though he were a machine driven by the two forces of his environment and his personality; his reason was someone looking on, observing the facts but powerless to interfere: it was like those gods of Epicurus, who saw the doings of men from their empyrean heights and had no might to alter one smallest particle of what occurred.

LXXIX

PHILIP went up to London a couple of days before the session began in order to find himself rooms. He hunted about the streets that led out of the Westminster Bridge Road, but their dinginess was distasteful to him; and at last he found one in Kennington which had a quiet and old-world air. It reminded one a little of the London which Thackeray knew on that side of the river, and in the Kennington Road, through which the great barouche of the Newcomes must have passed as it drove the family to the West of London, the plane-trees were bursting into leaf. The houses in the street which Philip fixed upon were two-storied, and in most of the windows was a notice to state that lodgings were to let. He knocked at one which announced that the lodgings were unfurnished, and was shown by an austere, silent woman four very small rooms, in one of which there was a kitchen range and a sink. The rent was nine shillings a week. Philip did not want so many rooms, but the rent was low and he wished to settle down at once. He asked the landlady if she could keep the place clean for him and cook his breakfast, but she replied that she had enough work to do without that; and he was pleased rather than otherwise because she intimated that she wished to have nothing more to do with him than to receive his rent. She told him that, if he inquired at the grocer's round the corner, which was also a post-office, he might hear of a woman who would 'do' for him.

Philip had a little furniture which he had gathered as he went along, an arm-chair that he had bought in Paris, and a table, a few drawings, and the small Persian rug which Cronshaw had given him. His uncle had offered a fold-up bed for which, now that he no longer let his house in August, he had no further use; and by spending another ten pounds Philip bought himself whatever else was essential. He spent ten shillings on putting a corn-coloured paper in the room he was making his parlour; and he hung on the walls a sketch which Lawson had given him of the Quai des Grands Augustins, and the photograph of the *Odalisque* by Ingres and Manet's *Olympia* which in Paris had been the objects of his contemplation while he shaved. To remind himself that he too had once been engaged in the practice of art, he put up a charcoal drawing of the young Spaniard Miguel Ajuria: it was the best thing he had ever done, a nude standing with clenched hands, his feet gripping the floor with a peculiar force, and on his face that air of determination which had been so impressive; and though Philip after the long interval saw very well the defects of his work its associations made him look upon it with tolerance. He wondered what had happened to Miguel. There is nothing so terrible as the pursuit of art by those who have no talent. Perhaps, worn

out by exposure, starvation, disease, he had found an end in some hospital, or in an access of despair had sought death in the turbid Seine; but perhaps with his Southern instability he had given up the struggle of his own accord, and now, a clerk in some office in Madrid, turned his fervent rhetoric to politics and bull-fighting.

Philip asked Lawson and Hayward to come and see his new rooms, and they came, one with a bottle of whiskey, the other with a *pâté de foie gras;* and he was delighted when they praised his taste. He would have invited the Scotch stockbroker too, but he had only three chairs, and thus could entertain only a definite number of guests. Lawson was aware that through him Philip had become very friendly with Norah Nesbit and now remarked that he had run across her a few days before.

"She was asking how you were."

Philip flushed at the mention of her name, (he could not get himself out of the awkward habit of reddening when he was embarrassed,) and Lawson looked at him quizzically. Lawson, who now spent most of the year in London, had so far surrendered to his environment as to wear his hair short and to dress himself in a neat serge suit and a bowler hat.

"I gather that all is over between you," he said.

"I've not seen her for months."

"She was looking rather nice. She had a very smart hat on with a lot of white ostrich feathers on it. She must be doing pretty well."

Philip changed the conversation, but he kept thinking of her, and after an interval, when the three of them were talking of something else, he asked suddenly:

"Did you gather that Norah was angry with me?"

"Not a bit. She talked very nicely of you."

"I've got half a mind to go and see her."

"She won't eat you."

Philip had thought of Norah often. When Mildred left him his first thought was of her, and he told himself bitterly that she would never have treated him so. His impulse was to go to her; he could depend on her pity; but he was ashamed: she had been good to him always, and he had treated her abominably.

"If I'd only had the sense to stick to her!" he said to himself, afterwards, when Lawson and Hayward had gone and he was smoking a last pipe before going to bed.

He remembered the pleasant hours they had spent together in the cosy sitting-room in Vincent Square, their visits to galleries and to the play, and the charming evenings of intimate conversation. He recollected her solicitude for his welfare and her interest in all that concerned him. She had loved him with a love that was kind and lasting, there was more than sensuality in it, it was almost maternal; he had always known that it was a precious thing for which with all his soul he should thank the gods. He made up his mind to throw himself on her mercy. She must have suffered horribly, but he felt she had the greatness of heart to forgive him: she was incapable of malice. Should he write to her? No. He would break in on her suddenly and cast himself at her feet —he knew that when the time came he would feel too shy to perform such a dramatic gesture, but that was how he liked to think of it—and tell her that if she would take him back she might rely on him for ever. He was cured of the hateful disease from which he had suffered, he knew her

worth, and now she might trust him. His imagination leaped forward to the future. He pictured himself rowing with her on the river on Sundays; he would take her to Greenwich, he had never forgotten that delightful excursion with Hayward, and the beauty of the Port of London remained a permanent treasure in his recollection; and on the warm summer afternoons they would sit in the Park together and talk: he laughed to himself as he remembered her gay chatter, which poured out like a brook bubbling over little stones, amusing, flippant, and full of character. The agony he had suffered would pass from his mind like a bad dream.

But when next day, about tea-time, an hour at which he was pretty certain to find Norah at home, he knocked at her door his courage suddenly failed him. Was it possible for her to forgive him? It would be abominable of him to force himself on her presence. The door was opened by a maid new since he had been in the habit of calling every day, and he inquired if Mrs. Nesbit was in.

"Will you ask her if she could see Mr. Carey?" he said. "I'll wait here."

The maid ran upstairs and in a moment clattered down again.

"Will you step up, please, sir. Second floor front."

"I know," said Philip, with a slight smile.

He went with a fluttering heart. He knocked at the door.

"Come in," said the well-known, cheerful voice.

It seemed to say come in to a new life of peace and happiness. When he entered Norah stepped forward to greet him. She shook hands with him as if they had parted the day before. A man stood up.

"Mr. Carey—Mr. Kingsford."

Philip, bitterly disappointed at not finding her alone, sat down and took stock of the stranger. He had never heard her mention his name, but he seemed to Philip to occupy his chair as though he were very much at home. He was a man of forty, clean-shaven, with long fair hair very neatly plastered down, and the reddish skin and pale, tired eyes which fair men get when their youth is passed. He had a large nose, a large mouth; the bones of his face were prominent, and he was heavily made; he was a man of more than average height, and broad-shouldered.

"I was wondering what had become of you," said Norah, in her sprightly manner. "I met Mr. Lawson the other day—did he tell you?—and I informed him that it was really high time you came to see me again."

Philip could see no shadow of embarrassment in her countenance, and he admired the ease with which she carried off an encounter of which himself felt the intense awkwardness. She gave him tea. She was about to put sugar in it when he stopped her.

"How stupid of me!" she cried. "I forgot."

He did not believe that. She must remember quite well that he never took sugar in his tea. He accepted the incident as a sign that her nonchalance was affected.

The conversation which Philip had interrupted went on, and presently he began to feel a little in the way. Kingsford took no particular notice of him. He talked fluently and well, not without humour, but with a slightly dogmatic manner: he was a journalist, it appeared, and had something amusing to say on every topic that was touched upon; but it exasperated Philip to find himself edged out of the conversation. He was determined to stay the visitor out. He wondered if he admired Norah. In the old days they had often talked of the men who wanted to flirt with her and had laughed at them together. Philip tried to bring back the conversation to matters which only he and Norah knew about, but each time the journalist broke in and succeeded in drawing it away to a subject upon which Philip was forced to be silent. He grew faintly angry with Norah, for she must see he was being made ridiculous; but perhaps she was inflicting this upon him as a punishment, and with this thought he regained his good humour. At last, however, the clock struck six, and Kingsford got up.

"I must go," he said.

Norah shook hands with him, and accompanied him to the landing. She shut the door behind her and stood outside for a couple of minutes. Philip wondered what they were talking about.

"Who is Mr. Kingsford?" he asked cheerfully, when she returned.

"Oh, he's the editor of one of Harmsworth's Magazines. He's been taking a good deal of my work lately."

"I thought he was never going."

"I'm glad you stayed. I wanted to have a talk with you." She curled herself into the large arm-chair, feet and all, in a way her small size made possible, and lit a cigarette. He smiled when he saw her assume the attitude which had always amused him.

"You look just like a cat."

She gave him a flash of her dark, fine eyes.

"I really ought to break myself of the habit. It's absurd to behave like a child when you're my age, but I'm comfortable with my legs under me."

"It's awfully jolly to be sitting in this room again," said Philip happily.

"You don't know how I've missed it."

"Why on earth didn't you come before?" she asked gaily.

"I was afraid to," he said, reddening.

She gave him a look full of kindness. Her lips outlined a charming smile.

"You needn't have been."

He hesitated for a moment. His heart beat quickly.

"D'you remember the last time we met? I treated you awfully badly— I'm dreadfully ashamed of myself."

She looked at him steadily. She did not answer. He was losing his head; he seemed to have come on an errand of which he was only now realising the outrageousness. She did not help him, and he could only blurt out bluntly:

"Can you ever forgive me?"

Then impetuously he told her that Mildred had left him and that his unhappiness had been so great that he almost killed himself. He told her of all that had happened between them, of the birth of the child, and of the meeting with Griffiths, of his folly and his trust and his immense deception. He told her how often he had thought of her kindness and of her love, and how bitterly he had regretted throwing it away: he had only been happy when he was with her, and he knew now how great was her worth. His voice was hoarse with emotion. Sometimes he was so ashamed of what he was saying that he spoke with his eyes fixed on the ground. His face was distorted with pain, and yet he felt it a strange relief to speak. At last he finished. He flung himself back in his chair, exhausted, and waited. He had concealed nothing, and even, in his self-abasement, he had striven to make himself more despicable than he had really been. He was surprised

that she did not speak, and at last he raised his eyes. She was not looking at him. Her face was quite white, and she seemed to be lost in thought.

"Haven't you got anything to say to me?"

She started and reddened.

"I'm afraid you've had a rotten time," she said. "I'm dreadfully sorry."

She seemed about to go on, but she stopped, and again he waited. At length she seemed to force herself to speak.

"I'm engaged to be married to Mr. Kingsford."

"Why didn't you tell me at once?" he cried. "You needn't have allowed me to humiliate myself before you."

"I'm sorry, I couldn't stop you. . . . I met him soon after you" —she seemed to search for an expression that should not wound him— "told me your friend had come back. I was very wretched for a bit, he was extremely kind to me. He knew someone had made me suffer, of course he doesn't know it was you, and I don't know what I should have done without him. And suddenly I felt I couldn't go on working, working, working; I was so tired, I felt so ill. I told him about my husband. He offered to give me the money to get my divorce if I would marry him as soon as I could. He had a very good job, and it wouldn't be necessary for me to do anything unless I wanted to. He was so fond of me and so anxious to take care of me. I was awfully touched. And now I'm very, very fond of him."

"Have you got your divorce then?" asked Philip.

"I've got the decree nisi. It'll be made absolute in July, and then we are going to be married at once."

For some time Philip did not say anything.

"I wish I hadn't made such a fool of myself," he muttered at length.

He was thinking of his long, humiliating confession. She looked at him curiously.

"You were never really in love with me," she said.

"It's not very pleasant being in love."

But he was always able to recover himself quickly, and, getting up now and holding out his hand, he said: "I hope you'll be very happy. After all, it's the best thing that could have happened to you."

She looked a little wistfully at him as she took his hand and held it.

"You'll come and see me again, won't you?" she asked.

"No," he said, shaking his head. "It would make me too envious to see you happy."

He walked slowly away from her house. After all she was right when she said he had never loved her. He was disappointed, irritated even, but his vanity was more affected than his heart. He knew that himself. And presently he grew conscious that the gods had played a very good practical joke on him, and he laughed at himself mirthlessly. It is not very comfortable to have the gift of being amused at one's own absurdity.

LXXX

For the next three months Philip worked on subjects which were new to him. The unwieldy crowd which had entered the Medical School nearly two years before had thinned out: some had left the hospital, finding the examinations more difficult to pass than they expected, some had been taken away by parents who had not foreseen the expense of life in London, and some had drifted away to other callings. One youth whom Philip knew had devised an ingenious plan to make money; he had bought things at sales and pawned them, but presently found it more profitable to pawn goods bought on credit; and it had caused a little excitement at the hospital when someone pointed out his name in police-court proceedings. There had been a remand, then assurances on the part of a harassed father, and the young man had gone out to bear the White Man's Burden overseas. The imagination of another, a lad who had never before been in a town at all, fell to the glamour of music-halls and bar parlours; he spent his time among racing-men, tipsters, and trainers, and now was become a book-maker's clerk. Philip had seen him once in a bar near Piccadilly Circus in a tight-waisted coat and a brown hat with a broad, flat brim. A third, with a gift for singing and mimicry, who had achieved success at the smoking concerts of the Medical School by his imitation of notorious comedians, had abandoned the hospital for the chorus of a musical comedy. Still another, and he interested Philip because his uncouth manner and interjectional speech did not suggest that he was capable of any deep emotion, had felt himself stifle among the houses of London. He grew haggard in shut-in spaces, and the soul he knew not he possessed struggled like a sparrow held in the hand, with little frightened gasps and a quick palpitation of the heart: he yearned for the broad skies and the open, desolate places among which his childhood had been spent; and he walked off one day, without a word to anybody, between one lecture and another; and the next thing his friends heard was that he had thrown up medicine and was working on a farm.

Philip attended now lectures on medicine and on surgery. On certain mornings in the week he practised bandaging on out-patients glad to earn a little money, and he was taught auscultation and how to use the stethoscope. He learned dispensing. He was taking the examination in *Materia Medica* in July, and it amused him to play with various drugs, concocting mixtures, rolling pills, and making ointments. He seized avidly upon anything from which he could extract a suggestion of human interest.

He saw Griffiths once in the distance, but, not to have the pain of cutting him dead, avoided him. Philip had felt a certain self-consciousness with Griffiths' friends, some of whom were now friends of his, when he realised they knew of his quarrel with Griffiths and surmised they were aware of the reason. One of them, a very tall fellow, with a small head and a languid air, a youth called Ramsden, who was one of Griffiths' most faithful admirers, copied his ties, his boots, his manner of talking and his gestures, told Philip that Griffiths was very much hurt because Philip had not answered his letter. He wanted to be reconciled with him.

"Has he asked you to give me the message?" asked Philip.

"Oh, no. I'm saying this entirely on my own," said Ramsden. "He's awfully sorry for what he did, and he says you always behaved like a perfect brick to him. I know he'd be glad to make it up. He doesn't come to the hospital because he's afraid of meeting you, and he thinks you'd cut him."

"I should."

"It makes him feel rather wretched, you know."

"I can bear the trifling inconvenience that he feels with a good deal of fortitude," said Philip.

"He'll do anything he can to make it up."

"How childish and hysterical! Why should he care? I'm a very insignificant person, and he can do very well without my company. I'm not interested in him any more."

Ramsden thought Philip hard and cold. He paused for a moment or two, looking about him in a perplexed way.

"Harry wishes to God he'd never had anything to do with the woman."

"Does he?" asked Philip.

He spoke with an indifference which he was satisfied with. No one could have guessed how violently his heart was beating. He waited impatiently for Ramsden to go on.

"I suppose you've quite got over it now, haven't you?"

"I?" said Philip. "Quite."

Little by little he discovered the history of Mildred's relations with Griffiths. He listened with a smile on his lips, feigning an equanimity which quite deceived the dull-witted boy who talked to him. The week-end she spent with Griffiths at Oxford inflamed rather than extinguished her sudden passion; and when Griffiths went home, with a feeling that was unexpected in her she determined to stay in Oxford by herself for a couple of days, because she had been so happy in it. She felt that nothing could induce her to go back to Philip. He revolted her. Griffiths was taken aback at the fire he had aroused, for he had found his two days with her in the country somewhat tedious; and he had no desire to turn an amusing episode into a tiresome affair. She made him promise to write to her, and, being an honest, decent fellow, with natural politeness and a desire to make himself pleasant to everybody, when he got home he wrote her a long and charming letter. She answered it with reams of passion, clumsy, for she had no gift of expression, ill-written, and vulgar; the letter bored him, and when it was followed next day by another, and the day after by a third, he began to think her love no longer flattering but alarming. He did not answer; and she bombarded him with telegrams, asking him if he were ill and had received her letters; she said his silence made her dreadfully anxious. He was forced to write, but he sought to make his reply as casual as was possible without being offensive: he begged her not to wire, since it was difficult to explain telegrams to his mother, an old-fashioned person for whom a telegram was still an event to excite tremor. She answered by return of post that she must see him and announced her intention to pawn things (she had the dressing-case which Philip had given her as a wedding-present and could raise eight pounds on that) in order to come up and stay at the market town four miles from which was the village in which his father practised. This frightened Griffiths; and he, this time, made use of the telegraph wires to tell her that she must do nothing of the kind. He promised to let her know the moment he came up to London, and, when he did, found that she had already been asking for him at the hospital at which he had an appointment. He did not like this, and, on seeing her, told Mildred that she was not to come there on any pretext; and now, after an absence of three weeks, he found that she bored him quite decidedly; he wondered why he had ever troubled about her, and made

up his mind to break with her as soon as he could. He was a person who dreaded quarrels, nor did he want to give pain; but at the same time he had other things to do, and he was quite determined not to let Mildred bother him. When he met her he was pleasant, cheerful, amusing, affectionate; he invented convincing excuses for the interval since last he had seen her; but he did everything he could to avoid her. When she forced him to make appointments he sent telegrams to her at the last moment to put himself off; and his landlady (the first three months of his appointment he was spending in rooms) had orders to say he was out when Mildred called. She would waylay him in the street and, knowing she had been waiting about for him to come out of the hospital for a couple of hours, he would give her a few charming, friendly words and bolt off with the excuse that he had a business engagement. He grew very skilful in slipping out of the hospital unseen. Once, when he went back to his lodgings at midnight, he saw a woman standing at the area railings and suspecting who it was went to beg a shake-down in Ramsden's rooms; next day the landlady told him that Mildred had sat crying on the doorsteps for hours, and she had been obliged to tell her at last that if she did not go away she would send for a policeman.

"I tell you, my boy," said Ramsden, "you're jolly well out of it. Harry says that if he'd suspected for half a second she was going to make such a blooming nuisance of herself he'd have seen himself damned before he had anything to do with her."

Philip thought of her sitting on that doorstep through the long hours of the night. He saw her face as she looked up dully at the landlady who sent her away.

"I wonder what she's doing now."

"Oh, she's got a job somewhere, thank God. That keeps her busy all day."

The last thing he heard, just before the end of the summer session, was that Griffiths' urbanity had given way at length under the exasperation of the constant persecution. He had told Mildred that he was sick of being pestered, and she had better take her-self off and not bother him again. "It was the only thing he could do," said Ramsden. "It was getting a bit too thick."

"Is it all over then?" asked Philip.

"Oh, he hasn't seen her for ten days. You know, Harry's wonderful at dropping people. This is about the toughest nut he's ever had to crack, but he's cracked it all right."

Then Philip heard nothing more of her at all. She vanished into the vast anonymous mass of the population of London.

LXXXI

At the beginning of the winter session Philip became an out-patients' clerk. There were three assistant-physicians who took out-patients, two days a week each, and Philip put his name down for Dr. Tyrell. He was popular with the students, and there was some competition to be his clerk. Dr. Tyrell was a tall, thin man of thirty-five, with a very small head, red hair cut short, and prominent blue eyes: his face was bright scarlet. He talked well in a pleasant voice, was fond of a little joke, and treated the world lightly. He was a successful man, with a large consulting practice and a knighthood in prospect. From commerce with students and poor people he had the patronising air, and from dealing always with the sick he had the healthy man's jovial condescension, which some consultants achieve as the professional manner. He made the patient feel like a boy confronted by a jolly schoolmaster; his illness was an absurd piece of naughtiness which amused rather than irritated.

The student was supposed to at-tend in the out-patients' room every day, see cases, and pick up what information he could; but on the days on which he clerked his duties were a little more definite. At that time the out-patients' department at St. Luke's consisted of three rooms, leading into one another, and a large, dark waiting-room with massive pillars of masonry and long benches. Here the patients waited after having been given their 'letters' at mid-day; and the long rows of them, bottles and gallipots in hand, some tattered and dirty, others decent enough, sitting in the dimness, men and women of all ages, children, gave one an impression which was weird and horrible. They suggested the grim drawings of Daumier. All the rooms were painted alike, in salmon-colour with a high dado of maroon; and there was in them an odour of disinfectants, mingling as the afternoon wore on with the crude stench of humanity. The first room was the largest and in the middle of it were a table and an office chair for the physician; on each side of this were two smaller tables, a little lower: at one of these sat the house-physician and at the other the clerk who took the 'book' for the day. This was a large volume in which were written down the name, age, sex, profession, of the patient and the diagnosis of his disease.

At half past one the house-physician came in, rang the bell, and told the porter to send in the old patients. There were always a good many of these, and it was necessary to get through as many of them as possible before Dr. Tyrell came at two. The H.P. with whom Philip came in contact was a dapper little man, excessively conscious of his importance: he treated the clerks with condescension and patently resented the familiarity of older students who had been his contemporaries and did not use him with the respect he felt his present position demanded. He set about the cases. A clerk helped him. The patients streamed in. The men came first. Chronic bronchitis, "a nasty 'acking cough," was what they chiefly suffered from; one went to the H.P. and the other to the clerk, handing in their letters: if they were going on well the words *Rep 14* were written on them, and they went to the dispensary with their bottles or gallipots in order to have medicine given them for fourteen days more. Some old stagers held back so that they might be seen by the physician himself, but they seldom succeeded in this; and only three or four, whose condition seemed to demand his attention, were kept.

Dr. Tyrell came in with quick movements and a breezy manner. He reminded one slightly of a clown leaping into the arena of a circus with the cry: Here we are again. His air seemed to indicate: What's all this nonsense about being ill? I'll soon put that right. He took his seat, asked if there were any old patients for him to see, rapidly passed them in review, looking at them with shrewd eyes as he discussed their symptoms, cracked a joke (at which all the clerks laughed heartily) with the H.P., who laughed heartily too but with an air as if he thought it was rather impudent for the clerks to laugh, remarked that it was a fine day or a hot one, and rang the bell for the porter to show in the new patients.

They came in one by one and walked up to the table at which sat Dr. Tyrell. They were old men and young men and middle-aged men, mostly of the labouring class, dock labourers, draymen, factory hands, barmen; but some, neatly dressed, were of a station which was obviously superior, shop-assistants, clerks, and the like. Dr. Tyrell looked at these with suspicion. Sometimes they put on shabby clothes in order to pretend they were poor; but he had a keen eye to prevent what he regarded as fraud and sometimes refused to see people who, he thought, could well pay for medical attendance. Women were the worst offenders and they managed the thing more clumsily. They would wear a cloak and a skirt which were almost in rags, and neglect to take the rings off their fingers.

"If you can afford to wear jewellery you can afford a doctor. A hospital is a charitable institution," said Dr. Tyrell.

He handed back the letter and called for the next case.

"But I've got my letter."

"I don't care a hang about your letter; you get out. You've got no business to come and steal the time which is wanted by the really poor."

The patient retired sulkily, with an angry scowl.

"She'll probably write a letter to

the papers on the gross mismanagement of the London hospitals," said Dr. Tyrell, with a smile, as he took the next paper and gave the patient one of his shrewd glances.

Most of them were under the impression that the hospital was an institution of the state, for which they paid out of the rates, and took the attendance they received as a right they could claim. They imagined the physician who gave them his time was heavily paid.

Dr. Tyrell gave each of his clerks a case to examine. The clerk took the patient into one of the inner rooms; they were smaller, and each had a couch in it covered with black horsehair: he asked his patient a variety of questions, examined his lungs, his heart, and his liver, made notes of fact on the hospital letter, formed in his own mind some idea of the diagnosis, and then waited for Dr. Tyrell to come in. This he did, followed by a small crowd of students, when he had finished the men, and the clerk read out what he had learned. The physician asked him one or two questions, and examined the patient himself. If there was anything interesting to hear, students applied their stethoscope: you would see a man with two or three to the chest, and two perhaps to his back, while others waited impatiently to listen. The patient stood among them a little embarrassed, but not altogether displeased to find himself the centre of attention: he listened confusedly while Dr. Tyrell discoursed glibly on the case. Two or three students listened again to recognise the murmur or the crepitation which the physician described, and then the man was told to put on his clothes.

When the various cases had been examined Dr. Tyrell went back into the large room and sat down again at his desk. He asked any student

who happened to be standing near him what he would prescribe for a patient he had just seen. The student mentioned one or two drugs.

"Would you?" said Dr. Tyrell. "Well, that's original at all events. I don't think we'll be rash."

This always made the students laugh, and with a twinkle of amusement at his own bright humour the physician prescribed some other drug than that which the student had suggested. When there were two cases of exactly the same sort and the student proposed the treatment which the physician had ordered for the first, Dr. Tyrell exercised considerable ingenuity in thinking of something else. Sometimes, knowing that in the dispensary they were worked off their legs and preferred to give the medicines which they had all ready, the good hospital mixtures which had been found by the experience of years to answer their purpose so well, he amused himself by writing an elaborate prescription.

"We'll give the dispenser something to do. If we go on prescribing *mist: alb:* he'll lose his cunning."

The students laughed, and the doctor gave them a circular glance of enjoyment in his joke. Then he touched the bell and, when the porter poked his head in, said:

"Old women, please."

He leaned back in his chair, chatting with the H.P. while the porter herded along the old patients. They came in, strings of anæmic girls, with large fringes and pallid lips, who could not digest their bad, insufficient food; old ladies, fat and thin, aged prematurely by frequent confinements, with winter coughs; women with this, that, and the other, the matter with them. Dr. Tyrell and his house-physician got through them quickly. Time was getting on, and the air in the small room was growing more sickly. The physician looked at his watch.

"Are there many new women to-day?" he asked.

"A good few, I think," said the H.P.

"We'd better have them in. You can go on with the old ones."

They entered. With the men the most common ailments were due to the excessive use of alcohol, but with the women they were due to defective nourishment. By about six o'clock they were finished. Philip, exhausted by standing all the time, by the bad air, and by the attention he had given, strolled over with his fellow-clerks to the Medical School to have tea. He found the work of absorbing interest. There was humanity there in the rough, the materials the artist worked on; and Philip felt a curious thrill when it occurred to him that he was in the position of the artist and the patients were like clay in his hands. He remembered with an amused shrug of the shoulders his life in Paris, absorbed in colour, tone, values, Heaven knows what, with the aim of producing beautiful things: the directness of contact with men and women gave a thrill of power which he had never known. He found an endless excitement in looking at their faces and hearing them speak; they came in each with his peculiarity, some shuffling uncouthly, some with a little trip, others with heavy, slow tread, some shyly. Often you could guess their trades by the look of them. You learnt in what way to put your questions so that they should be understood, you discovered on what subjects nearly all lied, and by what inquiries you could extort the truth notwithstanding. You saw the different way people took the same things. The diagnosis of dangerous illness would be accepted by one with a laugh and a joke,

by another with dumb despair. Philip found that he was less shy with these people than he had ever been with others; he felt not exactly sympathy, for sympathy suggests condescension; but he felt at home with them. He found that he was able to put them at their ease, and, when he had been given a case to find out what he could about it, it seemed to him that the patient delivered himself into his hands with a peculiar confidence.

"Perhaps," he thought to himself, with a smile, "perhaps I'm cut out to be a doctor. It would be rather a lark if I'd hit upon the one thing I'm fit for."

It seemed to Philip that he alone of the clerks saw the dramatic interest of those afternoons. To the others men and women were only cases, good if they were complicated, tiresome if obvious; they heard murmurs and were astonished at abnormal livers; an unexpected sound in the lungs gave them something to talk about. But to Philip there was much more. He found an interest in just looking at them, in the shape of their heads and their hands, in the look of their eyes and the length of their noses. You saw in that room human nature taken by surprise, and often the mask of custom was torn off rudely, showing you the soul all raw. Sometimes you saw an untaught stoicism which was profoundly moving. Once Philip saw a man, rough and illiterate, told his case was hopeless; and, self-controlled himself, he wondered at the splendid instinct which forced the fellow to keep a stiff upper-lip before strangers. But was it possible for him to be brave when he was by himself, face to face with his soul, or would he then surrender to despair? Sometimes there was tragedy. Once a young woman brought her sister to be examined, a girl of eighteen, with delicate features and large blue eyes, fair hair that sparkled with gold when a ray of autumn sunshine touched it for a moment, and a skin of amazing beauty. The students' eyes went to her with little smiles. They did not often see a pretty girl in these dingy rooms. The elder woman gave the family history, father and mother had died of phthisis, a brother and a sister, these two were the only ones left. The girl had been coughing lately and losing weight. She took off her blouse and the skin of her neck was like milk. Dr. Tyrell examined her quietly, with his usual rapid method; he told two or three of his clerks to apply their stethoscopes to a place he indicated with his finger; and then she was allowed to dress. The sister was standing a little apart and she spoke to him in a low voice, so that the girl should not hear. Her voice trembled with fear.

"She hasn't got it, doctor, has she?"

"I'm afraid there's no doubt about it."

"She was the last one. When she goes I shan't have anybody."

She began to cry, while the doctor looked at her gravely; he thought she too had the type; she would not make old bones either. The girl turned round and saw her sister's tears. She understood what they meant. The colour fled from her lovely face and tears fell down her cheeks. The two stood for a minute or two, crying silently, and then the older, forgetting the indifferent crowd that watched them, went up to her, took her in her arms, and rocked her gently to and fro as if she were a baby.

When they were gone a student asked:

"How long d'you think she'll last, sir?"

Dr. Tyrell shrugged his shoulders.

"Her brother and sister died within three months of the first symptoms.

She'll do the same. If they were rich one might do something. You can't tell these people to go to St. Moritz. Nothing can be done for them."

Once a man who was strong and in all the power of his manhood came because a persistent aching troubled him and his club-doctor did not seem to do him any good; and the verdict for him too was death, not the inevitable death that horrified and yet was tolerable because science was helpless before it, but the death which was inevitable because the man was a little wheel in the great machine of a complex civilisation, and had as little power of changing the circumstances as an automaton. Complete rest was his only chance. The physician did not ask impossibilities.

"You ought to get some very much lighter job."

"There ain't no light jobs in my business."

"Well, if you go on like this you'll kill yourself. You're very ill."

"D'you mean to say I'm going to die?"

"I shouldn't like to say that, but you're certainly unfit for hard work."

"If I don't work who's to keep the wife and the kids?"

Dr. Tyrell shrugged his shoulders. The dilemma had been presented to him a hundred times. Time was pressing and there were many patients to be seen.

"Well, I'll give you some medicine and you can come back in a week and tell me how you're getting on."

The man took his letter with the useless prescription written upon it and walked out. The doctor might say what he liked. He did not feel so bad that he could not go on working. He had a good job and he could not afford to throw it away.

"I give him a year," said Dr. Tyrell.

Sometimes there was comedy. Now

and then came a flash of cockney humour, now and then some old lady, a character such as Charles Dickens might have drawn, would amuse them by her garrulous oddities. Once a woman came who was a member of the ballet at a famous music-hall. She looked fifty, but gave her age as twenty-eight. She was outrageously painted and ogled the students impudently with large black eyes; her smiles were grossly alluring. She had abundant self-confidence and treated Dr. Tyrell, vastly amused, with the easy familiarity with which she might have used an intoxicated admirer. She had chronic bronchitis, and told him it hindered her in the exercise of her profession.

"I don't know why I should 'ave such a thing, upon my word I don't. I've never 'ad a day's illness in my life. You've only got to look at me to know that."

She rolled her eyes round the young men, with a long sweep of her painted eyelashes, and flashed her yellow teeth at them. She spoke with a cockney accent, but with an affectation of refinement which made every word a feast of fun.

"It's what they call a winter cough," answered Dr. Tyrell gravely. "A great many middle-aged women have it."

"Well, I never! That is a nice thing to say to a lady. No one ever called me middle-aged before."

She opened her eyes very wide and cocked her head on one side, looking at him with indescribable archness.

"That is the disadvantage of our profession," said he. "It forces us sometimes to be ungallant."

She took the prescription and gave him one last, luscious smile.

"You will come and see me dance, dearie, won't you?"

"I will indeed."

He rang the bell for the next case.

"I am glad you gentlemen were here to protect me."

But on the whole the impression was neither of tragedy nor of comedy. There was no describing it. It was manifold and various; there were tears and laughter, happiness and woe; it was tedious and interesting and indifferent; it was as you saw it: it was tumultuous and passionate; it was grave; it was sad and comic; it was trivial; it was simple and complex; joy was there and despair; the love of mothers for their children, and of men for women; lust trailed itself through the rooms with leaden feet, punishing the guilty and the innocent, helpless wives and wretched children; drink seized men and women and cost its inevitable price; death sighed in these rooms; and the beginning of life, filling some poor girl with terror and shame, was diagnosed there. There was neither good nor bad there. There were just facts. It was life.

LXXXII

TOWARDS the end of the year, when Philip was bringing to a close his three months as clerk in the out-patients' department, he received a letter from Lawson, who was in Paris.

Dear Philip,

Cronshaw is in London and would be glad to see you. He is living at 43 Hyde Street, Soho. I don't know where it is, but I daresay you will be able to find out. Be a brick and look after him a bit. He is very down on his luck. He will tell you what he is doing. Things are going on here very much as usual. Nothing seems to have changed since you were here. Clutton is back, but he has become quite impossible. He has quarrelled with everybody. As far as I can make out he hasn't got a cent, he lives in a little studio right away beyond the Jardin des Plantes, but he won't let anybody see his work. He doesn't show anywhere, so one doesn't know what he is doing. He may be a genius, but on the other hand he may be off his head. By the way, I ran against Flanagan the other day. He was showing Mrs. Flanagan round the Quarter. He has chucked art and is now in popper's business. He seems to be rolling. Mrs. Flanagan is very pretty and I'm trying to work a portrait. How much would you ask if you were me? I don't want to frighten them, and then on the other hand I don't want to be such an ass as to ask £150 if they're quite willing to give £300.

Yours ever,
Frederick Lawson.

Philip wrote to Cronshaw and received in reply the following letter. It was written on a half-sheet of common note-paper, and the flimsy envelope was dirtier than was justified by its passage through the post.

Dear Carey,

Of course I remember you very well. I have an idea that I had some part in rescuing you from the Slough of Despond in which myself am hopelessly immersed. I shall be glad to see you. I am a stranger in a strange city and I am buffeted by the Philistines. It will be pleasant to talk of Paris. I do not ask you to come and see me, since my lodging is not of a magnificence fit for the reception of an eminent member of Monsieur Purgon's profession, but you will find me eating modestly any evening between seven and eight at a restaurant yclept Au Bon Plaisir in Dean Street.

Your sincere
J. Cronshaw.

Philip went the day he received this letter. The restaurant, consisting of one small room, was of the poorest class, and Cronshaw seemed to be its only customer. He was sitting in the corner, well away from draughts, wearing the same shabby great-coat which Philip had never seen him without, with his old bowler on his head.

"I eat here because I can be alone," he said. "They are not doing well; the only people who come are a few trollops and one or two waiters out of a job; they are giving up business, and the food is execrable. But the ruin of their fortunes is my advantage."

Cronshaw had before him a glass of absinthe. It was nearly three years since they had met, and Philip was shocked by the change in his appearance. He had been rather corpulent, but now he had a dried-up, yellow look: the skin of his neck was loose and wrinkled; his clothes hung about him as though they had been bought for someone else; and his collar, three or four sizes too large, added to the slatternliness of his appearance. His hands trembled continually. Philip remembered the handwriting which scrawled over the page with shapeless, haphazard letters. Cronshaw was evidently very ill.

"I eat little these days," he said. "I'm very sick in the morning. I'm just having some soup for my dinner, and then I shall have a bit of cheese."

Philip's glance unconsciously went

to the absinthe, and Cronshaw, seeing it, gave him the quizzical look with which he reproved the admonitions of common sense.

"You have diagnosed my case, and you think it's very wrong of me to drink absinthe."

"You've evidently got cirrhosis of the liver," said Philip.

"Evidently."

He looked at Philip in the way which had formerly had the power of making him feel incredibly narrow. It seemed to point out that what he was thinking was distressingly obvious; and when you have agreed with the obvious what more is there to say? Philip changed the topic.

"When are you going back to Paris?"

"I'm not going back to Paris. I'm going to die."

The very naturalness with which he said this startled Philip. He thought of half a dozen things to say, but they seemed futile. He knew that Cronshaw was a dying man.

"Are you going to settle in London then?" he asked lamely.

"What is London to me? I am a fish out of water. I walk through the crowded streets, men jostle me, and I seem to walk in a dead city. I felt that I couldn't die in Paris. I wanted to die among my own people. I don't know what hidden instinct drew me back at the last."

Philip knew of the woman Cronshaw had lived with and the two draggle-tailed children, but Cronshaw had never mentioned them to him, and he did not like to speak of them. He wondered what had happened to them.

"I don't know why you talk of dying," he said.

"I had penumonia a couple of winters ago, and they told me then it was a miracle that I came through. It ap-

pears I'm extremely liable to it, and another bout will kill me."

"Oh, what nonsense! You're not so bad as all that. You've only got to take precautions. Why don't you give up drinking?"

"Because I don't choose. It doesn't matter what a man does if he's ready to take the consequences. Well, I'm ready to take the consequences. You talk glibly of giving up drinking, but it's the only thing I've got left now. What do you think life would be to me without it? Can you understand the happiness I get out of my absinthe? I yearn for it; and when I drink it I savour every drop, and afterwards I feel my soul swimming in ineffable happiness. It disgusts you. You are a puritan and in your heart you despise sensual pleasures. Sensual pleasures are the most violent and the most exquisite. I am a man blessed with vivid senses, and I have indulged them with all my soul. I have to pay the penalty now, and I am ready to pay."

Philip looked at him for a while steadily.

"Aren't you afraid?"

For a moment Cronshaw did not answer. He seemed to consider his reply.

"Sometimes, when I'm alone." He looked at Philip. "You think that's a condemnation? You're wrong. I'm not afraid of my fear. It's folly, the Christian argument that you should live always in view of your death. The only way to live is to forget that you're going to die. Death is unimportant. The fear of it should never influence a single action of the wise man. I know that I shall die struggling for breath, and I know that I shall be horribly afraid. I know that I shall not be able to keep myself from regretting bitterly the life that has brought me to such a pass; but I disown that regret. I now, weak, old, diseased, poor, dying, hold still my soul in my hands, and I regret nothing."

"D'you remember that Persian carpet you gave me?" asked Philip.

Cronshaw smiled his old, slow smile of past days.

"I told you that it would give you an answer to your question when you asked me what was the meaning of life. Well, have you discovered the answer?"

"No," smiled Philip. "Won't you tell it me?"

"No, no, I can't do that. The answer is meaningless unless you discover it for yourself."

LXXXIII

CRONSHAW was publishing his poems. His friends had been urging him to do this for years, but his laziness made it impossible for him to take the necessary steps. He had always answered their exhortations by telling them that the love of poetry was dead in England. You brought out a book which had cost you years of thought and labour; it was given two or three contemptuous lines among a batch of similar volumes, twenty or thirty copies were sold, and the rest of the edition was pulped. He had long since worn out the desire for fame. That was an illusion like all else. But one of his friends had taken the matter into his own hands. This was a man of letters, named Leonard Upjohn, whom Philip had met once or twice with Cronshaw in the cafés of the Quarter. He had a considerable reputation in England as a critic and was the accredited exponent in this country of modern French literature. He had lived a good deal in France among the men who made the *Mercure de France* the liveliest review of the day, and by the simple process of expressing in English their point of view he had acquired in England a reputation for originality. Philip had read some of his articles. He had formed a style for himself by a close imitation of Sir Thomas Browne; he used elaborate sentences, carefully balanced, and obsolete, resplendent words: it gave his writing an appearance of individuality. Leonard Upjohn had induced Cronshaw to give him all his poems and found that there were enough to make a volume of reasonable size. He promised to use his influence with publishers. Cronshaw was in want of money. Since his illness he had found it more difficult than ever to work steadily; he made barely enough to keep himself in liquor; and when Upjohn wrote to him that this publisher and the other, though admiring the poems, thought it not worth while to publish them, Cronshaw began to grow interested. He wrote impressing upon Upjohn his great need and urging him to make more strenuous efforts. Now that he was going to die he wanted to leave behind him a published book, and at the back of his mind was the feeling that he had produced great poetry. He expected to burst upon the world like a new star. There was something fine in keeping to himself these treasures of beauty all his life and giving them to the world disdainfully when, he and the world parting company, he had no further use for them.

His decision to come to England was caused directly by an announcement from Leonard Upjohn that a publisher had consented to print the poems. By a miracle of persuasion Upjohn had persuaded him to give ten pounds in advance of royalties.

"In advance of royalties, mind you," said Cronshaw to Philip. "Milton only got ten pounds down."

Upjohn had promised to write a signed article about them, and he would ask his friends who reviewed to do their best. Cronshaw pretended to treat the matter with detachment, but it was easy to see that he was delighted with the thought of the stir he would make.

One day Philip went to dine by arrangement at the wretched eating-house at which Cronshaw insisted on taking his meals, but Cronshaw did not appear. Philip learned that he had not been there for three days. He got himself something to eat and went round to the address from which Cronshaw had first written to him. He had some difficulty in finding Hyde Street. It was a street of dingy houses huddled together; many of the windows had been broken and were clumsily repaired with strips of French newspaper; the doors had not been painted for years; there were shabby little shops on the ground floor, laundries, cobblers, stationers. Ragged children played in the road, and an old barrel-organ was grinding out a vulgar tune. Philip knocked at the door of Cronshaw's house, (there was a shop of cheap sweetstuffs at the bottom,) and it was opened by an elderly Frenchwoman in a dirty apron. Philip asked her if Cronshaw was in.

"Ah, yes, there is an Englishman who lives at the top, at the back. I don't know if he's in. If you want him you had better go up and see."

The staircase was lit by one jet of gas. There was a revolting odour in the house. When Philip was passing up a woman came out of a room on the first floor, looked at him suspiciously, but made no remark. There were three doors on the top landing. Philip knocked at one, and knocked again; there was no reply; he tried the handle, but the door was locked. He knocked at another door, got no answer, and tried the door again. It opened. The room was dark.

"Who's that?"

He recognised Cronshaw's voice.

"Carey. Can I come in?"

He received no answer. He walked in. The window was closed and the stink was overpowering. There was a certain amount of light from the arc-lamp in the street, and he saw that it was a small room with two beds in it, end to end; there was a washing-stand and one chair, but they left little space for anyone to move in. Cronshaw was in the bed nearest the window. He made no movement, but gave a low chuckle.

"Why don't you light the candle?" he said then.

Philip struck a match and discovered that there was a candlestick on the floor beside the bed. He lit it and put it on the washing-stand. Cronshaw was lying on his back immobile; he looked very odd in his nightshirt; and his baldness was disconcerting. His face was earthy and deathlike.

"I say, old man, you look awfully ill. Is there anyone to look after you here?"

"George brings me in a bottle of milk in the morning before he goes to his work."

"Who's George?"

"I call him George because his name is Adolphe. He shares this palatial apartment with me."

Philip noticed then that the second bed had not been made since it was slept in. The pillow was black where the head had rested.

"You don't mean to say you're sharing this room with somebody else?" he cried.

"Why not? Lodging costs money in Soho. George is a waiter, he goes out at eight in the morning and does not come in till closing time, so he isn't in my way at all. We neither of us sleep well, and he helps to pass away the hours of the night by telling me stories of his life. He's a Swiss, and I've always had a taste for waiters. They see life from an entertaining angle."

"How long have you been in bed?"

"Three days."

"D'you mean to say you've had nothing but a bottle of milk for the last three days? Why on earth didn't you send me a line? I can't bear to think of you lying here all day long without a soul to attend to you."

Cronshaw gave a little laugh.

"Look at your face. Why, dear boy, I really believe you're distressed. You nice fellow."

Philip blushed. He had not suspected that his face showed the dismay he felt at the sight of that horrible room and the wretched circumstances of the poor poet. Cronshaw, watching Philip, went on with a gentle smile.

"I've been quite happy. Look, here are my proofs. Remember that I am indifferent to discomforts which would harass other folk. What do the circumstances of life matter if your dreams make you lord paramount of time and space?"

The proofs were lying on his bed, and as he lay in the darkness he had been able to place his hands on them. He showed them to Philip and his eyes glowed. He turned over the pages, rejoicing in the clear type; he read out a stanza.

"They don't look bad, do they?"

Philip had an idea. It would involve him in a little expense and he could not afford even the smallest increase of expenditure; but on the other hand this was a case where it revolted him to think of economy.

"I say, I can't bear the thought of your remaining here. I've got an extra room, it's empty at present, but I can easily get someone to lend me a bed. Won't you come and live with me for a while? It'll save you the rent of this."

"Oh, my dear boy, you'd insist on my keeping my window open."

"You shall have every window in the place sealed if you like."

"I shall be all right tomorrow. I could have got up today, only I felt lazy."

"Then you can very easily make the move. And then if you don't feel well at any time you can just go to bed, and I shall be there to look after you."

"If it'll please you I'll come," said Cronshaw, with his torpid not unpleasant smile.

"That'll be ripping."

They settled that Philip should fetch Cronshaw next day, and Philip snatched an hour from his busy morning to arrange the change. He found Cronshaw dressed, sitting in his hat and great-coat on the bed, with a small, shabby portmanteau, containing his clothes and books, already packed: it was on the floor by his feet, and he looked as if he were sitting in the waiting-room of a station. Philip laughed at the sight of him. They went over to Kennington in a four-wheeler, of which the windows were carefully closed, and Philip installed his guest in his own room. He had gone out early in the morning and bought for himself a second-hand bedstead, a cheap chest of drawers, and a looking-glass. Cronshaw settled down at once to correct his proofs. He was much better.

Philip found him, except for the irritability which was a symptom of his disease, an easy guest. He had a lecture at nine in the morning, so did not see Cronshaw till the night. Once or twice Philip persuaded him to share the scrappy meal he prepared for himself in the evening, but Cronshaw was too restless to stay in, and preferred generally to get himself something to eat in one or other of the cheapest restaurants in Soho. Philip asked him to see Dr. Tyrell, but he stoutly refused; he knew a doctor would tell him to stop drinking, and this he was resolved not to do. He always felt horribly ill in the morning, but his absinthe at mid-day put him on his feet again, and by the time he came home, at midnight, he was able to talk with the brilliancy which had astonished Philip when first he made his acquaintance. His proofs were corrected; and the volume was to come out among the publications of the early spring, when the public might be supposed to have recovered from the avalanche of Christmas books.

LXXXIV

AT THE new year Philip became dresser in the surgical out-patients' department. The work was of the same character as that which he had just been engaged on, but with the greater directness which surgery has than medicine; and a larger proportion of the patients suffered from those two diseases which a supine public allows, in its prudishness, to be spread broadcast. The assistant-surgeon for whom Philip dressed was called Jacobs. He was a short, fat man, with an exuberant joviality, a bald head, and a loud voice; he had a cockney accent, and was generally described by the students as an 'awful bounder'; but his cleverness, both as a surgeon and as a teacher, caused some of them to overlook this. He had also a considerable facetiousness, which he exercised impartially on the patients and on the students. He took a great pleasure in making his dressers look foolish. Since they were ignorant, nervous, and could not answer as if he were their equal, this was not very difficult. He enjoyed his afternoons, with the home truths he permitted himself, much more than the students who had to put up with them with a smile. One day a case came up of a boy with a club-foot. His parents wanted to know whether anything could be done. Mr. Jacobs turned to Philip.

"You'd better take this case, Carey. It's a subject you ought to know something about."

Philip flushed, all the more because the surgeon spoke obviously with a humorous intention, and his browbeaten dressers laughed obsequiously. It was in point of fact a subject which Philip, since coming to the hospital, had studied with anxious attention. He had read everything in the library which treated of talipes in its various forms. He made the boy take off his boot and stocking. He was fourteen, with a snub nose, blue eyes, and a freckled face. His father explained that they wanted something done if possible, it was such a hindrance to the kid in earning his living. Philip looked at him curiously. He was a jolly boy, not at all shy, but talkative and with a cheekiness which his father reproved. He was much interested in his foot.

"It's only for the looks of the thing, you know," he said to Philip. "I don't find it no trouble."

"Be quiet, Ernie," said his father. "There's too much gas about you."

Philip examined the foot and passed his hand slowly over the shapelessness of it. He could not understand why the boy felt none of the humiliation which always oppressed himself. He wondered why he could not take his deformity with that philosophic indifference. Presently Mr. Jacobs came up to him. The boy was sitting on the edge of a couch, the surgeon and Philip stood on each side of him; and in a semi-circle, crowding round, were students. With accustomed brilliancy Jacobs gave a graphic little discourse upon the club-foot: he spoke of its varieties and of the forms which followed upon different anatomical conditions.

"I suppose you've got talipes equinus?" he said, turning suddenly to Philip.

"Yes."

Philip felt the eyes of his fellow-students rest on him, and he cursed himself because he could not help blushing. He felt the sweat start up in the palms of his hands. The surgeon spoke with the fluency due to long practice and with the admirable perspicacity which distinguished him. He was tremendously interested in his profession. But Philip did not listen. He was only wishing that the fellow would get done quickly. Suddenly he realised that Jacobs was addressing him.

"You don't mind taking off your sock for a moment, Carey?"

Philip felt a shudder pass through him. He had an impulse to tell the surgeon to go to hell, but he had not the courage to make a scene. He feared his brutal ridicule. He forced himself to appear indifferent.

"Not a bit," he said.

He sat down and unlaced his boot. His fingers were trembling and he thought he should never untie the knot. He remembered how they had forced him at school to show his foot, and the misery which had eaten into his soul.

"He keeps his feet nice and clean, doesn't he?" said Jacobs, in his rasping, cockney voice.

The attendant students giggled. Philip noticed that the boy whom they were examining looked down at his foot with eager curiosity. Jacobs took the foot in his hands and said:

"Yes, that's what I thought. I see you've had an operation. When you were a child, I suppose?"

He went on with his fluent explanations. The students leaned over and looked at the foot. Two or three examined it minutely when Jacobs let it go.

"When you've quite done," said Philip, with a smile, ironically.

He could have killed them all. He thought how jolly it would be to jab a chisel (he didn't know why that particular instrument came into his mind) into their necks. What beasts men were! He wished he could believe in hell so as to comfort himself with the thought of the horrible tortures which would be theirs. Mr. Jacobs turned his attention to treatment. He talked partly to the boy's father and partly to the students. Philip put on his sock and laced his boot. At last the surgeon finished. But he seemed to have an afterthought and turned to Philip.

"You know, I think it might be worth your while to have an operation. Of course I couldn't give you a normal foot, but I think I can do something. You might think about it, and when you want a holiday you can just come into the hospital for a bit."

Philip had often asked himself whether anything could be done, but his distaste for any reference to the subject had prevented him from consulting any of the surgeons at the hospital. His reading told him that whatever might have been done when he was a small boy, and then treatment of talipes was not as skilful as in the present day, there was small chance now of any great benefit. Still it would be worth while if an operation made it possible for him to wear a more ordinary boot and to limp less. He remembered how passionately he had prayed for the miracle which his uncle had assured him was possible to omnipotence. He smiled ruefully.

"I was rather a simple soul in those days," he thought.

Towards the end of February it was clear that Cronshaw was growing much worse. He was no longer able to get up. He lay in bed, insisting that the window should be closed always, and refused to see a doctor; he would take little nourishment, but demanded whiskey and cigarettes: Philip knew that he should have neither, but Cronshaw's argument was unanswerable.

"I daresay they are killing me. I don't care. You've warned me, you've done all that was necessary: I ignore your warning. Give me something to drink and be damned to you."

Leonard Upjohn blew in two or three times a week, and there was something of the dead leaf in his appearance which made that word exactly descriptive of the manner of his appearance. He was a weedy-looking fellow of five-and-thirty, with long pale hair and a white face; he had

the look of a man who lived too little in the open air. He wore a hat like a dissenting minister's. Philip disliked him for his patronising manner and was bored by his fluent conversation. Leonard Upjohn liked to hear himself talk. He was not sensitive to the interest of his listeners, which is the first requisite of the good talker; and he never realised that he was telling people what they knew already. With measured words he told Philip what to think of Rodin, Albert Samain, and Cæsar Franck. Philip's charwoman only came in for an hour in the morning, and since Philip was obliged to be at the hospital all day Cronshaw was left much alone. Upjohn told Philip that he thought someone should remain with him, but did not offer to make it possible.

"It's dreadful to think of that great poet alone. Why, he might die without a soul at hand."

"I think he very probably will," said Philip.

"How can you be so callous!"

"Why don't you come and do your work here every day, and then you'd be near if he wanted anything?" asked Philip drily.

"I? My dear fellow, I can only work in the surroundings I'm used to, and besides I go out so much."

Upjohn was also a little put out because Philip had brought Cronshaw to his own rooms.

"I wish you had left him in Soho," he said, with a wave of his long, thin hands. "There was a touch of romance in that sordid attic. I could even bear it if it were Wapping or Shoreditch, but the respectability of Kennington! What a place for a poet to die!"

Cronshaw was often so ill-humoured that Philip could only keep his temper by remembering all the time that this irritability was a symptom of the disease. Upjohn came sometimes before Philip was in, and then Cronshaw would complain of him bitterly. Upjohn listened with complacency.

"The fact is that Carey has no sense of beauty," he smiled. "He has a middle-class mind."

He was very sarcastic to Philip, and Philip exercised a good deal of self-control in his dealings with him. But one evening he could not contain himself. He had had a hard day at the hospital and was tired out. Leonard Upjohn came to him, while he was making himself a cup of tea in the kitchen, and said that Cronshaw was complaining of Philip's insistence that he should have a doctor.

"Don't you realise that you're enjoying a very rare, a very exquisite privilege? You ought to do everything in your power, surely, to show your sense of the greatness of your trust."

"It's a rare and exquisite privilege which I can ill afford," said Philip.

Whenever there was any question of money, Leonard Upjohn assumed a slightly disdainful expression. His sensitive temperament was offended by the reference.

"There's something fine in Cronshaw's attitude, and you disturb it by your importunity. You should make allowances for the delicate imaginings which you cannot feel."

Philip's face darkened.

"Let us go in to Cronshaw," he said frigidly.

The poet was lying on his back, reading a book, with a pipe in his mouth. The air was musty; and the room, notwithstanding Philip's tidying up, had the bedraggled look which seemed to accompany Cronshaw wherever he went. He took off his spectacles as they came in. Philip was in a towering rage.

"Upjohn tells me you've been complaining to him because I've urged you

to have a doctor," he said. "I want you to have a doctor, because you may die any day, and if you hadn't been seen by anyone I shouldn't be able to get a certificate. There'd have to be an inquest and I should be blamed for not calling a doctor in."

"I hadn't thought of that. I thought you wanted me to see a doctor for my sake and not for your own. I'll see a doctor whenever you like."

Philip did not answer, but gave an almost imperceptible shrug of the shoulders. Cronshaw, watching him, gave a little chuckle.

"Don't look so angry, my dear. I know very well you want to do everything you can for me. Let's see your doctor, perhaps he can do something for me, and at any rate it'll comfort you." He turned his eyes to Upjohn. "You're a damned fool, Leonard. Why d'you want to worry the boy? He has quite enough to do to put up with me. You'll do nothing more for me than write a pretty article about me after my death. I know you."

Next day Philip went to Dr. Tyrell. He felt that he was the sort of man to be interested by the story, and as soon as Tyrell was free of his day's work he accompanied Philip to Kennington. He could only agree with what Philip had told him. The case was hopeless.

"I'll take him into the hospital if you like," he said. "He can have a small ward."

"Nothing would induce him to come."

"You know, he may die any minute, or else he may get another attack of penumonia."

Philip nodded. Dr. Tyrell made one or two suggestions, and promised to come again whenever Philip wanted him to. He left his address. When Philip went back to Cronshaw he found him quietly reading. He did not trouble to enquire what the doctor had said.

"Are you satisfied now, dear boy?" he asked.

"I suppose nothing will induce you to do any of the things Tyrell advised?"

"Nothing," smiled Cronshaw.

LXXXV

ABOUT a fortnight after this Philip, going home one evening after his day's work at the hospital, knocked at the door of Cronshaw's room. He got no answer and walked in. Cronshaw was lying huddled up on one side, and Philip went up to the bed. He did not know whether Cronshaw was asleep or merely lay there in one of his uncontrollable fits of irritability. He was surprised to see that his mouth was open. He touched his shoulder. Philip gave a cry of dismay. He slipped his hand under Cronshaw's shirt and felt his heart; he did not know what to do; helplessly, because he had heard of this being done, he held a looking-glass in front of his mouth. It startled him to be alone with Cronshaw. He had his hat and coat still on, and he ran down the stairs into the street; he hailed a cab and drove to Harley Street. Dr. Tyrell was in.

"I say, would you mind coming at once? I think Cronshaw's dead."

"If he is it's not much good my coming, is it?"

"I should be awfully grateful if you would. I've got a cab at the door. It'll only take half an hour."

Tyrell put on his hat. In the cab he asked him one or two questions.

"He seemed no worse than usual when I left this morning," said Philip. "It gave me an awful shock when I went in just now. And the thought of his dying all alone. . . . D'you think he knew he was going to die?"

Philip remembered what Cronshaw had said. He wondered whether at that last moment he had been seized with the terror of death. Philip imagined himself in such a plight, knowing it was inevitable and with no one, not a soul, to give an encouraging word when the fear seized him.

"You're rather upset," said Dr. Tyrell.

He looked at him with his bright blue eyes. They were not unsympathetic. When he saw Cronshaw, he said:

"He must have been dead for some hours. I should think he died in his sleep. They do sometimes."

The body looked shrunk and ignoble. It was not like anything human. Dr. Tyrell looked at it dispassionately. With a mechanical gesture he took out his watch.

"Well, I must be getting along. I'll send the certificate round. I suppose you'll communicate with the relatives."

"I don't think there are any," said Philip.

"How about the funeral?"

"Oh, I'll see to that."

Dr. Tyrell gave Philip a glance. He wondered whether he ought to offer a couple of sovereigns towards it. He knew nothing of Philip's circumstances; perhaps he could well afford the expense; Philip might think it impertinent if he made any suggestion.

"Well, let me know if there's anything I can do," he said.

Philip and he went out together, parting on the doorstep, and Philip went to a telegraph office in order to send a message to Leonard Upjohn. Then he went to an undertaker whose shop he passed every day on his way to the hospital. His attention had been drawn to it often by the three words in silver lettering on a black cloth, which, with two model coffins, adorned the window: Economy, Celerity, Propriety. They had always diverted him. The undertaker was a little fat Jew with curly black hair, long and greasy, in black, with a large diamond ring on a podgy finger. He received Philip with a peculiar manner formed by the mingling of his natural blatancy with the subdued air proper to his calling. He quickly saw that Philip was very helpless and promised to send round a woman at once to perform the needful offices. His suggestions for the funeral were very magnificent; and Philip felt ashamed of himself when the undertaker seemed to think his objections mean. It was horrible to haggle on such a matter, and finally Philip consented to an expensiveness which he could ill afford.

"I quite understand, sir," said the undertaker, "you don't want any show and that—I'm not a believer in ostentation myself, mind you—but you want it done gentlemanly-like. You leave it to me, I'll do it as cheap as it can be done, 'aving regard to what's right and proper. I can't say more than that, can I?"

Philip went home to eat his supper, and while he ate the woman came along to lay out the corpse. Presently a telegram arrived from Leonard Upjohn.

SHOCKED AND GRIEVED BEYOND MEASURE. REGRET CANNOT COME TONIGHT. DINING OUT. WITH YOU EARLY TO-MORROW. DEEPEST SYMPATHY. UPJOHN.

In a little while the woman knocked at the door of the sitting-room.

"I've done now, sir. Will you come and look at 'im and see it's all right?"

Philip followed her. Cronshaw was lying on his back, with his eyes closed and his hands folded piously across his chest.

"You ought by rights to 'ave a few flowers, sir."

"I'll get some tomorrow."

She gave the body a glance of satisfaction. She had performed her job, and now she rolled down her sleeves, took off her apron, and put on her bonnet. Philip asked her how much he owed her.

"Well, sir, some give me two and sixpence and some give me five shillings."

Philip was ashamed to give her less than the larger sum. She thanked him with just so much effusiveness as was seemly in presence of the grief he might be supposed to feel, and left him. Philip went back into his sitting-room, cleared away the remains of his supper, and sat down to read Walsham's *Surgery*. He found it difficult. He felt singularly nervous. When there was a sound on the stairs he jumped, and his heart beat violently. That thing in the adjoining room, which had been a man and now was nothing, frightened him. The silence seemed alive, as if some mysterious movement were taking place within it; the presence of death weighed upon these rooms, unearthly and terrifying: Philip felt a sudden horror for what had once been his friend. He tried to force himself to read, but presently pushed away his book in despair. What troubled him was the absolute futility of the life which had just ended. It did not matter if Cronshaw was alive or dead. It would have been just as well if he had never lived. Philip thought of Cronshaw young; and it needed an effort of imagination to picture him slender, with a springing step, and with hair on his head, buoyant and hopeful. Philip's rule of life, to follow one's instincts with due regard to the policeman round the corner, had not acted very well there: it was because Cronshaw had done this that he had made such a lamentable failure of existence. It seemed that the instincts could not be trusted. Philip was puzzled, and he asked himself what rule of life was there, if that one was useless, and why people acted in one way rather than in another. They acted according to their emotions, but their emotions might be good or bad; it seemed just a chance whether they led to triumph or disaster. Life seemed an inextricable confusion. Men hurried hither and thither, urged by forces they knew not; and the purpose of it all escaped them; they seemed to hurry just for hurrying's sake.

Next morning Leonard Upjohn appeared with a small wreath of laurel. He was pleased with his idea of crowning the dead poet with this; and attempted, notwithstanding Philip's disapproving silence, to fix it on the bald head; but the wreath fitted grotesquely. It looked like the brim of a hat worn by a low comedian in a music-hall.

"I'll put it over his heart instead," said Upjohn.

"You've put it on his stomach," remarked Philip.

Upjohn gave a thin smile.

"Only a poet knows where lies a poet's heart," he answered.

They went back into the sitting-room, and Philip told him what arrangements he had made for the funeral.

"I hoped you've spared no expense. I should like the hearse to be followed by a long string of empty coaches, and I should like the horses to wear tall nodding plumes, and there should be a vast number of mutes with long streamers on their hats. I like the thought of all those empty coaches."

"As the cost of the funeral will apparently fall on me and I'm not over flush just now, I've tried to make it as moderate as possible."

"But, my dear fellow, in that case, why didn't you get him a pauper's funeral? There would have been something poetic in that. You have an unerring instinct for mediocrity."

Philip flushed a little, but did not answer; and next day he and Upjohn followed the hearse in the one carriage which Philip had ordered. Lawson, unable to come, had sent a wreath; and Philip, so that the coffin should not seem too neglected, had bought a couple. On the way back the coachman whipped up his horses. Philip was dog-tired and presently went to sleep. He was awakened by Upjohn's voice.

"It's rather lucky the poems haven't come out yet. I think we'd better hold them back a bit and I'll write a preface. I began thinking of it during the drive to the cemetery. I believe I can do something rather good. Anyhow I'll start with an article in *The Saturday*."

Philip did not reply, and there was silence between them. At last Upjohn said:

"I daresay I'd be wiser not to whittle away my copy. I think I'll do an article for one of the reviews, and then I can just print it afterwards as a preface."

Philip kept his eye on the monthlies, and a few weeks later it appeared. The article made something of a stir, and extracts from it were printed in many of the papers. It was a very good article, vaguely biographical, for no one knew much of Cronshaw's early life, but delicate, tender, and picturesque. Leonard Upjohn in his intricate style drew graceful little pictures of Cronshaw in the Latin Quarter, talking, writing poetry: Cronshaw became a picturesque figure, an English Verlaine; and Leonard Upjohn's coloured phrases took on a tremulous dignity, a more pathetic grandiloquence, as he described the sordid end, the shabby little room in Soho; and, with a reticence which was wholly charming and suggested a much greater generosity than modesty allowed him to state, the efforts he made to transport the poet to some cottage embowered with honeysuckle amid a flowering orchard. And the lack of sympathy, well-meaning but so tactless, which had taken the poet instead to the vulgar respectability of Kennington! Leonard Upjohn described Kennington with that restrained humour which a strict adherence to the vocabulary of Sir Thomas Browne necessitated. With delicate sarcasm he narrated the last weeks, the patience with which Cronshaw bore the well-meaning clumsiness of the young student who had appointed himself his nurse, and the pitifulness of that divine vagabond in those hopelessly middle-class surroundings. Beauty from ashes, he quoted from Isaiah. It was a triumph of irony for that outcast poet to die amid the trappings of vulgar respectability; it reminded Leonard Upjohn of Christ among the Pharisees, and the analogy gave him opportunity for an exquisite passage. And then he told how a friend—his good taste did not suffer him more than to hint subtly who the friend was with such gracious fancies—had laid a laurel wreath on the dead poet's heart; and the beautiful dead hands had seemed to rest with a voluptuous passion upon Apollo's leaves, fragrant with the fragrance of art, and more green than jade brought by swart mariners from the manifold, inexplicable China. And, an admirable contrast, the article ended with a description of the middle-class, ordinary, prosaic funeral of him who should have been buried like a prince or like a pauper. It was the crowning buffet, the final victory of Philistia over art, beauty, and immaterial things.

Leonard Upjohn had never written anything better. It was a miracle of charm, grace, and pity. He printed all Cronshaw's best poems in the course of the article, so that when the volume appeared much of its point was gone; but he advanced his own position a good deal. He was thenceforth a critic to be reckoned with. He had seemed before a little aloof; but there was a warm humanity about this article which was infinitely attractive.

LXXXVI

In the spring Philip, having finished his dressing in the out-patients' department, became an in-patients' clerk. This appointment lasted six months. The clerk spent every morning in the wards, first in the men's, then in the women's, with the house-physician; he wrote up cases, made tests, and passed the time of day with the nurses. On two afternoons a week the physician in charge went round with a little knot of students, examined the cases, and dispensed information. The work had not the excitement, the constant change, the intimate contact with reality, of the work in the out-patients' department; but Philip picked up a good deal of knowledge. He got on very well with the patients, and he was a little flattered at the pleasure they showed in his attendance on them. He was not conscious of any deep sympathy in their sufferings, but he liked them; and because he put on no airs he was more popular with them than others of the clerks. He was pleasant, encouraging, and friendly. Like everyone connected with hospitals he found that male patients were more easy to get on with than female. The women were often querulous and ill-tempered. They complained bitterly of the hard-worked nurses, who did not show them the attention they thought their right; and they were troublesome, ungrateful, and rude.

Presently Philip was fortunate enough to make a friend. One morning the house-physician gave him a new case, a man; and, seating himself at the bedside, Philip proceeded to write down particulars on the 'letter.' He noticed on looking at this that the patient was described as a journalist: his name was Thorpe Athelny, an unusual one for a hospital patient, and his age was forty-eight. He was suffering from a sharp attack of jaundice, and had been taken into the ward on account of obscure symptoms which it seemed necessary to watch. He answered the various questions which it was Philip's duty to ask him in a pleasant, educated voice. Since he was lying in bed it was difficult to tell if he was short or tall, but his small head and small hands suggested that he was a man of less than average height. Philip had the habit of looking at people's hands, and Athelny's astonished him: they were very small, with long, tapering fingers and beautiful, rosy finger-nails; they were very smooth and except for the jaundice would have been of a surprising whiteness. The patient kept them outside the bed-clothes, one of them slightly spread out, the second and third fingers together, and, while he spoke to Philip, seemed to contemplate them with satisfaction. With a twinkle in his eyes Philip glanced at the man's face. Notwithstanding the yellowness it was distinguished; he had blue eyes, a nose of an imposing boldness, hooked, aggressive but not clumsy, and a small beard, pointed and gray: he was rather bald, but his hair had evidently been quite fine, curling prettily, and he still wore it long.

"I see you're a journalist," said Philip. "What papers d'you write for?"

"I write for all the papers. You cannot open a paper without seeing some of my writing."

There was one by the side of the bed and reaching for it he pointed out an advertisement. In large letters was the name of a firm well-known to Philip, Lynn and Sedley, Regent Street, London; and below, in type smaller but still of some magnitude, was the dogmatic statement: Procrastination is the Thief of Time. Then a question, startling because of its reasonableness: Why not order today? There was a repetition, in large letters, like the hammering of conscience on a murderer's heart: Why not? Then, boldly: Thousands of pairs of gloves from the leading markets of the world at astounding prices. Thousands of pairs of stockings from the most reliable manufacturers of the universe at sensational reductions. Finally the question recurred, but flung now like a challenging gauntlet in the lists: Why not order today?

"I'm the press representative of Lynn and Sedley." He gave a little wave of his beautiful hand. "To what base uses . . ."

Philip went on asking the regulation questions, some a mere matter of routine, others artfully devised to lead the patient to discover things which he might be expected to desire to conceal.

"Have you ever lived abroad?" asked Philip.

"I was in Spain for eleven years."

"What were you doing there?"

"I was secretary of the English water company at Toledo."

Philip remembered that Clutton had spent some months in Toledo, and the journalist's answer made him look at him with more interest; but he felt it would be improper to show this: it was necessary to preserve the distance between the hospital patient and the staff. When he had finished his examination he went on to other beds.

Thorpe Athelny's illness was not grave, and, though remaining very yellow, he soon felt much better: he stayed in bed only because the physician thought he should be kept under observation till certain reactions became normal. One day, on entering the ward, Philip noticed that Athelny, pencil in hand, was reading a book. He put it down when Philip came to his bed.

"May I see what you're reading?" asked Philip, who could never pass a book without looking at it.

Philip took it up and saw that it was a volume of Spanish verse, the poems of San Juan de la Cruz, and as he opened it a sheet of paper fell out. Philip picked it up and noticed that verse was written upon it.

"You're not going to tell me you've been occupying your leisure in writing poetry? That's a most improper proceeding in a hospital patient."

"I was trying to do some translations. D'you know Spanish?"

"No."

"Well, you know all about San Juan de la Cruz, don't you?"

"I don't indeed."

"He was one of the Spanish mystics. He's one of the best poets they've ever had. I thought it would be worth while translating him into English."

"May I look at your translation?"

"It's very rough," said Athelny, but he gave it to Philip with an alacrity which suggested that he was eager for him to read it.

It was written in pencil, in a fine but very peculiar handwriting, which was hard to read: it was just like black letter.

"Doesn't it take you an awful time to write like that? It's wonderful."

"I don't know why handwriting shouldn't be beautiful."

Philip read the first verse:

In an obscure night
With anxious love inflamed
O happy lot!
Forth unobserved I went,
My house being now at rest . . .

Philip looked curiously at Thorpe Athelny. He did not know whether he felt a little shy with him or was attracted by him. He was conscious that his manner had been slightly patronising, and he flushed as it struck him that Athelny might have thought him ridiculous.

"What an unusual name you've got," he remarked, for something to say.

"It's a very old Yorkshire name. Once it took the head of my family a day's hard riding to make the circuit of his estates, but the mighty are fallen. Fast women and slow horses."

He was short-sighted and when he spoke looked at you with a peculiar intensity. He took up his volume of poetry.

"You should read Spanish," he said. "It is a noble tongue. It has not the mellifluousness of Italian, Italian is the language of tenors and organ-grinders, but it has grandeur: it does not ripple like a brook in a garden, but it surges tumultuous like a mighty river in flood."

His grandiloquence amused Philip, but he was sensitive to rhetoric; and he listened with pleasure while Athelny, with picturesque expressions and the fire of a real enthusiasm, described to him the rich delight of reading *Don Quixote* in the original and the music, romantic, limpid, passionate, of the enchanting Calderon.

"I must get on with my work," said Philip presently.

"Oh, forgive me, I forgot. I will tell my wife to bring me a photograph of Toledo, and I will show it you. Come and talk to me when you have the chance. You don't know what a pleasure it gives me."

During the next few days, in moments snatched whenever there was opportunity, Philip's acquaintance with the journalist increased. Thorpe

Athelny was a good talker. He did not say brilliant things, but he talked inspiringly, with an eager vividness which fired the imagination; Philip, living so much in a world of make-believe, found his fancy teeming with new pictures. Athelny had very good manners. He knew much more than Philip, both of the world and of books; he was a much older man; and the readiness of his conversation gave him a certain superiority; but he was in the hospital a recipient of charity, subject to strict rules; and he held himself between the two positions with ease and humour. Once Philip asked him why he had come to the hospital.

"Oh, my principle is to profit by all the benefits that society provides. I take advantage of the age I live in. When I'm ill I get myself patched up in a hospital and I have no false shame, and I send my children to be educated at the board-school."

"Do you really?" said Philip.

"And a capital education they get too, much better than I got at Winchester. How else do you think I could educate them at all? I've got nine. You must come and see them all when I get home again. Will you?"

"I'd like to very much," said Philip.

LXXXVII

TEN days later Thorpe Athelny was well enough to leave the hospital. He gave Philip his address, and Philip promised to dine with him at one o'clock on the following Sunday. Athelny had told him that he lived in a house built by Inigo Jones; he had raved, as he raved over everything, over the balustrade of old oak; and when he came down to open the

door for Philip he made him at once admire the elegant carving of the lintel. It was a shabby house, badly needing a coat of paint, but with the dignity of its period, in a little street between Chancery Lane and Holborn, which had once been fashionable but was now little better than a slum: there was a plan to pull it down in order to put up handsome offices;

meanwhile the rents were small, and Athelny was able to get the two upper floors at a price which suited his income. Philip had not seen him up before and was surprised at his small size; he was not more than five feet and five inches high. He was dressed fantastically in blue linen trousers of the sort worn by working men in France, and a very old brown velvet coat; he wore a bright red sash round his waist, a low collar, and for tie a flowing bow of the kind used by the comic Frenchman in the pages of *Punch*. He greeted Philip with enthusiasm. He began talking at once of the house and passed his hand lovingly over the balusters.

"Look at it, feel it, it's like silk. What a miracle of grace! And in five years the house-breaker will sell it for firewood."

He insisted on taking Philip into a room on the first floor, where a man in shirt sleeves, a blousy woman, and three children were having their Sunday dinner.

"I've just brought this gentleman in to show him your ceiling. Did you ever see anything so wonderful? How are you, Mrs. Hodgson? This is Mr. Carey, who looked after me when I was in the hospital."

"Come in, sir," said the man. "Any friend of Mr. Athelny's is welcome. Mr. Athelny shows the ceiling to all his friends. And it don't matter what we're doing, if we're in bed or if I'm 'aving a wash, in 'e comes."

Philip could see that they looked upon Athelny as a little queer; but they liked him none the less and they listened open-mouthed while he discoursed with his impetuous fluency on the beauty of the seventeenth-century ceiling.

"What a crime to pull this down, eh, Hodgson? You're an influential citizen, why don't you write to the papers and protest?"

The man in shirt sleeves gave a laugh and said to Philip:

"Mr. Athelny will 'ave his little joke. They do say these 'ouses are that insanitary, it's not safe to live in them."

"Sanitation be damned, give me art," cried Athelny. "I've got nine children and they thrive on bad drains. No, no, I'm not going to take any risk. None of your new-fangled notions for me! When I move from here I'm going to make sure the drains are bad before I take anything."

There was a knock at the door, and a little fair-haired girl opened it.

"Daddy, mummy says, do stop talking and come and eat your dinner."

"This is my third daughter," said Athelny, pointing to her with a dramatic forefinger. "She is called Maria del Pilar, but she answers more willingly to the name of Jane. Jane, your nose wants blowing."

"I haven't got a hanky, daddy."

"Tut, tut, child," he answered, as he produced a vast, brilliant bandanna, "what do you suppose the Almighty gave you fingers for?"

They went upstairs, and Philip was taken into a room with walls panelled in dark oak. In the middle was a narrow table of teak on trestle legs, with two supporting bars of iron, of the kind called in Spain *mesa de hieraje*. They were to dine there, for two places were laid, and there were two large arm-chairs, with broad flat arms of oak and leathern backs, and leathern seats. They were severe, elegant, and uncomfortable. The only other piece of furniture was a *bargueño*, elaborately ornamented with gilt iron-work, on a stand of ecclesiastical design roughly but very finely carved. There stood on this two or three lustre plates, much broken but rich in colour; and on the walls were old masters of the Spanish school in beautiful though dilapidated frames: though gruesome in subject, ruined by age and bad treatment, and second rate in their conception, they had a glow of passion. There was nothing in the room of any value, but the effect was lovely. It was magnificent and yet austere. Philip felt that it offered the very spirit of old Spain. Athelny was in the middle of showing him the inside of the *bargueño,* with its beautiful ornamentation and secret drawers, when a tall girl, with two plaits of bright brown hair hanging down her back, came in.

"Mother says dinner's ready and waiting and I'm to bring it in as soon as you sit down."

"Come and shake hands with Mr. Carey, Sally." He turned to Philip. "Isn't she enormous? She's my eldest. How old are you, Sally?"

"Fifteen, father, come next June."

"I christened her Maria del Sol, because she was my first child and I dedicated her to the glorious sun of Castile; but her mother calls her Sally and her brother Pudding-Face."

The girl smiled shyly, she had even, white teeth, and blushed. She was well set-up, tall for her age, with pleasant gray eyes and a broad forehead. She had red cheeks.

"Go and tell your mother to come in and shake hands with Mr. Carey before he sits down."

"Mother says she'll come in after dinner. She hasn't washed herself yet."

"Then we'll go in and see her ourselves. He mustn't eat the Yorkshire pudding till he's shaken the hand that made it."

Philip followed his host into the kitchen. It was small and much overcrowded. There had been a lot of noise, but it stopped as soon as the stranger entered. There was a large table in the middle and round it, eager for dinner, were seated Athelny's children. A woman was standing at the oven, taking out baked potatoes one by one.

"Here's Mr. Carey, Betty," said Athelny.

"Fancy bringing him in here. What will he think?"

She wore a dirty apron, and the sleeves of her cotton dress were turned up above her elbows; she had curling pins in her hair. Mrs. Athelny was a large woman, a good three inches taller than her husband, fair, with blue eyes and a kindly expression; she had been a handsome creature, but advancing years and the bearing of many children had made her fat and blousy; her blue eyes had become pale, her skin was coarse and red, the colour had gone out of her hair. She straightened herself, wiped her hand on her apron, and held it out.

"You're welcome, sir," she said, in a slow voice, with an accent that seemed oddly familiar to Philip. "Athelny said you was very kind to him in the 'orspital."

"Now you must be introduced to the live stock," said Athelny. "That is Thorpe," he pointed to a chubby boy with curly hair, "he is my eldest son, heir to the title, estates, and responsibilities of the family. There is Athelstan, Harold, Edward." He pointed with his forefinger to three smaller boys, all rosy, healthy, and smiling, though when they felt Philip's smiling eyes upon them they looked shyly down at their plates. "Now the girls in order: Maria del Sol . . ."

"Pudding-Face," said one of the small boys.

"Your sense of humour is rudimentary, my son. Maria de los Mercedes, Maria del Pilar, Maria de la Concepcion, Maria del Rosario."

"I call them Sally, Molly, Connie, Rosie, and Jane," said Mrs. Athelny. "Now, Athelny, you go into your own room and I'll send you your dinner. I'll let the children come in afterwards for a bit when I've washed them."

"My dear, if I'd had the naming of you I should have called you Maria of the Soapsuds. You're always torturing these wretched brats with soap."

"You go first, Mr. Carey, or I shall never get him to sit down and eat his dinner."

Athelny and Philip installed themselves in the great monkish chairs, and Sally brought them in two plates of beef, Yorkshire pudding, baked potatoes, and cabbage. Athelny took sixpence out of his pocket and sent her for a jug of beer.

"I hope you didn't have the table laid here on my account," said Philip. "I should have been quite happy to eat with the children."

"Oh no, I always have my meals by myself. I like these antique customs. I don't think that women ought to sit down at table with men. It ruins conversation and I'm sure it's very bad for them. It puts ideas in their heads, and women are never at ease with themselves when they have ideas."

Both host and guest ate with a hearty appetite.

"Did you ever taste such Yorkshire pudding? No one can make it like my wife. That's the advantage of not marrying a lady. You noticed she wasn't a lady, didn't you?"

It was an awkward question, and Philip did not know how to answer it.

"I never thought about it," he said lamely.

Athelny laughed. He had a pe-culiarly joyous laugh.

"No, she's not a lady, nor anything like it. Her father was a farmer, and she's never bothered about aitches in her life. We've had twelve children and nine of them are alive. I tell her it's about time she stopped, but she's an obstinate woman, she's got into the habit of it now, and I don't believe she'll be satisfied till she's had twenty."

At that moment Sally came in with the beer, and, having poured out a glass for Philip, went to the other side of the table to pour some out for her father. He put his hand round her waist.

"Did you ever see such a handsome, strapping girl? Only fifteen and she might be twenty. Look at her cheeks. She's never had a day's illness in her life. It'll be a lucky man who marries her, won't it, Sally?"

Sally listened to all this with a slight, slow smile, not much embarrassed, for she was accustomed to her father's outbursts, but with an easy modesty which was very attractive.

"Don't let your dinner get cold, father," she said, drawing herself away from his arm. "You'll call when you're ready for your pudding, won't you?"

They were left alone, and Athelny lifted the pewter tankard to his lips. He drank long and deep.

"My word, is there anything better than English beer?" he said. "Let us thank God for simple pleasures, roast beef and rice pudding, a good appetite and beer. I was married to a lady once. My God! Don't marry a lady, my boy."

Philip laughed. He was exhilarated by the scene, the funny little man in his odd clothes, the panelled room and the Spanish furniture, the English fare: the whole thing had an exquisite incongruity.

"You laugh, my boy, you can't imagine marrying beneath you. You want a wife who's an intellectual equal. Your head is crammed full of ideas of comradeship. Stuff and nonsense, my boy! A man doesn't want to talk politics to his wife, and what do you think I care for Betty's views upon the Differential Calculus? A man wants a wife who can cook his dinner and look after his children. I've tried both and I know. Let's have the pudding in."

He clapped his hands and presently Sally came. When she took away the plates, Philip wanted to get up and help her, but Athelny stopped him.

"Let her alone, my boy. She doesn't want you to fuss about, do you, Sally? And she won't think it rude of you to sit still while she waits upon you. She don't care a damn for chivalry, do you, Sally?"

"No, father," answered Sally demurely.

"Do you know what I'm talking about, Sally?"

"No, father. But you know mother doesn't like you to swear."

Athelny laughed boisterously. Sally brought them plates of rice pudding, rich, creamy, and luscious. Athelny attacked his with gusto.

"One of the rules of this house is that Sunday dinner should never alter. It is a ritual. Roast beef and rice pudding for fifty Sundays in the year. On Easter Sunday lamb and green peas, and at Michaelmas roast goose and apple sauce. Thus we preserve the traditions of our people. When Sally marries she will forget many of the wise things I have taught her, but she will never forget that if you want to be good and happy you must eat on Sundays roast beef and rice pudding."

"You'll call when you're ready for cheese," said Sally impassively.

"D'you know the legend of the halcyon?" said Athelny: Philip was growing used to his rapid leaping from one subect to another. "When the kingfisher, flying over the sea, is exhausted, his mate places herself beneath him and bears him along upon her stronger wings. That is what a man wants in a wife, the halcyon. I lived with my first wife for three years. She was a lady, she had fifteen hundred a year, and we used to give nice little dinner parties in our little red brick house in Kensington. She was a charming woman; they all said so, the barristers and their wives who dined with us, and the literary stockbrokers, and the budding politicians; oh, she was a charming woman. She made me go to church in a silk hat and a frock coat, she took me to classical concerts, and she was very fond of lectures on Sunday afternoon; and she sat down to breakfast every morning at eight-thirty, and if I was late breakfast was cold; and she read the right books, admired the right pictures, and adored the right music. My God, how that woman bored me! She is charming still, and she lives in the little red brick house in Kensington, with Morris papers and Whistler's etchings on the walls, and gives the same nice little dinner parties, with veal creams and ices from Gunter's, as she did twenty years ago."

Philip did not ask by what means the ill-matched couple had separated, but Athelny told him.

"Betty's not my wife, you know; my wife wouldn't divorce me. The children are bastards, every jack one of them, and are they any the worse for that? Betty was one of the maids in the little red brick house in Kensington. Four or five years ago I was on my uppers, and I had seven children, and I went to my wife and asked her to help me. She said she'd make me an allowance if I'd give Betty up and go abroad. Can you see me giving Betty up? We starved for a while instead. My wife said I loved the gutter. I've degenerated; I've come down in the world; I earn three pounds a week as press agent to a linendraper, and every day I thank God that I'm not in the little red brick house in Kensington."

Sally brought in Cheddar cheese, and Athelny went on with his fluent conversation.

"It's the greatest mistake in the world to think that one needs money to bring up a family. You need money to make them gentlemen and ladies, but I don't want my children to be ladies and gentlemen. Sally's going to earn her living in another year. She's to be apprenticed to a dressmaker, aren't you, Sally? And the boys are going to serve their country. I want them all to go into the Navy; it's a jolly life and a healthy life, good food, good pay, and a pension to end their days on."

Philip lit his pipe. Athelny smoked cigarettes of Havana tobacco, which he rolled himself. Sally cleared away. Philip was reserved, and it embarrassed him to be the recipient of so many confidences. Athelny, with his powerful voice in the diminutive body, with his bombast, with his foreign look, with his emphasis, was an astonishing creature. He reminded Philip a good deal of Cronshaw. He appeared to have the same independence of thought, the same bohemianism, but he had an infinitely more vivacious temperament; his mind was coarser, and he had not that interest in the abstract which made Cronshaw's conversation so captivating. Athelny was very proud of the county family to which he belonged; he showed Philip photographs of an Elizabethan mansion, and told him:

"The Athelnys have lived there for seven centuries, my boy. Ah, if you saw the chimney-pieces and the ceilings!"

There was a cupboard in the wainscoting and from this he took a family tree. He showed it to Philip with child-like satisfaction. It was indeed imposing.

"You see how the family names recur, Thorpe, Athelstan, Harold, Edward; I've used the family names for my sons. And the girls, you see, I've given Spanish names to."

An uneasy feeling came to Philip that possibly the whole story was an elaborate imposture, not told with any base motive, but merely from a wish to impress, startle, and amaze. Athelny had told him that he was at Winchester; but Philip, sensitive to differences of manner, did not feel that his host had the characteristics of a man educated at a great public school. While he pointed out the great alliances which his ancestors had formed, Philip amused himself by wondering whether Athelny was not the son of some tradesman in Winchester, auctioneer or coal-merchant, and whether a similarity of surname was not his only connection with the ancient family whose tree he was displaying.

LXXXVIII

THERE was a knock at the door and a troop of children came in. They were clean and tidy now; their faces shone with soap, and their hair was plastered down; they were going to Sunday school under Sally's charge. Athelny joked with them in his dramatic, exuberant fashion, and you could see that he was devoted to them all. His pride in their good health and their good looks was touching. Philip felt that they were a little shy in his presence, and when their father sent them off they fled from the room in evident relief. In a few minutes Mrs. Athelny appeared. She had taken her hair out of the curling pins and now wore an elaborate fringe. She had on a plain black dress, a hat with cheap flowers, and was forcing her hands, red and coarse from much work, into black kid gloves.

"I'm going to church, Athelny," she said. "There's nothing you'll be wanting, is there?"

"Only your prayers, my Betty."

"They won't do you much good, you're too far gone for that," she smiled. Then, turning to Philip, she drawled: "I can't get him to go to church. He's no better than an atheist."

"Doesn't she look like Rubens' second wife?" cried Athelny. "Wouldn't she look splendid in a seventeenth-century costume? That's the sort of wife to marry, my boy. Look at her."

"I believe you'd talk the hind leg off a donkey, Athelny," she answered calmly.

She succeeded in buttoning her gloves, but before she went she turned to Philip with a kindly, slightly embarrassed smile.

"You'll stay to tea, won't you? Athelny likes someone to talk to, and it's not often he gets anybody who's clever enough."

"Of course he'll stay to tea," said Athelny. Then when his wife had gone: "I make a point of the children going to Sunday school, and I like Betty to go to church. I think women ought to be religious. I don't believe myself, but I like women and children to."

Philip, strait-laced in matters of truth, was a little shocked by this airy attitude.

"But how can you look on while your children are being taught things which you don't think are true?"

"If they're beautiful I don't much mind if they're not true. It's asking a great deal that things should appeal to your reason as well as to your sense of the æsthetic. I wanted Betty to become a Roman Catholic, I should have liked to see her converted in a crown of paper flowers, but she's hopelessly Protestant. Besides, religion is a matter of temperament; you will believe anything if you have the religious turn of mind, and if you haven't it doesn't matter what beliefs were instilled into you, you will grow out of them. Perhaps religion is the best school of morality. It is like one of those drugs you gentlemen use in medicine which carries another in solution: it is of no efficacy in itself, but enables the other to be absorbed. You take your morality because it is combined with religion; you lose the religion and the morality stays behind.

A man is more likely to be a good man if he has learned goodness through the love of God than through a perusal of Herbert Spencer."

This was contrary to all Philip's ideas. He still looked upon Christianity as a degrading bondage that must be cast away at any cost; it was connected subconsciously in his mind with the dreary services in the cathedral at Tercanbury, and the long hours of boredom in the cold church at Blackstable; and the morality of which Athelny spoke was to him no more than a part of the religion which a halting intelligence preserved, when it had laid aside the beliefs which alone made it reasonable. But while he was meditating a reply Athelny, more interested in hearing himself speak than in discussion, broke into a tirade upon Roman Catholicism. For him it was an essential part of Spain; and Spain meant much to him, because he had escaped to it from the conventionality which during his married life he had found so irksome. With large gestures and in the emphatic tone which made what he said so striking, Athelny described to Philip the Spanish cathedrals with their vast dark spaces, the massive gold of the altar-pieces, and the sumptuous iron-work, gilt and faded, the air laden with incense, the silence: Philip almost saw the Canons in their short surplices of lawn, the acolytes in red, passing from the sacristy to the choir; he almost heard the monotonous chanting of vespers. The names which Athelny mentioned, Avila, Tarragona, Saragossa, Segovia, Cordoba, were like trumpets in his heart. He seemed to see the great gray piles of granite set in old Spanish towns amid a landscape tawny, wild, and windswept.

"I've always thought I should love to go to Seville," he said casually, when Athelny, with one hand dramatically uplifted, paused for a moment.

"Seville!" cried Athelny. "No, no, don't go there. Seville: it brings to the mind girls dancing with castanets, singing in gardens by the Guadalquivir, bull-fights, orange-blossom, mantillas, *mantones de Manila*. It is the Spain of comic opera and Montmartre. Its facile charm can offer permanent entertainment only to an intelligence which is superficial. Théophile Gautier got out of Seville all that it has to offer. We who come after him can only repeat his sensations. He put large fat hands on the obvious and there is nothing but the obvious there; and it is all finger-marked and frayed. Murillo is its painter."

Athelny got up from his chair, walked over to the Spanish cabinet, let down the front with its great gilt hinges and gorgeous lock, and displayed a series of little drawers. He took out a bundle of photographs.

"Do you know El Greco?" he asked.

"Oh, I remember one of the men in Paris was awfully impressed by him."

"El Greco was the painter of Toledo. Betty couldn't find the photograph I wanted to show you. It's a picture that El Greco painted of the city he loved, and it's truer than any photograph. Come and sit at the table."

Philip dragged his chair forward, and Athelny set the photograph before him. He looked at it curiously, for a long time, in silence. He stretched out his hand for other photographs, and Athelny passed them to him. He had never before seen the work of that enigmatic master; and at the first glance he was bothered by the arbitrary drawing: the figures were extraordinarily elongated; the heads were very small; the attitudes were extravagant. This was not realism, and yet, and yet even in the photographs you had the impression of a troubling reality. Athelny was describing eagerly, with vivid phrases, but Philip only heard vaguely what he said. He was puzzled. He was curiously moved. These pictures seemed to offer some meaning to him, but he did not know what the meaning was. There were portraits of men with large, melancholy eyes which seemed to say you knew not what; there were long monks in the Franciscan habit or in the Dominican, with distraught faces, making gestures whose sense escaped you; there was an Assumption of the Virgin; there was a Crucifixion in which the painter by some magic of feeling had been able to suggest that the flesh of Christ's dead body was not human flesh only but divine; and there was an Ascension in which the Saviour seemed to surge up towards the empyrean and yet to stand upon the air as steadily as though it were solid ground: the uplifted arms of the Apostles, the sweep of their draperies, their ecstatic gestures, gave an impression of exultation and of holy joy. The background of nearly all was the sky by night, the dark night of the soul, with wild clouds swept by strange winds of hell and lit luridly by an uneasy moon.

"I've seen that sky in Toledo over and over again," said Athelny. "I have an idea that when first El Greco came to the city it was by such a night, and it made so vehement an impression upon him that he could never get away from it."

Philip remembered how Clutton had been affected by this strange master, whose work he now saw for the first time. He thought that Clutton was the most interesting of all the people he had known in Paris. His sardonic manner, his hostile aloofness, had made it difficult to know him; but

it seemed to Philip, looking back, that there had been in him a tragic force, which sought vainly to express itself in painting. He was a man of unusual character, mystical after the fashion of a time that had no leaning to mysticism, who was impatient with life because he found himself unable to say the things which the obscure impulses of his heart suggested. His intellect was not fashioned to the uses of the spirit. It was not surprising that he felt a deep sympathy with the Greek who had devised a new technique to express the yearnings of his soul. Philip looked again at the series of portraits of Spanish gentlemen, with ruffles and pointed beards, their faces pale against the sober black of their clothes and the darkness of the background. El Greco was the painter of the soul; and these gentlemen, wan and wasted, not by exhaustion but by restraint, with their tortured minds, seem to walk unaware of the beauty of the world; for their eyes look only in their hearts, and they are dazzled by the glory of the unseen. No painter has shown more pitilessly that the world is but a place of passage. The souls of the men he painted speak their strange longings through their eyes: their senses are miraculously acute, not for sounds and odours and colour, but for the very subtle sensations of the soul. The noble walks with the monkish heart within him, and his eyes see things which saints in their cells see too, and he is unastounded. His lips are not lips that smile.

Philip, silent still, returned to the photograph of Toledo, which seemed to him the most arresting picture of them all. He could not take his eyes off it. He felt strangely that he was on the threshold of some new discovery in life. He was tremulous with a sense of adventure. He thought for an instant of the love that had consumed him: love seemed very trivial beside the excitement which now leaped in his heart. The picture he looked at was a long one, with houses crowded upon a hill; in one corner a boy was holding a large map of the town; in another was a classical figure representing the river Tabus; and in the sky was the Virgin surrounded by angels. It was a landscape alien to all Philip's notion, for he had lived in circles that worshipped exact realism; and yet here again, strangely to himself, he felt a reality greater than any achieved by the masters in whose steps humbly he had sought to walk. He heard Athelny say that the representation was so precise that when the citizens of Toledo came to look at the picture they recognised their houses. The painter had painted exactly what he saw but he had seen with the eyes of the spirit. There was something unearthly in that city of pale gray. It was a city of the soul seen by a wan light that was neither that of night nor day. It stood on a green hill, but of a green not of this world, and it was surrounded by massive walls and bastions to be stormed by no machines or engines of man's invention, but by prayer and fasting, by contrite sighs and by mortifications of the flesh. It was a stronghold of God. Those gray houses were made of no stone known to masons, there was something terrifying in their aspect, and you did not know what men might live in them. You might walk through the streets and be unamazed to find them all deserted, and yet not empty; for you felt a presence invisible and yet manifest to every inner sense. It was a mystical city in which the imagination faltered like one who steps out of the light into darkness; the soul walked naked to and fro, knowing the unknowable, and conscious strangely of experience,

intimate but inexpressible, of the absolute. And without surprise, in that blue sky, real with a reality that not the eye but the soul confesses, with its rack of light clouds driven by strange breezes, like the cries and the sighs of lost souls, you saw the Blessed Virgin with a gown of red and a cloak of blue, surrounded by winged angels. Philip felt that the inhabitants of that city would have seen the apparition without astonishment, reverent and thankful, and have gone their ways.

Athelny spoke of the mystical writers of Spain, of Teresa de Avila, San Juan de la Cruz, Fray Diego de Leon; in all of them was that passion for the unseen which Philip felt in the pictures of El Greco: they seemed to have the power to touch the incorporeal and see the invisible. They were Spaniards of their age, in whom were tremulous all the mighty exploits of a great nation: their fancies were rich with the glories of America and the green islands of the Caribbean Sea; in their veins was the power that had come from age-long battling with the Moor; they were proud, for they were masters of the world; and they felt in themselves the wide distances, the tawny wastes, the snow-capped mountains of Castile, the sunshine and the blue sky, and the flowering plains of Andalusia. Life was passionate and manifold, and because it offered so much they felt a restless yearning for something more; because they were human they were unsatisfied; and they threw this eager vitality of theirs into a vehement striving after the ineffable. Athelny was not displeased to find someone to whom he could read the translations with which for some time he had amused his leisure; and in his fine, vibrating voice he recited the canticle of the Soul and Christ her lover, the lovely poem which begins with the words *en una noche oscura,* and the *noche serena* of Fray Luis de Leon. He had translated them quite simply, not without skill, and he had found words which at all events suggested the rough-hewn grandeur of the original. The pictures of El Greco explained them, and they explained the pictures.

Philip had cultivated a certain disdain for idealism. He had always had a passion for life, and the idealism he had come across seemed to him for the most part a cowardly shrinking from it. The idealist withdrew himself, because he could not suffer the jostling of the human crowd; he had not the strength to fight and so called the battle vulgar; he was vain, and since his fellows would not take him at his own estimate, consoled himself with despising his fellows. For Philip his type was Hayward, fair, languid, too fat now and rather bald, still cherishing the remains of his good looks and still delicately proposing to do exquisite things in the uncertain future; and at the back of this were whiskey and vulgar amours of the street. It was in reaction from what Hayward represented that Philip clamoured for life as it stood; sordidness, vice, deformity, did not offend him; he declared that he wanted man in his nakedness; and he rubbed his hands when an instance came before him of meanness, cruelty, selfishness, or lust: that was the real thing. In Paris he had learned that there was neither ugliness nor beauty, but only truth: the search after beauty was sentimental. Had he not painted an advertisement of *chocolat Menier* in a landscape in order to escape from the tyranny of prettiness?

But here he seemed to divine something new. He had been coming to it, all hesitating, for some time, but only now was conscious of the fact; he felt himself on the brink of a discovery. He felt vaguely that here was something better than the realism which he had adored; but certainly it was not the bloodless idealism which stepped aside from life in weakness; it was too strong; it was virile; it accepted life in all its vivacity, ugliness and beauty, squalor and heroism; it was realism still; but it was realism carried to some higher pitch, in which facts were transformed by the more vivid light in which they were seen. He seemed to see things more profoundly through the grave eyes of those dead noblemen of Castile; and the gestures of the saints, which at first had seemed wild and distorted, appeared to have some mysterious significance. But he could not tell what that significance was. It was like a message which it was very important for him to receive, but it was given him in an unknown tongue, and he could not understand. He was always seeking for a meaning in life, and here it seemed to him that a meaning was offered; but it was obscure and vague. He was profoundly troubled. He saw what looked like the truth as by flashes of lightning on a dark, stormy night you might see a mountain range. He seemed to see that a man need not leave his life to chance, but that his will was powerful; he seemed to see that self-control might be as passionate and as active as the surrender to passion; he seemed to see that the inward life might be as manifold, as varied, as rich with experience, as the life of one who conquered realms and explored unknown lands.

LXXXIX

THE conversation between Philip and Athelny was broken into by a clatter up the stairs. Athelny opened the door for the children coming back from Sunday school, and with laughter and shouting they came in. Gaily he asked them what they had learned. Sally appeared for a moment, with instructions from her mother that father was to amuse the children while she got tea ready; and Athelny began to tell them one of Hans Andersen's stories. They were not shy children, and they quickly came to the conclusion that Philip was not formidable. Jane came and stood by him and presently settled herself on his knees. It was the first time that Philip in his lonely life had been present in a family circle: his eyes smiled as they rested on the fair children engrossed in the fairy tale. The life of his new friend, eccentric as it appeared at first glance, seemed now to have the beauty of perfect naturalness. Sally came in once more.

"Now then, children, tea's ready," she said.

Jane slipped off Philip's knees, and they all went back to the kitchen. Sally began to lay the cloth on the long Spanish table.

"Mother says, shall she come and have tea with you?" she asked. "I can give the children their tea."

"Tell your mother that we shall be proud and honoured if she will favour us with her company," said Athelny.

It seemed to Philip that he could never say anything without an oratorical flourish.

"Then I'll lay for her," said Sally.

She came back again in a moment with a tray on which were a cottage loaf, a slab of butter, and a jar of strawberry jam. While she placed the things on the table her father chaffed her. He said it was quite time she was walking out; he told Philip that she was very proud, and would have nothing to do with aspirants to that honour who lined up at the door, two by two, outside the Sunday school and craved the honour of escorting her home.

"You do talk, father," said Sally, with her slow, good-natured smile.

"You wouldn't think to look at her that a tailor's assistant has enlisted in the army because she would not say how d'you do to him and an electrical engineer, an electrical engineer, mind you, has taken to drink because she refused to share her hymn-book with him in church. I shudder to think what will happen when she puts her hair up."

"Mother'll bring the tea along herself," said Sally.

"Sally never pays any attention to me," laughed Athelny, looking at her with fond, proud eyes. "She goes about her business indifferent to wars, revolutions, and cataclysms. What a wife she'll make to an honest man!"

Mrs. Athelny brought in the tea. She sat down and proceeded to cut bread and butter. It amused Philip to see that she treated her husband as though he were a child. She spread jam for him and cut up the bread and butter into convenient slices for him to eat. She had taken off her hat; and in her Sunday dress, which seemed a little tight for her, she looked like one of the farmers' wives whom Philip used to call on sometimes with his uncle when he was a small boy. Then he knew why the sound of her voice was familiar to him. She spoke just like the people round Blackstable.

"What part of the country d'you come from?" he asked her.

"I'm a Kentish woman. I come from Ferne."

"I thought as much. My uncle's Vicar of Blackstable."

"That's a funny thing now," she said. "I was wondering in church just now whether you was any connection of Mr. Carey. Many's the time I've seen 'im. A cousin of mine married Mr. Barker of Roxley Farm, over by Blackstable Church, and I used to go and stay there often when I was a girl. Isn't that a funny thing now?"

She looked at him with a new interest, and a brightness came into her faded eyes. She asked him whether he knew Ferne. It was a pretty village about ten miles across country from Blackstable, and the Vicar had come over sometimes to Blackstable for the harvest thanksgiving. She mentioned names of various farmers in the neighbourhood. She was delighted to talk again of the country in which her youth was spent, and it was a pleasure to her to recall scenes and people that had remained in her memory with the tenacity peculiar to her class. It gave Philip a queer sensation too. A breath of the country-side seemed to be wafted into that panelled room in the middle of London. He seemed to see the fat Kentish fields with their stately elms; and his nostrils dilated with the scent of the air; it is laden with the salt of the North Sea, and that makes it keen and sharp.

Philip did not leave the Athelnys' till ten o'clock. The children came in to say good-night at eight and quite naturally put up their faces for Philip to kiss. His heart went out to them. Sally only held out her hand.

"Sally never kisses gentlemen till she's seen them twice," said her father.

"You must ask me again then," said Philip.

"You mustn't take any notice of what father says," remarked Sally, with a smile.

"She's a most self-possessed young woman," added her parent.

They had supper of bread and cheese and beer, while Mrs. Athelny was putting the children to bed; and when Philip went into the kitchen to bid her good-night (she had been sitting there, resting herself and reading *The Weekly Despatch*) she invited him cordially to come again.

"There's always a good dinner on Sundays so long as Athelny's in work," she said, "and it's a charity to come and talk to him."

On the following Saturday Philip received a postcard from Athelny saying that they were expecting him to dinner next day; but fearing their means were not such that Mr. Athelny would desire him to accept, Philip wrote back that he would only come to tea. He bought a large plum cake so that his entertainment should cost nothing. He found the whole family glad to see him, and the cake completed his conquest of the children. He insisted that they should all have tea together in the kitchen, and the meal was noisy and hilarious.

Soon Philip got into the habit of going to Athelny's every Sunday. He became a great favourite with the children, because he was simple and unaffected and because it was so plain that he was fond of them. As soon as they heard his ring at the door one of them popped a head out of window to make sure it was he, and then they all rushed downstairs tumultuously to let him in. They flung themselves into his arms. At tea they fought for the privilege of sitting next to him. Soon they began to call him Uncle Philip.

Athelny was very communicative, and little by little Philip learned the various stages of his life. He had followed many occupations, and it occurred to Philip that he managed to make a mess of everything he attempted. He had been on a tea plantation in Ceylon and a traveller in America for Italian wines; his secretaryship of the water company in Toledo had lasted longer than any of his employments; he had been a journalist and for some time had worked as police-court reporter for an evening paper; he had been sub-editor of a paper in the Midlands and editor of another on the Riviera. From all his occupations he had gathered amusing anecdotes, which he told with a keen pleasure in his own powers of entertainment. He had read a great deal, chiefly delighting in books which were unusual; and he poured forth his stores of abstruse knowledge with childlike enjoyment of the amazement of his hearers. Three or four years before abject poverty had driven him to take the job of press-representative to a large firm of drapers; and though he felt the work unworthy his abilities, which he rated highly, the firmness of his wife and the needs of his family had made him stick to it.

XC

WHEN he left the Athelnys' Philip walked down Chancery Lane and along the Strand to get a 'bus at the top of Parliament Street. One Sunday, when he had known them about six weeks, he did this as usual, but he found the Kennington 'bus full. It was June, but it had rained during the day and the night was raw and cold. He walked up to Piccadilly Circus in order to get a seat; the 'bus waited at the fountain, and when it arrived there seldom had more than two or three people in it. This service ran every quarter of an hour, and he had some time to wait. He looked idly at the crowd. The public-houses were closing, and there were many people about. His mind was busy with the ideas Athelny had the charming gift of suggesting.

Suddenly his heart stood still. He saw Mildred. He had not thought of her for weeks. She was crossing over from the corner of Shaftesbury Avenue and stopped at the shelter till a string of cabs passed by. She was watching her opportunity and had no eyes for anything else. She wore a large black straw hat with a mass of feathers on it and a black silk dress; at that time it was fashionable for women to wear trains; the road was clear, and Mildred crossed, her skirt trailing on the ground, and walked down Piccadilly. Philip, his heart beating excitedly, followed her. He did not wish to speak to her, but he wondered where she was going at that hour; he wanted to get a look at her face. She walked slowly along and turned down Air Street and so got through into Regent Street. She walked up again towards the Circus. Philip was puzzled. He could not make out what she was doing. Perhaps she was waiting for somebody, and he felt a great curiosity to know who it was. She overtook a short man in a bowler hat, who was strolling very slowly in the same direction as herself; she gave him a sidelong glance as she passed. She walked a few steps more till she came to Swan and Edgar's, then stopped and waited, facing the road. When the man came up she smiled. The man stared at her for a moment, turned away his head, and sauntered on. Then Philip understood.

He was overwhelmed with horror. For a moment he felt such a weakness in his legs that he could hardly stand; then he walked after her quickly; he touched her on the arm.

"Mildred."

She turned round with a violent start. He thought that she reddened, but in the obscurity he could not see very well. For a while they stood and looked at one another without speaking. At last she said:

"Fancy seeing you!"

He did not know what to answer; he was horribly shaken; and the phrases that chased one another through his brain seemed incredibly melodramatic.

"It's awful," he gasped, almost to himself.

She did not say anything more, she turned away from him, and looked down at the pavement. He felt his face was distorted with misery.

"Isn't there anywhere we can go and talk?"

"I don't want to talk," she said sullenly. "Leave me alone, can't you?"

The thought struck him that perhaps she was in urgent need of money and could not afford to go away at that hour.

"I've got a couple of sovereigns on me if you're hard up," he blurted out.

"I don't know what you mean. I was just walking along here on my way back to my lodgings. I expected to meet one of the girls from where I work."

"For God's sake don't lie now," he said.

Then he saw that she was crying, and he repeated his question.

"Can't we go and talk somewhere? Can't I come back to your rooms?"

"No, you can't do that," she sobbed. "I'm not allowed to take gentlemen in there. If you like I'll meet you tomorrow."

He felt certain that she would not keep an appointment. He was not going to let her go.

"No. You must take me somewhere now."

"Well, there is a room I know, but they'll charge six shillings for it."

"I don't mind that. Where is it?"

She gave him the address, and he called a cab. They drove to a shabby street beyond the British Museum in the neighbourhood of the Gray's Inn Road, and she stopped the cab at the corner.

"They don't like you to drive up to the door," she said.

They were the first words either of them had spoken since getting into the cab. They walked a few yards and Mildred knocked three times, sharply, at a door. Philip noticed in the fan-light a cardboard on which was an announcement that apartments were to let. The door was opened quietly, and an elderly, tall woman let them in. She gave Philip a stare and then spoke to Mildred in an undertone. Mildred led Philip along a passage to a room at the back. It was quite dark; she asked him for a match, and lit the gas; there was no globe, and the gas flared shrilly. Philip saw that he was in a dingy little bed-room with a suite of furniture painted to look like pine much too large for it; the lace curtains were very dirty; the grate was hidden by a large paper fan. Mildred sank on the chair which stood by the side of the chimney-piece. Philip sat on the edge of the bed. He felt ashamed. He saw now that Mildred's cheeks were thick with rouge, her eyebrows were blackened; but she looked thin and ill, and the red on her cheeks exaggerated the greenish pallor of her skin. She stared at the paper fan in a listless fashion. Philip could not think what to say, and he had a choking in his throat as if he were going to cry. He covered his eyes with his hands.

"My God, it is awful," he groaned.

"I don't know what you've got to fuss about. I should have thought you'd have been rather pleased."

Philip did not answer, and in a moment she broke into a sob.

"You don't think I do it because I like it, do you?"

"Oh, my dear," he cried. "I'm so sorry, I'm so awfully sorry."

"That'll do me a fat lot of good."

Again Philip found nothing to say. He was desperately afraid of saying anything which she might take for a reproach or a sneer.

"Where's the baby?" he asked at last.

"I've got her with me in London. I hadn't got the money to keep her on at Brighton, so I had to take her. I've got a room up Highbury way. I told them I was on the stage. It's a long way to have to come down to the West End every day, but it's a rare job to find anyone who'll let to ladies at all."

"Wouldn't they take you back at the shop?"

"I couldn't get any work to do anywhere. I walked my legs off looking for work. I did get a job once, but I was off for a week because I was queer, and when I went back they said they didn't want me any more. You can't blame them either, can you? Them places, they can't afford to have girls that aren't strong."

"You don't look very well now," said Philip.

"I wasn't fit to come out tonight, but I couldn't help myself, I wanted the money. I wrote to Emil and told him I was broke, but he never even answered the letter."

"You might have written to me."

"I didn't like to, not after what happened, and I didn't want you to know I was in difficulties. I shouldn't have been surprised if you'd just told me I'd only got what I deserved."

"You don't know me very well, do you, even now?"

For a moment he remembered all the anguish he had suffered on her account, and he was sick with the recollection of his pain. But it was no more than recollection. When he looked at her he knew that he no longer loved her. He was very sorry for her, but he was glad to be free. Watching her gravely, he asked himself why he had been so besotted with passion for her.

"You're a gentleman in every sense of the word," she said. "You're the only one I've ever met." She paused for a minute and then flushed. "I hate asking you, Philip, but can you spare me anything?"

"It's lucky I've got some money on me. I'm afraid I've only got two pounds."

He gave her the sovereigns.

"I'll pay you back, Philip."

"Oh, that's all right," he smiled. "You needn't worry."

He had said nothing that he wanted to say. They had talked as if the whole thing were natural; and it looked as though she would go now, back to the horror of her life, and he would be able to do nothing to prevent it. She had got up to take the money, and they were both standing.

"Am I keeping you?" she asked. "I

suppose you want to be getting home."

"No, I'm in no hurry," he answered.

"I'm glad to have a chance of sitting down."

Those words, with all they implied, tore his heart, and it was dreadfully painful to see the weary way in which she sank back into the chair. The silence lasted so long that Philip in his embarrassment lit a cigarette.

"It's very good of you not to have said anything disagreeable to me, Philip. I thought you might say I didn't know what all."

He saw that she was crying again. He remembered how she had come to him when Emil Miller had deserted her and how she had wept. The recollection of her suffering and of his own humiliation seemed to render more overwhelming the compassion he felt now.

"If I could only get out of it!" she moaned. "I hate it so. I'm unfit for the life, I'm not the sort of girl for that. I'd do anything to get away from it, I'd be a servant if I could. Oh, I wish I was dead."

And in pity for herself she broke down now completely. She sobbed hysterically, and her thin body was shaken.

"Oh, you don't know what it is. Nobody knows till they've done it."

Philip could not bear to see her cry. He was tortured by the horror of her position.

"Poor child," he whispered. "Poor child."

He was deeply moved. Suddenly he had an inspiration. It filled him with a perfect ecstasy of happiness.

"Look here, if you want to get away from it, I've got an idea. I'm frightfully hard up just now, I've got to be as economical as I can; but I've got a sort of little flat now in Kennington and I've got a spare room. If you like

you and the baby can come and live there. I pay a woman three and sixpence a week to keep the place clean and to do a little cooking for me. You could do that and your food wouldn't come to much more than the money I should save on her. It doesn't cost any more to feed two than one, and I don't suppose the baby eats much."

She stopped crying and looked at him.

"D'you mean to say that you could take me back after all that's happened?"

Philip flushed a little in embarrassment at what he had to say.

"I don't want you to mistake me. I'm just giving you a room which doesn't cost me anything and your food. I don't expect anything more from you than that you should do exactly the same as the woman I have in does. Except for that I don't want anything from you at all. I daresay you can cook well enough for that."

She sprang to her feet and was about to come towards him.

"You are good to me, Philip."

"No, please stop where you are," he said hurriedly, putting out his hand as though to push her away.

He did not know why it was, but he could not bear the thought that she should touch him.

"I don't want to be anything more than a friend to you."

"You are good to me," she repeated. "You are good to me."

"Does that mean you'll come?"

"Oh, yes, I'd do anything to get away from this. You'll never regret what you've done, Philip, never. When can I come, Philip?"

"You'd better come tomorrow."

Suddenly she burst into tears again.

"What on earth are you crying for now?" he smiled.

"I'm so grateful to you. I don't know

how I can ever make it up to you?"

"Oh, that's all right. You'd better go home now."

He wrote out the address and told her that if she came at half past five he would be ready for her. It was so late that he had to walk home, but it did not seem a long way, for he was intoxicated with delight; he seemed to walk on air.

XCI

NEXT day he got up early to make the room ready for Mildred. He told the woman who had looked after him that he would not want her any more. Mildred came about six, and Philip, who was watching from the window, went down to let her in and help her to bring up the luggage: it consisted now of no more than three large parcels wrapped in brown paper, for she had been obliged to sell everything that was not absolutely needful. She wore the same black silk dress she had worn the night before, and, though she had now no rouge on her cheeks, there was still about her eyes the black which remained after a perfunctory wash in the morning: it made her look very ill. She was a pathetic figure as she stepped out of the cab with the baby in her arms. She seemed a little shy, and they found nothing but commonplace things to say to one another.

"So you've got here all right."

"I've never lived in this part of London before."

Philip showed her the room. It was that in which Cronshaw had died. Philip, though he thought it absurd, had never liked the idea of going back to it; and since Cronshaw's death he had remained in the little room, sleeping on a fold-up bed, into which he had first moved in order to make his friend comfortable. The baby was sleeping placidly.

"You don't recognise her, I expect," said Mildred.

"I've not seen her since we took her down to Brighton."

"Where shall I put her? She's so heavy I can't carry her very long."

"I'm afraid I haven't got a cradle," said Philip, with a nervous laugh.

"Oh, she'll sleep with me. She always does."

Mildred put the baby in an armchair and looked round the room. She recognised most of the things which she had known in his old diggings. Only one thing was new, a head and shoulders of Philip which Lawson had painted at the end of the preceding summer; it hung over the chimney-piece; Mildred looked at it critically.

"In some ways I like it and in some ways I don't. I think you're better looking than that."

"Things are looking up," laughed Philip. "You've never told me I was good-looking before."

"I'm not one to worry myself about a man's looks. I don't like good-looking men. They're too conceited for me."

Her eyes travelled round the room in an instinctive search for a looking-glass, but there was none; she put up her hand and patted her large fringe.

"What'll the other people in the house say to my being here?" she asked suddenly.

"Oh, there's only a man and his wife living here. He's out all day, and I never see her except on Saturday to pay my rent. They keep entirely to themselves. I've not spoken two words to either of them since I came."

Mildred went into the bed-room to undo her things and put them away. Philip tried to read, but his spirits were too high: he leaned back in his chair, smoking a cigarette, and with smiling eyes looked at the sleeping child. He felt very happy. He was quite sure that he was not at all in love with Mildred. He was surprised that the old feeling had left him so completely; he discerned in himself a faint physical repulsion from her; and he thought that if he touched her it would give him goose-flesh. He could not understand himself. Presently, knocking at the door, she came in again.

"I say, you needn't knock," he said. "Have you made the tour of the mansion?"

"It's the smallest kitchen I've ever seen."

"You'll find it large enough to cook our sumptuous repasts," he retorted lightly.

"I see there's nothing in. I'd better go out and get something."

"Yes, but I venture to remind you that we must be devilish economical."

"What shall I get for supper?"

"You'd better get what you think you can cook," laughed Philip.

He gave her some money and she went out. She came in half an hour later and put her purchases on the table. She was out of breath from climbing the stairs.

"I say, you are anæmic," said Philip. "I'll have to dose you with Blaud's Pills."

"It took me some time to find the shops. I bought some liver. That's tasty, isn't it? And you can't eat much of it, so it's more economical than butcher's meat."

There was a gas stove in the kitchen, and when she had put the liver on, Mildred came into the sitting-room to lay the cloth.

"Why are you only laying one place?" asked Philip. "Aren't you going to eat anything?"

Mildred flushed.

"I thought you mightn't like me to have my meals with you."

"Why on earth not?"

"Well, I'm only a servant, aren't I?"

"Don't be an ass. How can you be so silly?"

He smiled, but her humility gave him a curious twist in his heart. Poor thing! He remembered what she had been when first he knew her. He hesitated for an instant.

"Don't think I'm conferring any benefit on you," he said. "It's simply a business arrangement, I'm giving you board and lodging in return for your work. You don't owe me anything. And there's nothing humiliating to you in it."

She did not answer, but tears rolled heavily down her cheeks. Philip knew from his experience at the hospital that women of her class looked upon service as degrading: he could not help feeling a little impatient with her; but he blamed himself, for it was clear that she was tired and ill. He got up and helped her to lay another place at the table. The baby was awake now, and Mildred had prepared some Mellin's Food for it. The liver and bacon were ready and they sat down. For economy's sake Philip had given up drinking anything but water, but he had in the house a half a bottle of whiskey, and he thought a little would do Mildred good. He did his best to make the supper pass cheerfully, but Mildred was subdued and exhausted. When they had finished she got up to put the baby to bed.

"I think you'll do well to turn in early yourself," said Philip. "You look absolutely done up."

"I think I will after I've washed up."

Philip lit his pipe and began to read. It was pleasant to hear somebody moving about in the next room. Sometimes his loneliness had oppressed him. Mildred came in to clear the table, and he heard the clatter of plates as she washed up. Philip smiled as he thought how characteristic it was of her that she should do all that in a black silk dress. But he had work to do, and he brought his book up to the table. He was reading Osler's *Medicine,* which had recently taken the place in the students' favour of Taylor's work, for many years the textbook most in use. Presently Mildred came in, rolling down her sleeves. Philip gave her a casual glance, but did not move; the occasion was curious, and he felt a little nervous. He

feared that Mildred might imagine he was going to make a nuisance of himself, and he did not quite know how without brutality to reassure her.

"By the way, I've got a lecture at nine, so I should want breakfast at a quarter past eight. Can you manage that?"

"Oh, yes. Why, when I was in Parliament Street I used to catch the eight-twelve from Herne Hill every morning."

"I hope you'll find your room comfortable. You'll be a different woman tomorrow after a long night in bed."

"I suppose you work till late?"

"I generally work till about eleven or half-past."

"I'll say good-night then."

"Good-night."

The table was between them. He did not offer to shake hands with her. She shut the door quietly. He heard her moving about in the bed-room, and in a little while he heard the creaking of the bed as she got in.

XCII

THE following day was Tuesday. Philip as usual hurried through his breakfast and dashed off to get to his lecture at nine. He had only time to exchange a few words with Mildred. When he came back in the evening he found her seated at the window, darning his socks.

"I say, you are industrious," he smiled. "What have you been doing with yourself all day?"

"Oh, I gave the place a good cleaning and then I took baby out for a little."

She was wearing an old black dress, the same as she had worn as uniform when she served in the tea-shop;

it was shabby, but she looked better in it than in the silk of the day before. The baby was sitting on the floor. She looked up at Philip with large, mysterious eyes and broke into a laugh when he sat down beside her and began playing with her bare toes. The afternoon sun came into the room and shed a mellow light.

"It's rather jolly to come back and find someone about the place. A woman and a baby make very good decoration in a room."

He had gone to the hospital dispensary and got a bottle of Blaud's Pills. He gave them to Mildred and told her she must take them after each meal. It was a remedy she was used to, for she had taken it off and on ever since she was sixteen.

"I'm sure Lawson would love that green skin of yours," said Philip. "He'd say it was so paintable, but I'm terribly matter of fact nowadays, and I shan't be happy till you're as pink and white as a milkmaid."

"I feel better already."

After a frugal supper Philip filled his pouch with tobacco and put on his hat. It was on Tuesdays that he generally went to the tavern in Beak Street, and he was glad that this day came so soon after Mildred's arrival, for he wanted to make his relations with her perfectly clear.

"Are you going out?" she said.

"Yes, on Tuesdays I give myself a night off. I shall see you tomorrow. Good-night."

Philip always went to the tavern with a sense of pleasure. Macalister, the philosophic stockbroker, was generally there and glad to argue upon any subject under the sun; Hayward came regularly when he was in London; and though he and Macalister disliked one another they continued out of habit to meet on that one evening in the week. Macalister thought Hayward a poor creature, and sneered at his delicacies of sentiment: he asked satirically about Hayward's literary work and received with scornful smiles his vague suggestions of future masterpieces; their arguments were often heated; but the punch was good, and they were both fond of it; towards the end of the evening they generally composed their differences and thought each other capital fellows. This evening Philip found them both there, and Lawson also; Lawson came more seldom now that he was beginning to know people in London and went out to dinner a good deal. They were all on excellent terms with

themselves, for Macalister had given them a good thing on the Stock Exchange, and Hayward and Lawson had made fifty pounds apiece. It was a great thing for Lawson, who was extravagant and earned little money: he had arrived at that stage of the portrait-painter's career when he was noticed a good deal by the critics and found a number of aristocratic ladies who were willing to allow him to paint them for nothing (it advertised them both, and gave the great ladies quite an air of patronesses of the arts); but he very seldom got hold of the solid philistine who was ready to pay good money for a portrait of his wife. Lawson was brimming over with satisfaction.

"It's the most ripping way of making money that I've ever struck," he cried. "I didn't have to put my hand in my pocket for sixpence."

"You lost something by not being here last Tuesday, young man," said Macalister to Philip.

"My God, why didn't you write to me?" said Philip. "If you only knew how useful a hundred pounds would be to me."

"Oh, there wasn't time for that. One has to be on the spot. I heard of a good thing last Tuesday, and I asked these fellows if they'd like to have a flutter, I bought them a thousand shares on Wednesday morning, and there was a rise in the afternoon so I sold them at once. I made fifty pounds for each of them and a couple of hundred for myself."

Philip was sick with envy. He had recently sold the last mortgage in which his small fortune had been invested and now had only six hundred pounds left. He was panic-stricken sometimes when he thought of the future. He had still to keep himself for two years before he could be qualified, and then he meant to try for hospital appointments, so that he could not expect to earn anything for three years at least. With the most rigid economy he would not have more than a hundred pounds left then. It was very little to have as a stand-by in case he was ill and could not earn money or found himself at any time without work. A lucky gamble would make all the difference to him.

"Oh, well, it doesn't matter," said Macalister. "Something is sure to turn up soon. There'll be a boom in South Africans again one of these days, and then I'll see what I can do for you."

Macalister was in the Kaffir market and often told them stories of the sudden fortunes that had been made in the great boom of a year or two back.

"Well, don't forget next time."

They sat on talking till nearly midnight, and Philip, who lived furthest off, was the first to go. If he did not catch the last tram he had to walk, and that made him very late. As it was he did not reach home till nearly half past twelve. When he got upstairs he was surprised to find Mildred still sitting in his arm-chair.

"Why on earth aren't you in bed?" he cried.

"I wasn't sleepy."

"You ought to go to bed all the same. It would rest you."

She did not move. He noticed that since supper she had changed into her black silk dress.

"I thought I'd rather wait up for you in case you wanted anything."

She looked at him, and the shadow of a smile played upon her thin pale lips. Philip was not sure whether he understood or not. He was slightly embarrassed, but assumed a cheerful, matter-of-fact air.

"It's very nice of you, but it's very naughty also. Run off to bed as fast as you can, or you won't be able to get up tomorrow morning."

"I don't feel like going to bed."

"Nonsense," he said coldly.

She got up, a little sulkily, and went into her room. He smiled when he heard her lock the door loudly.

The next few days passed without incident. Mildred settled down in her new surroundings. When Philip hurried off after breakfast she had the whole morning to do the housework. They ate very simply, but she liked to take a long time to buy the few things they needed; she could not be bothered to cook anything for her dinner, but made herself some cocoa and ate bread and butter; then she took the baby out in the go-cart, and when she came in spent the rest of the afternoon in idleness. She was tired out, and it suited her to do so little. She made friends with Philip's forbidding landlady over the rent, which he left with Mildred to pay, and within a week was able to tell him more about his neighbours than he had learned in a year.

"She's a very nice woman," said Mildred. "Quite the lady. I told her we was married."

"D'you think that was necessary?"

"Well, I had to tell her something. It looks so funny me being here and not married to you. I didn't know what she'd think of me."

"I don't suppose she believed you for a moment."

"That she did, I lay. I told her we'd been married two years—I had to say that, you know, because of baby —only your people wouldn't hear of it, because you was only a student" —she pronounced it stoodent—"and so we had to keep it a secret, but they'd given way now and we were all going down to stay with them in the summer."

"You're a past mistress of the cock-and-bull story," said Philip.

He was vaguely irritated that Mildred still had this passion for telling fibs. In the last two years she had learnt nothing. But he shrugged his shoulders.

"When all's said and done," he reflected, "she hasn't had much chance."

It was a beautiful evening, warm and cloudless, and the people of South London seemed to have poured out into the streets. There was that restlessness in the air which seizes the cockney sometimes when a turn in the weather calls him into the open. After Mildred had cleared away the supper she went and stood at the window. The street noises came up to them, noises of people calling to one another, of the passing traffic, of a barrel-organ in the distance.

"I suppose you must work tonight, Philip?" she asked him, with a wistful expression.

"I ought, but I don't know that I must. Why, d'you want me to do anything else?"

"I'd like to go out for a bit. Couldn't we take a ride on the top of a tram?"

"If you like."

"I'll just go and put on my hat," she said joyfully.

The night made it almost impossible to stay indoors. The baby was asleep and could be safely left; Mildred said she had always left it alone at night when she went out; it never woke. She was in high spirits when she came back with her hat on. She had taken the opportunity to put on a little rouge. Philip thought it was excitement which had brought a faint colour to her pale cheeks; he was touched by her child-like delight, and reproached himself for the austerity with which he had treated her. She laughed when she got out into the air. The first tram they saw was going towards Westminster Bridge and they got on it. Philip smoked his pipe, and

they looked at the crowded street. The shops were open, gaily lit, and people were doing their shopping for the next day. They passed a music-hall called the Canterbury and Mildred cried out:

"Oh, Philip, do let's go there. I haven't been to a music-hall for months."

"We can't afford stalls, you know."

"Oh, I don't mind, I shall be quite happy in the gallery."

They got down and walked back a hundred yards till they came to the doors. They got capital seats for sixpence each, high up but not in the gallery, and the night was so fine that there was plenty of room. Mildred's eyes glistened. She enjoyed herself thoroughly. There was a simple-mindedness in her which touched Philip. She was a puzzle to him. Certain things in her still pleased him, and he thought that there was a lot in her which was very good: she had been badly brought up, and her life was hard; he had blamed her for much that she could not help; and it was his own fault if he had asked virtues from her which it was not in her power to give. Under different circumstances she might have been a charming girl. She was extraordinarily unfit for the battle of life. As he watched her now in profile, her mouth slightly open and that delicate flush on her cheeks, he thought she looked strangely virginal. He felt an overwhelming compassion for her, and with all his heart he forgave her for the misery she had caused him. The smoky atmosphere made Philip's eyes ache, but when he suggested going she turned to him with beseeching face and asked him to stay till the end. He smiled and consented. She took his hand and held it for the rest of the performance. When they streamed out with the audience into the crowded street she did not want to go home; they wandered up the Westminster Bridge Road, looking at the people.

"I've not had such a good time as this for months," she said.

Philip's heart was full, and he was thankful to the fates because he had carried out his sudden impulse to take Mildred and her baby into his flat. It was very pleasant to see her happy gratitude. At last she grew tired and they jumped on a tram to go home; it was late now, and when they got down and turned into their own street there was no one about. Mildred slipped her arm through his.

"It's just like old times, Phil," she said.

She had never called him Phil before, that was what Griffiths called him; and even now it gave him a curious pang. He remembered how much he had wanted to die then; his pain had been so great that he had thought quite seriously of committing suicide. It all seemed very long ago. He smiled at his past self. Now he felt nothing for Mildred but infinite pity. They reached the house, and when they got into the sitting-room Philip lit the gas.

"Is the baby all right?" he asked. "I'll just go in and see."

When she came back it was to say that it had not stirred since she left it. It was a wonderful child. Philip held out his hand.

"Well, good-night."

"D'you want to go to bed already?"

"It's nearly one. I'm not used to late hours these days," said Philip.

She took his hand and holding it looked into his eyes with a little smile.

"Phil, the other night in that room, when you asked me to come and stay here, I didn't mean what you thought I meant, when you said you didn't want me to be anything to you except just to cook and that sort of thing."

"Didn't you?" answered Philip, withdrawing his hand. "I did."

"Don't be such an old silly," she laughed.

He shook his head.

"I meant it quite seriously. I shouldn't have asked you to stay here on any other condition."

"Why not?"

"I feel I couldn't. I can't explain it, but it would spoil it all."

She shrugged her shoulders.

"Oh, very well, it's just as you choose. I'm not one to go down on my hands and knees for that, and chance it."

She went out, slamming the door behind her.

XCIII

NEXT morning Mildred was sulky and taciturn. She remained in her room till it was time to get the dinner ready. She was a bad cook and could do little more than chops and steaks; and she did not know how to use up odds and ends, so that Philip was obliged to spend more money than he had expected. When she served up she sat down opposite Philip, but would eat nothing; he remarked on it; she said she had a bad headache and was not hungry. He was glad that he had somewhere to spend the rest of the day; the Athelnys were cheerful and friendly: it was a delightful and an unexpected thing to realise that everyone in that household looked forward with pleasure to his visit. Mildred had gone to bed when he came back, but next day she was still silent. At supper she sat with a haughty expression on her face and a little frown between her eyes. It made Philip impatient, but he told himself that he must be considerate to her; he was bound to make allowance.

"You're very silent," he said, with a pleasant smile.

"I'm paid to cook and clean, I didn't know I was expected to talk as well."

He thought it an ungracious answer, but if they were going to live together he must do all he could to make things go easily.

"I'm afraid you're cross with me about the other night," he said.

It was an awkward thing to speak about, but apparently it was necessary to discuss it.

"I don't know what you mean," she answered.

"Please don't be angry with me. I should never have asked you to come and live here if I'd not meant our relations to be merely friendly. I suggested it because I thought you wanted a home and you would have a chance of looking about for something to do."

"Oh, don't think I care."

"I don't for a moment," he hastened to say. "You mustn't think I'm ungrateful. I realise that you only proposed it for my sake. It's just a feeling I have, and I can't help it, it would make the whole thing ugly and horrid."

"You are funny," she said, looking at him curiously. "I can't make you out."

She was not angry with him now, but puzzled; she had no idea what he meant: she accepted the situation, she had indeed a vague feeling that

he was behaving in a very noble fashion and that she ought to admire it; but also she felt inclined to laugh at him and perhaps even to despise him a little.

"He's a rum customer," she thought.

Life went smoothly enough with them. Philip spent all day at the hospital and worked at home in the evening except when he went to the Athelnys' or to the tavern in Beak Street. Once the physician for whom he clerked asked him to a solemn dinner, and two or three times he went to parties given by fellow-students. Mildred accepted the monotony of her life. If she minded that Philip left her sometimes by herself in the evening she never mentioned it. Occasionally he took her to a music-hall. He carried out his intention that the only tie between them should be the domestic service she did in return for board and lodging. She had made up her mind that it was no use trying to get work that summer, and with Philip's approval determined to stay where she was till the autumn. She thought it would be easy to get something to do then.

"As far as I'm concerned you can stay on here when you've got a job if it's convenient. The room's there, and the woman who did for me before can come in to look after the baby."

He grew very much attached to Mildred's child. He had a naturally affectionate disposition, which had had little opportunity to display itself. Mildred was not unkind to the little girl. She looked after her very well and once when she had a bad cold proved herself a devoted nurse; but the child bored her, and she spoke to her sharply when she bothered; she was fond of her, but had not the maternal passion which might have induced her to forget herself. Mildred had no demonstrativeness, and she found the manifestations of affection ridiculous. When Philip sat with the baby on his knees, playing with it and kissing it, she laughed at him. "You couldn't make more fuss of her if you was her father," she said. "You're perfectly silly with the child."

Philip flushed, for he hated to be laughed at. It was absurd to be so devoted to another man's baby, and he was a little ashamed of the overflowing of his heart. But the child, feeling Philip's attachment, would put her face against his or nestle in his arms.

"It's all very fine for you," said Mildred. "You don't have any of the disagreeable part of it. How would you like being kept awake for an hour in the middle of the night because her ladyship wouldn't go to sleep?"

Philip remembered all sorts of things of his childhood which he thought he had long forgotten. He took hold of the baby's toes. "This little pig went to market, this little pig stayed at home."

When he came home in the evening and entered the sitting-room his first glance was for the baby sprawling on the floor, and it gave him a little thrill of delight to hear the child's crow of pleasure at seeing him. Mildred taught her to call him daddy, and when the child did this for the first time of her own accord, laughed immoderately.

"I wonder if you're that stuck on baby because she's mine," asked Mildred, "or if you'd be the same with anybody's baby."

"I've never known anybody else's baby, so I can't say," said Philip.

Towards the end of his second term as in-patients' clerk a piece of good fortune befell Philip. It was the middle of July. He went one Tuesday evening to the tavern in Beak Street and found nobody there but Macalister. They sat together, chatting about their absent friends, and after a while Macalister said to him:

"Oh, by the way, I heard of a rather good thing today, New Kleinfonteins; it's a gold mine in Rhodesia. If you'd like to have a flutter you might make a bit."

Philip had been waiting anxiously for such an opportunity, but now that it came he hesitated. He was desperately afraid of losing money. He had little of the gambler's spirit.

"I'd love to, but I don't know if I dare risk it. How much could I lose if things went wrong?"

"I shouldn't have spoken of it, only you seemed so keen about it," Macalister answered coldly.

Philip felt that Macalister looked upon him as rather a donkey.

"I'm awfully keen on making a bit," he laughed.

"You can't make money unless you're prepared to risk money."

Macalister began to talk of other things and Philip, while he was answering him, kept thinking that if the venture turned out well the stockbroker would be very facetious at his expense next time they met. Macalister had a sarcastic tongue.

"I think I will have a flutter if you don't mind," said Philip anxiously.

"All right. I'll buy you two hundred and fifty shares and if I see a half-crown rise I'll sell them at once."

Philip quickly reckoned out how much that would amount to, and his mouth watered; thirty pounds would be a godsend just then, and he thought the fates owed him something. He told Mildred what he had done when he saw her at breakfast next morning. She thought him very silly.

"I never knew anyone who made

money on the Stock Exchange," she said. "That's what Emil always said, you can't expect to make money on the Stock Exchange, he said."

Philip bought an evening paper on his way home and turned at once to the money columns. He knew nothing about these things and had difficulty in finding the stock which Macalister had spoken of. He saw they had advanced a quarter. His heart leaped, and then he felt sick with apprehension in case Macalister had forgotten or for some reason had not bought. Macalister had promised to telegraph. Philip could not wait to take a tram home. He jumped into a cab. It was an unwonted extravagance.

"Is there a telegram for me?" he said, as he burst in.

"No," said Mildred.

His face fell, and in bitter disappointment he sank heavily into a chair.

"Then he didn't buy them for me after all. Curse him," he added violently. "What cruel luck! And I've been thinking all day of what I'd do with the money."

"Why, what were you going to do?" she asked.

"What's the good of thinking about that now? Oh, I wanted the money so badly."

She gave a laugh and handed him a telegram.

"I was only having a joke with you. I opened it."

He tore it out of her hands. Macalister had bought him two hundred and fifty shares and sold them at the half-crown profit he had suggested. The commission note was to follow next day. For one moment Philip was furious with Mildred for her cruel jest, but then he could only

think of his joy.

"It makes such a difference to me," he cried. "I'll stand you a new dress if you like."

"I want it badly enough," she answered.

"I'll tell you what I'm going to do. I'm going to be operated upon at the end of July."

"Why, have you got something the matter with you?" she interrupted.

It struck her that an illness she did not know might explain what had so much puzzled her. He flushed, for he hated to refer to his deformity.

"No, but they think they can do something to my foot. I couldn't spare the time before, but now it doesn't matter so much. I shall start my dressing in October instead of next month. I shall only be in hospital a few weeks and then we can go away to the seaside for the rest of the summer. It'll do us all good, you and the baby and me."

"Oh, let's go to Brighton, Philip, I like Brighton, you get such a nice class of people there."

Philip had vaguely thought of some little fishing village in Cornwall, but as she spoke it occurred to him that Mildred would be bored to death there.

"I don't mind where we go as long as I get the sea."

He did not know why, but he had suddenly an irresistible longing for the sea. He wanted to bathe, and he thought with delight of splashing about in the salt water. He was a good swimmer, and nothing exhilarated him like a rough sea.

"I say, it will be jolly," he cried.

"It'll be like a honeymoon, won't it?" she said. "How much can I have for my new dress, Phil?"

XCIV

PHILIP asked Mr. Jacobs, the assistant-surgeon for whom he had dressed, to do the operation. Jacobs accepted with pleasure, since he was interested just then in neglected talipes and was getting together materials for a paper. He warned Philip that he could not make his foot like the other, but he thought he could do a good deal; and though he would always limp he would be able to wear a boot less unsightly than that which he had been accustomed to. Philip remembered how he had prayed to a God who was able to remove mountains for him who had faith, and he smiled bitterly.

"I don't expect a miracle," he answered.

"I think you're wise to let me try what I can do. You'll find a club-foot rather a handicap in practice. The layman is full of fads, and he doesn't like his doctor to have anything the matter with him."

Philip went into a 'small ward', which was a room on the landing, outside each ward, reserved for special cases. He remained there a month, for the surgeon would not let him go till he could walk; and, bearing the operation very well, he had a pleasant enough time. Lawson and Athelny came to see him, and one day Mrs. Athelny brought two of her children; students whom he knew looked in now and again to have a chat; Mildred came twice a week. Everyone was very kind to him, and Philip, always surprised when anyone took trouble with him, was touched and grateful. He enjoyed the relief from care; he need not worry there about the future, neither whether his money

would last out nor whether he would pass his final examinations; and he could read to his heart's content. He had not been able to read much of late, since Mildred disturbed him: she would make an aimless remark when he was trying to concentrate his attention, and would not be satisfied unless he answered; whenever he was comfortably settled down with a book she would want something done and would come to him with a cork she could not draw or a hammer to drive in a nail.

They settled to go to Brighton in August. Philip wanted to take lodgings, but Mildred said that she would have to do housekeeping, and it would only be a holiday for her if they went to a boarding-house.

"I have to see about the food every day at home, I get that sick of it I want a thorough change."

Philip agreed, and it happened that Mildred knew of a boarding-house at Kemp Town where they would not be charged more than twenty-five shillings a week each. She arranged with Philip to write about rooms, but when he got back to Kennington he found that she had done nothing. He was irritated.

"I shouldn't have thought you had so much to do as all that," he said.

"Well, I can't think of everything. It's not my fault if I forget, is it?"

Philip was so anxious to get to the sea that he would not wait to communicate with the mistress of the boarding-house.

"We'll leave the luggage at the station and go to the house and see if they've got rooms, and if they have we can just send an outside porter for our traps."

"You can please yourself," said Mildred stiffly.

She did not like being reproached, and, retiring huffily into a haughty silence, she sat by listlessly while Philip made the preparations for their departure. The little flat was hot and stuffy under the August sun, and from the road beat up a malodorous sultriness. As he lay in his bed in the small ward with its red, distempered walls he had longed for fresh air and the splashing of the sea against his breast. He felt he would go mad if he had to spend another night in London. Mildred recovered her good temper when she saw the streets of Brighton crowded with people making holiday, and they were both in high spirits as they drove out to Kemp Town. Philip stroked the baby's cheek.

"We shall get a very different colour into them when we've been down here a few days," he said smiling.

They arrived at the boarding-house and dismissed the cab. An untidy maid opened the door and, when Philip asked if they had rooms, said she would inquire. She fetched her mistress. A middle-aged woman, stout and business-like, came downstairs, gave them the scrutinising glance of her profession, and asked what accommodation they required.

"Two single rooms, and if you've got such a thing we'd rather like a cot in one of them."

"I'm afraid I haven't got that. I've got one nice large double room, and I could let you have a cot."

"I don't think that would do," said Philip.

"I could give you another room next week. Brighton's very full just now, and people have to take what they can get."

"If it were only for a few days, Philip, I think we might be able to manage," said Mildred.

"I think two rooms would be more convenient. Can you recommend any other place where they take boarders?"

"I can, but I don't suppose they'd have room any more than I have."

"Perhaps you wouldn't mind giving me the address."

The house the stout woman suggested was in the next street, and they walked towards it. Philip could walk quite well, though he had to lean on a stick, and he was rather weak. Mildred carried the baby. They went for a little in silence, and then he saw she was crying. It annoyed him, and he took no notice, but she forced his attention.

"Lend me a hanky, will you? I can't get at mine with baby," she said in a voice strangled with sobs, turning her head away from him.

He gave her his handkerchief, but said nothing. She dried her eyes, and as he did not speak, went on.

"I might be poisonous."

"Please don't make a scene in the street," he said.

"It'll look so funny insisting on separate rooms like that. What'll they think of us?"

"If they knew the circumstances I imagine they'd think us surprisingly moral," said Philip.

She gave him a sidelong glance.

"You're not going to give it away that we're not married?" she asked quickly.

"No."

"Why won't you live with me as if we were married then?"

"My dear, I can't explain. I don't want to humiliate you, but I simply can't. I daresay it's very silly and unreasonable, but it's stronger than I am. I loved you so much that now . . ." he broke off. "After all, there's no accounting for that sort of thing."

"A fat lot you must have loved me!" she exclaimed.

The boarding-house to which they had been directed was kept by a bustling maiden lady, with shrewd eyes and voluble speech. They could have one double room for twenty-five shillings a week each, and five shillings extra for the baby, or they could have two single rooms for a pound a week more.

"I have to charge that much more," the woman explained apologetically, "because if I'm pushed to it I can put two beds even in the single rooms."

"I daresay that won't ruin us. What do you think, Mildred?"

"Oh, I don't mind. Anything's good enough for me," she answered.

Philip passed off her sulky reply with a laugh, and, the landlady having arranged to send for their luggage, they sat down to rest themselves. Philip's foot was hurting him a little, and he was glad to put it up on a chair.

"I suppose you don't mind my sitting in the same room with you," said Mildred aggressively.

"Don't let's quarrel, Mildred," he said gently.

"I didn't know you was so well off you could afford to throw away a pound a week."

"Don't be angry with me. I assure you it's the only way we can live together at all."

"I suppose you despise me, that's it."

"Of course I don't. Why should I?"

"It's so unnatural."

"Is it? You're not in love with me, are you?"

"Me? Who d'you take me for?"

"It's not as if you were a very passionate woman, you're not that."

"It's so humiliating," she said sulkily.

"Oh, I wouldn't fuss about that if I were you."

There were about a dozen people in the boarding-house. They ate in a narrow, dark room at a long table, at the head of which the landlady sat and carved. The food was bad. The landlady called it French cooking, by which she meant that the poor quality of the materials was disguised by ill-made sauces: plaice masqueraded as sole and New Zealand mutton as lamb. The kitchen was small and inconvenient, so that everything was served up lukewarm. The people were dull and pretentious; old ladies with elderly maiden daughters; funny old bachelors with mincing ways; pale-faced, middle-aged clerks with wives, who talked of their married daughters and their sons who were in a very good position in the Colonies. At table they discussed Miss Corelli's latest novel; some of them liked Lord Leighton better than Mr. Alma-Tadema, and some of them liked Mr. Alma-Tadema better than Lord Leighton. Mildred soon told the ladies of her romantic marriage with Philip; and he found himself an object of interest because his family, county people in a very good position, had cut him off with a shilling because he married while he was only a stoodent; and Mildred's father, who had a large place down Devonshire way, wouldn't do anything for them because she had married Philip. That was why they had come to a boarding-house and had not a nurse for the baby; but they had to have two rooms because they were both used to a good deal of accommodation and they didn't care to be cramped. The other visitors also had explanations of their presence: one of the single gentlemen generally went to the Metropole for his holiday, but he liked cheerful company and you couldn't get that at one of those expensive hotels; and the old lady with the middle-aged daughter was having her beautiful house in London done up and she said to her daughter: "Gwennie, my dear, we must have a cheap holiday this year," and so they had come there, though of course it wasn't at all the kind of thing they were used to. Mildred found them all very superior, and she hated a lot of common, rough people. She liked gentlemen to be gentlemen in every sense of the word.

"When people are gentlemen and ladies," she said, "I like them to be gentlemen and ladies."

The remark seemed cryptic to Philip, but when he heard her say it two or three times to different persons, and found that it aroused hearty agreement, he came to the conclusion that it was only obscure to his own intelligence. It was the first time that Philip and Mildred had been thrown entirely together. In London he did not see her all day, and when he came home the household affairs, the baby, the neighbours, gave them something to talk about till he settled down to work. Now he spent the whole day with her. After breakfast they went down to the beach; the morning went easily enough with a bathe and a stroll along the front; the evening, which they spent on the pier, having put the baby to bed, was tolerable, for there was music to listen to and a constant stream of people to look at; (Philip amused himself by imagining who they were and weaving little stories about them; he had got into the habit of answering Mildred's remarks with his mouth only so that his thoughts remained undisturbed;) but the afternoons were long and dreary. They sat on the beach. Mildred said they must get all the benefit they could out of Doctor Brighton, and he could not read because Mildred made observations frequently about things in general. If he paid no attention he complained.

"Oh, leave that silly old book alone. It can't be good for you always reading. You'll addle your brain, that's what you'll do, Philip."

"Oh, rot!" he answered.

"Besides, it's so unsociable."

He discovered that it was difficult to talk to her. She had not even the power of attending to what she was herself saying, so that a dog running in front of her or the passing of a man in a loud blazer would call forth a remark and then she would forget what she had been speaking of. She had a bad memory for names, and it irritated her not to be able to think of them, so that she would pause in the middle of some story to rack her brains. Sometimes she had to give it up, but it often occurred to her afterwards, and when Philip was talking of something she would interrupt him.

"Collins, that was it. I knew it would come back to me some time. Collins, that's the name I couldn't remember."

It exasperated him because it showed that she was not listening to anything he said, and yet, if he was silent, she reproached him for sulkiness. Her mind was of an order that could not deal for five minutes with the abstract, and when Philip gave way to his taste for generalising she very quickly showed that she was bored. Mildred dreamt a great deal, and she had an accurate memory for her dreams, which she would relate every day with prolixity.

One morning he received a long letter from Thorpe Athelny. He was taking his holiday in the theatrical way, in which there was much sound sense, which characterised him. He had done the same thing for ten years. He took his whole family to a hopfield in Kent, not far from Mrs. Athelny's home, and they spent three weeks hopping. It kept them in the open air, earned them money, much to Mrs. Athelny's satisfaction, and renewed their contact with mother earth. It was upon this that Athelny laid stress. The sojourn in the fields gave them a new strength; it was like a magic ceremony, by which they renewed their youth and the power of their limbs and the sweetness of the spirit: Philip had heard him say many fantastic, rhetorical, and picturesque things on the subject. Now Athelny invited him to come over for a day, he had certain meditations on Shakespeare and the musical glasses which he desired to impart, and the children were clamouring for a sight of Uncle Philip. Philip read the letter again in the afternoon when he was sitting with Mildred on the beach. He thought of Mrs. Athelny, cheerful mother of many children, with her kindly hospitality and her good humour; of Sally, grave for her years, with funny little maternal ways and an air of authority, with her long plait of fair hair and her broad forehead; and then in a bunch of all the others, merry, boisterous, healthy, and handsome. His heart went out to them. There was one quality which they had that he did not remember to have noticed in people before, and that was goodness. It had not occurred to him till now, but it was evidently the beauty of their goodness which attracted him. In theory he did not believe in it: if morality were no more than a matter of convenience good and evil had no meaning. He did not like to be illogical, but here was simple goodness, natural and without effort, and he thought it beautiful. Meditating, he slowly tore the letter into little pieces; he did not see how he could go without Mildred, and he did not want to go with her.

It was very hot, the sky was cloudless, and they had been driven to a shady corner. The baby was gravely playing with stones on the beach, and now and then she crawled up to Philip and gave him one to hold, then took it away again and placed it carefully down. She was playing a mysterious and complicated game known only to herself. Mildred was asleep. She lay with her head thrown back and her mouth slightly open; her legs were stretched out, and her boots protruded from her petticoats in a grotesque fashion. His eyes had been resting on her vaguely, but now he looked at her with peculiar attention. He remembered how passionately he had loved her, and he wondered why now he was entirely indifferent to her. The change in him filled him with dull pain. It seemed to him that all he had suffered had been sheer waste. The touch of her hand had filled him with ecstasy; he had desired to enter into her soul so that he could share every thought with her and every feeling; he had suffered acutely because, when silence had fallen between them, a remark of hers showed how far their thoughts had travelled apart, and he had rebelled against the unsurmountable wall which seemed to divide every personality from every other. He found it strangely tragic that he had loved her so madly and now loved her not at all. Sometimes he hated her. She was incapable of learning, and the experience of life had taught her nothing. She was as unmannerly as she had always been. It revolted Philip to hear the insolence with which she treated the hardworked servant at the boarding-house.

Presently he considered his own plans. At the end of his fourth year he would be able to take his examination in midwifery, and a year more would see him qualified. Then he might manage a journey to Spain. He wanted to see the pictures which he knew only from photographs; he felt deeply that El Greco held a secret of peculiar moment to him; and he fancied that in Toledo he would surely find it out. He did not wish to do things grandly, and on a hundred pounds he might live for six months in Spain: if Macalister put him on to another good thing he could make that easily. His heart warmed at the thought of those old beautiful cities, and the tawny plains of Castile. He was convinced that more might be got out of life than offered itself at present, and he thought that in Spain he could live with greater intensity: it might be possible to practise in one of those old cities, there were a good many foreigners, passing or resident, and he should be able to pick up a living. But that would be much later; first he must get one or two hospital appointments; they gave experience and made it easy to get jobs afterwards. He wished to get a berth as ship's doctor on one of the large tramps that took things leisurely enough for a man to see something of the places at which they stopped. He wanted to go to the East; and his fancy was rich with pictures of Bangkok and Shanghai, and the ports of Japan: he pictured to himself palm-trees and skies blue and hot, dark-skinned people, pagodas; the scents of the Orient intoxicated his nostrils. His heart beat with passionate desire for the beauty and the strangeness of the world.

Mildred awoke.

"I do believe I've been asleep," she said. "Now then, you naughty girl, what have you been doing to yourself? Her dress was clean yesterday and just look at it now, Philip."

XCV

WHEN they returned to London Philip began his dressing in the surgical wards. He was not so much interested in surgery as in medicine, which, a more empirical science, offered greater scope to the imagination. The work was a little harder than the corresponding work on the medical side. There was a lecture from nine till ten, when he went into the wards; there wounds had to be dressed, stitches taken out, bandages renewed: Philip prided himself a little on his skill in bandaging, and it amused him to wring a word of approval from a nurse. On certain afternoons in the week there were operations; and he stood in the well of the theatre, in a white jacket, ready to hand the operating surgeon any instrument he wanted or to sponge the blood away so that he could see what he was about. When some rare operation was to be performed the theatre would fill up, but generally there were not more than half a dozen students present, and then the proceedings had a cosiness which Philip enjoyed. At that time the world at large seemed to have a passion for appendicitis, and a good many cases came to the operating theatre for this complaint: the surgeon for whom Philip dressed was in friendly rivalry with a colleague as to which could remove an appendix in the shortest time and with the smallest incision.

In due course Philip was put on accident duty. The dressers took this in turn; it lasted three days, during which they lived in hospital and ate their meals in the common room; they had a room on the ground floor near the casualty ward, with a bed that shut up during the day into a cupboard. The dresser on duty had to be at hand day and night to see to any casualty that came in. You were on the move all the time, and not more than an hour or two passed during the night without the clanging of the bell just above your head which made you leap out of bed instinctively. Saturday night was of course the busiest time and the closing of the public-houses the busiest hour. Men would be brought in by the police dead drunk and it would be necessary to administer a stomach-pump; women, rather the worse for liquor themselves, would come in with a wound on the head or a bleeding nose which their husbands had given them: some would vow to have the law on him, and others, ashamed, would declare that it had been an accident. What the dresser could manage himself he did, but if there was anything important he sent for the house-surgeon: he did this with care, since the house-surgeon was not vastly pleased to be dragged down five flights of stairs for nothing. The cases ranged from a cut finger to a cut throat. Boys came in with hands mangled by some machine, men were brought who had been knocked down by a cab, and children who had broken a limb while playing: now and then attempted suicides were carried in by the police: Philip saw a ghastly, wild-eyed man with a great gash from ear to ear, and he was in the ward for weeks afterwards in charge of a constable, silent, angry because he was alive, and sullen; he made no secret of the fact that he would try again to kill himself as soon as he was released. The wards were crowded, and the house-surgeon was faced with a dilemma when patients were brought in by the police: if they were sent on to the station and died there disagreeable things were said in the papers; and it was very difficult sometimes to tell if a man was dying or drunk. Philip did not go to bed till he was tired out, so that he should not have the bother of getting up again in an hour; and he sat in the casualty ward talking in the intervals of work with the night-nurse. She was a gray-haired woman of masculine appearance, who had been night-nurse in the casualty department for twenty years. She liked the work because she was her own mistress and had no sister to bother her. Her movements were slow, but she was immensely capable and she never failed in an emergency. The dressers, often inexperienced or nervous, found her a tower of strength. She had seen thousands of them, and they made no impression upon her: she always called them Mr. Brown; and when they expostulated and told her their real names, she merely nodded and went on calling them Mr. Brown. It interested Philip to sit with her in the bare room, with its two horse-hair couches and the flaring gas, and listen to her. She had long ceased to look upon the people who came in as human beings; they were drunks, or broken arms, or cut throats. She took the vice and misery and cruelty of the world as a matter of course; she found nothing to praise or blame in human actions: she accepted. She had a certain grim humour.

"I remember one suicide," she said to Philip, "who threw himself into the Thames. They fished him out and brought him here, and ten days later he developed typhoid fever from swallowing Thames water."

"Did he die?"

"Yes, he did all right. I could never make up my mind if it was suicide or not. . . . They're a funny lot, suicides. I remember one man who couldn't get any work to do and his wife died, so he pawned his clothes and bought a revolver; but he made a mess of it, he only shot out an eye and he got all right. And then, if you please, with an eye gone and a piece of his face blown away, he came to the conclusion that the world wasn't such a bad place after all, and he lived happily ever afterwards. Thing I've always noticed, people don't commit suicide for love, as you'd expect, that's just a fancy of novelists; they commit suicide because they haven't got any money. I wonder why that is."

"I suppose money's more important than love," suggested Philip.

Money was in any case occupying Philip's thoughts a good deal just then. He discovered the little truth there was in the airy saying which himself had repeated, that two could live as cheaply as one, and his expenses were beginning to worry him. Mildred was not a good manager, and it cost them as much to live as if they had eaten in restaurants; the child needed clothes, and Mildred boots, an umbrella, and other small things which it was impossible for her to do without. When they returned from Brighton she had announced her intention of getting a job, but she took no definite steps, and presently a bad cold laid her up for a fortnight. When she was well she answered one or two advertisements, but nothing came of it: either she arrived too late and the vacant place was filled, or the work was more than she felt strong enough to do. Once she got an offer, but the wages were only fourteen shillings a week, and she thought she was worth more than that.

"It's no good letting oneself be put upon," she remarked. "People don't respect you if you let yourself go too cheap."

"I don't think fourteen shillings is so bad," answered Philip, drily.

He could not help thinking how useful it would be towards the expenses of the household, and Mildred was already beginning to hint that she did not get a place because she had not got a decent dress to interview employers in. He gave her the dress, and she made one or two more attempts, but Philip came to the conclusion that they were not serious. She did not want to work. The only way he knew to make money was on the Stock Exchange, and he was very anxious to repeat the lucky experiment of the summer; but war had broken out with the Transvaal and nothing was doing in South Africans. Macalister told him that Redvers Buller would march into Pretoria in a month and then everything would boom. The only thing was to wait patiently. What they wanted was a British reverse to knock things down a bit, and then it might be worth while buying. Philip began reading assiduously the 'city chat' of his favourite newspaper. He was worried and irritable. Once or twice he spoke sharply to Mildred and since she was neither tactful nor patient she answered with temper, and they quarrelled. Philip always expressed his regret for what he had said, but Mildred had not a forgiving nature, and she would sulk for a couple of days. She got on his nerves in all sorts of ways; by the manner in which she ate, and by the untidiness which made her leave articles of clothing about their sitting-room: Philip was excited by the war and devoured the papers, morning and evening; but she took no interest in anything that happened. She had made the acquaintance of two or three people who lived in the street, and one of them had asked if she would like the curate to call on her. She wore a wedding-ring and called herself Mrs. Carey. On Philip's walls were two or three of the drawings which he had made in Paris, nudes, two of women and one of Miguel Ajuria, standing very square on his feet, with clenched fists. Philip kept them because they were the best things he had done, and they reminded him of happy days. Mildred had long looked at them with disfavour.

"I wish you'd take those drawings down, Philip," she said to him at last. "Mrs. Foreman, of number thirteen, came in yesterday afternoon, and I didn't know which way to look. I saw her staring at them."

"What's the matter with them?"

"They're indecent. Disgusting, that's what I call it, to have drawings of naked people about. And it isn't nice for baby either. She's beginning to notice things now."

"How can you be so vulgar?"

"Vulgar? Modest, I call it. I've never said anything, but d'you think I like having to look at those naked people all day long."

"Have you no sense of humour at all, Mildred?" he asked frigidly.

"I don't know what sense of humour's got to do with it. I've got a good mind to take them down myself. If you want to know what I think about them, I think they're disgusting."

"I don't want to know what you think about them, and I forbid you to touch them."

When Mildred was cross with him she punished him through the baby. The little girl was as fond of Philip as he was of her, and it was her great pleasure every morning to crawl into his room, (she was getting on for two now and could walk pretty well,) and be taken up into his bed. When Mildred stopped this the poor child would cry bitterly. To Philip's remonstrances she replied:

"I don't want her to get into habits."

And if then he said anything more she said:

"It's nothing to do with you what I do with my child. To hear you talk one would think you was her father. I'm her mother, and I ought to know what's good for her, oughtn't I?"

Philip was exasperated by Mildred's stupidity; but he was so indifferent to her now that it was only at times she made him angry. He grew used to having her about. Christmas came, and with it a couple of days holiday for Philip. He brought some holly in and decorated the flat, and on Christmas Day he gave small presents to Mildred and the baby. There were only two of them so they could not have a turkey, but Mildred roasted a chicken and boiled a Christmas pudding which she had bought at a local grocer's. They stood themselves a bottle of wine. When they had dined Philip sat in his arm-chair by the fire, smoking his pipe; and the unaccustomed wine had made him forget for a while the anxiety about money which was so constantly with him. He felt happy and comfortable. Presently Mildred came in to tell him that the baby wanted him to kiss her goodnight, and with a smile he went into Mildred's bed-room. Then, telling the child to go to sleep, he turned down the gas and, leaving the door open in case she cried, went back into the sitting-room.

"Where are you going to sit?" he asked Mildred.

"You sit in your chair. I'm going to sit on the floor."

When he sat down she settled herself in front of the fire and leaned against his knees. He could not help remembering that this was how they had sat together in her rooms in the Vauxhall Bridge Road, but the positions had been reversed; it was he who had sat on the floor and leaned his head against her knee. How passionately he had loved her then! Now he felt for her a tenderness he had not known for a long time. He seemed still to feel twined round his neck the baby's soft little arms.

"Are you comfy?" he asked.

She looked up at him, gave a slight smile, and nodded. They gazed into the fire dreamily, without speaking to one another. At last she turned round and stared at him curiously.

"D'you know that you haven't kissed me once since I came here?" she said suddenly.

"D'you want me to?" he smiled.

"I suppose you don't care for me in that way any more?"

"I'm very fond of you."

"You're much fonder of baby."

He did not answer, and she laid her cheek against his hand.

"You're not angry with me any more?" she asked presently, with her eyes cast down.

"Why on earth should I be?"

"I've never cared for you as I do now. It's only since I passed through the fire that I've learnt to love you."

It chilled Philip to hear her make use of the sort of phrase she read in the penny novelettes which she devoured. Then he wondered whether what she said had any meaning for her: perhaps she knew no other way to express her genuine feelings than the stilted language of *The Family Herald*.

"It seems so funny our living together like this."

He did not reply for quite a long time, and silence fell upon them again; but at last he spoke and seemed conscious of no interval.

"You mustn't be angry with me. One can't help these things. I remember that I thought you wicked and cruel because you did this, that, and the other; but it was very silly of me. You didn't love me, and it was absurd to blame you for that. I thought I could make you love me, but I know now that was impossible. I don't know what it is that makes someone love you, but whatever it is, it's the only thing that matters, and if it isn't there you won't create it by kindness, or generosity, or anything of that sort."

"I should have thought if you'd loved me really you'd have loved me still."

"I should have thought so too. I remember how I used to think that it would last for ever, I felt I would rather die than be without you, and I used to long for the time when you would be faded and wrinkled so that nobody cared for you any more and I should have you all to myself."

She did not answer, and presently she got up and said she was going to bed. She gave a timid little smile.

"It's Christmas Day, Philip, won't you kiss me good-night?"

He gave a laugh, blushed slightly, and kissed her. She went to her bedroom and he began to read.

XCVI

THE climax came two or three weeks later. Mildred was driven by Philip's behaviour to a pitch of strange exasperation. There were many different emotions in her soul, and she passed from mood to mood with facility. She spent a great deal of time alone and brooded over her position. She did not put all her feelings into words, she did not even know what they were, but certain things stood out in her mind, and she thought of them over and over again. She had never understood Philip, nor had very much liked him; but she was pleased to have him about her because she thought he was a gentleman. She was impressed because his father had been a doctor and his uncle was a clergyman. She despised him a little because she had made such a fool of him, and at the same time was never quite comfortable in his presence; she could not let herself go, and she felt that he was criticising her manners.

When she first came to live in the little rooms in Kennington she was tired out and ashamed. She was glad to be left alone. It was a comfort to think that there was no rent to pay; she need not go out in all weathers, and she could lie quietly in bed if she did not feel well. She had hated the life she led. It was horrible to have to be affable and subservient; and even now when it crossed her mind she cried with pity for herself as she thought of the roughness of men and their brutal language. But it crossed her mind very seldom. She was grateful to Philip for coming to her rescue, and when she remembered how honestly he had loved her and how badly she had treated him, she felt a pang of remorse. It was easy to make it up to him. It meant very little to her. She was surprised when he refused her suggestion, but she shrugged her shoulders: let him put on airs if he liked, she did not care, he would be anxious enough in a little while, and then it would be her turn to refuse; if he thought it was any deprivation to her he was very much mistaken. She had no doubt of her power over him. He was peculiar, but she knew him through and through. He had so often quarrelled with her and sworn he would never see her again, and then in a little while he had come on his knees begging to be forgiven. It gave her a thrill to think how he had cringed before her. He would have been glad to lie down on the ground for her to walk on him. She had seen him cry. She knew exactly how to treat him, pay no attention to him, just pretend you didn't notice his tempers, leave him severely alone, and in a little while he was sure to grovel. She laughed a little to herself, good-humouredly, when she thought how he had come and eaten dirt before her. She had had her fling now. She knew what men were and did not want to have anything more to do with them. She was quite ready to settle down with Philip. When all was said, he was a gentleman in every sense of the word, and that was something not to be sneezed at, wasn't it? Anyhow she was in no hurry, and she was not going to take the first step. She was glad to see how fond he was growing of the baby, though it tickled her a good deal; it was comic that he should set so much store on another man's child. He *was* peculiar and no mistake.

But one or two things surprised her. She had been used to his subservience: he was only too glad to do anything for her in the old days, she was accustomed to see him cast down by a cross word and in ecstasy at a kind one; he was different now, and she said to herself that he had not improved in the last year. It never struck her for a moment that there could be any change in his feelings, and she thought it was only acting when he paid no heed to her bad temper. He wanted to read sometimes and told her to stop talking: she did not know whether to flare up or to sulk, and was so puzzled that she did neither. Then came the conversation in which he told her that he intended their relations to be platonic, and, remembering an incident of their common past, it occurred to her that he dreaded the possibility of her being pregnant. She took pains to reassure him. It made no difference. She was the sort of woman who was unable to realise that a man might not have her own obsession with sex; her relations with men had been purely on those lines; and she could not understand that they ever had other interests. The thought struck her that Philip was in love with somebody else, and she watched him, suspecting nurses at the hospital or people he met out; but artful questions led her to the conclusion that there was no one dangerous in the Athelny household; and it forced itself upon her also that Philip, like most medical students, was unconscious of the sex of the nurses with whom his work threw him in contact. They were associated in his mind with a faint odour of iodoform. Philip received no letters, and there was no girl's photograph among his belong-

ings. If he was in love with someone, he was very clever at hiding it; and he answered all Mildred's questions with frankness and apparently without suspicion that there was any motive in them.

"I don't believe he's in love with anybody else," she said to herself at last.

It was a relief, for in that case he was certainly still in love with her; but it made his behaviour very puzzling. If he was going to treat her like that why did he ask her to come and live at the flat? It was unnatural. Mildred was not a woman who conceived the possibility of compassion, generosity, or kindness. Her only conclusion was that Philip was queer. She took it into her head that the reasons for his conduct were chivalrous; and, her imagination filled with the extravagances of cheap fiction, she pictured to herself all sorts of romantic explanations for his delicacy. Her fancy ran riot with bitter misunderstandings, purifications by fire, snow-white souls, and death in the cruel cold of a Christmas night. She made up her mind that when they went to Brighton she would put an end to all his nonsense; they would be alone there, everyone would think them husband and wife, and there would be the pier and the band. When she found that nothing would induce Philip to share the same room with her, when he spoke to her about it with a tone in his voice she had never heard before, she suddenly realised that he did not want her. She was astounded. She remembered all he had said in the past and how desperately he had loved her. She felt humiliated and angry, but she had a sort of native insolence which carried her through. He needn't think she was in love with him, because she wasn't. She hated him sometimes, and she longed to humble him; but she found herself singularly powerless; she did not know which way to handle him. She began to be a little nervous with him. Once or twice she cried. Once or twice she set herself to be particularly nice to him; but when she took his arm while they walked along the front at night he made some excuse in a while to release himself, as though it were unpleasant for him to be touched by her. She could not make it out. The only hold she had over him was through the baby, of whom he seemed to grow fonder and fonder: she could make him white with anger by giving the child a slap or a push; and the only time the old, tender smile came back into his eyes was when she stood with the baby in her arms. She noticed it when she was being photographed like that by a man on the beach, and afterwards she often stood in the same way for Philip to look at her.

When they got back to London Mildred began looking for the work she had asserted was so easy to find; she wanted now to be independent of Philip; and she thought of the satisfaction with which she would announce to him that she was going into rooms and would take the child with her. But her heart failed her when she came into closer contact with the possibility. She had grown unused to the long hours, she did not want to be at the beck and call of a manageress, and her dignity revolted at the thought of wearing once more a uniform. She had made out to such of the neighbours as she knew that they were comfortably off: it would be a come-down if they heard that she had to go out and work. Her natural indolence asserted itself. She did not want to leave Philip, and so long as he was willing to provide for her, she did not see why she should. There was no money to throw away, but she got her

board and lodging, and he might get better off. His uncle was an old man and might die any day, he would come into a little then, and even as things were, it was better than slaving from morning till night for a few shillings a week. Her efforts relaxed; she kept on reading the advertisement columns of the daily paper merely to show that she wanted to do something if anything that was worth her while presented itself. But panic seized her, and she was afraid that Philip would grow tired of supporting her. She had no hold over him at all now, and she fancied that he only allowed her to stay there because he was fond of the baby. She brooded over it all, and she thought to herself angrily that she would make him pay for all this some day. She could not reconcile herself to the fact that he no longer cared for her. She would make him. She suffered from pique, and sometimes in a curious fashion she desired Philip. He was so cold now that it exasperated her. She thought of him in that way incessantly. She thought that he was treating her very badly, and she did not know what she had done to deserve it. She kept on saying to herself that it was unnatural they should live like that. Then she thought that if things were different and she were going to have a baby, he would be sure to marry her. He was funny, but he was a gentleman in every sense of the word, no one could deny that. At last it became an obsession with her, and she made up her mind to force a change in their relations. He never even kissed her now, and she wanted him to: she remembered how ardently he had been used to press her lips. It gave her a curious feeling to think of it. She often looked at his mouth.

One evening, at the beginning of February, Philip told her that he was dining with Lawson, who was giving a

party in his studio to celebrate his
birthday; and he would not be in till
late; Lawson had bought a couple of
bottles of the punch they favoured
from the tavern in Beak Street, and
they proposed to have a merry evening.
Mildred asked if there were going to
be women there, but Philip told her
there were not; only men had been
invited; and they were just going to sit
and talk and smoke: Mildred did not
think it sounded very amusing; if she
were a painter she would have half a
dozen models about. She went to bed,
but could not sleep, and presently an
idea struck her; she got up and fixed
the catch on the wicket at the landing, so that Philip could not get in.
He came back about one, and she
heard him curse when he found that
the wicket was closed. She got out of
bed and opened.

"Why on earth did you shut yourself in? I'm sorry I've dragged you
out of bed."

"I left it open on purpose, I can't
think how it came to be shut."

"Hurry up and get back to bed, or
you'll catch cold."

He walked into the sitting-room and
turned up the gas. She followed him
in. She went up to the fire.

"I want to warm my feet a bit.
They're like ice."

He sat down and began to take off
his boots. His eyes were shining and
his cheeks were flushed. She thought
he had been drinking.

"Have you been enjoying yourself?" she asked, with a smile.

"Yes, I've had a ripping time."

Philip was quite sober, but he had
been talking and laughing, and he was
excited still. An evening of that sort
reminded him of the old days in Paris.
He was in high spirits. He took his
pipe out of his pocket and filled it.

"Aren't you going to bed?" she
asked.

"Not yet, I'm not a bit sleepy. Lawson was in great form. He talked
sixteen to the dozen from the moment
I got there till the moment I left."

"What did you talk about?"

"Heaven knows! Of every subject
under the sun. You should have seen
us all shouting at the tops of our
voices and nobody listening."

Philip laughed with pleasure at the
recollection, and Mildred laughed too.
She was pretty sure he had drunk
more than was good for him. That
was exactly what she had expected.
She knew men.

"Can I sit down?" she said.

Before he could answer she settled
herself on his knees.

"If you're not going to bed you'd
better go and put on a dressing-gown."

"Oh, I'm all right as I am." Then
putting her arms round his neck, she
placed her face against his and said:
"Why are you so horrid to me, Phil?"

He tried to get up, but she would
not let him.

"I do love you, Philip," she said.

"Don't talk damned rot."

"It isn't, it's true. I can't live without you. I want you."

He released himself from her arms.

"Please get up. You're making a
fool of yourself and you're making me
feel a perfect idiot."

"I love you, Philip. I want to make
up for all the harm I did you. I can't
go on like this, it's not in human
nature."

He slipped out of the chair and
left her in it.

"I'm very sorry, but it's too late."

She gave a heart-rending sob.

"But why? How can you be so
cruel?"

"I suppose it's because I loved you
too much. I wore the passion out.
The thought of anything of that sort
horrifies me. I can't look at you now
without thinking of Emil and Grif-

fiths. One can't help those things, I suppose it's just nerves."

She seized his hand and covered it with kisses.

"Don't," he cried.

She sank back into the chair.

"I can't go on like this. If you won't love me, I'd rather go away."

"Don't be foolish, you haven't anywhere to go. You can stay here as long as you like, but it must be on the definite understanding that we're friends and nothing more."

Then she dropped suddenly the vehemence of passion and gave a soft, insinuating laugh. She sidled up to Philip and put her arms round him. She made her voice low and wheedling.

"Don't be such an old silly. I believe you're nervous. You don't know how nice I can be."

She put her face against his and rubbed his cheek with hers. To Philip her smile was an abominable leer, and the suggestive glitter of her eyes filled him with horror. He drew back instinctively.

"I won't," he said.

But she would not let him go. She sought his mouth with her lips. He took her hands and tore them roughly apart and pushed her away.

"You disgust me," he said.

"Me?"

She steadied herself with one hand on the chimney-piece. She looked at him for an instant, and two red spots suddenly appeared on her cheeks. She gave a shrill, angry laugh.

"I disgust *you.*"

She paused and drew in her breath sharply. Then she burst into a furious torrent of abuse. She shouted at the top of her voice. She called him every foul name she could think of. She used language so obscene that Philip was astounded; she was always so anxious to be refined, so shocked by coarseness, that it had never occurred to him that she knew the words she used now. She came up to him and thrust her face in his. It was distorted with passion, and in her tumultuous speech the spittle dribbled over her lips.

"I never cared for you, not once, I was making a fool of you always, you bored me, you bored me stiff, and I hated you, I would never have let you touch me only for the money, and it used to make me sick when I had to let you kiss me. We laughed at you, Griffiths and me, we laughed because you was such a mug. A mug! A mug!"

Then she burst again into abominable invective. She accused him of every mean fault; she said he was stingy, she said he was dull, she said he was vain, selfish; she cast virulent ridicule on everything upon which he was most sensitive. And at last she turned to go. She kept on, with hysterical violence, shouting at him an opprobrious, filthy epithet. She seized the hand of the door and flung it open. Then she turned round and hurled at him the injury which she knew was the only one that really touched him. She threw into the word all the malice and all the venom of which she was capable. She flung it at him as though it were a blow.

"Cripple!"

XCVII

PHILIP awoke with a start next morning, conscious that it was late, and looking at his watch found it was nine o'clock. He jumped out of bed and went into the kitchen to get himself some hot water to shave with. There was no sign of Mildred, and the things which she had used for her supper the night before still lay in the sink unwashed. He knocked at her door.

"Wake up, Mildred. It's awfully late."

She did not answer, even after a second louder knocking, and he concluded that she was sulking. He was in too great a hurry to bother about that. He put some water on to boil and jumped into his bath which was always poured out the night before in order to take the chill off. He presumed that Mildred would cook his breakfast while he was dressing and leave it in the sitting-room. She had done that two or three times when she was out of temper. But he heard no sound of her moving, and realised that if he wanted anything to eat he would have to get it himself. He was irritated that she should play him such a trick on a morning when he had overslept himself. There was still no sign of her when he was ready, but he heard her moving about her room. She was evidently getting up. He made himself some tea and cut himself a couple of pieces of bread and butter, which he ate while he was putting on his boots, then bolted downstairs and along the street into the main road to catch his tram. While his eyes sought out the newspaper shops to see the war news on the placards, he thought of the scene of the night before: now that it was over and he had slept on it, he could not help thinking it grotesque; he supposed he had been ridiculous, but he was not master of his feelings; at the time they had been overwhelming. He was angry with Mildred because she had forced him into that absurd position, and then renewed with astonishment he thought of her outburst and the filthy language she had used. He could not help flushing when he remembered her final jibe; but he shrugged his shoulders contemptuously. He had long known that when his fellows were angry with him they never failed to taunt him with his deformity. He had seen men at the hospital imitate his walk, not before him as they used at school, but when they thought he was not looking. He knew now that they did it from no wilful unkindness, but because man is naturally an imitative animal, and because it was an easy way to make people laugh: he knew it, but he could never resign himself to it.

He was glad to throw himself into his work. The ward seemed pleasant and friendly when he entered it. The sister greeted him with a quick, business-like smile.

"You're very late, Mr. Carey."

"I was out on the loose last night."

"You look it."

"Thank you."

Laughing, he went to the first of his cases, a boy with tuberculous ulcers, and removed his bandages. The boy was pleased to see him, and Philip chaffed him as he put a clean dressing on the wound. Philip was a favourite with the patients; he treated them good-humouredly; and he had gentle, sensitive hands which did not hurt them: some of the dressers were a little rough and happy-go-lucky in their methods. He lunched with his friends in the club-room, a frugal meal consisting of a scone and butter, with a cup of cocoa, and they talked of the war. Several men were going out, but the authorities were particular and refused everyone who had not had a hospital appointment. Someone suggested that, if the war went on, in a while they would be glad to take anyone who was qualified; but the general opinion was that it would be over in a month. Now that Roberts was there things would get all right in no time. This was Macalister's opinion too, and he had told Philip that they must watch their chance and buy just before peace was declared. There would be a boom then, and they might all make a bit of money. Philip had left with Macalister instructions to buy him stock whenever the opportunity presented itself. His appetite had been whetted by the thirty pounds he had made in the summer, and he wanted now to make a couple of hundred.

He finished his day's work and got on a tram to go back to Kennington. He wondered how Mildred would behave that evening. It was a nuisance to think that she would probably be surly and refuse to answer his questions. It was a warm evening for the time of year, and even in those gray streets of South London there was the languor of February; nature is restless then after the long winter months, growing things awake from their sleep, and there is a rustle in the earth, a forerunner of spring, as it resumes its eternal activities. Philip would have liked to drive on further, it was distasteful to him to go back to his rooms, and he wanted the air; but

the desire to see the child clutched suddenly at his heart-strings, and he smiled to himself as he thought of her toddling towards him with a crow of delight. He was surprised, when he reached the house and looked up mechanically at the windows, to see that there was no light. He went upstairs and knocked, but got no answer. When Mildred went out she left the key under the mat and he found it there now. He let himself in and going into the sitting-room struck a match. Something had happened, he did not at once know what; he turned the gas on full and lit it; the room was suddenly filled with the glare and he looked round. He gasped. The whole place was wrecked. Everything in it had been wilfully destroyed. Anger seized him, and he rushed into Mildred's room. It was dark and empty. When he had got a light he saw that she had taken away all her things and the baby's; (he had noticed on entering that the go-cart was not in its usual place on the landing, but thought Mildred had taken the baby out;) and all the things on the washing-stand had been broken, a knife had been drawn cross-ways through the seats of the two chairs, the pillow had been slit open, there were large gashes in the sheets and the counterpane, the looking-glass appeared to have been broken with a hammer. Philip was bewildered. He went into his own room, and here too everything was in confusion. The basin and the ewer had been smashed, the looking-glass was in fragments, and the sheets were in ribands. Mildred had made a slit large enough to put her hand into the pillow and had scattered the feathers about the room. She had jabbed a knife into the blankets. On the dressing-table were photographs of Philip's mother, the frames had been smashed and the glass shivered. Philip went into the tiny kitchen. Everything that was breakable was broken, glasses, pudding-basins, plates, dishes.

It took Philip's breath away. Mildred had left no letter, nothing but this ruin to mark her anger, and he could imagine the set face with which she had gone about her work. He went back into the sitting-room and looked about him. He was astonished that he no longer felt angry. He looked curiously at the kitchen-knife and the coal-hammer, which were lying on the table where she had left them. Then his eye caught a large carving-knife in the fireplace which had been broken. It must have taken her a long time to do so much damage. Lawson's portrait of him had been cut cross-ways and gaped hideously. His own drawings had been ripped in pieces; and the photographs, Manet's *Olympia* and the *Odalisque* of Ingres, the portrait of Philip IV, had been smashed with great blows of the coal-hammer. There were gashes in the table-cloth and in the curtains and in the two arm-chairs. They were quite ruined. On one wall over the table which Philip used as his desk was the little bit of Persian rug which Cronshaw had given him. Mildred had always hated it.

"If it's a rug it ought to go on the floor," she said, "and it's a dirty stinking bit of stuff, that's all it is."

It made her furious because Philip told her it contained the answer to a great riddle. She thought he was making fun of her. She had drawn the knife right through it three times, it must have required some strength, and it hung now in tatters. Philip had two or three blue and white plates, of no value, but he had bought them one by one for very small sums and liked them for their associations. They littered the floor in fragments. There

were long gashes on the backs of his books, and she had taken the trouble to tear pages out of the unbound French ones. The little ornaments on the chimney-piece lay on the hearth in bits. Everything that it had been possible to destroy with a knife or a hammer was destroyed.

The whole of Philip's belongings would not have sold for thirty pounds, but most of them were old friends, and he was a domestic creature, attached to all those odds and ends because they were his; he had been proud of his little home, and on so little money had made it pretty and characteristic. He sank down now in despair. He asked himself how she could have been so cruel. A sudden fear got him on his feet again and into the passage, where stood a cupboard in which he kept his clothes. He opened it and gave a sigh of relief. She had apparently forgotten it and none of his things was touched.

He went back into the sitting-room and, surveying the scene, wondered what to do; he had not the heart to begin trying to set things straight; besides there was no food in the house, and he was hungry. He went out and got himself something to eat. When he came in he was cooler. A little pang seized him as he thought of the child, and he wondered whether she would miss him, at first perhaps, but in a week she would have forgotten him; and he was thankful to be rid of Mildred. He did not think of her with wrath, but with an overwhelming sense of boredom.

"I hope to God I never see her again," he said aloud.

The only thing now was to leave the rooms, and he made up his mind to give notice the next morning. He could not afford to make good the damage done, and he had so little money left that he must find cheaper lodgings still. He would be glad to get out of them. The expense had worried him, and now the recollection of Mildred would be in them always. Philip was impatient and could never rest till he had put in action the plan which he had in mind; so on the following afternoon he got in a dealer in second-hand furniture who offered him three pounds for all his goods damaged and undamaged; and two days later he moved into the house opposite the hospital in which he had had rooms when first he became a medical student. The landlady was a very decent woman. He took a bedroom at the top, which she let him have for six shillings a week; it was small and shabby and looked on the yard of the house that backed on to it, but he had nothing now except his clothes and a box of books, and he was glad to lodge so cheaply.

XCVIII

AND now it happened that the fortunes of Philip Carey, of no consequence to any but himself, were affected by the events through which his country was passing. History was being made, and the process was so significant that it seemed absurd it should touch the life of an obscure medical student. Battle after battle, Magersfontein, Colenso, Spion Kop, lost on the playing fields of Eton, had humiliated the nation and dealt the death-blow to the prestige of the aristocracy and gentry who till then had found no one seriously to oppose their assertion that they possessed a natural instinct of government. The old order was being swept away: history was being made indeed. Then the colossus put forth his strength, and, blundering again, at last blundered into the semblance of victory. Cronje surrendered at Paardeberg, Ladysmith was relieved, and at the beginning of March Lord Roberts marched into Bloemfontein.

It was two or three days after the news of this reached London that Macalister came into the tavern in Beak Street and announced joyfully that things were looking brighter on the Stock Exchange. Peace was in sight, Roberts would march into Pretoria within a few weeks, and shares were going up already. There was bound to be a boom.

"Now's the time to come in," he told Philip. "It's no good waiting till the public gets on to it. It's now or never."

He had inside information. The manager of a mine in South Africa had cabled to the senior partner of his firm that the plant was uninjured. They would start working again as soon as possible. It wasn't a speculation, it was an investment. To show how good a thing the senior partner thought it Macalister told Philip that he had bought five hundred shares for both his sisters: he never put them into anything that wasn't as safe as the Bank of England.

"I'm going to put my shirt on it myself," he said.

The shares were two and an eighth to a quarter. He advised Philip not to be greedy, but to be satisfied with a ten-shilling rise. He was buying three hundred for himself and suggested that Philip should do the same. He would hold them and sell when he thought fit. Philip had great faith in him, partly because he was a Scotsman and therefore by nature cautious, and partly because he had been right before. He jumped at the suggestion.

"I daresay we shall be able to sell before the account," said Macalister, "but if not, I'll arrange to carry them over for you."

It seemed a capital system to Philip. You held on till you got your profit, and you never even had to put your hand in your pocket. He began to watch the Stock Exchange columns of the paper with new interest. Next day everything was up a little, and Macalister wrote to say that he had had to pay two and a quarter for the shares. He said that the market was firm. But in a day or two there was a set-back. The news that came from South Africa was less reassuring, and Philip with anxiety saw that his shares had fallen to two; but Macalister was optimistic, the Boers couldn't hold out much longer, and he was willing to bet a top-hat that Roberts would march into Johannesburg before the middle of April. At the account Philip had to pay out nearly forty pounds. It worried him considerably, but he felt that the only course was to hold on: in his circumstances the loss was too great for him to pocket. For two or three weeks nothing happened; the Boers would not understand that they were beaten and nothing remained for them but to surrender: in fact they had one or two small successes, and Philip's shares fell half a crown more. It became evident that the war was not finished. There was a lot of selling. When Macalister saw Philip he was pessimistic.

"I'm not sure if the best thing wouldn't be to cut the loss. I've been paying out about as much as I want to in differences."

Philip was sick with anxiety. He could not sleep at night; he bolted his breakfast, reduced now to tea and bread and butter, in order to get over to the club reading-room and see the paper; sometimes the news was bad, and sometimes there was no news at all, but when the shares moved it was to go down. He did not know what to do. If he sold now he would lose altogether hard on three hundred and fifty pounds; and that would leave him only eighty pounds to go on with. He wished with all his heart that he had never been such a fool as to dabble on the Stock Exchange, but the only thing was to hold on; something decisive might happen any day and the shares would go up; he did not hope now for a profit, but he wanted to make good his loss. It was his only chance of finishing his course at the hospital. The summer session was beginning in May, and at the end of it he meant to take the examination in midwifery. Then he would only have a year more; he reckoned it out carefully and came to the conclusion that he could manage it, fees and all, on a hundred and fifty pounds; but that was the least it could possibly be done on.

Early in April he went to the tavern in Beak Street anxious to see Macalister. It eased him a little to discuss the situation with him; and to realise that numerous people beside himself were suffering from loss of money made his own trouble a little less intolerable. But when Philip arrived no one was there but Hayward, and no sooner had Philip seated himself than he said:

"I'm sailing for the Cape on Sunday."

"Are you!" exclaimed Philip.

Hayward was the last person he would have expected to do anything of the kind. At the hospital men were going out now in numbers; the Government was glad to get anyone who was qualified; and others, going out as troopers, wrote home that they had been put on hospital work as soon as it was learned that they were medical students. A wave of patriotic feeling had swept over the country, and volunteers were coming from all ranks of society.

"What are you going as?" asked Philip.

"Oh, in the Dorset Yeomanry. I'm going as a trooper."

Philip had known Hayward for eight years. The youthful intimacy which had come from Philip's enthusiastic admiration for the man who could tell him of art and literature had long since vanished; but habit had taken its place; and when Hayward was in London they saw one another once or twice a week. He still talked about books with a delicate appreciation. Philip was not yet tolerant, and sometimes Hayward's conversation irritated him. He no longer believed implicitly that nothing in the world was of consequence but art. He resented Hayward's contempt for action and success. Philip, stirring his punch, thought of his early friendship and his ardent expectation that Hayward would do great things; it was long since he had lost all such illusions, and he knew now that Hayward would never do anything but talk. He found his three hundred a year more difficult to live on now that he was thirty-five than he had when he was a young man; and his clothes, though still made by a good tailor, were worn a good deal longer than at one time he would have thought possible. He was too stout, and no artful arrangement of his fair hair could conceal the fact that he was bald. His blue eyes were dull and pale. It was not hard to guess that he drank too much.

"What on earth made you think of going out to the Cape?" asked Philip.

"Oh, I don't know, I thought I ought to."

Philip was silent. He felt rather silly. He understood that Hayward was being driven by an uneasiness in his soul which he could not account for. Some power within him made it seem necessary to go and fight for his country. It was strange, since he considered patriotism no more than a prejudice, and, flattering himself on his cosmopolitanism, he had looked upon England as a place of exile. His countrymen in the mass wounded his susceptibilities. Philip wondered what it was that made people do things which were so contrary to all their theories of life. It would have been reasonable for Hayward to stand aside and watch with a smile while the barbarians slaughtered one another. It looked as though men were puppets in the hands of an unknown force, which drove them to do this and that; and sometimes they used their reason to justify their actions; and when this was impossible they did the actions in despite of reason.

"People are very extraordinary," said Philip. "I should never have expected you to go out as a trooper."

Hayward smiled, slightly embarrassed, and said nothing.

"I was examined yesterday," he remarked at last. "It was worth while undergoing the *gêne* of it to know that one was perfectly fit."

Philip noticed that he still used a French word in an affected way when an English one would have served. But just then Macalister came in.

"I wanted to see you, Carey," he said. "My people don't feel inclined to hold those shares any more, the market's in such an awful state, and they want you to take them up."

Philip's heart sank. He knew that was impossible. It meant that he must accept the loss. His pride made him answer calmly.

"I don't know that I think that's worth while. You'd better sell them."

"It's all very fine to say that, I'm not sure if I can. The market's stagnant, there are no buyers."

"But they're marked down at one and an eighth."

"Oh yes, but that doesn't mean anything. You can't get that for them."

Philip did not say anything for a moment. He was trying to collect himself.

"D'you mean to say they're worth nothing at all?"

"Oh, I don't say that. Of course they're worth something, but you see, nobody's buying them now."

"Then you must just sell them for what you can get."

Macalister looked at Philip narrowly. He wondered whether he was very hard hit.

"I'm awfully sorry, old man, but we're all in the same boat. No one thought the war was going to hang on this way. I put you into them, but I was in myself too."

"It doesn't matter at all," said Philip. "One has to take one's chance."

He moved back to the table from which he had got up to talk to Macalister. He was dumfounded; his head suddenly began to ache furiously; but he did not want them to think him unmanly. He sat on for an hour. He laughed feverishly at everything they said. At last he got up to go.

"You take it pretty coolly," said Macalister, shaking hands with him. "I don't suppose anyone likes losing between three and four hundred pounds."

When Philip got back to his shabby little room he flung himself on his bed, and gave himself over to his despair. He kept on regretting his folly bitterly; and though he told himself that it was absurd to regret, for what had happened was inevitable just because it had happened, he could not help himself. He was utterly miserable. He could not sleep. He remembered all the ways he had wasted money during the last few years. His head ached dreadfully.

The following evening there came by the last post the statement of his account. He examined his pass-book. He found that when he had paid everything he would have seven pounds left. Seven pounds! He was thankful he had been able to pay. It would have been horrible to be obliged to confess to Macalister that he had not the money. He was dressing in the eye-department during the summer session, and he had bought an ophthalmoscope off a student who had one to sell. He had not paid for this, but he lacked the courage to tell the student that he wanted to go back on his bargain. Also he had to buy certain books. He had about five pounds to on with. It lasted him six weeks; then he wrote to his uncle a letter which he thought very business-like; he said that owing to the war he had had grave losses and could not go on with his studies unless his uncle came to his help. He suggested that the Vicar should lend him a hundred and fifty pounds paid over the next eighteen months in monthly instalments; he would pay interest on this and promised to refund the capital by degrees when he began to earn money. He would be qualified in a year and a half at the latest, and he could be pretty sure then of getting an assistantship at three pounds a week. His uncle wrote back that he could do nothing. It was not fair to ask him to sell out when everything was at its worst, and the little he had he felt that his duty to himself made it necessary for him to keep in case of illness. He ended the letter with a little homily. He had warned Philip time after time, and Philip had never paid any attention to him; he could not honestly say he was surprised; he had long expected that this would be the end of Philip's extravagance and want of balance. Philip grew hot and cold when he read this. It had never occurred to him that his uncle would refuse, and he burst into furious anger; but this was succeeded by utter blankness: if his uncle would not help him he could not go on at the hospital.

Panic seized him and, putting aside his pride, he wrote again to the Vicar of Blackstable, placing the case before him more urgently; but perhaps he did not explain himself properly and his uncle did not realise in what desperate straits he was, for he answered that he could not change his mind; Philip was twenty-five and really ought to be earning his living. When he died Philip would come into a little, but till then he refused to give him a penny. Philip felt in the letter the satisfaction of a man who for many years had disapproved of his courses and now saw himself justified.

XCIX

PHILIP began to pawn his clothes. He reduced his expenses by eating only one meal a day beside his breakfast; and he ate it, bread and butter and cocoa, at four so that it should last him till next morning. He was so hungry by nine o'clock that he had to go to bed. He thought of borrowing money from Lawson, but the fear of a refusal held him back; at last he asked him for five pounds. Lawson lent it with pleasure, but, as he did so, said:

"You'll let me have it back in a week or so, won't you? I've got to pay my framer, and I'm awfully broke just now."

Philip knew he would not be able to return it, and the thought of what Lawson would think made him so ashamed that in a couple of days he took the money back untouched. Lawson was just going out to luncheon and asked Philip to come too. Philip could hardly eat, he was so glad to get some solid food. On Sunday he was sure of a good dinner from Athelny. He hesitated to tell the

Athelnys what had happened to him: they had always looked upon him as comparatively well-to-do, and he had a dread that they would think less well of him if they knew he was penniless.

Though he had always been poor, the possibility of not having enough to eat had never occurred to him; it was not the sort of thing that happened to the people among whom he lived; and he was as ashamed as if he had some disgraceful disease. The situation in which he found himself was quite outside the range of his experience. He was so taken aback that he did not know what else to do than to go on at the hospital; he had a vague hope that something would turn up; he could not quite believe that what was happening to him was true; and he remembered how during his first term at school he had often thought his life was a dream from which he would awake to find himself once more at home. But very soon he foresaw that in a week or so he would have no money at all. He must set about trying to earn something at once. If he had been qualified, even with a club-foot, he could have gone out to the Cape, since the demand for medical men was now great. Except for his deformity he might have enlisted in one of the yeomanry regiments which were constantly being sent out. He went to the secretary of the Medical School and asked if he could give him the coaching of some backward student; but the secretary held out no hope of getting him anything of the sort. Philip read the advertisement columns of the medical papers, and he applied for the post of unqualified assistant to a man who had a dispensary in the Fulham Road. When he went to see him, he saw the doctor glance at his club-foot; and on hearing that Philip was only in his fourth year at the hospital he said at once that his experience was insufficient: Philip understood that this was only an excuse; the man would not have an assistant who might not be as active as he wanted. Philip turned his attention to other means of earning money. He knew French and German and thought there might be some chance of finding a job as correspondence clerk; it made his heart sink, but he set his teeth; there was nothing else to do. Though too shy to answer the advertisements which demanded a personal application, he replied to those which asked for letters; but he had no experience to state and no recommendations: he was conscious that neither his German nor his French was commercial; he was ignorant of the terms used in business; he knew neither shorthand nor typewriting. He could not help recognising that his case was hopeless. He thought of writing to the solicitor who had been his father's executor, but he could not bring himself to, for it

was contrary to his express advice that he had sold the mortgages in which his money had been invested. He knew from his uncle that Mr. Nixon thoroughly disapproved of him. He had gathered from Philip's year in the accountant's office that he was idle and incompetent.

"I'd sooner starve," Philip muttered to himself.

Once or twice the possibility of suicide presented itself to him; it would be easy to get something from the hospital dispensary, and it was a comfort to think that if the worst came to the worst he had at hand means of making a painless end of himself; but it was not a course that he considered seriously. When Mildred had left him to go with Griffiths his anguish had been so great that he wanted to die in order to get rid of the pain. He did not feel like that now. He remembered that the Casualty Sister had told him how people oftener did away with themselves for want of money than for want of love; and he chuckled when he thought that he was an exception. He wished only that he could talk his worries over with somebody, but he could not bring himself to confess them. He was ashamed. He went on looking for work. He left his rent unpaid for three weeks, explaining to his landlady that he would get money at the end of the month; she did not say anything, but pursed her lips and looked grim. When the end of the month came and she asked if it would be convenient for him to pay something on account, it made him feel very sick to say that he could not; he told her he would write to his uncle and was sure to be able to settle his bill on the following Saturday.

"Well, I 'ope you will, Mr. Carey, because I 'ave my rent to pay, and I can't afford to let accounts run on."

She did not speak with anger, but with determination that was rather frightening. She paused for a moment and then said: "If you don't pay next Saturday, I shall 'ave to complain to the secretary of the 'ospital."

"Oh yes, that'll be all right."

She looked at him for a little and glanced round the bare room. When she spoke it was without any emphasis, as though it were quite a natural thing to say.

"I've got a nice 'ot joint downstairs, and if you like to come down to the kitchen you're welcome to a bit of dinner."

Philip felt himself redden to the soles of his feet, and a sob caught at his throat.

"Thank you very much, Mrs. Higgins, but I'm not at all hungry."

"Very good, sir."

When she left the room Philip threw himself on his bed. He had to clench his fists in order to prevent himself from crying.

C

SATURDAY. It was the day on which he had promised to pay his landlady. He had been expecting something to turn up all through the week. He had found no work. He had never been driven to extremities before, and he was so dazed that he did not know what to do. He had at the back of his mind a feeling that the whole thing was a preposterous joke. He had no more than a few coppers left, he had sold all the clothes he could do without; he had some books and one or two odds and ends upon which he might have got a shilling or two, but the landlady was keeping an eye on his comings and goings: he was afraid she would stop him if he took anything more from his room. The only thing was to tell her that he could not pay his bill. He had not the courage. It was the middle of June. The night was fine and warm. He made up his mind to stay out. He walked slowly along the Chelsea Embankment, because the river was restful and quiet, till he was tired, and then sat on a bench and dozed. He did not know how long he slept; he awoke with a start, dreaming that he was being shaken by a policeman and told to move on; but when he opened his eyes he found himself alone. He walked on, he did not know why, and at last came to Chiswick, where he slept again. Presently the hardness of the bench roused him. The night seemed very long. He shivered. He was seized with a sense of his misery; and he did not know what on earth to do: he was ashamed at having slept on the Embankment; it seemed peculiarly humiliating, and he felt his cheeks flush in the darkness. He remembered stories he had heard of those who did and how among them were officers, clergymen, and men who had been to universities: he wondered if he would become one of them, standing in a line to get soup from a charitable institution. It would be much better to commit suicide. He could not go on like that: Lawson would help him when he knew what straits he was in; it was absurd to let his pride prevent him from asking for assistance. He wondered why he had come such a cropper. He had always tried to do what he thought best, and everything had gone wrong. He had helped people when he could, he did not think he had been more selfish than anyone else, it seemed horribly unjust that he should be reduced to such a pass.

But it was no good thinking about it. He walked on. It was now light: the river was beautiful in the silence, and there was something mysterious in the early day; it was going to be very fine, and the sky, pale in the dawn, was cloudless. He felt very tired, and hunger was gnawing at his entrails, but he could not sit still; he was constantly afraid of being spoken to by a policeman. He dreaded the mortification of that. He felt dirty and wished he could have a wash. At last he found himself at Hampton Court. He felt that if he did not have something to eat he would cry. He chose a cheap eating-house and went in; there was a smell of hot things, and it made him feel slightly sick: he meant to eat something nourishing enough to keep up for the rest of the day, but his stomach revolted at the sight of food. He had a cup of tea and some bread and butter. He remembered then that it was Sunday and he could go to the Athelnys; he thought of the roast beef and the Yorkshire pudding they would eat; but he was fearfully tired and could not face the happy, noisy family. He was feeling morose and wretched. He wanted to be left alone. He made up his mind that he would go into the gardens of the palace and lie down. His bones ached. Perhaps he would find a pump so that he could wash his hands and face and drink something; he was very thirsty; and now that he was no longer hungry he thought with pleasure of the flowers and the lawns and the great leafy trees. He felt that there he could think out better what he must do. He lay on the grass, in the shade, and lit his pipe. For economy's sake he had

for a long time confined himself to two pipes a day; he was thankful now that his pouch was full. He did not know what people did when they had no money. Presently he fell asleep. When he awoke it was nearly mid-day, and he thought that soon he must be setting out for London so as to be there in the early morning and answer any advertisements which seemed to promise. He thought of his uncle, who had told him that he would leave him at his death the little he had; Philip did not in the least know how much this was: it could not be more than a few hundred pounds. He wondered whether he could raise money on the reversion. Not without the old man's consent, and that he would never give.

"The only thing I can do is to hang on somehow till he dies."

Philip reckoned his age. The Vicar of Blackstable was well over seventy. He had chronic bronchitis, but many old men had that and lived on indefinitely. Meanwhile something must turn up; Philip could not get away from the feeling that his position was altogether abnormal; people in his particular station did not starve. It was because he could not bring himself to believe in the reality of his experience that he did not give way to utter despair. He made up his mind to borrow half a sovereign from Lawson. He stayed in the garden all day and smoked when he felt very hungry; he did not mean to eat anything until he was setting out again for London: it was a long way and he must keep up his strength for that. He started when the day began to grow cooler, and slept on benches when he was tired. No one disturbed him. He had a wash and brush up, and a shave at Victoria, some tea and bread and butter, and while he was eating this read the advertisement col-

umns of the morning paper. As he
looked down them his eye fell upon
an announcement asking for a salesman in the 'furnishing drapery' department of some well-known stores.
He had a curious little sinking of the
heart, for with his middle-class prejudices it seemed dreadful to go into
a shop; but he shrugged his shoulders,
after all what did it matter? and he
made up his mind to have a shot at
it. He had a queer feeling that by
accepting every humiliation, by going
out to meet it even, he was forcing
the hand of fate. When he presented
himself, feeling horribly shy, in the
department at nine o'clock he found
that many others were there before
him. They were of all ages, from boys
of sixteen to men of forty; some were
talking to one another in undertones,
but most were silent; and when he
took up his place those around him
gave him a look of hostility. He heard
one man say:

"The only thing I look forward to
is getting my refusal soon enough to
give me time to look elsewhere."

The man, standing next him,
glanced at Philip and asked:

"Had any experience?"

"No," said Philip.

He paused a moment and then
made a remark: "Even the smaller
houses won't see you without appointment after lunch."

Philip looked at the assistants. Some
were draping chintzes and cretonnes,
and others, his neighbour told him
were preparing country orders that had
come in by post. At about a quarter
past nine the buyer arrived. He heard
one of the men who were waiting say
to another that it was Mr. Gibbons.
He was middle-aged, short and corpulent, with a black beard and dark,
greasy hair. He had brisk movements
and a clever face. He wore a silk hat
and a frock coat, the lapel of which

was adorned with a white geranium
surrounded by leaves. He went into
his office, leaving the door open; it
was very small and contained only
an American roll-desk in the corner,
a bookcase, and cupboard. The men
standing outside watched him mechanically take the geranium out of his
coat and put it in an ink-pot filled with
water. It was against the rules to wear
flowers in business.

[During the day the department
men who wanted to keep in with the
governor admired the flower.

"I've never seen better," they said,
"you didn't grow it yourself?"

"Yes I did," he smiled, and a gleam
of pride filled his intelligent eyes.]

He took off his hat and changed
his coat, glanced at the letters and
then at the men who were waiting
to see him. He made a slight sign
with one finger, and the first in the
queue stepped into the office. They
filed past him one by one and answered his questions. He put them very
briefly, keeping his eyes fixed on the
applicant's face.

"Age? Experience? Why did you
leave your job?"

He listened to the replies without
expression. When it came to Philip's
turn he fancied that Mr. Gibbons
stared at him curiously. Philip's clothes
were neat and tolerably cut. He
looked a little different from the
others.

"Experience?"

"I'm afraid I haven't any," said
Philip.

"No good."

Philip walked out of the office.
The ordeal had been so much less
painful than he expected that he felt
no particular disappointment. He
could hardly hope to succeed in getting a place the first time he tried.
He had kept the newspaper and now
looked at the advertisements again: a

shop in Holborn needed a salesman too, and he went there; but when he arrived he found that someone had already been engaged. If he wanted to get anything to eat that day he must go to Lawson's studio before he went out to luncheon, so he made his way along the Brompton Road to Yeoman's Row.

"I say, I'm rather broke till the end of the month," he said as soon as he found an opportunity. "I wish you'd lend me half a sovereign, will you?"

It was incredible the difficulty he found in asking for money; and he remembered the casual way, as though almost they were conferring a favour, men at the hospital had extracted small sums out of him which they had no intention of repaying.

"Like a shot," said Lawson.

But when he put his hand in his pocket he found that he had only eight shillings. Philip's heart sank.

"Oh well, lend me five bob, will you?" he said lightly.

"Here you are."

Philip went to the public baths in Westminster and spent sixpence on a bath. Then he got himself something to eat. He did not know what to do with himself in the afternoon. He would not go back to the hospital in case anyone should ask him questions, and besides, he had nothing to do there now; they would wonder in the two or three departments he had worked in why he did not come, but they must think what they chose, it did not matter: he would not be the first student who had dropped out without warning. He went to the free library, and looked at the papers till they wearied him, then he took out Stevenson's *New Arabian Nights;* but he found he could not read: the words meant nothing to him, and he continued to brood over his helpless-ness. He kept on thinking the same things all the time, and the fixity of his thoughts made his head ache. At last, craving for fresh air, he went into the Green Park and lay down on the grass. He thought miserably of his deformity, which made it impossible for him to go to the war. He went to sleep and dreamed that he was suddenly sound of foot and out at the Cape in a regiment of Yeomanry; the pictures he had looked at in the illustrated papers gave materials for his fancy; and he saw himself on the Veldt, in khaki, sitting with other men round a fire at night. When he awoke he found that it was still quite light, and presently he heard Big Ben strike seven. He had twelve hours to get through with nothing to do. He dreaded the interminable night. The sky was overcast and he feared it would rain; he would have to go to a lodging-house where he could get a bed; he had seen them advertised on lamps outside houses in Lambeth: Good Beds sixpence; he had never been inside one, and dreaded the foul smell and the vermin. He made up his mind to stay in the open air if he possibly could. He remained in the park till it was closed and then began to walk about. He was very tired. The thought came to him that an accident would be a piece of luck, so that he could be taken to a hospital and lie there, in a clean bed, for weeks. At midnight he was so hungry that he could not go without food any more, so he went to a coffee stall at Hyde Park Corner and ate a couple of potatoes and had a cup of coffee. Then he walked again. He felt too restless to sleep, and he had a horrible dread of being moved on by the police. He noted that he was beginning to look upon the constable from quite a new angle. This was the third night he had spent out. Now and then he sat on the benches in Piccadilly and towards morning he strolled down to the Embankment. He listened to the striking of Big Ben, marking every quarter of an hour, and reckoned out how long it left till the city woke again. In the morning he spent a few coppers on making himself neat and clean, bought a paper to read the advertisements, and set out once more on the search for work.

He went on in this way for several days. He had very little food and began to feel weak and ill, so that he had hardly enough energy to go on looking for the work which seemed so desperately hard to find. He was growing used now to the long waiting at the back of a shop on the chance that he would be taken on, and the curt dismissal. He walked to all parts of London in answer to the advertisements, and he came to know by sight men who applied as fruitlessly as himself. One or two tried to make friends with him, but he was too tired and too wretched to accept their advances. He did not go any more to Lawson, because he owed him five shillings. He began to be too dazed to think clearly and ceased very much to care what would happen to him. He cried a good deal. At first he was very angry with himself for this and ashamed, but he found it relieved him, and somehow made him feel less hungry. In the very early morning he suffered a good deal from cold. One night he went into his room to change his linen; he slipped in about three, when he was quite sure everyone would be asleep, and out again at five; he lay on the bed and its softness was enchanting; all his bones ached, and as he lay he revelled in the pleasure of it; it was so delicious that he did not want to go to sleep. He was grow-

ing used to want of food and did not feel very hungry, but only weak. Constantly now at the back of his mind was the thought of doing away with himself, but he used all the strength he had not to dwell on it, because he was afraid the temptation would get hold of him so that he would not be able to help himself. He kept on saying to himself that it would be absurd to commit suicide, since something must happen soon; he could not get over the impression that his situation was too preposterous to be taken quite seriously; it was like an illness which must be endured but from which he was bound to recover. Every night he swore that nothing would induce him to put up with such another and determined next morning to write to his uncle, or to Mr. Nixon, the solicitor, or to Lawson; but when the time came he could not bring himself to make the humiliating confession of his utter failure. He did not know how Lawson would take it. In their friendship Lawson had been scatterbrained and he had prided himself on his common sense. He would have to tell the whole history of his folly. He had an uneasy feeling that Lawson, after helping him, would turn the cold shoulder on him. His uncle and the solicitor would of course do something for him, but he dreaded their reproaches. He did not want anyone to reproach him: he clenched his teeth and repeated that what had happened was inevitable just because it had happened. Regret was absurd.

The days were unending, and the five shillings Lawson had lent him would not last much longer. Philip longed for Sunday to come so that he could go to Athelny's. He did not know what prevented him from going there sooner, except perhaps that he wanted so badly to get through on his own; for Athelny, who had been in straits as desperate, was the only person who could do anything for him. Perhaps after dinner he could bring himself to tell Athelny that he was in difficulties. Philip repeated to himself over and over again what he should say to him. He was dreadfully afraid that Athelny would put him off with airy phrases: that would be so horrible that he wanted to delay as long as possible the putting of him to test. Philip had lost all confidence in his fellows.

Saturday night was cold and raw. Philip suffered horribly. From mid-day on Saturday till he dragged himself wearily to Athelny's house he ate nothing. He spent his last twopence on Sunday morning on a wash and a brush up in the lavatory at Charing Cross.

CI

WHEN Philip rang a head was put out of the window, and in a minute he heard a noisy clatter on the stairs as the children ran down to let him in. It was a pale, anxious, thin face that he bent down for them to kiss. He was so moved by their exuberant affection that, to give himself time to recover, he made excuses to linger on the stairs. He was in a hysterical state and almost anything was enough to make him cry. They asked him why he had not come on the previous Sunday, and he told them he had been ill; they wanted to know what was the matter with him; and Philip, to amuse them, suggested a mysterious ailment, the name of which, double-barrelled and barbarous with its mixture of Greek and Latin (medical nomenclature bristled with such), made them shriek with delight. They dragged Philip into the parlour and made him repeat it for their father's edification. Athelny got up and shook hands with him. He stared at Philip, but with his round, bulging eyes he always seemed to stare, Philip did not know why on this occasion it made him self-conscious.

"We missed you last Sunday," he said.

Philip could never tell lies without embarrassment, and he was scarlet when he finished his explanation for not coming. Then Mrs. Athelny entered and shook hands with him.

"I hope you're better, Mr. Carey," she said.

He did not know why she imagined that anything had been the matter with him, for the kitchen door was closed when he came up with the children, and they had not left him.

"Dinner won't be ready for another ten minutes," she said, in her slow drawl. "Won't you have an egg beaten up in a glass of milk while you're waiting?"

There was a look of concern on her face which made Philip uncomfortable. He forced a laugh and answered that he was not at all hungry. Sally came in to lay the table, and Philip began to chaff her. It was the family joke that she would be as fat as an aunt of Mrs. Athelny, called Aunt Elizabeth, whom the children had never seen but regarded as the type of obscene corpulence.

"I say, what *has* happened since I saw you last, Sally?" Philip began.

"Nothing that I know of."

"I believe you've been putting on weight."

"I'm sure you haven't," she retorted. "You're a perfect skeleton."

Philip reddened.

"That's a *tu quoque*, Sally," cried her father. "You will be fined one golden hair of your head. Jane, fetch the shears."

"Well, he is thin, father," remonstrated Sally. "He's just skin and bone."

"That's not the question, child. He is at perfect liberty to be thin, but your obesity is contrary to decorum."

As he spoke he put his arm proudly round her waist and looked at her with admiring eyes.

"Let me get on with the table, father. If I am comfortable there are some who don't seem to mind it."

"The hussy!" cried Athelny, with a dramatic wave of the hand. "She taunts me with the notorious fact that Joseph, a son of Levi who sells jewels in Holborn, has made her an offer of marriage."

"Have you accepted him, Sally?" asked Philip.

"Don't you know father better than that by this time? There's not a word of truth in it."

"Well, if he hasn't made you an offer of marriage," cried Athelny, "by Saint George and Merry England, I will seize him by the nose and demand of him immediately what are his intentions."

"Sit down, father, dinner's ready. Now then, you children, get along with you and wash your hands all of you, and don't shirk it, because I mean to look at them before you have a scrap of dinner, so there."

Philip thought he was ravenous till he began to eat, but then discovered that his stomach turned against food, and he could eat hardly at all. His brain was weary; and he did not notice that Athelny, contrary to his habit, spoke very little. Philip was relieved to be sitting in a comfortable house, but every now and then he could not prevent himself from glancing out of the window. The day was tempestuous. The fine weather had broken; and it was cold, and there was a bitter wind; now and again gusts of rain drove against the window. Philip wondered what he should do that night. The Athelnys went to bed early, and he could not stay where he was after ten o'clock. His heart sank at the thought of going out into the bleak darkness. It seemed more terrible now that he was with his friends than when he was outside and alone. He kept on saying to himself that there were plenty more who would be spending the night out of doors. He strove to distract his mind by talking, but in the middle of his words a spatter of rain against the window would make him start.

"It's like March weather," said Athelny. "Not the sort of day one would like to be crossing the Channel."

Presently they finished, and Sally came in and cleared away.

"Would you like a twopenny stinker?" said Athelny, handing him a cigar.

Philip took it and inhaled the smoke with delight. It soothed him extraordinarily. When Sally had finished Athelny told her to shut the door after her.

"Now we shan't be disturbed," he said, turning to Philip. "I've arranged with Betty not to let the children come in till I call them."

Philip gave him a startled look, but before he could take in the meaning of his words, Athelny, fixing his glasses on his nose with the gesture habitual to him, went on.

"I wrote to you last Sunday to ask if anything was the matter with you, and as you didn't answer I went to your rooms on Wednesday."

Philip turned his head away and did not answer. His heart began to beat violently. Athelny did not speak, and presently the silence seemed intolerable to Philip. He could not think of a single word to say.

"Your landlady told me you hadn't been in since Saturday night, and she said you owed her for the last month. Where have you been sleeping all this week?"

It made Philip sick to answer. He stared out of the window.

"Nowhere."

"I tried to find you."

"Why?" asked Philip.

"Betty and I have been just as broke in our day, only we had babies to look after. Why didn't you come here?"

"I couldn't."

Philip was afraid he was going to cry. He felt very weak. He shut his eyes and frowned, trying to control himself. He felt a sudden flash of anger with Athelny because he would not leave him alone; but he was broken; and presently, his eyes still closed, slowly in order to keep his voice steady, he told him the story of his adventures during the last few weeks. As he spoke it seemed to him that he had behaved inanely, and it made it still harder to tell. He felt that Athelny would think him an utter fool.

"Now you're coming to live with us till you find something to do," said Athelny, when he had finished.

Philip flushed, he knew not why.

"Oh, it's awfully kind of you, but I don't think I'll do that."

"Why not?"

Philip did not answer. He had refused instinctively from fear that he would be a bother, and he had a natural bashfulness of accepting favours. He knew besides that the Athelnys lived from hand to mouth, and with their large family had neither space nor money to entertain a stranger.

"Of course you must come here," said Athelny. "Thorpe will tuck in with one of his brothers and you can sleep in his bed. You don't suppose your food's going to make any difference to us."

Philip was afraid to speak, and Athelny, going to the door, called his wife.

"Betty," he said, when she came in, "Mr. Carey's coming to live with us."

"Oh, that is nice," she said. "I'll go and get the bed ready."

She spoke in such a hearty, friendly tone, taking everything for granted, that Philip was deeply touched. He never expected people to be kind to him, and when they were it surprised and moved him. Now he could not prevent two large tears from rolling down his cheeks. The Athelnys discussed the arrangements and pretended not to notice to what a state his weakness had brought him. When Mrs. Athelny left them Philip leaned back in his chair, and looking out of the window laughed a little.

"It's not a very nice night to be out, is it?"

CII

ATHELNY told Philip that he could easily get him something to do in the large firm of linendrapers in which himself worked. Several of the assistants had gone to the war, and Lynn and Sedley with patriotic zeal had promised to keep their places open for them. They put the work of the heroes on those who remained, and since they did not increase the wages of these were able at once to exhibit public spirit and effect an economy; but the war continued and trade was less depressed; the holidays were coming, when numbers of the staff went away for a fortnight at a time: they were bound to engage more assistants. Philip's experience had made him doubtful whether even then they would engage him; but Athelny, representing himself as a person of consequence in the firm, insisted that the manager could refuse him nothing. Philip, with his training in Paris, would be very useful; it was only a matter of waiting a little and he was bound to get a well-paid job to design costumes and draw posters. Philip made a poster for the summer sale and Athelny took it away. Two days later he brought it back, saying that the manager admired it very much and regretted with all his heart that there was no vacancy just then in that department. Philip asked whether there was nothing else he could do.

"I'm afraid not."

"Are you quite sure?"

"Well, the fact is they're advertising for a shop-walker tomorrow," said Athelny, looking at him doubtfully through his glasses.

"D'you think I stand any chance of getting it?"

Athelny was a little confused; he had led Philip to expect something much more splendid; on the other hand he was too poor to go on providing him indefinitely with board and lodging.

"You might take it while you wait for something better. You always stand a better chance if you're engaged by the firm already."

"I'm not proud, you know," smiled Philip.

"If you decide on that you must be there at a quarter to nine tomorrow morning."

Notwithstanding the war there was evidently much difficulty in finding work, for when Philip went to the shop many men were waiting already. He recognised some whom he had seen in his own searching, and there was one whom he had noticed lying about the park in the afternoon. To Philip now that suggested that he was as homeless as himself and passed the night out of doors. The men were of all sorts, old and young, tall and short; but every one had tried to make himself smart for the interview with the manager: they had carefully brushed hair and scrupulously clean hands. They waited in a passage which Philip learnt afterwards led up to the dining-hall and the work rooms; it was broken every few yards by five or six steps. Though there was electric light in the shop here was only gas, with wire cages over it for protection, and it flared noisily. Philip arrived punctually, but it was nearly ten o'clock when he was admitted into the office. It was three-cornered, like a cut of cheese lying on its side: on the walls were pictures of women in corsets, and two poster-proofs, one of a man in pyjamas, green and white in large stripes, and the other of a ship in full sail ploughing an azure sea: on the sail was printed in large letters 'great white sale.' The widest side of the office was the back of one of the shop-windows, which was being dressed at the time, and an assistant went to and fro during the interview. The manager was reading a letter. He was a florid man, with sandy hair and a large sandy moustache; from the middle of his watch-chain hung a bunch of football medals. He sat in his shirt-sleeves at a large desk with a telephone by his side; before him were the day's advertisements, Athelny's work, and cuttings from newspapers pasted on a card. He gave Philip a glance but did not speak to him; he dictated a letter to the typist, a girl who sat at a small table in one corner; then he asked Philip his name, age, and what experience he had had. He spoke with a cockney twang in a high, metallic voice which he seemed not able always to control; Philip noticed that his upper teeth were large and protruding; they gave you the impression that they were loose and would come out if you gave them a sharp tug.

"I think Mr. Athelny has spoken to you about me," said Philip.

"Oh, you are the young feller who did that poster?"

"Yes, sir."

"No good to us, you know, not a bit of good."

He looked Philip up and down. He seemed to notice that Philip was in some way different from the men who had preceded him.

"You'd 'ave to get a frock coat, you know. I suppose you 'aven't got one. You seem a respectable young feller. I suppose you found art didn't pay."

Philip could not tell whether he meant to engage him or not. He threw remarks at him in a hostile way.

"Where's your home?"

"My father and mother died when I was a child."

"I like to give young fellers a chance. Many's the one I've given their chance to and they're managers of departments now. And they're grateful to me, I'll say that for them. They know what I done for them. Start at the bottom of the ladder, that's the only way to learn the business, and then if you stick to it there's no knowing what it can lead to. If you suit, one of these days you may find yourself in a position like what mine is. Bear that in mind, young feller."

"I'm very anxious to do my best, sir," said Philip.

He knew that he must put in the sir whenever he could, but it sounded odd to him, and he was afraid of overdoing it. The manager liked talking. It gave him a happy consciousness of his own importance, and he did not give Philip his decision till he had used a great many words.

"Well, I daresay you'll do," he said at last, in a pompous way. "Anyhow I don't mind giving you a trial."

"Thank you very much, sir."

"You can start at once. I'll give you six shillings a week and your keep. Everything found, you know; the six shillings is only pocket money, to do what you like with, paid monthly. Start on Monday. I suppose you've got no cause of complaint with that."

"No, sir."

"Harrington Street, d'you know where that is, Shaftesbury Avenue. That's where you sleep. Number ten, it is. You can sleep there on Sunday night, if you like; that's just as you please, or you can send your box there on Monday." The manager nodded: "Good-morning."

CIII

MRS. ATHELNY lent Philip money to pay his landlady enough of her bill to let him take his things away. For five shillings and the pawn-ticket on a suit he was able to get from a pawn-broker a frock coat which fitted him fairly well. He redeemed the rest of his clothes. He sent his box to Harrington Street by Carter Patterson and on Monday morning went with Athelny to the shop. Athelny introduced him to the buyer of the costumes and left him. The buyer was a pleasant, fussy little man of thirty, named Sampson; he shook hands with Philip, and, in order to show his own accomplishment of which he was very proud, asked him if he spoke French. He was surprised when Philip told him he did.

"Any other language?"

"I speak German."

"Oh! I go over to Paris myself occasionally. *Parlez-vous français?* Ever been to Maxim's?"

Philip was stationed at the top of the stairs in the 'costumes.' His work consisted in directing people to the various departments. There seemed a great many of them as Mr. Sampson tripped them off his tongue. Suddenly he noticed that Philip limped.

"What's the matter with your leg?" he asked.

"I've got a club-foot," said Philip. "But it doesn't prevent my walking or anything like that."

The buyer looked at it for a moment doubtfully, and Philip surmised that he was wondering why the manager had engaged him. Philip knew that he had not noticed there was anything the matter with him.

"I don't expect you to get them all correct the first day. If you're in any doubt all you've got to do is to ask one of the young ladies."

Mr. Sampson turned away; and Philip, trying to remember where this or the other department was, watched anxiously for the customer in search of information. At one o'clock he went up to dinner. The dining-room, on the top floor of the vast building, was large, long, and well lit; but all the windows were shut to keep out the dust, and there was a horrid smell of cooking. There were long tables covered with cloths, with big glass bottles of water at intervals, and down the centre salt cellars and bottles of vinegar. The assistants crowded in noisily, and sat down on forms still warm from those who had dined at twelve-thirty.

"No pickles," remarked the man next to Philip.

He was a tall thin young man, with a hooked nose and a pasty face; he had a long head, unevenly shaped as though the skull had been pushed in here and there oddly, and on his forehead and neck were large acne spots red and inflamed. His name was Harris. Philip discovered that on some days there were large soup-plates down the table full of mixed pickles. They were very popular. There were no knives and forks, but in a minute a large fat boy in a white coat came in with a couple of handfuls of them and threw them loudly on the middle of the table. Each man took what he wanted; they were warm and greasy from recent washing in dirty water. Plates of meat swimming in gravy were handed round by boys in white jackets, and as they flung each plate down with the quick gesture of a prestidigitator the gravy slopped over on to the table-cloth. Then they brought large dishes of cabbages and potatoes; the sight of them turned Philip's stomach; he noticed that everyone poured quantities of vinegar over them. The noise was awful. They talked and laughed and shouted, and there was the clatter of knives and forks, and strange sounds of eating. Philip was glad to get back into the department. He was beginning to remember where each one was, and had less often to ask one of the assistants, when somebody wanted to know the way.

"First to the right. Second on the left, madam."

One or two of the girls spoke to him, just a word when things were slack, and he felt they were taking his measure. At five he was sent up again to the dining-room for tea. He was glad to sit down. There were large slices of bread heavily spread with butter; and many had pots of jam, which were kept in the 'store' and had their names written on.

Philip was exhausted when work stopped at half past six. Harris, the man he had sat next to at dinner, offered to take him over to Harrington Street to show him where he was to sleep. He told Philip there was a spare bed in his room, and, as the other rooms were full, he expected Philip would be put there. The house in Harrington Street had been a boot-maker's; and the shop was used as a bed-room; but it was very dark, since the window had been boarded three parts up, and as this did not open the

only ventilation came from a small skylight at the far end. There was a musty smell, and Philip was thankful that he would not have to sleep there. Harris took him up to the sitting-room, which was on the first floor; it had an old piano in it with a keyboard that looked like a row of decayed teeth; and on the table in a cigar-box without a lid was a set of dominoes; old numbers of *The Strand Magazine* and of *The Graphic* were lying about. The other rooms were used as bed-rooms. That in which Philip was to sleep was at the top of the house. There were six beds in it, and a trunk or a box stood by the side of each. The only furniture was a chest of drawers: it had four large drawers and two small ones, and Philip as the new-comer had one of these; there were keys to them, but as they were all alike they were not of much use, and Harris advised him to keep his valuables in his trunk. There was a looking-glass on the chimney-piece. Harris showed Philip the lavatory, which was a fairly large room with eight basins in a row, and here all the inmates did their washing. It led into another room in which were two baths, discoloured, the woodwork stained with soap; and in them were dark rings at various intervals which indicated the water marks of different baths.

When Harris and Philip went back to their bed-room they found a tall man changing his clothes and a boy of sixteen whistling as loud as he could while he brushed his hair. In a minute or two without saying a word to anybody the tall man went out. Harris winked at the boy, and the boy, whistling still, winked back. Harris told Philip that the man was called Prior; he had been in the army and now served in the silks; he kept pretty much to himself, and he went off every night, just like that, without so much as a good-evening, to see his girl. Harris went out too, and only the boy remained to watch Philip curiously while he unpacked his things. His name was Bell and he was serving his time for nothing in the haberdashery. He was much interested in Philip's evening clothes. He told him about the other men in the room and asked him every sort of question about himself. He was a cheerful youth, and in the intervals of conversation sang in a half-broken voice snatches of music-hall songs. When Philip had finished he went out to walk about the streets and look at the crowd; occasionally he stopped outside the doors of restaurants and watched the people going in; he felt hungry, so he bought a bath bun and ate it while he strolled along. He had been given a latch-key by the prefect, the man who turned out the gas at a quarter past eleven, but afraid of being locked out he returned in good time; he had learned already the system of fines: you had to pay a shilling if you came in after eleven, and half a crown after a quarter past, and you were reported besides: if it happened three times you were dismissed.

All but the soldier were in when Philip arrived and two were already in bed. Philip was greeted with cries.

"Oh, Clarence! Naughty boy!"

He discovered that Bell had dressed up the bolster in his evening clothes. The boy was delighted with his joke.

"You must wear them at the social evening, Clarence."

"He'll catch the belle of Lynn's, if he's not careful."

Philip had already heard of the social evenings, for the money stopped from the wages to pay for them was one of the grievances of the staff. It was only two shillings a month, and it covered medical attendance and the use of a library of worn novels; but

as four shillings a month besides was stopped for washing, Philip discovered that a quarter of his six shillings a week would never be paid to him.

Most of the men were eating thick slices of fat bacon between a roll of bread cut in two. These sandwiches, the assistants' usual supper, were supplied by a small shop a few doors off at twopence each. The soldier rolled in; silently, rapidly, took off his clothes and threw himself into bed. At ten minutes past eleven the gas gave a big jump and five minutes later went out. The soldier went to sleep, but the others crowded round the big window in their pyjamas and night-shirts and, throwing remains of their sandwiches at the women who passed in the street below, shouted to them facetious remarks. The house opposite, six storeys high, was a workshop for Jewish tailors who left off work at eleven; the rooms were brightly lit and there were no blinds to the windows. The sweater's daughter—the family consisted of father, mother, two small boys, and a girl of twenty—went round the house to put out the lights when work was over, and sometimes she allowed herself to be made love to by one of the tailors. The shop assistants in Philip's room got a lot of amusement out of watching the manœuvres of one man or another to stay behind, and they made small bets on which would succeed. At midnight the people were turned out of the Harrington Arms at the end of the street, and soon after they all went to bed: Bell, who slept nearest the door, made his way across the room by jumping from bed to bed, and even when he got to his own would not stop talking. At last everything was silent but for the steady snoring of the soldier, and Philip went to sleep.

He was awaked at seven by the loud ringing of a bell, and by a quarter to eight they were all dressed and hurrying downstairs in their stockinged feet to pick out their boots. They laced them as they ran along to the shop in Oxford Street for breakfast. If they were a minute later than eight they got none, nor, once in, were they allowed out to get themselves anything to eat. Sometimes, if they knew they could not get into the building in time, they stopped at the little shop near their quarters and bought a couple of buns; but this cost money, and most went without food till dinner. Philip ate some bread and butter, drank a cup of tea, and at half past eight began his day's work again.

"First to the right. Second on the left, madam."

Soon he began to answer the questions quite mechanically. The work was monotonous and very tiring. After a few days his feet hurt him so that he could hardly stand: the thick soft carpets made them burn, and at night his socks were painful to remove. It was a common complaint, and his fellow 'floormen' told him that socks and boots just rotted away from the continual sweating. All the men in his room suffered in the same fashion, and they relieved the pain by sleeping with their feet outside the bed-clothes. At first Philip could not walk at all and was obliged to spend a good many of his evenings in the sitting-room at Harrington Street with his feet in a pail of cold water. His companion on these occasions was Bell, the lad in the haberdashery, who stayed in often to arrange the stamps he collected. As he fastened them with little pieces of stamp-paper he whistled monotonously.

CIV

THE social evenings took place on alternate Mondays. There was one at the beginning of Philip's second week at Lynn's. He arranged to go with one of the women in his department.

"Meet 'em 'alf-way," she said, "same as I do."

This was Mrs. Hodges, a little woman of five and forty, with badly dyed hair; she had a yellow face with a network of small red veins all over it, and yellow whites to her pale blue eyes. She took a fancy to Philip and called him by his Christian name before he had been in the shop a week.

"We've both known what it is to come down," she said.

She told Philip that her real name was not Hodges, but she always referred to "me 'usband Misterodges;" he was a barrister and he treated her simply shocking, so she left him as she preferred to be independent like; but she had known what it was to drive in her own carriage, dear—she called everyone dear—and they always had late dinner at home. She used to pick her teeth with the pin of an enormous silver brooch. It was in the form of a whip and a hunting-crop crossed, with two spurs in the middle. Philip was ill at ease in his new surroundings, and the girls in the shop called him 'sidey.' One addressed him as Phil, and he did not answer because he had not the least idea that she was speaking to him; so she tossed her head, saying he was a 'stuck-up thing,' and next time with ironical emphasis called him Mister Carey. She was a Miss Jewell, and she was going to marry a doctor. The other girls had never seen him, but they said he must be a gentleman as he gave her such lovely presents.

"Never you mind what they say, dear," said Mrs. Hodges. "I've 'ad to go through it same as you 'ave. They don't know any better, poor things. You take my word for it, they'll like you all right if you 'old your own same as I 'ave."

The social evening was held in the restaurant in the basement. The tables were put on one side so that there might be room for dancing, and smaller ones were set out for progressive whist.

"The 'eads 'ave to get there early," said Mrs. Hodges.

She introduced him to Miss Bennett, who was the belle of Lynn's. She was the buyer in the 'Petticoats,' and when Philip entered was engaged in conversation with the buyer in the 'Gentlemen's Hosiery:' Miss Bennett was a woman of massive proportions, with a very large red face heavily powdered and a bust of imposing dimensions; her flaxen hair was arranged with elaboration. She was overdressed, but not badly dressed, in black with a high collar, and she wore black *glacé* gloves, in which she played cards; she had several heavy gold chains round her neck, bangles on her wrists, and circular photograph pendants, one being of Queen Alexandra; she carried a black satin bag and chewed Sen-sens.

"Please to meet you, Mr. Carey," she said. "This is your first visit to our social evenings, ain't it? I expect you feel a bit shy, but there's no cause to, I promise you that."

She did her best to make people feel at home. She slapped them on the shoulders and laughed a great deal.

"Ain't I a pickle?" she cried, turning to Philip. "What must you think of me? But I can't 'elp meself."

Those who were going to take part in the social evening came in, the younger members of the staff mostly, boys who had not girls of their own, and girls who had not yet found anyone to walk with. Several of the young gentlemen wore lounge suits with white evening ties and red silk handkerchiefs; they were going to perform, and they had a busy, abstracted air; some were self-confident, but others were nervous, and they watched their public with an anxious eye. Presently a girl with a great deal of hair sat at the piano and ran her hands noisily across the keyboard. When the audience had settled itself she looked round and gave the name of her piece.

"A Drive in Russia."

There was a round of clapping during which she deftly fixed bells to her wrists. She smiled a little and immediately burst into energetic melody. There was a great deal more clapping when she finished, and when this was over, as an encore, she gave a piece which imitated the sea; there were little trills to represent the lapping waves and thundering chords, with the loud pedal down, to suggest a storm. After this a gentleman sang a song called *Bid me Good-bye,* and as an encore obliged with *Sing me to Sleep.* The audience measured their enthusiasm with a nice discrimination. Everyone was applauded till he gave an encore, and so that there might be no jealousy no one was applauded more than anyone else. Miss Bennett sailed up to Philip.

"I'm sure you play or sing, Mr. Carey," she said archly. "I can see it in your face."

"I'm afraid I don't."

"Don't you even recite?"

"I have no parlour tricks."

The buyer in the 'gentleman's hosiery' was a well-known reciter, and he was called upon loudly to perform by all the assistants in his department. Needing no pressing, he gave a long poem of tragic character, in which he rolled his eyes, put his hand on his chest, and acted as though he were in great agony. The point, that he had eaten cucumber for supper, was divulged in the last line and was greeted with laughter, a little forced because everyone knew the poem well, but loud and long. Miss Bennett did not sing, play, or recite.

"Oh no, she 'as a little game of her own," said Mrs. Hodges.

"Now, don't you begin chaffing me. The fact is I know quite a lot about palmistry and second sight."

"Oh, do tell my 'and, Miss Bennett," cried the girls in her department, eager to please her.

"I don't like telling 'ands, I don't really. I've told people such terrible things and they've all come true, it makes one superstitious like."

"Oh, Miss Bennett, just for once."

A little crowd collected round her, and, amid screams of embarrassment, giggles, blushings, and cries of dismay or admiration, she talked mysteriously of fair and dark men, of money in a letter, and of journeys, till the sweat stood in heavy beads on her painted face.

"Look at me," she said. "I'm all of a perspiration."

Supper was at nine. There were cakes, buns, sandwiches, tea and coffee, all free; but if you wanted mineral water you had to pay for it. Gallantry often led young men to offer the ladies ginger beer, but common decency made them refuse. Miss Bennett was very fond of ginger beer, and she drank two and sometimes three bottles during the evening; but she insisted on paying for them herself. The men liked her for that.

"She's a rum old bird," they said,

"but mind you, she's not a bad sort, she's not like what some are."

After supper progressive whist was played. This was very noisy, and there was a great deal of laughing and shouting, as people moved from table to table. Miss Bennett grew hotter and hotter.

"Look at me," she said. "I'm all of a perspiration."

In due course one of the more dashing of the young men remarked that if they wanted to dance they'd better begin. The girl who had played the accompaniments sat at the piano and placed a decided foot on the loud pedal. She played a dreamy waltz, marking the time with the bass, while with the right hand she 'tiddled' in alternate octaves. By way of a change she crossed her hands and played the air in the bass.

"She does play well, doesn't she?" Mrs. Hodges remarked to Philip. "And what's more she's never 'ad a lesson in 'er life; it's all ear."

Miss Bennett liked dancing and poetry better than anything in the world. She danced well, but very, very slowly, and an expression came into her eyes as though her thoughts were far, far away. She talked breathlessly of the floor and the heat and the supper. She said that the Portman Rooms had the best floor in London and she always liked the dances there; they were very select, and she couldn't bear dancing with all sorts of men you didn't know anything about; why, you might be exposing yourself to you didn't know what all. Nearly all the people danced very well, and they enjoyed themselves. Sweat poured down their faces, and the very high collars of the young men grew limp.

Philip looked on, and a greater depression seized him than he remembered to have felt for a long time. He felt intolerably alone. He did not go, because he was afraid to seem supercilious, and he talked with the girls and laughed, but in his heart was unhappiness. Miss Bennett asked him if he had a girl.

"No," he smiled.

"Oh, well, there's plenty to choose from here. And they're very nice respectable girls, some of them. I expect you'll have a girl before you've been here long."

She looked at him very archly.

"Meet 'em 'alf-way," said Mrs. Hodges. "That's what I tell him."

It was nearly eleven o'clock, and the party broke up. Philip could not get to sleep. Like the others he kept his aching feet outside the bed-clothes. He tried with all his might not to think of the life he was leading. The soldier was snoring quietly.

C V

THE wages were paid once a month by the secretary. On pay-day each batch of assistants, coming down from tea, went into the passage and joined the long line of people waiting orderly like the audience in a queue outside a gallery door. One by one they entered the office. The secretary sat at a desk with wooden bowls of money in front of him, and he asked the employé's name; he referred to a book, quickly, after a suspicious glance at the assistant, said aloud the sum due, and taking money out of the bowl counted it into his hand.

"Thank you," he said. "Next."

"Thank you," was the reply.

The assistant passed on to the second secretary and before leaving the room paid him four shillings for washing money, two shillings for the club, and any fines that he might have incurred. With what he had left he went back into his department and there waited till it was time to go. Most of the men in Philip's house were in debt with the woman who sold the sandwiches they generally ate for supper. She was a funny old thing, very fat, with a broad, red face, and black hair plastered neatly on each side of the forehead in the fashion shown in early pictures of Queen Victoria. She always wore a little black bonnet and a white apron; her sleeves were tucked up to the elbow; she cut the sandwiches with large, dirty, greasy hands; and there was grease on her bodice, grease on her apron, grease on her skirt. She was called Mrs. Fletcher, but everyone addressed her as 'Ma;' she was really fond of the shop assistants, whom she called her boys; she never minded giving credit towards the end of the month, and it was known that now and then she had lent someone or other a few shillings when he was in straits. She was a good woman. When they were leaving or when they came back from the holidays, the boys kissed her fat red cheek; and more than one, dismissed and unable to find another job, had got for nothing food to keep body and soul together. The boys were sensible of her large heart and repaid her with genuine affection. There was a story they liked to tell of a man who had done well for himself at Bradford, and had five shops of his own, and had come back after fifteen years and visited Ma Fletcher and given her a gold watch.

Philip found himself with eighteen shillings left out of his month's pay.

It was the first money he had ever earned in his life. It gave him none of the pride which might have been expected, but merely a feeling of dismay. The smallness of the sum emphasised the hopelessness of his position. He took fifteen shillings to Mrs. Athelny to pay back part of what he owed her, but she would not take more than half a sovereign.

"D'you know, at that rate it'll take me eight months to settle up with you."

"As long as Athelny's in work I can afford to wait, and who knows, p'raps they'll give you a rise."

Athelny kept on saying that he would speak to the manager about Philip, it was absurd that no use should be made of his talents; but he did nothing, and Philip soon came to the conclusion that the press-agent was not a person of so much importance in the manager's eyes as in his own. Occasionally he saw Athelny in the shop. His flamboyance was extinguished; and in neat, commonplace, shabby clothes he hurried, a subdued, unassuming little man, through the departments as though anxious to escape notice.

"When I think of how I'm wasted there," he said at home, "I'm almost tempted to give in my notice. There's no scope for a man like me. I'm stunted, I'm starved."

Mrs. Athelny, quietly sewing, took no notice of his complaints. Her mouth tightened a little.

"It's very hard to get jobs in these times. It's regular and it's safe; I expect you'll stay there as long as you give satisfaction."

It was evident that Athelny would. It was interesting to see the ascendency which the uneducated woman, bound to him by no legal tie, had acquired over the brilliant, unstable man. Mrs. Athelny treated Philip with motherly kindness now that he was in a different position, and he was touched by her anxiety that he should make a good meal. It was the solace of his life (and when he grew used to it, the monotony of it was what chiefly appalled him) that he could go every Sunday to that friendly house. It was a joy to sit in the stately Spanish chairs and discuss all manner of things with Athelny. Though his condition seemed so desperate he never left him to go back to Harrington Street without a feeling of exultation. At first Philip, in order not to forget what he had learned, tried to go on reading his medical books, but he found it useless; he could not fix his attention on them after the exhausting work of the day; and it seemed hopeless to continue working when he did not know in how long he would be able to go back to the hospital. He dreamed constantly that he was in the wards. The awakening was painful. The sensation of other people sleeping in the room was inexpressibly irksome to him; he had been used to solitude, and to be with others always, never to be by himself for an instant, was at these moments horrible to him. It was then that he found it most difficult to combat his despair. He saw himself going on with that life, first to the right, second on the left, madam, indefinitely; and having to be thankful if he was not sent away: the men who had gone to the war would be coming home soon, the firm had guaranteed to take them back, and this must mean that others would be sacked; he would have to stir himself even to keep the wretched post he had.

There was only one thing to free him and that was the death of his uncle. He would get a few hundred pounds then, and on this he could finish his course at the hospital. Philip began to wish with all his might for the old man's death. He reckoned out how long he could possibly live: he was well over seventy, Philip did not know his exact age, but he must be at least seventy-five; he suffered from chronic bronchitis and every winter had a bad cough. Though he knew them by heart Philip read over and over again the details in his text-book of medicine of chronic bronchitis in the old. A severe winter might be too much for the old man. With all his heart Philip longed for cold and rain. He thought of it constantly, so that it became a monomania. Uncle William was affected by the great heat too, and in August they had three weeks of sweltering weather. Philip imagined to himself that one day perhaps a telegram would come saying that the Vicar had died suddenly, and he pictured to himself his unutterable relief. As he stood at the top of the stairs and directed people to the departments they wanted, he occupied his mind with thinking incessantly what he would do with the money. He did not know how much it would be, perhaps no more than five hundred pounds, but even that would be enough. He would leave the shop at once, he would not bother to give notice, he would pack his box and go without saying a word to anybody; and then he would return to the hospital. That was the first thing. Would he have forgotten much? In six months he could get it all back, and then he would take his three examinations as soon as he could, midwifery first, then medicine and surgery. The awful fear seized him that his uncle, notwithstanding his promises, might leave everything he had to the parish or the church. The thought made

Philip sick. He could not be so cruel. But if that happened Philip was quite determined what to do, he would not go on in that way indefinitely; his life was only tolerable because he could look forward to something better. If he had no hope he would have no fear. The only brave thing to do then would be to commit suicide, and, thinking this over too, Philip decided minutely what painless drug he would take and how he would get hold of it. It encouraged him to think that, if things became unendurable, he had at all events a way out.

"Second to the right, madam, and down the stairs. First on the left and straight through. Mr. Philips, forward please."

Once a month, for a week, Philip was 'on duty.' He had to go to the department at seven in the morning and keep an eye on the sweepers. When they finished he had to take the sheets off the cases and the models. Then, in the evening when the assistants left, he had to put back the sheets on the models and the cases and 'gang' the sweepers again. It was a dusty, dirty job. He was not allowed to read or write or smoke, but just had to walk about, and the time hung heavily on his hands. When he went off at half past nine he had supper given him, and this was the only consolation; for tea at five o'clock had left him with a healthy appetite, and the bread and cheese, the abundant cocoa which the firm provided, were welcome.

One day when Philip had been at Lynn's for three months, Mr. Sampson, the buyer, came into the department, fuming with anger. The manager, happening to notice the costume window as he came in, had sent for the buyer and made satirical remarks upon the colour scheme. Forced to submit in silence to his superior's sarcasm, Mr. Sampson took it out of the assistants; and he rated the wretched fellow whose duty it was to dress the window.

"If you want a thing well done you must do it yourself," Mr. Sampson stormed. "I've always said it and I always shall. One can't leave anything to you chaps. Intelligent you call yourselves, do you? Intelligent!"

He threw the word at the assistants as though it were the bitterest term of reproach.

"Don't you know that if you put an electric blue in the window it'll kill all the other blues?"

He looked round the department ferociously, and his eye fell upon Philip.

"You'll dress the window next Friday, Carey. Let's see what you can make of it."

He went into his office, muttering angrily. Philip's heart sank. When Friday morning came he went into the window with a sickening sense of shame. His cheeks were burning. It was horrible to display himself to the passers-by, and though he told himself it was foolish to give way to such a feeling he turned his back to the street. There was not much chance that any of the students at the hospital would pass along Oxford Street at that hour, and he knew hardly anyone else in London; but as Philip worked, with a huge lump in his throat, he fancied that on turning round he would catch the eye of some man he knew. He made all the haste he could. By the simple observation that all reds went together, and by spacing the costumes more than was usual, Philip got a very good effect; and when the buyer went into the street to look at the result he was obviously pleased.

"I knew I shouldn't go far wrong in putting you on the window. The fact is, you and me are gentlemen, mind you I wouldn't say this in the department, but you and me are gentlemen, and that always tells. It's no good your telling me it doesn't tell, because I know it does tell."

Philip was put on the job regularly, but he could not accustom himself to the publicity; and he dreaded Friday morning, on which the window was dressed, with a terror that made him awake at five o'clock and lie sleepless with sickness in his heart. The girls in the department noticed his shamefaced way, and they very soon discovered his trick of standing with his back to the street. They laughed at him and called him 'sidey.'

"I suppose you're afraid your aunt'll come along and cut you out of her will."

On the whole he got on well enough with the girls. They thought him a little queer; but his club-foot seemed to excuse his not being like the rest, and they found in due course that he was good-natured. He never minded helping anyone, and he was polite and even tempered.

"You can see he's a gentleman," they said.

"Very reserved, isn't he?" said one young woman, to whose passionate enthusiasm for the theatre he had listened unmoved.

Most of them had 'fellers,' and those who hadn't said they had rather than have it supposed that no one had an inclination for them. One or two showed signs of being willing to start a flirtation with Philip, and he watched their manœuvres with grave amusement. He had had enough of love-making for some time; and he was nearly always tired and often hungry.

CVI

PHILIP avoided the places he had known in happier times. The little gatherings at the tavern in Beak Street were broken up: Macalister, having let down his friends, no longer went there, and Hayward was at the Cape. Only Lawson remained; and Philip, feeling that now the painter and he had nothing in common, did not wish to see him; but one Saturday afternoon, after dinner, having changed his clothes he walked down Regent Street to go to the free library in St. Martin's Lane, meaning to spend the afternoon there, and suddenly found himself face to face with him. His first instinct was to pass on without a word, but Lawson did not give him the opportunity.

"Where on earth have you been all this time?" he cried.

"I?" said Philip.

"I wrote you and asked you to come to the studio for a beano and you never even answered."

"I didn't get your letter."

"No, I know. I went to the hospital to ask for you, and I saw my letter in the rack. Have you chucked the Medical?"

Philip hesitated for a moment. He was ashamed to tell the truth, but the shame he felt angered him, and he forced himself to speak. He could not help reddening.

"Yes, I lost the little money I had. I couldn't afford to go on with it."

"I say, I'm awfully sorry. What are you doing?"

"I'm a shop-walker."

The words choked Philip, but he was determined not to shirk the truth.

He kept his eyes on Lawson and saw his embarrassment. Philip smiled savagely.

"If you went into Lynn and Sedley, and made your way into the 'made robes' department, you would see me in a frock coat, walking about with a *dégagé* air and directing ladies who want to buy petticoats or stockings. First to the right, madam, and second on the left."

Lawson, seeing that Philip was making a jest of it, laughed awkwardly. He did not know what to say. The picture that Philip called up horrified him, but he was afraid to show his sympathy.

"That's a bit of a change for you," he said.

His words seemed absurd to him, and immediately he wished he had not said them. Philip flushed darkly.

"A bit," he said. "By the way, I owe you five bob."

He put his hand in his pocket and pulled out some silver.

"Oh, it doesn't matter. I'd forgotten all about it."

"Go on, take it."

Lawson received the money silently. They stood in the middle of the pavement, and people jostled them as they passed. There was a sardonic twinkle in Philip's eyes, which made the painter intensely uncomfortable, and he could not tell that Philip's heart was heavy with despair. Lawson wanted dreadfully to do something, but he did not know what to do.

"I say, won't you come to the studio and have a talk?"

"No," said Philip.

"Why not?"

"There's nothing to talk about."

He saw the pain come into Lawson's eyes, he could not help it, he was sorry, but he had to think of himself; he could not bear the thought of discussing his situation, he could endure it only by determining resolutely not to think about it. He was afraid of his weakness if once he began to open his heart. Moreover, he took irresistible dislikes to the places where he had been miserable: he remembered the humiliation he had endured when he had waited in that studio, ravenous with hunger, for Lawson to offer him a meal, and the last occasion when he had taken the five shillings off him. He hated the sight of Lawson, because he recalled those days of utter abasement.

"Then look here, come and dine with me one night. Choose your own evening."

Philip was touched with the painter's kindness. All sorts of people were strangely kind to him, he thought. "It's awfully good of you, old man, but I'd rather not." He held out his hand. "Good-bye."

Lawson, troubled by a behaviour which seemed inexplicable, took his hand, and Philip quickly limped away. His heart was heavy; and, as was usual with him, he began to reproach himself for what he had done: he did not know what madness of pride had made him refuse the offered friendship. But he heard someone running behind him and presently Lawson's voice calling him; he stopped and suddenly the feeling of hostility got the better of him; he presented to Lawson a cold, set face.

"What is it?"

"I suppose you heard about Hayward, didn't you?"

"I know he went to the Cape."

"He died, you know, soon after landing."

For a moment Philip did not answer. He could hardly believe his ears. "How?" he asked.

"Oh, enteric. Hard luck, wasn't it? I thought you mightn't know. Gave me a bit of a turn when I heard it."

Lawson nodded quickly and walked away. Philip felt a shiver pass through his heart. He had never before lost a friend of his own age, for the death of Cronshaw, a man so much older than himself, had seemed to come in the normal course of things. The news gave him a peculiar shock. It reminded him of his own mortality, for like everyone else Philip, knowing perfectly that all men must die, had no intimate feeling that the same must apply to himself; and Hayward's death, though he had long ceased to have any warm feeling for him, affected him deeply. He remembered on a sudden all the good talks they had had, and it pained him to think that they would never talk with one another again; he remembered their first meeting and the pleasant months they had spent together in Heidelberg. Philip's heart sank as he thought of the lost years. He walked on mechanically, not noticing where he went, and realised suddenly, with a movement of irritation, that instead of turning down the Haymarket he had sauntered along Shaftesbury Avenue. It bored him to retrace his steps; and besides, with that news, he did not want to read, he wanted to sit alone and think. He made up his mind to go to the British Museum. Solitude was now his only luxury. Since he had been at Lynn's he had often gone there and sat in front of the groups from the Parthenon; and, not deliberately thinking, had allowed their divine masses to rest his troubled soul. But this afternoon they had nothing to say to him, and after a few minutes, impatiently, he wandered out of the room. There were too many people, provincials with foolish faces, foreigners poring over guide-books; their hideousness besmirched the everlasting masterpieces, their restlessness troubled the god's immortal repose. He went into another room and here there was hardly anyone. Philip sat down wearily. His nerves were on edge. He could not get the people out of his mind. Sometimes at Lynn's they affected him in the same way, and he looked at them file past him with horror; they were so ugly and there was such meanness in their faces, it was terrifying; their features were distorted with paltry desires, and you felt they were strange to any ideas of beauty. They had furtive eyes and weak chins. There was no wickedness in them, but only pettiness and vulgarity. Their humour was a low facetiousness. Sometimes he found himself looking at them to see what animal they resembled, (he tried not to, for it quickly became an obsession,) and he saw in them all the sheep or the horse or the fox or the goat. Human beings filled him with disgust.

But presently the influence of the place descended upon him. He felt quieter. He began to look absently at the tombstones with which the room was lined. They were the work of the Athenian stone masons of the fourth and fifth centuries before Christ, and they were very simple, work of no great talent but with the exquisite spirit of Athens upon them; time had mellowed the marble to the colour of honey, so that unconsciously one thought of the bees of Hymettus, and softened their outlines. Some represented a nude figure, seated on a bench, some the departure of the dead from those who loved him, and some the dead clasping hands with one who remained behind. On all was the

tragic word farewell; that and nothing more. Their simplicity was infinitely touching. Friend parted from friend, the son from his mother, and the restraint made the survivor's grief more poignant. It was so long, long ago, and century upon century had passed over that unhappiness; for two thousand years those who wept had been dust as those they wept for. Yet the woe was alive still, and it filled Philip's heart so that he felt compassion spring up in it, and he said:

"Poor things, poor things."

And it came to him that the gaping sight-seers and the fat strangers with their guide-books, and all those mean, common people who thronged the shop, with their trivial desires and vulgar cares, were mortal and must die. They too loved and must part from those they loved, the son from his mother, the wife from her husband; and perhaps it was more tragic because their lives were ugly and sordid, and they knew nothing that gave beauty to the world. There was one stone which was very beautiful, a bas relief of two young men holding each other's hand; and the reticence of line, the simplicity, made one like to think that the sculptor here had been touched with a genuine emotion. It was an exquisite memorial to that than which the world offers but one thing more precious, to a friendship; and as Philip looked at it, he felt the tears come to his eyes. He thought of Hayward and his eager admiration for him when first they met, and how disillusion had come and then indifference, till nothing held them together but habit and old memories. It was one of the queer things of life that you saw a person every day for months and were so intimate with him that you could not imagine existence without him; then separation came, and everything went on in the same way, and the companion who had seemed essential proved unnecessary. Your life proceeded and you did not even miss him. Philip thought of those early days in Heidelberg when Hayward, capable of great things, had been full of enthusiasm for the future, and how, little by little, achieving nothing, he had resigned himself to failure. Now he was dead. His death had been as futile as his life. He died ingloriously, of a stupid disease, failing once more, even at the end, to accomplish anything. It was just the same now as if he had never lived.

Philip asked himself desperately what was the use of living at all. It all seemed inane. It was the same with Cronshaw: it was quite unimportant that he had lived; he was dead and forgotten, his book of poems sold in remainder by second-hand booksellers; his life seemed to have served nothing except to give a pushing journalist occasion to write an article in a review. And Philip cried out in his soul:

"What is the use of it?"

The effort was so incommensurate with the result. The bright hopes of youth had to be paid for at such a bitter price of disillusionment. Pain and disease and unhappiness weighed down the scale so heavily. What did it all mean? He thought of his own life, the high hopes with which he had entered upon it, the limitations which his body forced upon him, his friendlessness, and the lack of affection which had surrounded his youth. He did not know that he had ever done anything but what seemed best to do, and what a cropper he had come! Other men, with no more advantages than he, succeeded, and others again, with many more, failed. It seemed pure chance. The rain fell alike upon the just and upon the unjust, and for nothing was there a why and a where-

fore.

Thinking of Cronshaw, Philip remembered the Persian rug which he had given him, telling him that it offered an answer to his question upon the meaning of life; and suddenly the answer occurred to him: he chuckled: now that he had it, it was like one of the puzzles which you worry over till you are shown the solution and then cannot imagine how it could ever have escaped you. The answer was obvious. Life had no meaning. On the earth, satellite of a star speeding through space, living things had arisen under the influence of conditions which were part of the planet's history; and as there had been a beginning of life upon it so, under the influence of other conditions, there would be an end: man, no more significant than other forms of life, had come not as the climax of creation but as a physical reaction to the environment. Philip remembered the story of the Eastern King who, desiring to know the history of man, was brought by a sage five hundred volumes; busy with affairs of state, he bade him go and condense it; in twenty years the sage returned and his history now was in no more than fifty volumes, but the King, too old then to read so many ponderous tomes, bade him go and shorten it once more; twenty years passed again and the sage, old and gray, brought a single book in which was the knowledge the King had sought; but the King lay on his death-bed, and he had no time to read even that; and then the sage gave him the history of man in a single line; it was this: he was born, he suffered, and he died. There was no meaning in life, and man by living served no end. It was immaterial whether he was born or not born, whether he lived or ceased to live. Life was insignificant and death without consequence.

Philip exulted, as he had exulted in his boyhood when the weight of a belief in God was lifted from his shoulders: it seemed to him that the last burden of responsibility was taken from him; and for the first time he was utterly free. His insignificance was turned to power, and he felt himself suddenly equal with the cruel fate which had seemed to persecute him; for, if life was meaningless, the world was robbed of its cruelty. What he did or left undone did not matter. Failure was unimportant and success amounted to nothing. He was the most inconsiderate creature in that swarming mass of mankind which for a brief space occupied the surface of the earth; and he was almighty because he had wrenched from chaos the secret of its nothingness. Thoughts came tumbling over one another in Philip's eager fancy, and he took long breaths of joyous satisfaction. He felt inclined to leap and sing. He had not been so happy for months.

"Oh, life," he cried in his heart, "Oh life, where is thy sting?"

For the same uprush of fancy which had shown him with all the force of mathematical demonstration that life had no meaning, brought with it another idea; and that was why Cronshaw, he imagined, had given him the Persian rug. As the weaver elaborated his pattern for no end but the pleasure of his æsthetic sense, so might a man live his life, or if one was forced to believe that his actions were outside his choosing, so might a man look at his life, that it made a pattern. There was as little need to do this as there was use. It was merely something he did for his own pleasure. Out of the manifold events of his life, his deeds, his feelings, his thoughts, he might make a design, regular, elaborate, complicated, or beautiful; and though it might be no more than an illusion that he had the power of selection, though it might be no more than a fantastic legerdemain in which appearances were interwoven with moonbeams, that did not matter: it seemed, and so to him it was. In the vast warp of life, (a river arising from no spring and flowing endlessly to no sea,) with the background to his fancies that there was no meaning and that nothing was important, a man might get a personal satisfaction in selecting the various strands that worked out the pattern. There was one pattern, the most obvious, perfect, and beautiful, in which a man was born, grew to manhood, married, produced children, toiled for his bread, and died; but there were others, intricate and wonderful, in which happiness did not enter and in which success was not attempted; and in them might be discovered a more troubling grace. Some lives, and Hayward's was among them, the blind indifference of chance cut off while the design was still imperfect; and then the solace was comfortable that it did not matter; other lives, such as Cronshaw's, offered a pattern which was difficult to follow, the point of view had to be shifted and old standards had to be altered before one could understand that such a life was its own justification. Philip thought that in throwing over the desire for happiness he was casting aside the last of his illusions. His life had seemed horrible when it was measured by its happiness, but now he seemed to gather strength as he realised that it might be measured by something else. Happiness mattered as little as pain. They came in, both of them, as all the other details of his life came in, to the elaboration of the design. He seemed for an instant to stand above the accidents of his existence, and he felt that they could not affect him again as they had done before. Whatever happened to him now would be one more motive to add to the complexity of the pattern, and when the end approached he would rejoice in its completion. It would be a work of art, and it would be none the less beautiful because he alone knew of its existence, and with his death it would at once cease to be. Philip was happy.

CVII

MR. SAMPSON, the buyer, took a fancy to Philip. Mr. Sampson was very dashing, and the girls in his department said they would not be surprised if he married one of the rich customers. He lived out of town and often impressed the assistants by putting on his evening clothes in the office. Sometimes he would be seen by those on sweeping duty coming in next morning still dressed, and they would wink gravely to one another while he went into his office and changed into a frock coat. On these occasions, having slipped out for a hurried breakfast, he also would wink at Philip as he walked up the stairs on his way back and rub his hands.

"What a night! What a night!" he said. "My word!"

He told Philip that he was the only gentleman there, and he and Philip were the only fellows who knew what life was. Having said this, he changed his manner suddenly, called Philip Mr. Carey instead of old boy, assumed the importance due to his position as buyer, and put Philip back into his place of shop-walker.

Lynn and Sedley received fashion papers from Paris once a week and adapted the costumes illustrated in them to the needs of their customers. Their clientèle was peculiar. The most substantial part consisted of women from the smaller manufacturing towns, who were too elegant to have their frocks made locally and not sufficiently acquainted with London to discover good dressmakers within their means. Beside these, incongruously, was a large number of music-hall artistes. This was a connection that Mr. Sampson had worked up for himself and took great pride in. They had begun by getting their stage-costumes at Lynn's, and he had induced many of them to get their other clothes there as well.

"As good as Paquin and half the price," he said.

He had a persuasive, hail-fellow well-met air with him which appealed to customers of this sort, and they said to one another:

"What's the good of throwing money away when you can get a coat and skirt at Lynn's that nobody knows don't come from Paris?"

Mr. Sampson was very proud of his friendship with the popular favourites whose frocks he made, and when he went out to dinner at two o'clock on Sunday with Miss Victoria Virgo—"she was wearing that powder blue we made her and I lay she didn't let on it come from us, I 'ad to tell her meself that if I 'adn't designed it with my own 'ands I'd have said it must come from Paquin"—at her beautiful house in Tulse Hill, he regaled the department next day with abundant details. Philip had never paid much attention to women's clothes, but in course of time he began, a little amused at himself, to take a technical interest in them. He had an eye for colour which was more highly trained than that of anyone in the department, and he had kept from his student days in Paris some knowledge of line. Mr. Sampson, an ignorant man conscious of his incompetence, but with a shrewdness that enabled him to combine other people's suggestions, constantly asked the opinion of the assistants in his department in making up new designs; and he had the quickness to see that Philip's criticisms were valuable. But he was very jealous and would never allow that he took anyone's advice. When he had altered some drawing in accordance with Philip's suggestion, he always finished up by saying:

"Well, it comes round to my own idea in the end."

One day, when Philip had been at the shop for five months, Miss Alice Antonia, the well-known seriocomic, came in and asked to see Mr. Sampson. She was a large woman, with flaxen hair, and a boldly painted face, a metallic voice, and the breezy manner of a comédienne accustomed to be on friendly terms with the gallery boys of provincial music-halls. She had a new song and wished Mr. Sampson to design a costume for her.

"I want something striking," she said. "I don't want any old thing, you know. I want something different from what anybody else has."

Mr. Sampson, bland and familiar, said he was quite certain they could get her the very thing she required. He showed her sketches.

"I know there's nothing here that would do, but I just want to show you the kind of thing I would suggest."

"Oh no, that's not the sort of thing at all," she said, as she glanced at them impatiently. "What I want is something that'll just hit 'em in the jaw and make their front teeth rattle."

"Yes, I quite understand, Miss Antonia," said the buyer, with a bland smile, but his eyes grew blank and stupid.

"I expect I shall 'ave to pop over to Paris for it in the end."

"Oh, I think we can give you satisfaction, Miss Antonia. What you can get in Paris you can get here."

When she had swept out of the department Mr. Sampson, a little worried, discussed the matter with Mrs. Hodges.

"She's a caution and no mistake," said Mrs. Hodges.

"Alice, where art thou?" remarked the buyer, irritably, and thought he had scored a point against her.

His ideas of music-hall costumes had never gone beyond short skirts, a swirl of lace, and glittering sequins; but Miss Antonia had expressed herself on that subject in no uncertain terms.

"Oh, my aunt!" she said.

And the invocation was uttered in such a tone as to indicate a rooted antipathy to anything so commonplace, even if she had not added that sequins gave her the sick. Mr. Sampson 'got out' one or two ideas, but Mrs. Hodges told him frankly she did not think they would do. It was she who gave Philip the suggestion:

"Can you draw, Phil? Why don't you try your 'and and see what you can do?"

Philip bought a cheap box of water colours, and in the evening while Bell, the noisy lad of sixteen, whistling three notes, busied himself with his stamps, he made one or two sketches. He remembered some of the costumes he had seen in Paris, and he adapted one of them, getting his effect from a combination of violent, unusual colours. The result amused him and next morning he showed it to Mrs. Hodges. She was somewhat astonished, but took it at once to the buyer.

"It's unusual," he said, "there's no denying that."

It puzzled him, and at the same time his trained eye saw that it would make up admirably. To save his face he began making suggestions for altering it, but Mrs. Hodges, with more sense, advised him to show it to Miss Antonia as it was.

"It's neck or nothing with her, and she may take a fancy to it."

"It's a good deal more nothing than neck," said Mr. Sampson, looking at the *décolletage*. "He can draw, can't he? Fancy 'im keeping it dark all this time."

When Miss Antonia was announced, the buyer placed the design on the table in such a position that it must catch her eye the moment she was shown into his office. She pounced on it at once.

"What's that?" she said. "Why can't I 'ave that?"

"That's just an idea we got out for you," said Mr. Sampson casually. "D'you like it?"

"Do I like it!" she said. "Give me 'alf a pint with a little drop of gin in it."

"Ah, you see, you don't have to go to Paris. You've only got to say what you want and there you are."

The work was put in hand at once, and Philip felt quite a thrill of satisfaction when he saw the costume completed. The buyer and Mrs. Hodges took all the credit of it; but he did not care, and when he went with them to the Tivoli to see Miss Antonia wear it for the first time he was filled with elation. In answer to her questions he at last told Mrs. Hodges how he had learnt to draw—fearing that the people he lived with would think he wanted to put on airs, he had always taken

the greatest care to say nothing about his past occupations—and she repeated the information to Mr. Sampson. The buyer said nothing to him on the subject, but began to treat him a little more deferentially and presently gave him designs to do for two of the country customers. They met with satisfaction. Then he began to speak to his clients of a "clever young feller, Paris art-student, you know," who worked for him; and soon Philip, ensconced behind a screen, in his shirt-sleeves, was drawing from morning till night. Sometimes he was so busy that he had to dine at three with the 'stragglers.' He liked it, because there were few of them and they were all too tired to talk; the food also was better, for it consisted of what was left over from the buyers' table. Philip's rise from shop-walker to designer of costumes had a great effect on the department. He realised that he was an object of envy. Harris, the assistant with the queer-shaped head, who was the first person he had known at the shop and had attached himself to Philip, could not conceal his bitterness.

"Some people 'ave all the luck," he said. "You'll be a buyer yourself one of these days, and we shall all be calling you sir."

He told Philip that he should demand higher wages, for notwithstanding the difficult work he was now engaged in, he received no more than the six shillings a week with which he started. But it was a ticklish matter to ask for a rise. The manager had a sardonic way of dealing with such applicants.

"Think you're worth more, do you? How much d'you think you're worth, eh?"

The assistant, with his heart in his mouth, would suggest that he thought he ought to have another two shillings a week.

"Oh, very well, if you think you're worth it. You can 'ave it." Then he paused and sometimes, with a steely eye, added: "And you can 'ave your notice too."

It was no use then to withdraw your request, you had to go. The manager's idea was that assistants who were dissatisfied did not work properly, and if they were not worth a rise it was better to sack them at once. The result was that they never asked for one unless they were prepared to leave. Philip hesitated. He was a little suspicious of the men in his room who told him that the buyer could not do without him. They were decent fellows, but their sense of humour was primitive, and it would have seemed funny to them if they had persuaded Philip to ask for more wages and he were sacked. He could not forget the mortification he had suffered in looking for work, he did not wish to expose himself to that again, and he knew there was small chance of his getting elsewhere a post as designer: there were hundreds of people about who could draw as well as he. But he wanted money very badly; his clothes were worn out, and the heavy carpets rotted his socks and boots; he had almost persuaded himself to take the venturesome step when one morning, passing up from breakfast in the basement through the passage that led to the manager's office, he saw a queue of men waiting in answer to an advertisement. There were about a hundred of them, and whichever was engaged would be offered his keep and the same six shillings a week that Philip had. He saw some of them cast envious glances at him because he had employment. It made him shudder. He dared not risk it.

CVIII

THE winter passed. Now and then Philip went to the hospital, slinking in when it was late and there was little chance of meeting anyone he knew, to see whether there were letters for him. At Easter he received one from his uncle. He was surprised to hear from him, for the Vicar of Blackstable had never written him more than half a dozen letters in his whole life, and they were on business matters.

Dear Philip,

If you are thinking of taking a holiday soon and care to come down here I shall be pleased to see you. I was very ill with my bronchitis in the winter and Doctor Wigram never expected me to pull through. I have a wonderful constitution and I made, thank God, a marvellous recovery.

Yours affectionately,
William Carey.

The letter made Philip angry. How did his uncle think he was living? He did not even trouble to inquire. He might have starved for all the old man cared. But as he walked home something struck him; he stopped under a lamp-post and read the letter again; the handwriting had no longer the business-like firmness which had characterised it; it was larger and wavering: perhaps the illness had shaken him more than he was willing to confess, and he sought in that formal note to express a yearning to see the only relation he had in the world. Philip wrote back that he could come down to Blackstable for a fortnight in July. The invitation was convenient, for he had not known what to do, with his brief holiday. The Athelnys went hopping in September, but he could not then be spared, since during that month the autumn models were prepared. The rule of Lynn's was that everyone must take a fortnight whether he wanted it or not; and during that time, if he had nowhere to go, the assistant might sleep in his room, but he was not allowed food. A number had no friends within reasonable distance of London, and to these the holiday was an awkward interval when they had to provide food out of their small wages and, with the whole day on their hands, had nothing to spend. Philip had not been out of London since his visit to Brighton with Mildred, now two years before, and he longed for fresh air and the silence of the sea. He thought of it with such a passionate desire, all through May and June, that, when at length the time came for him to go, he was listless.

On his last evening, when he talked with the buyer of one or two jobs he had to leave over, Mr. Sampson suddenly said to him:

"What wages have you been getting?"

"Six shillings."

"I don't think it's enough. I'll see that you're put up to twelve when you come back."

"Thank you very much," smiled Philip. "I'm beginning to want some new clothes badly."

"If you stick to your work and don't go larking about with the girls like what some of them do, I'll look after you, Carey. Mind you, you've got a lot to learn, but you're promising, I'll

say that for you, you're promising, and I'll see that you get a pound a week as soon as you deserve it."

Philip wondered how long he would have to wait for that. Two years?

He was startled at the change in his uncle. When last he had seen him he was a stout man, who held himself upright, clean-shaven, with a round, sensual face; but he had fallen in strangely, his skin was yellow; there were great bags under the eyes, and he was bent and old. He had grown a beard during his last illness, and he walked very slowly.

"I'm not at my best today," he said when Philip, having just arrived, was sitting with him in the dining-room. "The heat upsets me."

Philip, asking after the affairs of the parish, looked at him and wondered how much longer he could last. A hot summer would finish him; Philip noticed how thin his hands were; they trembled. It meant so much to Philip. If he died that summer he could go back to the hospital at the beginning of the winter session; his heart leaped at the thought of returning no more to Lynn's. At dinner the Vicar sat humped up on his chair, and the housekeeper who had been with him since his wife's death said:

"Shall Mr. Philip carve, sir?"

The old man, who had been about to do so from disinclination to confess his weakness, seemed glad at the first suggestion to relinquish the attempt.

"You've got a very good appetite," said Philip.

"Oh yes, I always eat well. But I'm thinner than when you were here last. I'm glad to be thinner, I didn't like being so fat. Dr. Wigram thinks I'm all the better for being thinner than I was."

When dinner was over the housekeeper brought him some medicine.

"Show the prescription to Master Philip," he said. "He's a doctor too. I'd like him to see that he thinks it's all right. I told Dr. Wigram that now you're studying to be a doctor he ought to make a reduction in his charges. It's dreadful the bills I've had to pay. He came every day for two months, and he charges five shillings a visit. It's a lot of money, isn't it? He comes twice a week still. I'm going to tell him he needn't come any more. I'll send for him if I want him."

He looked at Philip eagerly while he read the prescriptions. They were narcotics. There were two of them, and one was a medicine which the Vicar explained he was to use only if his neuritis grew unendurable.

"I'm very careful," he said. "I don't want to get into the opium habit."

He did not mention his nephew's affairs. Philip fancied that it was by way of precaution, in case he asked for money, that his uncle kept dwelling on the financial calls upon him. He had spent so much on the doctor and so much more on the chemist, while he was ill they had had to have a fire every day in his bed-room, and now on Sunday he needed a carriage to go to church in the evening as well as in the morning. Philip felt angrily inclined to say he need not be afraid, he was not going to borrow from him, but he held his tongue. It seemed to him that everything had left the old man now but two things, pleasure in his food and a grasping desire for money. It was a hideous old age.

In the afternoon Dr. Wigram came, and after the visit Philip walked with him to the garden gate.

"How d'you think he is?" said Philip.

Dr. Wigram was more anxious not to do wrong than to do right, and he never hazarded a definite opinion if he could help it. He had practised at

Blackstable for five-and-thirty years. He had the reputation of being very safe, and many of his patients thought it much better that a doctor should be safe than clever. There was a new man at Blackstable—he had been settled there for ten years, but they still looked upon him as an interloper— and he was said to be very clever; but he had not much practice among the better people, because no one really knew anything about him.

"Oh, he's as well as can be expected," said Dr. Wigram in answer to Philip's inquiry.

"Has he got anything seriously the matter with him?"

"Well, Philip, your uncle is no longer a young man," said the doctor with a cautious little smile, which suggested that after all the Vicar of Blackstable was not an old man either.

"He seems to think his heart's in a bad way."

"I'm not satisfied with his heart," hazarded the doctor, "I think he should be careful, very careful."

On the tip of Philip's tongue was the question: how much longer can he live? He was afraid it would shock. In these matters a periphrase was demanded by the decorum of life, but, as he asked another question instead, it flashed through him that the doctor must be accustomed to the impatience of a sick man's relatives. He must see through their sympathetic expressions. Philip, with a faint smile at his own hypocrisy, cast down his eyes.

"I suppose he's in no immediate danger?"

This was the kind of question the doctor hated. If you said a patient couldn't live another month the family prepared itself for a bereavement, and if then the patient lived on they visited the medical attendant with the resentment they felt at having tormented themselves before it was necessary. On the other hand, if you said the patient might live a year and he died in a week the family said you did not know your business. They thought of all the affection they would have lavished on the defunct if they had known the end was so near. Dr. Wigram made the gesture of washing his hands.

"I don't think there's any grave risk so long as he—remains as he is," he ventured at last. "But on the other hand, we mustn't forget that he's no longer a young man, and well, the machine is wearing out. If he gets over the hot weather I don't see why he shouldn't get on very comfortably till the winter, and then if the winter does not bother him too much, well, I don't see why anything should happen."

Philip went back to the dining-room where his uncle was sitting. With his skull-cap and a crochet shawl over his shoulders he looked grotesque. His eyes had been fixed on the door, and they rested on Philip's face as he entered. Philip saw that his uncle had been waiting anxiously for his return.

"Well, what did he say about me?"

Philip understood suddenly that the old man was frightened of dying. It made Philip a little ashamed, so that he looked away involuntarily. He was always embarrassed by the weakness of human nature.

"He says he thinks you're much better," said Philip.

A gleam of delight came into his uncle's eyes.

"I've got a wonderful constitution," he said. "What else did he say?" he added suspiciously.

Philip smiled.

"He said that if you take care of yourself there's no reason why you shouldn't live to be a hundred."

"I don't know that I can expect to do that, but I don't see why I shouldn't see eighty. My mother lived till she was eighty-four."

There was a little table by the side of Mr. Carey's chair, and on it were a Bible and the large volume of the Common Prayer from which for so many years he had been accustomed to read to his household. He stretched out now his shaking hand and took his Bible.

"Those old patriarchs lived to a jolly good old age, didn't they?" he said, with a queer little laugh in which Philip read a sort of timid appeal.

The old man clung to life. Yet he believed implicitly all that his religion taught him. He had no doubt in the immortality of the soul, and he felt that he had conducted himself well enough, according to his capacities, to make it very likely that he would go to heaven. In his long career to how many dying persons must he have administered the consolations of religion! Perhaps he was like the doctor who could get no benefit from his own prescriptions. Philip was puzzled and shocked by that eager cleaving to the earth. He wondered what nameless horror was at the back of the old man's mind. He would have liked to probe into his soul so that he might see in its nakedness the dreadful dismay of the unknown which he suspected.

The fortnight passed quickly and Philip returned to London. He passed a sweltering August behind his screen in the costumes department, drawing in his shirt-sleeves. The assistants in relays went for their holidays. In the evening Philip generally went into Hyde Park and listened to the band. Growing more accustomed to his work it tired him less, and his mind, recovering from its long stagnation, sought for fresh activity. His whole desire now was set on his uncle's death. He kept on dreaming the same dream: a telegram was handed to him one morning, early, which announced the Vicar's sudden demise, and freedom was in his grasp. When he awoke and found it was nothing but a dream he was filled with sombre rage. He occupied himself, now that the event seemed likely to happen at any time, with elaborate plans for the future. In these he passed rapidly over the year which he must spend before it was possible for him to be qualified and dwelt on the journey to Spain on which his heart was set. He read books about that country, which he borrowed from the free library, and already he knew from photographs exactly what each city looked like. He saw himself lingering in Cordova on the bridge that spanned the Guadalquivir; he wandered through tortuous streets in Toledo and sat in churches where he wrung from El Greco the secret which he felt the mysterious painter held for him. Athelny entered into his humour, and on Sunday afternoons they made out elaborate itineraries so that Philip should miss nothing that was noteworthy. To cheat his impatience Philip began to teach himself Spanish, and in the deserted sitting-room in Harrington Street he spent an hour every evening doing Spanish exercises and puzzling out with an English translation by his side the magnificent phrases of Don Quixote. Athelny gave him a lesson once a week, and Philip learned a few sentences to help him on his journey. Mrs. Athelny laughed at them.

"You two and your Spanish!" she said. "Why don't you do something useful?"

But Sally, who was growing up and was to put up her hair at Christmas, stood by sometimes and listened in her grave way while her father and Philip exchanged remarks in a language she did not understand. She thought her father the most wonderful man who had ever existed, and she expressed her opinion of Philip only through her father's commendations.

"Father thinks a rare lot of your Uncle Philip," she remarked to her brothers and sisters.

Thorpe, the eldest boy, was old enough to go on the Arethusa, and Athelny regaled his family with magnificent descriptions of the appearance the lad would make when he came back in uniform for his holidays. As soon as Sally was seventeen she was to be apprenticed to a dressmaker. Athelny in his rhetorical way talked of the birds, strong enough to fly now, who were leaving the parental nest, and with tears in his eyes told them that the nest would be there still if ever they wished to return to it. A shakedown and a dinner would always be theirs, and the heart of a father would never be closed to the troubles of his children.

"You do talk, Athelny," said his wife. "I don't know what trouble they're likely to get into so long as they're steady. So long as you're honest and not afraid of work you'll never be out of a job, that's what I think, and I can tell you I shan't be sorry when I see the last of them earning their own living."

Child-bearing, hard work, and constant anxiety were beginning to tell on Mrs. Athelny; and sometimes her back ached in the evening so that she had to sit down and rest herself. Her ideal of happiness was to have a girl to do the rough work so that she need not herself get up before seven. Athelny waved his beautiful white hand.

"Ah, my Betty, we've deserved well of the state, you and I. We've reared nine healthy children, and the boys shall serve their king; the girls shall cook and sew and in their turn breed healthy children." He turned to Sally, and to comfort her for the anti-climax of the contrast added grandiloquently: "They also serve who only stand and wait."

Athelny had lately added socialism to the other contradictory theories he vehemently believed in, and he stated now:

"In a socialist state we should be richly pensioned, you and I, Betty."

"Oh, don't talk to me about your socialists, I've got no patience with them," she cried. "It only means that another lot of lazy loafers will make a good thing out of the working classes. My motto is, leave me alone; I don't want anyone interfering with me; I'll make the best of a bad job, and the devil take the hindmost."

"D'you call life a bad job?" said Athelny. "Never! We've had our ups and downs, we've had our struggles, we've always been poor, but it's been worth it, ay, worth it a hundred times I say when I look round at my children."

"You do talk, Athelny," she said, looking at him, not with anger but with scornful calm. "You've had the pleasant part of the children, I've had the bearing of them, and the bearing with them. I don't say that I'm not fond of them, now they're there, but if I had my time over again I'd remain single. Why, if I'd remained single I might have a little shop by now, and four or five hundred pounds in the bank, and a girl to do the rough work. Oh, I wouldn't go over my life again, not for something."

Philip thought of the countless millions to whom life is no more than unending labour, neither beautiful nor ugly, but just to be accepted in the same spirit as one accepts the changes of the seasons. Fury seized him because it all seemed useless. He could not reconcile himself to the belief that life had no meaning and yet everything he saw, all his thoughts, added to the force of his conviction. But though fury seized him it was a joyful fury. Life was not so horrible if it was meaningless, and he faced it with a strange sense of power.

CIX

THE autumn passed into winter. Philip had left his address with Mrs. Foster, his uncle's housekeeper, so that she might communicate with him, but still went once a week to the hospital on the chance of there being a letter. One evening he saw his name on an envelope in a handwriting he had hoped never to see again. It gave him a queer feeling. For a little while he could not bring himself to take it. It brought back a host of hateful memories. But at length, impatient with himself, he ripped open the envelope.

7 *William Street,*
Fitzroy Square.
Dear Phil,
    Can I see you for a minute or two as soon as possible. I am in awful trouble and don't know what to do. It's not money.
                    Yours truly,
                        Mildred.

He tore the letter into little bits and going out into the street scattered them in the darkness.

"I'll see her damned," he muttered.

A feeling of disgust surged up in him at the thought of seeing her again. He did not care if she was in distress, it served her right whatever it was, he thought of her with hatred, and the love he had had for her aroused his loathing. His recollections filled him with nausea, and as he walked across the Thames he drew himself aside in an instinctive withdrawal from his thought of her. He went to bed, but he could not sleep; he wondered what was the matter with her, and he could not get out of his head the fear that she was ill and hungry; she would not have written to him unless she were desperate. He was angry with himself for his weakness, but he knew that he would have no peace unless he saw her. Next morning he wrote a letter-card and posted it on his way to the shop. He made it as stiff as he could and said merely that he was sorry she was in difficulties and would come to the address she had given at seven o'clock that evening.

It was that of a shabby lodging-house in a sordid street; and when, sick at the thought of seeing her, he asked whether she was in, a wild hope seized him that she had left. It looked the sort of place people moved in and out of frequently. He had not thought of looking at the postmark on her letter and did not know how many days it had lain in the rack. The woman who answered the bell did not reply to his inquiry, but silently preceded him along the passage and knocked on a door at the back.

"Mrs. Miller, a gentleman to see you," she called.

The door was slightly opened, and Mildred looked out suspiciously.

"Oh, it's you," she said. "Come in."

He walked in and she closed the door. It was a very small bed-room, untidy as was every place she lived in; there was a pair of shoes on the floor, lying apart from one another and uncleaned; a hat was on the chest of drawers, with false curls beside it; and there was a blouse on the table. Philip looked for somewhere to put his hat. The hooks behind the door were laden with skirts, and he noticed that they were muddy at the hem.

"Sit down, won't you?" she said. Then she gave a little awkward laugh. "I suppose you were surprised to hear from me again."

"You're awfully hoarse," he answered. "Have you got a sore throat?"

"Yes, I have had for some time."

He did not say anything. He waited for her to explain why she wanted to see him. The look of the room told him clearly enough that she had gone back to the life from which he had taken her. He wondered what had happened to the baby; there was a photograph of it on the chimney-piece, but no sign in the room that a child was ever there. Mildred was holding her handkerchief. She made it into a little ball, and passed it from hand to hand. He saw that she was very nervous. She was staring at the fire, and he could look at her without meeting her eyes. She was much thinner than when she had left him; and the skin, yellow and dryish, was drawn more tightly over her cheek-bones. She had dyed her hair and it was now flaxen: it altered her a good deal, and made her look more vulgar.

"I was relieved to get your letter, I can tell you," she said at last. "I thought p'raps you weren't at the 'ospital any more."

Philip did not speak.

"I suppose you're qualified by now, aren't you?"

"No."

"How's that?"

"I'm no longer at the hospital. I

had to give it up eighteen months ago."

"You are changeable. You don't seem as if you could stick to anything."

Philip was silent for another moment, and when he went on it was with coldness.

"I lost the little money I had in an unlucky speculation and I couldn't afford to go on with medical. I had to earn my living as best I could."

"What are you doing then?"

"I'm in a shop."

"Oh!"

She gave him a quick glance and turned her eyes away at once. He thought that she reddened. She dabbed her palms nervously with the handkerchief.

"You've not forgotten all your doctoring, have you?" She jerked the words out quite oddly.

"Not entirely."

"Because that's why I wanted to see you." Her voice sank to a hoarse whisper. "I don't know what's the matter with me."

"Why don't you go to a hospital?"

"I don't like to do that, and have all the stoodents staring at me, and I'm afraid they'd want to keep me."

"What are you complaining of?" asked Philip coldly, with the stereotyped phrase used in the out-patients' room.

"Well, I've come out in a rash, and I can't get rid of it."

Philip felt a twinge of horror in his heart. Sweat broke out on his forehead.

"Let me look at your throat?"

He took her over to the window and made such examination as he could. Suddenly he caught sight of her eyes. There was deadly fear in them. It was horrible to see. She was terrified. She wanted him to reassure her; she looked at him pleadingly, not daring to ask for words of comfort but with all her nerves astrung to receive them: he had none to offer her.

"I'm afraid you're very ill indeed," he said.

"What d'you think it is?"

When he told her she grew deathly pale, and her lips even turned yellow; she began to cry, hopelessly, quietly at first and then with choking sobs.

"I'm awfully sorry," he said at last. "But I had to tell you."

"I may just as well kill myself and have done with it."

He took no notice of the threat.

"Have you got any money?" he asked.

"Six or seven pounds."

"You must give up this life, you know. Don't you think you could find some work to do? I'm afraid I can't help you much. I only get twelve bob a week."

"What is there I can do now?" she cried impatiently.

"Damn it all, you *must* try to get something."

He spoke to her very gravely, telling her of her own danger and the danger to which she exposed others, and she listened sullenly. He tried to console her. At last he brought her to a sulky acquiescence in which she promised to do all he advised. He wrote a prescription, which he said he would leave at the nearest chemist's, and he impressed upon her the necessity of taking her medicine with the utmost regularity. Getting up to go, he held out his hand.

"Don't be downhearted, you'll soon get over your throat."

But as he went her face became suddenly distorted, and she caught hold of his coat.

"Oh, don't leave me," she cried hoarsely. "I'm so afraid, don't leave me alone yet. Phil, please. There's no one else I can go to, you're the only friend I've ever had."

He felt the terror of her soul, and it was strangely like that terror he had seen in his uncle's eyes when he feared that he might die. Philip looked down. Twice that woman had come into his life and made him wretched; she had no claim upon him; and yet, he knew not why, deep in his heart was a strange aching; it was that which, when he received her letter, had left him no peace till he obeyed her summons.

"I suppose I shall never really quite get over it," he said to himself.

What perplexed him was that he felt a curious physical distaste, which made it uncomfortable for him to be near her.

"What do you want me to do?" he asked.

"Let's go out and dine together. I'll pay."

He hesitated. He felt that she was creeping back again into his life when he thought she was gone out of it for ever. She watched him with sickening anxiety.

"Oh, I know I've treated you shocking, but don't leave me alone now. You've had your revenge. If you leave me by myself now I don't know what I shall do."

"All right, I don't mind," he said, "but we shall have to do it on the cheap, I haven't got money to throw away these days."

She sat down and put her shoes on, then changed her skirt and put on a hat; and they walked out together till they found a restaurant in the Tottenham Court Road. Philip had got out of the habit of eating at those hours, and Mildred's throat was so sore that she could not swallow. They had a little cold ham and Philip drank a glass of beer. They sat opposite one another, as they had so often sat before; he wondered if she remembered; they had nothing to say to one another and would have sat in silence if Philip had not forced himself to talk. In the bright light of the restaurant, with its vulgar looking-glasses that reflected in an endless series, she looked old and haggard. Philip was anxious to know about the child, but he had not the courage to ask. At last she said:

"You know baby died last summer."

"Oh!" he said.

"You might say you're sorry."

"I'm not," he answered, "I'm very glad."

She glanced at him and, understanding what he meant, looked away.

"You were rare stuck on it at one time, weren't you? I always thought it funny like how you could see so much in another man's child."

When they had finished eating they called at the chemist's for the medicine Philip had ordered, and going back to the shabby room he made her take a dose. Then they sat together till it was time for Philip to go back to Harrington Street. He was hideously bored.

Philip went to see her every day. She took the medicine he had prescribed and followed his directions, and soon the results were so apparent that she gained the greatest confidence in Philip's skill. As she grew better she grew less despondent. She talked more freely.

"As soon as I can get a job I shall be all right," she said. "I've had my lesson now and I mean to profit by it. No more racketing about for yours truly."

Each time he saw her, Philip asked whether she had found work. She told him not to worry, she would find something to do as soon as she wanted it; she had several strings to her bow; it was all the better not to do anything for a week or two. He could not deny this, but at the end of that time he became more insistent. She laughed at him, she was much more cheerful now, and said he was a fussy old thing. She told him long stories of the manageresses she interviewed, for her idea was to get work at some eating-house; what they said and what she answered. Nothing definite was fixed, but she was sure to settle something at the beginning of the following week: there was no use hurrying, and it would be a mistake to take something unsuitable.

"It's absurd to talk like that," he said impatiently. "You must take anything you can get. I can't help you, and your money won't last for ever."

"Oh, well, I've not come to the end of it yet and chance it."

He looked at her sharply. It was three weeks since his first visit, and she had then less than seven pounds. Suspicion seized him. He remembered some of the things she had said. He put two and two together. He wondered whether she had made any attempt to find work. Perhaps she had been lying to him all the time. It was very strange that her money should have lasted so long.

"What is your rent here?"

"Oh, the landlady's very nice, different from what some of them are; she's quite willing to wait till it's convenient for me to pay."

He was ·silent. What he suspected was so horrible that he hesitated. It was no use to ask her, she would deny everything; if he wanted to know he must find out for himself. He was in the habit of leaving her every evening at eight, and when the clock struck he got up; but instead of going back to Harrington Street he stationed him-

self at the corner of Fitzroy Square so that he could see anyone who came along William Street. It seemed to him that he waited an interminable time, and he was on the point of going away, thinking his surmise had been mistaken, when the door of No. 7 opened and Mildred came out. He fell back into the darkness and watched her walk towards him. She had on the hat with a quantity of feathers on it which he had seen in her room, and she wore a dress he recognised, too showy for the street and unsuitable to the time of year. He followed her slowly till she came into the Tottenham Court Road, where she slackened her pace; at the corner of Oxford Street she stopped, looked round, and crossed over to a music-hall. He went up to her and touched her on the arm. He saw that she had rouged her cheeks and painted her lips.

"Where are you going, Mildred?"

She started at the sound of his voice and reddened as she always did when she was caught in a lie; then the flash of anger which he knew so well came into her eyes as she instinctively sought to defend herself by abuse. But she did not say the words which were on the tip of her tongue.

"Oh, I was only going to see the show. It gives me the hump sitting every night by myself."

He did not pretend to believe her.

"You mustn't. Good heavens, I've told you fifty times how dangerous it is. You must stop this sort of thing at once."

"Oh, hold your jaw," she cried roughly. "How d'you suppose I'm going to live?"

He took hold of her arm and without thinking what he was doing tried to drag her away.

"For God's sake come along. Let

me take you home. You don't know what you're doing. It's criminal."

"What do I care? Let them take their chance. Men haven't been so good to me that I need bother my head about them."

She pushed him away and walking up to the box-office put down her money. Philip had threepence in his pocket. He could not follow. He turned away and walked slowly down Oxford Street.

"I can't do anything more," he said to himself.

That was the end. He did not see her again.

CX

CHRISTMAS that year falling on Thursday, the shop was to close for four days: Philip wrote to his uncle asking whether it would be convenient for him to spend the holidays at the vicarage. He received an answer from Mrs. Foster, saying that Mr. Carey was not well enough to write himself, but wished to see his nephew and would be glad if he came down. She met Philip at the door, and when she shook hands with him, said:

"You'll find him changed since you was here last, sir; but you'll pretend you don't notice anything, won't you, sir? He's that nervous about himself."

Philip nodded, and she led him into the dining-room.

"Here's Mr. Philip, sir."

The Vicar of Blackstable was a dying man. There was no mistaking that when you looked at the hollow cheeks and the shrunken body. He sat huddled in the arm-chair, with his head strangely thrown back, and a shawl over his shoulders. He could not walk now without the help of sticks, and his hands trembled so that he could only feed himself with difficulty.

"He can't last long now," thought Philip, as he looked at him.

"How d'you think I'm looking?" asked the Vicar. "D'you think I've changed since you were here last?"

"I think you look stronger than you did last summer."

"It was the heat. That always upsets me."

Mr. Carey's history of the last few months consisted in the number of weeks he had spent in his bed-room and the number of weeks he had spent downstairs. He had a hand-bell by his side and while he talked he rang it for Mrs. Foster, who sat in the next room ready to attend to his wants, to ask on what day of the month he had first left his room.

"On the seventh of November, sir."

Mr. Carey looked at Philip to see how he took the information.

"But I eat well still, don't I, Mrs. Foster?"

"Yes, sir, you've got a wonderful appetite."

"I don't seem to put on flesh though."

Nothing interested him now but his health. He was set upon one thing indomitably and that was living, just living, notwithstanding the monotony of his life and the constant pain which allowed him to sleep only when he was under the influence of morphia.

"It's terrible, the amount of money I have to spend on doctor's bills." He tinkled his bell again. "Mrs. Foster, show Master Philip the chemist's bill."

Patiently she took it off the chimney-piece and handed it to Philip.

"That's only one month. I was wondering if as you're doctoring yourself you couldn't get me the drugs cheaper. I thought of getting them down from the stores, but then there's the postage."

Though apparently taking so little interest in him that he did not trouble to inquire what Phil was doing, he seemed glad to have him there. He asked how long he could stay, and when Philip told him he must leave on Tuesday morning, expressed a wish that the visit might have been longer. He told him minutely all his symptoms and repeated what the doctor had said of him. He broke off to ring his bell, and when Mrs. Foster came in, said:

"Oh, I wasn't sure if you were there. I only rang to see if you were."

When she had gone he explained to Philip that it made him uneasy if he was not certain that Mrs. Foster was within earshot; she knew exactly what to do with him if anything happened. Philip, seeing that she was tired and that her eyes were heavy from want of sleep, suggested that he was working her too hard.

"Oh, nonsense," said the Vicar, "she's as strong as a horse." And when next she came in to give him his medicine he said to her:

"Master Philip says you've got too much to do, Mrs. Foster. You like looking after me, don't you?"

"Oh, I don't mind, sir. I want to do everything I can."

Presently the medicine took effect and Mr. Carey fell asleep. Philip went into the kitchen and asked Mrs. Foster whether she could stand the work. He saw that for some months she had had little peace.

"Well, sir, what can I do?" she an-swered. "The poor old gentleman's so dependent on me, and, although he is troublesome sometimes, you can't help liking him, can you? I've been here so many years now, I don't know what I shall do when he comes to go."

Philip saw that she was really fond of the old man. She washed and dressed him, gave him his food, and was up half a dozen times in the night; for she slept in the next room to his and whenever he awoke he tinkled his little bell till she came in. He might die at any moment, but he might live for months. It was wonderful that she should look after a stranger with such patient tenderness, and it was tragic and pitiful that she should be alone in the world to care for him.

It seemed to Philip that the religion which his uncle had preached all his life was now of no more than formal importance to him: every Sunday the curate came and administered to him Holy Communion, and he often read his Bible; but it was clear that he looked upon death with horror. He believed that it was the gateway to life everlasting, but he did not want to enter upon that life. In constant pain, chained to his chair and having given up the hope of ever getting out into the open again, like a child in the hands of a woman to whom he paid wages, he clung to the world he knew.

In Philip's head was a question he could not ask, because he was aware that his uncle would never give any but a conventional answer: he wondered whether at the very end, now that the machine was painfully wearing itself out, the clergyman still believed in immortality; perhaps at the bottom of his soul, not allowed to shape itself into words in case it became urgent, was the conviction that there was no God and after this life nothing.

On the evening of Boxing Day Philip sat in the dining-room with his uncle. He had to start very early next morning in order to get to the shop by nine, and he was to say good-night to Mr. Carey then. The Vicar of Blackstable was dozing and Philip, lying on the sofa by the window, let his book fall on his knees and looked idly round the room. He asked himself how much the furniture would fetch. He had walked round the house and looked at the things he had known from his childhood; there were a few pieces of china which might go for a decent price and Philip wondered if it would be worth while to take them up to London; but the furniture was of the Victorian order, of mahogany, solid and ugly; it would go for nothing at an auction. There were three or four thousand books, but everyone knew how badly they sold, and it was not probable that they would fetch more than a hundred pounds. Philip did not know how much his uncle would leave, and he reckoned out for the hundredth time what was the least sum upon which he could finish the curriculum at the hospital, take his degree, and live during the time he wished to spend on hospital appointments. He looked at the old man, sleeping restlessly: there was no humanity left in that shrivelled face; it was the face of some queer animal. Philip thought how easy it would be to finish that useless life. He had thought it each evening when Mrs. Foster prepared for his uncle the medicine which was to give him an easy night. There were two bottles: one contained a drug which he took regularly, and the other an opiate if the pain grew unendurable. This was poured out for him and left by his bed-side. He generally took it at three or four in the morning. It would be a simple thing to double the dose; he would die in the night, and no one would suspect anything; for that was how Doctor Wigram expected him to die. The end would be painless. Philip clenched his hands as he thought of the money he wanted so badly. A few more months of that wretched life could matter nothing to the old man, but the few more months meant everything to him: he was getting to the end of his endurance, and when he thought of going back to work in the morning he shuddered with horror. His heart beat quickly at the thought which obsessed him, and though he made an effort to put it out of his mind he could not. It would be so easy, so desperately easy. He had no feeling for the old man, he had never liked him; he had been selfish all his life, selfish to his wife who adored him, indifferent to the boy who had been put in his charge; he was not a cruel man, but a stupid, hard man, eaten up with a small sensuality. It would be easy, desperately easy. Philip did not dare. He was afraid of remorse; it would be no good having the money if he regretted all his life what he had done. Though he had told himself so often that regret was futile, there were certain things that came back to him occasionally and worried him. He wished they were not on his conscience.

His uncle opened his eyes; Philip was glad, for he looked a little more human then. He was frankly horrified at the idea that had come to him, it was murder that he was meditating; and he wondered if other people had such thoughts or whether he was abnormal and depraved. He supposed he could not have done it when it came to the point, but there the thought was, constantly recurring: if he held his hand it was from fear. His uncle spoke.

"You're not looking forward to my death, Philip?"

Philip felt his heart beat against his chest.

"Good heavens, no."

"That's a good boy. I shouldn't like you to do that. You'll get a little bit of money when I pass away, but you mustn't look forward to it. It wouldn't profit you if you did."

He spoke in a low voice, and there was a curious anxiety in his tone. It sent a pang in Philip's heart. He wondered what strange insight might have led the old man to surmise what strange desires were in Philip's mind.

"I hope you'll live for another twenty years," he said.

"Oh, well, I can't expect to do that, but if I take care of myself I don't see why I shouldn't last another three or four."

He was silent for a while, and Philip found nothing to say. Then, as if he had been thinking it all over, the old man spoke again.

"Everyone has the right to live as long as he can."

Philip wanted to distract his mind.

"By the way, I suppose you never hear from Miss Wilkinson now?"

"Yes, I had a letter some time this year. She's married, you know."

"Really?"

"Yes, she married a widower. I believe they're quite comfortable."

CXI

NEXT day Philip began work again, but the end which he expected within a few weeks did not come. The weeks passed into months. The winter wore away, and in the parks the trees burst into bud and into leaf. A terrible lassitude settled upon Philip. Time was passing, though it went with such heavy feet, and he thought that his youth was going and soon he would have lost it and nothing would have been accomplished. His work seemed more aimless now that there was the certainty of his leaving it. He became skilful in the designing of costumes, and though he had no inventive faculty acquired quickness in the adaptation of French fashions to the English market. Sometimes he was not displeased with his drawings, but they always bungled them in the execution. He was amused to notice that he suffered from a lively irritation when

his ideas were not adequately carried out. He had to walk warily. Whenever he suggested something original Mr. Sampson turned it down: their customers did not want anything outré, it was a very respectable class of business, and when you had a connection of that sort it wasn't worth while taking liberties with it. Once or twice he spoke sharply to Philip; he thought the young man was getting a bit above himself, because Philip's ideas did not always coincide with his own.

"You jolly well take care, my fine young fellow, or one of these days you'll find yourself in the street."

Philip longed to give him a punch on the nose, but he restrained himself. After all it could not possibly last much longer, and then he would be done with all these people for ever. Sometimes in comic desperation he cried out that his uncle must be made of iron. What a constitution! The ills he suffered from would have killed any decent person twelve months before. When at last the news came that the Vicar was dying Philip, who had been thinking of other things, was taken by surprise. It was in July, and in another fortnight he was to have gone for his holiday. He received a letter from Mrs. Foster to say the doctor did not give Mr. Carey many days to live, and if Philip wished to see him again he must come at once. Philip went to the buyer and told him he wanted to leave. Mr. Sampson was a decent fellow, and when he knew the circumstances made no difficulties. Philip said good-bye to the people in his department; the reason of his leaving had spread among them in an exaggerated form, and they thought he had come into a fortune. Mrs. Hodges had tears in her eyes when she shook hands with him.

"I suppose we shan't often see you again," she said.

"I'm glad to get away from Lynn's," he answered.

It was strange, but he was actually sorry to leave these people whom he thought he had loathed, and when he drove away from the house in Harrington Street it was with no exultation. He had so anticipated the emotions he would experience on this occasion that now he felt nothing: he was as unconcerned as though he were going for a few days' holiday.

"I've got a rotten nature," he said to himself. "I look forward to things awfully, and then when they come I'm always disappointed."

He reached Blackstable early in the afternoon. Mrs. Foster met him at the door, and her face told him that his uncle was not yet dead.

"He's a little better today," she said. "He's got a wonderful constitution."

She led him into the bedroom where Mr. Carey lay on his back. He gave Philip a slight smile, in which was a trace of satisfied cunning at having circumvented his enemy once more.

"I thought it was all up with me yesterday," he said, in an exhausted voice. "They'd all given me up, hadn't you, Mrs. Foster?"

"You've got a wonderful constitution, there's no denying that."

"There's life in the old dog yet."

Mrs. Foster said that the Vicar must not talk, it would tire him; she treated him like a child, with kindly despotism; and there was something childish in the old man's satisfaction at having cheated all their expectations. It struck him at once that Philip had been sent for, and he was amused that he had been brought on a fool's errand. If he could only avoid another of his heart attacks he would get well enough in a week or two; and he had had the attacks several times before; he always felt as if he were going to die, but he never did. They all talked of his constitution, but they none of them knew how strong it was.

"Are you going to stay a day or two?" he asked Philip, pretending to believe he had come down for a holiday.

"I was thinking of it," Philip answered cheerfully.

"A breath of sea-air will do you good."

Presently Dr. Wigram came, and after he had seen the Vicar talked with Philip. He adopted an appropriate manner.

"I'm afraid it is the end this time, Philip," he said. "It'll be a great loss to all of us. I've known him for five-and-thirty years."

"He seems well enough now," said Philip.

"I'm keeping him alive on drugs,

but it can't last. It was dreadful these last two days, I thought he was dead half a dozen times."

The doctor was silent for a minute or two, but at the gate he said suddenly to Philip:

"Has Mrs. Foster said anything to you?"

"What d'you mean?"

"They're very superstitious, these people: she's got hold of an idea that he's got something on his mind, and he can't die till he gets rid of it; and he can't bring himself to confess it."

Philip did not answer, and the doctor went on.

"Of course it's nonsense. He's led a very good life, he's done his duty, he's been a good parish priest, and I'm sure we shall all miss him; he can't have anything to reproach himself with. I very much doubt whether the next vicar will suit us half so well."

For several days Mr. Carey continued without change. His appetite which had been excellent left him, and he could eat little. Dr. Wigram did not hesitate now to still the pain of the neuritis which tormented him; and that, with the constant shaking of his palsied limbs, was gradually exhausting him. His mind remained clear. Philip and Mrs. Foster nursed him between them. She was so tired by the many months during which she had been attentive to all his wants that Philip insisted on sitting up with the patient so that she might have her night's rest. He passed the long hours in an arm-chair so that he should not sleep soundly, and read by the light of shaded candles The Thousand and One Nights. He had not read them since he was a little boy, and they brought back his childhood to him. Sometimes he sat and listened to the silence of the night. When the effects of the opiate wore off Mr. Carey grew restless and kept him constantly busy.

At last, early one morning, when the birds were chattering noisily in the trees, he heard his name called. He went up to the bed. Mr. Carey was lying on his back, with his eyes looking at the ceiling; he did not turn them on Philip. Philip saw that sweat was on his forehead, and he took a towel and wiped it.

"Is that you, Philip?" the old man asked.

Philip was startled because the voice was suddenly changed. It was hoarse and low. So would a man speak if he was cold with fear.

"Yes, d'you want anything?"

There was a pause, and still the unseeing eyes stared at the ceiling. Then a twitch passed over the face.

"I think I'm going to die," he said.

"Oh, what nonsense!" cried Philip. "You're not going to die for years."

Two tears were wrung from the old man's eyes. They moved Philip horribly. His uncle had never betrayed any particular emotion in the affairs of life; and it was dreadful to see them now, for they signified a terror that was unspeakable.

"Send for Mr. Simmonds," he said. "I want to take the Communion."

Mr. Simmonds was the curate.

"Now?" asked Philip.

"Soon, or else it'll be too late."

Philip went to awake Mrs. Foster, but it was later than he thought and she was up already. He told her to send the gardener with a message, and he went back to his uncle's room.

"Have you sent for Mr. Simmonds?"

"Yes."

There was a silence. Philip sat by the bed-side, and occasionally wiped the sweating forehead.

"Let me hold your hand, Philip," the old man said at last.

Philip gave him his hand and he clung to it as to life, for comfort in his extremity. Perhaps he had never really loved anyone in all his days, but now he turned instinctively to a human being. His hand was wet and cold. It grasped Philip's with feeble, despairing energy. The old man was fighting with the fear of death. And Philip thought that all must go through that. Oh, how monstrous it was, and they could believe in a God that allowed his creatures to suffer such a cruel torture! He had never cared for his uncle, and for two years he had longed every day for his death; but now he could not overcome the compassion that filled his heart. What a price it was to pay for being other than the beasts!

They remained in silence broken only once by a low inquiry from Mr. Carey.

"Hasn't he come yet?"

At last the housekeeper came in softly to say that Mr. Simmonds was there. He carried a bag in which were his surplice and his hood. Mrs. Foster brought the communion plate. Mr. Simmonds shook hands silently with Philip, and then with professional gravity went to the sick man's side. Philip and the maid went out of the room.

Philip walked round the garden all fresh and dewy in the morning. The birds were singing gaily. The sky was blue, but the air, salt-laden, was sweet and cool. The roses were in full bloom. The green of the trees, the green of the lawns, was eager and brilliant. Philip walked, and as he walked he thought of the mystery which was proceeding in that bedroom. It gave him a peculiar emotion. Presently Mrs. Foster came out to him and said that his uncle wished to see him. The curate was putting his things back into the black bag. The sick man turned his head a little and greeted him with a smile. Philip was

astonished, for there was a change in him, an extraordinary change; his eyes had no longer the terror-stricken look, and the pinching of his face had gone: he looked happy and serene.

"I'm quite prepared now," he said, and his voice had a different tone in it. "When the Lord sees fit to call me I am ready to give my soul into his hands."

Philip did not speak. He could see that his uncle was sincere. It was almost a miracle. He had taken the body and blood of his Saviour, and they had given him strength so that he no longer feared the inevitable passage into the night. He knew he was going to die: he was resigned. He only said one thing more:

"I shall rejoin my dear wife."

It startled Philip. He remembered with what a callous selfishness his uncle had treated her, how obtuse he had been to her humble, devoted love. The curate, deeply moved, went away and Mrs. Foster, weeping, accompanied him to the door. Mr. Carey, exhausted by his effort, fell into a light doze, and Philip sat down by the bed and waited for the end. The morning wore on, and the old man's breathing grew stertorous. The doctor came and said he was dying. He was unconscious and he pecked feebly at the sheets; he was restless and he cried out. Dr. Wigram gave him a hypodermic injection.

"It can't do any good now, he may die at any moment."

The doctor looked at his watch and then at the patient. Philip saw that it was one o'clock. Dr. Wigram was thinking of his dinner.

"It's no use your waiting," he said.

"There's nothing I can do," said the doctor.

When he was gone Mrs. Foster asked Philip if he would go to the carpenter, who was also the undertaker, and tell him to send up a woman to lay out the body.

"You want a little fresh air," she said, "it'll do you good."

The undertaker lived half a mile away. When Philip gave him his message, he said:

"When did the poor old gentleman die?"

Philip hesitated. It occurred to him that it would seem brutal to fetch a woman to wash the body while his uncle still lived, and he wondered why Mrs. Foster had asked him to come. They would think he was in a great hurry to kill the old man off. He thought the undertaker looked at him oddly. He repeated the question. It irritated Philip. It was no business of his.

"When did the Vicar pass away?"

Philip's first impulse was to say that it had just happened, but then it would seem inexplicable if the sick man lingered for several hours. He reddened and answered awkwardly.

"Oh, he isn't exactly dead yet."

The undertaker looked at him in perplexity, and he hurried to explain.

"Mrs. Foster is all alone and she wants a woman there. You understand, don't you? He may be dead by now."

The undertaker nodded.

"Oh, yes, I see. I'll send someone up at once."

When Philip got back to the vicarage he went up to the bed-room. Mrs. Foster rose from her chair by the bedside.

"He's just as he was when you left," she said.

She went down to get herself something to eat, and Philip watched curiously the process of death. There was nothing human now in the unconscious being that struggled feebly. Sometimes a muttered ejaculation issued from the loose mouth. The sun beat down hotly from a cloudless sky, but the trees in the garden were pleasant and cool. It was a lovely day. A bluebottle buzzed against the window-pane. Suddenly there was a loud rattle, it made Philip start, it was horribly frightening; a movement passed through the limbs and the old man was dead. The machine had run down. The bluebottle buzzed, buzzed noisily against the window-pane.

CXII

JOSIAH GRAVES in his masterful way made arrangements, becoming but economical, for the funeral; and when it was over came back to the vicarage with Philip. The will was in his charge, and with a due sense of the fitness of things he read it to Philip over an early cup of tea. It was written on half a sheet of paper and left everything Mr. Carey had to his nephew. There was the furniture, about eighty pounds at the bank, twenty shares in the A. B. C. company, a few in Allsop's brewery, some in the Oxford music-hall, and a few more in a London restaurant. They had been bought under Mr. Graves' direction, and he told Philip with satisfaction:

"You see, people must eat, they will drink, and they want amusement. You're always safe if you put your money in what the public thinks necessities."

His words showed a nice discrimination between the grossness of the vulgar, which he deplored but accepted, and the finer taste of the elect. Altogether in investments there was about five hundred pounds; and to that must be added the balance at the bank and what the furniture would fetch. It was riches to Philip. He was not happy but infinitely relieved.

Mr. Graves left him, after they had discussed the auction which must be held as soon as possible, and Philip sat himself down to go through the papers of the deceased. The Rev. William Carey had prided himself on never destroying anything, and there were piles of correspondence dating back for fifty years and bundles upon bundles of neatly docketed bills. He had kept not only letters addressed to him, but letters which himself had written. There was a yellow packet of letters which he had written to his father in the forties, when as an Oxford undergraduate he had gone to Germany for the long vacation. Philip read them idly. It was a different William Carey from the William Carey he had known, and yet there were traces in the boy which might to an acute observer have suggested the man. The letters were formal and a little stilted. He showed himself strenuous to see all that was noteworthy, and he described with a fine enthusiasm the castles of the Rhine. The falls of Schaffhausen made him 'offer reverent thanks to the all-powerful Creator of the universe, whose works were wondrous and beautiful,' and he could not help thinking that they who lived in sight of 'this handiwork of their blessed Maker must be moved by the contemplation to lead pure and holy lives.' Among some bills Philip found a miniature which had been painted of William Carey soon after he was ordained. It represented a thin young curate,

with long hair that fell over his head in natural curls, with dark eyes, large and dreamy, and a pale ascetic face. Philip remembered the chuckle with which his uncle used to tell of the dozens of slippers which were worked for him by adoring ladies.

The rest of the afternoon and all the evening Philip toiled through the innumerable correspondence. He glanced at the address and at the signature, then tore the letter in two and threw it into the washing-basket by his side. Suddenly he came upon one signed Helen. He did not know the writing. It was thin, angular, and old-fashioned. It began: my dear William, and ended: your affectionate sister. Then it struck him that it was from his own mother. He had never seen a letter of hers before, and her handwriting was strange to him. It was about himself.

My dear William,

Stephen wrote to you to thank you for your congratulations on the birth of our son and your kind wishes to myself. Thank God we are both well and I am deeply thankful for the great mercy which has been shown me. Now that I can hold a pen I want to tell you and dear Louisa myself how truly grateful I am to you both for all your kindness to me now and always since my marriage. I am going to ask you to do me a great favour. Both Stephen and I wish you to be the boy's godfather, and we hope that you will consent. I know I am not asking a small thing, for I am sure you will take the responsibilities of the position very seriously, but I am especially anxious that you should undertake this office because you are a clergyman as well as the boy's uncle. I am very anxious for the boy's welfare and I pray God night and day that he may grow into a good, honest,

*and Christian man. With you to guide
him I hope that he will become a soldier in Christ's Faith and be all the
days of his life God-fearing, humble,
and pious.*

Your affectionate sister,

Helen.

Philip pushed the letter away and,
leaning forward, rested his face on his
hands. It deeply touched and at the
same time surprised him. He was astonished at its religious tone, which
seemed to him neither mawkish nor
sentimental. He knew nothing of his
mother, dead now for nearly twenty
years, but that she was beautiful, and
it was strange to learn that she was
simple and pious. He had never
thought of that side of her. He read
again what she said about him, what
she expected and thought about him;
he had turned out very differently; he
looked at himself for a moment; perhaps it was better that she was dead.
Then a sudden impulse caused him
to tear up the letter; its tenderness and
simplicity made it seem peculiarly private; he had a queer feeling that there
was something indecent in his reading
what exposed his mother's gentle soul.
He went on with the Vicar's dreary
correspondence.

A few days later he went up to London, and for the first time for two
years entered by day the hall of St.
Luke's Hospital. He went to see the
secretary of the Medical School; he
was surprised to see him and asked
Philip curiously what he had been
doing. Philip's experiences had given
him a certain confidence in himself
and a different outlook upon many
things: such a question would have
embarrassed him before; but now he
answered coolly, with a deliberate
vagueness which prevented further inquiry, that private affairs had obliged
him to make a break in the curriculum; he was now anxious to qualify
as soon as possible. The first examination he could take was in Midwifery
and the Diseases of Women, and he
put his name down to be a clerk in
the ward devoted to feminine ailments; since it was holiday time there
happened to be no difficulty in getting
a post as obstetric clerk; he arranged
to undertake that duty during the last
week of August and the first two of
September. After this interview Philip
walked through the Medical School,
more or less deserted, for the examinations at the end of the summer session were all over; and he wandered
along the terrace by the river-side.
His heart was full. He thought that
now he could begin a new life, and
he would put behind him all the errors, follies, and miseries of the past.
The flowing river suggested that
everything passed, was passing always,
and nothing mattered; the future was
before him rich with possibilities.

He went back to Blackstable and
busied himself with the settling up of
his uncle's estate. The auction was
fixed for the middle of August, when
the presence of visitors for the summer holidays would make it possible
to get better prices. Catalogues were
made out and sent to the various
dealers in second-hand books at Tercanbury, Maidstone, and Ashford.

One afternoon Philip took it into
his head to go over to Tercanbury and
see his old school. He had not been
there since the day when, with relief
in his heart, he had left it with the
feeling that thenceforward he was his
own master. It was strange to wander
through the narrow streets of Tercanbury which he had known so well
for so many years. He looked at the
old shops, still there, still selling the
same things; the booksellers with
school-books, pious works, and the
latest novels in one window and

photographs of the Cathedral and of the city in the other; the games shop, with its cricket bats, fishing tackle, tennis rackets, and footballs; the tailor from whom he had got clothes all through his boyhood; and the fishmonger where his uncle whenever he came to Tercanbury bought fish. He wandered along the sordid street in which, behind a high wall, lay the red brick house which was the preparatory school. Further on was the gateway that led into King's School, and he stood in the quadrangle round which were the various buildings. It was just four and the boys were hurrying out of school. He saw the masters in their gowns and mortar-boards, and they were strange to him. It was more than ten years since he had left and many changes had taken place. He saw the headmaster; he walked slowly down from the schoolhouse to his own, talking to a big boy who Philip supposed was in the sixth; he was little changed, tall, cadaverous, romantic as Philip remembered him, with the same wild eyes; but the black beard was streaked with gray now and the dark, sallow face was more deeply lined. Philip had an impulse to go up and speak to him, but he was afraid he would have forgotten him, and he hated the thought of explaining who he was.

Boys lingered talking to one another, and presently some who had hurried to change came out to play fives; others straggled out in twos and threes and went out of the gateway, Philip knew they were going up to the cricket ground; others again went into the precincts to bat at the nets. Philip stood among them a stranger; one or two gave him an indifferent glance; but visitors, attracted by the Norman staircase, were not rare and excited little attention. Philip looked at them curiously. He thought with melancholy of the distance that separated him from them, and he thought bitterly how much he had wanted to do and how little done. It seemed to him that all those years, vanished beyond recall, had been utterly wasted. The boys, fresh and buoyant, were doing the same things that he had done, it seemed that not a day had passed since he left the school, and yet in that place where at least by name he had known everybody now he knew not a soul. In a few years these too, others taking their place, would stand alien as he stood; but the reflection brought him no solace; it merely impressed upon him the futility of human existence. Each generation repeated the trivial round. He wondered what had become of the boys who were his companions: they were nearly thirty now; some would be dead, but others were married and had children; they were soldiers and parsons, doctors, lawyers; they were staid men who were beginning to put youth behind them. Had any of them made such a hash of life as he? He thought of the boy he had been devoted to; it was funny, he could not recall his name; he remembered exactly what he looked like, he had been his greatest friend; but his name would not come back to him. He looked back with amusement on the jealous emotions he had suffered on his account. It was irritating not to recollect his name. He longed to be a boy again, like those he saw sauntering through the quadrangle, so that, avoiding his mistakes, he might start fresh and make something more out of life. He felt an intolerable loneliness. He almost regretted the penury which he had suffered during the last two years, since the desperate struggle merely to keep body and soul together had deadened the pain of living. *In the sweat of thy brow shalt thou earn thy daily bread*: it was not a curse upon mankind, but the balm which reconciled it to existence.

But Philip was impatient with himself; he called to mind his idea of the pattern of life: the unhappiness he had suffered was no more than part of a decoration which was elaborate and beautiful; he told himself strenuously that he must accept with gaiety everything, dreariness and excitement, pleasure and pain, because it added to the richness of the design. He sought for beauty consciously, and he remembered how even as a boy he had taken pleasure in the Gothic cathedral as one saw it from the precincts; he went there and looked at the massive pile, gray under the cloudy sky, with the central tower that rose like the praise of men to their God; but the boys were batting at the nets, and they were lissom and strong and active; he could not help hearing their shouts and laughter. The cry of youth was insistent, and he saw the beautiful thing before him only with his eyes.

CXIII

At the beginning of the last week in August Philip entered upon his duties in the 'district.' They were arduous, for he had to attend on an average three confinements a day. The patient had obtained a 'card' from the hospital some time before; and when her time came it was taken to the porter by a messenger, generally a little girl, who was then sent across the road to the house in which Philip lodged. At night the porter, who had a latch-key, himself came over and awoke Philip. It was mysterious then to get up in the darkness and walk through the deserted streets of the South Side. At those hours it was generally the husband who brought the card. If there had been a number of babies before he took it for the most part with surly indifference, but if newly married he was nervous and then sometimes strove to allay his anxiety by getting drunk. Often there was a mile or more to walk, during which Philip and the messenger discussed the conditions of labour and the cost of living; Philip learnt about the various trades which were practised on that side of the river. He inspired confidence in the people among whom he was thrown, and during the long hours that he waited in a stuffy room, the woman in labour lying on a large bed that took up half of it, her mother and the midwife talked to him as naturally as they talked to one another. The circumstances in which he had lived during the last two years had taught him several things about the life of the very poor, which it amused them to find he knew; and they were impressed because he was not deceived by their little subterfuges. He was kind, and he had gentle hands, and he did not lose his temper. They were pleased because he was not above drinking a cup of tea with them, and when the dawn came and they were still waiting they offered him a slice of bread and dripping; he was not squeamish and could eat most things now with a good appetite. Some of the houses he went to, in filthy courts off a dingy street, huddled against one another without light or air, were merely squalid; but others, unexpectedly, though dilapidated, with worm-eaten floors and leaking roofs, had the grand air: you found in them oak balusters exquisitely carved, and the walls had still their panelling. These were thickly inhabited. One family lived in each room, and in the daytime there was the incessant noise of children playing in the court. The old walls were the breeding-place of vermin; the air was so foul that often, feeling sick, Philip had to light his pipe. The people who dwelt here lived from hand to mouth. Babies were unwelcome, the man received them with surly anger, the mother with despair; it was one more mouth to feed, and there was little enough wherewith to feed those already there. Philip often discerned the wish that the child might be born dead or might die quickly. He delivered one woman of twins (a source of humour to the facetious) and when she was told she burst into a long, shrill wail of misery. Her mother said outright:

"I don't know how they're going to feed 'em."

"Maybe the Lord'll see fit to take 'em to 'imself," said the midwife.

Philip caught sight of the husband's face as he looked at the tiny pair lying side by side, and there was a ferocious sullenness in it which startled him. He felt in the family assembled there a hideous resentment against those poor atoms who had come into the world unwished for; and he had a suspicion that if he did not speak firmly an 'accident' would occur. Accidents occurred often; mothers 'overlay' their babies, and perhaps errors of diet were not always the result of carelessness.

"I shall come every day," he said. "I warn you that if anything happens to them there'll have to be an inquest."

The father made no reply, but he gave Philip a scowl. There was murder in his soul.

"Bless their little 'earts," said the grandmother, "what should 'appen to them?"

The great difficulty was to keep the mothers in bed for ten days, which was the minimum upon which the hospital practice insisted. It was awkward to look after the family, no one would see to the children without payment, and the husband grumbled because his tea was not right when he came home tired from his work and hungry. Philip had heard that the poor helped one another, but woman after woman complained to him that she could not get anyone in to clean up and see to the children's dinner without paying for the service, and she could not afford to pay. By listening to the women as they talked and by chance remarks from which he could deduce much that was left unsaid, Philip learned how little there was in common between the poor and the classes above them. They did not envy their betters, for the life was too different, and they had an ideal of ease which made the existence of the middle-classes seem formal and stiff; moreover, they had a certain contempt for them because they were soft and did not work with their hands. The proud merely wished to be left alone, but the majority looked upon the well-to-do as people to be exploited; they knew what to say in order to get such advantages as the charitable put at their disposal, and they accepted benefits as a right which came to them from the folly of their superiors and their own astuteness. They bore the curate with contemptuous indifference, but the district visitor excited their bitter hatred. She came in and opened your windows without so much as a by your leave or with your leave, 'and me with my bronchitis, enough to give me my death of cold;' she poked her nose into corners, and if she didn't say the place was dirty you saw what she thought right enough, 'an' it's all very well for them as 'as servants, but I'd like to see what she'd make of 'er room if she 'ad four children, and 'ad to do the cookin', and mend their clothes, and wash them.'

Philip discovered that the greatest tragedy of life to these people was not separation or death, that was natural and the grief of it could be assuaged with tears, but loss of work. He saw a man come home one afternoon, three days after his wife's confinement, and tell her he had been dismissed; he was a builder and at that time work was slack; he stated the fact, and sat down to his tea.

"Oh, Jim," she said.

The man ate stolidly some mess which had been stewing in a saucepan against his coming; he stared at his plate; his wife looked at him two or three times, with little startled glances, and then quite silently began to cry. The builder was an uncouth little fellow with a rough, weather-beaten face and a long white scar on his forehead; he had large, stubbly hands. Presently he pushed aside his plate as if he must give up the effort to force himself to eat, and turned a fixed gaze out of the window. The room was at the top of the house, at the back, and one saw nothing but sullen clouds. The silence seemed heavy with despair. Philip felt that there was nothing to be said, he could only go; and as he walked away wearily, for he had been up most of the night, his heart was filled with rage against the cruelty of the world. He knew the hopelessness of the search for work and the desolation which is harder to bear than hunger. He was thankful not to have to believe in God, for then such a condition of things would be intolerable;

one could reconcile oneself to existence only because it was meaningless.

It seemed to Philip that the people who spent their time in helping the poorer classes erred because they sought to remedy things which would harass them if themselves had to endure them without thinking that they did not in the least disturb those who were used to them. The poor did not want large airy rooms; they suffered from cold, for their food was not nourishing and their circulation bad; space gave them a feeling of chilliness, and they wanted to burn as little coal as need be; there was no hardship for several to sleep in one room, they preferred it; they were never alone for a moment, from the time they were born to the time they died, and loneliness oppressed them; they enjoyed the promiscuity in which they dwelt, and the constant noise of their surroundings pressed upon their ears unnoticed. They did not feel the need of taking a bath constantly, and Philip often heard them speak with indignation of the necessity to do so with which they were faced on entering the hospital: it was both an affront and a discomfort. They wanted chiefly to be left alone; then if the man was in regular work life went easily and was not without its pleasures: there was plenty of time for gossip, after the day's work a glass of beer was very good to drink, the streets were a constant source of entertainment, if you wanted to read there was *Reynolds'* or *The News of the World;* 'but there, you couldn't make out 'ow the time did fly, the truth was and that's a fact, you was a rare one for reading when you was a girl, but what with one thing and another you didn't get no time now not even to read the paper.'

The usual practice was to pay three visits after a confinement, and one Sunday Philip went to see a patient at the dinner hour. She was up for the first time.

"I couldn't stay in bed no longer, I really couldn't. I'm not one for idling, and it gives me the fidgets to be there and do nothing all day long, so I said to 'Erb, I'm just going to get up and cook your dinner for you."

'Erb was sitting at table with his knife and fork already in his hands. He was a young man, with an open face and blue eyes. He was earning good money, and as things went the couple were in easy circumstances. They had only been married a few months, and were both delighted with the rosy boy who lay in the cradle at the foot of the bed. There was a savoury smell of beefsteak in the room and Philip's eyes turned to the range.

"I was just going to dish up this minute," said the woman.

"Fire away," said Philip. "I'll just have a look at the son and heir and then I'll take myself off."

Husband and wife laughed at Philip's expression, and 'Erb getting up went over with Philip to the cradle. He looked at his baby proudly.

"There doesn't seem much wrong with him, does there?" said Philip.

He took up his hat, and by this time 'Erb's wife had dished up the beefsteak and put on the table a plate of green peas.

"You're going to have a nice dinner," smiled Philip.

"He's only in of a Sunday and I like to 'ave something special for him, so as he shall miss his 'ome when he's out at work."

"I suppose you'd be above sittin' down and 'avin' a bit of dinner with us?" said 'Erb.

"Oh, 'Erb," said his wife, in a shocked tone.

"Not if you ask me," answered Philip, with his attractive smile.

"Well, that's what I call friendly, I knew 'e wouldn't take offence, Polly. Just get another plate, my girl."

Polly was flustered, and she thought 'Erb a regular caution, you never knew what ideas 'e'd get in 'is 'ead next; but she got a plate and wiped it quickly with her apron, then took a new knife and fork from the chest of drawers, where her best cutlery rested among her best clothes. There was a jug of stout on the table, and 'Erb poured Philip out a glass. He wanted to give him the lion's share of the beefsteak, but Philip insisted that they should share alike. It was a sunny room with two windows that reached to the floor; it had been the parlour of a house which at one time was if not fashionable at least respectable: it might have been inhabited fifty years before by a well-to-do tradesman or an officer on half pay. 'Erb had been a football player before he married, and there were photographs on the wall of various teams in self-conscious attitudes, with neatly plastered hair, the captain seated proudly in the middle holding a cup. There were other signs of prosperity: photographs of the relations of 'Erb and his wife in Sunday clothes; on the chimney-piece an elaborate arrangement of shells stuck on a miniature rock; and on each side mugs, 'A present from Southend' in Gothic letters, with pictures of a pier and a parade on them. 'Erb was something of a character; he was a non-union man and expressed himself with indignation at the efforts of the union to force him to join. The union wasn't no good to him, he never found no difficulty in getting work, and there was good wages for anyone as 'ad a head on his shoulders and wasn't above puttin' 'is 'and to anything as come 'is way. Polly was timorous. If she was 'im she'd join the union, the last time there was a strike she was expectin' 'im to be brought back in an ambulance every time he went out. She turned to Philip.

"He's that obstinate, there's no doing anything with 'im."

"Well, what I say is, it's a free country, and I won't be dictated to."

"It's no good saying it's a free country," said Polly, "that won't prevent 'em bashin' your 'ead in if they get the chanst."

When they had finished Philip passed his pouch over to 'Erb and they lit their pipes; then he got up, for a 'call' might be waiting for him at his rooms, and shook hands. He saw that it had given them pleasure that he shared their meal, and they saw that he had thoroughly enjoyed it.

"Well, good-bye, sir," said 'Erb, "and I 'ope we shall 'ave as nice a doctor next time the missus disgraces 'erself."

"Go on with you, 'Erb," she retorted. "'Ow d'you know there's going to be a next time?"

CXIV

THE three weeks which the appointment lasted drew to an end. Philip had attended sixty-two cases, and he was tired out. When he came home about ten o'clock on his last night he hoped with all his heart that he would not be called out again. He had not had a whole night's rest for ten days. The case which he had just come from was horrible. He had been fetched by a huge, burly man, the worse for liquor, and taken to a room in an evil-smelling court, which was filthier than any he had seen: it was a tiny attic; most of the space was taken up by a wooden bed, with a canopy of dirty red hangings, and the ceiling was so low that Philip could touch it with the tips of his fingers; with the solitary candle that afforded what light there was he went over it, frizzling up the bugs that crawled upon it. The woman was a blowsy creature of middle age, who had had a long succession of still-born children. It was a story that Philip was not unaccustomed to: the husband had been a soldier in India; the legislation forced upon that country by the prudery of the English public had given a free run to the most distressing of all diseases; the innocent suffered. Yawning, Philip undressed and took a bath, then shook his clothes over the water and watched the animals that fell out wriggling. He was just going to get into bed when there was a knock at the door, and the hospital porter brought him a card.

"Curse you," said Philip. "You're the last person I wanted to see tonight. Who's brought it?"

"I think it's the 'usband, sir. Shall I tell him to wait?"

Philip looked at the address, saw that the street was familiar to him, and told the porter that he would find his own way. He dressed himself and in five minutes, with his black bag in his hand, stepped into the street. A man, whom he could not see in the darkness, came up to him, and said he was the husband.

"I thought I'd better wait, sir," he said. "It's a pretty rough neighbour'ood, and them not knowing who you was."

Philip laughed.

"Bless your heart, they all know the doctor, I've been in some damned sight rougher places than Waver Street."

It was quite true. The black bag was a passport through wretched alleys and down foul-smelling courts into which a policeman was not ready to venture by himself. Once or twice a little group of men had looked at Philip curiously as he passed; he heard a mutter of observations and then one say:

"It's the 'orspital doctor."

As he went by one or two of them said: "Good-night, sir."

"We shall 'ave to step out if you don't mind, sir," said the man who accompanied him now. "They told me there was no time to lose."

"Why did you leave it so late?" asked Philip, as he quickened his pace.

He glanced at the fellow as they passed a lamp-post.

"You look awfully young," he said.

"I'm turned eighteen, sir."

He was fair, and he had not a hair on his face, he looked no more than a boy; he was short, but thick set.

"You're young to be married," said Philip.

"We 'ad to."

"How much d'you earn?"

"Sixteen, sir."

Sixteen shillings a week was not much to keep a wife and child on. The room the couple lived in showed that their poverty was extreme. It was a fair size, but it looked quite large, since there was hardly any furniture in it; there was no carpet on the floor; there were no pictures on the walls; and most rooms had something, photographs or supplements in cheap frames from the Christmas numbers of the illustrated papers. The patient lay on a little iron bed of the cheapest sort. It startled Philip to see how young she was.

"By Jove, she can't be more than sixteen," he said to the woman who had come in to 'see her through.'

She had given her age as eighteen on the card, but when they were very young they often put on a year or two. Also she was pretty, which was rare in those classes in which the constitution has been undermined by bad food, bad air, and unhealthy occupations; she had delicate features and large blue eyes, and a mass of dark hair done in the elaborate fashion of the coster girl. She and her husband were very nervous.

"You'd better wait outside, so as to be at hand if I want you," Philip said to him.

Now that he saw him better Philip was surprised again at his boyish air: you felt that he should be larking in the street with the other lads instead of waiting anxiously for the birth of a child. The hours passed, and it was not till nearly two that the baby was born. Everything seemed to be going satisfactorily; the husband was called in, and it touched Philip to see the awkward, shy way in which he kissed his wife; Philip packed up his things. Before going he felt once more his patient's pulse.

"Hulloa!" he said.

He looked at her quickly: something had happened. In cases of emergency the S. O. C.—senior obstetric clerk—had to be sent for; he was a qualified man, and the 'district' was in his charge. Philip scribbled a note, and giving it to the husband, told him to run with it to the hospital; he bade him hurry, for his wife was in a dangerous state. The man set off. Philip waited anxiously; he knew the woman was bleeding to death; he was afraid she would die before his chief arrived; he took what steps he could. He hoped fervently that the S. O. C. would not have been called elsewhere. The minutes were interminable. He came at last, and, while he examined the patient, in a low voice asked Philip questions. Philip saw by his face that he thought the case very grave. His name was Chandler. He was a tall man of few words, with a long nose and a thin face much lined for his age. He shook his head.

"It was hopeless from the beginning. Where's the husband?"

"I told him to wait on the stairs," said Philip.

"You'd better bring him in."

Philip opened the door and called him. He was sitting in the dark on the first step of the flight that led to the next floor. He came up to the bed.

"What's the matter?" he asked.

"Why, there's internal bleeding. It's impossible to stop it." The S. O. C. hesitated a moment, and because it was a painful thing to say he forced his voice to become brusque. "She's dying."

The man did not say a word; he stopped quite still, looking at his wife, who lay, pale and unconscious, on the bed. It was the midwife who spoke.

"The gentlemen 'ave done all they could, 'Arry," she said. "I saw what was comin' from the first."

"Shut up," said Chandler.

There were no curtains on the windows, and gradually the night seemed to lighten; it was not yet the dawn, but the dawn was at hand. Chandler was keeping the woman alive by all the means in his power, but life was slipping away from her, and suddenly she died. The boy who was her husband stood at the end of the cheap iron bed with his hands resting on the rail; he did not speak; but he looked very pale and once or twice Chandler gave him an uneasy glance, thinking he was going to faint: his lips were gray. The midwife sobbed noisily, but he took no notice of her. His eyes were fixed upon his wife, and in them was an utter bewilderment. He reminded you of a dog whipped for something he did not know was wrong. When Chandler and Philip had gathered together their things Chandler turned to the husband.

"You'd better lie down for a bit. I expect you're about done up."

"There's nowhere for me to lie down, sir," he answered, and there was in his voice a humbleness which was very distressing.

"Don't you know anyone in the house who'll give you a shakedown?"

"No, sir."

"They only moved in last week," said the midwife. "They don't know nobody yet."

Chandler hesitated a moment awkwardly, then he went up to the man and said:

"I'm very sorry this has happened."

He held out his hand and the man, with an instinctive glance at his own to see if it was clean, shook it.

"Thank you, sir."

Philip shook hands with him too. Chandler told the midwife to come and fetch the certificate in the morning. They left the house and walked along together in silence.

"It upsets one a bit at first, doesn't it?" said Chandler at last.

"A bit," answered Philip.

"If you like I'll tell the porter not to bring you any more calls tonight."

"I'm off duty at eight in the morning in any case."

"How many cases have you had?"

"Sixty-three."

"Good. You'll get your certificate then."

They arrived at the hospital, and the S. O. C. went in to see if anyone wanted him. Philip walked on. It had been very hot all the day before, and even now in the early morning there was a balminess in the air. The street was very still. Philip did not feel inclined to go to bed. It was the end of his work and he need not hurry. He strolled along, glad of the fresh air and the silence; he thought that he would go on to the bridge and look at day break on the river. A policeman at the corner bade him good-morning. He knew who Philip was from his bag.

"Out late tonight, sir," he said.

Philip nodded and passed. He leaned against the parapet and looked towards the morning. At that hour the great city was like a city of the dead. The sky was cloudless, but the stars were dim at the approach of day; there was a light mist on the river, and the great buildings on the north side were like palaces in an enchanted island. A group of barges were moored in midstream. It was all of an unearthy violet, troubling somehow and awe-inspiring; but quickly everything grew pale, and cold, and gray. Then the sun rose, a ray of yellow gold stole across the sky, and the sky was iridescent. Philip could not get out of his eyes the dead girl lying on the bed, wan and white, and the boy who stood at the end of it like a stricken beast. The bareness of the squalid room made the pain of it more poignant. It was cruel that a stupid chance should have cut off her life when she was just entering upon it; but in the very moment of saying this to himself, Philip thought of the life which had been in store for her, the bearing of children, the dreary fight with poverty, the youth broken by toil and deprivation into a slatternly middle age—he saw the pretty face grow thin and white, the hair grow scanty, the pretty hands, worn down brutally by work, become like the claws of an old animal—then, when the man was past his prime, the difficulty of getting jobs, the small wages he had to take; and the inevitable, abject penury of the end: she might be energetic, thrifty, industrious, it would not have saved her; in the end was the workhouse or subsistence on the charity of her children. Who could pity her because she had died when life offered so little?

But pity was inane. Philip felt it was not that which these people needed. They did not pity themselves. They accepted their fate. It was the natural order of things. Otherwise, good heavens! otherwise they would swarm over the river in their multitude to the side where those great buildings were, secure and stately; and they would pillage, burn, and sack. But the day, tender and pale, had broken now, and the mist was tenuous; it bathed everything in a soft radiance; and the Thames was gray, rosy, and green; gray like mother-of-pearl and green like the heart of a yellow rose. The wharves and store-houses of the Surrey Side were massed in disorderly loveliness. The scene was so exquisite that Philip's heart beat passionately. He was overwhelmed by the beauty of the world. Beside that nothing seemed to matter.

CXV

PHILIP spent the few weeks that remained before the beginning of the winter session in the out-patients' department, and in October settled down to regular work. He had been away from the hospital for so long that he found himself very largely among new people; the men of different years had little to do with one another, and his contemporaries were now mostly qualified: some had left to take up assistantships or posts in country hospitals and infirmaries, and some held appointments at St. Luke's. The two years during which his mind had lain fallow had refreshed him, he fancied, and he was able now to work with energy.

The Athelnys were delighted with his change of fortune. He had kept aside a few things from the sale of his uncle's effects and gave them all presents. He gave Sally a gold chain that had belonged to his aunt. She was now grown up. She was apprenticed to a dressmaker and set out every morning at eight to work all day in a shop in Regent Street. Sally had frank blue eyes, a broad brow, and plentiful shining hair; she was buxom, with broad hips and full breasts; and her father, who was fond of discussing her appearance, warned her constantly that she must not grow fat. She attracted because she was healthy, animal, and feminine. She had many admirers, but they left her unmoved; she gave one the impression that she looked upon love-making as nonsense; and it was easy to imagine that young men found her unapproachable. Sally was old for her years: she had been used to help her mother in the house-

hold work and in the care of the children, so that she had acquired a managing air, which made her mother say that Sally was a bit too fond of having things her own way. She did not speak very much, but as she grew older she seemed to be acquiring a quiet sense of humour, and sometimes uttered a remark which suggested that beneath her impassive exterior she was quietly bubbling with amusement at her fellow-creatures. Philip found that with her he never got on the terms of affectionate intimacy upon which he was with the rest of Athelny's huge family. Now and then her indifference slightly irritated him. There was something enigmatic in her.

When Philip gave her the necklace Athelny in his boisterous way insisted that she must kiss him; but Sally reddened and drew back.

"No, I'm not going to," she said.

"Ungrateful hussy!" cried Athelny. "Why not?"

"I don't like being kissed by men," she said.

Philip saw her embarrassment, and, amused, turned Athelny's attention to something else. That was never a very difficult thing to do. But evidently her mother spoke of the matter later, for next time Philip came she took the opportunity when they were alone for a couple of minutes to refer to it.

"You didn't think it disagreeable of me last week when I wouldn't kiss you?"

"Not a bit," he laughed.

"It's not because I wasn't grateful." She blushed a little as she uttered the formal phrase which she had prepared. "I shall always value the necklace, and it was very kind of you to give it me."

Philip found it always a little difficult to talk to her. She did all that she had to do very competently, but seemed to feel no need of conversation; yet there was nothing unsociable in her. One Sunday afternoon when Athelny and his wife had gone out together, and Philip, treated as one of the family, sat reading in the parlour, Sally came in and sat by the window to sew. The girls' clothes were made at home and Sally could not afford to spend Sundays in idleness. Philip thought she wished to talk and put down his book.

"Go on reading," she said. "I only thought as you were alone I'd come and sit with you."

"You're the most silent person I've ever struck," said Philip.

"We don't want another one who's talkative in this house," she said.

There was no irony in her tone: she was merely stating a fact. But it suggested to Philip that she measured her father, alas, no longer the hero he was to her childhood, and in her mind joined together his entertaining conversation and the thriftlessness which often brought difficulties into their life; she compared his rhetoric with her mother's practical common sense; and though the liveliness of her father amused her she was perhaps sometimes a little impatient with it. Philip looked at her as she bent over her work; she was healthy, strong, and normal; it must be odd to see her among the other girls in the shop with their flat chests and anæmic faces. Mildred suffered from anæmia.

After a time it appeared that Sally had a suitor. She went out occasionally with friends she had made in the work-room, and had met a young man, an electrical engineer in a very good way of business, who was a most eligible person. One day she told her mother that he had asked her to marry him.

"What did you say?" said her mother.

"Oh, I told him I wasn't over-anxious to marry anyone just yet awhile." She paused a little as was her habit between observations. "He took on so that I said he might come to tea on Sunday."

It was an occasion that thoroughly appealed to Athelny. He rehearsed all the afternoon how he should play the heavy father for the young man's edification till he reduced his children to helpless giggling. Just before he was due Athelny routed out an Egyptian tarboosh and insisted on putting it on.

"Go on with you, Athelny," said his wife, who was in her best, which was of black velvet, and, since she was growing stouter every year, very tight for her. "You'll spoil the girl's chances."

She tried to pull it off, but the little man skipped nimbly out of her way.

"Unhand me, woman. Nothing will induce me to take it off. This young man must be shown at once that it is no ordinary family he is preparing to enter."

"Let him keep it on, mother," said Sally, in her even, indifferent fashion. "If Mr. Donaldson doesn't take it the way it's meant he can take himself off, and good riddance."

Philip thought it was a severe ordeal that the young man was being exposed to, since Athelny, in his brown velvet jacket, flowing black tie, and red tarboosh, was a startling spectacle for an innocent electrical engineer. When he came he was greeted by his host with the proud courtesy of a Spanish grandee and by Mrs. Athelny in an altogether homely and natural fashion. They sat down at the old ironing-table in the high-backed monkish chairs, and Mrs. Athelny poured tea out of a lustre teapot which gave a note of England and the countryside to the festivity. She had made little cakes with her own hand, and on the table was home-made jam. It was a farmhouse tea, and to Philip very quaint and charming in that Jacobean house. Athelny for some fantastic reason took it into his head to discourse upon Byzantine history; he had been reading the later volumes of the *Decline and Fall*; and, his forefinger dramatically extended, he poured into the astonished ears of the suitor scandalous stories about Theodora and Irene. He addressed himself directly to his guest with a torrent of rhodomontade; and the young man, reduced to helpless silence and shy, nodded his head at intervals to show that he took an intelligent interest. Mrs. Athelny paid no attention to Thorpe's conversation, but interrupted now and then to offer the young man more tea or to press upon him cake and jam. Philip watched Sally; she sat with downcast eyes, calm, silent, and observant; and her long eye-lashes cast a pretty shadow on her cheek. You could not tell whether she was amused at the scene or if she cared for the young man. She was inscrutable. But one thing was certain: the electrical engineer was good-looking, fair and clean-shaven, with pleasant, regular features, and an honest face; he was tall and well-made. Philip could not help thinking he would make an excellent mate for her, and he felt a pang of envy for the happiness which he fancied was in store for them.

Presently the suitor said he thought it was about time he was getting along. Sally rose to her feet without a word and accompanied him to the door. When she came back her father

burst out:

"Well, Sally, we think your young man very nice. We are prepared to welcome him into our family. Let the banns be called and I will compose a nuptial song."

Sally set about clearing away the tea-things. She did not answer. Suddenly she shot a swift glance at Philip.

"What did you think of him, Mr. Philip?"

She had always refused to call him Uncle Phil as the other children did, and would not call him Philip.

"I think you'd make an awfully handsome pair."

She looked at him quickly once more, and then with a slight blush went on with her business.

"I thought him a very nice civil-spoken young fellow," said Mrs. Athelny, "and I think he's just the sort to make any girl happy."

Sally did not reply for a minute or two, and Philip looked at her curiously: it might be thought that she was meditating upon what her mother had said, and on the other hand she might be thinking of the man in the moon.

"Why don't you answer when you're spoken to, Sally?" remarked her mother, a little irritably.

"I thought he was a silly."

"Aren't you going to have him then?"

"No, I'm not."

"I don't know how much more you want," said Mrs. Athelny, and it was quite clear now that she was put out. "He's a very decent young fellow and he can afford to give you a thorough good home. We've got quite enough to feed here without you. If you get a chance like that it's wicked not to take it. And I daresay you'd be able to have a girl to do the rough work."

Philip had never before heard Mrs.

Athelny refer so directly to the difficulties of her life. He saw how important it was that each child should be provided for.

"It's no good your carrying on, mother," said Sally in her quiet way. "I'm not going to marry him."

"I think you're a very hard-hearted, cruel, selfish girl."

"If you want me to earn my own living, mother, I can always go into service."

"Don't be so silly, you know your father would never let you do that."

Philip caught Sally's eye, and he thought there was in it a glimmer of amusement. He wondered what there had been in the conversation to touch her sense of humour. She was an odd girl.

CXVI

DURING his last year at St. Luke's Philip had to work hard. He was contented with life. He found it very comfortable to be heart-free and to have enough money for his needs. He had heard people speak contemptuously of money: he wondered if they had ever tried to do without it. He knew that the lack made a man petty, mean, grasping; it distorted his character and caused him to view the world from a vulgar angle; when you had to consider every penny, money became of grotesque importance: you needed a competency to rate it at its proper value. He lived a solitary life, seeing no one except the Athelnys, but he was not lonely; he busied himself with plans for the future, and sometimes he thought of the past. His recollection dwelt now and then on old friends, but he made no effort to see them. He would have liked to know what was become of Norah Nesbit; she was Norah something else now, but he could not remember the name of the man she was going to marry; he was glad to have known her: she was a good and a brave soul. One evening about half past eleven he saw Lawson, walking along Piccadilly; he was in evening clothes and might be supposed to be coming back from a theatre. Philip gave way to a sudden impulse and quickly turned down a side street. He had not seen him for two years and felt that he could not now take up again the interrupted friendship. He and Lawson had nothing more to say to one another. Philip was no longer interested in art; it seemed to him that he was able to enjoy beauty with greater force than when he was a boy; but art appeared to him unimportant. He was occupied with the forming of a pattern out of the manifold chaos of life, and the materials with which he worked seemed to make preoccupation with pigments and words very trivial. Lawson had served his turn. Philip's friendship with him had been a motive in the design he was elaborating: it was merely sentimental to ignore the fact that the painter was of no further interest to him.

Sometimes Philip thought of Mildred. He avoided deliberately the streets in which there was a chance of seeing her; but occasionally some feeling, perhaps curiosity, perhaps something deeper which he would not acknowledge, made him wander about Piccadilly and Regent Street during the hours when she might be expected to be there. He did not know then whether he wished to see her or dreaded it. Once he saw a back which reminded him of hers, and for a moment he thought it was she; it gave him a curious sensation: it was a strange sharp pain in his heart, there was fear in it and a sickening dismay; and when he hurried on and found that he was mistaken he did not know whether it was relief that he experienced or disappointment.

At the beginning of August Philip passed his Surgery, his last examination, and received his diploma. It was seven years since he had entered St. Luke's Hospital. He was nearly thirty. He walked down the stairs of the Royal College of Surgeons with the roll in his hand which qualified him to practice, and his heart beat with satisfaction.

"Now I'm really going to begin life," he thought.

Next day he went to the secretary's office to put his name down for one of the hospital appointments. The secretary was a pleasant little man with a black beard, whom Philip had always found very affable. He congratulated him on his success, and then said:

"I suppose you wouldn't like to do a locum for a month on the South coast? Three guineas a week with board and lodging."

"I wouldn't mind," said Philip.

"It's at Farnley, in Dorsetshire. Doctor South. You'd have to go down at once; his assistant has developed mumps. I believe it's a very pleasant place."

There was something in the secretary's manner that puzzled Philip. It was a little doubtful.

"What's the crab in it?" he asked.

The secretary hesitated a moment and laughed in a conciliating fashion.

"Well, the fact is, I understand he's rather a crusty, funny old fellow. The agencies won't send him anyone any more. He speaks his mind very openly, and men don't like it."

"But d'you think he'll be satisfied with a man who's only just qualified? After all I have no experience."

"He ought to be glad to get you," said the secretary diplomatically.

Philip thought for a moment. He had nothing to do for the next few weeks, and he was glad of the chance to earn a bit of money. He could put it aside for the holiday in Spain which he had promised himself when he had finished his appointment at St. Luke's or, if they would not give him anything there, at some other hospital.

"All right. I'll go."

"The only thing is, you must go this afternoon. Will that suit you? If so, I'll send a wire at once."

Philip would have liked a few days to himself; but he had seen the Athelnys the night before (he had gone at once to take them his good news) and there was really no reason why he should not start immediately. He had little luggage to pack. Soon after seven that evening he got out of the station at Farnley and took a cab to Doctor South's. It was a broad low stucco house, with a Virginia creeper growing over it. He was shown into the consulting-room. An old man was writing at a desk. He looked up as the maid ushered Philip in. He did not get up, and he did not speak; he merely stared at Philip. Philip was taken aback.

"I think you're expecting me," he said. "The secretary of St. Luke's wired to you this morning."

"I kept dinner back for half an hour. D'you want to wash?"

"I do," said Philip.

Doctor South amused him by his odd manner. He got up now, and Philip saw that he was a man of middle height, thin, with white hair cut very short and a long mouth closed so tightly that he seemed to have no lips at all; he was clean-shaven but for small white whiskers, and they increased the squareness of face which his firm jaw gave him. He wore a brown tweed suit and a white stock. His clothes hung loosely about him as though they had been made for a much larger man. He looked like a respectable farmer of the middle of the nineteenth century. He opened the door.

"There is the dining-room," he said, pointing to the door opposite. "Your bed-room is the first door you come to when you get on the landing. Come downstairs when you're ready."

During dinner Philip knew that Doctor South was examining him, but he spoke little, and Philip felt that he did not want to hear his assistant talk.

"When were you qualified?" he asked suddenly.

"Yesterday."

"Were you at a university?"

"No."

"Last year when my assistant took a holiday they sent me a 'Varsity man. I told 'em not to do it again. Too damned gentlemanly for me."

There was another pause. The dinner was very simple and very good. Philip preserved a sedate exterior, but in his heart he was bubbling over with excitement. He was immensely elated at being engaged as a locum; it made him feel extremely grown up; he had an insane desire to laugh at nothing in particular; and the more he thought of his professional dignity the more he was inclined to chuckle.

But Doctor South broke suddenly into his thoughts.

"How old are you?"

"Getting on for thirty."

"How is it you're only just qualified?"

"I didn't go in for the medical till I was nearly twenty-three, and I had to give it up for two years in the middle."

"Why?"

"Poverty."

Doctor South gave him an odd look and relapsed into silence. At the end of dinner he got up from the table.

"D'you know what sort of a practice this is?"

"No," answered Philip.

"Mostly fishermen and their families. I have the Union and the Seamen's Hospital. I used to be alone here, but since they tried to make this into a fashionable sea-side resort a man has set up on the cliff, and the well-to-do people go to him. I only have those who can't afford to pay for a doctor at all."

Philip saw that the rivalry was a sore point with the old man.

"You know that I have no experience," said Philip.

"You none of you know anything."

He walked out of the room without another word and left Philip by himself. When the maid came in to clear away she told Philip that Doctor South saw patients from six till seven. Work for that night was over. Philip fetched a book from his room, lit his pipe, and settled himself down to read. It was a great comfort, since he had read nothing but medical books for the last few months. At ten o'clock Doctor South came in and looked at him. Philip hated not to have his feet up, and he had dragged up a chair for them.

"You seem able to make yourself pretty comfortable," said Doctor South, with a grimness which would have disturbed Philip if he had not been in such high spirits.

Philip's eyes twinkled as he answered.

"Have you any objection?"

Doctor South gave him a look, but did not reply directly.

"What's that you're reading?"

"*Peregrine Pickle*. Smollett."

"I happen to know that Smollett wrote *Peregrine Pickle*."

"I beg your pardon. Medical men aren't much interested in literature, are they?"

Philip had put the book down on the table, and Doctor South took it up. It was a volume of an edition which had belonged to the Vicar of Blackstable. It was a thin book bound in faded morocco, with a copper-plate engraving as a frontispiece; the pages were musty with age and stained with mould. Philip, without meaning to, started forward a little as Doctor South took the volume in his hands, and a slight smile came into his eyes. Very little escaped the old doctor.

"Do I amuse you?" he asked icily.

"I see you're fond of books. You can always tell by the way people handle them."

Doctor South put down the novel immediately.

"Breakfast at eight-thirty," he said and left the room.

"What a funny old fellow!" thought Philip.

He soon discovered why Doctor South's assistants found it difficult to get on with him. In the first place, he set his face firmly against all the discoveries of the last thirty years: he had no patience with the drugs which became modish, were thought to work marvellous cures, and in a few years were discarded; he had stock mixtures which he had brought from St. Luke's, where he had been a student, and

had used all his life; he found them just as efficacious as anything that had come into fashion since. Philip was startled at Dr. South's suspicion of asepsis; he had accepted it in deference to universal opinion; but he used the precautions which Philip had known insisted upon so scrupulously at the hospital with the disdainful tolerance of a man playing at soldiers with children.

"I've seen antiseptics come along and sweep everything before them, and then I've seen asepsis take their place. Bunkum!"

The young men who were sent down to him knew only hospital practice; and they came with the unconcealed scorn for the General Practitioner which they had absorbed in the air at the hospital; but they had seen only the complicated cases which appeared in the wards; they knew how to treat an obscure disease of the suprarenal bodies, but were helpless when consulted for a cold in the head. Their knowledge was theoretical and their self-assurance unbounded. Doctor South watched them with tightened lips; he took a savage pleasure in showing them how great was their ignorance and how unjustified their conceit. It was a poor practice, of fishing folk, and the doctor made up his own prescriptions. Doctor South asked his assistant how he expected to make both ends meet if he gave a fisherman with a stomach-ache a mixture consisting of half a dozen expensive drugs. He complained too that the young medical men were uneducated: their reading consisted of *The Sporting Times* and *The British Medical Journal;* they could neither write a legible hand nor spell correctly. For two or three days Doctor South watched Philip closely, ready to fall on him with acid sarcasm if he gave him the opportunity; and Philip, aware of this, went about his work with a quiet sense of amusement. He was pleased with the change of occupation. He liked the feeling of independence and of responsibility. All sorts of people came to the consulting-room. He was gratified because he seemed able to inspire his patients with confidence; and it was entertaining to watch the process of cure which at a hospital necessarily could be watched only at distant intervals. His rounds took him into low-roofed cottages in which were fishing tackle and sails and here and there mementoes of deep-sea travelling, a lacquer box from Japan, spears and oars from Melanesia, or daggers from the bazaars of Stamboul; there was an air of romance in the stuffy little rooms, and the salt of the sea gave them a bitter freshness. Philip liked to talk to the sailor-men, and when they found that he was not supercilious they told him long yarns of the distant journeys of their youth.

Once or twice he made a mistake in diagnosis: (he had never seen a case of measles before, and when he was confronted with the rash took it for an obscure disease of the skin;)

and once or twice his ideas of treatment differed from Doctor South's. The first time this happened Doctor South attacked him with savage irony; but Philip took it with good humour; he had some gift for repartee, and he made one or two answers which caused Doctor South to stop and look at him curiously. Philip's face was grave, but his eyes were twinkling. The old gentleman could not avoid the impression that Philip was chaffing him. He was used to being disliked and feared by his assistants, and this was a new experience. He had half a mind to fly into a passion and pack Philip off by the next train, he had done that before with his assistants; but he had an uneasy feeling that Philip would simply laugh at him outright; and suddenly he felt amused. His mouth formed itself into a smile against his will, and he turned away. In a little while he grew conscious that Philip was amusing himself systematically at his expense. He was taken aback at first and then diverted.

"Damn his impudence," he chuckled to himself. "Damn his impudence."

CXVII

Philip had written to Athelny to tell him that he was doing a locum in Dorsetshire and in due course received an answer from him. It was written in the formal manner he affected, studded with pompous epithets as a Persian diadem was studded with precious stones; and in the beautiful hand, like black letter and as difficult to read, upon which he prided himself. He suggested that Philip should join him and his family in the Kentish hop-field to which he went every year;

and to persuade him said various beautiful and complicated things about Philip's soul and the winding tendrils of the hops. Philip replied at once that he would come on the first day he was free. Though not born there, he had a peculiar affection for the Isle of Thanet, and he was fired with enthusiasm at the thought of spending a fortnight so close to the earth and amid conditions which needed only a blue sky to be as idyllic as the olive groves of Arcady.

The four weeks of his engagement at Farnley passed quickly. On the cliff a new town was springing up, with red brick villas round golf links, and a large hotel had recently been opened to cater for the summer visitors; but Philip went there seldom. Down below, by the harbour, the little stone houses of a past century were clustered in a delightful confusion, and the narrow streets, climbing down steeply, had an air of antiquity which appealed to the imagination. By the water's edge were neat cottages with trim, tiny gardens in front of them; they were inhabited by retired captains in the merchant service, and by mothers or widows of men who had gained their living by the sea; and they had an appearance which was quaint and peaceful. In the little harbour came tramps from Spain and the Levant, ships of small tonnage; and now and then a windjammer was borne in by the winds of romance. It reminded Philip of the dirty little harbour with its colliers at Blackstable, and he thought that there he had first acquired the desire, which was now an obsession, for Eastern lands and sunlit islands in a tropic sea. But here you felt yourself closer to the wide, deep ocean than on the shore of that North Sea which seemed always circumscribed; here you could draw a long breath as you looked out upon the even vastness; and the west wind, the dear soft salt wind of England, uplifted the heart and at the same time melted it to tenderness.

One evening, when Philip had reached his last week with Doctor South, a child came to the surgery door while the old doctor and Philip were making up prescriptions. It was a little ragged girl with a dirty face and bare feet. Philip opened the door.

"Please, sir, will you come to Mrs. Fletcher's in Ivy Lane at once?"

"What's the matter with Mrs. Fletcher?" called out Doctor South in his rasping voice.

The child took no notice of him, but addressed herself again to Philip.

"Please, sir, her little boy's had an accident and will you come at once?"

"Tell Mrs. Fletcher I'm coming," called out Doctor South.

The little girl hesitated for a moment, and putting a dirty finger in a dirty mouth stood still and looked at Philip.

"What's the matter, Kid?" said Philip, smiling.

"Please, sir, Mrs. Fletcher says, will the new doctor come?"

There was a sound in the dispensary and Doctor South came out into the passage.

"Isn't Mrs. Fletcher satisfied with me?" he barked. "I've attended Mrs. Fletcher since she was born. Why aren't I good enough to attend her filthy brat?"

The little girl looked for a moment as though she were going to cry, then she thought better of it; she put out her tongue deliberately at Doctor South, and, before he could recover from his astonishment, bolted off as fast as she could run. Philip saw that the old gentleman was annoyed.

"You look rather fagged, and it's a goodish way to Ivy Lane," he said, by way of giving him an excuse not to go himself.

Doctor South gave a low snarl.

"It's a damned sight nearer for a man who's got the use of both legs than for a man who's got only one and a half."

Philip reddened and stood silent for a while.

"Do you wish me to go or will you go yourself?" he said at last frigidly.

"What's the good of my going? They want you."

Philip took up his hat and went to

see the patient. It was hard upon eight o'clock when he came back. Doctor South was standing in the dining-room with his back to the fireplace.

"You've been a long time," he said.

"I'm sorry. Why didn't you start dinner?"

"Because I chose to wait. Have you been all this while at Mrs. Fletcher's?"

"No, I'm afraid I haven't. I stopped to look at the sunset on my way back, and I didn't think of the time."

Doctor South did not reply, and the servant brought in some grilled sprats. Philip ate them with an excellent appetite. Suddenly Doctor South shot a question at him.

"Why did you look at the sunset?"

Philip answered with his mouth full.

"Because I was happy."

Doctor South gave him an odd look, and the shadow of a smile flickered across his old, tired face. They ate the rest of the dinner in silence; but when the maid had given them the port and left the room, the old man leaned back and fixed his sharp eyes on Philip.

"It stung you up a bit when I spoke of your game leg, young fellow?" he said.

"People always do, directly or indirectly, when they get angry with me."

"I suppose they know it's your weak point."

Philip faced him and looked at him steadily.

"Are you very glad to have discovered it?"

The doctor did not answer, but he gave a chuckle of bitter mirth. They sat for a while staring at one another. Then Doctor South surprised Philip extremely.

"Why don't you stay here and I'll get rid of that damned fool with his mumps?"

"It's very kind of you, but I hope to get an appointment at the hospital in the autumn. It'll help me so much in getting other work later."

"I'm offering you a partnership," said Doctor South grumpily.

"Why?" asked Philip, with surprise.

"They seem to like you down here."

"I didn't think that was a fact which altogether met with your approval," Philip said drily.

"D'you suppose that after forty years' practice I care a twopenny damn whether people prefer my assistant to me? No, my friend. There's no sentiment between my patients and me. I don't expect gratitude from them, I expect them to pay my fees. Well, what d'you say to it?"

Philip made no reply, not because he was thinking over the proposal, but because he was astonished. It was evidently very unusual for someone to offer a partnership to a newly qualified man; and he realised with wonder that, although nothing would induce him to say so, Doctor South had taken a fancy to him. He thought how amused the secretary at St. Luke's would be when he told him.

"The practice brings in about seven hundred a year. We can reckon out how much your share would be worth, and you can pay me off by degrees. And when I die you can succeed me. I think that's better than knocking about hospitals for two or three years, and then taking assistantships until you can afford to set up for yourself."

Philip knew it was a chance that most people in his profession would jump at; the profession was overcrowded, and half the men he knew would be thankful to accept the certainty of even so modest a competence as that.

"I'm awfully sorry, but I can't,"

he said. "It means giving up everything I've aimed at for years. In one way and another I've had a roughish time, but I always had that one hope before me, to get qualified so that I might travel; and now, when I wake in the morning, my bones simply ache to get off, I don't mind where particularly, but just away, to places I've never been to."

Now the goal seemed very near. He would have finished his appointment at St. Luke's by the middle of the following year, and then he would go to Spain; he could afford to spend several months there, rambling up and down the land which stood to him for romance; after that he would get a ship and go to the East. Life was before him and time of no account. He could wander, for years if he chose, in unfrequented places, amid strange peoples, where life was led in strange ways. He did not know what he sought or what his journeys would bring him; but he had a feeling that he would learn something new about life and gain some clue to the mystery that he had solved only to find more mysterious. And even if he found nothing he would allay the unrest which gnawed at his heart. But Doctor South was showing him a great kindness, and it seemed ungrateful to refuse his offer for no adequate reason; so in his shy way, trying to appear as matter of fact as possible, he made some attempt to explain why it was so important to him to carry out the plans he had cherished so passionately.

Doctor South listened quietly, and a gentle look came into his shrewd old eyes. It seemed to Philip an added kindness that he did not press him to accept his offer. Benevolence is often very peremptory. He appeared to look upon Philip's reasons as sound. Dropping the subject, he began to talk of his own youth; he had been in the Royal Navy, and it was his long connection with the sea that, when he retired, had made him settle at Farnley. He told Philip of old days in the Pacific and of wild adventures in China. He had taken part in an expedition against the head-hunters of Borneo and had known Samoa when it was still an independent state. He had touched at coral islands. Philip listened to him entranced. Little by little he told Philip about himself. Doctor South was a widower, his wife had died thirty years before, and his daughter had married a farmer in Rhodesia; he had quarrelled with him, and she had not come to England for ten years. It was just as if he had never had wife or child. He was very lonely. His gruffness was little more than a protection which he wore to hide a complete disillusionment; and to Philip it seemed tragic to see him just waiting for death, not impatiently, but rather with loathing for it, hating old age and unable to resign himself to its limitations, and yet with the feeling that death was the only solution of the bitterness of his life. Philip crossed his path, and the natural affection which long separation from his daughter had killed—she had taken her husband's part in the quarrel and her children he had never seen—settled itself upon Philip. At first it made him angry, he told himself it was a sign of dotage; but there was something in Philip that attracted him, and he found himself smiling at him he knew not why. Philip did not bore him. Once or twice he put his hand on his shoulder: it was as near a caress as he had got since his daughter left England so many years before. When the time came for Philip to go Doctor South accompanied him to the station: he found himself unaccountably depressed.

"I've had a ripping time here," said Philip. "You've been awfully kind to me."

"I suppose you're very glad to go?"

"I've enjoyed myself here."

"But you want to get out into the world? Ah, you have youth." He hesitated a moment. "I want you to remember that if you change your mind my offer still stands."

"That's awfully kind of you."

Philip shook hands with him out of the carriage window, and the train steamed out of the station. Philip thought of the fortnight he was going to spend in the hop-field: he was happy at the idea of seeing his friends again, and he rejoiced because the day was fine. But Doctor South walked slowly back to his empty house. He felt very old and very lonely.

CXVIII

It was late in the evening when Philip arrived at Ferne. It was Mrs. Athelny's native village, and she had been accustomed from her childhood to pick in the hop-field to which with her husband and her children she still went every year. Like many Kentish folk her family had gone out regularly, glad to earn a little money, but especially regarding the annual outing, looked forward to for months, as the best of holidays. The work was not hard, it was done in common, in the open air, and for the children it was a long, delightful picnic; here the young men met the maidens; in the long evenings when work was over they wandered about the lanes, making love; and the hopping season was generally followed by weddings. They went out in carts with bedding, pots and pans, chairs and tables; and Ferne while the hopping lasted was deserted. They were very exclusive and would have resented the intrusion of foreigners, as they called the people who came from London; they looked down upon them and feared them too; they were a rough lot, and the respectable country folk did not want to mix with them. In the old days the hoppers slept in barns, but ten years ago a row of huts had been erected at the side of a meadow; and the Athelnys, like many others, had the same hut every year.

Athelny met Philip at the station in a cart he had borrowed from the public-house at which he had got a room for Philip. It was a quarter of a mile from the hop-field. They left his bag there and walked over to the meadow in which were the huts. They were nothing more than a long, low shed, divided into little rooms about twelve feet square. In front of each was a fire of sticks, round which a family was grouped, eagerly watching the cooking of supper. The sea-air and the sun had browned already the faces of Athelny's children. Mrs. Athelny seemed a different woman in her sun-bonnet: you felt that the long years in the city had made no real difference to her; she was the country woman born and bred, and you could see how much at home she found herself in the country. She was frying bacon and at the same time keeping an eye on the younger children, but she had a hearty handshake and a jolly smile for Philip. Athelny was enthusiastic over the delights of a rural existence.

"We're starved for sun and light in the cities we live in. It isn't life, it's a long imprisonment. Let us sell all we have, Betty, and take a farm in the country."

"I can see you in the country," she answered with good-humoured scorn. "Why, the first rainy day we had in the winter you'd be crying for London." She turned to Philip. "Athelny's always like this when we come down here. Country, I like that! Why, he don't know a swede from a mangel wurzel."

"Daddy was lazy today," remarked Jane, with the frankness which characterized her, "he didn't fill one bin."

"I'm getting into practice, child, and tomorrow I shall fill more bins than all of you put together."

"Come and eat your supper, children," said Mrs. Athelny. "Where's Sally?"

"Here I am, mother."

She stepped out of their little hut, and the flames of the wood fire leaped up and cast sharp colour upon her face. Of late Philip had only seen her in the trim frocks she had taken to since she was at the dressmaker's, and there was something very charming in the print dress she wore now, loose and easy to work in; the sleeves were tucked up and showed her strong, round arms. She too had a sun-bonnet.

"You look like a milkmaid in a fairy story," said Philip, as he shook hands with her.

"She's the belle of the hop-fields," said Athelny. "My word, if the Squire's son sees you he'll make you an offer of marriage before you can say Jack Robinson."

"The Squire hasn't got a son, fa-

ther," said Sally.

She looked about for a place to sit down in, and Philip made room for her beside him. She looked wonderful in the night lit by wood fires. She was like some rural goddess, and you thought of those fresh, strong girls whom old Herrick had praised in exquisite numbers. The supper was simple, bread and butter, crisp bacon, tea for the children, and beer for Mr. and Mrs. Athelny and Philip. Athelny, eating hungrily, praised loudly all he ate. He flung words of scorn at Lucullus and piled invectives upon Brillat-Savarin.

"There's one thing one can say for you, Athelny," said his wife, "you do enjoy your food and no mistake!"

"Cooked by your hand, my Betty," he said, stretching out an eloquent forefinger.

Philip felt himself very comfortable. He looked happily at the line of fires, with people grouped about them, and the colour of the flames against the night; at the end of the meadow was a line of great elms, and above the starry sky. The children talked and laughed, and Athelny, a child among them, made them roar by his tricks and fancies.

"They think a rare lot of Athelny down here," said his wife. "Why, Mrs. Bridges said to me, I don't know what we should do without Mr. Athelny now, she said. He's always up to something, he's more like a schoolboy than the father of a family."

Sally sat in silence, but she attended to Philip's wants in a thoughtful fashion that charmed him. It was pleasant to have her beside him, and now and then he glanced at her sunburned, healthy face. Once he caught her eyes, and she smiled quietly. When supper was over Jane and a small brother were sent down to a brook that ran at the bottom of the meadow to fetch a pail of water for washing up.

"You children, show your Uncle Philip where we sleep, and then you must be thinking of going to bed."

Small hands seized Philip, and he was dragged towards the hut. He went in and struck a match. There was no furniture in it; and beside a tin box, in which clothes were kept, there was nothing but the beds; there were three of them, one against each wall. Athelny followed Philip in and showed them proudly.

"That's the stuff to sleep on," he cried. "None of your spring-mattresses and swansdown. I never sleep so soundly anywhere as here. *You* will sleep between sheets. My dear fellow, I pity you from the bottom of my soul."

The beds consisted of a thick layer of hopbine, on the top of which was a coating of straw, and this was covered with a blanket. After a day in the open air, with the aromatic scent of the hops all round them, the happy pickers slept like tops. By nine o'clock all was quiet in the meadow and everyone in bed but one or two men who still lingered in the public-house and would not come back till it was closed at ten. Athelny walked there with Philip. But before he went Mrs. Athelny said to him:

"We breakfast about a quarter to six, but I daresay you won't want to get up as early as that. You see, we have to set to work at six."

"Of course he must get up early," cried Athelny, "and he must work like the rest of us. He's got to earn his board. No work, no dinner, my lad."

"The children go down to bathe before breakfast, and they can give you a call on their way back. They pass The Jolly Sailor."

"If they'll wake me I'll come and bathe with them," said Philip.

Jane and Harold and Edward shouted with delight at the prospect, and next morning Philip was wakened out of a sound sleep by their bursting into his room. The boys jumped on his bed, and he had to chase them out with his slippers. He put on a coat and a pair of trousers and went down. The day had only just broken, and there was a nip in the air; but the sky was cloudless, and the sun shining yellow. Sally, holding Connie's hand, was standing in the middle of the road, with a towel and a bathing-dress over her arm. He saw now that her sun-bonnet was of the colour of lavender, and against it her face, red and brown, was like an apple. She greeted him with her slow, sweet smile, and he noticed suddenly that her teeth were small and regular and very white. He wondered why they had never caught his attention before.

"I was for letting you sleep on," she said, "but they would go up and wake you. I said you didn't really want to come."

"Oh, yes, I did."

They walked down the road and then cut across the marshes. That way it was under a mile to the sea. The water looked cold and gray, and Philip shivered at the sight of it; but the others tore off their clothes and ran in shouting. Sally did everything a little slowly, and she did not come into the water till all the rest were splashing round Philip. Swimming was his only accomplishment; he felt at home in the water; and soon he had them all imitating him as he played at being a porpoise, and a drowning man, and a fat lady afraid of wetting her hair. The bathe was uproarious, and it was necessary for Sally to be very severe to induce them all to come out.

"You're as bad as any of them," she said to Philip, in her grave, maternal way, which was at once comic and touching. "They're not anything like so naughty when you're not here."

They walked back, Sally with her bright hair streaming over one shoulder and her sun-bonnet in her hand, but when they got to the huts Mrs. Athelny had already started for the hop-garden. Athelny, in a pair of the oldest trousers anyone had ever worn, his jacket buttoned up to show he had no shirt on, and in a wide-brimmed soft hat, was frying kippers over a fire of sticks. He was delighted with himself: he looked every inch a brigand. As soon as he saw the party he began to shout the witches' chorus from *Macbeth* over the odorous kippers.

"You mustn't dawdle over your breakfast or mother will be angry," he said, when they came up.

And in a few minutes, Harold and Jane with pieces of bread and butter in their hands, they sauntered through the meadow into the hop-field. They were the last to leave. A hop-garden was one of the sights connected with Philip's boyhood and the oast-houses to him the most typical feature of the Kentish scene. It was with no sense of strangeness, but as though he were at home, that Philip followed Sally through the long lines of the hops. The sun was bright now and cast a sharp shadow. Philip feasted his eyes on the richness of the green leaves. The hops were yellowing, and to him they had the beauty and the passion which poets in Sicily have found in the purple grape. As they walked along Philip felt himself overwhelmed by the rich luxuriance. A sweet scent arose from the fat Kentish soil, and the fitful September breeze was heavy with the goodly perfume of the hops. Athelstan felt

the exhilaration instinctively, for he lifted up his voice and sang; it was the cracked voice of the boy of fifteen, and Sally turned round.

"You be quiet, Athelstan, or we shall have a thunderstorm."

In a moment they heard the hum of voices, and in a moment more came upon the pickers. They were all hard at work, talking and laughing as they picked. They sat on chairs, on stools, on boxes, with their baskets by their sides, and some stood by the bin throwing the hops they picked straight into it. There were a lot of children about and a good many babies, some in makeshift cradles, some tucked up in a rug on the soft brown dry earth. The children picked a little and played a great deal. The women worked busily, they had been pickers from childhood, and they could pick twice as fast as foreigners from London. They boasted about the number of bushels they had picked in a day, but they complained you could not make money now as in former times: then they paid you a shilling for five bushels, but now the rate was eight and even nine bushels to the shilling. In the old days a good picker could earn enough in the season to keep her for the rest of the year, but now there was nothing in it; you got a holiday for nothing, and that was about all. Mrs. Hill had bought herself a pianner out of what she made picking, so she said, but she was very near, one wouldn't like to be near like that, and most people thought it was only what she said, if the truth was known pehaps it would be found that she had put a bit of money from the savings bank towards it.

The hoppers were divided into bin companies of ten pickers, not counting children, and Athelny loudly boasted of the day when he would have a company consisting entirely of his own family. Each company had a bin-man, whose duty it was to supply it with strings of hops at their bins; (the bin was a large sack on a wooden frame, about seven feet high, and long rows of them were placed between the rows of hops;) and it was to this position that Athelny aspired when his family was old enough to form a company. Meanwhile he worked rather by encouraging others than by exertions of his own. He sauntered up to Mrs. Athelny, who had been busy for half an hour and had already emptied a basket into the bin, and with his cigarette between his lips began to pick. He asserted that he was going to pick more than anyone that day, but mother; of course no one could pick so much as mother; that reminded him of the trials which Aphrodite put upon the curious Psyche, and he began to tell his children the story of her love for the unseen bridegroom. He told it very well. It seemed to Philip, listening with a smile on his lips, that the old tale fitted in with the scene. The sky was very blue now, and he thought it could not be more lovely even in Greece. The children with their fair hair and rosy cheeks, strong, healthy, and vivacious; the delicate form of the hops; the challenging emerald of the leaves, like a blare of trumpets; the magic of the green alley, narrowing to a point as you looked down the row, with the pickers in their sun-bonnets: perhaps there was more of the Greek spirit there than you could find in the books of professors or in museums. He was thankful for the beauty of England. He thought of the winding white roads and the hedgerows, the green meadows with their elm-trees, the delicate line of the hills and the copses that crowned them, the flatness of the marshes, and the melancholy of the North Sea. He was very glad that he felt its loveliness. But presently Athelny grew restless and announced that he would go and ask how Robert Kemp's mother was. He knew everyone in the garden and called them all by their Christian names; he knew their family histories and all that had happened to them from birth. With harmless vanity he played the fine gentleman among them, and there was a touch of condescension in his familiarity. Philip would not go with him.

"I'm going to earn my dinner," he said.

"Quite right, my boy," answered Athelny, with a wave of the hand, as he strolled away. "No work, no dinner."

CXIX

PHILIP had not a basket of his own, but sat with Sally. Jane thought it monstrous that he should help her elder sister rather than herself, and he had to promise to pick for her when Sally's basket was full. Sally was almost as quick as her mother.

"Won't it hurt your hands for sewing?" asked Philip.

"Oh, no, it wants soft hands. That's why women pick better than men. If your hands are hard and your fingers all stiff with a lot of rough work you can't pick near so well."

He liked to see her deft movements, and she watched him too now and then with that maternal spirit of hers which was so amusing and yet so charming. He was clumsy at first, and she laughed at him. When she bent over and showed him how best to deal with a whole line their hands met. He was surprised to see her blush. He could not persuade himself that she was a woman; because he had known her as a flapper, he could not help looking upon her as a child still; yet the number of her admirers showed that she was a child no longer; and though they had only been down a few days one of Sally's cousins was already so attentive that she had to endure a lot of chaffing. His name was Peter Gann, and he was the son of Mrs. Athelny's sister, who had married a farmer near Ferne. Everyone knew why he found it necessary to walk through the hop-field every day.

A call-off by the sounding of a horn was made for breakfast at eight, and though Mrs. Athelny told them they had not deserved it, they ate it very heartily. They set to work again and worked till twelve, when the horn sounded once more for dinner. At intervals the measurer went his round from bin to bin, accompanied by the booker, who entered first in his own book and then in the hopper's the number of bushels picked. As each bin was filled it was measured out in bushel baskets into a huge bag called a poke; and this the measurer and the pole-puller carried off between them and put on the waggon. Athelny came back now and then with stories of how much Mrs. Heath or Mrs. Jones had picked, and he conjured his family to beat her: he was always wanting to make records, and sometimes in his enthusiasm picked steadily for an hour. His chief amusement in it, however, was that it showed the beauty of his graceful hands, of which he was excessively proud. He spent much time manicuring them.

He told Philip, as he stretched out his tapering fingers, that the Spanish grandees had always slept in oiled gloves to preserve their whiteness. The hand that wrung the throat of Europe, he remarked dramatically, was as shapely and exquisite as a woman's; and he looked at his own, as he delicately picked the hops, and sighed with self-satisfaction. When he grew tired of this he rolled himself a cigarette and discoursed to Philip of art and literature. In the afternoon it grew very hot. Work did not proceed so actively and conversation halted. The incessant chatter of the morning dwindled now to desultory remarks. Tiny beads of sweat stood on Sally's upper lip, and as she worked her lips were slightly parted. She was like a rosebud bursting into flower.

Calling-off time depended on the state of the oast-house. Sometimes it was filled early, and as many hops had been picked by three or four as could be dried during the night. Then work was stopped. But generally the last measuring of the day began at five. As each company had its bin measured it gathered up its things and, chatting again now that work was over, sauntered out of the garden. The women went back to the huts to clean up and prepare the supper, while a good many of the men strolled down the road to the public-house. A glass of beer was very pleasant after the day's work.

The Athelnys' bin was the last to be dealt with. When the measurer came Mrs. Athelny, with a sigh of relief, stood up and stretched her arms: she had been sitting in the same position for many hours and was stiff.

"Now, let's go to The Jolly Sailor," said Athelny. "The rites of the day must be duly performed, and there is none more sacred than that."

"Take a jug with you, Athelny,"

said his wife, "and bring back a pint and a half for supper."

She gave him the money, copper by copper. The bar-parlour was already well filled. It had a sanded floor, benches round it, and yellow pictures of Victorian prize-fighters on the walls. The licencee knew all his customers by name, and he leaned over his bar smiling benignly at two young men who were throwing rings on a stick that stood up from the floor: their failure was greeted with a good deal of hearty chaff from the rest of the company. Room was made for the new arrivals. Philip found himself sitting between an old labourer in corduroys, with string tied under his knees, and a shiny-faced lad of seventeen with a love-lock neatly plastered on his red forehead. Athelny insisted on trying his hand at the throwing of rings. He backed himself for half a pint and won it. As he drank the loser's health he said:

"I would sooner have won this than won the Derby, my boy."

He was an outlandish figure, with his wide-brimmed hat and pointed beard, among those country folk, and it was easy to see that they thought him very queer; but his spirits were so high, his enthusiasm so contagious, that it was impossible not to like him. Conversation went easily. A certain number of pleasantries were exchanged in the broad, slow accent of the Isle of Thanet, and there was uproarious laughter at the sallies of the local wag. A pleasant gathering! It would have been a hard-hearted person who did not feel a glow of satisfaction in his fellows. Philip's eyes wandered out of the window where it was bright and sunny still; there were little white curtains in it tied up with red ribbon like those of a cottage window, and on the sill were pots of geraniums. In due course one by one

the idlers got up and sauntered back to the meadow where supper was cooking.

"I expect you'll be ready for your bed," said Mrs. Athelny to Philip. "You're not used to getting up at five and staying in the open air all day."

"You're coming to bathe with us, Uncle Phil, aren't you?" the boys cried.

"Rather."

He was tired and happy. After supper, balancing himself against the wall of the hut on a chair without a back, he smoked his pipe and looked at the night. Sally was busy. She passed in and out of the hut, and he lazily watched her methodical actions. Her walk attracted his notice; it was not particularly graceful, but it was easy and assured; she swung her legs from the hips, and her feet seemed to tread the earth with decision. Athelny had gone off to gossip with one of the neighbours, and presently Philip heard his wife address the world in general.

"There now, I'm out of tea and I wanted Athelny to go down to Mrs. Black's and get some." A pause, and then her voice was raised: "Sally, just run down to Mrs. Black's and get me half a pound of tea, will you? I've run quite out of it."

"All right, mother."

Mrs. Black had a cottage about half a mile along the road, and she combined the office of postmistress with that of universal provider. Sally came out of the hut, turning down her sleeves.

"Shall I come with you, Sally?" asked Philip.

"Don't you trouble. I'm not afraid to go alone."

"I didn't think you were; but it's getting near my bedtime, and I was just thinking I'd like to stretch my legs."

Sally did not answer, and they set

out together. The road was white and silent. There was not a sound in the summer night. They did not speak much.

"It's quite hot even now, isn't it?" said Philip.

"I think it's wonderful for the time of year."

But their silence did not seem awkward. They found it was pleasant to walk side by side and felt no need of words. Suddenly at a stile in the hedgerow they heard a low murmur of voices, and in the darkness they saw the outline of two people. They were sitting very close to one another and did not move as Philip and Sally passed.

"I wonder who that was," said Sally.

"They looked happy enough, didn't they?"

"I expect they took us for lovers too."

They saw the light of the cottage in front of them, and in a minute went into the little shop. The glare dazzled them for a moment.

"You are late," said Mrs. Black. "I was just going to shut up." She looked at the clock. "Getting on for nine."

Sally asked for her half pound of tea, (Mrs. Athelny could never bring herself to buy more than half a pound at a time,) and they set off up the road again. Now and then some beast of the night made a short, sharp sound, but it seemed only to make the silence more marked.

"I believe if you stood still you could hear the sea," said Sally.

They strained their ears, and their fancy presented them with a faint sound of little waves lapping up against the shingle. When they passed the stile again the lovers were still there, but now they were not speaking; they were in one another's arms,

and the man's lips were pressed against the girl's.

"They seem busy," said Sally.

They turned a corner, and a breath of warm wind beat for a moment against their faces. The earth gave forth its freshness. There was something strange in the tremulous night, and something, you knew not what, seemed to be waiting; the silence was on a sudden pregnant with meaning. Philip had a queer feeling in his heart, it seemed very full, it seemed to melt, (the hackneyed phrases expressed precisely the curious sensation,) he felt happy and anxious and expectant. To his memory came back those lines in which Jessica and Lorenzo murmur melodious words to one another, capping each other's utterance; but passion shines bright and clear through the conceits that amuse them. He did not know what there was in the air that made his senses so strangely alert; it seemed to him that he was pure soul to enjoy the scents and the sounds and the savours of the earth. He had never felt such an exquisite capacity for beauty. He was afraid that Sally by speaking would break the spell, but she said never a word, and he wanted to hear the sound of her voice. Its low richness was the voice of the country night itself.

They arrived at the field through which she had to walk to get back to the huts. Philip went in to hold the gate open for her.

"Well, here I think I'll say good-night."

"Thank you for coming all that way with me."

She gave him her hand, and as he took it, he said:

"If you were very nice you'd kiss me good-night like the rest of the family."

"I don't mind," she said.

Philip had spoken in jest. He merely wanted to kiss her, because he was happy and he liked her and the night was so lovely.

"Good-night then," he said, with a little laugh, drawing her towards him. She gave him her lips; they were warm and full and soft; he lingered a little, they were like a flower; then, he knew not how, without meaning it, he flung his arms round her. She yielded quite silently. Her body was firm and strong. He felt her heart beat against his. Then he lost his head. His senses overwhelmed him like a flood of rushing waters. He drew her into the darker shadow of the hedge.

CXX

PHILIP slept like a log and awoke with a start to find Harold tickling his face with a feather. There was a shout of delight when he opened his eyes. He was drunken with sleep.

"Come on, lazy bones," said Jane. "Sally says she won't wait for you unless you hurry up."

Then he remembered what had happened. His heart sank, and, half out of bed already, he stopped; he did not know how he was going to face her; he was overwhelmed with a sudden rush of self-reproach, and bitterly, bitterly, he regretted what he had done. What would she say to him that morning? He dreaded meeting her, and he asked himself how he could have been such a fool. But the children gave him no time; Edward took his bathing-drawers and his towel, Athelstan tore the bed-clothes away; and in three minutes they all clattered down into the road. Sally gave him a smile. It was as sweet and innocent as it had ever been.

"You do take a time to dress yourself," she said. "I thought you was never coming."

There was not a particle of difference in her manner. He had expected some change, subtle or abrupt; he fancied that there would be shame in the way she treated him, or anger, or perhaps some increase of familiarity; but there was nothing. She was exactly the same as before. They walked towards the sea all together, talking and laughing; and Sally was quiet, but she was always that, reserved, but he had never seen her otherwise, and gentle. She neither sought conversation with him nor avoided it. Philip was astounded. He had expected the incident of the night before to have caused some revolution in her, but it was just as though nothing had happened; it might have been a dream; and as he walked along, a little girl holding on to one hand and a little boy to the other, while he chatted as unconcernedly as he could, he sought for an explanation. He wondered whether Sally meant the affair to be forgotten. Perhaps her senses had run away with her just as his had, and, treating what had occurred as an accident due to unusual circumstances, it might be that she had decided to put the matter out of her mind. It was ascribing to her a power of thought and a mature wisdom which fitted neither with her age nor with her character. But he realised that he knew nothing of her. There had been in her always something enigmatic.

They played leap-frog in the water, and the bathe was as uproarious as on the previous day. Sally mothered them all, keeping a watchful eye on them, and calling to them when they went out too far. She swam staidly backwards and forwards while the others got up to their larks, and now and then turned on her back to float. Presently she went out and began drying herself; she called to the others more or less peremptorily, and at last only Philip was left in the water. He took the opportunity to have a good hard swim. He was more used to the cold water this second morning, and he revelled in its salt freshness; it rejoiced him to use his limbs freely, and he covered the water with long, firm strokes. But Sally, with a towel round her, went down to the water's edge.

"You're to come out this minute, Philip," she called, as though he were a small boy under her charge.

And when, smiling with amusement at her authoritative way, he came towards her, she upbraided him.

"It is naughty of you to stay in so long. Your lips are quite blue, and just look at your teeth, they're chattering."

"All right. I'll come out."

She had never talked to him in that manner before. It was as though what had happened gave her a sort of right over him, and she looked upon him as a child to be cared for. In a few minutes they were dressed, and they started to walk back. Sally noticed his hands.

"Just look, they're quite blue."

"Oh, that's all right. It's only the circulation. I shall get the blood back in a minute."

"Give them to me."

She took his hands in hers and rubbed them, first one and then the other, till the colour returned. Philip, touched and puzzled, watched her. He could not say anything to her on account of the children, and he did not

meet her eyes; but he was sure they did not avoid his purposely, it just happened that they did not meet. And during the day there was nothing in her behaviour to suggest a consciousness in her that anything had passed between them. Perhaps she was a little more talkative than usual. When they were all sitting again in the hopfield she told her mother how naughty Philip had been in not coming out of the water till he was blue with cold. It was incredible, and yet it seemed that the only effect of the incident of the night before was to arouse in her a feeling of protection towards him: she had the same instinctive desire to mother him as she had with regard to her brothers and sisters.

It was not till the evening that he found himself alone with her. She was cooking the supper, and Philip was sitting on the grass by the side of the fire. Mrs. Athelny had gone down to the village to do some shopping, and the children were scattered in various pursuits of their own. Philip hesitated to speak. He was very nervous. Sally attended to her business with serene competence and she accepted placidly the silence which to him was so embarrassing. He did not know how to begin. Sally seldom spoke unless she was spoken to or had something particular to say. At last he could not bear it any longer.

"You're not angry with me, Sally?" he blurted out suddenly.

She raised her eyes quietly and looked at him without emotion.

"Me? No. Why should I be?"

He was taken aback and did not reply. She took the lid off the pot, stirred the contents, and put it on again. A savoury smell spread over the air. She looked at him once more, with a quiet smile which barely separated her lips; it was more a smile of the eyes.

"I always liked you," she said.

His heart gave a great thump against his ribs, and he felt the blood rushing to his cheeks. He forced a faint laugh.

"I didn't know that."

"That's because you're a silly."

"I don't know why you liked me."

"I don't either." She put a little more wood on the fire. "I knew I liked you that day you came when you'd been sleeping out and hadn't had anything to eat, d'you remember? And me and mother, we got Thorpy's bed ready for you."

He flushed again, for he did not know that she was aware of that incident. He remembered it himself with horror and shame.

"That's why I wouldn't have anything to do with the others. You remember that young fellow mother wanted me to have? I let him come to tea because he bothered so, but I knew I'd say no."

Philip was so surprised that he found nothing to say. There was a queer feeling in his heart; he did not know what it was, unless it was happiness. Sally stirred the pot once more.

"I wish those children would make haste and come. I don't know where they've got to. Supper's ready now."

"Shall I go and see if I can find them?" said Philip.

It was a relief to talk about practical things.

"Well, it wouldn't be a bad idea, I must say. . . . There's mother coming."

Then, as he got up, she looked at him without embarrassment.

"Shall I come for a walk with you tonight when I've put the children to bed?"

"Yes."

"Well, you wait for me down by the stile, and I'll come when I'm ready."

He waited under the stars, sitting on the stile, and the hedges with their ripening blackberries were high on each side of him. From the earth rose rich scents of the night, and the air was soft and still. His heart was beating madly. He could not understand anything of what happened to him. He associated passion with cries and tears and vehemence, and there was nothing of this in Sally; but he did not know what else but passion could have caused her to give herself. But passion for him? He would not have been surprised if she had fallen to her cousin, Peter Gann, tall, spare, and straight, with his sunburned face and long, easy stride. Philip wondered what she saw in him. He did not know if she loved him as he reckoned love. And yet? He was convinced of her purity. He had a vague inkling that many things had combined, things that she felt though was unconscious of, the intoxication of the air and the hops and the night, the healthy instincts of the natural woman, a tenderness that overflowed, and an affection that had in it something maternal and something sisterly; and she gave all she had to give because her heart was full of charity.

He heard a step on the road, and a figure came out of the darkness.

"Sally," he murmured.

She stopped and came to the stile, and with her came sweet, clean odours of the country-side. She seemed to carry with her scents of the new-mown hay, and the savour of ripe hops, and the freshness of young grass. Her lips were soft and full against his, and her lovely, strong body was firm within his arms.

"Milk and honey," he said. "You're like milk and honey."

He made her close her eyes and kissed her eyelids, first one and then the other. Her arm, strong and muscular, was bare to the elbow; he passed his hand over it and wondered at its beauty; it gleamed in the darkness; she had the skin that Rubens painted, astonishingly fair and transparent, and on one side were little golden hairs. It was the arm of a Saxon goddess; but no immortal had that exquisite, homely naturalness; and Philip thought of a cottage garden with the dear flowers which bloom in all men's hearts, of the hollyhock and the red and white rose which is called York and Lancaster, and of love-in-a-mist and Sweet William, and honeysuckle, larkspur, and London Pride.

"How can you care for me?" he said. "I'm insignificant and crippled and ordinary and ugly."

She took his face in both her hands and kissed his lips.

"You're an old silly, that's what you are," she said.

CXXI

When the hops were picked, Philip with the news in his pocket that he had got the appointment as assistant house-physician at St. Luke's, accompanied the Athelnys back to London. He took modest rooms in Westminster and at the beginning of October entered upon his duties. The work was interesting and varied; every day he learned something new; he felt himself of some consequence; and he saw a good deal of Sally. He found life uncommonly pleasant. He was free about six, except on the days on which he had out-patients, and then he went to the shop at which Sally worked to meet her when she came out. There were several young men, who hung about opposite the 'trade entrance' or a little further along, at the first corner; and the girls, coming out two and two or in little groups, nudged one another and giggled as they recognised them. Sally in her plain black dress looked very different from the country lass who had picked hops side by side with him. She walked away from the shop quickly, but she slackened her pace when they met, and greeted him with her quiet smile. They walked together through the busy street. He talked to her of his work at the hospital, and she told him what she had been doing in the shop that day. He came to know the names of the girls she worked with. He found that Sally had a restrained, but keen, sense of the ridiculous, and she made remarks about the girls or the men who were set over them which amused him by their unexpected drollery. She had a way of saying a thing which was very characteristic, quite gravely, as though there were nothing funny in it at all, and yet it was so sharp-sighted that Philip broke into delighted laughter. Then she would give him a little glance in which the smiling eyes showed she was not unaware of her own humour. They met with a handshake and parted as formally. Once Philip asked her to come and have tea with him in his rooms, but she refused.

"No, I won't do that. It would look funny."

Never a word of love passed between them. She seemed not to desire anything more than the companionship of those walks. Yet Philip was positive that she was glad to be with him. She puzzled him as much as she had done at the beginning. He did not begin to understand her conduct;

but the more he knew her the fonder he grew of her; she was competent and self-controlled, and there was a charming honesty in her: you felt that you could rely upon her in every circumstance.

"You are an awfully good sort," he said to her once à propos of nothing at all.

"I expect I'm just the same as everyone else," she answered.

He knew that he did not love her. It was a great affection that he felt for her, and he liked her company; it was curiously soothing; and he had a feeling for her which seemed to him ridiculous to entertain towards a shop-girl of nineteen: he respected her. And he admired her magnificent healthiness. She was a splendid animal, without defect; and physical perfection filled him always with admiring awe. She made him feel unworthy.

Then, one day, about three weeks after they had come back to London as they walked together, he noticed that she was unusually silent. The serenity of her expression was altered by a slight line between the eyebrows: it was the beginning of a frown.

"What's the matter, Sally?" he asked.

She did not look at him, but straight in front of her, and her colour darkened.

"I don't know."

He understood at once what she meant. His heart gave a sudden, quick beat, and he felt the colour leave his cheeks.

"What d'you mean? Are you afraid that . . . ?"

He stopped. He could not go on. The possibility that anything of the sort could happen had never crossed his mind. Then he saw that her lips were trembling, and she was trying not to cry.

"I'm not certain yet. Perhaps it'll be all right."

They walked on in silence till they came to the corner of Chancery Lane, where he always left her. She held out her hand and smiled.

"Don't worry about it yet. Let's hope for the best."

He walked away with a tumult of thoughts in his head. What a fool he had been! That was the first thing that struck him, an abject, miserable fool, and he repeated it to himself a dozen times in a rush of angry feeling. He despised himself. How could he have got into such a mess? But at the same time, for his thoughts chased one another through his brain and yet seemed to stand together, in a hopeless confusion, like the pieces of a jig-saw puzzle seen in a nightmare, he asked himself what he was going to do. Everything was so clear before him, all he had aimed at so long within reach at last, and now his inconceivable stupidity had erected this new obstacle. Philip had never been able to surmount what he acknowledged was a defeat in his resolute desire for a well-ordered life, and that was his passion for living in the future; and no sooner was he settled in his work at the hospital than he had busied himself with arrangements for his travels. In the past he had often tried not to think too circumstantially of his plans for the future, it was only discouraging; but now that his goal was so near he saw no harm in giving away to a longing that was so difficult to resist. First of all he meant to go to Spain. That was the land of his heart; and by now he was imbued with its spirit, its romance and colour and history and grandeur; he felt that it had a message for him in particular which no other country could give. He knew the fine old cities already as though he had trodden their tortuous streets from childhood. Cordova, Seville, Toledo, Leon, Tarragona, Burgos. The great painters of Spain were the painters of his soul, and his pulse beat quickly as he pictured his ecstasy on standing face to face with those works which were more significant than any others to his own tortured, restless heart. He had read the great poets, more characteristic of their race than the poets of other lands; for they seemed to have drawn their inspiration not at all from the general currents of the world's literature but directly from the torrid, scented plains and the bleak mountains of their country. A few short months now, and he would hear with his own ears all around him the language which seemed most apt for grandeur of soul and passion. His fine taste had given him an inkling that Andalusia was too soft and sensuous, a little vulgar even, to satisfy his ardour; and his imagination dwelt more willingly among the wind-swept distances of Castile and the rugged magnificence of Aragon and Leon. He did not know quite what those unknown contacts would give him, but he felt that he would gather from them a strength and a purpose which would make him more capable of affronting and comprehending the manifold wonders of places more distant and more strange.

For this was only a beginning. He had got into communication with the various companies which took surgeons out on their ships, and knew exactly what were their routes, and from men who had been on them what were the advantages and disadvantages of each line. He put aside the Orient and the P. & O. It was difficult to get a berth with them; and besides their passenger traffic allowed the medical officer little freedom; but there were other services which sent large tramps on leisurely expeditions to the East, stopping at all sorts of ports for various periods, from a day or two to a fortnight, so that you had plenty of time, and it was often possible to make a trip inland. The pay was poor and the food no more than adequate, so that there was not much demand for the posts, and a man with a London degree was pretty sure to get one if he applied. Since there were no passengers other than a casual man or so, shipping on business from some out-of-the-way port to another, the life on board was friendly and pleasant. Philip knew by heart the list of places at which they touched; and each one called up in him visions of tropical sunshine, and magic colour, and of a teeming, mysterious, intense life. Life! That was what he wanted. At last he would come to close quarters with life. And perhaps, from Tokio or Shanghai it would be possible to tranship into some other line and dip down to the islands of the South Pacific. A doctor was useful anywhere. There might be an opportunity to go up country in Burmah, and what rich jungles in Sumatra or Borneo might he not visit? He was young still and time was no object to him. He had no ties in England, no friends; he could go up and down the world for years, learning the beauty and the wonder and the variedness of life.

Now this thing had come. He put aside the possibility that Sally was mistaken; he felt strangely certain that she was right; after all, it was so likely; anyone could see that Nature had built her to be the mother of children. He knew what he ought to do. He ought not to let the incident divert him a hair's breadth from his path. He thought of Griffiths; he could easily imagine with what indifference that young man would have received such a piece of news; he would have thought it an awful nuisance and would at once have taken to his heels, like a wise fellow; he would have left the girl to deal with her troubles as best she could. Philip told himself that if this had happened it was because it was inevitable. He was no more to blame than Sally; she was a girl who knew the world and the facts of life, and she had taken the risk with her eyes open. It would be madness to allow such an accident to disturb the whole pattern of his life. He was one of the few people who was acutely conscious of the transitoriness of life, and how necessary it was to make the most of it. He would do what he could for Sally; he could afford to give her a sufficient sum of money. A strong man would never allow himself to be turned from his purpose.

Philip said all this to himself, but he knew he could not do it. He simply could not. He knew himself. "I'm so damned weak," he muttered despairingly.

She had trusted him and been kind to him. He simply could not do a thing which, notwithstanding all his reason, he felt was horrible. He knew he would have no peace on his travels if he had the thought constantly with him that she was wretched. Besides, there were her father and mother: they had always treated him well; it was not possible to repay them with ingratitude. The only thing was to marry Sally as quickly as possible. He would write to Doctor South, tell him he was going to be married at once, and say that if his offer still held he was willing to accept it. That sort of practice, among poor people, was the only one possible for him; there his deformity did not matter, and they would not sneer at the simple manners of his wife. It was curious to think of her as his wife, it gave him a queer, soft feeling; and a wave of emotion spread over him as he thought of the child which was his. He had little doubt that Doctor South would be glad to have him, and he pictured to himself the life he would lead with Sally in the fishing village. They would have a little house within sight of the sea, and he would watch the mighty ships passing to the lands he would never know. Perhaps that was the wisest thing. Cronshaw had told him that the facts of life mattered nothing to him who by the power of fancy held in fee the twin realms of space and time. It was true. *Forever wilt thou love and she be fair!*

His wedding present to his wife would be all his high hopes. Self-sacrifice! Philip was uplifted by its beauty, and all through the evening he thought of it. He was so excited that he could not read. He seemed to be driven out of his rooms into the streets, and he walked up and down Birdcage Walk, his heart throbbing with joy. He could hardly bear his impatience. He wanted to see Sally's happiness when he made her his offer, and if it had not been so late he would have gone to her there and then. He pictured to himself the long evenings he would spend with Sally in the cosy sitting-room, the blinds undrawn so that they could watch the sea; he with his books, while she bent over her work, and the shaded lamp made her sweet face more fair. They would talk over the growing child, and when she turned her eyes to his there was in them the light of love. And the fishermen and their wives who were his patients would come to feel a great affection for them, and they in their turn would enter into the pleasures and pains of those simple lives. But his thoughts returned to the son who would be his and hers. Already he felt in himself a passionate devotion to it. He thought of passing his hands over his little perfect limbs, he knew he would be beautiful; and he would make over to him all his dreams of a rich and varied life. And thinking over the long pilgrimage of his past he accepted it joyfully. He accepted the deformity which had made life so hard for him; he knew that it had warped his character, but now he saw also that by reason of it he had acquired that power of introspection which had given him so much delight. Without it he would never have had his keen appreciation of beauty, his passion for art and literature, and his interest in the varied spectacle of life. The ridicule and the contempt which had so often been heaped upon him had turned his mind inward and called forth those flowers which he felt would never lose their fragrance. Then he saw that the normal was the rarest thing in the world. Everyone had some defect, of body or of mind: he thought of all the people he had known, (the whole world was like a sick-house, and there was no rhyme or reason in it,) he saw a long procession, deformed in body and warped in mind, some with illness of the flesh, weak hearts or weak lungs, and some with illness of the spirit, languor of will, or a craving for liquor. At this moment he could feel a holy compassion for them all. They were the helpless instruments of blind chance. He could pardon Griffiths for his treachery and Mildred for the pain she had caused him. They could not help themselves. The only reasonable thing was to accept the good of men and be patient with their faults. The words of the dying God crossed his memory:

Forgive them, for they know not what they do.

CXXII

HE HAD arranged to meet Sally on Saturday in the National Gallery. She was to come there as soon as she was released from the shop and had agreed to lunch with him. Two days had passed since he had seen her, and his exultation had not left him for a moment. It was because he rejoiced in the feeling that he had not attempted to see her. He had repeated to himself exactly what he would say to her and how he should say it. Now his impatience was unbearable. He had written to Doctor South and had in his pocket a telegram from him received that morning: *"Sacking the mumpish fool. When will you come?"* Philip walked along Parliament Street.

It was a fine day, and there was a bright, frosty sun which made the light dance in the street. It was crowded. There was a tenuous mist in the distance, and it softened exquisitely the noble lines of the buildings. He crossed Trafalgar Square. Suddenly his heart gave a sort of twist in his body; he saw a woman in front of him who he thought was Mildred. She had the same figure, and she walked with that slight dragging of the feet which was so characteristic of her. Without thinking, but with a beating heart, he hurried till he came alongside, and then, when the woman turned, he saw it was someone unknown to him. It was the face of a much older person, with a lined, yellow skin. He slackened his pace. He was infinitely relieved, but it was not only relief that he felt; it was disappointment too; he was seized with horror of himself. Would he never be free from that passion? At the bottom of his heart, notwithstanding everything, he felt that a strange, desperate thirst for that vile woman would always linger. That love had caused him so much suffering that he knew he would never, never quite be free of it. Only death could finally assuage his desire.

But he wrenched the pang from his heart. He thought of Sally, with her kind blue eyes; and his lips unconsciously formed themselves into a smile. He walked up the steps of the National Gallery and sat down in the first room, so that he should see her the moment she came in. It always comforted him to get among pictures. He looked at none in particular, but allowed the magnificence of their colour, the beauty of their lines, to work upon his soul. His imagination was busy with Sally. It would be pleasant to take her away from that London in which she seemed an unusual figure, like a cornflower in a shop among orchids and azaleas; he had learned in the Kentish hop-field that she did not belong to the town; and he was sure that she would blossom under the soft skies of Dorset to a rarer beauty. She came in, and he got up to meet her. She was in black, with white cuffs at her wrists and a lawn collar round her neck. They shook hands.

"Have you been waiting long?"

"No. Ten minutes. Are you hungry?"

"Not very."

"Let's sit here for a bit, shall we?"

"If you like."

They sat quietly, side by side, without speaking. Philip enjoyed having her near him. He was warmed by her radiant health. A glow of life seemed like an aureole to shine about her.

"Well, how have you been?" he said at last, with a little smile.

"Oh, it's all right. It was a false alarm."

"Was it?"

"Aren't you glad?"

An extraordinary sensation filled him. He had felt certain that Sally's suspicion was well-founded; it had never occurred to him for an instant that there was a possibility of error. All his plans were suddenly overthrown, and the existence, so elaborately pictured, was no more than a dream which would never be realised. He was free once more. Free! He need give up none of his projects, and life still was in his hands for him to do what he liked with. He felt no exhilaration, but only dismay. His heart sank. The future stretched out before him in desolate emptiness. It was as though he had sailed for many years over a great waste of waters, with peril and privation, and at last had come upon a fair haven, but as he was about to enter, some contrary wind had arisen and drove him out again into the open sea; and because he had let his mind dwell on these soft meads and pleasant woods of the land, the vast deserts of the ocean filled him with anguish. He could not confront again the loneliness and the tempest. Sally looked at him with her clear eyes.

"Aren't you glad?" she asked again. "I thought you'd be as pleased as Punch."

He met her gaze haggardly.

"I'm not sure," he muttered.

"You are funny. Most men would."

He realised that he had deceived himself; it was no self-sacrifice that had driven him to think of marrying, but the desire for a wife and a home and love; and now that it all seemed to slip through his fingers he was seized with despair. He wanted all that more than anything in the world. What did he care for Spain and its cities, Cordova, Toledo, Leon; what to him were the pagodas of Burmah and the lagoons of South Sea Islands? America was here and now. It seemed to him that all his life he had followed the ideals that other people, by their words or their writings, had instilled into him, and never the desires of his own heart. Always his course had been swayed by what he thought he should do and never by what he wanted with his whole soul to do. He put all that aside now with a gesture of impatience. He had lived always in the future, and the present always, always had slipped through his fingers. His ideals? He thought of his desire to make a design, intricate and beautiful, out of the myriad, meaningless facts of life: had he not seen also that the simplest pattern, that in which a man was born, worked, married, had children, and died, was likewise the most perfect? It might be that to surrender to happiness was to accept defeat, but it was a defeat better than many victories.

He glanced quickly at Sally, he wondered what she was thinking, and then looked away again.

"I was going to ask you to marry me," he said.

"I thought p'raps you might, but I shouldn't have liked to stand in your way."

"You wouldn't have done that."

"How about your travels, Spain and all that?"

"How d'you know I want to travel?"

"I ought to know something about it. I've heard you and Dad talk about it till you were blue in the face."

"I don't care a damn about all that." He paused for an instant and then spoke in a low, hoarse whisper. "I don't want to leave you! I can't leave you."

She did not answer. He could not tell what she thought.

"I wonder if you'll marry me, Sally."

She did not move and there was no flicker of emotion on her face, but she did not look at him when she answered.

"If you like."

"Don't you want to?"

"Oh, of course I'd like to have a house of my own, and it's about time I was settling down."

He smiled a little. He knew her pretty well by now, and her manner did not surprise him.

"But don't you want to marry *me*?"

"There's no one else I would marry."

"Then that settles it."

"Mother and Dad will be surprised, won't they?"

"I'm so happy."

"I want my lunch," she said.

"Dear!"

He smiled and took her hand and pressed it. They got up and walked out of the gallery. They stood for a moment at the balustrade and looked at Trafalgar Square. Cabs and omnibuses hurried to and fro, and crowds passed, hastening in every direction, and the sun was shining.

Four Short Pieces

SOME NOVELISTS I HAVE KNOWN

ONE OF Hazlitt's most enchanting essays is *My First Acquaintance with Poets*, in which he relates how he came to know Coleridge and Wordsworth. Coleridge had come to Shrewsbury to take charge of its Unitarian Congregation, and Mr. Rowe, whom he was succeeding, went down to the coach to meet him; but though he saw a round-faced man in a short black coat who seemed to be talking at a great rate to his fellow passengers he could find no one answering the description of the man he was expecting. He went home, but had scarcely got there when the round-faced man in the black coat entered and "dissipated all doubts on the subject, by beginning to talk. He did not cease while he stayed; nor has he since, that I know of." Hazlitt's father, a dissenting minister, lived ten miles from Shrewsbury and a few days later Coleridge walked over to see him. Hazlitt, then twenty years old, was presented to him. The poet found the young man an enthusiastic and intelligent listener and invited him to come to Nether-Stowey in the spring. This Hazlitt did, and after he had been there a day or two Wordsworth arrived. "He instantly began to make havoc of the half of a Cheshire cheese on the table, and said triumphantly that his marriage with experience had not been so unproductive as Mr. Southey's in teaching him a knowledge of the good things of this life." Next day Coleridge and Hazlitt accompanied Wordsworth to Alfoxden, where he read in the open air the story of Peter Bell. "There is a charm in the recitation both of Coleridge and Wordsworth," says Hazlitt, "which acts as a spell upon the heart, and disarms the judgment. Perhaps they have deceived themselves by making use of this ambiguous accompaniment." Hazlitt, though excited and admiring, relinquished neither his critical acumen nor his sense of humour.

It is the delight I take in this essay that has prompted me to write the following pages. Alas, I have no such great figures to write about as Coleridge and Wordsworth. *The Ancient Mariner, Kubla Khan*, the great ode and *The Solitary Reaper* will be read as long as English poetry is read; but who can tell whether any of the authors with whom I propose to deal in this essay will be remembered by posterity? Brahma, the Indian monists think, created the world for sport, thus exercising in this little bit of fun the infinite activity which is one of his attributes; and it is with just such sardonic and unscrupulous humour that posterity orders literary fame. Its wilfulness is beyond reason. It takes no account of virtue and little of industry; it is indifferent to high endeavour and sincerity of purpose. How unjust it is that Mrs. Humphry Ward, with her well-stored mind and her command of language, with her solid gifts, her conscientiousness and her seriousness, should be so forgotten that even her name will be unknown to most readers of today, whereas a dissipated French abbé, a hack-writer of the eighteenth century who wrote interminable and unreadable novels, should have achieved immortality because in the long course of one of them he wrote the story of a little baggage called Manon Lescaut!

Before I begin I should like to make it quite clear that though I knew the authors I am going to speak of over a long period I was not really intimate with any of them. One reason of this is that until I made a success as a writer of light comedies I knew very few authors, and for the most part those I know, and only casually, were like myself very small fry. One's intimate friends are those one makes in one's teens or early twenties. I was thirty-four when I became a popular playwright, and though after that I came in contact with many of the literary figures of the day they were a good deal older than me and they were by then too much occupied with their own activities and the friends these had brought them for me to become anything more than a random acquaintance. I have been a wanderer all my life and when I was not wanted in London for the rehearsals of a play I spent long periods out of England, so that I lost touch with the people my success had enabled me to meet.

French authors live for the greater part of the year in Paris. They form cliques and the members of a clique meet constantly, in cafés, in newspaper offices, in their apartments; they dine together and talk and criticise one another's books; they write to one another (with a view to future publication) immense letters. They defend one another; they attack one another. English authors are different. On the whole they are not much interested in their fellow-writers. They are apt to live in the country and only go to London when they need to. They are more indiscriminately social than the French and mix freely in circles other than literary. Their close friends are, as with Henry James, a little group of fervent admirers or, as with H. G. Wells, the persons who share their particular interests. If you are not numbered among one or other of these classes you have little chance of admittance into their intimacy. But the chief reason why I have never become easily familiar with the men of letters I propose to write about is owing to some fault in my own character. I am either too self-centred, or too diffident, or too reserved, or too shy to be able to be on confidential terms with anyone I know at all well, and when on occasion a friend in trouble has opened his heart to me I have been too embarrassed to be of much help to him. Most people like to talk about themselves and when they tell me things I should have thought they would prefer to keep to themselves I am abashed. I prefer to guess at the secrets of their hearts. It is not in me to take people at their face value and I am not easily impressed. I have no power of veneration. It is more in my humour to be amused by people than to respect them.

Many have been on terms of much closer friendship with the more or less illustrious persons my recollections of whom I am now offering to the reader, and I have written the above only to impress upon him that they (my recollections) can suggest no more than a partial portrait of my subjects.

I saw Henry James long before I knew him. Somehow or other I was allotted two seats in the dress circle for the first night of *Guy Domville*. I can't think why, because I was still a medical student and one of George Alexander's first nights was a fashionable affair and seats in the better parts of the house were distributed among critics, regular first-nighters, friends of the management and persons of consequence. The play was a dreadful failure. The dialogue was graceful, but perhaps not quite direct enough to be taken in by an audience and there was a certain monotony in its rhythm. Henry James was fifty when he wrote the play and it is hard to understand how such a practised writer could have invented such a tissue of absurdities as was that night presented to the public. There was in the second act a distressing scene of pretended drunkenness which gave one goose-flesh. One blushed for the author. The play reached its tedious end and Henry James was very unwisely brought on the stage to take a' bow, as was the undignified custom of the time. He was greeted with such an outburst of boos and catcalls as only then have I heard in the theatre. From my seat in the dress circle he seemed oddly foreshortened. A stout man on stumpy legs, and owing to his baldness, notwithstanding his beard, a vast expanse of naked face. He confronted the hostile audience, his jaw fallen so that his mouth was slightly open and on his countenance a look of complete bewilderment. He was paralysed. I don't know why the curtain wasn't immediately brought down. He seemed to stand there interminably while the gallery and the pit continued to bawl. There was clapping in the stalls and dress circle, and he said afterwards that it was enthusiastic, but there he was mistaken. It was half-hearted. People clapped in protest at the rudeness of pit and gallery, and out of pity because they could not bear to see the wretched man's humiliation. At last George Alexander came out and led him, crushed and cowed, away.

In a letter he wrote to his brother William after that disastrous evening Henry James, like many another dramatist who has had a failure, said that his play was "over the heads of the usual vulgar theatre-going London public." That was not the fact. It was a bad play. It is possible that the outcry would have been less violent if the audience had not been exasperated by the incredible conduct of the characters. Their motives were, as in so much of Henry James's work, not the motives of normal human beings, and though in his fiction he was persuasive enough very often to conceal the fact from the reader, presented on the stage they glaringly lacked plausibility. The audience felt instinctively that people did not behave with the lack of common sense with which he made them behave and, so feeling, felt that they had been made fools of. In their boos there was more than irritation because they had been bored, there was resentment.

One can see the play Henry James wanted to write and perhaps thought he had written, but it is wretchedly evident that he fell very far short of his intention. He despised the English theatre and was convinced that he could write much better plays himself. Years before in Paris he wrote that he had "mastered Dumas, Augier and Sardou," and claimed that he knew "all they knew and a great deal more besides." Why he failed as a dramatist is obvious enough. He was like a man who, because he can ride a bicycle, thinks he can ride a horse. If under that impression he goes out for a day with the Pytchley he will come a cropper at the first fence. One unfortunate result of Henry James's misadventure was that it confirmed managers in the belief that no novelist could write a play.

II

It was not till many years later, when I had myself written successful plays, that I met Henry James. It was at a luncheon party given by Lady Russell, the author of *Elizabeth and Her German Garden*, in a flat she then had, if I remember rightly, near Buckingham Gate. It was by way of being a literary party and Henry James was of course the lion of the occasion. He said a few polite words to me, but I received the impression that they meant very little. I forget how long it was after this that I happened to go to an afternoon performance of *The Cherry Orchard* given by the Stage Society and found myself sitting next to Henry James and Mrs. W. K. Clifford, the widow of the mathematician, and herself the author of two good novels, *Mrs. Keith's Crime* and *Aunt Anne*. The intervals were long and we had ample time to talk. Henry James was perplexed by *The Cherry Orchard*, as well he might be when his dramatic values were founded on the plays of Alexandre Dumas and Sardou, and in the second interval he set out to explain to us how antagonistic to his French sympathies was this Russian incoherence. Lumbering through his tortuous phrases, he hesitated now and again in search of the exact word to express his dismay; but Mrs. Clifford had a quick and agile mind; she knew the word he was looking for and every time he paused immediately supplied it. This was the last thing he wanted. He was too well-mannered to protest, but an almost imperceptible expression on his face betrayed his irritation and, obstinately refusing the word she offered, he laboriously sought another, and again Mrs. Clifford suggested it, only to have it again turned down. It was a scene of high comedy.

Ethel Irving was playing the part of Chekov's feckless heroine. She was herself moody, neurotic and emotional, which suited the character, and her performance was excellent. She had made a great success in a play of mine and Henry James was curious to know about her. I told him what I could. Then he put me a very simple question, but he felt it would be crude and perhaps a trifle snobbish to put it simply. Both Mrs. Clifford and I knew exactly what he wanted to say. He led up to his enquiry like a big-game hunter stalking an antelope. He approached stealthily and drew back when he suspected that the shy creature winded him. He wrapped up his meaning in an increasingly embarrassed maze of circumlocution till at last Mrs. Clifford could stand it no longer and blurted out: "Do you mean, is she a lady?" A look of real suffering crossed his face. Put so, the question had a vulgarity that outraged him. He pretended not to hear. He made a little gesture of desperation and said: "Is she, *enfin*, what you'd call if you were asked point-blank, if so to speak you were put with your back to the wall, is she a *femme du monde?*"

In 1910 I went to America for the first time and in due course paid a visit to Boston. Henry James, his brother having recently died, was staying at Cambridge, Massachusetts, with his sister-in-law, and Mrs. James asked me to dinner. There were but the three of us. I can remember nothing of the conversation, but I could not help noticing that Henry James was troubled in spirit, and after dinner, when the widow had left us alone in the dining-room, he told me that he had promised his brother to remain at Cambridge for, I think, six months after his death, so that if he found himself able to make a communication from beyond the grave there would be two sympathetic witnesses on the spot ready to receive it. I could not but reflect that Henry James was in so nervous a state that it would be difficult to place implicit confidence in any report he might make. His sensibility was so exacerbated that he was capable of imagining anything. But hitherto no message had come and the six months were drawing to their end.

When it was time for me to go Henry James insisted on accompanying me to the corner where I could take the street-car back to Boston. I protested that I was perfectly capable of getting there by myself, but he would not hear of it, not only on account of the kindness and the great courtesy which were natural to him, but also because America seemed to him a strange and terrifying labyrinth in which without his guidance I was bound to get hopelessly lost.

As we walked along, he told me what his good manners had prevented him from saying before Mrs. James, that he was counting the days that must elapse before, having fulfilled his promise, he could sail for the blessed shores of England. He yearned for it. There, in Cambridge, he felt himself forlorn. He was determined never to set foot again on that bewildering and unknown country that America was to him. It was then that he uttered the phrase which seemed to me so fantastic that I have never forgotten it. "I wander about these great empty streets of Boston," he said, "and I never see a soul. I could not be more alone in the Sahara." The street-car hove in sight and Henry James was seized with agitation. He began waving frantically when it was still a quarter of a mile away. He was afraid it wouldn't stop, and he besought me to jump on with the greatest agility of which I was capable, for it would not pause more than an instant, and if I were not very careful I might be dragged along and, if not killed, at least mangled and dismembered. I assured him I was quite accustomed to getting on street-cars. Not American street-cars, he told me, they were of a savagery, an inhumanity, a ruthlessness beyond any conception. I was so infected by his anxiety that when the car pulled up and I leapt on I had almost the sensation that I had had a miraculous escape from certain death. I saw him standing on his short legs in the middle of the road, looking after the car, and I felt that he was trembling still at my narrow shave.

But homesick as he was for England, I don't believe that he ever felt himself quite at home there. He remained a friendly but critical alien. He did not know the English as an Englishman instinctively knows them and so his English characters never to my mind ring quite true. His American characters, at least to an Englishman, on the whole do. He had certain remarkable gifts, but he lacked the quality of empathy which enables a novelist to feel himself into his characters, think their thoughts and suffer their emotions. Flaubert vomited as though he too had swallowed arsenic when he was describing the suicide of Emma Bovary. It is impossible to imagine Henry James being similarly affected if he had had to narrate a similar episode. Take *The Author of Beltraffio*. In that a mother lets her only child, a little boy, die of diphtheria so that he should not be corrupted by his father's books, of which she profoundly disapproves. No one could have conceived such a monstrous episode who could imagine a mother's love for her son and in his nerves feel the anguish of the child tossing restlessly on his bed and the pitiful, agonizing struggle for breath. That is what the French call *littérature*. There is no precise English equivalent. On the pattern of writer's cramp you might call it writer's hokum. It signifies the sort of writing produced purely for literary effect without a relation to truth or probability. A novelist may ask himself what it feels like to commit a murder and then may invent a character who commits one to know what it feels like. That is *littérature*. People commit murders for reasons that seem good to them, not in order to enjoy a curious experience. The great novelists, even in seclusion, have lived life passionately. Henry James was content to observe it from a window. But you cannot describe life convincingly unless you have partaken of it; nor, should your object be different, can you fantasticate upon it (as Balzac and Dickens did) unless you know it first. Something escapes you unless you have been an actor in the tragi-comedy. However realistic he tries to be, the novelist cannot hope to give a representation of life as exactly as a litho-

graph can give a representation of a drawing. With his characters and the experiences he causes them to undergo he draws a pattern, but he is more likely to convince his readers that the pattern is acceptable if the people he depicts have the same sort of motives, foibles and passions as they know they have themselves and if the experiences of the persons in question are such as their characters render plausible.

Henry James regarded his relations and friends with deep affection, but this is no indication that he was capable of love. Indeed he showed a singular obtuseness in his stories and novels when he came to deal with the most deeply seated of human emotions; so that interested and amused as you are (often amused at him rather than with him), you are constantly jolted back to reality by your feeling that human beings simply do not behave as he makes them do. You cannot take Henry James's fiction quite seriously as, for instance, you take *Anna Karenina* or *Madame Bovary;* you read it with a smile, and with the suspension of disbelief with which you read the Restoration dramatists. (This notion is not so far-fetched as it may seem at first sight: if Congreve had been a novelist he might well have written the bawdy narrative of promiscuous fornication which Henry James entitled *What Maisie Knew*.) There is all the difference between his novels and those of Flaubert and Tolstoi as there is between the paintings of Daumier and the drawings of Constantin Guys. The draughtsman's pretty women drive in the Bois in their smart carriages, luxurious and fashionable, but they have no bodies in their elegant clothes. They amuse, they charm; but they are as unsubstantial as the stuff that dreams are made of. Henry James's fictions are like the cobwebs which a spider may spin in the attic of some old house, intricate, delicate and even beautiful, but which at any moment the housemaid's broom with brutal common sense may sweep away.

It is not my purpose to criticise Henry James's work, yet it is impossible in his case to write of the man rather than of the author. They are in fact inseparable. The author absorbed the man. To him it was art that made life significant, but he cared little for any of the arts except the one he practised. He was little interested in music or painting. When Gosse was going to Venice he conjured him without fail to see Tintoretto's *Crucifixion* at San Cassiano. It is odd that he should have picked out this fine but stagey picture to commend rather than Titian's grand *Presentation of the Virgin* or Veronese's *Jesus in the House of Levi*. No one who knew Henry James in the flesh can read his stories dispassionately. He got the sound of his voice into every line he wrote, and you accept (not willingly, but with indulgence) the abominable style of his later work, with its ugly Gallicisms, its abuse of adverbs, its too elaborate metaphors, the tortuosity of its long sentences, because they are part and parcel of the charm, benignity and amusing pomposity of the man you remember.

I am not sure that Henry James was fortunate in his friends. They were disposed to be possessive, and they regarded one another's claim to be in the inner circle of his confidence with no conspicuous amiability. Like a dog with a bone, each was inclined to growl when another showed an inclination to dispute his exclusive right to the precious object of his devotion. The reverence with which they treated him was of no great service to him. They seemed to me, indeed, sometimes a trifle silly: they whispered to one another with delighted giggles that Henry James privately stated that the article in *The Ambassadors* on the manufacture of which the fortune of the widow Newsome was founded, and the nature of which he had left in polite obscurity, was in fact a chamber pot. I did not find this so amusing as they did. I think it would be unfair to say that Henry James demanded the admiration of his friends, but he certainly enjoyed it. English authors, unlike their fellows in France and Germany, are chary of assuming an attitude. The pose of *Cher Maître* makes them feel faintly ridiculous. Perhaps because Henry James had first come to know distinguished writers in France he took the pedestal on which his admirers placed him as a natural prerogative. He was touchy and could be cross when he was not treated with what he thought proper respect. On one occasion a young Irish friend of mine was staying at Hill for the week-end in company with Henry James. Mrs. Hunter, their hostess, told him that he was a talented young man and Henry James on the Saturday afternoon engaged him in conversation. My friend was petulant and impatient, and at length, driven to desperation by James's interminable struggle to find the one word that would express exactly what he wanted to say, blurted out: "Oh, Mr. James, I'm not of any importance. Don't bother about rooting around for the right word. Any old word is good enough for me." Henry James was deeply affronted and complained to Mrs. Hunter that the young man had been very rude to him, whereupon Mrs. Hunter gave him a severe scolding and insisted that he should apologise to her distinguished guest. This he accordingly did. Once Jane Wells inveigled Henry James and me to go with her to a subscription dance in aid of some worthy object in which H. G. was interested. Mrs. Wells, Henry James and I were chatting in a kind of anteroom adjoining the ballroom when a brash young man bounced in, interrupting Henry James in his discourse, and, seizing Jane Wells's hands, said: "Come on and dance, Mrs. Wells, you don't want to sit there listening to that old man talking his head off." It wasn't very polite. Jane Wells gave Henry James an anxious glance and then with a strained smile went off with the brash young man. Henry James was too little accustomed to be treated like that to take it, as he might sensibly have done, with a good-natured laugh, and he was much offended. When Mrs. Wells came back he got up and a little too formally bade her good night.

When someone transplants himself from one country to another he is more likely to assimilate the defects of its inhabitants than their virtues. The England in which Henry James lived was excessively class-conscious, and I think it is to this that must be ascribed the somewhat disconcerting attitude he adopted in his fiction to those who were so unfortunate as to be of humble origin. Unless he were an artist, by choice a writer, it seemed to him more than a little ridiculous that anyone should be under the necessity of earning a living. The death of a member of the lower orders could be

trusted to give him a mild chuckle. I think this attitude was emphasized by the fact that, himself of good family, he could not have dwelt long in England without becoming aware that to the English one American was very like another. He saw compatriots on the strength of a fortune acquired in Michigan or Ohio received with as great cordiality as though they belonged to the eminent families of Boston and New York, and in self-defence somewhat exaggerated his native fastidiousness in social relations. Sometimes he made rather ludicrous mistakes and would attribute to some young man who had taken his fancy a distinction which he obviously did not possess.

If in these pages I have made Henry James, I hope not unkindly, a trifle absurd it is because that is what I found him. I think he took himself a good deal too seriously. We look askance at a man who keeps on telling you he is a gentleman; I think it would have been more becoming in Henry James if he had not insisted so often on his being an artist. It is better to leave others to say that. But he was gracious, hospitable and, when in the mood, uncommonly amusing. He had uncommon gifts and if I think they were too often ill-directed that is only what I think and I ask no one to agree with me. The fact remains that those last novels of his, notwithstanding their unreality, make all other novels, except the very best, unreadable.

III

I met H. G. Wells for the first time at a flat which Reggie Turner had near Berkeley Square. I was living then in Mount Street and sometimes I would drop in to see him. Reggie

Turner was on the whole the most amusing man I have known. I will not attempt to describe his humour, since Max Beerbohm has done it to perfection in the essay called *Laugh-*

ter. Reggie was not so well pleased as he might have been with this flattering tribute because Max had added that he was not very responsive to the humour of others. He asked me if it was true, and I was bound to admit that it was. Reggie liked an audience, though he was quite content with one of three or four, and then he would take a theme and embroider upon it with such drollery that he made your sides so ache with laughter that at last you had to beg him to stop. He was by way of being a novelist, but somehow, when he took up his pen his gaiety, his extravagant invention, his lightness deserted him, and his novels were dull. They were unsuccessful. He said of them: "With most novelists it's their first edition that is valuable, but with mine it's the second. It doesn't exist." I will set down here a quip of his because I do not think it is well known. He was one of the few of Oscar Wilde's friends who remained faithful to him after his disgrace. Reggie was in Paris when Wilde, living in a cheap, dingy hotel on the left bank of the Seine, was dying. Reggie went to see him every day. One morning he found him distraught. He asked him what was the matter. "I had a terrible dream last night," said Oscar. "I dreamt I was supping with the dead." "Well," said Reggie, "I'm sure you were the life and soul of the party, Oscar." Wilde burst into a roar of laughter and regained his spirits. It was not only witty, but kind.

On the day on which I was first introduced to H. G. he had been lunching with Reggie and they had gone back to his flat to continue their conversation. H. G. was then, I suppose, at the height of his fame. I had not expected to find him there and was slightly disconcerted. I had re-

cently made a success as a dramatist which the newspapers described as spectacular, but I was well aware that I had thereby lost caste with the intelligentsia. H. G. was cordial enough, but, perhaps because I was sensitive, I received the impression that he looked upon me with a sort of offhand amusement as he might have looked upon Arthur Roberts or Dan Leno. He was busy reconstructing the world according to his own notions of how it should be shaped, and he had no time for anyone who was not with him, so that he could be enlisted to serve his ideas, or against him, so that he could be reasoned with, argued with, and, if not brought round, ignominiously discarded.

Though after that I saw him now and then, it was not till a number of years later, when I had settled down on the Riviera and H. G. had a house there too at which he spent a considerable part of the year, that our slight acquaintance ripened into friendship. Later still, when he had parted with the companion who shared the house with him (carved on the chimney-piece in the sitting room was the phrase: "This house was built by two lovers") and abandoned it to her, he would from time to time come to stay with me. He was very good company. He was not a wit as Max Beerbohm or Reggie Turner was, but he had a lively sense of humour and could laugh at himself as well as at others. Once he asked me to lunch to meet Barbusse, the author of a novel called *Le Feu* that had made a great stir. It is a long time ago and I can only remember that Barbusse was a long, thin, hirsute man dressed in shabby black like a mute at a French funeral. He had dark angry eyes and a restless manner. He was an ardent, violent socialist and his speech was torrential. Though H. G.

understood French well enough he spoke it haltingly, so that Barbusse had the conversation pretty much to himself. He treated us as though we were a public meeting. When he left, H. G. turned to me with a wry smile and said: "How silly our own ideas sound when we hear them out of somebody else's mouth." He was sharp-witted and, though apt to find persons who didn't agree with him stupid and so objects of ridicule, the humour he exercised at their expense was devoid of malice.

H. G. had strong sexual instincts and he said to me more than once that the need to satisfy these instincts had nothing to do with love. It was a purely physiological matter. If humour, as some say, is incompatible with love, then H. G. was never in love, for he was keenly alive to what was rather absurd in the objects of his unstable affections and sometimes seemed almost to look upon them as creatures of farce. He was incapable of the idealization of the desired person which most of us experience when we fall in love. If his companion was not intelligent he soon grew bored with her, and if she was, her intelligence sooner or later palled on him. He did not like his cake unsweetened and if it was sweet it cloyed. He loved his liberty and when he found that a woman wished to restrict it he became exasperated and somewhat ruthlessly broke off the connection. Sometimes this was not so easily done and he had to put up with scenes and recriminations that even he found difficult to treat with levity. He was of course, like most creative persons, self-centred. That to sever a tie that had lasted for years might cause the other party pain and humiliation appeared to him merely silly. I was somewhat closely concerned in one of these upheavals in his life, and speak-

ing of the trouble it was causing him, he said: "You know, women often mistake possessiveness for passion and when they are left it is not so much that their heart is broken as that their claim to property is repudiated." He thought it unreasonable that what on his side was merely the relaxation from what he regarded as his life's work on the other might be enduring passion. This he aroused. It surprised me, since his physical appearance was not particularly pleasing. He was fat and homely. I once asked one of his mistresses what especially attracted her in him. I expected her to say his acute mind and his sense of fun; not at all; she said that his body smelt of honey.

Notwithstanding H. G.'s immense reputation and the great influence he had had on his contemporaries, he was devoid of conceit. There was nothing of the stuffed shirt in him. He never put on airs. He had naturally good manners and he would treat some unknown scribbler, the assistant librarian, for instance, of a provincial library, with the same charming civility as if he were as important as himself. It was only later that by a grin and a quip you could tell what a donkey he had thought him. I remember attending a dinner of the P.E.N., of which H. G. was then president. There were a great many people present and after H. G. had read a report a number of them got up to ask questions. Most of them were silly, but H. G. replied to them all with great courtesy. One thickly bearded man, which marked him out as a conscious intellectual, leapt to his feet time and time again to make short speeches of a singular ineptitude and it was only too obvious that he was trying merely to attract attention to himself. H. G. could have crushed him with a retort, but he listened to him attentively and then reasoned with him as if he had been talking sense. After the proceedings were over I told H. G. how much I admired the wonderful patience with which he had dealt with the silly fellow. He chuckled and said: "When I was a member of the Fabian Society I got a lot of practice in dealing with fools."

He had no illusions about himself as an author. He always insisted that he made no pretension to be an artist. That was, indeed, something he despised rather than admired, and when he spoke of Henry James, an old friend, who claimed, as I have hinted, perhaps a little too often that he was an artist and nothing else, it was good-humouredly to ridicule him. "I'm not an author," H. G. would say, "I'm a publicist. My work is just high-class journalism." On one occasion, after he had been staying with me, he sent me a complete edition of his works and next time he came he saw them displayed in an imposing row on my shelves. They were well printed on good paper and handsomely bound in red. He ran his finger along them and with a cheerful grin said: "They're as dead as mutton, you know. They all dealt with matters of topical interest and now that the matters aren't topical any more they're unreadable." There is a good deal of truth in what he said. He had a fluent pen and too often it ran away with him. I have never seen any of his manuscripts, but I surmise that he wrote with facility and corrected little. He had a way of repeating in one sentence, but in other words, exactly what he said in the previous one. I suppose it was because he was so full of the idea he wanted to express that he was not satisfied to say it only once. It made him unnecessarily verbose.

H. G.'s theory of the short story was a sensible one. It enabled him to write a number that were very good and several that were masterly. His theory of the novel was different. His early novels, which he had written to earn a living, did not accord with it and he spoke of them slightingly. His notion was that the function of the novelist was to deal with the pressing problems of the day and to persuade the reader to adopt the views for the betterment of the world which he, H. G., held. He was fond of likening the novel to a woven tapestry of varied interest, and he would not accept my objection that after all a tapestry has unity. The artist who designed it has given it form, balance, coherence and arrangement. It is not a jumble of unrelated items.

His later novels are, if not, as he said, unreadable, at least difficult to read with delight. You begin to read them with interest, but as you go on you find your interest dwindle and it is only by an effort of will that you continue to read. I think *Tono Bungay* is generally considered his best novel. It is written with his usual liveliness, though perhaps the style is better suited to a treatise than to a novel, and the characters are well presented. He has deliberately avoided the suspense which most novelists attempt to create and he tells you more or less early on what is going to happen. His theory of the novelist's function allows him to digress abundantly, which, if you are interested in the characters and their behaviour, can hardly fail to arouse in you some impatience.

One day when he was staying with me, in the course of conversation he made the remark: "I'm only interested in people in the mass, I'm indifferent to the individual." Then with a smile: "I like you, in fact I've got a real affection for you, but I'm not interested in you." I laughed. I knew it was true. "I'm afraid I can't multiply myself by ten thousand to arouse your interest, old boy," I said. "Ten thousand?" he cried. "That's nothing. Ten million." During the course of his life he came in contact with a great many people, but with rare exceptions, though consistently pleasant and courteous, they made no more impression on him than the "extras" who compose the crowd in a moving picture.

I think that is why his novels are less satisfactory than one would have liked them to be. The people he puts before you are not individuals, but lively and talkative marionettes whose function it is to express the ideas he was out to attack or to defend. They do not develop according to their dispositions, but change for the purposes of the theme. It is as though a tadpole did not become a frog, but a squirrel

—because you had a cage that you wanted to pop him into. H. G. seems often to have grown tired of his characters before he was halfway through and then, frankly discarding any attempt at characterisation, he becomes an out-and-out pamphleteer. One curious thing that you can hardly help noticing if you have read most of H. G.'s novels is that he deals with very much the same people in book after book. He appears to have been content to use with little variation the few persons who had played an intimate part in his own life. He was always a little impatient with his heroines. He regarded his heroes with greater indulgence. He had of course put more of himself in them; most of them in fact are merely himself in a different guise. Trafford in *Marriage* is indeed the portrait of the man H. G. thought he was, added to the man he would have liked to be.

IV

In the last twenty-five years I have had a lot of people staying with me and sometimes I am tempted to write an essay on guests. There are the guests who never shut a door after them and never turn out the light when they leave their room. There are the guests who throw themselves on their bed in muddy boots to have a nap after lunch, so that the counterpane has to be cleaned on their departure. There are the guests who smoke in bed and burn holes in your sheets. There are the guests who are on a regime and have to have special food cooked for them and there are the guests who wait till their glass is filled with a vintage claret and then say: "I won't have any, thank you."

There are the guests who never put back a book in the place from which they took it and there are the guests who take away a volume from a set and never return it. There are the guests who borrow money from you when they are leaving and do not pay it back. There are the guests who can never be alone for a minute and there are the guests who are seized with a desire to talk the moment they see you glancing at a paper. There are the guests who, wherever they are, want to be somewhere else and there are the guests who want to be doing something from the time they get up in the morning till the time they go to bed at night. There are the guests who treat you as though they were gauleiters in a conquered province. There are the guests who bring three weeks' laundry with them to have washed at your expense and there are the guests who send their clothes to the cleaners and leave you to pay the bill. There are the guests who telephone to London, Paris, Rome, Madrid and New York, and never think of inquiring how much it costs. There are the guests who take all they can get and offer nothing in return.

There are also the guests who are happy just to be with you, who seek to please, who have resources of their own, who amuse you, whose conversation is delightful, whose interests are varied, who exhilarate and excite you, who in short give you far more than you can ever hope to give them and whose visits are only too brief. Such a guest was H. G. He had a social sense. When there was a party he wanted to make it go. Now and then there were neighbours who had to be asked to lunch or dine and sometimes they were dull. H. G. would talk to them as entertainingly as if they had the wits to understand him. One such occasion stands out in my memory because it is the only time I saw him defeated. One of my neighbours, hearing that he was staying with me, called me up and told me that she had a great admiration for him and that she'd always been told that he was a marvellous talker and would so much like to meet him. I asked her to lunch. We sat down and H. G., who liked to talk, began to do so. He had just got into his stride when the lady interrupted him with a remark which showed that she hadn't listened to a word he said. He stopped and, when she had finished, went on. Again she interrupted him and again he stopped. When she paused he started once more and again she interrupted. It was evident that her wish was not to hear

H. G. talk, but to have him listen to her talk. He gave me one of his funny grins and relapsed into silence. For the rest of lunch he sat mute while she cheerfully gave utterance to a stream of shattering platitudes. When she went away she said she'd had a wonderful time.

I saw H. G. for the last time during the war. I was in New York and he had come to America to deliver a series of lectures. He came to lunch with me just before his return to England. He looked old, tired and shrivelled. He was as perky as ever, but with something of an effort. His lectures were a dismal failure. He was not a good speaker. It was odd that after so much public speaking he had never been able to deliver a discourse, but was obliged to read it. His voice was thin and squeaky and he read with his nose in his manuscript. People couldn't hear what he said and they left in droves. He had also seen a number of highly influential persons, but though they listened to him politely he could not but see that they paid little attention to what he said. He was hurt and disappointed. "I've been saying the same things to people for the last thirty years," he said to me with exasperation, "and they won't listen." That was the trouble. He had said the same things too often. Many of his ideas were sensible, none of them was complicated; but, like Goethe, he thought that one must always repeat truth: *Man muss das Wahre immer wiederholen.* He was so constituted that never a doubt entered his mind that he was definitely possessed of *das Wahre.* Naturally people grew impatient when they were asked once more to listen to views they knew only too well. He had had an immense influence on a whole generation and had done a great deal to alter the climate of opinion. But he had had his say. He was mortified to find that people looked upon him as a has-been. They agreed with him or they didn't. When they listened to him it was no

longer with the old thrill of excitement, but with the indulgence you accord to an old man who has outlived his interest.

He died a disappointed man.

V

H. G. SET little store on the pure novelist. I think he would have segregated the novelists who seek primarily to entertain on an island next to the one on which in *A New Utopia* he settled the drunkards, where, well-fed and comfortably housed, they could spend their leisure in reading one another's works. The only straight novelist with whom he was on terms of real intimacy was Arnold Bennett. A woman I knew told me how once, standing next to Henry James at a very grand party at Londonderry House, one of those parties graced by royalty, where decorations were worn, stars and impressive ribbons, and the women blazed with diamonds, she had perhaps flippantly said to him: "Fun, isn't it, for middle-class people like you and me to find ourselves hobnobbing with all these swells." She saw at once by the look on his face that she had said the wrong thing. He didn't at all like being called middle class, and the look of amusement in her eyes when she noticed his annoyance increased his displeasure. Henry James was wrong to take offence, for after all it is the middle class that has created the wealth of English literature. That is natural enough. The boy of poor parents has received a scanty education and is forced to go to work at an early age. He has had little opportunity to read. The boy born in the

upper ranks of society is seduced by the amusements his circumstances put within his easy reach, and his ambition, if he has any, is more likely to lead him to seek distinction in the way approved of by the people among whom his happy lot is cast. In either case his urge to create must be very strong to overcome the hindrances, though very different in character, which combine to thwart him. The nobility and gentry, so far as I know, have only produced two poets whose work is definitely a part of English literature, Shelley and Byron, and only one novelist, Fielding. The youth of middle-class parentage who has an irresistible impulse to write has received an education which is at least adequate; he has had access to something of a library; he has probably come in contact with a greater variety of people than either the son of an artisan or the son of a country squire; and though his family may deplore his taking to the hazardous profession of literature, the idea is not quite foreign to their prepossessions and may even make a certain appeal to their pride. The English middle class is never without the desire to rise in the social scale, and to have a writer in the family is to the clergyman, the solicitor, the Civil Servant something of a prestige item.

I think H. G. and Arnold were drawn together because both were of modest origin and both had had an arduous struggle to win recognition. After they had achieved success both felt that, though for somewhat different reasons, they stood slightly apart from the rest of the literary world, and that again was a bond between them. But the chief cause of H. G.'s genuine attachment to Arnold was that Arnold was a very lovable man.

I first knew him in 1905, when we were both living in Paris. I had taken a tiny apartment near the Lion de Belfort, on the fifth floor, from which I had a spacious view of the cemetery of Montparnasse. I used to dine at a restaurant in the Rue d'Odessa. A number of painters, illustrators, sculptors and writers were in the habit of dining there and we had a little room to ourselves. We got a very good dinner, *vin compris,* for two francs fifty, and it was usual to give four sous to Marie, the good-humoured and sharp-tongued maid who waited on us. We were of various nationalities and the conversation was carried on indifferently in English and French. On occasion someone would bring his mistress and her mother, whom he introduced politely to the company as *ma belle mère,* but for the most part we were all men. We discussed every subject under the sun, generally with heat, and by the time we came to coffee (with which, I seem to remember, a *fine* was thrown in) and lit our cigars, *demi londrès* at three sous apiece, the air was heady. We differed with extreme acrimony. Arnold used to come there once a week. He reminded me years later that the first time we met, which was at this restaurant, I was white with passion. The conversation was upon the merits of Hérédia. I asserted that there was no sense in him, and a painter scorn-

fully replied that you didn't want sense in poetry, you wanted sound. Someone contributed an anecdote about Mallarmé and Degas. Degas arrived late at one of Mallarmé's celebrated Tuesdays and said he'd been trying all day to write a sonnet and couldn't get an idea. To this Mallarmé replied: "But, my dear Degas, one doesn't write a sonnet with ideas, one writes it with words." From this an argument arose upon the objects and limitations of poetry which soon enlivened the whole company. I exercised such powers as I had of sarcasm, invective and vituperation, and my antagonist, Roderic O'Connor by name, a taciturn Irishman, than whom there is no man more difficult to cope with, was coldly and bitingly virulent. The entire table took up the dispute and I have still a dim recollection of Arnold, smiling a little, calm and a trifle Olympian, putting in now and then a brief, dogmatic, but, I am certain, judicious remark. He was older than most of us. He was then a thin man, with dark hair very smoothly done in a fashion that suggested the private soldier of the day. He was much more neatly dressed than we were and more conventionally. He looked like a managing clerk in a city office. At that time the only book he had written that we knew of was *The Grand Babylon Hotel* and our attitude towards him was somewhat patronising. We were arrogantly high-brow. Some of us had read the book and enjoyed it, which was enough for us to decide that there was nothing in it, but the rest shrugged their shoulders and declined to waste their time over such trash. Had you read *Bubu de Montparnasse?* That was the stuff to give the troops.

Arnold was living at that time in Montmartre, I think in the Rue de

Calais, in a small dark apartment which he had filled with Empire furniture. It was certainly not genuine, but this he did not know, and he was exceedingly proud of it. Arnold was a tidy man and his apartment was very neat, with every article in an appointed place, but it was not very comfortable and you could not imagine anyone making a home of it. It gave you the impression of a "set" arranged for a man who saw himself in a certain role which he was playing conscientiously, but into the skin of which he hadn't quite got. On deciding to live in Paris, Arnold had given up the editorship of a magazine called *Woman* and was settled down to train himself for the profession of literature. Through Marcel Schwob he had got to know several of the French writers of the day, and I seem to remember his telling me that Schwob had taken him to see Anatole France, who was then the high priest of French letters. Arnold diligently read the French literary reviews, of which at that time the *Mercure de France* was the most distinguished; he read Stendhal and Flaubert, but chiefly Balzac, and I think he told me that he had read through the whole of the *Comédie Humaine* in a year. When I first knew him he was starting on the Russians and talked with enthusiasm of *Anna Karenina*. He thought it the greatest of all novels. I am under the impression that he did not discover Chekov till somewhat later. When he did, he began to admire Tolstoi less.

Arnold's plan of campaign to achieve success in his calling was cut-and-dried. He proposed to make his annual expenditure by writing novels, and by writing plays to make provision for his old age. He meant to write two or three books to get his hand in and then write a masterpiece.

When I asked him what sort of book this was going to be he said, something on the lines of *A Great Man;* but that, he added, had brought him in nothing at all and he couldn't afford to go on in that style till he was properly established. I listened, but attached no importance to what he said. I did not think him capable of writing anything of consequence. Because I had lately had my first play produced by the Stage Society he asked me to read one of his. The characters were plausible and the dialogue natural, but in his determination to be realistic he had allowed none of them to make a witty or even a clever remark and had, so it seemed to me, gone out of his way to eschew anything in the nature of dramatic action. As a picture of middle-class life the play had verisimilitude, but I found it dull. Perhaps only it was before its time.

Like everyone else who lives in Paris, Arnold had come across a particular little restaurant where you could get a better dinner for less money than anywhere else. This one was on the first floor, somewhere in Montmartre, and now and then I used to go over to dine, Dutch treat, with him. After dinner we went back to his apartment and he would play Beethoven on a cottage piano. He was nothing if not thorough, and it was obvious that if you were living in Montmartre as a man of letters and a Bohemian (though a clean, respectable one) to complete the picture you must have a mistress. But that costs money and Arnold, who had come to Paris for a definite purpose and had only a certain sum to dispose of, was too cagey to squander on luxuries what he needed for necessities. He was not a son of the Five Towns for nothing and he solved the problem in a characteristic fashion. One night after we had been dining together and were sitting amid the Empire furniture of his apartment, he said:

"Look here, I have a proposal to make to you."

"Oh?"

"I have a mistress with whom I spend two nights a week. She has another gentleman with whom she spends two other nights. She likes to have her Sundays to herself and she's looking for someone who'll take the two nights she has free. I've told her about you. She likes writers. I'd like to see her nicely fixed up and I thought it would be a good plan if you took the two nights that she has vacant."

The suggestion startled me.

"It sounds rather cold-blooded to me," I said.

"She's not an ignorant woman, you know," Arnold insisted. "Not by any manner of means. She reads a great deal, Madame de Sévigné and all that, and she can talk very intelligently."

But even that didn't tempt me.

Arnold was good company, and I always enjoyed spending an evening with him, but I didn't very much like him. He was cocksure and bumptious, and he was rather common. I don't say this depreciatingly, but as I might say that someone was short and fat. I left Paris after a year or so and lost touch with him. He wrote one or two books which I did not read. The Stage Society produced a play of his which I liked. I wrote and told him so and he wrote to thank me and in the course of his letter laid out the critics who had not thought so well of the play as I had. I can't remember whether it was before or after this that The Old Wives' Tale was published. I began reading it with misgiving, but this quickly changed to astonishment. I had never supposed that Arnold could write anything so

good. I was deeply impressed. I thought it a great book. I have read many appreciations of it, and I think everything has been said but one thing, which is that it is eminently readable. I should not mention a merit that is so obvious except that many great books do not possess it. It is the novelist's most precious gift, and it is one that Arnold had even in his slightest and most trivial pieces. I have of late read The Old Wives' Tale again. Though written in rather a drab style, with an occasional use of "literatese" which gives you a jolt, and without elegance, it is still extremely readable. The characters ring true: they are not intrinsically interesting, it was not to Arnold's purpose to make them brilliant, and it is a mark of his skill that, notwithstanding, you follow their fortunes with interest and sympathy. Their motives are plausible and they behave as from what you know of them you would expect them to behave. The incidents are completely probable: Sophia is in Paris during the siege and the Commune; an author less determined to avoid the sensational would have looked upon it as an opportunity, by describing scenes of terror, anguish and bloodshed, to give his narrative a lift. Not Arnold. Sophia goes about her business unperturbed; she looks after her lodgers, buys and hoards food, makes money when she can, and in fact conducts herself precisely as of course the great mass of the people did.

The Old Wives' Tale was slow to make its way. I think I am right in saying that it was received favourably, but not with frantic eulogy, and that its circulation was inconsiderable. For a time it looked as though it would have no more than the sort of succès d'estime that Maurice Guest had and be forgotten as all but one novel out of a thousand are forgotten. By a happy chance, however, it was brought to the attention of George Doran, an American publisher, and he bought sheets; he then acquired the American rights, set it up and launched it on its triumphal course. It was not until after its great success in America that it was taken over by another publisher in England and won favour with the British public.

For many years, what with one thing and another, I do not think I met Arnold, or if I did it was only at a party, literary or otherwise, at which I had the opportunity to say no more than a few words to him; but after the First World War and until his death I saw him frequently. By this time he had become a "character." He was very different from the thin, rather insignificant man that I had known in Paris. He had grown stout. His hair, very grey, was worn long and he had cultivated the amusing cock's comb that the caricaturists made famous. He walked with an arrogant strut, his back arched and his head thrown back. He had always been neat in his dress, disconcertingly even, but now he was grand. He wore a fob and frilled shirts in the evening and took an immense pride in his white waistcoats. At one time he had a yacht and he dressed the part of the owner in style. Yachting cap, blue coat with brass buttons, white trousers: no actor playing the role in a musical comedy could have arrayed himself more perfectly in character. In one of his diaries he has related the story of a picnic I took him on while he was staying with me in the South of France. I had a motor-boat then and after picking up the rest of my guests in Cannes we went over to the Isle Sainte Marguerite to bathe, eat *bouillabaisse* and gossip. The women wore pyjamas and the men tennis shirts, ducks and espadrilles, but Arnold, refusing to permit himself such *sans gène,* was dressed in a check suit of a sort of mustard colour, fancy socks and fancy shoes, a striped shirt, a starched collar and a foulard tie. After lunch a violent mistral sprang up which prevented us from leaving the island. Some of the persons present took the prospect without amenity of being marooned for an indefinite period and when twelve hours later the sea had sufficiently calmed down to allow us to risk the crossing more than one of them faced the slight danger we were in with a good deal of anxiety. Arnold throughout remained dignified, self-possessed, good-tempered and interested. When at six in the morning, bedraggled and unshaven, we at last got home, he, in his smart shirt and neat suit, looked as dapper and well-groomed as he had looked eighteen hours before.

But it was not only in appearance that Arnold differed from the man I had known before. Life had changed him. I think it possible that when I first knew him he was hampered by a certain diffidence and his bumptiousness was assumed to conceal it. Success had given him confidence. It had certainly mellowed him. He had acquired a proper assurance of his own merit. He told me once that there were only two novels written during the first twenty years of the century that he was confident would survive and one of them was *The Old Wives' Tale.* It may be that he was right. That depends on the whirligig of taste. Realism is a fashion that comes and goes. When readers ask their novels to give them fantasy, romance, excitement, suspense, surprise, they will find Arnold's masterpiece pedestrian and rather dull. When the pendulum swings back and they want homely truth, verisimilitude, good sense and sympathetic delineation of character they will find it in *The Old Wives' Tale*.

I have said before that Arnold was a lovable man. His very oddities were endearing. Indeed it was to them that the great affection in which he was held was largely owing, for people laughed at foibles in him of which they believed themselves exempt and thus mitigated the oppression which his talent must otherwise have made them feel. They liked him all the better for the absurdities which gave them a comfortable sense of superiority. He was never what in England is technically known as a gentleman, but he was never vulgar any more than the traffic surging up Ludgate Hill is vulgar. He was devoid of envy. He was generous. He was courageous. He always said with perfect frankness what he thought and because it never struck him that he could offend he seldom did; but if, with his quick sensitiveness, he imagined that he had hurt somebody's feelings, he did everything in reason to salve the wound. But only in reason. If the affronted person continued to bear a grudge he dismissed him with a shrug of the shoulders and a "silly ass." He retained to the end an engaging naïvety. He was convinced that there were two things he knew all about—money and women. His friends were unanimous in agreeing that this was an illusion. It got him now and then into trouble. With all his common sense, and he had more common sense than most of us, he made the mistake, to which many novelists are prone, of ordering his life after the pattern of one of the novels he might very well have written. In a work of fiction the author can pull the strings and with sufficient skill on the whole get his characters to act as he wants them to. In real life people are more difficult to cope with.

I was surprised to see how patronising in general were the obituary notices written at Arnold's death. A good deal of fun was made of his obsession with grandeur and luxury, and the pleasure he took in *trains de luxe* and first-class hotels. He never grew quite accustomed to the appurtenances of wealth. Once he said to me: "If you've ever really been poor you remain poor at heart all your life. I've often walked," he added, "when I could very well afford to take a taxi because I simply couldn't bring myself to waste the shilling it would cost." He admired and disapproved of extravagance.

The criticism to which he devoted much time during his later years came in for a good deal of adverse comment. He loved his position on the *Evening Standard*. He liked the power it gave him and enjoyed the interest his articles aroused. The immediate response, like the applause an actor receives after an effective scene, gratified his appetite for actuality. It gave him the illusion, peculiarly pleasant to the author whose avocation necessarily entails a sense of apartness, that he was in the midst of things. Whatever he thought, he said without fear or favour. He had no patience with the precious, the affected or the pompous. If he thought little of writers who are now more praised than read it is not certain that he thought wrongly. He was more interested in life than in art. In criticism he was an amateur. The professional critic is probably somewhat shy of life, for otherwise it is unlikely that he will devote himself to the reading and judging of books rather than to the stress and turmoil of living. He is more at ease with it when the sweat has dried and the acrid odour of humanity has ceased to offend the nostrils. He can be sympathetic enough to the realism of Defoe and the tumultuous vitality of Balzac, but when it comes to the productions of his own day he feels more comfortable with works in which a deliberately literary attitude has softened the asperities of reality.

That is why, I suppose, the praise that was accorded to Arnold for *The Old Wives' Tale* after his death was cooler than one would have expected. Some of the critics said that, notwithstanding everything, he had a sense of beauty, and they quoted passages to show his poetic power and his feeling for the mystery of existence. I do not see the point of making out that he had something of what you would have liked him to have a great deal more of and ignoring that in which his power and value lay. He was neither mystic nor poet. He was interested in material things and in the humours of common men in general and he described life, as every writer does, in the terms of his own temperament.

Arnold was afflicted with a very bad stammer; it was painful to watch the struggle he sometimes had to get the words out. It was torture to him. Few realised the exhaustion it caused him to speak. What to most men is as easy as breathing was to him a constant strain. It tore his nerves to pieces. Few knew the humiliations it exposed him to, the ridicule it excited in many, the impatience it aroused, the awkwardness of feeling that it made people find him tiresome, the minor exasperation of thinking of a good, amusing or apt remark and not venturing to say it in case the stammer ruined it. Few knew the distressing sense it gave rise to of a bar to complete contact with other men. It may be that except for the stammer which forced him to introspection Arnold would never have become a writer. But I think it is no small proof of his strong and sane character that, notwithstanding this impediment, he was able to retain his splendid balance and regard the normal life of man from a normal point of view.

The Old Wives' Tale is certainly the best book he wrote. He never lost the desire to write another as good and because it was written by an effort of will he thought he could repeat it. He tried in *Clayhanger,* and for a time it looked as though he might succeed. I think he failed only because his material fizzled out. After *The Old Wives' Tale* he had not enough left to complete the vast structure he had designed. No writer can get more than a certain amount of ore out of one seam; when he has got that, though it remains, miraculously, as rich as before, it is only others who can profitably work it. Arnold tried again in *Lord Raingo,* and he tried for the last time in *Imperial Palace.* In this I think the subject was at fault. Because it profoundly interested him he thought it was of universal interest. He gathered his data systematically, but they were jotted down in notebooks and not garnered (as were those of *The Old Wives' Tale*) unconsciously, and preserved, not in black and white, but as old memories in his bones, in his nerves, in his heart. But that Arnold should have spent the last of his energy and determination on the description of an hotel seems to me to have symbolic significance. For I feel that he was never quite at home in the world. It was to him perhaps a sumptuous hotel, with marble bathrooms and a perfect cuisine, in which he was a transient guest. I feel that he was, here among men, impressed, delighted, but a little afraid of doing the wrong thing and never entirely at his ease. Just as his little apartment in the Rue de Calais years before had suggested to me a part played carefully, but from the outside, I feel that to him life was a role that he played conscientiously, and with ability, but into the skin of which he never quite got.

I remember that once, beating his knee with his clenched fist to force the words from his writhing lips, he said: "I am a nice man." He was.

VI

I MENTIONED early in this essay that I was introduced to Henry James by Elizabeth Russell. I knew her slightly over a number of years, but when she built herself a house near Mougins, which is an easy hour's drive from my own, I saw her fairly often, and so came to know her much better. She made her reputation with three books, starting with *Elizabeth and Her German Garden,* when she was still Countess von Arnim, but later on wrote a number of novels in a style in which the English have never had much success. This is the light, amusing novel which is not an outrage to the intelligence. I think the English are apt to be suspicious of books that are so entertaining and so easy to read. Farce they wallow in, but high comedy causes them a vague discomfort. Perhaps it makes them feel that the author is poking fun at them. And it is true that Elizabeth was inclined to be flippant about matters that we are more inclined to take seriously. She was a little, rather plump woman, not pretty, but with a pleasant, open, frank face, which was a very fallacious indication of her character. In one of his aphorisms Pearsal Smith said: "Hearts that are delicate and kind and tongues that are neither —these make the finest company in the world." I do not know whether Elizabeth's heart, except where dogs were concerned, was delicate and kind, but her tongue was neither and she was very good company. She regarded her fellow creatures with a robust common sense which some thought verged on the cynical. It was typical of her that over her writing-room she should have affixed the quotation: "Peace, perfect peace, with loved ones far away." She had a low voice and an innocent manner which added to the effect of the devastating things she said. She could be very malicious. I remember one occasion when I asked her to lunch because H. G., a very old friend of hers, was staying with me. He had recently published his autobiography and in the course of conversation he mentioned that he had gone down to see again the house, Up Park, where in his boyhood he had spent his holidays. His mother had been lady's maid to the owner and much later had returned as housekeeper. From time to time H. G. spent considerable periods there and as was natural enough lived, as the phrase goes, "below stairs."

"And this time, H. G.," asked Elizabeth with her most ingenuous air, "did you go in by the front door?"

It was said of course to embarrass him and for a moment succeeded. He flushed a little, grinned and did not answer. Afterwards another of my guests asked Elizabeth why she had put that awkward question to him. She opened her eyes wide and with a wonderful assumption of innocence answered: "I wanted to know."

I asked Elizabeth once whether the story I had often heard was true, that when her husband was very ill she read to him as he lay in bed the book in which she had drawn a caustic portrait of him. When she reached the last page, so the story ran, shattered by what he had been made to listen to, he turned his face to the wall and died. She looked at me blandly and said:

"He was very ill. He would have died in any case."

Elizabeth lived to a ripe old age and retained to the end the complacent air of a woman who knows she is attractive to men. Before I leave her I will recount a story she told me which is not only characteristic, but so diverting that I think it would be a pity if it were forgotten. I don't know whether she told it to anybody else. She was living with her second husband, Lord Russell, on Telegraph Hill. When she went into the kitchen one morning she found the cook gasping; she asked what was the matter, and the cook told her that she had just cut off the head of the chicken they were to have for dinner that night, and then the headless chicken had laid an egg.

"Show it me," said Elizabeth.

She looked at it pensively for a moment and then said:

"Give it to his lordship for breakfast tomorrow."

Next morning, sitting at table opposite her husband, she watched him as he ate the boiled egg. When he finished she asked him:

"Did you notice anything funny about that egg, Frank?"

"No," he answered. "Was there anything peculiar about it?"

"No, nothing," she said, "except that it was laid by a dead hen."

He gave her a startled look, sprang to the window and vomited. With a demure smile she added to me:

"And d'you know, I don't believe he ever really loved me after that."

I will end this essay with an account of my one and only meeting with Mrs. Wharton. She was then a well-known and highly esteemed novelist. Her short stories are ingenious and well-contrived, and in *Ethan Frome* she wrote a remarkably able novel about the country folk of New England; but her main interests lay with the rich and fashionable people who lived on Fifth Avenue and had sumptuous palaces at Newport. She described a phase of American civilisation which has long since passed away, and the manners and customs of her characters, their attitude towards the problems and difficulties that confront them, are so different from those of today that we can only believe what she tells us because we know that she wrote of what she knew. Her novels have now the same sort of charm that time gives to certain pictures regardless of their artistic merit. The crinolines, the bustles that women wore, as fashion changed made them absurd, but today, with the passing of the years, they have become "costume" and give us an amused delight. Mrs. Wharton's style was easy, pleasant and not undistinguished. She deserves a place, even though but a minor one, in American literature.

Mrs. Wharton lived in Paris but sometimes came to England, chiefly, I think, to see Henry James, who was an intimate and revered friend; and on these visits she spent a few days in London. On one of these occasions Lady St. Helier asked her to lunch and asked me too. She had a large house in Portland Place and she entertained a great deal. People were inclined to laugh at her because she was something of a lion-hunter, but they accepted her invitations with alacrity since they were pretty sure to find themselves in company with persons who were either eminent, amusing or notorious. When a certain man was being tried for what looked like a peculiarly callous murder and his birth and antecedents made the case the talk of high society one bright young spark asked another if he knew the accused. "No," he answered, "but if he isn't hanged I shall certainly meet him at Lady St. Helier's next week." The party to which I was bidden was choice and rather select, and because besides Mrs. Wharton I was the only author present, when lunch was over my hostess took me up to her so that we could have a chat. She was seated in the middle of a small French sofa in such a way as to give it the appearance of a throne, and since she gave no indication that she wished to share it with me I took a chair and sat down in front of her. She was a smallish woman, with fine eyes, regular features and a pale clear skin drawn rather tightly over the bones of her face. She was dressed with the sober magnificence suitable to a woman of birth, of wealth and of letters. She made the other ladies there, all of exalted rank, look dowdy and provincial. She talked and I listened. She talked very well. She talked for twenty minutes. In that time, with a light touch and well-chosen words, she traversed the fields of painting, music and literature. Nothing she said was commonplace, everything she said was just. She said exactly the right things about Maurice Barrès, André Gide and Paul Valéry; it was impossible not to concur with her admirable remarks upon Debussy and Stravinsky; and of course what she had to say about Rodin and Maillol, about Cézanne, Degas and Renoir was just what one would have wished her to say. I have never met anyone whose perceptions were so sensitive, whose opinions so sound and whose artistic sentiments so exemplary.

Though my literary friends do not, I am sorry to say, look upon me as a member of the intelligentsia, I very much enjoy the conversation of cultured persons and I think (perhaps mistakenly) that I can adequately hold my own with them. Indeed sometimes I gently lead them down the garden path of mysticism and when I talk to them of Denis the Areopagite and Fray Luis de Leon, throwing in Samkaracharia for good measure, I often have them gasping for breath like speckled trout on a river bank. But Mrs. Wharton got me down. Most people have a blind spot; many suffer from vagaries of taste. I was once sitting at the opera behind a distinguished and talented woman. The opera was *Tristan and Isolde*. At the end of the second act she gathered her ermine cloak around her shoulders and, turning to her companion, said: "Let's go. There's not enough action in this play." Of course she was right, but perhaps that wasn't quite the point. There are persons of intelligence and susceptibility who prefer Verdi to Wagner, Charlotte Brontë to Jane Austen and cold mutton to cold grouse. Mrs. Wharton was devoid of frailty. Her taste was faultless. She admired only what was admirable. But such is the frowardness of human nature (of mine at all events), in the end I began to grow a trifle restive. It would have been a comfort to me if I could have found a chink in the shining armour of her impeccable refinement, if she had unaccountably expressed a sneaking tenderness for something that was downright vulgar; if, for instance, she had admitted to a secret passion for Marie Lloyd, or, though it had not yet burst on an enraptured world, had confided in me that she went to the

Victoria Palace every night to hear *The Lambeth Walk*. But no. She said nothing but the right thing about the right person. The worst of it was that I could not but agree with everything she said. I could not bring myself to affirm that I thought Maillol boring and André Gide silly. She said about everyone that she so lightly touched upon, for there was nothing pedantic in her discourse, precisely what I thought myself and what every right-minded person should think. I cannot imagine anything more exasperating.

At last I said to her: "And what do you think of Edgar Wallace?"

"Who is Edgar Wallace?" she replied.

"Do you never read thrillers?" I asked.

"No."

Never has a monosyllable contained more frigid displeasure, more shocked disapproval nor more wounded surprise. I will not say she blenched, for she was a woman of the world and she knew instinctively how to deal with a solecism, but her eyes wandered away and a little forced smile slightly curled her lips. The moment was embarrassing for both of us. Her manner was that of a woman to whom a man has made proposals offensive to her modesty, but which her good breeding tells her it will be more dignified to ignore than to make a scene about.

"I'm afraid it's getting very late," said Mrs. Wharton.

I knew that my audience was at an end. I never saw her again. She was an admirable creature, but not my cup of tea.

MR. HARRINGTON'S WASHING

WHEN Ashenden went on deck and saw before him a low-lying coast and a white town he felt a pleasant flutter of excitement. It was early and the sun had not long risen, but the sea was glassy and the sky was blue; it was warm already and one knew that the day would be sweltering. Vladivostok. It really gave one the sensation of being at the end of the world. It was a long journey that Ashenden had made from New York to San Francisco, across the Pacific in a Japanese boat to Yokohama, then from Tsuruki in a Russian boat, he the only Englishman on board, up the Sea of Japan. From Vladivostok he was to take the Trans-Siberian to Petrograd. It was the most important mission that he had ever

had and he was pleased with the sense of responsibility that it gave him. He had no one to give him orders, unlimited funds (he carried in a belt next to his skin bills of exchange for a sum so enormous that he was staggered when he thought of them), and though he had been sent to do something that was beyond human possibility he did not know this and was prepared to set about his task with confidence. He believed in his own astuteness. Though he had both esteem and admiration for the sensibility of the human race he had little respect for their intelligence: man has always found it easier to sacrifice his life than to learn the multiplication table.

Ashenden did not much look forward to ten days on a Russian train and in Yokohama he had heard rumours that in one or two places bridges had been blown up and the line cut. He was told that the soldiers, completely out of hand, would rob him of everything he possessed and turn him out on the steppe to shift for himself. It was a cheerful prospect. But the train was certainly starting and whatever happened later (and Ashenden had always a feeling that things never turned out as badly as you expected) he was determined to get a place on it. His intention on landing was to go at once to the British Consulate and find out what arrangements had been made for him; but as they neared the shore and he was able to discern the untidy and bedraggled town he felt not a little forlorn. He knew but a few words of Russian. The only man on the ship who spoke English was the purser and though he promised Ashenden to do anything he could to help him Ashenden had the impression that he must not too greatly count upon him. It was a relief then, when they docked, to have a young man, small and with a mop of untidy hair, obviously a Jew, come up to him and ask if his name was Ashenden.

"Mine is Benedict. I'm the interpreter at the British Consulate. I've been told to look after you. We've got you a place on the train to-night."

Ashenden's spirits went up. They landed. The little Jew looked after his luggage and had his passport examined and then, getting into a car that waited for them, they drove off to the Consulate.

"I've had instructions to offer you every facility," said the Consul, "and you've only got to tell me what you want. I've fixed you up all right on the train, but God knows if you'll ever get to Petrograd. Oh, by the way, I've got a travelling companion for you. He's a man called Harrington, an American, and he's going to Petrograd for a firm in Philadelphia. He's trying to fix up some deal with the Provisional Government."

"What's he like?" asked Ashenden.

"Oh, he's all right. I wanted him to come with the American Consul to luncheon, but they've gone for an excursion in the country. You must get to the station a couple of hours before the train starts. There's always an awful scrimmage and if you're not there in good time someone will pinch your seat."

The train started at midnight and Ashenden dined with Benedict at the station restaurant which was, it appeared, the only place in that slatternly town where you could get a decent meal. It was crowded. The service was intolerably slow. Then they went on to the platform, where, though they had still two hours to spare, there was already a seething mob. Whole families, sitting on piles of luggage, seemed to be camped there. People rushed to and fro, or stood in little groups violently arguing. Women screamed. Others were silently weeping. Here two men were engaged in a fierce quarrel. It was a scene of indescribable confusion. The light in the station was wan and cold and the white faces of all those people were like the white faces of the dead waiting, patient or anxious, distraught or penitent, for the judgment of the last day. The train was made up and most of the carriages were already filled to overflowing. When at last Benedict found that in which Ashenden had his place a man sprang out of it excitedly.

"Come in and sit down," he said. "I've had the greatest difficulty in keeping your seat. A fellow wanted to come in here with a wife and two children. My Consul has just gone off with him to see the station-master."

"This is Mr. Harrington," said Benedict.

Ashenden stepped into the carriage. It had two berths in it. The porter stowed his luggage away. He shook hands with his travelling companion.

Mr. John Quincy Harrington was a very thin man of somewhat less than middle height, he had a yellow, bony face, with large, pale-blue eyes and when he took off his hat to wipe his brow wet from the perturbation he had endured he showed a large, bald skull; it was very bony and the ridges and protuberances stood out disconcertingly. He wore a bowler hat, a black coat and waistcoat, and a pair of striped trousers; a very high white collar and a neat, unobtrusive tie. Ashenden did not know precisely how you should dress in order to take a ten days' journey across Siberia, but he could not but think that Mr. Harrington's costume was eccentric. He spoke with precision in a high-pitched voice and in an accent that Ashenden recognized as that of New England.

In a minute the station-master came accompanied by a bearded Russian, suffering evidently from profound emotion, and followed by a lady holding two children by the hand. The Russian, tears running down his face, was talking with quivering lips to the station-master and his wife between sobs was apparently telling him the story of her life. When they arrived at the carriage the altercation became more violent and Benedict joined in with his fluent Russian. Mr. Harrington did not know a word of the language, but being obviously of an excitable turn broke in and explained in voluble English that these seats had been booked by the Consuls of Great Britain and the United States respectively, and though he didn't know about the King of England, he could tell them straight and they could take it from him that the President of the United States would never permit an American citizen to be done out of a seat on the train that he had duly paid for. He would yield to force, but to nothing else, and if they touched him he would register a complaint with the Consul at once. He said all this and a great deal more to the station-master, who of course had no notion what he was talking about, but with much emphasis and a good deal of gesticulation made him in reply a passionate speech. This roused Mr. Harrington to the utmost pitch of indignation, for shaking his fist in the station-master's face, his own pale with fury, he cried out:

"Tell him I don't understand a word he says and I don't want to understand. If the Russians want us to look upon them as a civilized people why don't they talk a civilized language? Tell him that I am Mr. John Quincy Harrington and I'm travelling on behalf of Messrs Crewe and Adams of Philadelphia with a special letter of introduction to Mr. Kerensky and if I'm not left in peaceful possession of this carriage, Mr. Crewe will take the matter up with the Administration in Washington."

Mr. Harrington's manner was so truculent and his gestures so menacing that the station-master, throwing up the sponge, turned on his heel without another word and walked moodily away. He was followed by the bearded Russian and his wife arguing heatedly with him and the two apathetic children. Mr. Harrington jumped back into the carriage.

"I'm terribly sorry to have to refuse to give up my seat to a lady with two children," he said. "No one knows better than I the respect due to a woman and a mother, but I've got to get to Petrograd by this train if I don't want to lose a very important order and I'm not going to spend ten days in a corridor for all the mothers in Russia."

"I don't blame you," said Ashenden. "I am a married man and I have two children myself. I know that travelling with your family is a difficult matter, but there's nothing that I know to prevent you from staying at home."

When you are shut up with a man for ten days in a railway carriage you can hardly fail to learn most of what there is to know about him, and for ten days (for eleven to be exact) Ashenden spent twenty-four hours a day with Mr. Harrington. It is true that they went into the dining-room three times a day for their meals, but they sat opposite to one another; it is true that the train stopped for an hour morning and afternoon so that they were able to have a tramp up and down the platform, but they walked side by side. Ashenden made acquaintance with some of his fellow-travellers and sometimes they came into the compartment to have a chat, but if they only spoke French or German Mr. Harrington would watch them with acidulous disapproval and if they spoke English he would never let them get a word in. For Mr. Harrington was a talker. He talked as though it were a natural function of the human being, automatically, as men breathe or digest their food; he talked not because he had something to say, but because he could not help himself, in a high-pitched, nasal voice, without inflection, at one dead level of tone. He talked with precision, using a copious vocabulary and forming his sentences with deliberation; he never used a short word when a longer one

would do; he never paused. He went on and on. It was not a torrent, for there was nothing impetuous about it, it was like a stream of lava pouring irresistibly down the side of a volcano. It flowed with a quiet and steady force that overwhelmed everything that was in its path.

Ashenden thought he had never known as much about anyone as he knew about Mr. Harrington, and not only about him, with all his opinions, habits and circumstances, but about his wife and his wife's family, his children and their schoolfellows, his employers and the alliances they had made for three or four generations with the best families of Philadelphia. His own family had come from Devonshire early in the eighteenth century and Mr. Harrington had been to the village where the graves of his forebears were still to be seen in the churchyard. He was proud of his English ancestry, but proud too of his American birth, though to him America was a little strip of land along the Atlantic coast and Americans were a small number of persons of English or Dutch origin whose blood had never been sullied by foreign admixture. He looked upon the Germans, Swedes, Irish and the inhabitants of Central and Eastern Europe who for the last hundred years have descended upon the United States as interlopers. He turned his attention away from them as a maiden lady who lived in a secluded manor might avert her eyes from the factory chimneys that had trespassed upon her retirement.

When Ashenden mentioned a man of vast wealth who owned some of the finest pictures in America Mr. Harrington said:

"I've never met him. My great-aunt Maria Penn Warmington always said his grandmother was a very good cook.

My great-aunt Maria was terribly sorry when she left her to get married. She said she never knew anyone who could make an apple pancake as she could."

Mr. Harrington was devoted to his wife and he told Ashenden at unbelievable length how cultivated and what a perfect mother she was. She had delicate health and had undergone a great number of operations all of which he described in detail. He had had two operations himself, one on his tonsils and one to remove his appendix and he took Ashenden day by day through his experiences. All his friends had had operations and his knowledge of surgery was encyclopædic. He had two sons, both at school, and he was seriously considering whether he would not be well-advised to have them operated on. It was curious that one of them should have enlarged tonsils, and he was not at all happy about the appendix of the other. They were more devoted to one another than he had ever seen two brothers be and a very good friend of his, the brightest surgeon in Philadelphia, had offered to operate on them both together so that they should not be separated. He showed Ashenden photographs of the boys and their mother. This journey of his to Russia was the first time in their lives that he had been separated from them and every morning he wrote a long letter to his wife telling her everything that had happened and a good deal of what he had said during the day. Ashenden watched him cover sheet after sheet of paper with his neat, legible and precise handwriting.

Mr. Harrington had read all the books on conversation and knew its technique to the last detail. He had a little book in which he noted down the stories he heard and he told Ashenden that when he was going out to dinner he always looked up half a dozen so that he should not be at a loss. They were marked with a G if they could be told in general society and with an M (for men) if they were more fit for rough masculine ears. He was a specialist in that peculiar form of anecdote that consists in narrating a long serious incident, piling detail upon detail, till a comic end is reached. He spared you nothing and Ashenden foreseeing the point long before it arrived would clench his hands and knit his brows in the strenuous effort not to betray his impatience and at last force from his unwilling mouth a grim and hollow laugh. If someone came into the compartment in the middle Mr. Harrington would greet him with cordiality.

"Come right in and sit down. I was just telling my friend a story. You must listen to it, it's one of the funniest things you ever heard."

Then he would begin again from the very beginning and repeat it word for word, without altering a single apt epithet, till he reached the humorous end. Ashenden suggested once that they should see whether they could find two people on the train who played cards so that they might while away the time with a game of bridge, but Mr. Harrington said he never touched cards and when Ashenden in desperation began to play patience he pulled a wry face.

"It beats me how an intelligent man can waste his time card playing, and of all the unintellectual pursuits I have ever seen it seems to me that solitaire is the worst. It kills conversation. Man is a social animal and he exercises the highest part of his nature when he takes part in social intercourse."

"There is a certain elegance in wasting time," said Ashenden. "Any fool can waste money, but when you waste time you waste what is priceless. Besides," he added with bitterness, "you can still talk."

"How can I talk when your attention is taken up by whether you are going to get a black seven to put on a red eight? Conversation calls forth the highest powers of the intellect and if you have made a study of it you have the right to expect that the person you're talking to will give you the fullest attention he is capable of."

He did not say this acrimoniously, but with the good-humoured patience of a man who has been much tried. He was just stating a plain fact and Ashenden could take it or leave it. It was the claim of the artist to have his work taken seriously.

Mr. Harrington was a diligent reader. He read pencil in hand, underlining passages that attracted his attention and on the margin making in his neat writing comments on what he read. This he was fond of discussing and when Ashenden himself was reading and felt on a sudden that Mr. Harrington, book in one hand and pencil in the other, was looking at him with his large pale eyes he began to have violent palpitations of the heart. He dared not look up, he dared not even turn the page, for he knew that Mr. Harrington would regard this as ample excuse to break into a discourse, but remained with his eyes fixed desperately on a single word, like a chicken with its beak to a chalk line, and only ventured to breathe when he realized that Mr. Harrington, having given up the attempt, had resumed his reading. He was then engaged on a History of the American Constitution in two volumes and for recreation was perusing a stout volume that purported to contain all the great speeches of the world. For Mr. Harrington was an after-dinner speaker and had read all the best books on

speaking in public. He knew exactly how to get on good terms with his audience, just where to put in the serious words that touched their hearts, how to catch their attention by a few apt stories and finally with what degree of eloquence, suiting the occasion, to deliver his peroration.

Mr. Harrington was very fond of reading aloud. Ashenden had had frequent occasion to observe the distressing propensity of Americans for this pastime. In hotel drawing-rooms at night after dinner he had often seen the father of a family seated in a retired corner and surrounded by his wife, his two sons and his daughter, reading to them. On ships crossing the Atlantic he had sometimes watched with awe the tall, spare gentleman of commanding aspect who sat in the centre of fifteen ladies no longer in their first youth and in a resonant voice read to them the history of Art. Walking up and down the promenade deck he had passed honeymooning couples lying on deck-chairs and caught the unhurried tones of the bride as she read to her young husband the pages of a popular novel. It had always seemed to him a curious way of showing affection. He had had friends who had offered to read to him and he had known women who had said they loved being read to, but he had always politely refused the invitation and firmly ignored the hint. He liked neither reading aloud nor being read aloud to. In his heart he thought the national predilection for this form of entertainment the only flaw in the perfection of the American character. But the immortal gods love a good laugh at the expense of human beings and now delivered him, bound and helpless, to the knife of the high priest. Mr. Harrington flattered himself that he was a very good reader and he explained to Ashenden the theory and practice of the art. Ashenden learned that there were two schools, the dramatic and the natural: in the first you imitated the voices of those who spoke (if you were reading a novel) and when the heroine wailed you wailed and when emotion choked her you choked too; but in the other you read as impassively as though you were reading the price-list of a mail-order house in Chicago. This was the school Mr. Harrington belonged to. In the seventeen years of his married life he had read aloud to his wife, and to his sons as soon as they were old enough to appreciate them, the novels of Sir Walter Scott, Jane Austen, Dickens, the Brontë Sisters, Thackeray, George Eliot, Nathaniel Hawthorne and W. J. Howells. Ashenden came to the conclusion that it was second nature with Mr. Harrington to read aloud and to prevent him from doing so made him as uneasy as cutting off his tobacco made the confirmed smoker. He would take you unawares.

"Listen to this," he would say, "you must listen to this," as though he were suddenly struck by the excellence of a maxim or the neatness of a phrase. "Now just tell me if you don't think this is remarkably well put. It's only three lines."

He read them and Ashenden was willing to give him a moment's attention, but having finished them, without pausing for a moment to take breath, he went on. He went right on. On and on. In his measured high-pitched voice, without emphasis or expression, he read page after page. Ashenden fidgeted, crossed and uncrossed his legs, lit cigarettes and smoked them, sat first in one position, then in another. Mr. Harrington went on and on. The train went leisurely through the interminable steppes of Siberia. They passed villages and crossed rivers. Mr. Harrington went

on and on. When he finished a great speech by Edmund Burke he put down the book in triumph.

"Now that in my opinion is one of the finest orations in the English language. It is certainly a part of our common heritage that we can look upon with genuine pride."

"Doesn't it seem to you a little ominous that the people to whom Edmund Burke made that speech are all dead?" asked Ashenden gloomily.

Mr. Harrington was about to reply that this was hardly to be wondered at since the speech was made in the eighteenth century when it dawned upon him that Ashenden (bearing up wonderfully under affliction as any unprejudiced person could not fail to admit) was making a joke. He slapped his knee and laughed heartily.

"Gee, that's a good one," he said. "I'll write that down in my little book. I see exactly how I can bring it in one time when I have to speak at our luncheon club."

Mr. Harrington was a highbrow; but that appellation, invented by the vulgar as a term of abuse, he had accepted like the instrument of a saint's martyrdom, the gridiron of Saint Laurence for instance or the wheel of Saint Catherine, as an honorific title. He gloried in it.

"Emerson was a highbrow," he said. "Longfellow was a highbrow. Oliver Wendell Holmes was a highbrow. James Russell Lowell was a highbrow."

Mr. Harrington's study of American literature had taken him no further down the years than the period during which those eminent, but not precisely thrilling, authors flourished.

Mr. Harrington was a bore. He exasperated Ashenden, and enraged him; he got on his nerves, and drove him to frenzy. But Ashenden did not dislike him. His self-satisfaction was enormous but so ingenuous that you could not resent it; his conceit was so child-like that you could only smile at it. He was so well-meaning, so thought-ful, so deferential, so polite that though Ashenden would willingly have killed him he could not but own that in that short while he had con-ceived for Mr. Harrington something very like affection. His manners were exquisite, formal, a trifle elaborate per-haps (there is no harm in that, for good manners are the product of an artificial state of society and so can bear a touch of the powdered wig and the lace ruffle) but though natural to his good breeding they gained a pleasant significance from his good heart. He was ready to do anyone a kindness and seemed to find nothing too much trouble if he could thereby oblige his fellow man. He was emi-nently *serviable*. And it may be that this is a word for which there is no exact translation because the charm-ing quality it denotes is not very com-mon among our practical people. When Ashenden was ill for a couple of days Mr. Harrington nursed him with devotion. Ashenden was embar-rassed by the care he took of him and though racked with pain could not help laughing at the fussy attention with which Mr. Harrington took his temperature, from his neatly packed valise extracted a whole regiment of tabloids and firmly doctored him; and he was touched by the trouble he gave himself to get from the dining-car the things that he thought Ashenden could eat. He did everything in the world for him but stop talking.

It was only when he was dressing that Mr. Harrington was silent, for then his maidenly mind was singly occupied with the problem of chang-ing his clothes before Ashenden with-out indelicacy. He was extremely mod-est. He changed his linen every day,

neatly taking it out of his suit-case and neatly putting back what was soiled; but he performed miracles of dexterity in order during the process not to show an inch of bare skin. After a day or two Ashenden gave up the struggle to keep neat and clean in that dirty train, with one lavatory for the whole carriage, and soon was as grubby as the rest of the passengers; but Mr. Harrington refused to yield to the difficulties. He performed his toilet with deliberation, notwithstand-ing the impatient persons who rattled the door-handle, and returned from the lavatory every morning washed, shining and smelling of soap. Once dressed, in his black coat, striped trou-sers and well-polished shoes, he looked as spruce as though he had just stepped out of his tidy little red-brick house in Philadelphia and was about to board the street-car that would take him down town to his office. At one point of the journey it was announced that an attempt had been made to blow up a bridge and that there were disturbances at the next station over the river; it might be that the train would be stopped and the passengers turned adrift or taken prisoners. Ash-enden, thinking he might be separated from his luggage, took the precaution to change into his thickest clothes so that if he had to pass the winter in Siberia he need suffer as little as neces-sary from the cold; but Mr. Harring-ton would not listen to reason; he made no preparations for the possible experience and Ashenden had the con-viction that if he spent three months in a Russian prison he would still preserve that smart and natty appear-ance. A troop of Cossacks boarded the train and stood on the platform of each carriage with their guns loaded, and the train rattled gingerly over the damaged bridge; then they came to the station at which they had been warned of danger, put on steam and dashed straight through it. Mr. Harrington was mildly satirical when Ashenden changed back into a light summer suit.

Mr. Harrington was a keen business man. It was obvious that it would need someone very astute to over-reach him and Ashenden was sure that his employers had been well-advised to send him on this errand. He would safeguard their interests with all his might and if he succeeded in driving a bargain with the Russians it would be a hard one. His loyalty to his firm demanded that. He spoke of the partners with affectionate reverence. He loved them and was proud of them; but he did not envy them because their wealth was great. He was quite content to work on a salary and thought himself adequately paid; so long as he could educate his boys and leave his widow enough to live on what was money to him? He thought it a trifle vulgar to be rich. He looked upon culture as more important than money. He was careful of it and after every meal put down in his note-book exactly what it had cost him. His firm might be certain that he would not charge a penny more for his expenses than he had spent. But having discovered that poor people came to the station at the stopping places of the train to beg and seeing that the war had really brought them to destitution he took care before each halt to supply himself with ample small change and in a shame-faced way, mocking himself for being taken in by such impostors, distributed everything in his pocket.

"Of course I know they don't deserve it," he said, "and I don't do it for them. I do it entirely for my own peace of mind. I should feel so terribly badly if I thought some man really was hungry and I'd refused to give him the price of a meal."

Mr. Harrington was absurd, but lovable. It was inconceivable that anyone should be rude to him, it would have seemed as dreadful as hitting a child; and Ashenden, chafing inwardly but with a pretence of amiability, suffered meekly and with a truly Christian spirit the affliction of the gentle, ruthless creature's society. It took eleven days at that time to get from Vladivostok to Petrograd and Ashenden felt that he could not have borne another day. If it had been twelve he would have killed Mr. Harrington.

When at last (Ashenden tired and dirty, Mr. Harrington neat, sprightly and sententious) they reached the outskirts of Petrograd and stood at the window looking at the crowded houses of the city, Mr. Harrington turned to Ashenden and said:

"Well, I never would have thought that eleven days in the train would pass so quickly. We've had a wonderful time. I've enjoyed your company and I know you've enjoyed mine. I'm not going to pretend I don't know that I'm a pretty good conversationalist. But now we've come together like this we must take care to stay together. We must see as much of one another as we can while I'm in Petrograd."

"I shall have a great deal to do," said Ashenden. "I'm afraid my time won't be altogether my own."

"I know," answered Mr. Harrington cordially. "I expect to be pretty busy myself, but we can have breakfast together anyway and we'll meet in the evening and compare notes. It would be too bad if we drifted apart now."

"Too bad," sighed Ashenden.

When Ashenden found himself alone in his bedroom for the first time, he sat down and looked about him. It had seemed an age. He had not the energy to start immediately to unpack.

How many of these hotel bedrooms had he known since the beginning of the war, grand or shabby, in one place and one land after another! It seemed to him that he had been living in his luggage for as long as he could remember. He was weary. He asked himself how he was going to set about the work that he had been sent to do. He felt lost in the immensity of Russia and very solitary. He had protested when he was chosen for this mission, it looked too large an order, but his protests were ignored. He was chosen not because those in authority thought him particularly suited for the job, but because there was no one to be found who was more suited. There was a knock at the door and Ashenden, pleased to make use of the few words of the language he knew, called out in Russian. The door was opened. He sprang to his feet.

"Come in, come in," he cried. "I'm awfully glad to see you."

Three men entered. He knew them by sight, since they had travelled on the same boat with him from San Francisco to Yokohama, but following their instructions no communications had passed between them and Ashenden. They were Czechs, exiled from their country for their revolutionary activity and long settled in America, who had been sent over to Russia to help Ashenden in his mission and put him in touch with Professor Z. whose authority over the Czechs in Russia was absolute. Their chief was a certain Dr. Egon Orth, a tall thin man, with a little grey head; he was minister to some church in the Middle West and a doctor of divinity; but had abandoned his cure to work for the liberation of his country, and Ashenden had the impression that he was an intelligent fellow who would not put too fine a point on matters of conscience. A parson with a fixed idea has this advantage over common men that he can persuade himself of the Almighty's approval for almost any goings on. Dr. Orth had a merry twinkle in his eye and a dry humour.

Ashenden had had two secret interviews with him in Yokohama and had learnt that Professor Z., though eager to free his country from the Austrian rule and since he knew that this could only come about by the downfall of the Central Powers with the allies body and soul, yet had scruples; he would not do things that outraged his conscience, all must be straightforward and above board, and so some things that it was necessary to do had to be done without his knowledge. His influence was so great that his wishes could not be disregarded, but on occasion it was felt better not to let him know too much of what was going on.

Dr. Orth had arrived in Petrograd a week before Ashenden and now put before him what he had learned of the situation. It seemed to Ashenden that it was critical and if anything was to be done it must be done quickly. The army was dissatisfied and mutinous, the Government under the weak Kerensky was tottering and held power only because no one else had the courage to seize it, famine was staring the country in the face and already the possibility had to be considered that the Germans would march on Petrograd. The ambassadors of Great Britain and the United States had been apprised of Ashenden's coming, but his mission was secret even from them, and there were particular reasons why he could demand no assistance from them. He arranged with Dr. Orth to make an appointment with Professor Z. so that he could learn his views and explain to him that he had the financial means to support any scheme that seemed likely to prevent the catastrophe that the Allied governments foresaw of Russia's making a separate peace. But he had to get in touch with influential persons in all classes. Mr. Harrington with his business proposition and his letters to Ministers of State would be thrown in contact with members of the Government and Mr. Harrington wanted an interpreter. Dr. Orth spoke Russian almost as well as his own language and it struck Ashenden that he would be admirably suited to the post. He explained the circumstances to him and it was arranged that while Ashenden and Mr. Harrington were at luncheon Dr. Orth should come in, greeting Ashenden as though he had not seen him before, and be introduced to Mr. Harrington; then Ashenden, guiding the conversation, would suggest to Mr. Harrington that the heavens had sent in Dr. Orth the ideal man for his purpose.

But there was another person on whom Ashenden had fixed as possibly useful to him and now he said:

"Have you ever heard of a woman called Anastasia Alexandrovna Leonidov? She's the daughter of Alexander Denisiev."

"I know all about him of course."

"I have reason to believe she's in Petrograd. Will you find out where she lives and what she's doing."

"Certainly."

Dr. Orth spoke in Czech to one of the two men who accompanied him. They were sharp-looking fellows both of them, one was tall and fair and the other was short and dark, but they were younger than Dr. Orth and Ashenden understood that they were there to do as he bade them. The man nodded, got up, shook hands with Ashenden and went out.

"You shall have all the information possible this afternoon."

"Well, I think there's nothing more we can do for the present," said Ashenden. "To tell you the truth I haven't had a bath for eleven days and I badly want one."

Ashenden had never quite made up his mind whether the pleasure of reflection was better pursued in a railway carriage or in a bath. So far as the act of invention was concerned he was inclined to prefer a train that went smoothly and not too fast, and many of his best ideas had come to him when he was thus traversing the plains of France; but for the delight of reminiscence or the entertainment of embroidery upon a theme already in his head he had no doubt that nothing could compare with a hot bath. He considered now, wallowing in soapy water like a water-buffalo in a muddy pond, the grim pleasantry of his relations with Anastasia Alexandrovna Leonidov.

In these stories no more than the barest suggestion has been made that Ashenden was capable on occasions of the passion ironically called tender. The specialists in this matter, those charming creatures who make a business of what philosophers know is but a diversion, assert that writers, painters and musicians, all in short who are connected with the arts, in the relation of love cut no very conspicuous figure. There is much cry but little wool. They rave or sigh, make phrases and strike many a romantic attitude, but in the end, loving art or themselves (which with them is one and the same thing) better than the object of their emotion offer a shadow when the said object, with the practical common sense of the sex, demands a substance. It may be so and this may be the reason (never before suggested) why women in their souls look upon art with such a virulent hatred. Be this as it may Ashenden in the last twenty years had felt his heart go pit-a-pat because of one charming person after another. He had had a good deal of fun and had paid for it with a great deal of misery, but even when suffering most acutely from the pangs of unrequited love he had been able to say to himself, albeit with a wry face, after all, it's grist to the mill. Anastasia Alexandrovna Leonidov was the daughter of a revolutionary who had escaped from Siberia after being sentenced to penal servitude for life and had settled in England. He was an able man and had supported himself for thirty years by the activity of a restless pen and had even made himself a distinguished position in English letters. When Anastasia Alexandrovna reached a suitable age she married Vladimir Semenovich Leonidov, also an exile from his native country, and it was after she had been married to him for some years that Ashenden made her acquaintance. It was at the time when Europe discovered Russia. Everyone was reading the Russian novelists, the Russian dancers captivated the civilized world, and the Russian composers set shivering the sensibility of persons who were beginning to want a change from Wagner. Russian art seized upon Europe with the virulence of an epidemic of influenza. New phrases became the fashion, new colours, new emotions, and the highbrows described themselves without a moment's hesitation as members of the intelligentsia. It was a difficult word to spell but an easy one to say. Ashenden fell like the rest, changed the cushions of his sitting-room, hung an eikon on the wall, read Chekov and went to the ballet. Anastasia Alexandrovna was by birth, circumstances and education very much a member of the intelli-

gentsia. She lived with her husband in a tiny house near Regent's Park and here all the literary folk in London might gaze with humble reverence at pale-faced bearded giants who leaned against the wall like caryatids taking a day off; they were revolutionaries to a man and it was a miracle that they were not in the mines of Siberia. Women of letters tremulously put their lips to a glass of vodka. If you were lucky and greatly favoured you might shake hands there with Diaghileff and now and again, like a peach-blossom wafted by the breeze, Pavlova herself hovered in and out. At this time Ashenden's success had not been so great as to affront the highbrows, he had very distinctly been one of them in his youth, and though some already looked askance, others (optimistic creatures with a faith in human nature) still had hopes of him. Anastasia Alexandrovna told him to his face that he was a member of the intelligentsia. Ashenden was quite ready to believe it. He was in a state when he was ready to believe anything. He was thrilled and excited. It seemed to him that at last he was about to capture that illusive spirit of romance that he had so long been chasing. Anastasia Alexandrovna had fine eyes and a good, though for these days, too voluptuous figure, high cheek bones and a snub nose (this was very Tartar), a wide mouth full of large square teeth and a pale skin. She dressed somewhat flamboyantly. In her dark melancholy eyes Ashenden saw the boundless steppes of Russia, and the Kremlin with its pealing bells, and the solemn ceremonies of Easter at St. Isaac's, and forests of silver beeches and the Nevsky Prospekt; it was astonishing how much he saw in her eyes. They were round and shining and slightly protuberant like those of a Pekinese. They talked together of Alyosha in the *Brothers Karamazov*, of Natasha in *War and Peace*, of Anna Karenina and of *Fathers and Sons*.

Ashenden soon discovered that her husband was quite unworthy of her and presently learned that she shared his opinion. Vladimir Semenovich was a little man with a large, long head that looked as though it had been pulled like a piece of liquorice, and he had a great shock of unruly Russian hair. He was a gentle, unobtrusive creature and it was hard to believe that the Czarist government had really feared his revolutionary activities. He taught Russian and wrote for papers in Moscow. He was amiable and obliging. He needed these qualities for Anastasia Alexandrovna was a woman of character: when she had a toothache Vladimir Semenovich suffered the agonies of the damned and when her heart was wrung by the suffering of her unhappy country Vladimir Semenovich might well have wished he had never been born. Ashenden could not help admitting that he was a poor thing, but he was so harmless that he conceived quite a liking for him, and when in due course he had disclosed his passion to Anastasia Alexandrovna and to his joy found it was returned he was puzzled to know what to do about Vladimir Semenovich. Neither Anastasia Alexandrovna nor he felt that they could live another minute out of one another's pockets, and Ashenden feared that with her revolutionary views and all that she would never consent to marry him; but somewhat to his surprise, and very much to his relief, she accepted the suggestion with alacrity.

"Would Vladimir Semenovich let himself be divorced, do you think?" he asked, as he sat on the sofa, leaning against cushions the colour of which

reminded him of raw meat just gone bad, and held her hand.

"Vladimir adores me," she answered. "It'll break his heart."

"He's a nice fellow, I shouldn't like him to be very unhappy. I hope he'll get over it."

"He'll never get over it. That is the Russian spirit. I know that when I leave him he'll feel that he has lost everything that made life worth living for him. I've never known anyone so wrapped up in a woman as he is in me. But of course he wouldn't want to stand in the way of my happiness. He's far too great for that. He'll see that when it's a question of my own self-development I haven't the right to hesitate. Vladimir will give me my freedom without question."

At that time the divorce law in England was even more complicated and absurd than it is now and in case she was not acquainted with its peculiarities Ashenden explained to Anastasia Alexandrovna the difficulties of the case. She put her hand gently on his.

"Vladimir would never expose me to the vulgar notoriety of the divorce court. When I tell him that I have decided to marry you he will commit suicide."

"That would be terrible," said Ashenden.

He was startled, but thrilled. It was really very much like a Russian novel and he saw the moving and terrible pages, pages and pages, in which Dostoievsky would have described the situation. He knew the lacerations his characters would have suffered, the broken bottles of champagne, the visits to the gipsies, the vodka, the swoonings, the catalepsy and the long, long speeches everyone would have made. It was all very dreadful and wonderful and shattering.

"It would make us horribly unhappy," said Anastasia Alexandrovna, "but I don't know what else he could do. I couldn't ask him to live without me. He would be like a ship without a rudder or a car without a carburettor. I know Vladimir so well. He will commit suicide."

"How?" asked Ashenden, who had the realist's passion for the exact detail.

"He will blow his brains out."

Ashenden remembered *Rosmerholm*. In his day he had been an ardent Ibsenite and had even flirted with the notion of learning Norwegian so that he might, by reading the master in the original, get at the secret essence of his thought. He had once seen Ibsen in the flesh drink a glass of Munich beer.

"But do you think we could ever pass another easy hour if we had the death of that man on our conscience?" he asked. "I have a feeling that he would always be between us."

"I know we shall suffer, we shall suffer dreadfully," said Anastasia Alexandrovna, "but how can we help it? Life is like that. We must think of Vladimir. There is his happiness to be considered too. He will prefer to commit suicide."

She turned her face away and Ashenden saw that the heavy tears were coursing down her cheeks. He was much moved. For he had a soft heart and it was dreadful to think of poor Vladimir lying there with a bullet in his brain.

These Russians, what fun they have!

But when Anastasia Alexandrovna had mastered her emotion she turned to him gravely. She looked at him with her humid, round and slightly protuberant eyes.

"We must be quite sure that we're doing the right thing," she said. "I should never forgive myself if I'd allowed Vladimir to commit suicide and then found I'd made a mistake. I think we ought to make sure that we really love one another."

"But don't you know?" exclaimed Ashenden in a low, tense voice. "I know."

"Let's go over to Paris for a week and see how we get on. Then we shall know."

Ashenden was a trifle conventional and the suggestion took him by surprise. But only for a moment. Anastasia was wonderful. She was very quick and she saw the hesitation that for an instant troubled him.

"Surely you have no bourgeois prejudices?" she said.

"Of course not," he assured her hurriedly, for he would much sooner have been thought knavish than bourgeois, "I think it's a splendid idea."

"Why should a woman hazard her whole life on a throw? It's impossible to know what a man is really like till you've lived with him. It's only fair to give her the opportunity to change her mind before it's too late."

"Quite so," said Ashenden.

Anastasia Alexandrovna was not a woman to let the grass grow under her feet and so having made their arrangements forthwith on the following Saturday they started for Paris.

"I shall not tell Vladimir that I am going with you," she said. "It would only distress him."

"It would be a pity to do that," said Ashenden.

"And if at the end of the week I come to the conclusion that we've made a mistake he need never know anything about it."

"Quite so," said Ashenden.

They met at Victoria station.

"What class have you got?" she asked him.

"First."

"I'm glad of that. Father and Vladimir travel third on account of their principles, but I always feel sick on a train and I like to be able to lean my head on somebody's shoulder. It's easier in a first-class carriage."

When the train started Anastasia Alexandrovna said she felt dizzy, so she took off her hat and leaned her head on Ashenden's shoulder. He put his arm round her waist.

"Keep quite still, won't you?" she said.

When they got on to the boat she went down to the ladies' cabin and at Calais was able to eat a very hearty meal, but when they got into the train she took off her hat again and rested her head on Ashenden's shoulder. He thought he would like to read and took up a book.

"Do you mind not reading?" she said. "I have to be held and when you turn the pages it makes me feel all funny."

Finally they reached Paris and went to a little hotel on the Left Bank that Anastasia Alexandrovna knew of. She said it had atmosphere. She could not bear those great big grand hotels on the other side; they were hopelessly vulgar and bourgeois.

"I'll go anywhere you like," said Ashenden, "as long as there's a bathroom."

She smiled and pinched his cheek.

"How adorably English you are. Can't you do without a bathroom for a week? My dear, my dear, you have so much to learn."

They talked far into the night about Maxim Gorki and Karl Marx, human destiny, love and the brotherhood of man; and drank innumerable cups of Russian tea, so that in the morning Ashenden would willingly have breakfasted in bed and got up for luncheon; but Anastasia Alexandrovna was an early riser. When

life was so short and there was so much to do it was a sinful thing to have breakfast a minute after half-past eight. They sat down in a dingy little dining-room the windows of which showed no signs of having been opened for a month. It was full of atmosphere. Ashenden asked Anastasia Alexandrovna what she would have for breakfast.

"Scrambled eggs," she said.

She ate heartily. Ashenden had already noticed that she had a healthy appetite. He supposed it was a Russian trait: you could not picture Anna Karenina making her midday meal off a bath-bun and a cup of coffee, could you?

After breakfast they went to the Louvre and in the afternoon they went to the Luxembourg. They dined early in order to go to the Comédie Française; then they went to a Russian cabaret where they danced. When next morning at eight-thirty they took their places in the dining-room and Ashenden asked Anastasia Alexandrovna what she fancied, her reply was:

"Scrambled eggs."

"But we had scrambled eggs yesterday," he expostulated.

"Let's have them again to-day," she smiled.

"All right."

They spent the day in the same manner except that they went to the Carnavalet instead of the Louvre and the Musée Guimet instead of the Luxembourg. But when the morning after in answer to Ashenden's enquiry Anastasia Alexandrovna again asked for scrambled eggs, his heart sank.

"But we had scrambled eggs yesterday and the day before," he said.

"Don't you think that's a very good reason to have them again to-day?"

"No, I don't."

"Is it possible that your sense of

humour is a little deficient this morning?" she asked. "I eat scrambled eggs every day. It's the only way I like them."

"Oh, very well. In that case of course we'll have scrambled eggs."

But the following morning he could not face them.

"Will you have scrambled eggs as usual?" he asked her.

"Of course," she smiled affectionately, showing him two rows of large square teeth.

"All right, I'll order them for you, I shall have mine fried."

The smile vanished from her lips.

"Oh?" She paused a moment. "Don't you think that's rather inconsiderate? Do you think it's fair to give the cook unnecessary work? You English, you're all the same, you look upon servants as machines. Does it occur to you that they have hearts like yours, the same feelings and the same emotions? How can you be surprised that the proletariat are seething with discontent when the bourgeoisie like you are so monstrously selfish?"

"Do you really think that there'll be a revolution in England if I have my eggs in Paris fried rather than scrambled?"

She tossed her pretty head in indignation.

"You don't understand. It's the principle of the thing. You think it's a jest, of course I know you're being funny, I can laugh at a joke as well as anyone, Chekov was well-known in Russia as a humorist; but don't you see what is involved? Your whole attitude is wrong. It's a lack of feeling. You wouldn't talk like that if you had been through the events of 1905 in Petersburg. When I think of the crowds in front of the Winter Palace kneeling in the snow while the Cossacks charged them, women and children! No, no, no."

Her eyes filled with tears and her face was all twisted with pain. She took Ashenden's hand.

"I know you have a good heart. It was just thoughtless on your part and we won't say anything more about it. You have imagination. You're very sensitive. I know. You'll have your eggs done in the same way as mine, won't you?"

"Of course," said Ashenden.

He ate scrambled eggs for breakfast every morning after that. The waiter said: *"Monsieur aime les œufs brouillés."* At the end of the week they returned to London. He held Anastasia Alexandrovna in his arms, her head resting on his shoulder, from Paris to Calais and again from Dover to London. He reflected that the journey from New York to San Francisco took five days. When they arrived at Victoria and stood on the platform waiting for a cab she looked at him with her round, shining and slightly protuberant eyes.

"We've had a wonderful time, haven't we?" she said.

"Wonderful."

"I've quite made up my mind. The experiment has justified itself. I'm willing to marry you whenever you like."

But Ashenden saw himself eating scrambled eggs every morning for the rest of his life. When he had put her in a cab, he called another for himself, went to the Cunard office and took a berth on the first ship that was going to America. No immigrant, eager for freedom and a new life, ever looked upon the statue of Liberty with more heartfelt thankfulness than did Ashenden, when on that bright and sunny morning his ship steamed into the harbour of New York.

Some years had passed since then and Ashenden had not seen Anastasia Alexandrovna again. He knew that on the outbreak of the revolution in March she and Vladimir Semenovich had gone to Russia. It might be that they would be able to help him, in a way Vladimir Semenovich owed him his life, and he made up his mind to write to Anastasia Alexandrovna to ask if he might come to see her.

When Ashenden went down to lunch he felt somewhat rested. Mr. Harrington was waiting for him and they sat down. They ate what was put before them.

"Ask the waiter to bring us some bread," said Mr. Harrington.

"Bread?" replied Ashenden. "There's no bread."

"I can't eat without bread," said Mr. Harrington.

"I'm afraid you'll have to. There's no bread, no butter, no sugar, no eggs, no potatoes. There's fish and meat and green vegetables, and that's all."

Mr. Harrington's jaw dropped.

"But this is war," he said.

"It looks very much like it."

Mr. Harrington was for a moment speechless; then he said: "I'll tell you what I'm going to do, I'm going to get through with my business as quick as I can and then I'm going to get out of this country. I'm sure Mrs. Harrington wouldn't like me to go without sugar or butter. I've got a very delicate stomach. The firm would never have sent me here if they'd thought I wasn't going to have the best of everything."

In a little while Dr. Egon Orth came in and gave Ashenden an envelope. On it was written Anastasia Alexandrovna's address. He introduced him to Mr. Harrington. It was soon clear that he was pleased with Dr. Egon Orth and so without further to do he suggested that here was the perfect interpreter for him.

"He talks Russian like a Russian. But he's an American citizen so that he won't do you down. I've known him a considerable time and I can assure you that he's absolutely trustworthy."

Mr. Harrington was pleased with the notion and after luncheon Ashenden left them to settle the matter by themselves. He wrote a note to Anastasia Alexandrovna and presently received an answer to say that she was going to a meeting, but would look in at his hotel about seven. He awaited her with apprehension. Of course he knew now that he had not loved her, but Tolstoi and Dostoievsky, Rimsky-Korsakoff, Stravinsky and Bakst; but he was not quite sure if the point had occurred to her. When between eight and half-past she arrived he suggested that she should join Mr. Harrington and him at dinner. The presence of a third party, he thought, would prevent any awkwardness their meeting might have; but he need not have had any anxiety, for five minutes after they had sat down to a plate of soup it was borne in upon him that the feelings of Anastasia Alexandrovna towards him were as cool as were his towards her. It gave him a momentary shock. It is very hard for a man, however modest, to grasp the possibility that a woman who has once loved him may love him no longer, and though of course he did not imagine that Anastasia Alexandrovna had languished for five years with a hopeless passion for him, he did think that by a heightening of colour, a flutter of the eyelashes, or a quiver of the lips she would betray the fact that she had still a soft place in her heart for him. Not at all. She talked to him as though he were a friend she was very glad to see again after an absence of a few days, but whose intimacy with her was purely social. He asked after Vladimir Semenovich.

"He has been a disappointment to me," she said. "I never thought he was a clever man, but I thought he was an honest one. He's going to have a baby."

Mr. Harrington who was about to put a piece of fish into his mouth, stopped, his fork in the air, and stared at Anastasia Alexandrovna with astonishment. In extenuation it must be explained that he had never read a Russian novel in his life. Ashenden, slightly perplexed too, gave her a questioning look.

"I'm not the mother," she said with a laugh. "I am not interested in that sort of thing. The mother is a friend of mine and a well-known writer on Political Economy. I do not think her views are sound, but I should be the last to deny that they deserve consideration. She has a good brain, quite a good brain." She turned to Mr. Harrington. "Are you interested in Political Economy?"

For once in his life Mr. Harrington was speechless. Anastasia Alexandrovna gave them her views on the subject and they began to speak on the situation in Russia. She seemed to be on intimate terms with the leaders of the various political parties and Ashenden made up his mind to sound her on the possibility of her working with him. His infatuation had not blinded him to the fact that she was an extremely intelligent woman. After dinner he told Mr. Harrington that he wished to talk business with Anastasia Alexandrovna and took her to a retired corner of the lounge. He told her all he thought necessary and found her interested and anxious to help. She had a passion for intrigue and a desire for power. When he hinted that he had command of large sums of money she saw at once that through him she might acquire an influence in the affairs of Russia. It tickled her

vanity. She was immensely patriotic, but like many patriots she had an impression that her own aggrandisement tended to the good of her country. When they parted they had come to a working agreement.

"That was a very remarkable woman," said Mr. Harrington next morning when they met at breakfast.

"Don't fall in love with her," smiled Ashenden.

This, however, was not a matter on which Mr. Harrington was prepared to jest.

"I have never looked at a woman since I married Mrs. Harrington," he said. "That husband of hers must be a bad man."

"I could do with a plate of scrambled eggs," said Ashenden, irrelevantly, for their breakfast consisted of a cup of tea without milk and a little jam instead of sugar.

With Anastasia Alexandrovna to help him and Dr. Orth in the background, Ashenden set to work. Things in Russia were going from bad to worse. Kerensky, the head of the Provisional Government, was devoured by vanity and dismissed any minister who gave evidence of a capacity that might endanger his own position. He made speeches. He made endless speeches. At one moment there was a possibility that the Germans would make a dash for Petrograd. Kerensky made speeches. The food shortage grew more serious, the winter was approaching and there was no fuel. Kerensky made speeches. In the background the Bolsheviks were active, Lenin was hiding in Petrograd, it was said that Kerensky knew where he was, but dared not arrest him. He made speeches.

It amused Ashenden to see the unconcern with which Mr. Harrington wandered through this turmoil. History was in the making and Mr. Harrington minded his own business. It was uphill work. He was made to pay bribes to secretaries and underlings under the pretence that the ear of great men would be granted to him. He was kept waiting for hours in antechambers and then sent away without ceremony. When at last he saw the great men he found they had nothing to give him but idle words. They made him promises and in a day or two he discovered that the promises meant nothing. Ashenden advised him to throw in his hand and return to America; but Mr. Harrington would not hear of it; his firm had sent him to do a particular job, and by gum, he was going to do it or perish in the attempt. Then Anastasia Alexandrovna took him in hand. A singular friendship had arisen between the pair. Mr. Harrington thought her a very remarkable and deeply wronged woman; he told her all about his wife and his two sons, he told her all about the Constitution of the United States; she on her side told him all about Vladimir Semenovich, and she told him about Tolstoi, Turgeniev and Dostoievski. They had great times together. He said he couldn't manage to call her Anastasia Alexandrovna, it was too much of a mouthful; so he called her Delilah. And now she placed her inexhaustible energy at his service and they went together to the persons who might be useful to him. But things were coming to a head. Riots broke out and the streets were growing dangerous. Now and then armoured cars filled with discontented reservists careered wildly along the Nevsky Prospekt and in order to show that they were not happy took pot-shots at the passers-by. On one occasion when Mr. Harrington and Anastasia Alexandrovna were in a tram together shots peppered the windows and they had

to lie down on the floor for safety. Mr. Harrington was highly indignant.

"An old fat woman was lying right on top of me and when I wriggled to get out Delilah caught me a clip on the side of the head and said, stop still, you fool. I don't like your Russian ways, Delilah."

"Anyhow you stopped still," she giggled.

"What you want in this country is a little less art and a little more civilization."

"You are bourgeoisie, Mr. Harrington, you are not a member of the intelligentsia."

"You are the first person who's ever said that, Delilah. If I'm not a member of the intelligentsia I don't know who is," retorted Mr. Harrington with dignity.

Then one day when Ashenden was working in his room there was a knock at the door and Anastasia Alexandrovna stalked in followed, somewhat sheepishly, by Mr. Harrington. Ashenden saw that she was excited.

"What's the matter?" he asked.

"Unless this man goes back to America he'll get killed. You really must talk to him. If I hadn't been there something very unpleasant might have happened to him."

"Not at all, Delilah," said Mr. Harrington, with asperity. "I'm perfectly capable of taking care of myself and I wasn't in the smallest danger."

"What is it all about?" asked Ashenden.

"I'd taken Mr. Harrington to the Lavra of Alexander Nevsky to see Dostoievski's grave," said Anastasia Alexandrovna, "and on our way back we saw a soldier being rather rough with an old woman."

"Rather rough!" cried Mr. Harrington. "There was an old woman walking along the side-walk with a basket of provisions on her arm. Two soldiers came up behind her and one of them snatched the basket from her and walked off with it. She burst out screaming and crying, I don't know what she was saying, but I can guess, and the other soldier took his gun and with the butt-end of it hit her over the head. Isn't that right, Delilah?"

"Yes," she answered, unable to help smiling. "And before I could prevent it Mr. Harrington jumped out of the cab and ran up to the soldier who had the basket, wrenched it from him and began to abuse the pair of them like pickpockets. At first they were so taken aback they didn't know what to do and then they got in a rage. I ran after Mr. Harrington and explained to them that he was a foreigner and drunk."

"Drunk?" cried Mr. Harrington.

"Yes, drunk. Of course a crowd collected. It looked as though it wasn't going to be very nice."

Mr. Harrington smiled with those large, pale-blue eyes of his.

"It sounded to me as though you were giving them a piece of your mind, Delilah. It was as good as a play to watch you."

"Don't be stupid, Mr. Harrington," cried Anastasia, in a sudden fury, stamping her foot. "Don't you know that those soldiers might very easily have killed you and me too, and not one of the bystanders would have raised a finger to help us?"

"Me? I'm an American citizen, Delilah. They wouldn't dare touch a hair of my head."

"They'd have difficulty in finding one," said Anastasia Alexandrovna, who when she was in a temper had no manners. "But if you think Russian soldiers are going to hesitate to kill you because you're an American citizen you'll get a big surprise one of these days."

"Well, what happened to the old woman?" asked Ashenden.

"The soldiers went off after a little and we went back to her."

"Still with the basket?"

"Yes. Mr. Harrington clung on to that like grim death. She was lying on the ground with the blood pouring from her head. We got her into the cab and when she could speak enough to tell us where she lived we drove her home. She was bleeding dreadfully and we had some difficulty in staunching the blood."

Anastasia Alexandrovna gave Mr. Harrington an odd look and to his surprise Ashenden saw him turn scarlet.

"What's the matter now?"

"You see, we had nothing to bind her up with. Mr. Harrington's handkerchief was soaked. There was only one thing about me that I could get off quickly and so I took off my . . ."

But before she could finish Mr. Harrington interrupted her.

"You need not tell Mr. Ashenden what you took off. I'm a married man and I know ladies wear them, but I see no need to refer to them in general society."

Anastasia Alexandrovna giggled.

"Then you must kiss me, Mr. Harrington. If you don't I shall say."

Mr. Harrington hesitated a moment, considering evidently the pros and cons of the matter, but he saw that Anastasia Alexandrovna was determined.

"Go on then, you may kiss me, Delilah, though I'm bound to say I don't see what pleasure it can be to you."

She put her arms round his neck and kissed him on both cheeks, then without a word of warning burst into a flood of tears.

"You're a brave little man, Mr. Harrington. You're absurd but magnificent," she sobbed.

Mr. Harrington was less surprised than Ashenden would have expected him to be. He looked at Anastasia with a thin, quizzical smile and gently patted her.

"Come, come, Delilah, pull yourself together. It gave you a nasty turn, didn't it? You're quite upset. I shall have terrible rheumatism in my shoulder if you go on weeping all over it."

The scene was ridiculous and touching, Ashenden laughed, but he had the beginnings of a lump in his throat.

When Anastasia Alexandrovna had left them Mr. Harrington sat in a brown study.

"They're very queer, these Russians. Do you know what Delilah did?" he said, suddenly. "She stood up in the cab, in the middle of the street, with people passing on both sides, and took her pants off. She tore them in two and gave me one to hold while she made a bandage of the other. I was never so embarrassed in my life."

"Tell me what gave you the idea of calling her Delilah?" smiled Ashenden.

Mr. Harrington reddened a little.

"She's a very fascinating woman, Mr. Ashenden. She's been deeply wronged by her husband and I naturally felt a great deal of sympathy for her. These Russians are very emotional people and I did not want her to mistake my sympathy for anything else. I told her I was very much attached to Mrs. Harrington."

"You're not under the impression that Delilah was Potiphar's wife?" asked Ashenden.

"I don't know what you mean by that, Mr. Ashenden," replied Mr. Harrington. "Mrs. Harrington has always given me to understand that I'm very fascinating to women, and I thought if I called our little friend Delilah it would make my position quite clear."

"I don't think Russia's any place for you, Mr. Harrington," said Ashenden smiling. "If I were you I'd get out of it as quick as I could."

"I can't go now. I've got them to agree to my terms at last and we're going to sign next week. Then I shall pack my grip and go."

"I wonder if your signatures will be worth the paper they're written on," said Ashenden.

He had at length devised a plan of campaign. It took him twenty-four hours' hard work to code a telegram in which he put his scheme before the persons who had sent him to Petrograd. It was accepted and he was promised all the money he needed. Ashenden knew he could do nothing unless the Provisional Government remained in power for another three months; but winter was at hand and food was getting scarcer every day. The army was mutinous. The people clamoured for peace. Every evening at the Europe Ashenden drank a cup of chocolate with Professor Z. and discussed with him how best to make use of his devoted Czechs. Anastasia Alexandrovna had a flat in a retired spot and here he had meetings with all manner of persons. Plans were drawn up. Measures were taken. Ashenden argued, persuaded, promised. He had to overcome the vacillation of one and wrestle with the fatalism of another. He had to judge who was resolute and who was self-sufficient, who was honest and who was infirm of purpose. He had to curb his impatience with the Russian verbosity; he had to be good-tempered with people who were willing to talk of everything but the matter in hand; he had to listen sympathetically to ranting and rhodomontade. He had to beware of treachery. He had to humour the vanity of fools and elude the greed of the ambitious. Time was pressing. The rumours grew hot and many of the activities of the Bolsheviks. Kerensky ran hither and thither like a frightened hen.

Then the blow fell. On the night of November 7th, 1917, the Bolsheviks rose, Kerensky's ministers were arrested and the Winter Palace was sacked by the mob; the reins of power were seized by Lenin and Trotsky. Anastasia Alexandrovna came to Ashenden's room at the hotel early in the morning. Ashenden was coding a telegram. He had been up all night, first at the Smolny, and then at the Winter Palace. He was tired out. Her face was white and her shining brown eyes were tragic.

"Have you heard?" she asked Ashenden.

He nodded.

"It's all over then. They say Kerensky has fled. They never even showed fight." Rage seized her. "The buffoon!" she screamed.

At that moment there was a knock at the door and Anastasia Alexandrovna looked at it with sudden apprehension.

"You know the Bolsheviks have got a list of people they've decided to execute. My name is on it, and it may be that yours is too."

"If it's they and they want to come in they only have to turn the handle," said Ashenden, smiling, but with ever so slightly odd a feeling at the pit of his stomach. "Come in."

The door was opened and Mr. Harrington stepped into the room. He was as dapper as ever, in his short black coat and striped trousers, his shoes neatly polished and a derby on his bald head. He took it off when he saw Anastasia Alexandrovna.

"Oh, fancy finding you here so early. I looked in on my way out, I wanted to tell you my news. I tried to find you yesterday evening, but

couldn't. You didn't come in to dinner."

"No, I was at a meeting," said Ashenden.

"You must both congratulate me, I got my signatures yesterday, and my business is done."

Mr. Harrington beamed on them, the picture of self-satisfaction, and he arched himself like a bantam-cock who has chased away all rivals. Anastasia Alexandrovna burst into a sudden shriek of hysterical laughter. He stared at her in perplexity.

"Why, Delilah, what is the matter?" he said.

Anastasia laughed till the tears ran from her eyes and then began to sob in earnest. Ashenden explained.

"The Bolsheviks have overthrown the Government. Kerensky's ministers are in prison. The Bolsheviks are out to kill. Delilah says her name is on the list. Your minister signed your documents yesterday because he knew it did not matter what he did then. Your contracts are worth nothing. The Bolsheviks are going to make peace with Germany as soon as they can."

Anastasia Alexandrovna had recovered her self-control as quickly as she had lost it.

"You had better get out of Russia as soon as you can, Mr. Harrington. It's no place for a foreigner now and it may be that in a few days you won't be able to."

Mr. Harrington looked from one to the other.

"O my," he said. "O my!" It seemed inadequate. "Are you going to tell me that that Russian minister was just making a fool of me?"

Ashenden shrugged his shoulders. "How can one tell what he was thinking of? He may have a keen sense of humour and perhaps he thought it funny to sign a fifty million dollar contract yesterday when there was every chance of his being stood against the wall and shot to-day. Anastasia Alexandrovna's right, Mr. Harrington, you'd better take the first train that'll get you to Sweden."

"And what about you?"

"There's nothing for me to do here any more. I'm cabling for instructions and I shall go as soon as I get leave. The Bolsheviks have got in ahead of us and the people I was working with will have their work cut out to save their lives."

"Boris Petrovich was shot this morning," said Anastasia Alexandrovna with a frown.

They both looked at Mr. Harrington and he stared at the floor. His pride in this achievement of his was shattered and he sagged like a pricked balloon. But in a minute he looked up. He gave Anastasia Alexandrovna a little smile and for the first time Ashenden noticed how attractive and kindly his smile was. There was something peculiarly disarming about it.

"If the Bolsheviks are after you, Delilah, don't you think you'd better come with me? I'll take care of you and if you like to come to America I'm sure Mrs. Harrington would be glad to do anything she could for you."

"I can see Mrs. Harrington's face if you arrived in Philadelphia with a Russian refugee," laughed Anastasia Alexandrovna. "I'm afraid it would need more explaining than you could ever manage. No, I shall stay here."

"But if you're in danger?"

"I'm a Russian. My place is here. I will not leave my country when most my country needs me."

"That is the bunk, Delilah," said Mr. Harrington very quietly.

Anastasia Alexandrovna had spoken with deep emotion, but now with a little start she shot a sudden quizzical look at him.

"I know it is, Samson," she answered. "To tell you the truth I think we're all going to have a hell of a time, God knows what's going to happen, but I want to see; I wouldn't miss a minute of it for the world."

Mr. Harrington shook his head.

"Curiosity is the bane of your sex, Delilah," he said.

"Go along and do your packing, Mr. Harrington," said Ashenden, smiling, "and then we'll take you to the station. The train will be besieged."

"Very well, I'll go. And I shan't be sorry either. I haven't had a decent meal since I came here and I've done a thing I never thought I should have to do in my life, I've drunk my coffee without sugar and when I've been lucky enough to get a little piece of black bread I've had to eat it without butter. Mrs. Harrington will never believe me when I tell her what I've gone through. What this country wants is organization."

When he left them Ashenden and Anastasia Alexandrovna talked over the situation. Ashenden was depressed because all his careful schemes had come to nothing, but Anastasia Alexandrovna was excited and she hazarded every sort of guess about the outcome of this new revolution. She pretended to be very serious, but in her heart she looked upon it all very much as a thrilling play. She wanted more and more things to happen. Then there was another knock at the door and before Ashenden could answer Mr. Harrington burst in.

"Really the service at this hotel is a scandal," he cried heatedly, "I've been ringing my bell for fifteen minutes and I can't get anyone to pay the smallest attention to me."

"Service?" exclaimed Anastasia Alexandrovna. "There is not a servant left in the hotel."

"But I want my washing. They

promised to let me have it back last night."

"I'm afraid you haven't got much chance of getting it now," said Ashenden.

"I'm not going to leave without my washing. Four shirts, two union suits, a pair of pyjamas, and four collars. I wash my handkerchiefs and socks in my room. I want my washing and I'm not going to leave this hotel without it."

"Don't be a fool," cried Ashenden. "What you've got to do is to get out of here while the going's good. If there are no servants to get it you'll just have to leave your washing behind you."

"Pardon me, sir, I shall do nothing of the kind. I'll go and fetch it myself. I've suffered enough at the hands of this country and I'm not going to leave four perfectly good shirts to be worn by a lot of dirty Bolsheviks. No, sir. I do not leave Russia till I have my washing."

Anastasia Alexandrovna stared at the floor for a moment; then with a little smile looked up. It seemed to Ashenden that there was something in her that responded to Mr. Harrington's futile obstinacy. In her Russian way she understood that Mr. Harrington could not leave Petrograd without his washing. His insistence had given it the value of a symbol.

"I'll go downstairs and see if I can find anybody about who knows where the laundry is and if I can, I'll go with you and you can bring your washing away with you."

Mr. Harrington unbent. He answered with that sweet and disarming smile of his.

"That's terribly kind of you, Delilah. I don't mind if it's ready or not, I'll take it just as it is."

Anastasia Alexandrovna left them.

"Well, what do you think of Russia and the Russians now?" Mr. Harring-

ton asked Ashenden.

"I'm fed up with them. I'm fed up with Tolstoi, I'm fed up with Turgeniev and Dostoievski, I'm fed up with Chekov. I'm fed up with the Intelligentsia. I hanker after people who know their mind from one minute to another, who mean what they say an hour after they've said it, whose word you can rely on; I'm sick of fine phrases, and oratory and attitudinizing."

Ashenden, bitten by the prevailing ill, was about to make a speech when he was interrupted by a rattle as of peas on a drum. In the city, so strangely silent, it sounded abrupt and odd.

"What's that?" asked Mr. Harrington.

"Rifle firing. On the other side of the river I should think."

Mr. Harrington gave a funny little look. He laughed, but his face was a trifle pale; he did not like it, and Ashenden did not blame him.

"I think it's high time I got out. I shouldn't so much mind for myself, but I've got a wife and children to think of. I haven't had a letter from Mrs. Harrington for so long I'm a bit worried." He paused an instant. "I'd like you to know Mrs. Harrington, she's a very wonderful woman. She's the best wife a man ever had. Until I came here I'd not been separated from her for more than three days since we were married."

Anastasia Alexandrovna came back and told them that she had found the address.

"It's about forty minutes' walk from here and if you'll come now I'll go with you," she said.

"I'm ready."

"You'd better look out," said Ashenden. "I don't believe the streets are very healthy to-day."

Anastasia Alexandrovna looked at Mr. Harrington.

"I must have my washing, Delilah," he said. "I should never rest in peace if I left it behind me and Mrs. Harrington would never let me hear the last of it."

"Come on then."

They set out and Ashenden went on with the dreary business of translating into a very complicated code the shattering news he had to give. It was a long message, and then he had to ask for instructions upon his own movements. It was a mechanical job and yet it was one in which you could not allow your attention to wander. The mistake of a single figure might make a whole sentence incomprehensible.

Suddenly his door was burst open and Anastasia Alexandrovna flung into the room. She had lost her hat and was dishevelled. She was panting. Her eyes were starting out of her head and she was obviously in a state of great excitement.

"Where's Mr. Harrington?" she cried. "Isn't he here?"

"No."

"Is he in his bedroom?"

"I don't know. Why, what's the matter? We'll go and look if you like. Why didn't you bring him along with you?"

They walked down the passage and knocked at Mr. Harrington's door; there was no answer; they tried the handle; the door was locked.

"He's not there."

They went back to Ashenden's room. Anastasia Alexandrovna sank into a chair.

"Give me a glass of water, will you. I'm out of breath. I've been running."

She drank the water Ashenden poured out for her. She gave a sudden sob.

"I hope he's all right. I should never forgive myself if he was hurt. I was hoping he would have got here before me. He got his washing all right. We found the place. There was only an old woman there and they didn't want to let us take it, but we insisted. Mr. Harrington was furious because it hadn't been touched. It was exactly as he had sent it. They'd promised it last night and it was still in the bundle that Mr. Harrington had made himself. I said that was Russia and Mr. Harrington said he preferred coloured people. I'd led him by side streets because I thought it was better, and we started to come back again. We passed at the top of a street and at the bottom of it I saw a little crowd. There was a man addressing them.

"'Let's go and hear what he's saying,' I said.

"I could see they were arguing. It looked exciting. I wanted to know what was happening.

"'Come along, Delilah,' he said. 'Let us mind our own business.'

"'You go back to the hotel and do your packing. I'm going to see the fun,' I said.

"I ran down the street and he followed me. There were about two or three hundred people there and a student was addressing them. There were some working men and they were shouting at him. I love a row and I edged my way into the crowd. Suddenly we heard the sound of shots and before you could realize what was happening two armoured cars came dashing down the street. There were soldiers in them and they were firing as they went. I don't know why. For fun, I suppose, or because they were drunk. We all scattered like a lot of rabbits. We just ran for our lives. I lost Mr. Harrington. I can't make out why he isn't here. Do you think something has happened to him?"

Ashenden was silent for a while. "We'd better go out and look for him," he said. "I don't know why the devil he couldn't leave his washing." "I understand, I understand so well." "That's a comfort," said Ashenden irritably. "Let's go."

He put on his hat and coat, and they walked downstairs. The hotel seemed strangely empty. They went out into the street. There was hardly anyone to be seen. They walked along. The trams were not running and the silence in the great city was uncanny. The shops were closed. It was quite startling when a motor car dashed by at breakneck speed. The people they passed looked frightened and downcast. When they had to go through a main thoroughfare they hastened their steps. A lot of people were there and they stood about irresolutely as though they did not know what to do next. Reservists in their shabby grey were walking down the middle of the roadway in little bunches. They did not speak. They looked like sheep looking for their shepherd. Then they came to the street down which Anastasia Alexandrovna had run, but they entered it from the opposite end. A number of windows had been broken by the wild shooting. It was quite empty. You could see where the people had scattered, for strewn about were articles they had dropped in their haste, books, a man's hat, a lady's bag and a basket. Anastasia Alexandrovna touched Ashenden's arm to draw his attention: sitting on the pavement, her head bent right down to her lap, was a woman and she was dead. A little way on two men had fallen together. They were dead too. The wounded, one supposed, had managed to drag themselves away or their friends had carried them. Then they found Mr. Harrington. His derby had rolled in the gutter. He lay on his face, in a pool of blood, his bald head, with its prominent bones, very white; his neat black coat smeared and muddy. But his hand was clenched tight on the parcel that contained four shirts, two union suits, a pair of pyjamas and four collars. Mr. Harrington had not let his washing go.

THE BOOK-BAG

SOME people read for instruction, which is praiseworthy, and some for pleasure, which is innocent, but not a few read from habit, and I suppose that this is neither innocent nor praiseworthy. Of that lamentable company am I. Conversation after a time bores me, games tire me and my own thoughts, which we are told are the unfailing resource of a sensible man, have a tendency to run dry. Then I fly to my book as the opium-smoker to his pipe. I would sooner read the catalogue of the Army and Navy Stores or Bradshaw's Guide than nothing at all, and indeed I have spent many delightful hours over both these works. At one time I never went out without a second-hand bookseller's list in my pocket. I know no reading more fruity. Of course to read in this way is as reprehensible as doping, and I never cease to wonder at the impertinence of great readers who, because they are such, look down on the illiterate. From the standpoint of what eternity is it better to have read a thousand books than to have ploughed a million furrows? Let us admit that reading with us is just a drug that we cannot do without—who of this band does not know the restlessness that attacks him when he has been severed from reading too long, the apprehension and irritability, and the sigh of relief which the sight of a printed page extracts from him?—and so let us be no more vainglorious than the poor slaves of the hypodermic needle or the pint-pot.

And like the dope-fiend who cannot move from place to place without taking with him a plentiful supply of his deadly balm I never venture far without a sufficiency of reading matter. Books are so necessary to me that when in a railway train I have become aware that fellow-travellers have come away without a single one I have been seized with a veritable dismay. But when I am starting on a long journey the problem is formidable. I have learnt my lesson. Once, imprisoned by illness for three months in a hill-town in Java, I came to the end of all the books I had brought with me, and knowing no Dutch was obliged to buy the school-books from which intelligent Javanese, I suppose, acquired knowledge of French and German. So I read again after five and twenty years the frigid plays of Goethe, the fables of La Fontaine and the tragedies of the tender and exact Racine. I have the greatest admiration for Racine, but I admit that to read his plays one after the other requires a certain effort in a person who is suffering from colitis. Since then I have made a point of travelling with the largest sack made for carrying soiled linen and filling it to the brim with books to suit every possible occasion

and every mood. It weighs a ton and strong porters reel under its weight. Customhouse officials look at it askance, but recoil from it with consternation when I give them my word that it contains nothing but books. Its inconvenience is that the particular work I suddenly hanker to read is always at the bottom and it is impossible for me to get it without emptying the book-bag's entire contents upon the floor. Except for this, however, I should perhaps never have heard the singular history of Olive Hardy.

I was wandering about Malaya, staying here and there, a week or two if there was a rest-house or a hotel, and a day or so if I was obliged to inflict myself on a planter or a District Officer whose hospitality I had no wish to abuse; and at the moment I happened to be at Penang. It is a pleasant little town, with a hotel that has always seemed to me very agreeable, but the stranger finds little to do there and time hung a trifle heavily on my hands. One morning I received a letter from a man I knew only by name. This was Mark Featherstone. He was Acting Resident, in the absence on leave of the Resident, at a place called Tenggarah. There was a sultan there and it appeared that a water festival of some sort was to take place which Featherstone thought would interest me. He said that he would be glad if I would come and stay with him for a few days. I wired to tell him that I should be delighted and next day took the train to Tenggarah. Featherstone met me at the station. He was a man of about thirty-five, I should think, tall and handsome, with fine eyes and a strong, stern face. He had a wiry black moustache and bushy eyebrows. He looked more like a soldier than a government official. He was very smart in white ducks, with a white topi, and he wore his clothes with elegance. He was a little shy, which seemed odd in a strapping fellow of resolute mien, but I surmised that this was only because he was unused to the society of that strange fish, a writer, and I hoped in a little to put him at his ease.

"My boys'll look after your barang," he said. "We'll go down to the club. Give them your keys and they'll unpack before we get back."

I told him that I had a good deal of luggage and thought it better to leave everything at the station but what I particularly wanted. He would not hear of it.

"It doesn't matter a bit. It'll be safer at my house. It's always better to have one's barang with one."

"All right."

I gave my keys and the ticket for my trunk and my book-bag to a Chinese boy who stood at my host's elbow. Outside the station a car was waiting for us and we stepped in.

"Do you play bridge?" asked Featherstone.

"I do."

"I thought most writers didn't."

"They don't," I said. "It's generally considered among authors a sign of deficient intelligence to play cards."

The club was a bungalow, pleasing but unpretentious; it had a large reading-room, a billiard-room with one table, and a small card-room. When we arrived it was empty but for one or two persons reading the English weeklies, and we walked through to the tennis courts where a couple of sets were being played. A number of people were sitting on the verandah, looking on, smoking and sipping long drinks. I was introduced to one or two of them. But the light was failing and soon the players could hardly see the ball. Featherstone asked one of the men I had been introduced to if he

would like a rubber. He said he would. Featherstone looked about for a fourth. He caught sight of a man sitting a little by himself, paused for a second, and went up to him. The two exchanged a few words and then came towards us. We strolled in to the card-room. We had a very nice game. I did not pay much attention to the two men who made up the four. They stood me drinks, and I, a temporary member of the club, returned the compliment. The drinks were very small, quarter whiskies, and in the two hours we played each of us was able to show his open-handedness without an excessive consumption of alcohol. When the advancing hour suggested that the next rubber must be the last we changed from whisky to gin pahits. The rubber came to an end. Featherstone called for the book and the winnings and losings of each one of us were set down. One of the men got up.

"Well, I must be going," he said.

"Going back to the Estate?" asked Featherstone.

"Yes," he nodded. He turned to me. "Shall you be here to-morrow?"

"I hope so."

He went out of the room.

"I'll collect my mem and get along home to dinner," said the other.

"We might be going too," said Featherstone.

"I'm ready whenever you are," I replied.

We got into the car and drove to his house. It was a longish drive. In the darkness I could see nothing much, but presently I realized that we were going up a rather steep hill. We reached the Residency.

It had been an evening like any other, pleasant, but not at all exciting, and I had spent I don't know how many just like it. I did not expect it to leave any sort of impression on me.

Featherstone led me into his sitting-room. It looked comfortable, but it was a trifle ordinary. It had large basket arm-chairs covered with cretonne and on the walls were a great many framed photographs; the tables were littered with papers, magazines and official reports, with pipes, yellow tins of straight-cut cigarettes and pink tins of tobacco. In a row of shelves were untidily stacked a good many books, their bindings stained with damp and the ravages of white ants. Featherstone showed me my room and left me with the words:

"Shall you be ready for a gin pahit in ten minutes?"

"Easily," I said.

I had a bath and changed and went downstairs. Featherstone, ready before me, mixed our drinks as he heard me clatter down the wooden staircase. We dined. We talked. The festival which I had been invited to see was the next day but one, but Featherstone told me he had arranged for me before that to be received by the Sultan.

"He's a jolly old boy," he said. "And the palace is a sight for sore eyes."

After dinner we talked a little more, Featherstone put on the gramophone, and we looked at the latest illustrated papers that had arrived from England. Then we went to bed. Featherstone came to my room to see that I had everything I wanted.

"I suppose you haven't any books with you," he said. "I haven't got a thing to read."

"Books?" I cried.

I pointed to my book-bag. It stood upright, bulging oddly, so that it looked like a humpbacked gnome somewhat the worse for liquor.

"Have you got books in there? I thought that was your dirty linen or a camp-bed or something. Is there anything you can lend me?"

"Look for yourself."

Featherstone's boys had unlocked the bag, but quailing before the sight that then discovered itself had done no more. I knew from long experience how to unpack it. I threw it over on its side, seized its leather bottom and, walking backwards, dragged the sack away from its contents. A river of books poured on to the floor. A look of stupefaction came upon Featherstone's face.

"You don't mean to say you travel with as many books as that? By George, what a snip."

He bent down and turning them over rapidly looked at the titles. There were books of all kinds. Volumes of verse, novels, philosophical works, critical studies (they say books about books are profitless, but they certainly make very pleasant reading), biographies, history; there were books to read when you were ill and books to read when your brain, all alert, craved for something to grapple with, there were books that you had always wanted to read, but in the hurry of life at home had never found time to, there were books to read at sea when you were meandering through narrow waters on a tramp steamer, and there were books for bad weather when your whole cabin creaked and you had to wedge yourself in your bunk in order not to fall out; there were books chosen solely for their length, which you took with you when on some expedition you had to travel light, and there were the books you could read when you could read nothing else. Finally Featherstone picked out a life of Byron that had recently appeared.

"Hullo, what's this?" he said. "I read a review of it some time ago."

"I believe it's very good," I replied. "I haven't read it yet."

"May I take it? It'll do me for to-night at all events."

"Of course. Take anything you like."

"No, that's enough. Well, good-night. Breakfast at eight-thirty."

When I came down next morning the head boy told me that Feather-stone, who had been at work since six, would be in shortly. While I waited for him I glanced at his shelves.

"I see you've got a grand library of books on bridge," I remarked as we sat down to breakfast.

"Yes, I get every one that comes out. I'm very keen on it."

"That fellow we were playing with yesterday plays a good game."

"Which? Hardy?"

"I don't know. Not the one who said he was going to collect his wife. The other."

"Yes, that was Hardy. That was why I asked him to play. He doesn't come to the club very often."

"I hope he will to-night."

"I wouldn't bank on it. He has an estate about thirty miles away. It's a longish ride to come just for a rubber of bridge."

"Is he married?"

"No. Well, yes. But his wife is in England."

"It must be awfully lonely for those men who live by themselves on those estates," I said.

"Oh, he's not so badly off as some. I don't think he much cares about seeing people. I think he'd be just as lonely in London."

There was something in the way Featherstone spoke that struck me as a little strange. His voice had what I can only describe as a shuttered tone. He seemed suddenly to have moved away from me. It was as though one were passing along a street at night and paused for a second to look in at a lighted window that showed a comfortable room and suddenly an in-visible hand pulled down a blind. His eyes, which habitually met those of the person he was talking to with frankness, now avoided mine and I had a notion that it was not only my fancy that read in his face an expression of pain. It was drawn for a moment as it might be by a twinge of neuralgia. I could not think of anything to say and Featherstone did not speak. I was conscious that his thoughts, withdrawn from me and what we were about, were turned upon a subject unknown to me. Pres-ently he gave a little sigh, very slight, but unmistakable, and seemed with a deliberate effort to pull himself to-gether.

"I'm going down to the office im-mediately after breakfast," he said. "What are you going to do with your-self?"

"Oh, don't bother about me. I shall slack around. I'll stroll down and look at the town."

"There's not much to see."

"All the better. I'm fed up with sights."

I found that Featherstone's veran-dah gave me sufficient entertainment for the morning. It had one of the most enchanting views I had seen in the F.M.S. The Residency was built on the top of a hill and the garden was large and well-cared for. Great trees gave it almost the look of an English park. It had vast lawns and there Tamils, black and emaciated, were scything with deliberate and beautiful gestures. Beyond and below, the jungle grew thickly to the bank of a broad, winding and swiftly flowing river, and on the other side of this, as far as the eye could reach, stretched the wooded hills of Tenggarah. The contrast between the trim lawns, so strangely English, and the savage growth of the jungle beyond pleas-antly titillated the fancy. I sat and read and smoked. It is my business to be curious about people and I asked myself how the peace of this scene, charged nevertheless with a tremulous and dark significance, affected Featherstone who lived with it. He knew it under every aspect: at dawn when the mist rising from the river shrouded it with a ghostly pall; in the splendour of noon; and at last when the shadowy gloaming crept softly out of the jungle, like an army making its way with caution in unknown country, and presently enveloped the green lawns and the great flowering trees and the flaunting cassias in the silent night. I wondered whether, unbeknownst to him, the tender and yet strangely sinister aspect of the scene, acting on his nerves and his loneliness, imbued him with some mystical quality so that the life he led, the life of the capable administrator, the sportsman and the good fellow, on occasion seemed to him not quite real. I smiled at my own fancies, for certainly the conversation we had had the night before had not indicated in him any stirrings of the soul. I had thought him quite nice. He had been at Oxford and was a member of a good London club. He seemed to attach a good deal of importance to social things. He was a gentleman and slightly conscious of the fact that he belonged to a better class than most of the Englishmen his life brought him in contact with. I gathered from the various silver pots that adorned his dining-room that he excelled in games. He played tennis and billiards.

When he went on leave he hunted and, anxious to keep his weight down, he dieted carefully. He talked a good deal of what he would do when he retired. He hankered after the life of a country gentleman. A little house in Leicestershire, a couple of hunters and neighbours to play bridge with.

He would have his pension and he had a little money of his own. But meanwhile he worked hard and did his work, if not brilliantly, certainly with competence. I have no doubt that he was looked upon by his superiors as a reliable officer. He was cut upon a pattern that I knew too well to find very interesting. He was like a novel that is careful, honest and efficient, yet a little ordinary, so that you seem to have read it all before, and you turn the pages listlessly knowing that it will never afford you a surprise or move you to excitement.

But human beings are incalculable and he is a fool who tells himself that he knows what a man is capable of.

In the afternoon Featherstone took me to see the Sultan. We were received by one of his sons, a shy, smiling youth who acted as his A.D.C. He was dressed in a neat blue suit, but round his waist he wore a sarong, white flowers on a yellow ground, on his head a red fez, and on his feet knobby American shoes. The palace, built in the Moorish style, was like a very big doll's house and it was painted bright yellow, which is the royal colour. We were led into a spacious room, furnished with the sort of furniture you would find in an English lodging-house at the seaside, but the chairs were covered with yellow silk. On the floor was a Brussels carpet and on the walls photographs in very grand gilt frames of the Sultan at various state functions. In a cabinet was a large collection of all kinds of fruit done entirely in crochet work. The Sultan came in with several attendants. He was a man of fifty, perhaps, short and stout, dressed in trousers and tunic of a large white and yellow check; round his middle he wore a very beautiful yellow sarong and on his head a white fez. He had large, handsome, friendly eyes. He gave us coffee to drink, sweet cakes to eat and cheroots to smoke. Conversation was not difficult, for he was affable, and he told me that he had never been to a theatre or played cards, for he was very religious, and he had four wives and twenty-four children. The only bar to the happiness of his life seemed to be that common decency obliged him to divide his time equally between his four wives. He said that an hour with one was a month and with another five minutes. I remarked that Professor Einstein—or was it Bergson?—had made similar observations upon time and indeed on this question had given the world much to ponder over. Presently we took our leave and the Sultan presented me with some beautiful white Malaccas.

In the evening we went to the club. One of the men we had played with the day before got up from his chair as we entered.

"Ready for a rubber?" he said.

"Where's our fourth?" I asked.

"Oh, there are several fellows here who'll be glad to play."

"What about that man we played with yesterday?" I had forgotten his name.

"Hardy? He's not here."

"It's not worth while waiting for him," said Featherstone.

"He very seldom comes to the club. I was surprised to see him last night."

I did not know why I had the impression that behind the very ordinary words of these two men there was an odd sense of embarrassment. Hardy had made no impression on me and I did not even remember what he looked like. He was just a fourth at the bridge table. I had a feeling that they had something against him. It was no business of mine and I was quite content to play with a man who at that moment joined us. We certainly had a more cheerful game than before. A

good deal of chaff passed from one side of the table to the other. We played less serious bridge. We laughed. I wondered if it was only that they were less shy of the stranger who had happened in upon them or if the presence of Hardy had caused in the other two a certain constraint. At half-past eight we broke up and Featherstone and I went back to dine at his house.

After dinner we lounged in armchairs and smoked cheroots. For some reason our conversation did not flow easily. I tried topic after topic, but could not get Featherstone to interest himself in any of them. I began to think that in the last twenty-four hours he had said all he had to say. I fell somewhat discouraged into silence. It prolonged itself and again, I did not know why, I had a faint sensation that it was charged with a significance that escaped me. I felt slightly uncomfortable. I had that queer feeling that one sometimes has when sitting in an empty room that one is not by oneself. Presently I was conscious that Featherstone was steadily looking at me. I was sitting by a lamp, but he was in shadow so that the play of his features was hidden from me. But he had very large brilliant eyes and in the half darkness they seemed to shine dimly. They were like new boot-buttons that caught a reflected light. I wondered why he looked at me like that. I gave him a glance and catching his eyes insistently fixed upon me faintly smiled.

"Interesting book that one you lent me last night," he said suddenly, and I could not help thinking his voice did not sound quite natural. The words issued from his lips as though they were pushed from behind.

"Oh, the Life of Byron?" I said breezily. "Have you read it already?"

"A good deal of it. I read till three."

"I've heard it's very well done. I'm not sure that Byron interests me so much as all that. There was so much in him that was so frightfully second-rate. It makes one rather uncomfortable."

"What do you think is the real truth of that story about him and his sister?"

"Augusta Leigh? I don't know very much about it. I've never read Astarte."

"Do you think they were really in love with one another?"

"I suppose so. Isn't it generally believed that she was the only woman he ever genuinely loved?"

"Can you understand it?"

"I can't really. It doesn't particularly shock me. It just seems to me very unnatural. Perhaps 'unnatural' isn't the right word. It's incomprehensible to me. I can't throw myself into the state of feeling in which such a thing seems possible. You know, that's how a writer gets to know the people he writes about, by standing himself in their shoes and feeling with their hearts."

I knew I did not make myself very clear, but I was trying to describe a sensation, an action of the subconscious, which from experience was perfectly familiar to me, but which no words I knew could precisely indicate. I went on.

"Of course she was only his half-sister, but just as habit kills love I should have thought habit would prevent its arising. When two persons have known one another all their lives and lived together in close contact I can't imagine how or why that sudden spark should flash that results in love. The probabilities are that they would be joined by mutual affection and I don't know anything that is more contrary to love than affection."

I could just see in the dimness the outline of a smile flicker for a moment on my host's heavy, and it seemed to me then, somewhat saturnine face.

"You only believe in love at first sight?"

"Well, I suppose I do, but with the proviso that people may have met twenty times before seeing one another. 'Seeing' has an active side and a passive one. Most people we run across mean so little to us that we never bestir ourselves to look at them. We just suffer the impression they make on us."

"Oh, but one's often heard of couples who've known one another for years and it's never occurred to one they cared two straws for each other and suddenly they go and get married. How do you explain that?"

"Well, if you're going to bully me into being logical and consistent, I should suggest that their love is of a different kind. After all, passion isn't the only reason for marriage. It may not even be the best one. Two people may marry because they're lonely or because they're good friends or for convenience' sake. Though I said that affection was the greatest enemy of love, I would never deny that it's a very good substitute. I'm not sure that a marriage founded on it isn't the happiest."

"What did you think of Tim Hardy?"

I was a little surprised at the sudden question, which seemed to have nothing to do with the subject of our conversation.

"I didn't think of him very much. He seemed quite nice. Why?"

"Did he seem to you just like everybody else?"

"Yes. Is there anything peculiar about him? If you'd told me that I'd have paid more attention to him."

"He's very quiet, isn't he? I suppose

no one who knew nothing about him would give him a second thought."

I tried to remember what he looked like. The only thing that had struck me when we were playing cards was that he had fine hands. It passed idly through my mind that they were not the sort of hands I should have expected a planter to have. But why a planter should have different hands from anybody else I did not trouble to ask myself. His were somewhat large, but very well formed, with peculiarly long fingers, and the nails were of an admirable shape. They were virile and yet oddly sensitive hands. I noticed this and thought no more about it. But if you are a writer, instinct and the habit of years enable you to store up impressions that you are not aware of. Sometimes of course they do not correspond with the facts and a woman for example may remain in your subconsciousness as a dark, massive and ox-eyed creature when she is indeed rather small and of a nondescript colouring. But that is of no consequence. The impression may very well be more exact than the sober truth. And now, seeking to call up from the depths of me a picture of this man I had a feeling of some ambiguity. He was clean-shaven and his face, oval but not thin, seemed strangely pale under the tan of long exposure to the tropical sun. His features were vague. I did not know whether I remembered it or only imagined now that his rounded chin gave one the impression of a certain weakness. He had thick brown hair, just turning grey, and a long wisp fell down constantly over his forehead. He pushed it back with a gesture that had become habitual. His brown eyes were rather large and gentle, but perhaps a little sad; they had a melting softness which, I could imagine, might be very appealing.

After a pause Featherstone continued:

"It's rather strange that I should run across Tim Hardy here after all these years. But that's the way of the F.M.S. People move about and you find yourself in the same place as a man you'd known years before in another part of the country. I first knew Tim when he had an estate near Sibuku. Have you ever been there?"

"No. Where is it?"

"Oh, it's up north. Towards Siam. It wouldn't be worth your while to go. It's just like every other place in the F.M.S. But it was rather nice. It had a very jolly little club and there were some quite decent people. There was the schoolmaster and the head of the police, the doctor, the padre and the government engineer. The usual lot, you know. A few planters. Three or four women. I was A.D.O. It was one of my first jobs. Tim Hardy had an estate about twenty-five miles away. He lived there with his sister. They had a bit of money of their own and he'd bought the place. Rubber was pretty good then and he wasn't doing at all badly. We rather cottoned on to one another. Of course it's a toss-up with planters. Some of them are very good fellows, but they're not exactly . . ." he sought for a word or a phrase that did not sound snobbish. "Well, they're not the sort of people you'd be likely to meet at home. Tim and Olive were of one's own class, if you understand what I mean."

"Olive was the sister?"

"Yes. They'd had a rather unfortunate past. Their parents had separated when they were quite small, seven or eight, and the mother had taken Olive and the father had kept Tim. Tim went to Clifton, they were West Country people, and only came home for the holidays. His father was a retired naval man who lived at Fowey.

But Olive went with her mother to Italy. She was educated in Florence; she spoke Italian perfectly and French too. For all those years Tim and Olive never saw one another once, but they used to write to one another regularly. They'd been very much attached when they were children. As far as I could understand, life when their people were living together had been rather stormy with all sorts of scenes and upsets, you know the sort of thing that happens when two people who are married don't get on together, and that had thrown them on their own resources. They were left a good deal to themselves. Then Mrs. Hardy died and Olive came home to England and went back to her father. She was eighteen then and Tim was seventeen. A year later the war broke out, Tim joined up and his father, who was over fifty, got some job at Portsmouth. I take it he had been a hard liver and a heavy drinker. He broke down before the end of the war and died after a lingering illness. They don't seem to have had any relations. They were the last of a rather old family; they had a fine old house in Dorsetshire that had belonged to them for a good many generations, but they had never been able to afford to live in it and it was always let. I remember seeing photographs of it. It was very much a gentleman's house, of grey stone and rather stately, with a coat of arms carved over the front door and mullioned windows. Their great ambition was to make enough money to be able to live in it. They used to talk about it a lot. They never spoke as though either of them would marry, but always as though it were a settled thing that they would remain together. It was rather funny considering how young they were."

"How old were they then?" I asked.

"Well, I suppose he was twenty-five or twenty-six and she was a year older. They were awfully kind to me when I first went up to Sibuku. They took a fancy to me at once. You see, we had more in common than most of the people there. I think they were glad of my company. They weren't particularly popular."

"Why not?" I asked.

"They were rather reserved and you couldn't help seeing that they liked their own society better than other people's. I don't know if you've noticed it, but that always seems to put people's backs up. They resent it somehow if they have a feeling that you can get along very well without them."

"It's tiresome, isn't it?" I said.

"It was rather a grievance to the other planters that Tim was his own master and had private means. They had to put up with an old Ford to get about in, but Tim had a real car. Tim and Olive were very nice when they came to the club and they played in the tennis tournaments and all that sort of thing, but you had an impression that they were always glad to get away again. They'd dine out with people and make themselves very pleasant, but it was pretty obvious that they'd just as soon have stayed at home. If you had any sense you couldn't blame them. I don't know if you've been much to planters' houses. They're a bit dreary. A lot of gimcrack furniture and silver ornaments and tiger skins. And the food's uneatable. But the Hardys had made their bungalow rather nice. There was nothing very grand in it; it was just easy and homelike and comfortable. Their living-room was like a drawing-room in an English country house. You felt that their things meant something to them and that they had had them a long time. It was a very jolly house to stay at. The bungalow was in the middle of the estate, but it was on the brow of a little hill and you looked right over the rubber trees to the sea in the distance. Olive took a lot of trouble with her garden and it was really topping. I never saw such a show of cannas. I used to go there for week-ends. It was only about half an hour's drive to the sea and we'd take our lunch with us and bathe and sail. Tim kept a small boat there. Those days were grand. I never knew one could enjoy oneself so much. It's a beautiful bit of coast and it was really extraordinarily romantic. Then in the evenings we'd play patience and chess or turn on the gramophone. The cooking was damned good too. It was a change from what one generally got. Olive had taught their cook to make all sorts of Italian dishes and we used to have great wallops of macaroni and risotto and gnocchi and things like that. I couldn't help envying them their life, it was so jolly and peaceful, and when they talked of what they'd do when they went back to England for good I used to tell them they'd always regret what they'd left.

" 'We've been very happy here,' said Olive.

"She had a way of looking at Tim, with a slow, sidelong glance from under her long eyelashes, that was rather engaging.

"In their own house they were quite different from what they were when they went out. They were so easy and cordial. Everybody admitted that and I'm bound to say that people enjoyed going there. They often asked people over. They had the gift of making you feel at home. It was a very happy house, if you know what I mean. Of course no one could help seeing how attached they were to one another. And whatever people said about their being standoffish and self-centred, they were bound to be rather touched by the affection they had for one another. People said they couldn't have been more united if they were married, and when you saw how some couples got on you couldn't help thinking they made most marriages look rather like a wash-out. They seemed to think the same things at the same time. They had little private jokes that made them laugh like children. They were so charming with one another, so gay and happy, that really to stay with them was, well, a spiritual refreshment. I don't know what else you could call it. When you left them, after a couple of days at the bungalow, you felt that you'd absorbed some of their peace and their sober gaiety. It was as though your soul had been sluiced with cool clear water. You felt strangely purified."

It was singular to hear Featherstone talking in this exalted strain. He looked so spruce in his smart white coat, technically known as a bum-freezer, his moustache was so trim, his thick curly hair so carefully brushed, that his high-flown language made me a trifle uncomfortable. But I realized that he was trying to express in his clumsy way a very sincerely felt emotion.

"What was Olive Hardy like?" I asked.

"I'll show you. I've got quite a lot of snapshots."

He got up from his chair and going to a shelf brought me a large album. It was the usual thing, indifferent photographs of people in groups and unflattering likenesses of single figures. They were in bathing dress or in shorts or tennis things, generally with their faces all screwed up because the sun blinded them, or puckered by the distortion of laughter. I recognized Hardy, not much changed after ten years, with his wisp of hair hanging across his forehead. I remembered him better now that I saw the snapshots. In them he looked nice and fresh and young. He had an alertness of expression that was attractive and that I certainly had not noticed when I saw him. In his eyes was a sort of eagerness for life that danced and sparkled through the fading print. I glanced at the photographs of his sister. Her bathing dress showed that she had a good figure, well-developed, but slender; and her legs were long and slim.

"They look rather alike," I said.

"Yes, although she was a year older they might have been twins, they were so much alike. They both had the same oval face and that pale skin without any colour in the cheeks, and they both had those soft brown eyes, very liquid and appealing, so that you felt whatever they did you could never be angry with them. And they both had a sort of careless elegance that made them look charming whatever they wore and however untidy they were. He's lost that now, I suppose, but he certainly had it when I first knew him. They always rather reminded me of the brother and sister in Twelfth Night. You know whom I mean."

"Viola and Sebastian."

"They never seemed to belong quite to the present. There was something Elizabethan about them. I don't think it was only because I was very young then that I couldn't help feeling they were strangely romantic somehow. I could see them living in Illyria."

I gave one of the snapshots another glance.

"The girl looks as though she had a good deal more character than her brother," I remarked.

"She had. I don't know if you'd have called Olive beautiful, but she was awfully attractive. There was

something poetic in her, a sort of lyrical quality as it were, that coloured her movements, her acts and everything about her. It seemed to exalt her above common cares. There was something so candid in her expression, so courageous and independent in her bearing, that—oh, I don't know, it made mere beauty just flat and dull."

"You speak as if you'd been in love with her," I interrupted.

"Of course I was. I should have thought you'd guessed that at once. I was frightfully in love with her."

"Was it love at first sight?" I smiled.

"Yes, I think it was, but I didn't know it for a month or so. When it suddenly struck me that what I felt for her—I don't know how to explain it, it was a sort of shattering turmoil that affected every bit of me—that that was love, I knew I'd felt it all along. It was not only her looks, though they were awfully alluring, the smoothness of her pale skin and the way her hair fell over her forehead and the grave sweetness of her brown eyes, it was more than that; you had a sensation of well-being when you were with her, as though you could relax and be quite natural and needn't pretend to be anything you weren't. You felt she was incapable of meanness. It was impossible to think of her as envious of other people or catty. She seemed to have a natural generosity of soul. One could be silent with her for an hour at a time and yet feel that one had had a good time."

"A rare gift," I said.

"She was a wonderful companion. If you made a suggestion to do something she was always glad to fall in with it. She was the least exacting girl I ever knew. You could throw her over at the last minute and however disappointed she was it made no difference. Next time you saw her she was just as cordial and serene as ever."

"Why didn't you marry her?"

Featherstone's cheroot had gone out. He threw the stub away and deliberately lit another. He did not answer for a while. It may seem strange to persons who live in a highly civilized state that he should confide these intimate things to a stranger; it did not seem strange to me. I was used to it. People who live so desperately alone, in the remote places of the earth, find it a relief to tell someone whom in all probability they will never meet again the story that has burdened perhaps for years their waking thoughts and their dreams at night. And I have an inkling that the fact of your being a writer attracts their confidence. They feel that what they tell you will excite your interest in an impersonal way that makes it easier for them to discharge their souls. Besides, as we all know from our own experience, it is never unpleasant to talk about oneself.

"Why didn't you marry her?" I had asked him.

"I wanted to badly enough," Featherstone answered at length. "But I hesitated to ask her. Although she was always so nice to me and so easy to get on with, and we were such good friends, I always felt that there was something a little mysterious in her. Although she was so simple, so frank and natural, you never quite got over the feeling of an inner kernel of aloofness, as if deep in her heart she guarded, not a secret, but a sort of privacy of the soul that not a living person would ever be allowed to know. I don't know if I make myself clear."

"I think so."

"I put it down to her upbringing. They never talked of their mother, but somehow I got the impression that she was one of those neurotic, emotional women who wreck their own happiness and are a pest to everyone connected with them. I had a suspicion that she'd led rather a hectic life in Florence and it struck me that Olive owed her beautiful serenity to a disciplined effort of her own will and that her aloofness was a sort of citadel she'd built to protect herself from the knowledge of all sorts of shameful things. But of course that aloofness was awfully captivating. It was strangely exciting to think that if she loved you, and you were married to her, you would at last pierce right into the hidden heart of that mystery; and you felt that if you could share that with her it would be as it were a consummation of all you'd ever desired in your life. Heaven wouldn't be in it. You know, I felt about it just like Bluebeard's wife about the forbidden chamber in the castle. Every room was open to me, but I should never rest till I had gone into that last one that was locked against me."

My eye was caught by a chik-chak, a little brown house lizard with a large head, high up on the wall. It is a friendly little beast and it is good to see it in a house. It watched a fly. It was quite still. On a sudden it made a dart and then as the fly flew away fell back with a sort of jerk into a strange immobility.

"And there was another thing that made me hesitate. I couldn't bear the thought that if I proposed to her and she refused me she wouldn't let me come to the bungalow in the same old way. I should have hated that, I enjoyed going there so awfully. It made me so happy to be with her. But you know, sometimes one can't help oneself. I did ask her at last, but it was almost by accident. One evening, after dinner, when we were sitting on the verandah by ourselves, I took her hand. She withdrew it at once.

" 'Why did you do that?' I asked her.

" 'I don't very much like being touched,' she said. She turned her head a little and smiled. 'Are you hurt? You mustn't mind, it's just a funny feeling I have. I can't help it.'

" 'I wonder if it's ever occurred to you that I'm frightfully fond of you,' I said.

"I expect I was terribly awkward about it, but I'd never proposed to anyone before." Featherstone gave a little sound that was not quite a chuckle and not quite a sigh. "For the matter of that, I've never proposed to anyone since. She didn't say anything for a minute. Then she said:

" 'I'm very glad, but I don't think I want you to be anything more than that.'

" 'Why not?' I asked.

" 'I could never leave Tim.'

" 'But supposing he marries?'

" 'He never will.'

"I'd gone so far then that I thought I'd better go on. But my throat was so dry that I could hardly speak. I was shaking with nervousness.

" 'I'm frightfully in love with you, Olive. I want to marry you more than anything in the world.'

"She put her hand very gently on my arm. It was like a flower falling to the ground.

" 'No, dear, I can't,' she said.

"I was silent. It was difficult for me to say what I wanted to. I'm naturally rather shy. She was a girl. I couldn't very well tell her that it wasn't quite the same thing living with a husband and living with a brother. She was normal and healthy; she must want to have babies; it wasn't reasonable to starve her natural instincts. It was such waste of her youth. But it was she who spoke first.

" 'Don't let's talk about this any more,' she said. 'D'you mind? It did strike me once or twice that perhaps you cared for me. Tim noticed it. I was sorry because I was afraid it would break up our friendship. I don't want it to do that, Mark. We do get on so well together, the three of us, and we have such jolly times. I don't know what we should do without you now.'

" 'I thought of that too,' I said.

" 'D'you think it need?' she asked me.

" 'My dear, I don't want it to,' I said. 'You must know how much I love coming here. I've never been so happy anywhere before!'

" 'You're not angry with me?'

" 'Why should I be? It's not your fault. It only means that you're not in love with me. If you were you wouldn't care a hang about Tim.'

" 'You are rather sweet,' she said.

"She put her arm round my neck and kissed me lightly on the cheek. I had a notion that in her mind it settled our relation. She adopted me as a second brother.

"A few weeks later Tim went back to England. The tenant of their house in Dorset was leaving and though there was another in the offing, he thought he ought to be on the spot to conduct negotiations. And he wanted some new machinery for the estate. He thought he'd get it at the same time. He didn't expect to be gone more than three months and Olive made up her mind not to go. She knew hardly anyone in England, and it was practically a foreign country to her, she didn't mind being left alone, and she wanted to look after the estate. Of course they could have put a manager in charge, but that wasn't the same thing. Rubber was falling and in case of accidents it was just as well that one or other of them should be there.

I promised Tim I'd look after her and if she wanted me she could always call me up. My proposal hadn't changed anything. We carried on as though nothing had happened. I don't know whether she'd told Tim. He made no sign that he knew. Of course I loved her as much as ever, but I kept it to myself. I have a good deal of self-control, you know. I had a sort of feeling I hadn't a chance. I hoped eventually my love would change into something else and we could just be wonderful friends. It's funny, it never has, you know. I suppose I was hit too badly ever to get quite over it.

"She went down to Penang to see Tim off and when she came back I met her at the station and drove her home. I couldn't very well stay at the bungalow while Tim was away, but I went over every Sunday and had tiffin and we'd go down to the sea and have a bathe. People tried to be kind to her and asked her to stay with them, but she wouldn't. She seldom left the estate. She had plenty to do. She read a lot. She was never bored. She seemed quite happy in her own company, and when she had visitors it was only from a sense of duty. She didn't want them to think her ungracious. But it was an effort and she told me she heaved a sigh of relief when she saw the last of them and could again enjoy without disturbance the peaceful loneliness of the bungalow. She was a very curious girl. It was strange that at her age she should be so indifferent to parties and the other small gaieties the station afforded. Spiritually, if you know what I mean, she was entirely self-supporting. I don't know how people found out that I was in love with her; I thought I'd never given myself away in anything, but I had hints here and there that they knew. I gathered they thought Olive hadn't gone home with her brother on my account. One woman, a Mrs. Sergison, the policeman's wife, actually asked me when they were going to be able to congratulate me. Of course I pretended I didn't know what she was talking about, but it didn't go down very well. I couldn't help being amused. I meant so little to Olive in that way that I really believe she'd entirely forgotten that I'd asked her to marry me. I can't say she was unkind to me, I don't think she could have been unkind to anyone; but she treated me with just the casualness with which a sister might treat a younger brother. She was two or three years older than I. She was always terribly glad to see me, but it never occurred to her to put herself out for me, she was almost amazingly intimate with me; but unconsciously, you know, as you might be with a person you'd known so well all your life that you never thought of putting on frills with him. I might not have been a man at all, but an old coat that she wore all the time because it was easy and comfortable and she didn't mind what she did in it. I should have been crazy not to see that she was a thousand miles away from loving me.

"Then one day, three or four weeks before Tim was due back, when I went to the bungalow I saw she'd been crying. I was startled. She was always so composed. I'd never seen her upset over anything.

" 'Hullo, what's the matter?' I said.

" 'Nothing.'

" 'Come off it, darling,' I said. 'What have you been crying about?'

"She tried to smile.

" 'I wish you hadn't got such sharp eyes,' she said. 'I think I'm being silly.

I've just had a cable from Tim to say he's postponed his sailing.'

" 'Oh, my dear, I am sorry,' I said. 'You must be awfully disappointed.'

" 'I've been counting the days. I want him back so badly.'

" 'Does he say why he's postponing?' I asked.

" 'No, he says he's writing. I'll show you the cable.'

"I saw that she was very nervous. Her slow quiet eyes were filled with apprehension and there was a little frown of anxiety between her brows. She went into her bedroom and in a moment came back with the cable. I felt that she was watching me anxiously as I read. So far as I remember it ran: *Darling, I cannot sail on the seventh after all. Please forgive me. Am writing fully. Fondest love. Tim.*

" 'Well, perhaps the machinery he wanted isn't ready and he can't bring himself to sail without it,' I said.

" 'What could it matter if it came by a later ship? Anyhow, it'll be hung up at Penang.'

" 'It may be something about the house.'

" 'If it is why doesn't he say so? He must know how frightfully anxious I am.'

" 'It wouldn't occur to him,' I said. 'After all, when you're away you don't realize that the people you've left behind don't know something that you take as a matter of course.'

"She smiled again, but now more happily.

" 'I daresay you're right. In point of fact Tim is a little like that. He's always been rather slack and casual. I daresay I've been making a mountain out of a molehill. I must just wait patiently for his letter.'

"Olive was a girl with a lot of self-control and I saw her by an effort of will pull herself together. The little line between her eyebrows vanished

and she was once more her serene, smiling and kindly self. She was always gentle: that day she had a mildness so heavenly that it was shattering. But for the rest of the time I could see that she kept her restlessness in check only by the deliberate exercise of her common sense. It was as though she had a foreboding of ill. I was with her the day before the mail was due. Her anxiety was all the more pitiful to see because she took such pains to hide it. I was always busy on mail day, but I promised to go up to the estate later on and hear the news. I was just thinking of starting when Hardy's seis came along in the car with a message from the amah asking me to go at once to her mistress. The amah was a decent, elderly woman to whom I had given a dollar or two and said that if anything went wrong on the estate she was to let me know at once. I jumped into my car. When I arrived I found the amah waiting for me on the steps.

" 'A letter came this morning,' she said.

"I interrupted her. I ran up the steps. The sitting-room was empty. " 'Olive,' I called.

"I went into the passage and suddenly I heard a sound that froze my heart. The amah had followed me and now she opened the door of Olive's room. The sound I had heard was the sound of Olive crying. I went in. She was lying on her bed, on her face, and her sobs shook her from head to foot. I put my hand on her shoulder.

" 'Olive, what is it?' I asked.

" 'Who's that?' she cried. She sprang to her feet suddenly, as though she were scared out of her wits. And then: 'Oh, it's you,' she said. She stood in front of me, with her head thrown back and her eyes closed, and the tears streamed from them. It was dreadful. 'Tim's married,' she gasped, and her face screwed up in a sort of grimace of pain.

"I must admit that for one moment I had a thrill of exultation, it was like a little electric shock tingling through my heart; it struck me that now I had a chance, she might be willing to marry me; I know it was terribly selfish of me; you see, the news had taken me by surprise; but it was only for a moment, after that I was melted by her awful distress and the only thing I felt was deep sorrow because she was unhappy. I put my arm round her waist.

"'Oh, my dear, I'm so sorry,' I said. 'Don't stay here. Come into the sitting-room and sit down and we'll talk about it. Let me give you something to drink.'

"She let me lead her into the next room and we sat down on the sofa. I told the amah to fetch the whisky and syphon and I mixed her a good strong stengah and made her drink a little. I took her in my arms and rested her head on my shoulder. She let me do what I liked with her. The great tears streamed down her poor face.

"'How could he?' she moaned. 'How could he?'

"'My darling,' I said, 'it was bound to happen sooner or later. He's a young man. How could you expect him never to marry? It's only natural.'

"'No, no, no,' she gasped.

"Tight-clenched in her hand I saw that she had a letter and I guessed that it was Tim's.

"'What does he say?' I asked.

"She gave a frightened movement and clutched the letter to her heart as though she thought I would take it from her.

"'He says he couldn't help himself. He says he had to. What does it mean?'

"'Well, you know, in his way he's

just as attractive as you are. He has so much charm. I suppose he just fell madly in love with some girl and she with him.'

"'He's so weak,' she moaned.

"'Are they coming out?' I asked.

"'They sailed yesterday. He says it won't make any difference. He's insane. How *can* I stay here?'

"She began to cry hysterically. It was torture to see that girl, usually so calm, utterly shattered by her emotion. I had always felt that her lovely serenity masked a capacity for deep feeling. But the abandon of her distress simply broke me up. I held her in my arms and kissed her, her eyes and her wet cheek and her hair. I don't think she knew what I was doing. I was hardly conscious of it myself. I was so deeply moved.

"'What shall I do?' she wailed.

"'Why won't you marry me?' I said.

"She tried to withdraw herself from me, but I wouldn't let her go.

"'After all, it would be a way out,' I said.

"'How can I marry you?' she moaned. 'I'm years older than you are.'

"'Oh, what nonsense, two or three. What do I care?'

"'No, no.'

"'Why not?' I said.

"'I don't love you,' she said.

"'What does that matter? I love you.'

"I don't know what I said. I told her that I'd try to make her happy. I said I'd never ask anything from her but what she was prepared to give me. I talked and talked. I tried to make her see reason. I felt that she didn't want to stay there, in the same place as Tim, and I told her that I'd be moved soon to some other district. I thought that might tempt her. She couldn't deny that we'd always got on awfully well together. After a time she did seem to grow a little quieter. I had a feeling that she was listening to me. I had even a sort of feeling that she knew that she was lying in my arms and that it comforted her. I made her drink a drop more whisky. I gave her a cigarette. At last I thought I might be just mildly facetious.

" 'You know, I'm not a bad sort really,' I said. 'You might do worse.'

" 'You don't know me,' she said. 'You know nothing whatever about me.'

" 'I'm capable of learning,' I said.

"She smiled a little.

" 'You're awfully kind, Mark,' she said.

" 'Say yes, Olive,' I begged.

"She gave a deep sigh. For a long time she stared at the ground. But she did not move and I felt the softness of her body in my arms. I waited. I was frightfully nervous and the minutes seemed endless.

" 'All right,' she said at last, as though she were not conscious that any time had passed between my prayer and her answer.

"I was so moved that I had nothing to say. But when I wanted to kiss her lips, she turned her face away, and wouldn't let me. I wanted us to be married at once, but she was quite firm that she wouldn't. She insisted on waiting till Tim came back. You know how sometimes you see so clearly in people's thoughts that you're more certain of them than if they'd spoken them; I saw that she couldn't quite believe that what Tim had written was true and that she had a sort of miserable hope that it was all a mistake and he wasn't married after all. It gave me a pang, but I loved her so much, I just bore it. I was willing to bear anything. I adored her. She wouldn't even let me tell anyone that we were engaged. She made me prom- ise not to say a word till Tim's return. She said she couldn't bear the thought of the congratulations and all that. She wouldn't even let me make any announcement of Tim's marriage. She was obstinate about it. I had a notion that she felt if the fact were spread about it gave it a certainty that she didn't want it to have.

"But the matter was taken out of her hands. News travels mysteriously in the East. I don't know what Olive had said in the amah's hearing when first she received the news of Tim's marriage; anyhow, the Hardys' seis told the Sergisons' and Mrs. Sergison attacked me the next time I went into the club.

" 'I hear Tim Hardy's married,' she said.

" 'Oh?' I answered, unwilling to commit myself.

"She smiled at my blank face, and told me that her amah having told her the rumour she had rung up Olive and asked her if it was true. Olive's answer had been rather odd. She had not exactly confirmed it, but said that she had received a letter from Tim telling her he was married.

" 'She's a strange girl,' said Mrs. Sergison. 'When I asked her for details she said she had none to give and when I said: "Aren't you thrilled?" she didn't answer.'

" 'Olive's devoted to Tim, Mrs. Sergison,' I said. 'His marriage has naturally been a shock to her. She knows nothing about Tim's wife. She's nervous about her.'

" 'And when are you two going to be married?' she asked me abruptly.

" 'What an embarrassing question!' I said, trying to laugh it off.

"She looked at me shrewdly.

" 'Will you give me your word of honour that you're not engaged to her?'

"I didn't like to tell her a deliberate

lie, nor to ask her to mind her own business, and I'd promised Olive faithfully that I would say nothing till Tim got back. I hedged.

" 'Mrs. Sergison,' I said, 'when there's anything to tell I promise that you'll be the first person to hear it. All I can say to you now is that I do want to marry Olive more than anything in the world.'

" 'I'm very glad that Tim's married,' she answered. 'And I hope she'll marry you very soon. It was a morbid and unhealthy life that they led up there, those two, they kept far too much to themselves and they were far too much absorbed in one another.'

"I saw Olive practically every day. I felt that she didn't want me to make love to her, and I contented myself with kissing her when I came and when I went. She was very nice to me, kindly and thoughtful; I knew she was glad to see me and sorry when it was time for me to go. Ordinarily, she was apt to fall into silence, but during this time she talked more than I had ever heard her talk before. But never of the future and never of Tim and his wife. She told me a lot about her life in Florence with her mother. She had led a strange lonely life, mostly with servants and governesses, while her mother, I suspected, engaged in one affair after another with vague Italian counts and Russian princes. I guessed that by the time she was fourteen there wasn't much she didn't know. It was natural for her to be quite unconventional: in the only world she knew till she was eighteen conventions weren't mentioned because they didn't exist. Gradually, Olive seemed to regain her serenity and I should have thought that she was beginning to accustom herself to the thought of Tim's marriage if it hadn't been that I couldn't but notice how pale and tired she looked. I

made up my mind that the moment he arrived I'd press her to marry me at once. I could get short leave whenever I asked for it, and by the time that was up I thought I could manage a transfer to some other post. What she wanted was change of air and fresh scenes.

"We knew, of course, within a day when Tim's ship would reach Penang, but it was a question whether she'd get in soon enough for him to catch the train and I wrote to the P. & O. agent asking him to telegraph as soon as he had definite news. When I got the wire and took it up to Olive I found that she'd just received one from Tim. The ship had docked early and he was arriving next day. The train was supposed to get in at eight o'clock in the morning, but it was liable to be anything from one to six hours late, and I bore with me an invitation from Mrs. Sergison asking Olive to come back with me to stay the night with her so that she would be on the spot and need not go to the station till the news came through that the train was coming.

"I was immensely relieved. I thought that when the blow at last fell Olive wouldn't feel it so much. She had worked herself up into such a state that I couldn't help thinking that she must have a reaction now. She might take a fancy to her sister-in-law. There was no reason why they shouldn't all three get on very well together. To my surprise Olive said she wasn't coming down to the station to meet them.

" 'They'll be awfully disappointed,' I said.

" 'I'd rather wait here,' she answered. She smiled a little. 'Don't argue with me, Mark, I've quite made up my mind.'

" 'I've ordered breakfast in my house,' I said.

" 'That's all right. You meet them and take them to your house and give them breakfast, and then they can come along here afterwards. Of course I'll send the car down.'

" 'I don't suppose they'll want to breakfast if you're not there,' I said.

" 'Oh, I'm sure they will. If the train gets in on time they wouldn't have thought of breakfasting before it arrived and they'll be hungry. They won't want to take this long drive without anything to eat.'

"I was puzzled. She had been looking forward so intensely to Tim's coming, it seemed strange that she should want to wait all by herself while the rest of us were having a jolly breakfast. I supposed she was nervous and wanted to delay as long as possible meeting the strange woman who had come to take her place. It seemed unreasonable. I couldn't see that an hour sooner or an hour later could make any difference, but I knew women were funny, and anyhow I felt Olive wasn't in the mood for me to press it.

" 'Telephone when you're starting so that I shall know when to expect you,' she said.

" 'All right,' I said, 'but you know I shan't be able to come with them. It's my day for going to Lahad.'

"This was a town that I had to go to once a week to take cases. It was a good way off and one had to ferry across a river, which took some time, so that I never got back till late. There were a few Europeans there and a club. I generally had to go on there for a bit to be sociable and see that things were getting along all right.

" 'Besides,' I added, 'with Tim bringing his wife home for the first time I don't suppose he'll want me about. But if you'd like to ask me to dinner I'll be glad to come to that.'

"Olive smiled.

" 'I don't think it'll be my place to issue any more invitations, will it?' she said. 'You must ask the bride.'

"She said this so lightly that my heart leaped. I had a feeling that at last she had made up her mind to accept the altered circumstances and, what was more, was accepting them with cheerfulness. She asked me to stay to dinner. Generally I left about eight and dined at home. She was very sweet, almost tender, and I was happier than I'd been for weeks, I had never been more desperately in love with her. I had a couple of gin pahits and I think I was in rather good form at dinner. I know I made her laugh. I felt that at last she was casting away the load of misery that had oppressed her. That was why I didn't let myself be very much disturbed by what happened at the end.

" 'Don't you think it's about time you were leaving a presumably maiden lady?' she said.

"She spoke in a manner that was so quietly gay that I answered without hesitation:

" 'Oh, my dear, if you think you've got a shred of reputation left you deceive yourself. You're surely not under the impression that the ladies of Sibuku don't know that I've been coming to see you every day for a month. The general feeling is that if we're not married it's high time we were. Don't you think it would be just as well if I broke it to them that we're engaged?'

" 'Oh, Mark, you mustn't take our engagement very seriously,' she said.

"I laughed.

" 'How else do you expect me to take it? It is serious.'

"She shook her head a little.

" 'No. I was upset and hysterical that day. You were being very sweet to me. I said yes because I was too miserable to say no. But now I've had time to collect myself. Don't think me unkind. I made a mistake. I've been very much to blame. You must forgive me.'

" 'Oh, darling, you're talking nonsense. You've got nothing against me.'

"She looked at me steadily. She was quite calm. She had even a little smile at the back of her eyes.

" 'I can't marry you. I can't marry anyone. It was absurd of me ever to think I could.'

"I didn't answer at once. She was in a queer state and I thought it better not to insist.

" 'I suppose I can't drag you to the altar by main force,' I said.

"I held out my hand and she gave me hers. I put my arm round her, and she made no attempt to withdraw. She suffered me to kiss her as usual on her cheek.

"Next morning I met the train. For once in a way it was punctual. Tim waved to me as his carriage passed the place where I was standing, and by the time I had walked up he had already jumped out and was handing down his wife. He grasped my hand warmly.

" 'Where's Olive?' he said, with a glance along the platform. 'This is Sally.'

"I shook hands with her and at the same time explained why Olive was not there.

" 'It was frightfully early, wasn't it?' said Mrs. Hardy.

"I told them that the plan was for them to come and have a bit of breakfast at my house and then drive home.

" 'I'd love a bath,' said Mrs. Hardy.

" 'You shall have one,' I said.

"She was really an extremely pretty little thing, very fair, with enormous blue eyes and a lovely little straight nose. Her skin, all milk and roses, was exquisite. A little of the chorus girl type, of course, and you may happen to think that rather namby-pamby, but in that style she was enchanting. We drove to my house, they both had a bath and Tim a shave; I just had two minutes alone with him. He asked me how Olive had taken his marriage. I told her she'd been upset.

" 'I was afraid so,' he said, frowning a little. He gave a short sigh. 'I couldn't do anything else.'

"I didn't understand what he meant. At that moment Mrs. Hardy joined us and slipped her arm through her husband's. He took her hand in his and gently pressed it. He gave her a look that had in it something pleased and humorously affectionate, as though he didn't take her quite seriously, but enjoyed his sense of proprietorship and was proud of her beauty. She really was lovely. She was not at all shy, she asked me to call her Sally before we'd known one another ten minutes, and she was quick in the uptake. Of course, just then she was excited at arriving. She'd never been East and everything thrilled her. It was quite obvious that she was head over heels in love with Tim. Her eyes never left him and she hung on his words. We had a jolly breakfast and then we parted. They got into their car to go home and I into mine to go to Lahad. I promised to go straight to the estate from there and in point of fact it was out of my way to pass by my house. I took a change with me. I didn't see why Olive shouldn't like Sally very much, she was frank and gay, and ingenuous; she was extremely young, she couldn't have been more than nineteen, and her wonderful prettiness couldn't fail to appeal to Olive. I was just as glad to have had a reasonable excuse to leave the three of them by themselves for the day, but as I started out from Lahad I had a notion that by the time I arrived they would all be pleased to see me. I drove up to the bungalow and blew my horn two or three times, expecting someone to appear. Not a soul. The place was in total darkness. I was surprised. It was absolutely silent. I couldn't make it out. They must be in. Very odd, I thought. I waited a moment, then got out of the car and walked up the steps. At the top of them I stumbled over something. I swore and bent down to see what it was; it had felt like a body. There was a cry and I saw it was the amah. She shrank back cowering as I touched her and broke into loud wails.

" 'What the hell's the matter?' I cried, and then I felt a hand on my arm and heard a voice. Tuan, Tuan. I turned and in the darkness recognized Tim's head boy. He began to speak in little frightened gasps. I listened to him with horror. What he told me was unspeakable. I pushed him aside and rushed into the house. The sitting-room was dark. I turned on the light. The first thing I saw was Sally huddled up in an armchair. She was startled by my sudden appearance and cried out. I could hardly speak. I asked her if it was true. When she told me it was I felt the room suddenly going round and round me. I had to sit down. As the car that bore Tim and Sally drove up the road that led to the house and Tim sounded the claxon to announce their arrival and the boys and the amah ran out to greet them there was the sound of a shot. They ran to Olive's room and found her lying in front of the looking-glass in a pool of blood. She had shot herself with Tim's revolver.

" 'Is she dead?' I said.

" 'No, they sent for the doctor, and he took her to the hospital.'

"I hardly knew what I was doing. I didn't even trouble to tell Sally

where I was going. I got up and staggered to the door. I got into the car and told my seis to drive like hell to the hospital. I rushed in. I asked where she was. They tried to bar my way, but I pushed them aside. I knew where the private rooms were. Someone clung to my arm, but I shook him off. I vaguely understood that the doctor had given instructions that no one was to go into the room. I didn't care about that. There was an orderly at the door; he put out his arm to prevent me from passing. I swore at him and told him to get out of my way. I suppose I made a row, I was beside myself; the door was opened and the doctor came out.

" 'Who's making all this noise?' he said. 'Oh, it's you. What do you want?'

" 'Is she dead?' I asked.

" 'No. But she's unconscious. She never regained consciousness. It's only a matter of an hour or two.'

" 'I want to see her.'

" 'You can't.'

" 'I'm engaged to her.'

" 'You?' he cried, and even at that moment I was aware that he looked at me strangely. 'That's all the more reason.'

"I didn't know what he meant. I was stupid with horror.

" 'Surely you can do something to save her,' I cried.

"He shook his head.

" 'If you saw her you wouldn't wish it,' he said.

"I stared at him aghast. In the silence I heard a man's convulsive sobbing.

" 'Who's that?' I asked.

" 'Her brother.'

"Then I felt a hand on my arm. I looked round and saw it was Mrs. Sergison.

" 'My poor boy,' she said, 'I'm so sorry for you.'

" 'What on earth made her do it?'
I groaned.

" 'Come away, my dear,' said Mrs.
Sergison. 'You can do no good here.'

" 'No. I must stay,' I said.

" 'Well, go and sit in my room,'
said the doctor.

"I was so broken that I let Mrs.
Sergison take me by the arm and lead
me into the doctor's private room. She
made me sit down. I couldn't bring
myself to realize that it was true. I
thought it was a horrible nightmare
from which I must awake. I don't
know how long we sat there. Three
hours. Four hours. At last the doctor
came in.

" 'It's all over,' he said.

"Then I couldn't help myself, I
began to cry. I didn't care what they
thought of me. I was so frightfully
unhappy.

"We buried her next day.

"Mrs. Sergison came back to my
house and sat with me for a while.
She wanted me to go to the club with
her. I hadn't the heart. She was very
kind, but I was glad when she left
me by myself. I tried to read, but the
words meant nothing to me. I felt
dead inside. My boy came in and
turned on the lights. My head was
aching like mad. Then he came back
and said that a lady wished to see
me. I asked who it was. He wasn't
quite sure, but he thought it must be
the new wife of the tuan at Putatan.
I couldn't imagine what she wanted.
I got up and went to the door. He
was right. It was Sally. I asked her to
come in. I noticed that she was deathly
white. I felt sorry for her. It was a
frightful experience for a girl of that
age and for a bride a miserable home-
coming. She sat down. She was very
nervous. I tried to put her at her ease
by saying conventional things. She
made me very uncomfortable because
she stared at me with those enormous

blue eyes of hers, and they
were simply ghastly with horror. She
interrupted me suddenly.

" 'You're the only person here I
know,' she said. 'I had to come to
you. I want you to get me away from
here.'

"I was dumbfounded.

" 'What do you mean?' I said.

" 'I don't want you to ask me any
questions. I just want you to get me
away. At once. I want to go back to
England!'

" 'But you can't leave Tim like that
just now,' I said. 'My dear, you must
pull yourself together. I know it's been
awful for you. But think of Tim. I
mean, he'll be miserable. If you have
any love for him the least you can do
is to try and make him a little less
unhappy.'

" 'Oh, you don't know,' she cried.
'I can't tell you. It's too horrible. I
beseech you to help me. If there's a
train to-night let me get on it. If I
can only get to Penang I can get a
ship. I can't stay in this place another
night. I shall go mad.'

"I was absolutely bewildered.

" 'Does Tim know?' I asked her.

" 'I haven't seen Tim since last
night. I'll never see him again. I'd
rather die.'

"I wanted to gain a little time.

" 'But how can you go without
your things? Have you got any luggage?'

" 'What does that matter?' she cried
impatiently. 'I've got what I want for
the journey.'

" 'Have you any money?'

" 'Enough. Is there a train to-night?'

" 'Yes,' I said. 'It's due just after
midnight.'

" 'Thank God. Will you arrange
everything? Can I stay here till then?'

" 'You're putting me in a frightful
position,' I said. 'I don't know what

to do for the best. You know, it's an awfully serious step you're taking.'

" 'If you knew everything you'd know it was the only possible thing to do.'

" 'It'll create an awful scandal here. I don't know what people'll say. Have you thought of the effect on Tim?' I was worried and unhappy. 'God knows I don't want to interfere in what isn't my business. But if you want me to help you I ought to know enough to feel justified in doing so. You must tell me what's happened.'

" 'I can't. I can only tell you that I know everything.'

"She hid her face with her hands and shuddered. Then she gave herself a shake as though she were recoiling from some frightful sight.

" 'He had no right to marry me. It was monstrous.'

"And as she spoke her voice rose shrill and piercing. I was afraid she was going to have an attack of hysterics. Her pretty doll-like face was terrified and her eyes stared as though she could never close them again.

" 'Don't you love him any more?' I asked.

" 'After that?'

" 'What will you do if I refuse to help you?' I said.

" 'I suppose there's a clergyman here or a doctor. You can't refuse to take me to one of them.'

" 'How did you get here?'

" 'The head boy drove me. He got a car from somewhere.'

" 'Does Tim know you've gone?'

" 'I left a letter for him.'

" 'He'll know you're here.'

" 'He won't try to stop me. I promise you that. He daren't. For God's sake don't you try either. I tell you I shall go mad if I stay here another night.'

"I sighed. After all she was of an age to decide for herself."

I, the writer of this, hadn't spoken for a long time.

"Did you know what she meant?" I asked Featherstone.

He gave me a long, haggard look.

"There was only one thing she could mean. It was unspeakable. Yes, I knew all right. It explained everything. Poor Olive. Poor sweet. I suppose it was unreasonable of me, at that moment I only felt a horror of that little pretty fair-haired thing with her terrified eyes. I hated her. I didn't say anything for a while. Then I told her I'd do as she wished. She didn't even say thank you. I think she knew what I felt about her. When it was dinner time I made her eat something and then she asked me if there was a room she could go and lie down in till it was time to go to the station. I showed her into my spare room and left her. I sat in the sitting-room and waited. My God, I don't think the time has ever passed so slowly for me. I thought twelve would never strike. I rang up the station and was told the train wouldn't be in till nearly two. At midnight she came back to the sitting-room and we sat there for an hour and a half. We had nothing to say to one another and we didn't speak. Then I took her to the station and put her on the train."

"Was there an awful scandal?"

Featherstone frowned.

"I don't know. I applied for short leave. After that I was moved to another post. I heard that Tim had sold his estate and bought another. But I didn't know where. It was a shock to me at first when I found him here."

Featherstone, getting up, went over to a table and mixed himself a whisky and soda. In the silence that fell now I heard the monotonous chorus of the croaking frogs. And suddenly the bird that is known as the fever-bird, perched in a tree close to the house, began to call. First, three notes in a descending, chromatic scale, then five, then four. The varying notes of the scale succeeded one another with maddening persistence. One was compelled to listen and to count them, and because one did not know how many there would be it tortured one's nerves.

"Blast that bird," said Featherstone. "That means no sleep for me to-night."

EL GRECO

An Essay

PAINTERS, not unnaturally, since so much nonsense has been written on the subject, have always resented writers expressing their opinions on pictures. They have insisted, often with great vehemence, that only the painter can speak of painting with authority, and that the man of letters, looking at a picture from his literary point of view, can know nothing of its specific value. His part is to admire in silence and if he has the money, buy. This seems to me a narrow way of thinking. Doubtless they are right when they claim that only painters should discuss technique, but technique is not the whole of painting. You might as well say that only a dramatist can appreciate a play. The drama also has its technique, though it is not so abstruse as some of its professors like to pretend, but it is the business only of the dramatist. To understand the technique of an art may be a diversion, it may even give the layman the feeling, agreeable to some people, of being in the know (like addressing the head-waiter of a fashionable restaurant by his first name), but it is not essential to appreciation. It may greatly interfere with it. We know that painters are often very bad judges of pictures, for their interest in technique absorbs them so that they cannot recognise merits, unconnected with it, that may give a picture value. For technique is only the method by which the artist achieves his aim. It is no more than the knowledge that has gradually been acquired of the best ways to attain the specific excellencies of which a medium is capable. It cannot touch the heart nor excite the mind. An inadequate technique will not prevent the artist from doing this. I do not think people are sufficiently conscious of the great difference there is between the attitude of the artist towards the work he creates and the attitude of the beholder. The connection between them is slight. For the moment I will leave on one side the position of the artist and consider the work of art in relation with the beholder.

But first I should like to deal with the meaning of a word. To the term artist is now attached a judgement of value, and (though painters are not so squeamish) most of us who practise an art are as shy of calling ourselves artists as we are of calling ourselves gentlemen. In this sense the term is the sport of fashion. A painter may be at one period considered an artist and at another a charlatan. What makes it more confusing is that it does not always correspond with pre-ëminence. I suppose few people would deny that Addison was a greater artist than Charles Dickens, but few could doubt which was the greater writer. The word craftsman has unfortunate associations, nor does it indicate the act of creation, which is the essence of the matter; and the word creator is intolerably pretentious. I do not know any word that will do but artist; I must use it, but I mean by it only someone who is engaged in the arts. He may be a good artist or a bad one.

I have long since abjured the heresy prevalent in my youth of art for art's sake. Oscar Wilde popularized it in England and Oscar Wilde learnt it from Whistler. It gave art an esoteric quality that flattered the artist and it was accepted by the cultured public with the humility that characterises them. The cultured public have always taken a masochistic pleasure in the contempt that artists have shown them and, browbeaten and intimidated, have comforted themselves with a feeling of superiority over the common herd. It was believed that the object of a work of art was to arouse the æsthetic emotion and when you had felt that you had got all it had to give you. But what is an emotion that results in nothing? To experience the æsthetic emotion is pleasurable and all pleasure is good; but it is pleasurable also to drink a glass of beer and no one has ever been able to show that, taken simply as pleasure, one surpasses the other. Attempts have been made by moralists to prove that spiritual pleasures are keener and more lasting than sensual pleasures; they carry no conviction. No pleasure endures and to please it must be taken in small doses and at not too frequent intervals. It would be no less tedious to hear Beethoven's Fifth Symphony every day than it would be to eat caviare. And until age has blunted the sensibilities the general experience is surely that the pleasures of sense are more vivid than the pleasures of the spirit. We have all known omnivorous readers who read for the delight of it; they absorb books as the machines in Chicago absorb hogs, but no sausages come out of them at the other end; and we have all known the people who moon their days away in picture galleries in imbecile contemplation; they are no better than opium smokers, worse if anything, for the opium smoker at all events is not self-complacent. The value of emotion lies in its effects. Santa Teresa insisted on this over and over again: the ecstasy of union with the Godhead was precious only if it resulted in greater capacity for works. The æsthetic emotion, however delightful and however subtle, has worth only if it leads to action.

The work of art, whether the artist intended it or not, and for my part I think he seldom does, proffers a communication. This has nothing to do with the artist. From his standpoint it may only be a by-product of his activity: so the esculent swallows build nests to rear their young and are unaware that for their aphrodisiac qualities they will go to make soup for the enfeebled but amative Chinese. This communication is made in two voices. For the work of art is a diversion, an escape from the bitterness of life and a solace in the world's inevitable cruelty, a rest from its turmoil and a relief from labour. This is much, and if a work of art has only this communication to make it justifies itself. But great works speak with another voice too; they enrich the soul so that it is capable of a nobler and more fruitful activity. Their effects are worthy deeds. But should you ask me what these are I must confess that I should find it hard to reply. Provisionally at all events I should be willing enough to accept the maxim of Fray Luis de Leon: "The beauty of life," he says, "is nothing but this, that each should act in conformity with his nature and his business."

Notwithstanding this long preamble I do not wish to say much of El Greco's pictures. Nothing is so tedious as a description of the greens, yellows and blues that are in a picture; you cannot visualise them even with a photograph before you and the narrator's enthusiasm does not matter to you a row of pins. It is enough to say that El Greco's cool, silvery colours are lovely. When the art critics begin to talk of upper triangles and lower triangles, as they do with the Burial of Count Orgaz, or of inner and outer ellipses in the San Maurizio, I sigh. Do they really think that an artist bothers his head with such things? You look at a picture as a whole, that is one of the advantages the plastic arts have over the descriptive, and it is as a whole that it must affect you. The study of its parts is merely amusement. An emotion analysed is no longer an emotion. I do not suppose the painter creates a work of art differently from any other artist. The artist works by instinct combined with knowledge and his knowledge he acquires partly from his predecessors and partly from his own errors. I have had the greatest admiration for El Greco and if now my admiration is a trifle qualified that is perhaps because I have got out of him all that I am capable of getting. For my own part I find that when a work of art has given me a powerful emotion I cannot recapture it any more than I can eat a dinner I have already eaten. In this I am very unlike a cow. One gets tired of everything. But what remains is the personality behind the work of art; that to some minds is the great interest in the artist's work; and that, so complex is man, is an interest that endures when you know his work by heart.

It is with the personality then of the Greek that I am concerned. There is only one word that I know to describe it and that is one we are told to eschew. The late, but excellent, Fowler tells us that there is no excuse for the use of the word intriguing. He asks plaintively why we should not say interesting or perplexing, but really they do not mean quite the same thing, and if ever the word is justified it is here. To me it suggests an ambiguity, a puzzle that invites you to solve it and a secret that demands all your subtlety to discover it. It is all very well to tell us that it is formed from the word intrigue; the adjective has by now acquired a meaning of its own. I would say boldly then that no great artist is more intriguing than El Greco. I have wondered whether from the little that is known of his life, from some acquaintance with the circumstances in which he lived and from his strange and beautiful paintings, it was possible to get a coherent idea of the person he was. This indeed was essential if I was in my pages to draw the portrait of a living man. I thought also that I might thus explain, at least to my own satisfaction, something of the mysteriousness of his pictures.

Of his life very little is known and that little is unexpected. Until recently he was thought to have been born about 1545, or even later, for there is a letter, dated 1570, from Julio Clovio recommending him to the attention of Cardinal Farnese in which he is described as a youth; but lately an erudite Spaniard, Don Francisco San Roman, has proved that he was born in 1541. It seems strange that Julio Clovio should have called him a youth when he was hard on thirty; at that time, and indeed much later, that age was looked upon as the flower of manhood and youth already passed; but it agrees well enough with the statement made by Jusepe Martinez that he died at an advanced age. It is known that he died in 1614. The explanation may be that Julio Clovio thought thus to excite the sympathy of a possible patron and it may be that, being himself seventy-three, he looked upon a man of thirty as no more than a boy. In his letter he describes him further as a pupil of Titian, and this is at first sight surprising, since the works by which we chiefly know him show the influence of Tintoretto rather than of Titian. But it appears that El Greco's early pictures owe much to him, and the wily Julio Clovio may well have thought it more useful to describe the young man as the pupil of the better known master. He was born in Crete. Of his boyhood nothing is known, but it is supposed that he learnt to paint in the monastery schools in which the manufacture of icons had long been a flourishing industry. He went to Venice, but at what age is uncertain, and after a lengthy sojourn there settled down in Rome. Here he seems to have passed five or six years, and sometime between 1575 and 1577, being then about thirty-five, he went to Spain. He stayed there for the rest of his life. The common view is that in Toledo he recognised his spiritual home. It is held that he acquired his magic colour from the grey walls of that city built upon a rock and from the austere tones of the surrounding country; in his encounter with the Spanish character it is held that he developed an originality that his early works had given small hint of, and in his contact with the passionate Spanish faith achieved the mystical exaltation that inspires his great religious pictures. He has been seen as a man of an austere temper, indifferent to the things of the earth, who went his lonely ascetic way intent only on expressing his rapt vision; and those later pictures of his with their fantastic distortions seemed the final effort to represent a spiritual experience.

This is plausible, romantic enough to please the fancy, and coherent. But it is only credible if you leave out everything that is known of El Greco and that can be seen in his pictures that does not fit in with it. Those cool colours of his were there before ever he went to Spain: it may be that they were the colours he learnt in the Cretan monastery in which he had been taught to paint icons, or it may be that he discovered them in his own sensibility. There is no reason to believe that they would have been different if he had never left Italy. It is singular to find in the portrait of Julio Clovio, painted before his journey to Spain, a landscape with the same tortured sky that he painted so often in his later pictures. It is a sky that in point of fact you do not see in Toledo nearly so often as you do in Venice and indeed you will find it in several of Tintoretto's pictures in the Scuola di San Rocco. In the Madonna del Orto you will find the heavy grey clouds, with their abrupt outlines, looking as though they were cut out of tufa, that are so characteristic of El Greco.

There is no knowing why he went to Spain. It may be of course that he went because he hoped to get work. Artists were engaged to decorate the

Escorial and a painter who could find little to do at home might well think it worth his while to try his luck abroad. So English actors who cannot get a job in London go to New York and often achieve a success that their own country denied them. A certain Mancini, a contemporary, states that he left Rome because the painters and patrons of the arts resented a remark he had made about Michael Angelo's Last Judgement. The Pope, considering certain figures indecent, desired to have them painted over, whereupon El Greco said that if he would destroy the whole work he would do another, "not a whit worse than Michael Angelo's as a work of art, which would be both chaste and decorous in addition." Painters must have changed very much since then if they took so much to heart a fellow painter's criticism of a dead painter, and patrons of the arts had much to learn if they attached great importance to what one artist said of another. I can see nothing in El Greco's character to persuade me that any indignation a flout of his might arouse would have driven him from a place he did not want to leave. In a dispute between El Greco and the chapter of Toledo over his picture El Espolio, when asked during the legal proceedings that took place why he had come to Spain, he refused to answer. Considering that he was a foreigner, living among people who did not like foreigners, and at loggerheads with the Church, which few were inclined to affront, it seems strange that he should have declined to give his reason without good cause. It looks very much as though he had something to hide. When you read the novels and biographies of the day it occurs to you how often a journey was occasioned by the tragic outcome of a quarrel. Swords were drawn quickly, often on trivial grounds, and if you were unlucky enough to kill your antagonist it was usual to go while the going was good. I have wondered whether research in the police records of Rome, if such still exist, would not reward the industrious investigator with the explanation why El Greco went to Spain and stayed there. At the same trial he stated that he did not understand Spanish very well. This does not seem to have been questioned. He had then been in Toledo for three or four years. El Greco had provided himself with a sleeping dictionary; which our empire-builders recommend as the best way to acquire the speech of the country they inhabit and so make themselves more competent to bear the white man's burden. He took a mistress, Doña Jeronima de las Cubas, and in 1578, it is supposed, had a son by her. Levantines are quick at learning languages. El Greco's indifference to acquiring Spanish does not look as though he were very much interested in the country which was to be his home for the rest of his life. He never lost his pride in his Greek birth. As is well known he signed his pictures with his full name in Greek characters and added the fact that he was a Cretan. A list of the books in his possession at his death has been found. There were about two hundred of them. Of these only seventeen were in Spanish; but unfortunately their titles are not given. The rest were in Italian or Greek. It is hard to resist the conclusion that his curiosity about Spanish literature was not intense.

Toledo, when El Greco settled there, was no longer the capital of Spain, but it was still the centre of much artistic and literary activity. Churches were being built that had to be decorated. Ecclesiastics lived splendidly. Poets and dramatists made lengthy sojourns. The painter might very well have known Lope de Vega and Cervantes; he certainly knew Gongora, the obscure, irascible and conceptist poet. Plays were given by professional actors and by aristocratic amateurs, and every possible occasion was seized upon, the birth of a royal prince, the signing of a peace, for splendid festivities. An attractive picture of the life of the place is given in the Cigarrales de Toledo to which I have already referred. It is a dull book, it must be confessed, and the euphuistic style in which it is written is tedious. The time of day is told you with such witty conceits that to discover what it is you need not only some acquaintance with astronomy but also with mythology. When you are told that a curtain is indebted to the labours of architectural worms it is easy to guess that it is made of silk, but you have to think a moment before you discover that when the author informs you that snow, transformed into wax by the parturition of the republican but tiny birds, was burning, he means that the candles were lit. To our modern taste it seems a roundabout way of saying that you threw a letter into the fire unopened to state that only the flames were given leave to unseal it. But for all that you get an impression of leisured, courtly, well-bred persons who took delight in beautiful things. They passed the summer mornings in the pleasures of the chase and fishing (the fish biting with avidity because the bait was offered them by such fair hands); the afternoons in peaceful games, tilting and racing; and the nights in dancing, delectable argument and ingenious devising.

The reader may think that this picture does not correspond very well with what I have said before about the poverty that so constantly oppressed the Spaniards of the Golden Age. Let him go to the Mall on the evening of a Court and look at the long line of cars driving up in which sit dowagers in their diamonds and débutantes in grand new dresses. They tell me that the scene within the Palace is gorgeous beyond description. Then let him stroll along to the Admiralty Arch. He will find a coffee-stall where the hungry are given for nothing a cup of tea and a bite to eat. There he will see a string of men a quarter of a mile long, patiently waiting, one hour, two hours, for the stall to open. He will admit that there is nothing contradictory in what I have said and indeed that it is just what you would expect.

It has been supposed that El Greco lived in the cultured society of the city, consorting with grave ecclesiastics and eminent lawyers; but the only evidence I know of this is that he painted portraits of such personages. He was a man of education and of a pleasant discourse. Among his Greek books, besides classics such as Homer, Euripides, Plutarch and Lucian were the works of certain of the Fathers, St. John Chrysostom, St. Justin, St. Basil; and it is probable that he could converse suitably with the reverend gentlemen who were his principal patrons. Among his Italian books were Petrarch, Ariosto, and Bernardo Tasso. In his life, which was described as singular and extravagant, there is nothing to suggest the ascetic. He dwelt in a large house with a display that was thought ostentatious, and he had musicians come from Venice to play to him while he was at dinner. Nothing of this is surprising, for it is an error to suppose that the artist lives in a garret from choice. Philosophers may content themselves with plain living, but painters, writers and musicians are occupied with the things of sense and whenever they have been able, have lived with splendour. They have liked grand houses, with as many servants to wait upon them as they could pay for, and they have seldom hesitated to run into debt to provide themselves with fine clothes. El Greco had a keen eye on the profits of his trade. He made a great deal of money. Of the few documents concerning him that have come down to us several have to do with his quarrels over payment with the patrons who had commissioned him to paint a picture. When the authorities taxed him upon the profits of his work at Illescas he fought them and got a judgement in his favour. So far as I can understand the argument his contention was that what he sold was not canvas and paint, but the art with which he had arranged the paint, and this was not dutiable. Like many another artist before and after him, he was a shrewd business man. He kept in his studio sketches of his pictures so that when the patron came along for an altarpiece he could order what he wanted, a St. Francis or a Magdalen, an Assumption of the Virgin or Christ bearing the Cross: they were all there, you paid your money and you took your choice. He repeated pictures as often as he was required to. There are two or three versions at least of most of his paintings and of St. Francis in Meditation there are, it appears, over twenty.

There is a peculiar thing about the process of artistic creation which I should not have thought was any different in a painter and a writer. When a writer has been occupied with a subject and has done what he could with it, he is so sick of it that he takes no more interest in it at all. He is like a snake that has sloughed its skin. The subject that has absorbed him ceases to be a part of him; the emotion that filled him when he was working at it is dead and he cannot by any effort of will recapture it. When a writer must take up a theme out of which he has got all he could, making a play out of a novel, to take an example, the labour is mechanical. He cannot expect to have any inspiration. It is a task he performs by exercise of the knowledge he has acquired. I cannot understand how El Greco could have painted the same pictures over and over again if he was really filled with the religious emotion people find in them. I should have thought he could only do this if the subject was of no consequence to him.

The authorities have dealt with this matter in a very simple way. They have divided El Greco's pictures into good, indifferent, and bad. They claim that he painted the good ones by himself, the indifferent with the help of his assistants, who painted the bad ones all by themselves. It seems to me a little too simple. He must have been a very wonderful artist indeed if he never painted a bad picture. It is strange that Tristan, the best of his pupils, when he worked on his own, painted no pictures so good as the worst of those that are with any probability ascribed to his master. Of course El Greco had assistants who prepared the canvas, squared up the design, and presumably did some underpainting; but the contracts that various religious bodies made with him go into such particular detail, they are so careful to state what they want, you cannot persuade yourself that they would have accepted work which they were not reasonably sure was from his own hand. Indeed when there was a possibility that through death or other hindrance he could not finish a certain work a clause was inserted in the contract that it should be finished by his son Jorge Manuel or by some other specified person. I think some explanation must be sought for the fact that no painter of genius so often repeated his pictures as did El Greco.

Now let us look at the portraits he painted of himself. There is one in the Burial of Count Orgaz and another in the St. Maurizio in the Escorial. It is not certain that they are his portraits, it is only a tradition that they are, but they are evidently portraits of the same man and it is likely that the tradition is true. Accepting them then, on the great authority of Don Manuel Cossio, as authentic I think one may safely say that El Greco may not have looked like this, but this is what he thought he looked like. It is a thin, intelligent face, fresh-coloured, a rather long face; the beard, of a palish, reddish brown, is well trimmed; the hair is dark; the forehead is high and noble; the eyes, somewhat close-set, are cool, observant and reflective. You have the impression of a man who gave a good deal of thought to his appearance. You would have said from the look of him that this was a composed, intelligently curious man, but one capable neither of great passion nor of deep emotion. In neither of these pictures is there in the expression any of the seriousness which one would have thought the occasion demanded. This person seems to preserve a strangely ironic detachment; it would never occur to you that he was a mystic; you might have taken him for a sardonic humorist.

Often the portraits that an artist paints will tell you as much about himself as about his sitters, and I have wondered whether El Greco's would not offer some clue to what I sought. Now when you look at a collection of El Greco's portraits, in the Prado for instance, the first thing that strikes you is their distinction. They have a well-bred elegance. They have gravity and decorum. But it would be absurd to say that they are profound. They seem indeed to be painted in the most perfunctory fashion. The colour is cool and subdued, but no effort is made to use the mass in an effective manner; the bony structure is barely indicated; the heads have no backs to them and the bodies no weight. You get the impression that the Greek was not interested in the people he painted. These men were the contemporaries of the conquistadores and of the saints; they are as empty of character as lord mayors. When you compare these portraits with those of Zurbaran, so actual, so strongly individualized, they cease to exist. More than once certainly El Greco painted a magnificent portrait, but only when some eccentricity in the sitter's appearance gave him the obvious opportunity. Now in fiction it is easy to make a striking character of a person with marked characteristics; the difficulty is to make a man live when he is more or less like everybody else. Any competent novelist could create the father in the Brothers Karamazov; he needed to be more than that who created the old servant in Un Cœur Simple. I should have thought it was the same in portrait painting. More insight and more imagination were needed, I should have thought, to paint the Man with the Glove than the Grand Inquisitor. It looks as though El Greco regarded his sitters with a singular detachment. Is it possible that this mystic took no interest in the human soul? Though infinitely well-born these people look terribly stupid. They were. The history of Spain during the Golden Age is a history of the abysmal ineptitude of which the human race is capable. A

Greek, subtle and quick-witted, a man of culture, it may well be that he was impatient of these fine gentlemen's stupidity.

Years ago I went to Crete, not hoping to find any trace of El Greco, but curious to see the island that had given him birth. From the sea it offers a jagged aspect. It seems to consist of ridge upon ridge of rough, barren and stony hills. Their sharp outlines silhouetted against the sky have an austere and unapproachable beauty. Yet when you go into the interior you find that these hills, tawny, arid and sparsely covered with coarse herbage, separate into pleasing valleys. Here flourish great plantations of ancient olives and in more favourable places vines. Ash-trees and cypresses grow along the streams and oleanders luxuriate at their brim. But when you come away it is not so much the memory of the smiling valleys and the shallow rippling streams that you take with you, but rather of the desolate, wild and tawny hills. When the Greek looked at the gaunt mountain ranges of Castile it must have seemed to him that he was very close to the landscape he had known in childhood.

Candia, outside the main street untidy and bedraggled, is a town of narrow tortuous streets, with low houses that offer a blank wall to the view; and the unpaved road, all holes, is dusty in dry weather and a morass in wet. You might think yourself back in the sixteenth century. By the side of the grand new Greek church is a little old one, very low, dark, and heavy with stale incense. Its reredos is richly carved and gilt and on the walls hang large icons that you can scarcely see. In the sacristy are others. Some of them are very old and one or two are fine. In several a foreign influence is manifest. In them the Byzantine

feeling is swamped, but not entirely destroyed, by the easy splendour and the courtly formality of Venetian art. It is not unreasonable to suppose that it was the exciting charm of this new style that impelled the young painter to make his way to Venice.

No one knows how long the Cretan lived in Italy, ten, twelve or fifteen years; but they were the impressionable years of his youth and we know the sort of circumstances he was thrown in. Venice had lost much of its political power and the population was declining, but it was the playground of Europe and life, splendid still, was led by the rich with pomp. Manners were easy, scruples were few. The Bride of the Adriatic resisted as well as she could the efforts of the Papacy to reform her morals and to purify her faith. Thought was free and the intelligent were elegantly sceptical. Rome, alarmed by the Reformation, was making some effort to set her house in order, but there is no evidence that the individual was much inconvenienced by the fervour that reigned in high places. Artists have ever proved hostile to the limitations that puritanism has sought to impose on their private behaviour. From the little that is known of El Greco it seems likely that he would have remained an indifferent spectator of a spiritual movement that his foreign birth made of no great moment to him. Since he died fortified by the rites of the Catholic Church he was presumably received into it, but when you look at his coolly sceptical face you cannot but wonder whether it meant as much to him as those have thought who see in his pictures the most fervent expression of the passion of the Counter-reformation.

Everyone knows how Philip II commissioned El Greco to paint a picture of St. Maurice and his companions for one of the altars of the Escorial and when it was delivered liked it so little that he would not let it be placed in the church but banished it to a cellar. It hangs now in the Sala Capitular and is the greatest glory of the Escorial. In the eyes of the cultured not one of the actions of his long reign has redounded more to the discredit of Philip II. I think he has been harshly treated. He was a sufficiently enlightened patron of the arts to buy the pictures of Titian and to ask Paul Veronese to come to Spain to decorate the stupendous building on which he lavished such vast treasure. He was a deeply and sincerely religious man. He shared the common (and not unreasonable) opinion of his time that saints should be painted in such a manner that one did not lose the desire to pray before them, nay, that they should engender devotion, "since the chief effect and the end of painting them must be this." El Greco's picture is of superb vivacity, its colouring is so brilliant and original that the neighboring pictures look dull beside it; but Philip knew a religious picture when he saw one. In the San Maurizio the three chief figures wear what I suppose are leather jerkins, but they are in effect nudes; their muscles are drawn as in a studio study and even the navels are shown. The angels that fly about the clouds or in easy attitudes rest upon them, playing musical instruments and singing, seem to take part in a divertisement like those prepared by great nobles to honour a royal guest. The figures in the background, the Theban legion, might be stripped for the Olympian games rather than to attest their faith by martyrdom. It would not be strange if Philip was shocked by the frivolity with which El Greco had treated the scene. The attitude of those various personages is a triumph of elegance.

Never did El Greco more obviously paint gestures for their beauty rather than their significance. It is a picture that gives enjoyment; it does not excite devotion.

I cannot but ask myself why El Greco, who could draw so beautifully when he wanted to, should, apart from his deliberate distortions, at times have drawn so carelessly. Why does he put a Virgin's eye half way down her face or make it pop out of her head as though, poor thing, she had exophthalmic goitre? Why does he sometimes give his saints the look of ducks dying of fright in a thunderstorm? The Virgin in the Crucifixion in the Prado is grotesque; that face would not be out of keeping in a satyric painting by Goya. (But how lovely is the colour, the green tunic worn by St. John, the exquisite tone of the body hanging on the cross, so tender and ethereal, and the richness of that tempestuous sky!) I am tempted to ask myself whether when he painted a religious picture he did not give way sometimes to a sardonic humour. It is difficult to see more than a conventional devotion in those single figures of Franciscan saints which as we know he painted wholesale. The St. Antony in the Prado is composed so perfunctorily that it does not even make sense. In one hand the saint delicately holds a madonna lily, while with the other he supports a heavy open book in which is a small brown object that he seems to study in pitch-black night; for the background is that stormy sky which El Greco used with amazing pertinacity. And beautiful as I find the Resurrection in the Prado, with the slender, soaring, movingly painted figure; exciting as I find the sweep of those others with their arms raised in such expressive gesture; I am not conscious of any depth of religious feeling. Nor is there any that I can see in the Baptism of Christ. It is a lovely picture, with colour of an intoxicating beauty; those elongated forms, nude but for their loin-cloths, of the Saviour and the Baptist, have an exquisite sophisticated grace; but I feel there no fervour of belief nor rapture of ecstasy. It is disconcerting in that fine picture of Christ bearing the Cross to see the elegance with which the Saviour clasps it. Indeed it is on the hands that El Greco has concentrated the interest. The face, with the eyes showing a great deal of white under the pupil, which was the Cretan's simple way of expressing religious emotion, is the face of a comic actor. Ernest Thesiger might have sat for it. The right hand rests on the cross with the third and fourth fingers together, an old trick of the painter's to get away from the awkwardness of those five odd digits; while the left, again with the third and fourth fingers together, has the little one slightly crooked as ladies of easy virtue to show their refinement crook their little fingers when they drink a glass of champagne.

Not far from the San Maurizio in the Sala Capitular of the Escorial is a picture that portrays religious emotion in a very different manner. It is a Deposition from the Cross, and it is by Van der Weyden. Here the emotion is sincere and natural. The expressions are real. The painter felt what he painted and expressed what he felt. You are moved because he was moved himself. It is an awful moment that is represented and there is a sense of despair in the droop of those figures that makes you feel that here is the most terrifying moment in the world's history. The men are stricken with grief, but gravely masters of it; Mary has swooned and there is another woman, Mary Magdalen, I suppose, whose clumsy, broken attitude gives

you a tragic impression of hopelessness. All these people feel as they would feel and act as they would act. It is a beautiful picture, a terrible scene, and one to bring home to a rude and brutal people the horror of the event represented. Its sincerity is shattering. You cannot look at it and again believe in El Greco's religious sense.

I do not doubt that he was one of the greatest painters that ever lived. I think the Burial of Count Orgaz is one of the greatest pictures in the world. It has a sweep, a freshness and a vitality that are amazing. It fills you with stupefaction. El Greco was a master of gesture. You would never think that an outflung arm, a raised hand, a foot on tip-toe or an extended leg, could have such a miraculous grace. He had indeed a wonderful sense of the beautiful though limited gestures permitted to the hand. The general effect of a large number of his pictures together, as you may see them in the room in the Prado, is thrilling; it is not only that distinguished, cool yet not cold, colour that moves you, but something in the pictures themselves, apart also from their subjects, their form and architecture. It is something troubling, sinister and enigmatic; I can only suppose it is the personality of the painter. It is like looking into the darkness of a lake in the mountains. You feel vaguely scared. You wonder whether there is anything there at the bottom, a secret that it would be good for you to know, or whether it is an aimless depth that has no purpose. For depth in itself has no greater significance than breadth. The lake may look bottomless only because it is muddy, and if you take a header into it you can easily crack your skull. In literature, I know, the obscure is very often taken for the profound. Here, however, time plays an odd trick; it dissipates obscurity as a breeze dissipates fog, and then are discovered, not the great truths we hoped for, but painted trifles. Thus time has made most of Mallarmé's poems quite clear and we see that all that labyrinthine imagery hid from the vulgar nothing more abstruse than the poetic commonplaces of the day. All that remains to delight us is a number of pellucid and beautiful phrases.

It gives you a curious sensation to go from the room in which the El Grecos are hung into the Velasquez room next door. It is like coming into the warm light of common day. You cannot but feel that Velasquez is somewhat superficial, but he is superficial on the grand scale. He had an equable, sunny temperament and his pictures are delightfully gay. He had that alegria which is the Andalusian's most cherished and characteristic grace. He does not in his portraits suggest a criticism of his sitters. He takes them at their face value. He was the greatest of court-painters. His charm was combined with a genial heartlessness. His dwarfs and fools are painted with amusement. So might Shakespeare have drawn them. He had no feeling for the horror of their deformity or the misery of their lot. His cheerful temper enabled him to look upon these loathsome abortions with the good humour of one who knew that the Almighty had created them to be the playthings of princes. I suppose no one can deny his miraculous skill in painting, the silvery lustre of his blacks and the richness of his sober tones. He could paint the dress of an infanta in such a manner as to take one's breath away. But even as one admires one is filled with a slight sense of uneasiness and one asks oneself whether this wonderful skill is worth while. It reminds one of a writer who says things with exquisite

sobriety, but says nothing of any great consequence. But how skilfully these figures are placed on the canvas to make a pattern pleasing to the eye! In the full length of Philip IV with his gun and in the companion picture of the Cardinal-Infante pure representation seems to achieve perfect beauty. There is nothing to be said. You can only stand and gape.

When you go back to the El Greco room you enter a troubled world. Here is a wild intensity that seems to seek utterance for no emotion that can be made clear by symbols. It is a vague and tormenting sensation that seems to oppress him, like that anxiety, common at times to us all, I suppose, to which no cause can be assigned; you do not know whether it is of the body or the spirit. It was not a man of equable and sunny temper who painted these pictures, but a man of uncertain humour perplexed by fantastic longings; it was a man striving with pain for an expression that he sought in the abyss of his soul as though it were a memory hovering just below consciousness that it exasperated him to be unable to recall. But if he was a mystic his mysticism must surely be sought in another sphere than the religious. Pacheco, who saw him in his old age, says of El Greco that he was a great philosopher, very witty in his speech, personal, profound, with an original answer to everything. We know that he was luxurious and improvident; indeed he died insolvent; the portraits he painted of himself suggest scepticism and irony; and one's own sensibility persuades one that he was very lonely. Even in Rome he had a high conceit of himself and later on his arrogance was overweening. In the action over his remuneration for the Burial of Count Orgaz he finished his pleadings with the words: "As true as it is that the payment is inferior to the value of my sublime work, my name will pass to posterity, which will recompense my work and glorify the author as one of the greatest geniuses of Spanish painting." He was a Levantine and the Levantines are apt to express themselves with grandiloquence. No writer can have gone to Alexandria or Beyrout without being visited by some young author who tells him in bad but fluent French that he has written a novel vastly better than anything that Balzac, Anatole France or —Zola ever wrote. It is a bombastic use of words that does not preclude a real and often touching modesty. But humility is the very substance of the soil on which religious mysticism grows and it would be absurd to say that El Greco had it. There is a story which, if true, shows that he was something of an actor and the art of bluff was not unfamiliar to him. The story runs as follows: Tristan, his pupil, had painted for a stipulated price a picture for the Jeronimite monks of the convent of Sisla, but when the picture was finished the monks (doubtless with justice) thought it was not worth it and wanted to pay less. The matter was submitted to the arbitration of El Greco. He looked at the picture and then, flying into a passion, began to beat Tristan with his stick. The monks interposed. "Tristan is but young," they said, "and does not understand that he is asking too much." "Too much!" cried El Greco. "It is a sublime and beautiful work and I am beating him for daring to ask two hundred ducats for a picture that is worth five hundred, and if you don't pay the money at once I'm going to take it myself." The monks paid.

Taking it all in all you have the impression of a man who possessed most of the traits that we generally hold to be typical of the Levantine, and if you combined these ingeniously I do not think it would be impossible to construct an image coherent enough to be credible. The various particulars fit like the pieces of a jig-saw puzzle. The flaw lies in the fact that there is nothing in the sort of man you have thus created to account for the pictures he painted. One must look further.

Not long ago I came across the suggestion, made in a ribald spirit, that El Greco was homosexual. I have thought it worth considering. So far as an artist's work is concerned there is as a rule little interest in knowing about his sexual life, upon which indeed an exaggerated stress is generally laid. There is a notion that men who have in any way greatly distinguished themselves should in this respect be different from their fellows, and when the student discovers that they have had love affairs he is apt to think the fact strangely significant. For all the to-do that has been made over the amours of Shelley and Byron I cannot but doubt whether they were very different from those of other young men of their class. Many a smart young broker in the City of London would have looked upon them with supercilious amusement as extremely meagre. But when it comes to an abnormality the case is different. I have suggested that talent consists in an individual way of seeing the world combined with a natural aptitude for creation and that genius is talent with a greater capacity and a universal sympathy. Now it cannot be denied that the homosexual has a narrower outlook on the world than the normal man. In certain respects the natural responses of the species are denied to him. Some at least of the broad and typical human emotions he can never experience. However subtly he sees life he cannot see it whole. If it were not for the perplexing sonnets I should say that the homosexual can never reach the supreme heights of genius. I cannot now help asking myself whether what I see in El Greco's work of tortured fantasy and sinister strangeness is not due to such a sexual abnormality as this. I hasten to add that this can be nothing but surmise, as is all else I have said of him. Besides his pictures, the letter of Julio Clovio, certain legal documents, his death certificate and the list of his effects there is no material for any direct knowledge of him. Whatever does not proceed from this, however confidently it is stated, can be no more than plausible.

When you survey possibilities it must be admitted that there is in this one a good deal that saves it from being wildly improbable. El Greco spent his childhood and youth in places where he can have conceived no instinctive aversion to that idiosyncrasy. I should say that a distinctive trait of the homosexual is a lack of deep seriousness over certain things that normal men take seriously. This ranges from an inane flippancy to a sardonic humour. He has a wilfulness that attaches importance to things that most men find trivial and on the other hand regards cynically the subjects which the common opinion of mankind has held essential to its spiritual welfare. He has a lively sense of beauty, but is apt to see beauty especially in decoration. He loves luxury and attaches peculiar value to elegance. He is emotional, but fantastic. He is vain, loquacious, witty and theatrical. With his keen insight and quick sensibility he can pierce the depths, but in his innate frivolity he fetches up from them not a priceless jewel but a tinsel ornament. He has small power of invention, but a wonderful gift for delightful embroidery. He has vitality, brilliance, but seldom strength. He stands on the bank, aloof and ironical, and watches the river of life flow on. He is persuaded that opinion is no more than prejudice. In short he has many of the characteristics that surprise us in El Greco. It may be that in this abnormality lies the explanation why his pictures fail of that ultimate greatness which is release. They thrill; they do not give you peace. They excite; but do not satisfy. We know that whatever imagination El Greco had he did not apply it to the composition of his pictures. The learned have traced the patterns of some of them to the Byzantine icons with which he may be presumed to have been familiar in his early youth and of others to pictures he had seen in Italy. It is curious that in the full flush of his early manhood, when fancy is generally exuberant, he should have been content so often to take his designs from the woodcuts, engravings and etchings that were at that time current articles of commerce in Italy. When he had to invent something out of his head he was not remarkable. The Burial of Count Orgaz betrays its Byzantine inspiration. A dozen artists in Italy could have arranged it on a more satisfactory plan. It is only the miraculous painting that prevents that row of heads, cutting the picture into two parts, from being disconcerting. And when he had to represent the martyrdom of St. Maurice he shirked it and painted a group of young men who might be discussing the handicapping for the school sports. There is in Toledo a San Bernardino, with a tiny head, a courtly little pointed beard and an immensely long body against a gloomy sky, which is quite charming; but in the same way as the twisted pillars of a plateresque patio are charming. It is a delicious picture for a great lady's oratory. But it could hardly arouse devotion. It is perfectly frivolous. I think no religious painter ever expressed emotion so perfunctorily as El Greco. This would not be strange if he were entirely devoid of it.

A little while ago, confessing a former error, I made a distinction between the artist's work from his creative standpoint and its communication, which is what the layman is concerned with. I think a good deal of criticism is rendered less illuminating than it should be because critics often do not clearly distinguish between the two. They step from one to the other without realising that they are doing so. There need be no relation between them. The artist is not justified in claiming to be judged from the standpoint of his intention. That is important to him, and to anyone who cares to study his personality, but it is of no importance to the observer. The artist is driven to produce by an instinct within him that impels him to express his personality. He does not try to do this; it is an inevitable accident that he does so. He is in all probability not very much interested in his personality. (I am not speaking of the journeyman who busies himself with the arts to earn an honest living or the spent worker who continues to do so from habit.) The artist can no more help creating than water can help running down hill. It is a release from the burden on his soul. It is a spiritual exercise which is infinitely pleasurable, and it is accompanied by a sense of power that is in itself delightful. When production fulfills it he enjoys a heavenly sense of liberation. For one delicious moment he rests in a state of equilibrium. What the painter paints or the writer writes is an experience of himself and the theorists of art for art's

sake were right when they claimed that it had no moral value. Nor need this experience and its expression, whatever its importance for the person who feels it, have any value for anybody else. That must depend on the interest for the world of the personality that has thus been forced to exteriorise itself.

I think there are two ways in which El Greco sought deliverance. One was in decoration. To my mind he was singularly indifferent to his subjects. They were given him and like all artists he worked out his own intentions within the limitations imposed upon him by the circumstances of his time. That is why he could paint the same picture over and over again. These saints, Francis or Antony, meant no more to him than did their abstract designs to the early cubists. To him they were merely excuses for his decorative inventions. And that is why he was so much more interested in the hand than in the head. The hand has a possibility of lovely gesture that is denied to the head. No one has painted hands more exquisitely. But in many of the pictures they are placed with such affected grace that, considering the episode represented, you are shocked by the unseemliness. El Greco was ready to sacrifice truth of gesture to beauty of attitude. His reaction was, in short, baroque.

The reader must pardon me if I indulge now in a short disquisition on baroque. I do this not only because I think the subject in itself interesting, but because I seem to discern in that form of art and the circumstances that brought it about much that corresponds with the art of the present day and the conditions in which we are now living. I suppose everyone is agreed that massivity and movement are the essentials of baroque. It used decoration, not to complete a composition, but for its own sake; and its wonderful discovery was that movement was decorative. The spectacular nature of architecture has caused the learned to study baroque particularly in that art. This has made it a little more difficult to discover its distinctive features. The decorative element is not so noticeable in a building because the architect has made it for a certain use and this use conditions his treatment. But when you look more closely you cannot but see how much these great artists were concerned with it. They aimed at unity, whereas the Renaissance architects were content to make a harmonious composition of self-subsisting parts; and unity of effect is the first demand of decoration. We hesitate when we are told that the baroque architects sought to represent movement and our inclination is to think that they were aiming at something foreign to the spirit of their art and therefore necessarily bad. The play they made with light and shade seems like a device to deceive the eye into accepting what is contrary to nature. It takes a little while to recognise that mass is but an instant in the unending curve of movement. It is not my business here to point out the various uses they made of the expedients at their command and the triumphant success with which they achieved their ends. But the sway of baroque was by no means confined to architecture; it affected the painters and sculptors too, the writers, and I should imagine the musicians. Indeed I suspect that it gave their art for the first time the possibility of reaching the cloud-capped heights which Beethoven and Wagner attained. But of music I know nothing. I went to Cambridge to ask a great authority whether there was anything in my surmise, but thinking perhaps

that it was no affair of mine he would not tell me.

Baroque is often considered to be the characteristic expression of the Counter-reformation. It seems unlikely that it was created by it. The Counter-reformation built new churches and restored old ones. The artists who worked in them were baroque artists. They were sentimental, violent and theatrical as was the religion of the period, but not necessarily on account of it. Religion was declamatory; it exaggerated the manifestations of its piety in reaction from the pagan scepticism of the Renaissance and in challenge to the Lutheran strenuousness. It suited very well the new style the artists were now making use of; the extravagant emotions they were asked to express gave them an opportunity to use movement for purely decorative purposes and movement they could only represent by mass. I should have said that the Counter-reformation, so far as it was not dictated by fear, corresponded to a feeling that was in the the air and it was this feeling that created the universal tendency towards the baroque.

It is interesting to consider why this absorption in decoration, which to my mind is the essence of the style, should just at this time have made itself felt. Some writers have ascribed it to a normal reaction from the preceding period. The Renaissance was over and people were tired of the works it had produced. That was very natural, for man desires change and he wearies even of perfection. Beauty is a full stop and when you have reached it you can do nothing but start another sentence. The inspiration that the discovery of the antique had brought was exhausted. But boredom with one style cannot give rise to another; a new style arises from a new state of the spirit.

The Renaissance cultivated measure and repose. It cherished the golden mean. Its strength was tranquil. Art not only occupied an important part in men's lives, but the artists felt themselves in conformity with the life about them. They were citizens of the state as well as artists. Sin was original sin and the individual did not feel himself answerable for it. Man was free, if not always in fact, in imagination. And freedom was the most cherished of his ideals.

But the attempt to think again the thoughts and live once more the life enshrined in the literatures of Greece and Rome failed. Liberty died. Half of Italy was in the hands of Spain and the rest in the power of petty tyrants. The Inquisition, fostered by the Spanish kings as an instrument of state, acquired a new power in Italy. Incidents here and there in the picaresque novels prove the terror it inspired. Catholicism was restored by force. The Church claimed control over all the activities of the human mind, its philosophy, its science and its art. A strange disquiet oppressed the spirits of men. It seemed as though in their long struggle with intellect they had grown exhausted. Believers, notwithstanding, were uneasy, and they drowned their hesitations in a sea of declamation. They were intolerant because they were afraid. Man was deprived of his inalienable right of self-realisation and freedom was lost to him it seemed for ever.

Freedom is man's greatest good. When you rob the artist of this you force him back upon himself. When he can no longer deal with the great issues of life that in happier times occupy the souls of men, his instinct of creation, which nevertheless demands expression, can but turn to decoration. When men are wretched they look into their hearts and some inexplicable instinct leads them to ascribe their misery to their own shortcomings. Their minds turn to another world and they look for solace to their vexed spirits in the eternal. Sin was no longer original sin; it was personal, and a rigid reckoning would be demanded of the sinner. Decoration with its vague meanings can very well express the desire for the unearthly, the vague fear and the sense of guilt that haunted the souls of men to whom the healthy and inspiring activity of free men was denied. The Renaissance, essentially objective, copied and idealised nature; but baroque used nature as a vehicle to display its own morbid sensibility. It was subjective. And the most direct expression of the subjective is decoration. It is worth while to consider for a moment how the writers reacted to the conditions in which they found themselves. They turned away from matter and busied themselves with form. They sought brilliant and exquisite conceits, no matter how frivolous, and put them in the manner most calculated to surprise. They cultivated rhetoric, the play upon words, flowers of speech, archaisms and suchlike toys. They wanted to show their cleverness rather than to discover their hearts. All artists have in them something of the child. They like to play and if they lack serious and great convictions are very likely to squander their faculties on spiritual kickshaws. They do not try to make bread without leaven; they try to make bread with nothing but leaven. Michael Angelo, resuming in himself the restlessness and dissatisfaction of the age, tried by vastness, by violence, to express the passion of his tortured heart, and so became in the plastic arts the father of baroque. His contemporaries and successors felt the significance of what he had invented. Realising quickly the immense decorative value of mass and movement they began with growing assurance to make them the principles of their activity. But because they lacked his spiritual power their works seldom achieved his complete sincerity; and decoration, which had been grave and sincere because it corresponded to a deep instinct in the artist's nature, degenerated with time to the frivolous ornament of rococo.

Now let me return to El Greco. There was in him to my mind a temper that exactly suited the spirit that he found prevalent to some extent in Venice, and at its height in Rome. So he became the greatest of baroque painters. Looking at the whole series of his pictures I seem to see his interest in decoration for decoration's sake grow in intensity. His contemporaries thought that he painted in an increasingly fantastic manner because he went mad. I do not believe it. More recently it has been suggested that he suffered from astigmatism and it has been said that if you put on the right glasses his vertiginous figures would assume normal proportions. I do not belive it. Their immense elongation, which, I may remind the reader, he will find also in many of Tintoretto's pictures, seems to me a natural development of treating the human form as decoration. Because El Greco was aiming at this and nothing else I think he grew more and more indifferent to fact. This, I think, explains also his cock-eyed virgins. If the body, with its mass, is treated as a unit of expression the face becomes of no importance. It is not strange that the moderns should have set such great store by El Greco. If he were alive to-day I imagine he would paint pictures as abstract as the later work of Bracque, Picasso and Fernand Léger. And it may be that the interest in formal design of the present day is due to the same causes as produced baroque art in the sixteenth century. Now too we are spiritually at sixes and sevens. Afraid of the sublime, we take refuge in the multiplication table.

For now the world is sullen and jealous as was the world of the Counter-reformation. The great issues that occupied the Victorians, which seemed to offer the spirit boundless horizons, have played us false. We mock at those who maunder of truth, goodness and beauty. We are afraid of greatness. And we too have lost the inestimable blessing of freedom. Liberty throughout the world is dying or dead. Like the Jesuit novice who lost his personality to find it again in the Company we are asked to surrender our own to find it again in the State. Nobody dares tackle great subjects and the heresy has become orthodox that subject is of no consequence. Only the pretty, the ingenious, the amusing are cultivated. Artists have not yet learnt how to deal with what really matters to our world and so are driven to devote themselves to decoration. They make technical devices the end and aim of their endeavour. They cast off the shackles of tradition, use their independence to stand on their heads and, like Hippokleides, kick their legs in the air. Modern critics are wrong when they blame writers for writing about themselves. When art is no more than a side issue they have nothing else to write about.

But of course there is more in El Greco than the fantastic patterns he devised, his grace and distinction, the elegance of his gestures and his dramatic intensity, seldom falling into theatricalism, with which as I take it he satisfied the sardonic, ironic, sumptuous, sinister side of his nature. When you see many of a painter's pictures together you find in them often a certain monotony. An artist can only give you himself and he is unfortunately always very like himself. The startling thing about El Greco is that, such is his vitality, he can under the most unlikely conditions give you an impression of variety. Take for instance that collection of the Apostles which is in what is now called la casa del Greco. They are three-quarter lengths, canvases of the same size, and the personages are not happily individualised; but the vigour with which they are painted makes them lively and different. You feel in them the stubborn idiosyncrasy of their creator, in wonderful possession of his faculties, who, regardless of what people thought, was getting marvellous satisfaction out of their exercise. Then there is his colour. This, I think, was the second of the two methods by which he strove to release his spirit from its burden; and it is his colour that makes him so wonderful an artist. A painter thinks with his brushes. Such thoughts as he has that can be

put into words are for the most part commonplace. Why artists are often incomprehensible to other people is that they express their profoundest feelings in a language of their own. I think El Greco put the most serious emotion of his strange, perhaps inexplicable personality into the colours that he set down on canvas. However he acquired his palette, he gave it an intensity, a significance, which were his own. Colour was his complete and unique experience. They are not so far wrong who see in him a mystic, though I cannot help thinking that to look upon him as a religious mystic is superficial. If mysticism is that state that renders you conscious of depths of truth unknown to the intellect, revealing like "glimpses of forgotten dreams" a greater significance in life and union with some larger reality, then I think you can hardly fail to find it in El Greco's painting. I seem to see as great a mystic rapture in the painting of the right side of the body of Christ in the Crucifixion in the Louvre as in any of the experiences of Santa Teresa.

The Summing Up

I

THIS is not an autobiography nor is it a book of recollections. In one way and another I have used in my writings whatever has happened to me in the course of my life. Sometimes an experience I have had has served as a theme and I have invented a series of incidents to illustrate it; more often I have taken persons with whom I have been slightly or intimately acquainted and used them as the foundation for characters of my invention. Fact and fiction are so intermingled in my work that now, looking back on it, I can hardly distinguish one from the other. It would not interest me to record the facts, even if I could remember them, of which I have already made a better use. They would seem, moreover, very tame. I have had a varied, and often an interesting, life, but not an adventurous one. I have a poor memory. I can never remember a good story till I hear it again and then I forget it before I have had a chance to tell it to somebody else. I have never been able to remember even my own jokes, so that I have been forced to go on making new ones. This disability, I am aware, has made my company less agreeable than it might otherwise have been.

I have never kept a diary. I wish now that during the year that followed my first success as a dramatist I had done so, for I met then many persons of consequence and it might have proved an interesting document. At that period the confidence of the people in the aristocracy and the landed gentry had been shattered by the muddle they had made of things in South Africa, but the aristocracy and the landed gentry had not realized this and they preserved their old self-confidence. At certain political houses I frequented they still talked as though to run the British Empire were their private business. It gave me a peculiar sensation to hear it discussed, when a general election was in the air, whether Tom should have the Home Office and whether Dick would be satisfied with Ireland. I do not suppose that anyone today reads the novels of Mrs. Humphry Ward, but dull though they may be, my recollection is that some of them give a very good picture of what the life of the ruling class was then. Novelists were still much concerned with it and even writers who had never known a lord thought it necessary to write largely about persons of rank. It would astonish anyone now who looked at the playbills of the day to see how many of the characters were titled. Managers thought that they attracted the public, and actors liked to portray them. But as the political importance of the aristocracy dwindled the public took less interest in it. Playgoers began to be ready to observe the actions of people of their own class, the well-to-do merchants and professional men who were then conducting the affairs of the country; and the rule, though never formulated, prevailed that the writer should not introduce persons of title unless they were essential to his theme. It was still impossible to interest the public in the lower classes. Novels and plays that dealt with them were very generally considered sordid. It will be curious to see if now that these classes have acquired political power the public at large will take the same interest in their lives that for so long it took in the lives of the titled, and for a while in those of the opulent bourgeoisie.

During this period I met persons who by their rank, fame or position might very well have thought themselves destined to become historical figures. I did not find them as brilliant as my fancy had painted them. The English are a political nation and I was often asked to houses where politics were the ruling interest. I could not discover in the eminent statesmen I met there any marked capacity. I concluded, perhaps rashly, that no great degree of intelligence was needed to rule a nation. Since then I have known in various countries a good many politicians who have attained high office. I have continued to be puzzled by what seemed to me the mediocrity of their minds. I have found them ill-informed upon the ordinary affairs of life and I have not often discovered in them either subtlety of intellect or liveliness of imagination. At one time I was inclined to think that they owed their illustrious position only to their gift of speech, for it must be next door to impossible to rise to power in a democratic community unless you can catch the ears of the public; and the gift of speech, as we know, is not often accompanied by the power of thought. But since I have seen statesmen who did not seem to me very clever conduct public affairs with reasonable success I cannot but think I was wrong: it must be that to govern a nation you need a specific talent and that this may very well exist without general ability. In the same way I have known men of affairs who have made great fortunes and brought vast enterprises to prosperity, but in everything unconcerned with their business appear to be devoid even of common sense.

Nor was the conversation that I heard then as clever as I had expected. It seldom gave you much to think about. It was easy, though not always; gay, amiable and superficial. Serious topics were not dealt with, for there was a feeling that to discuss them in general company was embarrassing, and the fear of "shop" seemed to prevent people from speaking of the subjects in which they were most interested. So far as I could judge conversation consisted in little more than a decorous badinage; but it was not often that you heard a witticism worth repeating. One might have thought that the only use of culture was to enable one to talk nonsense with distinction. On the whole I think the most interesting and consistently amusing talker I ever knew was Edmund Gosse. He had read a great deal, though not very carefully, it appears, and his conversation was extremely intelligent. He had a prodigious memory, a keen sense of humour, and malice. He had known Swinburne intimately and could talk about him in an entrancing fashion, but he could also talk of Shelley, whom after all he could not possibly have known, as if he had been a bosom friend. For many years he had been acquainted with eminent persons. I think he was a vain man and he had observed their absurdities with satisfaction. I am sure he made them much more amusing than they really were.

II

I HAVE always wondered at the passion many people have to meet the celebrated. The prestige you acquire by being able to tell your friends that you know famous men proves only that you are yourself of small account. The celebrated develop a technique to deal with the persons they come across. They show the world a mask, often an impressive one, but take care to conceal their real selves. They play the part that is expected from them and with practice learn to play it very well, but you are stupid if you think that this public performance of theirs corresponds with the man within.

I have been attached, deeply attached, to a few people; but I have been interested in men in general not for their own sakes, but for the sake of my work. I have not, as Kant enjoined, regarded each man as an end in himself, but as material that might be useful to me as a writer. I have been more concerned with the obscure than with the famous. They are more often themselves. They have had no need to create a figure to protect themselves from the world or to impress it. Their idiosyncrasies have had more chance to develop in the limited circle of their activity, and since they have never been in the public eye it has never occurred to them that they have anything to conceal. They display their oddities because it has never struck them that they are odd. And after all it is with the common run of men that we writers have to deal; kings, dictators, commercial magnates are from our point of view very unsatisfactory. To write about them is a venture that has often tempted writers, but the failure that has attended their efforts shows that such beings are too exceptional to form a proper ground for a work of art. They cannot be made real. The ordinary is the writer's richer field. Its unexpectedness, its singularity, its infinite variety afford unending material. The great man is too often all of a piece; it is the little man that is a bundle of contradictory elements. He is inexhaustible. You never come to the end of the surprises he has in store for you. For my part I would much sooner spend a month on a desert island with a veterinary surgeon than with a prime minister.

III

IN THIS book I am going to try to sort out my thoughts on the subjects that have chiefly interested me during the course of my life. But such conclusions as I have come to have drifted about my mind like the wreckage of a foundered ship on a restless sea. It has seemed to me that if I set them down in some sort of order I should see for myself more distinctly what they really were and so might get some kind of coherence into them. I have long thought I should like to make such an attempt and more than once, when starting on a journey that was to last for several months, have determined to set about it. The opportunity seemed ideal. But I have always found that I was assailed by so many impressions, I saw so many strange things and met so many people who excited my fancy, that I had no time to reflect. The experience of the moment was so vivid that I could not attune my mind to introspection.

I have been held back also by the irksomeness of setting down my thoughts in my own person. For though I have written a good deal from this standpoint I have written as a novelist and so in a manner have been able to regard myself as a character in the story. Long habit has made it more comfortable for me to speak through the creatures of my invention. I can decide what they would think more readily than I can decide what I think myself. The one has always been a pleasure to me; the other has been a labour that I have willingly put off. But now I can afford to put it off no longer. In youth the years stretch before one so long that it is hard to realize that they will ever pass, and even in middle age, with the ordinary expectation of life in these days, it is easy to find excuses for delaying what one would like to do but does not want to; but at last a time comes when death must be considered. Here and there one's contemporaries drop off. We know that all men are mortal (Socrates was a man; therefore —and so forth), but it remains for us little more than a logical premiss till we are forced to recognize that in the ordinary course of things our end can no longer be remote. An occasional glance at the obituary column of *The Times* has suggested to me that the sixties are very unhealthy; I have long thought that it would exasperate me to die before I had written this book and so it seemed to me that I had better set about it at once. When I have finished it I can face the future with serenity, for I shall have rounded off my life's work. I can no longer persuade myself that I am not ready to write it, since if I have not by now made up my mind about the things that seem of importance to me there is small likelihood that I shall ever do so. I am glad at last to collect all these thoughts that for so long have floated at haphazard on the various levels of my consciousness. When they are written down I shall have finished with them and my mind will be free to occupy itself with other things. For I hope that this will not be the last book I shall write. One does not die immediately one has made one's will; one makes one's will as a precaution. To have settled one's affairs is a very good preparation to leading the rest of one's life without concern for the future. When I have finished this book I shall know where I stand. I can afford then to do what I choose with the years that remain to me.

IV

It is inevitable that in it I should say many things that I have said before; that is why I have called it *The Summing Up*. When a judge sums up a case he recapitulates the facts that have been put before the jury and comments on the speeches of counsel. He does not offer new evidence. And since I have put the whole of my life into my books much of what I have to say will naturally have found a place in them. There are few subjects within the compass of my interests that I have not lightly or seriously touched upon. All I can attempt to do now is to give a coherent picture of my feelings and opinions; and here and there, maybe, to state with greater elaboration some idea which the limitations I have thought fit to accept in fiction and in the drama have only allowed me to hint at.

This book must be egotistic. It is about certain subjects that are important to me and it is about myself because I can only treat of these subjects as they have affected me. But it is not about my doings. I have no desire to lay bare my heart, and I put limits to the intimacy that I wish the reader to enter upon with me. There are matters on which I am content to maintain my privacy. No one can tell the whole truth about himself. It is not only vanity that has prevented those who have tried to reveal themselves to the world from telling the whole truth; it is direction of interest; their disappointment with themselves, their surprise that they can do things that seem to them so abnormal, make them place too great an emphasis on occurrences that are more common than they suppose. Rousseau in the course of his *Confessions* narrates incidents that have profoundly shocked the sensibility of mankind. By describing them so frankly he falsified his values and so gave them in his book a greater importance than they had in his life. There were events among a multitude of others, virtuous or at least neutral, that he omitted because they were too ordinary to seem worth recording. There is a sort of man who pays no attention to his good actions, but is tormented by his bad ones. This is the type that most often writes about himself. He leaves out his redeeming qualities and so appears only weak, unprincipled and vicious.

V

I write this book to disembarrass my soul of certain notions that have hovered about in it too long for my comfort. I do not seek to persuade anybody. I am devoid of the pedagogic instinct and when I know a thing never feel in myself the desire to impart it to others. I do not much care if people agree with me. Of course I think I am right, otherwise I should not think as I do, and they are wrong, but it does not offend me that they should be wrong. Nor does it greatly disturb me to discover that my judgment is at variance with that of the majority. I have a certain confidence in my instinct.

I must write as though I were a person of importance; and indeed, I am—to myself. To myself I am the most important person in the world; though I do not forget that, not even taking into consideration so grand a conception as the Absolute, but from the standpoint of common sense, I am of no consequence whatever. It would have made small difference to the universe if I had never existed. Though I may seem to write as though significance must necessarily be attached to certain of my works, I mean only that they are of moment to me for the purpose of any discussion during which I may have occasion to mention them. I think few serious writers, by which I do not only mean writers of serious things, can be entirely indifferent to the fate that will befall their works after their death. It is pleasant to think, not that one may achieve immortality (immortality for literary productions lasts in any case but a few hundred years and then is seldom more than the immortality of the schoolroom) but that one may be read with interest by a few generations and find a place, however small, in the history of one's country's literature. But so far as I am concerned, I look upon this modest possibility with scepticism. Even in my life I have seen writers who made much more stir in the world of letters than ever I have, sink into oblivion. When I was young George Meredith and Thomas Hardy seemed certain of survival. They have ceased to mean very much to the youth of to-day. From time to time they will doubtless find a critic in search of a subject to write an article about them, which may cause readers here and there to get out one or other of their books from a library; but I think it is clear that neither of them wrote anything that will be read as *Gulliver's Travels*, *Tristram Shandy* or *Tom Jones* is read.

If in the following pages I seem to express myself dogmatically, it is only because I find it very boring to qualify every phrase with an "I think" or "to my mind." Everything I say is merely an opinion of my own. The reader can take it or leave it. If he has the patience to read what follows he will see that there is only one thing about which I am certain, and this is that there is very little about which one can be certain.

VI

WHEN I began to write I did so as though it were the most natural thing in the world. I took to it as a duck takes to water. I have never quite got over my astonishment at being a writer; there seems no reason for my having become one except an irresistible inclination, and I do not see why such an inclination should have arisen in me. For well over a hundred years my family has practised law. According to the Dictionary of National Biography my grandfather was one of the two founders of the Incorporated Law Society, and in the catalogue of the library at the British Museum there is a long list of his legal works. He wrote only one book that was not of this character. It was a collection of essays that he had contributed to the solid magazines of the day and he issued it, as became his sense of decorum, anonymously. I once had the book in my hands, a handsome volume bound in calf, but I never read it and I have not been able to get hold of a copy since. I wish I had, for I might have learnt from it something of the kind of man he was. For many years he lived in Chancery Lane, for he became secretary of the society he had founded, and when he retired to a house in Kensington Gore overlooking the Park, he was presented with a salver, a tea and coffee service and an épergne, in silver, so massive and ornate that they have been ever since an embarrassment to his descendants. An old solicitor, whom I knew when I was a boy, told me that as an articled clerk he was once invited to dine with my grandfather. My grandfather carved the beef and then a servant handed him a dish of potatoes baked in their skins. There are few things better to eat than a potato in its skin, with plenty of butter, pepper and salt, but apparently my grandfather did not think so. He rose in his chair at the head of the table and took the potatoes out of the dish one by one and threw one at each picture on the walls. Then without a word he sat down again

and went on with his dinner. I asked my friend what effect this behaviour had on the rest of the company. He told me that no one took any notice. He also told me that my grandfather was the ugliest little man he ever saw. I went once to the building of the Incorporated Society in Chancery Lane to see for myself if he was really so ugly as all that, for there is a portrait of him there. If what my old gentleman said was true the painter must have grossly flattered my grandfather; he has given him very fine dark eyes under black eyebrows, and there is a faintly ironic twinkle in them; a firm jaw, a straight nose and pouting red lips. His dark hair is wind-swept as becomingly as that of Miss Anita Loos. He is holding a quill and there is a pile of books, doubtless his own, by his side. Notwithstanding his black coat, he does not look so respectable as I should have expected, but slightly mischievous. Many years ago when I was destroying the papers of one of his sons, my uncle, who had died, I came across the diary that my grandfather kept when as a young man at the beginning of the nineteenth century he did what I believe was called the Little Tour, France, Germany and Switzerland; and I remember that when he described the not very impressive fall of the Rhine at Schaffhausen he offered thanks to God Almighty because in creating "this stupendous cataract" he had given "His miserable creatures occasion to realize their insignificance in comparison with the prodigious greatness of His works."

VII

My parents died when I was so young, my mother when I was eight, my father when I was ten, that I know little of them but from hearsay. My father, I do not know why unless he was drawn by some such restlessness for the unknown as has consumed his son, went to Paris and became solicitor to the British Embassy. He had offices just opposite, in the Faubourg St. Honoré, but he lived in what was then called the Avenue d'Antin, a broad street with chestnut trees on each side of it that leads from the Rond Point. He was a great traveller for those days. He had been to Turkey, Greece and Asia Minor and in Morocco as far as Fez, which was a place few people then visited. He had a considerable library of travel books and the apartment in the Avenue d'Antin was filled with the things he had brought back, Tanagra statuettes, Rhodes ware and Turkish daggers in hilts of richly decorated silver. He was forty when he married my mother, who was more than twenty years younger. She was a very beautiful woman and he was a very ugly man. I have been told that they were known in the Paris of that day as Beauty and the Beast. Her father was in the army; he died in India and his widow, my grandmother, after squandering a considerable fortune, settled down in France to live on her pension. She was a woman of character, I suspect, and perhaps of some talent, for she wrote novels in French *pour jeunes filles* and composed the music for drawing-room ballads. I like to think that the novels were read and the ballads sung by Octave Feuillet's

high-born heroines. I have a little photograph of her, a middle-aged woman in a crinoline with fine eyes and a look of good-humoured determination. My mother was very small, with large brown eyes and hair of a rich reddish gold, exquisite features and a lovely skin. She was very much admired. One of her great friends was Lady Anglesey, an American woman who died at an advanced age not very long ago, and she told me that she had once said to my mother: "You're so beautiful and there are so many people in love with you, why are you faithful to that ugly little man you've married?" And my mother answered: "He never hurts my feelings."

The only letter of hers I ever saw was one that I came across when I was going through my uncle's papers after his death. He was a clergyman and she asked him to be godfather to one of her sons. She expressed, very simply and piously, the hope that by reason of his holy calling the relationship into which she invited him to enter would have such an influence on the new-born child that he would grow up to be a good, God-fearing man. She was a great novel-reader and in the billiard-room of the apartment in the Avenue d'Antin were two great bookcases filled with Tauchnitz. She suffered from tuberculosis of the lungs and I remember the string of donkeys that stopped at the door to provide her with asses' milk, which at that time was thought to be good for that malady. In the summer we used to take a house at Deauville, not then a fashionable spot, but a little fishing village overshadowed by the smarter Trouville, and towards the end of her life we spent winters at Pau. Once when she was lying in bed, I suppose after a hæmorrhage, and knew she could not live much longer, the thought came to her that her sons when they grew up would not know what she was like when she died, so she called her maid, had herself dressed in an evening gown of white satin and went to the photographer's. She had six sons and died in childbirth. The doctors of the period had a theory that to have a child was beneficial to women suffering from consumption. She was thirty-eight.

After my mother's death, her maid became my nurse. I had till then had French nurses and I had been sent to a French school for children. My knowledge of English must have been slight. I have been told that on one occasion, seeing a horse out of the window of a railway carriage, I cried: "Regardez, Maman, voilà un 'orse."

I think my father had a romantic mind. He took it into his head to build a house to live in during the summer. He bought a piece of land on the top of a hill at Suresnes. The view was splendid over the plain, and in the distance was Paris. There was a road down to the river and by the river lay a little village. It was to be like a villa on the Bosphorus and on the top floor it was surrounded by loggias. I used to go down with him every Sunday by the Seine on a *bateau-mouche* to see how it was getting on. When the roof was on, my father began to furnish it by buying a pair of antique fire irons. He ordered a great quantity of glass on which he had engraved a sign against the Evil Eye which he had found in Morocco and which the reader may see on the cover of this book. It was a white house and the shutters were painted red. The garden was laid out. The rooms were furnished and then my father died.

VIII

I HAD been taken away from the French school and went for my lessons every day to the apartment of the English clergyman at the church attached to the Embassy. His method of teaching me English was to make me read aloud the police-court news in *The Standard* and I can still remember the horror with which I read the ghastly details of a murder in the train between Paris and Calais. I must then have been nine. I was for long uncertain about the pronunciation of English words and I have never forgotten the roar of laughter that abashed me when in my preparatory school I read out the phrase "un-

stable as water" as though unstable rhymed with Dunstable.

I have never had more than two English lessons in my life, for though I wrote essays at school, I do not remember that I ever received any instruction on how to put sentences together. The two lessons I have had were given me so late in life that I am afraid I cannot hope greatly to profit by them. The first was only a few years ago. I was spending some weeks in London and had engaged as temporary secretary a young woman. She was shy, rather pretty, and absorbed in a love affair with a married man. I had written a book called *Cakes and*

Ale and, the typescript arriving one Saturday morning, I asked her if she would be good enough to take it home and correct it over the week-end. I meant her only to make a note of mistakes in spelling that the typist might have made and point out errors occasioned by a handwriting that is not always easy to decipher. But she was a conscientious young person and she took me more literally than I intended. When she brought back the typescript on Monday morning it was accompanied by four foolscap sheets of corrections. I must confess that at the first glance I was a trifle vexed; but then I thought that it would be silly of me not to profit, if I could, by the trouble she had taken and so sat me down to examine them. I suppose the young woman had taken a course at a secretarial college and she had gone through my novel in the same methodical way as her masters had gone through her essays. The remarks that filled the four neat pages of foolscap were incisive and severe. I could not but surmise that the professor of English at the secretarial college did not mince matters. He took a marked line, there could be no doubt about that; and he did not allow that there might be two opinions about anything. His apt pupil would have nothing to do with a preposition at the end of a sentence. A mark of exclamation betokened her disapproval of a colloquial phrase. She had a feeling that you must not use the same word twice on a page and she was ready every time with a synonym to put in its place. If I had indulged myself in the luxury of a sentence of ten lines, she wrote: "Clarify this. Better break it up into two or more periods." When I had availed myself of the pleasant pause that is indicated by a semicolon, she noted: "A full stop"; and if I had ventured upon a colon she remarked stingingly: "Obsolete." But the harshest stroke of all was her comment on what I thought was rather a good joke: "Are you sure of your facts?" Taking it all in all I am bound to conclude that the professor at her college would not have given me very high marks.

The second lesson I had was given me by a don, both intelligent and charming, who happened to be staying with me when I was myself correcting the typescript of another book. He was good enough to offer to read it. I hesitated, because I knew that he judged from a standpoint of excellence that is hard to attain; and though I was aware that he had a profound knowledge of Elizabethan literature, his inordinate admiration for *Esther Waters* made me doubtful of his discernment in the productions of our own day: no one could attach so great a value to that work who had an intimate knowledge of the French novel during the nineteenth century. But I was anxious to make my book as good as I could and I hoped to benefit by his criticisms. They were in point of fact lenient. They interested me peculiarly because I inferred that this was the way in which he dealt with the compositions of undergraduates. My don had, I think, a natural gift for language, which it has been his business to cultivate; his taste appeared to me faultless. I was much struck by his insistence on the force of individual words. He liked the stronger word rather than the euphonious. To give an example, I had written that a statue would be placed in a certain square and he suggested that I should write: the statue will stand. I had not done that because my ear was offended by the alliteration. I noticed also that he had a feeling that words should be used not only to balance a sentence but to balance an idea. This is sound, for an idea may lose its effect if it is delivered abruptly; but it is a matter of delicacy, since it may well lead to verbiage. Here a knowledge of stage dialogue should help. An actor will sometimes say to an author: "Couldn't you give me a word or two more in this speech? It seems to take away all the point of my line if I have nothing else to say." As I listened to my don's remarks I could not but think how much better I should write now if in my youth I had had the advantage of such sensible, broad-minded and kindly advice.

IX

As it is, I have had to teach myself. I have looked at the stories I wrote when I was very young in order to discover what natural aptitude I had, my original stock-in-trade, before I developed it by taking thought. The manner had a superciliousness that perhaps my years excused and an irascibility that was a defect of nature; but I am speaking now only of the way in which I expressed myself. It seems to me that I had a natural lucidity and a knack for writing easy dialogue.

When Henry Arthur Jones, then a well-known playwright, read my first novel, he told a friend that in due course I should be one of the most successful dramatists of the day. I suppose he saw in it directness and an effective way of presenting a scene that suggested a sense of the theatre. My language was commonplace, my vocabulary limited, my grammar shaky and my phrases hackneyed. But to write was an instinct that seemed as natural to me as to breathe, and I did not stop to consider if I wrote well or badly. It was not till some years later that it dawned upon me that it was a delicate art that must be painfully acquired. The discovery was forced upon me by the difficulty I found in getting my meaning down on paper. I wrote dialogue fluently, but when it came to a page of description I found myself entangled in all sorts of quandaries. I would struggle for a couple of hours over two or three sentences that I could in no way manage to straighten out. I made up my mind to teach myself how to write. Unfortunately I had no one to help me. I made many mistakes. If I had had someone to guide me like the charming don of whom I spoke just now I might have been saved much time. Such a one might have told me that such gifts as I had lay in one direction and that they must be cultivated in that direction; it was useless to try to do something for which I had no aptitude. But at that time a florid prose was admired. Richness of texture was sought by means of a jewelled phrase and sentences stiff with exotic epithets: the ideal was a brocade so heavy with gold that it stood up by itself. The intelligent young read Walter Pater with enthusiasm. My common sense suggested to me that it was anæmic stuff; behind those elaborate, gracious periods I was conscious of a tired, wan personality. I was young, lusty and energetic; I wanted fresh air, action, violence, and I found it hard to breathe that dead, heavily scented atmosphere and sit in those hushed rooms in which it was indecorous to speak above a whisper. But I would not listen to my common sense. I persuaded myself that this was the height of culture and turned a scornful shoulder on the outside world where men shouted and swore, played the fool, wenched and got drunk. I read *Intentions* and *The Picture of Dorian Gray*. I was intoxicated by the colour and rareness of the fantastic words that thickly stud the pages of *Salome*. Shocked by the poverty of my own vocabulary, I went to the British Museum with pencil and paper and noted down the names of curious jewels, the Byzantine hues of old enamels, the sensual feel of textiles, and made elaborate sentences to bring them in. Fortunately I could never find an opportunity to use them and they lie there yet in an old notebook ready for anyone who has a mind to write nonsense. It was generally thought then that the Authorized Version of the Bible was the greatest piece of prose that the English language has produced. I read it diligently, especially the Song of Solomon, jotting down for future use turns of phrase that struck me and making lists of unusual or beautiful words. I studied Jeremy Taylor's *Holy Dying*.

In order to assimilate his style I copied out passages and then tried to write them down from memory.

The first fruit of this labour was a little book about Andalusia called *The Land of the Blessed Virgin*. I had occasion to read parts of it the other day. I know Andalusia a great deal better now than I knew it then, and I have changed my mind about a good many things of which I wrote. Since it has continued in America to have a small sale it occurred to me that it might be worth while to revise it. I soon saw that this was impossible. The book was written by someone I have completely forgotten. It bored me to distraction. But what I am concerned with is the prose, for it was as an exercise in style that I wrote it. It is wistful, allusive and elaborate. It has neither ease nor spontaneity. It smells of hothouse plants and Sunday dinner like the air in the greenhouse that leads out of the dining-room of a big house in Bayswater. There are a great many melodious adjectives. The vocabulary is sentimental. It does not remind one of an Italian brocade, with its rich pattern of gold, but of a curtain material designed by Burne-Jones and reproduced by Morris.

X

I DO not know whether it was a subconscious feeling that this sort of writing was contrary to my bent or a naturally methodical cast of mind that led me then to turn my attention to the writers of the Augustan Period. The prose of Swift enchanted me. I made up my mind that this was the perfect way to write and I started to work on him in the same way as I had done with Jeremy Taylor. I chose

The Tale of a Tub. It is said that when the Dean re-read it in his old age he cried: "What genius I had then!" To my mind his genius was better shown in other works. It is a tiresome allegory and the irony is facile. But the style is admirable. I cannot imagine that English can be better written. Here are no flowery periods, fantastic turns of phrase or high-flown images. It is a civilized prose, natural, discreet and pointed. There is no attempt to surprise by an extravagant vocabulary. It looks as though Swift made do with the first word that came to hand, but since he had an acute and logical brain it was always the right one, and he put it in the right place. The strength and balance of his sentences are due to an exquisite taste. As I had done before I copied passages and then tried to write them out again from memory. I tried altering words or the order in which they were set. I found that the only possible words were those Swift had used and that the order in which he had placed them was the only possible order. It is an impeccable prose.

But perfection has one grave defect: it is apt to be dull. Swift's prose is like a French canal, bordered with poplars, that runs through a gracious and undulating country. Its tranquil charm fills you with satisfaction, but it neither excites the emotions nor stimulates the imagination. You go on and on and presently you are a trifle bored. So, much as you may admire Swift's wonderful lucidity, his terseness, his naturalness, his lack of affectation, you find your attention wandering after a while unless his matter peculiarly interests you. I think if I had my time over again I would give to the prose of Dryden the close study I gave to that of Swift. I did not come across it till I had lost the inclination to take so much pains. The prose of Dryden is delicious. It has not the perfection of Swift nor the easy elegance of Addison, but it has a springtime gaiety, a conversational ease, a blithe spontaneousness that are enchanting. Dryden was a very good poet, but it is not the general opinion that he had a lyrical quality; it is strange that it is just this that sings in his softly sparkling prose. Prose had never been written in England like that before; it has seldom been written like that since. Dryden flourished at a happy moment. He had in his bones the sonorous periods and the baroque massiveness of Jacobean language and under the influence of the nimble and well-bred felicity that he learnt from the French he turned it into an instrument that was fit not only for solemn themes but also to express the light thought of the passing moment. He was the first of the rococo artists. If Swift reminds you of a French canal Dryden recalls an English river winding its cheerful way round hills, through quietly busy towns and by nestling villages, pausing now in a noble reach and then running powerfully through a woodland country. It is alive, varied, windswept; and it has the pleasant open-air smell of England.

The work I did was certainly very good for me. I began to write better; I did not write well. I wrote stiffly and self-consciously. I tried to get a pattern into my sentences, but did not see that the pattern was evident. I took care how I placed my words, but did not reflect that an order that was natural at the beginning of the eighteenth century was most unnatural at the beginning of ours. My attempt to write in the manner of Swift made it impossible for me to achieve the effect of inevitable rightness that was just what I so much admired in him. I then wrote a number of plays and ceased to occupy myself with anything but dialogue. It was not till five years had passed that I set out again to write a novel. By then I no longer had any ambition to be a stylist; I put aside all thought of fine writing. I wanted to write without any frills of language, in as bare and unaffected a manner as I could. I had so much to say that I could afford to waste no words. I wanted merely to set down the facts. I began with the impossible aim of using no adjectives at all. I thought that if you could find the exact term a qualifying epithet could be dispensed with. As I saw it in my mind's eye my book would have the appearance of an immensely long telegram in which for economy's sake you had left out every word that was not necessary to make the sense clear. I have not read it since I corrected the proofs and do not know how near I came to doing what I tried. My impression is that it is written at least more naturally than anything I had written before; but I am sure that it is often slipshod and I daresay there are in it a good many mistakes in grammar.

Since then I have written many other books; and though ceasing my methodical study of the old masters (for though the spirit is willing, the flesh is weak), I have continued with increasing assiduity to try to write better. I discovered my limitations and it seemed to me that the only sensible thing was to aim at what excellence I could within them. I knew that I had no lyrical quality. I had a small vocabulary and no efforts that I could make to enlarge it much availed me. I had little gift of metaphor; the original and striking simile seldom occurred to me. Poetic flights and the great imaginative sweep were beyond my powers. I could admire them in others as I could admire their far-fetched tropes and the unusual but suggestive language in which they clothed their thoughts, but my own invention never presented me with such embellishments; and I was tired of trying to do what did not come easily to me. On the other hand, I had an acute power of observation and it seemed to me that I could see a great many things that other people missed. I could put down in clear terms what I saw. I had a logical sense, and if no great feeling for the richness and strangeness of words, at all events a lively appreciation of their sound. I knew that I should never write as well as I could wish, but I thought with pains I could arrive at writing as well as my natural defects allowed. On taking thought it seemed to me that I must aim at lucidity, simplicity and euphony. I have put these three qualities in the order of the importance I assigned to them.

XI

I HAVE never had much patience with the writers who claim from the reader an effort to understand their meaning. You have only to go to the great philosophers to see that it is possible to express with lucidity the most subtle reflections. You may find it difficult to understand the thought of Hume, and if you have no philosophical training its implications will doubtless escape you; but no one with any education at all can fail to understand exactly what the meaning of each sentence is. Few people have written English with more grace than Berkeley. There are two sorts of obscurity that you find in writers. One is due to negligence and the other to wilfulness. People often write obscurely because they have never taken the trouble to learn to write clearly. This sort of obscurity you find too often in modern philosophers, in men of science, and even in literary critics. Here it is indeed strange. You would have thought that men who passed their lives in the study of the great masters of literature would be sufficiently sensitive to the beauty of language to write if not beautifully at least with perspicuity. Yet you will find in their works sentence after sentence that you must read twice to discover the sense. Often you can only guess at it, for the writers have evidently not said what they intended.

Another cause of obscurity is that the writer is himself not quite sure of his meaning. He has a vague impression of what he wants to say, but has not, either from lack of mental power or from laziness, exactly formulated it in his mind and it is natural enough that he should not find a precise expression for a confused idea. This is due largely to the fact that many writers think, not before, but as they write. The pen originates the thought. The disadvantage of this, and indeed it is a danger against which the author must be always on his guard, is that there is a sort of magic in the written word. The idea acquires substance by taking on a visible nature, and then stands in the way of its own clarification. But this sort of obscurity merges very easily into the wilful. Some writers who do not think clearly are inclined to suppose that their thoughts have a significance greater than at first sight appears. It is flattering to believe that they are too profound to be expressed so clearly that all who run may read, and very naturally it does

not occur to such writers that the fault is with their own minds which have not the faculty of precise reflection. Here again the magic of the written word obtains. It is very easy to persuade oneself that a phrase that one does not quite understand may mean a great deal more than one realizes. From this there is only a little way to go to fall into the habit of setting down one's impressions in all their original vagueness. Fools can always be found to discover a hidden sense in them. There is another form of wilful obscurity that masquerades as aristocratic exclusiveness. The author wraps his meaning in mystery so that the vulgar shall not participate in it. His soul is a secret garden into which the elect may penetrate only after overcoming a number of perilous obstacles. But this kind of obscurity is not only pretentious; it is short-sighted. For time plays it an odd trick. If the sense is meagre time reduces it to a meaningless verbiage that no one thinks of reading. This is the fate that has befallen the lucubrations of those French writers who were seduced by the example of Guillaume Apollinaire. But occasionally it throws a sharp cold light on what had seemed profound and thus discloses the fact that these contortions of language disguised very commonplace notions. There are few of Mallarmé's poems now that are not clear; one cannot fail to notice that his thought singularly lacked originality. Some of his phrases were beautiful; the materials of his verse were the poetic platitudes of his day.

XII

SIMPLICITY is not such an obvious merit as lucidity. I have aimed

at it because I have no gift for richness. Within limits I admire richness in others, though I find it difficult to digest in quantity. I can read one page of Ruskin with delight, but twenty only with weariness. The rolling period, the stately epithet, the noun rich in poetic associations, the subordinate clauses that give the sentence weight and magnificence, the grandeur like that of wave following wave in the open sea; there is no doubt that in all this there is something inspiring. Words thus strung together fall on the ear like music. The appeal is sensuous rather than intellectual, and the beauty of the sound leads you easily to conclude that you need not bother about the meaning. But words are tyrannical things, they exist for their meanings, and if you will not pay attention to these, you cannot pay attention at all. Your mind wanders. This kind of writing demands a subject that will suit it. It is surely out of place to write in the grand style of inconsiderable things. No one wrote in this manner with greater success than Sir Thomas Browne, but even he did not always escape this pitfall. In the last chapter of *Hydriotaphia* the matter, which is the destiny of man, wonderfully fits the baroque splendour of the language, and here the Norwich doctor produced a piece of prose that has never been surpassed in our literature; but when he describes the finding of his urns in the same splendid manner the effect (at least to my taste) is less happy. When a modern writer is grandiloquent to tell you whether or no a little trollop shall hop into bed with a commonplace young man you are right to be disgusted.

But if richness needs gifts with which everyone is not endowed, simplicity by no means comes by nature. To achieve it needs rigid discipline. So far as I know ours is the only language in which it has been found necessary to give a name to the piece of prose which is described as the purple patch; it would not have been necessary to do so unless it were characteristic. English prose is elaborate rather than simple. It was not always so. Nothing could be more racy, straightforward and alive than the prose of Shakespeare; but it must be remembered that this was dialogue written to be spoken. We do not know how he would have written if like Corneille he had composed prefaces to his plays. It may be that they would have been as euphuistic as the letters of Queen Elizabeth. But earlier prose, the prose of Sir Thomas More, for instance, is neither ponderous, flowery nor oratorical. It smacks of the English soil. To my mind King James's Bible has been a very harmful influence on English prose. I am not so stupid as to deny its great beauty, and it is obvious that there are passages in it of a simplicity which is deeply moving. But the Bible is an oriental book. Its alien imagery has nothing to do with us. Those hyperboles, those luscious metaphors, are foreign to our genius. I cannot but think that not the least of the misfortunes that the Secession from Rome brought upon the spiritual life of our country is that this work for so long a period became the daily, and with many the only, reading of our people. Those rhythms, that powerful vocabulary, that grandiloquence, became part and parcel of the national sensibility. The plain, honest English speech was overwhelmed with ornament. Blunt Englishmen twisted their tongues to speak like Hebrew prophets. There was evidently something in the English temper to which this was congenial, perhaps a native lack of precision in thought, perhaps a naïve delight in fine words for their own sake, an innate eccentricity and love of embroidery, I do not know; but the fact remains that ever since, English prose has had to struggle against the tendency to luxuriance. When from time to time the spirit of the language has reasserted itself, as it did with Dryden and the writers of Queen Anne, it was only to be submerged once more by the pomposities of Gibbon and Dr. Johnson. When English prose recovered simplicity with Hazlitt, the Shelley of the letters and Charles Lamb at his best, it lost it again with De Quincey, Carlyle, Meredith and Walter Pater. It is obvious that the grand style is more striking than the plain. Indeed many people think that a style that does not attract notice is not style. They will admire Walter Pater's, but will read an essay by Matthew Arnold without giving a moment's attention to the elegance, distinction and sobriety with which he set down what he had to say.

The dictum that the style is the man is well known. It is one of those aphorisms that say too much to mean a great deal. Where is the man in Goethe, in his birdlike lyrics or in his clumsy prose? And Hazlitt? But I suppose that if a man has a confused mind he will write in a confused way, if his temper is capricious his prose will be fantastical, and if he has a quick, darting intelligence that is reminded by the matter in hand of a hundred things he will, unless he has great self-control, load his pages with metaphor and simile. There is a great difference between the magniloquence of the Jacobean writers, who were intoxicated with the new wealth that had lately been brought into the language, and the turgidity of Gibbon and Dr. Johnson, who were the victims of bad theories. I can read every word that Dr. Johnson wrote with delight, for he had good sense, charm and wit. No one could have written better if he had not wilfully set himself to

write in the grand style. He knew good English when he saw it. No critic has praised Dryden's prose more aptly. He said of him that he appeared to have no art other than that of expressing with clearness what he thought with vigour. And one of his Lives he finished with the words: "Whoever wishes to attain an English style, familiar but not coarse, and elegant but not ostentatious, must give his days and nights to the volumes of Addison." But when he himself sat down to write it was with a very different aim. He mistook the orotund for the dignified. He had not the good breeding to see that simplicity and naturalness are the truest marks of distinction.

For to write good prose is an affair of good manners. It is, unlike verse, a civil art. Poetry is baroque. Baroque is tragic, massive and mystical. It is elemental. It demands depth and insight. I cannot but feel that the prose writers of the baroque period, the authors of King James's Bible, Sir Thomas Browne, Glanville, were poets who had lost their way. Prose is a rococo art. It needs taste rather than power, decorum rather than inspiration and vigour rather than grandeur. Form for the poet is the bit and the bridle without which (unless you are an acrobat) you cannot ride your horse; but for the writer of prose it is the chassis without which your car does not exist. It is not an accident that the best prose was written when rococo with its elegance and moderation at its birth attained its greatest excellence. For rococo was evolved when baroque had become declamatory and the world, tired of the stupendous, asked for restraint. It was the natural expression of persons who valued a civilized life. Humour, tolerance and horse sense made the great tragic issues that had preoccupied the first half of the seventeenth century seem excessive. The world was a more comfortable place to live in and perhaps for the first time in centuries the cultivated classes could sit back and enjoy their leisure. It has been said that good prose should resemble the conversation of a well-bred man. Conversation is only possible when men's minds are free from pressing anxieties. Their lives must be reasonably secure and they must have no grave concern about their souls. They must attach importance to the refinements of civilization. They must value courtesy, they must pay attention to their persons (and have we not also been told that good prose should be like the clothes of a well-dressed man, appropriate but unobtrusive?), they must fear to bore, they must be neither flippant nor solemn, but always apt; and they must look upon "enthusiasm" with a critical glance. This is a soil very suitable for prose. It is not to be wondered at that it gave a fitting opportunity for the appearance of the best writer of prose that our modern world has seen, Voltaire. The writers of English, perhaps owing to the poetic nature of the language, have seldom reached the excellence that seems to have come so naturally to him. It is in so far as they have approached the ease, sobriety and precision of the great French masters that they are admirable.

XIII

WHETHER you ascribe importance to euphony, the last of the three characteristics that I mentioned, must depend on the sensitiveness of your ear. A great many readers, and many admirable writers, are devoid of this quality. Poets as we know have always made a great use of alliteration. They are persuaded that the repetition of a sound gives an effect of beauty. I do not think it does so in prose. It seems to me that in prose alliteration should be used only for a special reason; when used by accident it falls on the ear very disagreeably. But its accidental use is so common that one can only suppose that the sound of it is not universally offensive. Many writers without distress will put two rhyming words together, join a monstrous long adjective to a monstrous long noun, or between the end of one word and the beginning of another have a conjunction of consonants that almost breaks your jaw. These are trivial and obvious instances. I mention them only to prove that if careful writers can do such things it is only because they have no ear. Words have weight, sound and appearance; it is only by considering these that you can write a sentence that is good to look at and good to listen to.

I have read many books on English prose, but have found it hard to profit by them; for the most part they are vague, unduly theoretical, and often scolding. But you cannot say this of Fowler's Dictionary of Modern English Usage. It is a valuable work. I do not think anyone writes so well that he cannot learn much from it. It is lively reading. Fowler liked simplicity, straightforwardness and common sense. He had no patience with pretentiousness. He had a sound feeling that idiom was the backbone of a language and he was all for the racy phrase. He was no slavish admirer of logic and was willing enough to give usage right of way through the exact demesnes of grammar. English grammar is very difficult and few writers have avoided making mistakes in it. So heedful a writer as Henry James, for instance, on occasion wrote so ungrammatically that a schoolmaster, finding such errors in a schoolboy's essay, would be justly indignant. It is necessary to know grammar, and it is better to write grammatically than not, but it is well to remember that grammar is common speech formulated. Usage is the only test. I would prefer a phrase that was easy and unaffected to a phrase that was grammatical. One of the differences between French and English is that in French you can be grammatical with complete naturalness, but in English not invariably. It is a difficulty in writing English that the sound of the living voice dominates the look of the printed word. I have given the matter of style a great deal of thought and have taken great pains. I have written few pages that I feel I could not improve and far too many that I have left with dissatisfaction because, try as I would, I could do no better. I cannot say of myself what Johnson said of Pope: "He never passed a fault unamended by indifference, nor quitted it by despair." I do not write as I want to; I write as I can.

But Fowler had no ear. He did not see that simplicity may sometimes make concessions to euphony. I do not think a far-fetched, an archaic or even an affected word is out of place when it sounds better than the blunt, obvious one or when it gives a sentence a better balance. But, I hasten to add, though I think you may without mis-

giving make this concession to pleasant sound, I think you should make none to what may obscure your meaning. Anything is better than not to write clearly. There is nothing to be said against lucidity, and against simplicity only the possibility of dryness. This is a risk that is well worth taking when you reflect how much better it is to be bald than to wear a curly wig. But there is in euphony a danger that must be considered. It is very likely to be monotonous. When George Moore began to write, his style was poor; it gave you the impression that he wrote on wrapping paper with a blunt pencil. But he developed gradually a very musical English. He learnt to write sentences that fall away on the ear with a misty languor and it delighted him so much that he could never have enough of it. He did not escape monotony. It is like the sound of water lapping a shingly beach, so soothing that you presently cease to be sensible of it. It is so mellifluous that you hanker for some harshness, for an abrupt dissonance, that will interrupt the silky concord. I do not know how one can guard against this. I suppose the best chance is to have a more lively faculty of boredom than one's readers so that one is wearied before they are. One must always be on the watch for mannerisms and when certain cadences come too easily to the pen ask oneself whether they have not become mechanical. It is very hard to discover the exact point where the idiom one has formed to express oneself has lost its tang. As Dr. Johnson said: "He that has once studiously formed a style, rarely writes afterwards with complete ease." Admirably as I think Matthew Arnold's style was suited to his particular purposes, I must admit that his mannerisms are

558 MR. MAUGHAM HIMSELF

often irritating. His style was an instrument that he had forged once for all; it was not like the human hand capable of performing a variety of actions.

If you could write lucidly, simply, euphoniously and yet with liveliness you would write perfectly: you would write like Voltaire. And yet we know how fatal the pursuit of liveliness may be: it may result in the tiresome acrobatics of Meredith. Macaulay and Carlyle were in their different ways arresting; but at the heavy cost of naturalness. Their flashy effects distract the mind. They destroy their persuasiveness; you would not believe a man was very intent on ploughing a furrow if he carried a hoop with him and jumped through it at every other step. A good style should show no sign of effort. What is written should seem a happy accident. I think no one in France now writes more admirably than Colette, and such is the ease of her expression that you cannot bring yourself to believe that she takes any trouble over it. I am told that there are pianists who have a natural technique so that they can play in a manner that most executants can achieve only as the result of unremitting toil, and I am willing to believe that there are writers who are equally fortunate. Among them I was much inclined to place Colette. I asked her. I was exceedingly surprised to hear that she wrote everything over and over again. She told me that she would often spend a whole morning working upon a single page. But it does not matter how one gets the effect of ease. For my part, if I get it at all, it is only by strenuous effort. Nature seldom provides me with the word, the turn of phrase, that is appropriate without being farfetched or commonplace.

XIV

I HAVE read that Anatole France tried to use only the constructions and the vocabulary of the writers of the seventeenth century whom he so greatly admired. I do not know if it is true. If so, it may explain why there is some lack of vitality in his beautiful and simple French. But simplicity is false when you do not say a thing that you should say because you cannot say it in a certain way. One should write in the manner of one's period. The language is alive and constantly changing; to try to write like the authors of a distant past can only give rise to artificiality. I should not hesitate to use the common phrases of the day, knowing that their vogue was ephemeral, or slang, though aware that in ten years it might be incomprehensible, if they gave vividness and actuality. If the style has a classical form it can support the discreet use of a phraseology that has only a local and temporary aptness. I would sooner a writer were vulgar than mincing; for life is vulgar, and it is life he seeks.

I think that we English authors have much to learn from our fellow authors in America. For American writing has escaped the tyranny of King James's Bible and American writers have been less affected by the old masters whose mode of writing is part of our culture. They have formed their style, unconsciously perhaps, more directly from the living speech that surrounds them; and at its best it has a directness, a vitality and a drive that give our more urbane manner an air of languor. It has been an advantage to American writers, many of whom at one time or another have been reporters, that their journalism has been written in a more trenchant, nervous, graphic English than ours. For we read the newspaper now as our ancestors read the Bible. Not without profit either; for the newspaper, especially when it is of the popular sort, offers us a part of experience that we writers cannot afford to miss. It is raw material straight from the knacker's yard, and we are stupid if we turn up our noses because it smells of blood and sweat. We cannot, however willingly we would, escape the influence of this workaday prose. But the journalism of a period has very much the same style; it might all have been written by the same hand; it is impersonal. It is well to counteract its effect by reading of another kind. One can do this only by keeping constantly in touch with the writing of an age not too remote from one's own. So can one have a standard by which to test one's own style and an ideal which in one's modern way one can aim at. For my part the two writers I have found most useful to study for this purpose are Hazlitt and Cardinal Newman. I would try to imitate neither. Hazlitt can be unduly rhetorical; and sometimes his decoration is as fussy as Victorian Gothic. Newman can be a trifle flowery. But at their best both are admirable. Time has little touched their style; it is almost contemporary. Hazlitt is vivid, bracing and energetic; he has strength and liveliness. You feel the man in his phrases, not the mean, querulous, disagreeable man that he appeared to the world that knew him, but the man within of his own ideal vision. (And the man within us is as true in reality as the man, pitiful and halting, of our outward seeming.) Newman had an exquisite grace, music, playful sometimes and sometimes grave, a woodland beauty of phrase, dignity and mellowness. Both wrote with extreme lucidity. Neither is quite as simple as the purest taste demands. Here I think Matthew Arnold excels them. Both had a wonderful balance of phrase and both knew how to write sentences pleasing to the eye. Both had an ear of extreme sensitiveness.

If anyone could combine their merits in the manner of writing of the present day he would write as well as it is possible for anyone to write.

XV

FROM time to time I have asked myself whether I should have been a better writer if I had devoted my whole life to literature. Somewhat early, but at what age I cannot remember, I made up my mind that, having but one life, I should like to get the most I could out of it. It did not seem to me enough merely to write. I wanted to make a pattern of my life, in which writing would be an essential element, but which would include all the other activities proper to man, and which death would in the end round off in complete fulfilment. I had many disabilities. I was small; I had endurance but little physical strength; I stammered; I was shy; I had poor health. I had no facility for games, which play so great a part in the normal life of Englishmen; and I had, whether for any of these reasons or from nature I do not know, an instinctive shrinking from my fellow men that has made it difficult for me to enter into any familiarity with them. I have loved individuals; I have never much cared for men in the mass. I have none of that engaging come-hitherness that makes people take to one another on first acquaintance. Though in the course of years I have learnt to assume an air of heartiness when forced into contact with a stranger, I have never liked anyone at first sight. I do not think I have ever addressed someone I did not know in a railway carriage or spoken to a fellow-passenger on board ship unless he first spoke to me. The weakness of my flesh has prevented me from enjoying that communion with the human race that is engendered by alcohol; long before I could reach the state of intoxication that enables so many, more happily constituted, to look upon all men as their brothers, my stomach has turned upon me and I have been as sick as a dog. These are grave disadvantages both to the writer and the man. I have had to make the best of them. I have followed the pattern I made with persistence. I do not claim that it was a perfect one. I think it was the best that I could hope for in the circumstances and with the very limited powers that were granted to me by nature.

Looking for the special function of man Aristotle decided that since he shares growth with the plants and perception with the beasts, and alone has a rational element, his function is the activity of the soul. From this he concluded, not as you would have thought sensible, that man should cultivate the three forms of activity which he ascribed to him, but that he should

pursue only that which is especial to him. Philosophers and moralists have looked at the body with misgiving. They have pointed out that its satisfactions are brief. But a pleasure is none the less a pleasure because it does not please forever. It is delightful to plunge into cold water on a hot day even though in a moment your skin is no longer sensitive to the coldness. White is no whiter if it lasts for a year or a day. I looked upon it then as a part of the pattern I was attempting to draw to experience all the pleasures of sense. I have not been afraid of excess: excess on occasion is exhilarating. It prevents moderation from acquiring the deadening effect of a habit. It tonifies the system and rests the nerves. The spirit is often most free when the body is satiated with pleasure; indeed, sometimes the stars shine more brightly seen from the gutter than from the hilltop. The keenest pleasure to which the body is susceptible is that of sexual congress. I have known men who gave up their whole lives to this; they are grown old now, but I have noticed, not without surprise, that they look upon them as well spent. It has been my misfortune that a native fastidiousness has prevented me from indulging as much in this particular delight as I might have. I have exercised moderation because I was hard to please. When from time to time I have seen the persons with whom the great lovers satisfied their desires I have been more often astonished by the robustness of their appetites than envious of their successes. It is obvious that you need not often go hungry if you are willing to dine off mutton hash and turnip tops.

Most people live haphazard lives subject to the varying winds of fortune. Many are forced by the situation in which they were born and the necessity of earning a living to keep to a straight and narrow road in which there is no possibility of turning to the right or to the left. Upon these the pattern is imposed. Life itself has forced it on them. There is no reason why such a pattern should not be as complete as that which anyone has tried self-consciously to make. But the artist is in a privileged position. I use the word artist, not meaning to attach any measure of value to what he produces, but merely to signify someone who is occupied with the arts. I wish I could find a better word. Creator is pretentious and seems to make a claim to orginality that can seldom be justified. Craftsman is not enough. A carpenter is a craftsman, and though he may be in the narrower sense an artist, he has not as a rule the freedom of action which the most incompetent scribbler, the poorest dauber, possesses. The artist can with certain limits make what he likes of his life. In other callings, in medicine for instance or the law, you are free to choose whether you will adopt them or not, but having chosen, you are free no longer. You are bound by the rules of your profession; a standard of conduct is imposed upon you. The pattern is predetermined. It is only the artist, and maybe the criminal, who can make his own.

Perhaps it was a natural sense of tidiness that engaged me, when still so young, to design a pattern for my life; perhaps it was due to something I discovered in myself about which I shall have a little to say later. The defect of such an undertaking is that it may kill spontaneity. One great difference between the persons of real life and the persons of fiction is that the persons of real life are creatures of impulse. It has been said that metaphysics is the finding of bad reasons for what we believe upon instinct; and it might be said also that in the

conduct of life we make use of deliberation to justify ourselves in doing what we want to do. And to surrender to impulse is part of the pattern. I think a greater defect is that it leads you to live too much in the future. I have long known that this was a fault of mine and have in vain tried to correct it. I have never, except by an effort of will, wished that the passing moment might linger so that I could get more enjoyment from it, for even when it has brought me something I had immensely looked forward to, my imagination in the very moment of fulfilment has been busy with the problematical delight of whatever was to come. I have never walked down the south side of Piccadilly without being all in a dither about what was happening on the north. This is folly. The passing moment is all we can be sure of; it is only common sense to extract its utmost value from it; the future will one day be the present and will seem as unimportant as the present does now. But common sense avails me little. I do not find the present unsatisfactory; I merely take it for granted. It is interwoven in the pattern and what interests me is what remains to come.

I have made a great many mistakes. I have at times fallen victim to a snare to which the writer is peculiarly liable, the desire to carry out in my own life certain actions which I made the characters of my invention do. I have attempted things that were foreign to my nature and obstinately persevered in them because in my vanity I would not confess myself beaten. I have paid too much attention to the opinion of others. I have made sacrifices to unworthy objects because I had not the courage to inflict pain. I have committed follies. I have a sensitive conscience, and I have done certain things in my life that I am unable entirely to forget; if I had been fortunate enough to be a Catholic I could have delivered myself of them at confession and after performing the penance imposed received absolution and put them out of my mind forever. I have had to deal with them as my common sense suggested. I do not regret them, for I think it is because of my own grave faults that I have learnt indulgence for others. It took me a long time. In youth I was harshly intolerant. I remember my indignation upon hearing someone make the remark, not an original one, but new to me then, that hypocrisy was the tribute that vice paid to virtue. I thought that one should have the courage of one's vices. I had ideals of honesty, uprightness, truth; I was impatient not of human weakness, but of cowardice, and I would make no allowances for those who hedged and temporized. It never occurred to me that no one stood in greater need of indulgence than I.

XVI

AT FIRST sight it is curious that our own offences should seem to us so much less heinous than the offences of others. I suppose the reason is that we know all the circumstances that have occasioned them and so manage to excuse in ourselves what we cannot excuse in others. We turn our attention away from our own defects, and when we are forced by untoward events to consider them find it easy to condone them. For all I know we are right to do this; they are part of us and we must accept the good and the bad in ourselves together. But when we come to judge others it is not by ourselves as we really are that we judge them, but by an image that we have formed of ourselves from which we have left out everything that offends our vanity or would discredit us in the eyes of the world. To take a trivial instance: how scornful we are when we catch someone out telling a lie; but who can say that he has never told not one, but a hundred? We are shocked when we discover that great men were weak and petty, dishonest or selfish, sexually vicious, vain or intemperate; and many people think it disgraceful to disclose to the public its heroes' failings. There is not much to choose between men. They are all a hotch-potch of greatness and littleness, of virtue and vice, of nobility and baseness. Some have more strength of character, or more opportunity, and so in one direction or another give their instincts freer play, but potentially they are the same. For my part I do not think I am any better or any worse than most people, but I know that if I set down every action in my life and every thought that has crossed my mind the world would consider me a monster of depravity.

I wonder how anyone can have the face to condemn others when he reflects upon his own thoughts. A great part of our lives is occupied in reverie, and the more imaginative we are, the more varied and vivid this will be. How many of us could face having our reveries automatically registered and set before us? We should be overcome with shame. We should cry that we could not really be as mean, as wicked, as petty, as selfish, as obscene, as snobbish, as vain, as sentimental, as that. Yet surely our reveries are as much part of us as our actions, and if there were a being to whom our inmost thoughts were known we might just as well be held responsible for them as for our deeds. Men forget the horrible thoughts that wander through their own minds, and are indignant when they discover them in others. In Goethe's *Wahrheit und Dichtung* he relates how in his youth he could not bear the idea that his father was a middle-class lawyer in Frankfurt. He felt that noble blood must flow in his veins. So he sought to persuade himself that some prince travelling through the city had met and loved his mother, and that he was the offspring of the union. The editor of the copy I read wrote an indignant footnote on the subject. It seemed to him unworthy of so great a poet that he should impugn the undoubted virtue of his mother in order snobbishly to plume himself on his bastard aristocracy. Of course it was disgraceful, but it was not unnatural and I venture to say not uncommon. There must be few romantic, rebellious and imaginative boys who have not toyed with the idea that they could not be the son of their dull and respectable father, but ascribe the superiority they feel in themselves, according to their own idiosyncrasies, to an unknown poet, great statesman or ruling prince. The Olympian attitude of Goethe's later years inspires me with esteem; this confession arouses in me a warmer feeling. Because a man can write great works he is none the less a man.

It is, I suppose, these lewd, ugly, base and selfish thoughts, dwelling in their minds against their will, that have tormented the saints when their lives were devoted to good works and repentance had redeemed the sins of their past. St. Ignatius Loyola, as we know, when he went to Monserrat made a general confession and received absolution; but he continued to be obsessed by a sense of sin so that he was on the point of killing himself. Till his conversion he had led the ordinary life of the young man of good birth at that time; he was somewhat vain of his appearance, he had wenched and gambled; but at least on one occasion he had shown rare magnanimity and he had always been honourable, loyal, generous and brave. If peace was still denied him it looks as though it was his thoughts that he could not forgive himself. It would be a comfort to know that even the saints were thus afflicted. When I have seen the great ones of the earth, so upright and dignified, sitting in state I have often asked myself whether at such moments they ever remembered how their minds in solitude were sometimes occupied and whether it ever made them uneasy to think of the secrets that their subliminal self harboured. It seems to me that the knowledge that these reveries are common to all men should inspire one with tolerance to oneself as well as to others. It is well also if they enable us to look upon our fellows, even the most eminent and respectable, with humour and if they lead us to take ourselves not too seriously. When I have heard judges on the bench moralizing with unction I have asked myself whether it was possible for them to have forgotten their humanity so completely as their words suggested. I have wished that beside his bunch of flowers at the Old Bailey, his lordship had a packet of toilet paper. It would remind him that he was a man like any other.

XVII

I HAVE been called cynical. I have been accused of making men out worse than they are. I do not think I have done this. All I have done is to bring into prominence certain traits that many writers shut their eyes to. I think what has chiefly struck me in human beings is their lack of consistency. I have never seen people all of a piece. It has amazed me that the most incongruous traits should exist in the same person and for all that yield a plausible harmony. I have often asked myself how characteristics, seemingly irreconcilable, can exist in the same person. I have known crooks who were capable of self-sacrifice, sneak-thieves who were sweet-natured and harlots for whom it was a point of honour to give good value for money. The only explanation I can offer is that so instinctive is each one's conviction that he is unique in the world, and privileged, that he feels that, however wrong it might be for others, what he for his part does, if not natural and right, is at least venial. The contrast that I have found in people has interested me, but I do not think I have unduly emphasized it. The censure that has from time to time been passed on me is due perhaps to the fact that I have not expressly condemned what was bad in the characters of my invention and praised what was good. It must be a fault in me that I am not gravely shocked at the sins of others unless they personally affect me, and even when they do I have learnt at last generally to excuse them. It is meet not to expect too much of others. You should be grateful when they treat you well, but unperturbed when they treat you ill. "For every one of us," as the Athenian Stranger said, "is made pretty much what he is by the bent of his desires and the nature of his soul." It is want of imagination that prevents people from seeing things from any point of view but their own, and it is unreasonable to be angry with them because they lack this faculty.

I think I could be justly blamed if I saw only people's faults and were blind to their virtues. I am not conscious that this is the case. There is nothing more beautiful than goodness and it has pleased me very often to show how much of it there is in persons who by common standards would be relentlessly condemned. I have shown it because I have seen it. It has seemed to me sometimes to shine more brightly in them because it was surrounded by the darkness of sin. I take the goodness of the good for granted and I am amused when I discover their defects or their vices; I am touched when I see the goodness of the wicked and I am willing enough to shrug a tolerant shoulder at their wickedness. I am not my brother's keeper. I cannot bring myself to judge my fellows; I am content to observe them. My observation has led me to believe that, all in all, there is not so much difference between the good and the bad as the moralists would have us believe.

I have not on the whole taken people at their face value. I do not know if this coolness of scrutiny has been inherited from my fathers; they could hardly have been successful lawyers if they had not possessed a shrewdness that prevented them from being deceived by appearances; or if I owe it to the lack in me of that joyful uprush of emotion on meeting people that makes many, as the saying is, take their geese for swans. It was certainly encouraged by my training as a medical student. I did not want to be a doctor. I did not want to be anything but a writer, but I was much too shy to say so, and in any case at that time it was unheard of that a boy of eighteen, belonging to a respectable family, should adopt literature as a profession. The notion was so preposterous that I never even dreamt of imparting it to anybody. I had always supposed that I should enter the law, but my three brothers, much older than I, were practising it and there did not seem room for me too.

<h1 style="text-align:center">XVIII</h1>

I LEFT school early. I had been unhappy at the preparatory school to which I was sent on my father's death because it was at Canterbury and only six miles from Whitstable of which my uncle and guardian was vicar. It was an annex of the King's School, an ancient foundation, and to this when I was thirteen I duly went. After I had got out of the lower forms, the masters of which were frightening bullies, I was contented enough, and I was miserable when an illness forced me to spend a term in the South of France. My mother and her only sister had died of tuberculosis and when it was found that my lungs were affected my uncle and aunt were concerned. I was placed at a tutor's at Hyères. When I went back to Canterbury I did not like it so well. My friends had made new friends. I was lonely. I had been moved into a higher form in which, with three months lost, I could not find my place. My form-master nagged me. I persuaded my uncle that it would be very good for my lungs if instead of staying at school I spent the following winter on the Riviera and that it would be of value to me after that to go to Germany and learn German. I could continue to work there on the subjects which were necessary for me to get into Cambridge. He was a weak man and my arguments were specious. He did not much like me, for which I cannot blame him, since I do not think I was a likeable boy, and as it was my own money that was being spent on my education, he was willing enough to let me do as I chose. My aunt greatly favoured my plan. She was herself German, penniless but of noble birth; her family had a coat of arms with supporters and a great number of quarterings, of which she was primly arrogant. I have related elsewhere how, though but a poor clergyman's wife, she would not call on the wife of an opulent banker who had taken a house for the summer near by because he was in trade. It was she who arranged that I should go to a family in Heidelberg whom she had heard of through her relations in Munich.

But when I came back from Germany, aged eighteen, I had very decided views of my own about my future. I had been happier than ever before. I had for the first time tasted freedom and I could not bear the thought of going to Cambridge and being subjected once more to restraint. I felt myself a man and I had a great eagerness to enter at once upon life. I felt that there was not a moment to waste. My uncle had always hoped that I would go into the church, though he should have known that, stammering as I did, no profession could have been more unsuitable; and when I told him that I wouldn't, he accepted with his usual indifference my refusal to go to Cambridge. I still remember the rather absurd arguments that were held about the calling I should adopt. A suggestion was made that I should become a civil servant and my uncle wrote to an old Oxford friend of his who held an important position in the Home Office for his advice. It was that, owing to the system of examinations and the class of persons it had introduced into the government service, it was now no place for a gentleman. That settled that. It was finally decided that I should become a doctor.

The medical profession did not interest me, but it gave me the chance of living in London and so gaining the experience of life that I hankered after. I entered St. Thomas's Hospital in the autumn of 1892. I found the first two years of the curriculum very dull and gave my work no more attention than was necessary to scrape through the examinations. I was an unsatisfactory student. But I had the freedom I yearned for. I liked having lodgings of my own, where I could be by myself; I took pride in making them pretty and comfortable. All my spare time, and much that I should have devoted to my medical studies, I spent reading and writing. I read enormously; I filled notebooks with ideas for stories and plays, scraps of dialogue and reflections, very ingenuous ones, on what my reading and the various experiences that I was undergoing suggested to me. I entered little into the life of the hospital and made few friends there, for I was occupied with other things; but when, after two years, I became a clerk in the out-patients' departments I began to grow interested. In due course I started to work in the wards and then my interest so much increased that when I caught septic tonsillitis through doing a post-mortem on a corpse that was in an unreasonable state of decomposition and had to take to my bed, I could not wait to get well to resume my duties. I had to attend a certain number of confinements to get a certificate and this meant going into the slums of Lambeth, often into foul courts that the police hesitated to enter, but in which my black bag amply protected me: I found the work absorbing. For a short period I was on accident duty day and night to give first aid to urgent cases. It left me tired out but wonderfully exhilarated.

XIX

For here I was in contact with what I most wanted, life in the raw. In those three years I must have witnessed pretty well every emotion of which man is capable. It appealed to my dramatic instinct. It excited the novel-ist in me. Even now that forty years have passed I can remember certain people so exactly that I could draw a picture of them. Phrases that I heard then still linger on my ears. I saw how men died. I saw how they bore pain. I saw what hope looked like, fear and relief; I saw the dark lines that despair drew on a face; I saw courage and steadfastness. I saw faith shine in the eyes of those who trusted in what I could only think was an illusion and I saw the gallantry that made a man greet the prognosis of death with an ironic joke because he was too proud to let those about him see the terror of his soul.

At that time (a time to most people of sufficient ease, when peace seemed certain and prosperity secure) there was a school of writers who enlarged upon the moral value of suffering. They claimed that it was salutary. They claimed that it increased sympathy and enhanced the sensibilities. They claimed that it opened to the spirit new avenues of beauty and enabled it to get into touch with the mystical kingdom of God. They claimed that it strengthened the character, purified it from its human grossness and brought to him who did not avoid but sought it a more perfect happiness. Several books on these lines had a great success and their authors, who lived in comfortable homes, had three meals a day and were in robust health, gained much reputation. I set down in my notebook, not once or twice, but in a dozen places, the facts that I had seen. I knew that suffering did not ennoble; it degraded. It made men selfish, mean, petty and suspicious. It absorbed them in small things. It did not make them more than men; it made them less than men; and I wrote ferociously that we learn resignation not by our own suffering, but by the suffering of others.

All this was a valuable experience to me. I do not know a better training for a writer than to spend some years in the medical profession. I suppose that you can learn a good deal about human nature in a solicitor's office; but there on the whole you have to deal with men in full control of themselves. They lie perhaps as much as they lie to the doctor, but they lie more consistently, and it may be that for the solicitor it is not so necessary to know the truth. The interests he deals with, besides, are usually material. He sees human nature from a specialized standpoint. But the doctor, especially the hospital doctor, sees it bare. Reticences can generally be undermined; very often there are none. Fear for the most part will shatter every defence; even vanity is unnerved by it. Most people have a furious itch to talk about themselves and are restrained only by the disinclination of others to listen. Reserve is an artificial quality that is developed in most of us but as the result of innumerable rebuffs. The doctor is discreet. It is his business to listen and no details are too intimate for his ears.

But of course human nature may be displayed before you and if you have not the eyes to see you will learn nothing. If you are hidebound with prejudice, if your temper is sentimental, you can go through the wards of a hospital and be as ignorant of man at the end as you were at the beginning. If you want to get any benefit from such an experience you must have an open mind and an interest in human beings. I look upon myself as very fortunate in that though I have never much liked men I have found them so interesting that I am almost incapable of being bored by them. I do not particularly want to talk and I am very willing to listen. I do not care if people are interested in me or not. I have no desire to impart any knowledge I have to others nor do I feel the need to correct them if they are wrong. You can get a great deal of entertainment out of tedious people if you keep your head. I remember being taken for a drive in a foreign country by a kind lady who wanted to show me round. Her conversation was composed entirely of truisms and she had so large a vocabulary of hackneyed phrases that I despaired of remembering them. But one remark she made has stuck in my memory as have few witticisms; we passed a row of little houses by the sea and she said to me: "Those are week-end bungalows, if you understand what I mean; in other words they're bungalows that people go to on Saturdays and leave on Mondays." I should have been sorry to miss that.

I do not want to spend too long a time with boring people, but then I do not want to spend too long a time with amusing ones. I find social intercourse fatiguing. Most persons, I think, are both exhilarated and rested by conversation; to me it has always been an effort. When I was young and stammered, to talk for long singularly exhausted me, and even now that I have to some extent cured myself, it is a strain. It is a relief to me when I can get away and read a book.

XX

I WOULD not claim for a moment that those years I spent at St. Thomas's Hospital gave me a complete knowledge of human nature. I do not suppose anyone can hope to have that. I have been studying it, consciously and subconsciously, for forty years and I still find men unaccountable; people I know intimately can surprise me by some action of which I never thought them capable or by the discovery of some trait exhibit a side of themselves that I never even suspected. It is possible that my training gave me a warped view, for at St. Thomas's the persons I came in contact with were for the most part sick and poor and ill-educated. I have tried to guard against this. I have tried also to guard against my own prepossessions. I have no natural trust in others. I am more inclined to expect them to do ill than to do good. This is the price one has to pay for having a sense of humour. A sense of humour leads you to take pleasure in the discrepancies of human nature; it leads you to mistrust great professions and look for the unworthy motive that they conceal; the disparity between appearance and reality diverts you and you are apt when you cannot find it to create it. You tend to close your eyes to truth, beauty and goodness because they give no scope to your sense of the ridiculous. The humourist has a quick eye for the humbug; he does not always recognize the saint. But if to see men one-sidedly is a heavy price to pay for a sense of humour there is a compensation that has a value too. You are not angry with people when you laugh at them. Humour teaches tolerance, and the humourist, with a smile and perhaps a sigh, is more likely to shrug his shoulders than to condemn. He does not moralize, he is content to understand; and it is true that to understand is to pity and forgive.

But I must admit that, with these reservations that I have tried always to remember, the experience of all the years that have followed has only confirmed the observations on human nature that I made, not deliberately, for I was too young, but unconsciously, in the out-patients' departments and in the wards of St. Thomas's Hospital. I have seen men since as I saw them then, and thus have I drawn them. It may not be a true picture and I know that many have thought it an unpleasant one. It is doubtless partial, for naturally I have seen men through my own idiosyncrasies. A buoyant, optimistic, healthy and sentimental person would have seen the same people quite differently. I can only claim to have seen them coherently. Many writers seem to me not to observe at all, but to create their characters in stock sizes from images in their own fancy. They are like draughtsmen who draw their figures from recollections of the antique and have never attempted to draw from the living model. At their best they can only give living shape to the fantasies of their own minds. If their minds are noble they can give you noble figures and perhaps it does not matter if they lack the infinite complication of common life.

I have always worked from the living model. I remember that once in the dissecting room when I was going over my "part" with the demonstrator, he asked me what some nerve was and I did not know. He told me; whereupon I remonstrated, for it was in the wrong place. Nevertheless he insisted that it was the nerve I had been in vain looking for. I complained of the abnormality and he, smiling, said that in anatomy it was the normal that was uncommon. I was only annoyed at the time, but the remark sank into my mind and since then it has been forced upon me that it was true of man as well as of anatomy. The normal is what you find but rarely. The normal is an ideal. It is a picture that one fabricates of the average characteristics of men, and to find them all in a single man is hardly to be expected. It is this false picture that the writers

I have spoken of take as their model and it is because they describe what is so exceptional that they seldom achieve the effect of life. Selfishness and kindliness, idealism and sensuality, vanity, shyness, disinterestedness, courage, laziness, nervousness, obstinacy, and diffidence, they can all exist in a single person and form a plausible harmony. It has taken a long time to persuade readers of the truth of this.

I do not suppose men in past centuries were any different from the men we know, but they must surely have appeared to their contemporaries more of a piece than they do to us now, or writers would not have thus represented them. It seemed reasonable to describe every man in his humour. The miser was nothing but miserly, the fop foppish, and the glutton gluttonous. It never occurred to anyone that the miser might be foppish and gluttonous; and yet we see constantly people who are; still less, that he might be an honest and upright man with a disinterested zeal for public service and a genuine passion for art. When novelists began to disclose the diversity that they had found in themselves or seen in others they were accused of maligning the human race. So far as I know the first novelist who did this with deliberate intention was Stendhal in *Le Rouge et le Noir*. Contemporary criticism was outraged. Even Sainte-Beuve, who needed only to look into his own heart to discover what contrary qualities could exist side by side in some kind of harmony, took him to task. Julien Sorel is one of the most interesting characters that a novelist has ever created. I do not think that Stendhal has succeeded in making him entirely plausible, but that, I believe, is due to causes that I shall mention in another part of this book. For the first three quarters of the novel he is perfectly consistent. Sometimes he fills you with horror; sometimes he is entirely sympathetic; but he has an inner coherence, so that though you often shudder you accept.

But it was long before Stendhal's example bore fruit. Balzac, with all his genius, drew his characters after the old models. He gave them his own immense vitality so that you accept them as real; but in fact they are humours as definitely as are the characters of old comedy. His people are unforgettable, but they are seen from the standpoint of the ruling passion that affected those with whom they were brought in contact. I suppose it is a natural prepossession of mankind to take people as though they were homogeneous. It is evidently less trouble to make up one's mind about a man one way or the other and dismiss suspense with the phrase, he's one of the best or he's a dirty dog. It is disconcerting to find that the saviour of his country may be stingy or that the poet who has opened new horizons to our consciousness may be a snob. Our natural egoism leads us to judge people by their relations to ourselves. We want them to be certain things to us, and for us that is what they are; because the rest of them is no good to us, we ignore it.

These reasons perhaps explain why there is so great a disinclination to accept the attempts to portray man with his incongruous and diverse qualities and why people turn away with dismay when candid biographers reveal the truth about famous persons. It is distressing to think that the composer of the quintet in the *Meistersinger* was dishonest in money matters and treacherous to those who had benefited him. But it may be that he could not have had great qualities if he had not also had great failings. I do not believe they are right who say that the defects of famous men should be ignored; I think it is better that we should know them. Then, though we are conscious of having faults as glaring as theirs, we can believe that that is no hindrance to our achieving also something of their virtues.

XXI

BESIDES teaching me something about human nature my training in a medical school furnished me with an elementary knowledge of science and scientific method. Till then I had been concerned only with art and literature. It was a very limited knowledge, for the demands of the curriculum at that time were small, but at all events it showed me the road that led to a region of which I was completely ignorant. I grew familiar with certain principles. The scientific world of which I thus obtained a cursory glimpse was rigidly materialistic and because its conceptions coincided with my own prepossessions I embraced them with alacrity; "For men," as Pope observed, "let them say what they will, never approve any other's sense, but as it squares with their own." I was glad to learn that the mind of man (himself the product of natural causes) was a function of the brain subject like the rest of his body to the laws of cause and effect and that these laws were the same as those that governed the movements of star and atom. I exulted at the thought that the universe was no more than a vast machine in which every event was determined by a preceding event so that nothing could be other than it was. These conceptions not only appealed to my dramatic instinct; they filled me besides with a very delectable sense of liberation. With the ferocity of youth I welcomed the hypothesis of the Survival of the Fittest. It gave me much satisfaction to learn that the earth was a speck of mud whirling round a second-rate star which was gradually cooling; and that evolution, which had produced man, would by forcing him to adapt himself to his environment deprive him of all the qualities he had acquired but those that were necessary to enable him to combat the increasing cold till at last the planet, an icy cinder, would no longer support even a vestige of life. I believed that we were wretched puppets at the mercy of a ruthless fate; and that, bound by the inexorable laws of nature, we were doomed to take part in the ceaseless struggle for existence with nothing to look forward to but inevitable defeat. I learnt that men were moved by a savage egoism, that love was only the dirty trick nature played on us to achieve the continuation of the species, and I decided that,

whatever aims men set themselves, they were deluded, for it was impossible for them to aim at anything but their own selfish pleasures. When once I happened to do a friend a good turn (for what reasons, since I knew that all our actions were purely selfish, I did not stop to think) and wanting to show his gratitude (which of course he had no business to feel, for my apparent kindness was rigidly determined) he asked me what I would like as a present, I answered without hesitation Herbert Spencer's *First Principles*. I read it with complacency. But I was impatient of Spencer's maudlin belief in progress: the world I knew was going from bad to worse and I was as pleased as Punch at the thought of my remote descendants having long forgotten art and science and handicraft, cowering skin-clad in caverns as they watched the approach of the cold and eternal night. I was violently pessimistic. All the same, having abundant vitality, I was getting on the whole a lot of fun out of life. I was ambitious to make a name for myself as a writer. I exposed myself to every vicissitude that seemed to offer a chance of gaining the greater experience that I wanted and I read everything I could lay my hands on.

XXII

I LIVED at this time in a group of young men who had by nature gifts that seemed to me much superior to mine. They could write and draw and compose with a facility that aroused my envy. They had an appreciation of art and a critical instinct that I despaired of attaining. Of these some died without fulfilling the promise I thought they had and the rest have

lived on without distinction. I know now that all they had was the natural creativity of youth. To write prose and verse, to hammer out little tunes on the piano and to draw and paint, are instinctive with a great many young persons. It is a form of play, due merely to the exuberance of their years, and is no more significant than a child's building of a castle on the sands. I suspect that it was my own ingenuousness that led me to admire so much the gifts of my friends. If I had been less ignorant I might have seen that the opinions that seemed to me so original were theirs only at second-hand and that their verses and their music owed more to a retentive memory than to a lively imagination. The point I want to make is that this facility is, if not universal, so common that one can draw no conclusions from it. Youth is the inspiration. One of the tragedies of the arts is the spectacle of the vast number of persons who have been misled by this passing fertility to devote their lives to the effort of creation. Their invention deserts them as they grow older, and they are faced with the long years before them in which, unfitted by now for a more humdrum calling, they harass their wearied brain to beat out material it is incapable of giving them. They are lucky when, with what bitterness we know, they can make a living in ways, like journalism or teaching, that are allied to the arts.

Of course it is from among those who possess by nature this facility that the artist is produced. Without it he cannot have talent; but it is only a part of talent. We start by living, each one of us, in the solitariness of our own minds and from the data given us and our communications with other minds we construct the outside world to suit our needs. Because we are all the result of one evolutionary process, and our environment is more or less the same, the constructions we make are roughly similar. For convenience and simplicity we accept them as identical and speak of a common world. The peculiarity of the artist is that he is in some particular different from other men and so the world of his construction is different too. It is this idiosyncrasy that is the better part of his equipment. When the picture he draws of his private world appeals to a certain number of persons, either by its strangeness, its intrinsic interest or its correspondence with their own prepossessions (for none of us is quite the same as his neighbour, only rather like, and not everyone accepts the world common to us all in every respect) his talent will be acknowledged. If he is a writer he will fulfill some need in the nature of his readers and they will lead with him a life of the spirit that satisfies them better than the life circumstances have forced on them. But there are others to whom this idiosyncrasy does not appeal. They have no patience with the world constructed by its instrumentality. It may actually revolt them. Then the artist has nothing to say to them and they will deny his talent.

I do not believe that genius is an entirely different thing from talent. I am not even sure that it depends on any great difference in the artist's natural gifts. For example, I do not think that Cervantes had an exceptional gift for writing; few people would deny him genius. Nor would it be easy in English literature to find a poet with a happier gift than Herrick and yet no one would claim that he had more than a delightful talent. It seems to me that what makes genius is the combination of natural gifts for creation with an idiosyncrasy that enables its possessor to see the world personally in the highest degree and yet with such catholicity that his appeal is not to this type of man or to that type, but to all men. His private world is that of common men, but ampler and more pithy. His communication is universal and though men may not be able to tell exactly what it signifies they feel that it is important. He is supremely normal. By a happy accident of nature seeing life with immense vivacity, as it were at concert pitch, he sees it, with its infinite diversity, in the healthy way that mankind at large sees it. In Matthew Arnold's phrase he sees it steadily and sees it whole. But genius arises once or twice in a century. The lesson of anatomy applies: there is nothing so rare as the normal. It is foolish to do as many do now and call a man a genius because he has written half-a-dozen clever plays or painted a score of good pictures. It is very well to have talent; few people have. With talent the artist will only reach the second class, but that need not disturb him for it contains the names of many whose works have uncommon merit. When you think it has produced such novels as *Le Rouge et le Noir,* such poems as *The Shropshire Lad,* such paintings as those of Watteau, there is not much to be ashamed of. Talent cannot reach the utmost heights, but it can show you many an unexpected and delicious view, an unfrequented dell, a bubbling brook or a romantic cavern, on the way that leads to them. The frowardness of human nature is such that it falters sometimes when it is bidden to take the broadest of all surveys of human nature. It will shrink from the splendour of Tolstoi's *War and Peace* to turn with complacency to Voltaire's *Candide.* It would be hard to live always with Michelangelo's ceiling in the Sistine Chapel, but anyone could do with one of Constable's pictures of Salisbury Cathedral.

My sympathies are limited. I can only be myself, and partly by nature, partly by the circumstances of my life,

it is a partial self. I am not a social person. I cannot get drunk and feel a great love for my fellow men. Convivial amusement has always somewhat bored me. When people sit in an ale house or drifting down the river in a boat start singing I am silent. I have never even sung a hymn. I do not much like being touched and I have always to make a slight effort over myself not to draw away when someone links his arm in mine. I can never forget myself. The hysteria of the world repels me and I never feel more aloof than when I am in the midst of a throng surrendered to a violent feeling of mirth or sorrow. Though I have been in love a good many times I have never experienced the bliss of requited love. I know that this is the best thing that life can offer and it is a thing that almost all men, though perhaps only for a short time, have enjoyed. I have most loved people who cared little or nothing for me and when people have loved me I have been embarrassed. It has been a predicament that I have not quite known how to deal with. In order not to hurt their feelings I have often acted a passion that I did not feel. I have tried, with gentleness when possible, and if not, with irritation, to escape from the trammels with which their love bound me. I have been jealous of my independence. I am incapable of complete surrender. And so, never having felt some of the fundamental emotions of normal men, it is impossible that my work should have the intimacy, the broad human touch and the animal serenity which the greatest writers alone can give.

XXIII

IT IS dangerous to let the public behind the scenes. They are easily disillusioned and then they are angry with you, for it was the illusion they loved; they do not understand that what interests you is the way in which you have created the illusion. Anthony Trollope ceased to be read for thirty years because he confessed that he wrote at regular hours and took care to get the best price he could for his work.

But for me the race now is nearly run and it would ill become me to conceal the truth. I do not want anyone to think better of me than I deserve. Let those who like me take me as I am and let the rest leave me. I have more character than brains and more brains than specific gifts. I said something of this sort many years ago to a charming and distinguished critic. I do not know what led me to do so, since I am not much inclined to talk about myself in general company. It was at Montdidier, during the first months of the war, and we were lunching there on our way to Péronne. We had been very hardworked for some days and it was a pleasure to linger over a meal that seemed to our healthy appetites uncommonly good. I suppose I was flushed with wine and I daresay excited by the discovery, from a statue in the market-place, that Montdidier was the birthplace of Parmentier, who introduced the potato into France. Anyhow as we idled over our coffee and liqueurs I was moved to give an acute and candid analysis of my talent. I was disconcerted some years later to read it, almost in my very words,

in the columns of an important paper. I was a trifle vexed, for it is a very different thing to tell the truth about yourself and to have somebody else tell it, and I should have liked the critic to do me the compliment of saying that he had heard it all from my own lips. But I chid myself. I thought it very natural that he should like to think that he had so much perspicacity. And it was the truth. It has been a little unfortunate for me, since the critic is deservedly influential and what he said in this article has been very generally repeated. In another moment of frankness I informed my readers that I was unusually competent. One would think that except for this the critics would never have discovered it; but since then the adjective has been much and depreciatingly applied to me. It has seemed strange to me that so many people concerned, though only at second hand, with the arts should regard competence with so little favour.

I am told that there are natural singers and made singers. Though of course he must have something of a voice the made singer owes the better part of his accomplishment to training; with taste and musical ability he can eke out the relative poverty of his organ and his singing can afford a great deal of pleasure, especially to the connoisseur; but he will never move you as you are moved to ecstasy by the pure, birdlike notes of the natural singer. The natural singer may be inadequately trained, he may have neither tact or knowledge, he may outrage all the canons of art, but such is the magic of his voice that you are captivated. You forgive the liberties he takes, his vulgarities, his appeals to obvious emotion, when those heavenly sounds enchant your ear. I am a made writer. But it would be vanity if I thought that such results as I have achieved on myself were due to a design that I deliberately carried out. I was drawn to various courses by very simple motives and it is only on looking back that I discover myself subconsciously working to a certain end. The end was to develop my character and so make up for the deficiencies in my natural gifts.

I have a clear and logical brain, but not a very subtle nor a very powerful one. For long I wished it were better. I used to get exasperated because it would not do for me nearly as much as I wished. I was like a mathematician who could do no more than add and subtract and though he wanted to tackle all manner of complicated operations knew that he simply had not the capacity. It took me a long time to resign myself to making the best of what I had. I think it was a good enough brain to have brought me success in whatever profession I had adopted. I am not one of those persons who is a fool at everything but his own specialty. In law, medicine and politics a clear mind and insight into men are useful.

I have had one advantage; I have never wanted a subject. I have always had more stories in my head than I ever had time to write. I have often heard writers complain that they wanted to write but had nothing to write about, and I remember one distinguished author telling me that she was reading through some books in which were epitomized all the plots that had ever been used in order to find a theme. I have never found myself in such a predicament. Swift, as we know, who claimed that he could write on any subject whatever, when he was challenged to write a discourse on a broomstick acquitted himself very creditably. I am almost inclined to say that I could not spend an hour in anyone's company without getting the material to write at least a readable story about him. It is pleasant to have so many stories in mind that whatever your mood you have one upon which, for an hour or two, for a week or so, you can let your fancy linger. Reverie is the groundwork of creative imagination; it is the privilege of the artist that with him it is not as with other men an escape from reality, but the means by which he accedes to it. His reverie is purposeful. It affords him a delight in comparison with which the pleasures of sense are pale and it affords him the assurance of his freedom. One cannot wonder if sometimes he is unwilling to exchange its enjoyment for the drudgery and loss of execution.

But though I have had variety of invention, and this is not strange since it is the outcome of the variety of mankind, I have had small power of imagination. I have taken living people and put them into the situations, tragic or comic, that their characters suggested. I might well say that they invented their own stories. I have been incapable of those great, sustained flights that carry the author on broad pinions into a celestial sphere. My fancy, never very strong, has been hampered by my sense of probability. I have painted easel pictures, not frescoes.

XXIV

I HEARTILY wish that in my youth I had had someone of good sense to direct my reading. I sigh when I reflect on the amount of time I have wasted on books that were of no great profit to me. What little guidance I had I owe to a young man who came to live with the same family in Heidelberg as I was living with. I will call him Brown. He was then twenty-six. After leaving Cambridge he was called to the bar, but he had a little money, enough to live on in those inexpensive days, and finding the law distasteful he had made up his mind to devote himself to literature. He came to Heidelberg to learn German. I knew him till his death forty years later. For twenty years he amused himself with thinking what he would write when he really got down to it and for another twenty with what he could have written if the fates had been kinder. He wrote a good deal of verse. He had neither imagination, nor passion; and he had a defective ear. He spent some years translating those dialogues of Plato that already had been most often translated. I doubt, however, if he ever got to the end of one. He was completely devoid of will-power. He was sentimental and vain. Though short he was handsome, with finely cut features and curly hair; he had pale blue eyes and a wistful expression. He looked as one imagines a poet should look. As an old man, after a life of complete indolence, bald and emaciated, he had an ascetic air so that you might have taken him for a don who had spent long years in ardent and disinterested research. The spirituality of his expression suggested the tired scepticism of a philosopher who had plumbed the secrets of existence and discovered nothing but vanity. Having gradually wasted his small fortune, he preferred to live on the generosity of others rather than work, and often he found it difficult to make both ends meet. His self-complacency never deserted him. It enabled him to endure poverty with resignation and failure with indifference. I do not think he ever had an inkling that he was an outrageous sham. His whole life was a lie, but when he was dying, if he had known he was going to, which mercifully he didn't, I am convinced he would have looked upon it as well-spent. He had charm, he was devoid of envy, and though too selfish to do anyone a good turn, he was incapable of unkindness. He had a real appreciation of literature. During the long walks we took together over the hills of Heidelberg he talked to me of books. He talked to me of Italy and Greece, neither of which in point of fact he knew, but he fired my young imagination and I began to learn Italian. I accepted everything he told me with the fervour of the proselyte. I should not blame him because he inspired me with a passionate admiration for certain works that time has shown to be not so admirable. When he arrived he found me reading *Tom Jones*, which I had got out of the public library, and he told me that of course there was no harm in it, but I should do better to read *Diana of the Crossways*. Even then he was a Platonist and he gave me Shelley's translation of the Symposium. He talked to me of Renan,

Cardinal Newman and Matthew Arnold. But Matthew Arnold, he thought, was a bit of a philistine himself. He talked to me of Swinburne's *Poems and Ballads* and of *Omar Khayyám*. He knew a great many of the quatrains by heart and recited them to me on our walks. I was divided between enthusiasm for the romantic epicureanism of the matter and the embarrassment occasioned by Brown's delivery, for he recited poetry like a high-church curate intoning the Litany in an ill-lit crypt. But the two writers that it was really necessary to admire if you would be a person of culture and not a British philistine were Walter Pater and George Meredith. I was very ready to do what I was told to achieve this desirable end and incredible as it must seem I read *The Shaving of Shagpat* with roars of laughter. It seemed to me superlatively funny. Then I read the novels of George Meredith one after the other. I thought them wonderful; but not so wonderful as even to myself I pretended. My admiration was factitious. I admired because it was the part of a cultured young man to admire. I intoxicated myself with my own enthusiasm. I would not listen to the still small voice within me that carped. Now I know that there is a great deal of fustian in these novels. But the strange thing is that, reading them again, I recapture the days when I first read them. They are rich for me now with sunny mornings and my awakening intelligence and the delicious dreams of youth, so that even as I close a novel of Meredith's, *Evan Harrington* for instance, and decide that its insincerity is exasperating, its snobbishness loathsome, its verbosity intolerable and I will never read another, my heart melts and I think it's grand.

On the other hand I have no such feeling about Walter Pater whom I read at the same time and with a similar excitement. No pleasant associations give him for me a merit to which he has no claim. I find him as dull as a picture of Alma Tadema. It is strange that one can ever have admired that prose. It does not flow. There is no air in it. A careful mosaic constructed by someone without great technical skill to decorate the walls of a station dining-room. Pater's attitude towards the life about him, cloistered, faintly supercilious, gentlemanly, donnish in short, repels me. Art should be appreciated with passion and violence, not with a tepid, deprecating elegance that fears the censoriousness of a common room. But Walter Pater was a feeble creature: it is unnecessary to condemn him with intensity. I dislike him not for himself, but because he is an example of a type in the literary world that is common and detestable. This is the person who is filled with the conceit of culture.

The value of culture is its effect on character. It avails nothing unless it ennobles and strengthens that. Its use is for life. Its aim is not beauty but goodness. Too often, as we know, it gives rise to self-complacency. Who has not seen the scholar's thin-lipped smile when he corrects a misquotation and the connoisseur's pained look when someone praises a picture he does not care for? There is no more merit in having read a thousand books than in having ploughed a thousand fields. There is no more merit in being able to attach a correct description to a picture than in being able to find out what is wrong with a stalled motor-car. In each case it is special knowledge. The stockbroker has his knowledge too and so has the artizan. It is a silly prejudice of the intellectual that his is the only one that counts. The True, the Good and the Beautiful are not the perquisites of those who have been to expensive schools, burrowed in libraries and frequented museums. The artist has no excuse when he uses others with condescen- sion. He is a fool if he thinks his knowledge is more important than theirs and an oaf if he cannot comfortably meet them on an equal footing. Matthew Arnold did a great disservice to culture when he insisted on its opposition to philistinism.

XXV

AT EIGHTEEN I knew French, German and some Italian, but I was extremely uneducated and I was deeply conscious of my ignorance. I read everything that came my way. My curiosity was such that I was as willing to read a history of Peru or the reminiscences of a cowboy as a treatise on Provençal poetry or the *Confessions* of St. Augustine. I suppose it gained me a certain amount of general knowledge which is useful for the novelist to have. One never knows when an out-of-the-way bit of information will come in handy. I made lists of what I read and one of these lists by some accident I still have. It is my reading for two months and, but that I made it only for myself, I could not believe that it was veracious. It shows that I read three of Shakespeare's plays, two volumes of Mommsen's *History of Rome,* a large part of Lanson's *Littérature Française,* two or three novels, some of the French classics, a couple of scientific works and a play of Ibsen's. I was indeed the industrious apprentice. During the time I was at St. Thomas's Hospital I went systematically through English, French, Italian and Latin literature. I read a lot of history, a little philosophy and a good deal of science. My curiosity was too great to allow me to give much time to reflect upon what I read; I could hardly wait to finish one book, so eager was I to begin another. This was always an adventure, and I would start upon a famous work as excitedly as a reasonable young man would go in to bat for his side or a nice girl go to a dance. Now and then journalists in search of copy ask me what is the most thrilling moment of my life. If I were not ashamed to, I might answer that it is the moment when I began to read Goethe's *Faust.* I have never quite lost this feeling, and even now the first pages of a book sometimes send the blood racing through my veins. To me reading is a rest as to other people conversation or a game of cards. It is more than that; it is a necessity, and if I am deprived of it for a little while I find myself as irritable as the addict deprived of his drug. I would sooner read a time-table or a catalogue than nothing at all. That is putting it too low. I have spent many delightful hours poring over the price list of the Army and Navy Stores, the lists of second-hand booksellers and the A.B.C. All these are redolent of romance. They are much more entertaining than half the novels that are written.

I have put books aside only because I was conscious that time was passing and that it was my business to live. I have gone into the world because I thought it was necessary in order to get the experience without which I could not write, but I have gone into it also because I wanted experience for its own sake. It did not seem to me enough only to be a writer. The pattern I had designed for myself insisted that I should take the utmost part I could in this fantastic affair of being a man. I desired to feel the common pains and enjoy the common pleasures that are part of the common human lot. I saw no reason to subordinate the claims of sense to the tempting lure of spirit and I was determined to get whatever fulfilment I could out of social intercourse and human relations, out of food, drink and fornication, luxury, sport, art, travel, and as Henry James says, whatever. But it was an effort and I have always returned to my books and my own company with relief.

And yet, though I have read so much, I am a bad reader. I read slowly and I am a poor skipper. I find it difficult to leave a book, however bad and however much it bores me, unfinished. I could count on my fingers the number of books that I have not read from cover to cover. On the other hand there are few books that I have read twice. I know very well that there are many of which I cannot get the full value on a single reading, but in that they have given me all I was capable of getting at the time, and this, though I may forget their details, remains a permanent enrichment. I know people who read the same book over and over again. It can only be that they read with their eyes and not with their sensibility. It is a mechanical exercise like the Tibetan's turning of a praying-wheel. It is doubtless a harmless occupation, but they are wrong if they think it an intelligent one.

XXVI

In my youth, when my instinctive feeling about a book differed from that of authoritative critics I did not hesitate to conclude that I was wrong. I did not know how often critics accept the conventional view and it never occurred to me that they could talk with assurance of what they did not know very much about. It was long before I realized that the only thing that mattered to me in a work of art was what I thought about it. I have acquired now a certain confidence in my own judgment, for I have noticed that what I felt instinctively forty years ago about the writers I read then, and what I would not heed because it did not agree with current opinion, is now pretty generally accepted. For all that I still read a great deal of criticism, for I think it a very agreeable form of literary composition. One does not always want to be reading to the profit of one's soul and there is no pleasanter way of idling away an hour or two than reading a volume of criticism. It is diverting to agree; it is diverting to differ; and it is always interesting to know what an intelligent man has to say about some writer, Henry More, for instance, or Richardson, whom you have never had occasion to read.

But the only important thing in a book is the meaning it has for you; it may have other and much more profound meanings for the critic, but at second hand they can be of small service to you. I do not read a book for the book's sake, but for my own. It is not my business to judge it, but to absorb what I can of it, as the amœba absorbs a particle of a foreign body, and what I cannot assimilate has nothing to do with me. I am not a scholar, a student or a critic; I am a professional writer and now I read only what is useful to me professionally. Anyone can write a book that will revolutionize the ideas that have been held for centuries on the Ptolemies and I shall contentedly leave it unread; he can describe an incredibly adventurous journey in the heart of Patagonia and I shall remain ignorant of it. There is no need for the writer of fiction to be an expert on any subject but his own; on the contrary, it is hurtful to him, since, human nature being weak, he is hard put to it to resist the temptation of inappositely using his special knowledge. The novelist is ill-advised to be too technical. The practice, which came into fashion in the nineties, of using a multitude of cant terms is tiresome. It should be possible to give verisimilitude without that, and atmosphere is dearly bought at the price of tediousness. The novelist should know something about the great issues that occupy men, who are his topics, but it is generally enough if he knows a little. He must avoid pedantry at all costs. But even at that the field is vast and I have tried to limit myself to such works as were significant to my purpose. You can never know enough about your characters. Biographies and reminiscences, technical works, will give you often an intimate detail, a telling touch, a revealing hint, that you might never have got from a living model. People are hard to know. It is a slow business to induce them to tell you the particular thing about themselves that can be of use to you. They have the disadvantage that often you cannot look at them and put them aside, as you can a book, and you have to read the whole volume, as it were, only to learn that it had nothing much to tell you.

XXVII

Young persons, who are anxious to write, sometimes pay me the compliment of asking me to tell them of certain books necessary for them to read. I do. They seldom read them, for they seem to have little curiosity. They do not care what their predecessors have done. They think they know everything that it is necessary to know of the art of fiction when they have read two or three novels by Mrs. Woolf, one by E. M. Forster, several by D. H. Lawrence and, oddly enough, the *Forsyte Saga*. It is true that contemporary literature has a vividness of appeal that classical literature can never have and it is well for a young writer to know what his contemporaries are writing about and how. But there are fashions in literature and it is not easy to tell what intrinsic value there is in a style of writing that happens to be the vogue at the moment. An acquaintance with the great works of the past serves as a very good standard of comparison. I have sometimes wondered whether it is due to their ignorance that many young writers, notwithstanding their facility and cleverness, their skilful technique, so frequently fizzle out. They write two or three books that are not only brilliant, but mature, and then they are done for. But that is not what enriches the literature of a country. For that you must have writers who can produce not just two or three books, but a great body of work. Of course it will be uneven, because so many fortunate circumstances must go together to produce a masterpiece; but a masterpiece is more likely to come as the culminating point of a laborious career than as the lucky fluke of untaught genius. The writer can only be fertile if he renews himself and he can only renew himself if his soul is constantly enriched by fresh experience. There is no more fruitful source of this than the enchanting exploration of the great literatures of the past.

For the production of a work of art is not the result of a miracle. It requires preparation. The soil, be it ever so rich, must be fed. By taking thought, by deliberate effort, the artist must enlarge, deepen and diversify his personality. Then the soil must lie fallow. Like the bride of Christ, the artist waits for the illumination that shall bring forth a new spiritual life. He goes about his ordinary avocations with patience; the subconscious does its mysterious business; and then, suddenly springing, you might think from nowhere, the idea is produced. But like the corn that was sown on stony ground it may easily wither away; it must be tended with anxious care. All the power of the artist's mind must be set to work on it, all his technical skill, all his experience, and whatever he has in him of character and individuality, so that with infinite pains he may present it with the completeness that is fitting to it.

But I am not impatient with the young when, only at their request, I insist, I advise them to read Shakespeare and Swift, and they tell me that they read *Gulliver's Travels* in their nursery and *Henry IV* at school; and if they find *Vanity Fair* unendurable and *Anna Karenina* footling it is their own affair. No reading is worth while unless you enjoy it. There is at least this to be said for them that they do not suffer from the self-conceit of knowledge. They are not withdrawn by a wide culture from sympathy with the common run of men who are after all their material. They are nearer to their fellows and the art they practise is not a mystery, but a craft on the same footing as any other. They write novels and plays as unaffectedly as other men build motorcars. This is much to the good. For the artist, the writer especially, in the solitariness of his own mind constructs a world that is different from other men's; the idiosyncrasy that makes him a writer separates him from them and the paradox emerges that though his aim is to describe them truthfully his gift prevents him from knowing them as they really are. It is as though he wanted urgently to see a certain thing and by the act of looking at it drew before it a veil that obscured it. The writer stands outside the very action he is engaged in. He is the comedian who never quite loses himself in the part, for he is at the same time spectator and actor. It is all very well to say that poetry is emotion remembered in tranquillity; but a poet's emotion is specific, a poet's rather than a man's, and it is never quite disinterested. That is why women with their instinctive common sense have so often found the love of poets unsatisfying. It may be that the writers of the present day, who seem to be so much nearer to their raw material, ordinary men among ordinary men, rather than artists in an alien crowd, may break down the barrier that their peculiar gift cannot but raise and so come nearer to the plain truth than has ever been done before. But then you have to make up your mind about the relations between truth and art.

XXVIII

I HAD my full share of the intellectual's arrogance and if, as I hope, I have lost it, I must ascribe it not to my own virtue or wisdom but to the chance that made me more of a traveller than most writers. I am attached to England, but I have never felt myself very much at home there. I have always been shy with English people. To me England has been a country where I had obligations that I did not want to fulfil and responsibilities that irked me. I have never felt entirely myself till I had put at least the Channel between my native country and me. Some fortunate persons find freedom in their own minds; I, with less spiritual power than they, find it in travel. While still at Heidelberg I managed to visit a good many places in Germany (at Munich I saw Ibsen drinking a glass of beer at the Maximilianerhof and with a scowl on his face reading the paper) and I went to Switzerland; but the first real journey I made was to Italy. I went primed with much reading of Walter Pater, Ruskin and John Addington Symonds. I had the six weeks of the Easter vacation at my disposal and twenty pounds in my pocket. After going to Genoa and Pisa, where I trudged the interminable distance to sit for a while in the pine wood in which Shelley read Sophocles and wrote verses on a guitar, I settled down for the inside of a month in Florence in the house of a widow lady, with whose daughter I read the *Purgatorio*, and spent laborious days, Ruskin in hand, visiting the sights. I admired everything that Ruskin told me to admire (even that horrible tower of Giotto) and turned away in disgust from what he condemned. Never can he have had a more ardent disciple. After that I went to Venice, Verona and Milan. I returned to England very much pleased with myself and actively contemptuous of anyone who did not share my views (and Ruskin's) of Botticelli and Bellini. I was twenty.

A year later I went to Italy again, travelling as far down as Naples, and discovered Capri. It was the most enchanting spot I had ever seen and the following summer I spent the whole of my vacation there. Capri was then little known. There was no funicular from the beach to the town. Few people went there in summer and you could get board and lodging, with wine included, and from your bedroom window a view of Vesuvius, for four shillings a day. There was a poet there then, a Belgian composer, my friend from Heidelberg, Brown, a painter or two, a sculptor (Harvard Thomas) and an American colonel who had fought on the Southern side in the Civil War. I listened with transport to conversations, up at Anacapri at the colonel's house, or at Morgano's, the wine shop just off the Piazza, when they talked of art and beauty, literature and Roman history. I saw two men fly at one another's throats because they disagreed over the poetic merit of Heredia's sonnets. I thought it all grand. Art, art for art's sake, was the only thing that mattered in the world; and the artist alone gave this ridiculous world significance. Politics, commerce, the learned professions—what did they amount to from the standpoint of the Absolute? They might disagree, these friends of mine (dead, dead every jack one of them), about the value of a sonnet or the excellence of a Greek bas-relief (Greek, my eye! I tell you it's a Roman copy and if I tell you a thing it is so); but they were all agreed about this, that they burned with a hard, gemlike flame. I was too shy to tell them that I had written a novel and was halfway through another and it was a great mortification to me, burning as I was too with a hard, gemlike flame, to be treated as a philistine who cared for nothing but dissecting dead bodies and would seize an unguarded moment to give his best friend an enema.

XXIX

PRESENTLY I was qualified. I had already published a novel and it had had an unexpected success. I thought my fortune was made, and, abandoning medicine to become a writer, I went to Spain. I was then twenty-three. I was much more ignorant than are, it seems to me, young men of that age at the present day. I settled down in Seville. I grew a moustache, smoked Filipino cigars, learnt the guitar, bought a broad-brimmed hat with a flat crown, in which I swaggered down the Sierpes, and hankered for a flowing cape, lined with green and red velvet. But on account of the expense I did not buy it. I rode about the countryside on a horse lent me by a friend. Life was too pleasant to allow me to give an undivided attention to literature. My plan was to spend a year there till I had learnt Spanish, then go to Rome which I knew only as a tripper and perfect my superficial knowledge of Italian, follow that up with a journey to Greece where I intended to learn the vernacular as an approach to ancient Greek, and finally go to Cairo and learn Arabic. It was an ambitious programme, but I am glad now that I did not carry it out. I duly went to Rome (where I wrote my first play) but then I went back to Spain; for something had occurred that I had not anticipated. I fell in love with Seville and the life one led there and incidentally with a young thing with green eyes and a gay smile (but I got over that) and I could not resist its lure. I returned year after year. I wandered through the white and silent streets and strolled along the Guadalquivir, I dawdled about the Cathedral, I went to bullfights and made light love to pretty little creatures whose demands on me were no more than my exiguous means could satisfy. It was heavenly to live in Seville in the flower of one's youth. I postponed my education to a more convenient moment. The result is that I have never read the *Odyssey* but in English and I have never achieved my ambition to read *A Thousand Nights and a Night* in Arabic.

When the intelligentsia took up Russia I, remembering that Cato had begun to learn Greek when he was eighty, set about learning Russian, but

I had by then lost my youthful enthusiasm; I never got farther than being able to read the plays of Chekhov and have long since forgotten the little I knew. I think now that these schemes of mine were a trifle nonsensical. Words are not important, but their meanings, and it is of no spiritual advantage that I can see to know half-a-dozen languages. I have met polyglots; I have not noticed that they were wiser than the rest of us. It is convenient if you are travelling in a country to have a sufficient smattering of its speech to find your way about and get what you want to eat; and if it has a considerable literature it is pleasant to be able to read it. But such a knowledge as this can be acquired easily. To attempt to learn more is futile. Unless you devote your whole life to it, you will never learn to speak the language of another country to perfection; you will never know its people and its literature with complete intimacy. For they, and the literature which is their expression, are wrought, not only of the actions they perform and the words they use, neither of which offer great difficulty, but of ancestral instincts, shades of feeling that they have absorbed with their mothers' milk, and innate attitudes which the foreigner can never quite seize. It is hard enough for us to know our own people; we deceive ourselves, we English especially, if we think we can know those of other lands. For the sea-girt isle sets us apart and the link that a common religion gave, which once mitigated our insularity, was snapped with the Reformation. It seems hardly worth while to take much trouble to acquire a knowledge that can never be more than superficial. I think then it is merely waste of time to learn more than a smattering of foreign tongues. The only exception I would make to this is French. For French is the common language of educated men and it is certainly convenient to speak it well enough to be able to treat of any subject of discourse that may arise. It has a great literature; other countries, with the exception of England, have great writers, rather than a great literature; and its influence on the rest of the world has, till the last twenty years, been profound. It is very well to be able to read French as easily as if it were your native tongue. There are limits, however, to the excellence with which you should allow yourself to speak it. As a matter of practice it is good to be on your guard against an Englishman who speaks French perfectly; he is very likely to be a card-sharper or an attaché in the diplomatic service.

XXX

I WAS never stage-struck. I have known dramatists who wandered in every night to the theatre in which their play was being acted. They said they did it in order to see that the cast was not getting slack: I suspect it was because they could never hear their own words spoken often enough. Their delight was to sit in the dressing-room during the intervals and talk over this scene or the other, wondering why it had fallen flat that night or congratulating themselves on how well it had gone, and watch an actor make up. They never ceased to find the theatrical gossip of the day absorbing. They loved the theatre and everything connected with it. They had grease-paint in their bones.

I have never been like that. I like a theatre best when it is under dustsheets, the auditorium in darkness, and the unset stage, with the flats stacked against the back wall, is lit only by footlights. I have passed many happy hours at rehearsals; I have liked their easy camaraderie, the hurried lunch at a restaurant round the corner with a member of the cast and the cup of strong bitter tea, with thick bread and butter, brought in by the charwoman at four o'clock. I have never quite lost that little thrill of surprised amusement I felt when in my first play I heard grown men and women repeat the lines that had come so easily to my pen. It has interested me to watch the way in which a part grows in the actor's hands from the first lifeless reading of the typescript to something like the character that I have seen in my mind's eye. I have been diverted by the important discussions about the exact place where a piece of furniture should stand, the self-sufficiency of the director, the tantrums of an actress displeased with her positions, the artfulness of old players determined to get the centre of the stage for their scene, and the desultory talk about any subject that came to hand. But the consummation is the dress rehearsal. There are half-a-dozen people in the front-row of the dress circle. They are the dressmakers, subdued as though they were in church, but very businesslike; they exchange short, sharp whispers with one another during the performance and make little significant gestures. You know that they are speaking of the length of a skirt, the cut of a

sleeve or the feather in a hat; and the moment the curtain falls, the pins already in their mouths, they hurry through the door on to the stage. The director shouts "curtain up" and when it rises an actress snatches herself away from an agitated colloquy with two grim ladies in black.

"Oh, Mr. Thing," she calls out, "I know that passementerie is wrong, but Madame Floss says she'll take it off and put a bit of lace instead."

In the stalls are the photographers, the management and the man from the box office, the mothers of the actresses in the cast and the wives of the actors, your own agent, a girl friend of yours, and three or four old actors who haven't had a part for twenty years. It is the perfect audience. After each act the director reads out the remarks he has jotted down. There is a row with the electrician who, with nothing to do but attend to his switches, has turned on the wrong ones; and the author is indignant with him for being so careless and at the same time indulgent because he has a notion that the electrician only forgot his work because he was so absorbed in the play. Perhaps a little scene is repeated; then effective positions are arranged and with sudden blares of flashlight photographs are taken. The curtain is lowered to set the scene for the next act and the cast separate to their dressing-rooms to change. The dressmakers vanish and the old actors slink round the corner to have a drink. The management despondently smoke gaspers, the wives and mothers of the cast talk to one another in undertones and the author's agent reads the racing news in the evening paper. It is all unreal and exciting. At last the dressmakers filter through the fire-proof door and resume their seats, the representatives of rival firms at a haughty distance from one another, and the stage manager puts his head round the curtain.

"All ready, Mr. Thing," he says. "All right. Fire away. Curtain up."

But the dress rehearsal was the last pleasure my play ever had to give me. At the first nights of my early plays I was on tenterhooks, for on their result my future depended. When *Lady Frederick* was produced I had reached the end of the little money I had come into when I was twenty-one, my novels did not bring me in enough to live upon, and I could earn nothing by journalism. I had been given a little reviewing now and then and once persuaded an editor to let me do the notice of a play, but I evidently had no gifts in that direction; indeed, the editor in question told me that I had no sense of the theatre. If *Lady Frederick* was a failure it seemed to me that there was nothing for me but to go back to the hospital for a year to refresh my knowledge of medicine and then get a post as surgeon on a ship. At that time this was a position not much sought after and few men with London degrees applied for it. Later, when I had become a successful dramatist, I went to first nights with

my senses alert to discern from the reactions of the public whether there was any falling off in my ability. I did my best to lose myself in the audience. For the audience a first night is a more or less interesting event which they take between a snack at seven-thirty and supper at eleven, and the success or failure of which is no great matter. I tried to go to my own first nights as though they were somebody else's; but even at that I found it a disagreeable experience. It did me no good to hear the laughter that rewarded a happy jest or the applause that broke out on the fall of the curtain when an act had pleased. The fact is that, even in my lightest pieces, I had put in so much of myself that I was embarrassed to hear it disclosed to a crowd of people. Because they were words I had written myself they had for me an intimacy that I shrank from sharing with all and sundry. This unreasonable feeling I have had even when I have gone to see a play of mine in a translation and have sat in the theatre as an entirely unknown member of the public. Indeed I should never have gone to see my plays at all, on the first night or any other, if I had not thought it necessary to see the effect they had on the audience in order to learn how to write them.

XXXI

THE actor's calling is a hard one. I am not speaking now of the young women who go on the stage because they have a pretty face and if good looks were a qualification for typists might just as well have gone into an office, or of the young men who do so because they have a good figure and no particular aptitude for any-

thing else. They drift in and out of the profession; the women marry and the men get into a wine-merchant's office or take up interior decoration. I am speaking of the actors by vocation. They have a natural gift and the desire to use it. It is a profession that requires assiduous labour to achieve proficiency, so that by the time an actor knows how to act any sort of part he is often too old to act any but a few; it requires boundless patience; it is fraught with disappointments. Long stretches of enforced idleness must be endured. The prizes are few and can be held but for a brief period. The rewards are inadequate. The actor is at the mercy of fortune and the inconstant favour of the public. He is forgotten as soon as he ceases to please. Then it will avail him nothing to have been the idol of the crowd. He can starve for all they care. It is when I think of this that I find it easy to be indulgent to the actor's airs and graces, his exigence and vanity, when he is on the crest of the wave. Let him be flamboyant and absurd if he likes. It all lasts such a little while. And after all his egotism is part of his talent.

There was a period when the stage was the doorway to romance and everyone connected with it seemed exciting and mysterious. In the civilized world of the eighteenth century the actors gave life a touch of fantasy. Their disorderly existence was a lure to the imagination in the Age of Reason and the heroic parts they played, the verse they spoke, invested them with a halo. In Goethe's *Wilhelm Meister,* that wonderful and neglected book, you can see with what tenderness the poet regarded what can have been nothing but a second-rate touring company. And in the nineteenth century the actors offered an escape from the respectability of an industrial era. The bohemianism that was ascribed to them excited the imagination of young men who were forced to earn their living in an office. They were extravagant persons in a sober world, thoughtless in a careful one, and fancy clothed them with glamour. There is in Victor Hugo's *Choses Vues* a passage, touching in its unconscious humour, in which with awe, astonishment and a spark of envy for such wildness, the sensible little man describes a supper party with an actress. For once in his life he felt a devil of a fellow. Good gracious, how the champagne flowed and what luxury, what silver, what tiger skins, were to be seen in her apartment!

This glory has vanished. The actors have become settled, respectable and well-to-do. It offended them to be thought a race apart and they have done their best to be like everybody else. They have shown themselves to us without their make up in the broad light of day, and besought us to see for ourselves that they are golfers and taxpayers and thinking men and women. To my mind this is all stuff and nonsense.

I have known a number of actors very well. I have found them good company. Their gift of mimicry, their knack of telling a story, their quick wit, make them often highly entertaining. They are generous, kindly and courageous. But I have never quite been able to look upon them as human beings. I have never succeeded in achieving any intimacy with them. They are like crossword puzzles in which there are no words to fit the clues. The fact is, I suppose, that their personality is made up of the parts they play and that the basis of it is something amorphous. It is a soft, malleable thing that is capable of taking any shape and being painted in any colour. An ingenious writer has suggested that it is not surprising if for so long they were refused burial in consecrated ground because it is preposterous to suppose that they have souls. This is probably an extravagance. They are certainly very interesting. And the novelist, if he is sincere, cannot but acknowledge that there is between him and them a certain affinity: their character, like his, is a harmony that is none too plausible; they are all the persons they can mirror, while he is all the persons he can beget. The writer and the actor represent emotions they do not, at the moment at all events, feel; and stand-ing with one side of themselves outside life portray it for the satisfaction of their creative instincts. Make-believe is their reality, and the public, which is at once their material and their judge, is also their dupe. Because make-believe is their reality they can look upon reality as make-believe.

XXXII

I BEGAN to write plays, as do most young writers, I expect, because it seemed less difficult to set down on paper the things people said than to construct a narrative. Dr. Johnson remarked long ago that it is much more easy to form dialogues than to contrive adventures. Looking through the old notebooks in which from eighteen to twenty I wrote down scenes for the plays I had in mind I find the dialogue on the whole easy and probable. The jokes no longer make me smile, but they are said in the words people would have used then. I caught the colloquial note by instinct. But the jokes are few and savage. The themes of my plays were sombre; and they ended in gloom, despair and death. On my first journey to Florence, I took *Ghosts* with me, and by way of relaxation, for I was seriously studying Dante, translated it into English from a German version in order to acquire a knowledge of technique. I remember that with all my admiration for Ibsen I could not help thinking Pastor Manders a bit of a bore. The *Second Mrs. Tanqueray* was then running at the St. James's Theatre.

During the next two or three years I finished several curtain-raisers and sent them to various managers. One or two were never returned and since I had no copies were lost; the others I got discouraged over and put away or destroyed. At that time, and for long after, it was much more difficult than it is now for an unknown playwright to get a production. Runs were long, for expenses were small, and a small band of authors, headed by Pinero and Henry Arthur Jones, could be counted upon to provide the principal theatres with a play whenever one was needed. The French stage was still flourishing and adaptations from the French in bowdlerized versions were popular. I got it into my head, I think from the fact that George Moore's *Strike at Arlingford* was done by the Independent Theatre, that my only chance of being acted was by making a reputation for myself as a novelist. So I put the drama aside and set myself to writing fiction. The reader may think that this methodical fashion of going to work was unbecomingly businesslike in a young author. It suggests a matter-of-fact turn of mind rather than a heaven-sent compulsion to enrich the world with works of art. When I had published a couple of novels and had a volume of short stories ready for the press, I sat down and wrote my first full-length play. It was called *A Man of Honour*. I sent it to Forbes-Robertson, who was then a popular actor, with the reputation of having artistic inclinations, and when he returned it to me after three or four months, to Charles Frohman. He also returned it. I rewrote it and at last, having by then published two more novels, one of which (*Mrs. Craddock*) had a considerable success, so that I was beginning to be looked upon as a serious and promising novelist, I sent it to the Stage Society. They accepted it and W. L. Courtney, a member of the committee, liked it well enough to print it in *The Fortnightly Review*. He had only published one play before, Mrs. Clifford's *The Likeness of the Night*, so that it was a great honour.

Since the Stage Society was at that time the only organization of its kind, its productions attracted a good deal of attention and my play was treated by the critics as seriously as though it had been put on for a run in an important theatre. The old hacks, with Clement Scott at their head, abused it soundly; the critic of the *Sunday Times* stated that it showed no sign of any talent for the stage. I have forgotten who he was. But the critics who had succumbed to the influence of Ibsen treated it as a work worthy of consideration. They were sympathetic and encouraging.

I thought I had taken such a step forward that my course from then on would offer no great difficulties. It did not take me long to discover that, beyond learning a good deal about the technique of playwriting, I had achieved nothing. After its two performances my play was dead. My name was known to the small body of people who were interested in the experimental theatre and if I had written suitable plays I have no doubt that the Stage Society would have performed them. But that seemed to me unsatis-factory. During the rehearsals I had come in contact with the people who were interested in the society and especially with Granville Barker, who played the leading part in my play. The attitude I found there was antagonistic to me. It seemed to me patronizing and narrow. Granville Barker was very young; I was only twenty-eight, and he, I think, was a year younger. He had charm and gaiety and a coltish grace. He was brimming over with other people's ideas. But I felt in him a fear of life which he sought to cheat by contempt of the common herd. It was difficult to find anything he did not despise. He lacked spiritual vitality. I thought that an artist needed more force, more go, more bluntness, more guts, more beef. He had written a play, *The Marriage of Ann Leete*, which seemed to me anæmic and affected. I liked life and wanted to enjoy it. I wanted to get all I possibly could out of it. I was not satisfied with the appreciation of a small band of intellectuals. I had my doubts about their quality, for I had been to a stupid and rather common little farce that the Stage Society had unaccountably given and had seen its members consumed with laughter. I was not at all certain that there was not a great deal of pose in their concern for the higher drama. I wanted no such audience as this, but the great public. Moreover I was poor. I had no notion of living on a crust in a garret if I could help it. I had found out that money was like a sixth sense without which you could not make the most of the other five.

During the rehearsals of *A Man of Honour* I had discovered that some scenes of flirtatious badinage in the first act were amusing and I decided that I could write a comedy. I made up my mind to write one now. I called it *Loaves and Fishes*. Its hero was a worldly, ambitious parson and the story dealt with his courtship of a rich widow, his intrigues to get a bishopric and his final capture of a pretty heiress. No manager would consider it; it was thought impossible that a play that held a clergyman up to ridicule would be tolerated. I came to the conclusion then that my best chance was to write a comedy with a big part for an actress, who, if she liked it, might induce a manager to give the play a trial. I asked myself what sort of part would be likely to appeal to a leading lady, and having made up my mind on this point, wrote *Lady Frederick*. But its most effective scene, the scene that afterwards made it so successful, was one in which the heroine in order to disillusion a young lover let him come into her dressing-room and discover her without any make up on her face and with her hair dishevelled. At that distant time make up was not universal and most women wore false hair. But no actress would consent to let an audience see her in this condition and manager after manager refused it. I made up my mind then to devise a play in which no one could find anything to object to. I wrote *Mrs. Dot*. It suffered the same fate as the others. The managers thought it too slight. They complained that there was not enough action and Miss Mary Moore, then a popular actress, suggested that I should insert a burglary to make it

more exciting. I began to think that I should never be able to write a piece that a leading lady liked well enough to insist on playing and so tried my hand at a man's play. I wrote *Jack Straw*.

I had been under the impression that the small success I had had with the Stage Society would impress managers in my favour. To my mortification I found that this was not so. In fact my connection with that body prejudiced me with them, for they decided that I could only write gloomy and unprofitable plays. They could not say that my comedies were gloomy; but they felt them vaguely unpleasant and were convinced that they were uncommercial. I should certainly have given up in despair the attempt to get acted, for one rejection of a manuscript has always discouraged me; but fortunately for me Golding Bright thought that my plays were marketable and took them in hand. He submitted them to manager after manager and at last, in 1907, when I had written six full-length pieces, after ten years' waiting, *Lady Frederick* was produced at the Court Theater. Three months later *Mrs. Dot* was being played at the Comedy and *Jack Straw* at the Vaudeville. In June Lewis Waller put on at the Lyric a play called *The Explorer* which I had written immediately after *A Man of Honour*. I had achieved what I wanted.

XXXIII

THE first three had long runs. *The Explorer* was only just not a failure. I did not make a great deal of money, for in those days the takings of a popular play were much less than they are now, and my royalties were

small, but I was at all events relieved from financial anxiety and my future seemed sure. The fact that I had four plays running at once brought me great notoriety and Bernard Partridge drew a cartoon for *Punch* in which

William Shakespeare was shown biting his fingers in front of the boards that advertised my plays. I was much photographed and much interviewed. Distinguished people sought my acquaintance. My success was spectacular and unexpected. I was more relieved than excited. I think I lack the quality of being surprised, and just as in my journeys I have accepted the most curious sights and the most novel circumstances as perfectly ordinary, so that I have had to force myself to notice that they were remarkable, so now I took all this to-do as natural. One evening when I was dining alone at my club a fellow member, but a stranger to me, was entertaining a guest at the next table to mine; they were going to one of my plays and began to talk of me. The stranger mentioned that I was a member of the club, whereupon his guest said:

"D'you know him at all? I suppose he's about as swollen-headed as he can be."

"Oh, yes, I know him well," answered my fellow member. "He can't get a hat big enough to fit him."

He did me an injustice. I took the success as my due. I was amused at my notoriety, but not impressed by it. The only definite reaction that I can recall of that period was a reflection that occurred to me when I was walking along Panton Street one evening. Passing the Comedy Theatre I happened to look up and saw the clouds lit by the setting sun. I paused to look at the lovely sight and I thought to myself: Thank God, I can look at a sunset now without having to think how to describe it. I meant then never to write another book, but to devote myself for the rest of my life to the drama.

Though the public accepted my plays with enthusiasm, not only in England and America, but on the Continent, critical opinion was by no means unanimous. The more popular organs praised their wit, gaiety and theatrical effectiveness, but found fault with their cynicism; the more serious critics, on the other hand, fell very foul of them. They found them cheap and trivial. They told me that I had sold my soul to mammon; and the intelligentsia, of which I had been a modest but respected member, not only turned a cold shoulder on me, that would have been bad enough, but flung me, like Lucifer, headlong into the bottomless pit. I was taken aback and a trifle mortified, but I bore my disgrace with fortitude, for I knew it was not the end of the story. I had desired a certain end and had taken what I thought were the only possible means to attain it; I could only shrug my shoulders if there were people so stupid as not to see that. If I had continued to write plays as bitter as *A Man of Honour* or as sardonic as *Loaves and Fishes* I should never have been given the opportunity of producing certain pieces to which not even the most severe have refused praise. The critics accused me of writing down to the public; I did not exactly do that; I had then very high spirits, a facility for amusing dialogue, an eye for a comic situation and a flippant gaiety; there was more in me than that, but this I put away for the time, and wrote my comedies with those sides of myself only that were useful to my purpose. They were designed to please and they achieved their aim.

I had no intention of fizzling out with a passing success and I wrote my next two plays to consolidate my hold on the public. They were a little bolder and, mild and unsophisticated as they must seem now, they were attacked by the more strait-laced for their indecency. One of them, *Penel-*

ope, must have had some merit, for when it was revived in Berlin twenty years later it filled the theatre for a whole season.

I had by now learnt all that I was ever able to learn of the technique of the drama, and with the exception of *The Explorer,* which for a reason I saw very clearly had failed to please so well, I had had an uninterrupted series of successes. I thought it time to try my hand at more serious work. I wanted to see what I could do with more complicated subjects, I wanted to make one or two small technical experiments which I thought would be theatrically effective, and I wanted to see how far I could go with the public. I wrote *The Tenth Man* and *Landed Gentry,* and finally, after it had been lying in my desk a dozen years, produced *Loaves and Fishes.* None of them was a failure; none of them was a success. The managers neither made nor lost money on them. *Loaves and Fishes* failed to have a long run because the public of that day was uneasy at seeing a clergyman made fun of. The play is written somewhat extravagantly, so that it suggests farce rather than comedy, but it has some amusing scenes in it. The others fell between two stools. One portrayed the narrow, hidebound life of country gentlefolk; the other, the political and financial world; with both of which I had some acquaintance. I knew that I must interest, move and amuse, and I heightened the note. They were neither frankly realistic nor frankly theatrical. My indecision was fatal. The audiences found them rather disagreeable and not quite real. Then I took a rest for two years and at the end of it wrote *The Land of Promise.* This had been played to crowded houses for some months when the war broke out. I had produced ten plays in seven years. The intelligentsia, having passed judgment, ignored me, but I was securely fixed in the public favour.

XXXIV

From time to time I had a good deal of leisure during the war; at first because the work I was doing took up but part of my day and to write plays was a convenient means of distracting attention from the activities I was engaged in; and later, when, having contracted tuberculosis, I had to lie long in bed, because it was a pleasant way of passing the time. I wrote a series of plays in quick succession. It began with *Our Betters,* which was written in 1915, and ended with *The Constant Wife,* which was written in 1927.

Most of these plays were comedies. They are written in the tradition which flourished so brightly in the Restoration Period, which was carried on by Goldsmith and Sheridan, and which, since it has had so long a vogue, may be supposed to have something in it that peculiarly appeals to the English temper. The people who do not like it describe it as artificial comedy and by the epithet foolishly think they condemn it. It is drama not of action, but of conversation. It treats with indulgent cynicism the humours, follies and vices of the world of fashion. It is urbane, sentimental at times, for that is in the English character, and a trifle unreal. It does not preach: sometimes it draws a moral, but with a shrug of the shoulders as if to invite you to lay no too great stress on it. When the busy Monsieur de Voltaire went to see Congreve to discuss the current drama with him, Mr. Congreve pointed out to him that he was a gentleman rather than a dramatist. The interviewer answered: "If you were nothing but a gentleman I should not have troubled to call upon you." Monsieur de Voltaire was certainly the wittiest man of his age, but here he showed want of intelligence. Mr. Congreve's remark was profound. It showed that he knew very well that the first person the author of comedy must consider from the standpoint of comedy is himself.

XXXV

I HAD by then made up my mind on many things connected with the drama.

One of the conclusions I had come to was that a prose play was scarcely less ephemeral than a news sheet. The playwright and the journalist need very similar gifts, a quick eye for a good story and a telling point, animation and a vivid way of writing. All the dramatist needs besides is a specific knack. I do not know that anyone has been able to discover what this knack consists of. It cannot be learnt. It can exist without education or culture. It is a faculty that enables the playwright so to put words that they carry across the footlights and to tell a story, as it were stereoscopically, so that it visibly moves before an audience. It is a very rare faculty: that is why dramatists are so much more highly paid than other artists. It has nothing to do with literary ability as we know from the fact that the most distinguished novelists have generally failed lamentably when they have tried to write plays. It is a faculty, like that of being able to play by ear, of no spiritual importance. But without it, though your ideas may be profound, your theme original and your characterization acute, you will never be able to write a play.

A good deal has been written about the technique of playwriting. I have read most of the books on the subject with interest. The best way of learning how to write a play is to see one of your own produced. That will teach you how to write lines that the actors find easy to say and, if you have an ear, how far you can carry the rhythm of a sentence without losing the spontaneity of conversation. It will show you what sort of speech and what sort of scene are effective. But I think the secret of playwriting can be given in two maxims: stick to the point and whenever you can, cut. The first of these demands a logical mind. Few of us have it. One idea suggests another; it is very pleasant to pursue it, even though it is not directly concerned with the subject. The inclination to digress is human. But the dramatist must avoid it even more strenuously than the saint must avoid sin, for while sin may be venial, digression is mortal. The principle is that of direction of interest. It is important in a novel too, but here greater space permits of greater latitude and, just as according to the idealists evil is transformed into the perfect good of the Absolute, so certain digressions may take their necessary part in the development of the main theme. (A very good example of this is the early history of the Elder Zossima in the *Brothers Karamazov*.) Perhaps I should explain what I mean by direction of interest. It is the method by which an author causes you to concern yourself with the fortunes of certain people under certain conditions and keeps you attached to them till he has reached his solution. If he lets you wander from the main point it is very likely that he will never recapture your attention. It is a psychological trait in human nature that interest is established in the persons whom the playwright introduces at the beginning of his play so firmly that if the interest is then switched off to other persons who enter upon the scene later, a sense of disappointment ensues. The astute dramatist presents his subject as early as possible, and if for theatrical effectiveness he does not introduce his principal characters till later, the conversation of the persons on the stage at the rising of the curtain concentrates the attention of the audience on them so that the delay in their appearance increases the expectation. No one followed this practice more scrupulously than that very competent dramatist William Shakespeare.

It is the difficulty of directing the interest that makes it so hard to write the plays that are known as plays of atmosphere. The best known of them, of course, are Chekhov's. Since the interest is not concentrated on two or three persons, but on a group, and since the theme is their relations with one another and the environment, the author must take care to counteract the natural inclination of the audience to concern themselves with one character or two more than with the rest. With the interest thus dispersed it is possible that the audience will not feel warmly about any of the persons of the play,

and since the author must beware that none of his threads is more important than the other, and thus attracts more vividly the attention of the audience, every incident must be subdued to the minor key. So it is very difficult to prevent the audience from feeling a certain monotony and because nothing, either incident or character, has been very forcibly impressed upon them they are very likely to take away with them, when the play is over, some confusion of spirit. In practice it has been shown that such plays are only tolerable when they are perfectly acted.

Now I come to my second maxim. However brilliant a scene may be, however witty a line or profound a reflection, if it is not essential to his play the dramatist must cut it. Here it may serve him if he is also a man of letters. The pure dramatist looks upon it as something of a miracle that he should be able to put words on paper at all, and when they are there, out of his own brain, if not straight from heaven, he looks upon them as sacred. He cannot bear to sacrifice one of them. I well remember Henry Arthur Jones showing me one of his manuscripts and my surprise on noticing that he had written such a simple sentence as, will you have sugar in your tea? in three different ways. It is no wonder that people to whom words come so reluctantly should attach an inordinate importance to them. The man of letters is accustomed to writing; he has learnt how to express himself without intolerable labour and so can cut with fortitude. Of course every writer hits now and then upon a thought that seems to him so happy, a repartee that amuses him so much, that to cut it is worse than having a tooth out: it is then that it is well to have engraved on his heart the maxim, if you can, cut.

To do so is now more than ever necessary, for audiences are at once quicker-witted and more impatient than ever before in the history of the theatre. Plays have been written in such and such a way because they satisfied audiences. Audiences in the past seem to have been willing to sit out scenes that were elaborately developed and to listen to speeches in which the characters fully explained themselves. It is very different now, and the difference has been occasioned, I suppose, by the advent of the cinema. Today, audiences, especially in English-speaking countries, have learnt to see the point of a scene at once and having seen it want to pass on to the next; they catch the gist of a speech in a few words and having caught it, their attention quickly wanders. The author must curb his natural desire to get the full value out of a scene or to let his characters display themselves in ample expression. Indications are enough. They will be seized. His dialogue must be a sort of spoken shorthand. He must cut and cut till he has arrived at the maximum of concentration.

XXXVI

A PLAY is the result of a collaboration between the author, the actors, the audience, and, I suppose one must add now, the director. For the moment I will consider the audience. All the best dramatists have written with their eye on it and though they have more often spoken of it with contempt than with good will they have known that they were dependent on it. It is the public that pays, and if it is not pleased with the entertainment that is offered it, stays away. A play does not exist without an audience. Indeed the definition of a play is a piece of writing in dialogue devised to be spoken by actors and heard by an indefinite number of persons. A play written to be read in the study is a form of the novel in dialogue in which the author for some reason of his own (obscure to most of us) has eschewed the ordinary advantages of narrative. A play that does not appeal to an audience may have merits, but it is no more a play than a mule is a horse. (Alas, all of us dramatists from time to time give birth to these unsatisfactory hybrids.) Everyone who has had to do with the theatre knows how strangely audiences affect plays; a matinée audience and an evening audience may see quite different plays. We are told that the Norwegian public looks upon Ibsen's plays as comedies rich in laughter; the English public has never seen anything to laugh at in those harassing dramas. The emotion of the audience, its interests, its laughter, are part of the action of the play. It creates it in the same way as we through our senses from the objective data create the beauty of the sunrise and the peace of the sea. The audience is not the least important actor in the play and if it will not do its allotted share the play falls to pieces. The dramatist then is in the position of a tennis player who is left on the court with nobody to play with.

Now the audience is a very curious animal. It is shrewd rather than intelligent. Its mental capacity is less than that of its most intellectual members. If these were graded from A to Z, decreasing with succeeding letters to the zero of the hysterical shop-girl, I should say its mental capacity would come round about the letter O. It is immensely suggestible; individuals will laugh at a joke they have not seen because others who see it do. It is emotional; but it instinctively resents having its emotions stirred and is always ready to escape with a giggle. It is sentimental; but will only accept sentimentality of its own brand: thus in England it will accept the emotions attached to the concept of home, but the concept of a son's love for his mother only excites its ridicule. It is careless of probability if the situation excites its interest, a trait of which Shakespeare made extravagant use, but jibs at a lack of plausibility. Individuals know that they constantly give way to impulse, but an audience insists that every action must have its cogent reason. Its morality is the average morality of the crowd and it will be sincerely shocked by a sentiment that will offend none of its members taken one by one. It does not think with its brain, but with its solar plexus. It is easily bored. It likes novelty, but a novelty that will fit in with old notions, so that it excites but does not alarm. It likes ideas, so long as they are put in dramatic form, only they must be ideas that it has itself had, but for want of courage has never expressed. It will not play if it is hurt or affronted. Its chief desire is to be assured that the make-believe is real.

In essentials audiences never change, but at different periods and in different countries at the same period they rise to different levels of sophis-tication. The drama pictures the manners and customs of the day, and in its turn affects them, and as these change minor changes follow both in the trappings of a play and in its themes. The invention of the telephone, for instance, has made many scenes redundant, has quickened the pace of plays and has made it possible to avoid certain improbabilities. Probability is a variable factor. It is merely what the audience is prepared to accept. Often there is no rhyme nor reason for this. People leave compromising letters about or accidentally hear things they are not supposed to hear as often as they did in Elizabethan times and it is merely a convention that rejects such incidents as improbable. But what is more important is that there has been a change of heart among us, owing to changes in civilization, and so certain themes that dramatists favoured have now fallen into desuetude. We are less revengeful than we were and now a play devoted to revenge would be scarcely plausible. Perhaps because our passions are less strong, perhaps even because the teaching of Christ has at last penetrated our thick heads, we look upon revenge as discreditable. I ventured once to suggest that the liberation of women and their new-won sexual freedom had so altered men's views on the importance of chastity that jealousy was no longer a theme for tragedy, but only for comedy; but this observation was received with so much indignation that I will not enlarge upon it.

XXXVII

I HAVE given this little analysis of an audience because the nature of the audience is for the dramatist the most important of the conventions within which he must work. Every artist must accept the conventions of the art which he pursues, but it may be that these are of such a nature as to make the art a minor one. It was a poetic convention in the eighteenth century that enthusiasm was objectionable and that imagination must be curbed by reasonableness; so it was only minor poetry that was produced. Now, the fact that the general mentality of an audience is so very much lower than that of its more intellectual members is a factor that the author must deal with. I think it definitely reduces prose drama to a minor place. It has been noticed over and over again that, intellectually, the theatre is thirty years behind the times, and the intelligent, owing to its poverty of thought, have largely ceased to frequent it. I have a notion that when the intelligent look for thought in a playhouse, they show less intelligence than one would have expected of them. Thought is a private thing. It is the offspring of reason. It depends on the mental capacity of the individual and on his education. Its communication is private from the mind that conceives it to the mind that is prepared to receive it, and if one man's meat is another man's poison, still more is one man's thought another man's truism. But an audience is affected by mass suggestion and mass suggestion is excited by emotion. I have hazarded the opinion that if you classified the members of an audience from A to Z, starting, say, with the

critic of The Times and ending with the girl who sells sweet-stuffs in a shop off the Tottenham Court Road, its mental capacity would stand about the letter O. How can you write a play of which the ideas are so significant that they will make the critic of The Times sit up in his stall and at the same time induce the shop-girl in the gallery to forget the young man who is holding her hand? The only ideas that can affect them when they are welded together in that unity which is an audience, are those commonplace, fundamental ideas that are almost feelings. These, the root ideas of poetry, are love, death and the destiny of man. It is not any sort of dramatist who can find anything to say about them that has not been said a thousand times already; the great truths are too important to be new.

Besides, ideas do not grow on a gooseberry bush and few people in a generation can devise new ones. It is very unlikely that the dramatist who is lucky enough to have been born with the faculty of putting things so that they carry across the footlights will also be an original thinker. He would not be a dramatist if his mind did not work in the concrete. He has a quick eye for the instance; there is no reason to expect that he will have a faculty for conceptual thinking. He may have a meditative cast of mind and be interested in the speculations of his time, but there is a long way between this and having the power of creative thought. It might be very well if dramatists were philosophers, but in point of fact they are as little likely to be so as are kings. The only two dramatists in our time who have made their mark as thinkers are Ibsen and Shaw. Both were fortunate in the time of their appearance. Ibsen's advent coincided with the movement for the liberation of women from the inferior position in which they had so long stood; Shaw's with the revolt of youth from the conventionality of the Victorian epoch and the trammels that age had set upon it. They had to their hands subjects new to the theatre that could be displayed with dramatic effectiveness. Shaw had the advantage, useful to any dramatist, of high spirits, rollicking humour, wit and fertility of comic invention. Ibsen as we know had a meagre power of invention; his characters under different names are very dully repeated and his intrigue from play to play is little varied. It is not a gross exaggeration to say that his only gambit is the sudden arrival of a stranger who comes into a stuffy room and opens the windows; whereupon the people who were sitting there catch their death of cold and everything ends unhappily. When you consider the mental content of what these authors had to offer, you can, unless you are but ill educated, hardly fail to see that it consisted of no more than the common culture of the day. Shaw's ideas were expressed with great vivacity. They could only have surprised because the intellectual capacity of the audience was inconsiderable. They surprise no longer; indeed, the young tend to look on them now as antiquated buffooneries. The disadvantage of ideas in the theatre is that if they are acceptable, they are accepted and so kill the play that helped to diffuse them. For nothing is so tiresome in the theatre as to be forced to listen to the exposition of ideas that you are willing to take for granted. Now that everyone admits the right of a woman to her own personality it is impossible to listen to *A Doll's House* without impatience. The dramatist of ideas loads the dice against himself. Plays are ephemeral enough in any case, because they must be dressed in the fashion of the moment and fashions change so that they lose the actuality which is one of their attractive features; it seems a pity to make them more ephemeral still by founding them on ideas that will be stale the day after tomorrow. When I say that plays are ephemeral, I am of course not speaking of plays in verse; the greatest and noblest of the arts can lend its own life to the humble partner; I am speaking of the plays in prose with which our modern theatre is alone occupied. I can think of no serious prose play that has survived the generation that gave it birth. A few comedies have haphazardly travelled down a couple of centuries or so. They are revived now and then because a famous part tempts a leading actor, or a manager in want of a stop-gap thinks he will put on a play on which he has no royalties to pay. They are museum pieces. The audience laughs at their wit with politeness and at their farce with embarrassment. They are not held nor taken out of themselves. They cannot believe and so are never caught by the illusion of the theatre.

But if a play is naturally ephemeral why, the dramatist may ask, should he not look upon himself as a journalist, a journalist of the better class who writes for the sixpenny weeklies, and produce plays of the current topics, political and social, of the day? His ideas will be neither more nor less original than those of the serious young men who write in these journals. There is no reason why they should be less interesting; and if by the time the play has run its course they are out of date, what of it? The play is dead anyway. Now to this question the answer is that there is no reason at all, if he can get away with it and if he thinks it worth while. But he must be warned that he will get little thanks from the critics. For though they clamour for the play of ideas, when he presents it to them they sniff at it if the ideas are familiar to them, thinking modestly that what they know already is commonplace, and if the ideas are unfamiliar to them, they think them perfect nonsense and come down on him like a thousand of bricks. Even the licensed Shaw has not escaped the horns of this dilemma.

Societies have been founded in order to produce plays that people may go to who disdain the commercial theatre. They languish. The intelligentsia cannot be persuaded to patronize these performances, and if they do, want to go without paying. There are a number of dramatists who spend their whole careers writing plays which are only produced by these societies. They are trying to do something for which the drama is unsuited; once they have got a number of persons into the playhouse, these become an audience, and then, even though their average mentality is higher than the ordinary, they are subject to the reactions by which an audience is governed. They are swayed by emotion rather than by reasoning. They demand action rather than debate. (By action of course I do not mean merely physical action: from the standpoint of the theatre a character who says, I have a headache, performs an action as much as one who falls off a steeple.) When the plays these authors write fail, they claim it is because audiences have not the sense to appreciate them. I do not think they are right. Their plays fail because they have no dramatic value. Let no one think that commercial plays succeed because they are bad plays. The story they tell may be hackneyed, the dialogue commonplace and the characterization ordinary, they succeed notwithstanding because they have the essential, though doubtless trivial, merit of holding their audiences by the specific appeal of drama. But that this need not be the only merit of the commercial play is shown by those of Lope de Vega, Shakespeare and Molière.

XXXVIII

I f I have thus enlarged on the play of ideas, it is because I think the demand for it is responsible for the lamentable decadence of our theatre. The critics clamour for them. Now, the critics are of necessity the worst judges of plays. For consider, the play appeals to the audience as a unity, the current that passes infectiously from one person to another is essential to the dramatist; he wants to excite a contagion; he must take people out of themselves so that they become an instrument for him to play on, and what they give back, the resonance, the tone, the emotion, is part of his play. But the critic is there not to feel but to judge. He must hold aloof from the contagion that has captured the group and keep his self-possession. He must not allow his heart to carry him away; his head must remain well screwed on his shoulders. He must take care not to become part of the audience. He is not there to play his part in the play, but to watch it from the outside. The result is that he does not see the play they see because he has not, as they have, acted in it. It is natural enough then that he should ask for different things in a play from those the audience asks for. There is no reason why he should get it. Plays are not written for critics. Or at least, they should not be. But playwrights are sensitive creatures, and when they are told that the plays they write are an insult to the adult intelligence, they are distressed. They would like to do better, and so the young, aspiring ones, still trailing clouds of glory, sit down to write plays of ideas. That it can be done, and bring fame and fortune, the example of Bernard Shaw is there to show them.

The influence of Shaw on the English stage of today has been devastating. The public have not always liked his plays, any more than they liked Ibsen's, but after seeing them they have liked those written according to the old conventions even less. Disciples arose who sought to follow in his steps, but the event has proved that it was impossible to do so without his great gifts. The most talented of these was Granville Barker. As many scenes in his plays show, Granville Barker had it in him to be a very good playwright; he had a dramatic gift, facility for writing easy, natural and amusing dialogue, and an eye for theatrically effective character. The influence of Shaw led him to attach importance to ideas that were somewhat commonplace and to suppose that the natural discursiveness of his mind was a virtue. If he had not been persuaded that the public were fools, who must be bullied rather than cajoled, he would by the usual method of trial and error have learnt to correct his faults, and then might

have added to the drama of this country a number of popular plays of great excellence. The lesser followers of Bernard Shaw have only copied his defects. Shaw has succeeded on the stage not because he is a dramatist of ideas, but because he is a dramatist. But he is inimitable. He owes his originality to an idiosyncrasy, not of course peculiar to himself, that had never before found expression on the stage. The English, whatever they were in the Elizabethan era, are not an amorous race. Love with them is more sentimental than passionate. They are of course sufficiently sexual for the purpose of reproducing their species, but they cannot control the instinctive feeling that the sexual act is disgusting. They are more inclined to look upon love as affection or benevolence than as passion. They regard with approval its sublimations which dons describe in scholarly books, and with repulsion or with ridicule its frank expression. English is the only modern language in which it has been found necessary to borrow from the Latin a word with a depreciatory meaning, the word uxorious, for a man's devoted love for his wife. That love should absorb a man has seemed to them unworthy. In France a man who has ruined himself for women is generally regarded with sympathy and admiration; there is a feeling that it was worth while, and the man who has done it feels even a certain pride in the fact; in England he will be thought and will think himself a damned fool. That is why *Antony and Cleopatra* has always been the least popular of Shakespeare's greater plays. Audiences have felt that it was contemptible to throw away an empire for a woman's sake. Indeed if it were not founded on an accepted legend they would be unanimous in asserting that such a thing was incredible.

To audiences who had been forced to sit through plays in which love was the motive of the intrigue, but who had an instinctive feeling that love, though all very well in its way, was not really quite so important as the dramatists pretended, for after all there were politics, golf, getting on with one's job and all sorts of other things, it was a welcome relief to come upon a dramatist for whom love was a tiresome, secondary business, a quick gratification of a momentary impulse whose consequences were generally awkward. Though put as things must be put on the stage in an exaggerated way (and it should never be forgot-

ten that Shaw is an extremely skilful dramatist) there was enough truth in this attitude to impress. It responded to the deep-seated puritanism of the Anglo-Saxon race. But, if not amorous, the English are sentimental and emotional, and they felt that it was not the whole truth. When other dramatists repeated it, not because it was, as with Shaw, a natural expression of a personality, but because it was striking and effective, its onesidedness became tediously apparent. The author describes for you his private world, and if it interests you, you will give him your attention. There is no reason why you should trouble yourself with a description of it at second hand. It is inept to say again what Shaw has said so well.

XXXIX

To my mind, the drama took a wrong turning when the demand for realism led it to abandon the ornament of verse. Verse has a specific dramatic value as anyone can see by observing in himself the thrilling effect of a tirade in one of Racine's plays or of any of Shakespeare's great set pieces; and this is independent of the sense; it is due to the emotional power of rhythmical speech. But more than that: verse forces on the matter a conventional form that heightens the æsthetic effect. It enables the drama to achieve a beauty that is out of the question in a prose play. However much you may admire *The Wild Duck, The Importance of Being Earnest* or *Man and Superman,* you cannot without abuse of the word claim that they are beautiful. But the chief value of verse is that it delivers a play from

sober reality. It puts it on another level, at one remove from life, and so makes it easier for the audience to attune themselves to that state of feeling in which they are most susceptible to the drama's specific appeal. In that artificial medium life is not presented in a word-for-word translation, but in a free rendering, and thus the dramatist has ample scope for the effects of which his art is capable. For the drama is make-believe. It does not deal with truth but with effect. That willing suspension of disbelief of which Coleridge wrote is essential to it. The importance of truth to the dramatist is that it adds to interest, but to the dramatist truth is only verisimilitude. It is what he can persuade his audience to accept. If they will believe that a man can doubt his wife's fidelity because someone tells him he has found her handkerchief in somebody else's possession, well and good, that is sufficient motive for his jealousy; if they will believe that a six-course dinner can be eaten in ten minutes, well and good again, the dramatist can get on with his play. But when a greater and greater realism, both in motive and in action, is demanded of him and he is asked not to embroider gaily or romantically upon life but to copy it, he is robbed of a great part of his resources. He is forced to forego asides because people do not naturally talk to themselves out loud; he may not telescope events, by which he was able to accelerate his action, but he must cause them to occur as deliberately as in real life; he must eschew accident and chance, for we know (in the theatre) that things do not happen like that. The result has shown that realism too often can only produce plays that are drab and dull.

When the movies learnt to talk the prose play was powerless to defend itself. The movies could represent action much more effectively, and action is the essence of drama. The screen gave that artificiality which verse had once given to drama so that a different standard of verisimilitude was set and improbability was acceptable if only it gave rise to situation. It gave the opportunity for all manner of novel, picturesque and dramatic effects that stimulated and excited the public. The dramatist of ideas had to swallow the bitter pill that the intelligentsia for which he wrote would have nothing to do with his plays, but roared with laughter at the farce and wallowed in the thrills and spectacle of the moving pictures. The fact was of course that they had succumbed to the atmosphere the stage play has taken pains to lose and were delivered to the sway of make-believe that had held the audiences who first saw the plays of Lope de Vega and William Shakespeare.

I have always eschewed the prophetic role and have left to others the reformation of my fellows, but I cannot but state my belief that the prose drama to which I have given so much of my life will soon be dead. The minor arts, which depend on the manners and customs of the time rather than on deep-seated human necessities, come and go. The madrigal which was once a popular form of musical entertainment, exciting composers to write for it and producing an elaborate school of performers, succumbed when musical instruments were invented that produced more beautifully the peculiar effects it sought; and there is no reason why prose drama should not suffer the same fate. It may be said that the screen can never give exactly the sympathetic thrill you feel when you see living persons in flesh and blood before you. It might very well have been said that strings and wood could never make up for the intimate quality of the human voice. The event has proved that they could.

One thing seems certain, and that is that if the stage play has any chance at all of survival, it is not by trying to do any longer what the pictures can do better. Those dramatists have followed a false trail who by a multitude of little scenes have tried to reproduce the rapid action and varied setting of the cinematograph. It has occurred to me that possibly the dramatist would be wise now to go back to the origins of modern drama and call to his aid verse, dancing, music and pageantry so that he might appeal to all possible sources of entertainment; but I am conscious that here again the cinema with its great resources can do better whatever the spoken theatre can do; and of course a play of this kind would need a dramatist who was also a poet. Perhaps the best chance the realistic dramatist has today is to occupy himself with what, till now at all events, the screen has not succeeded very well in presenting—the drama in which the action is inner rather than outer and the comedy of wit. The screen demands physical action. Emotion which cannot be translated into this, and the humour whose appeal is mental, have little value for it. It may be that, for some time at all events, such plays would have their appeal.

But so far as comedy is concerned, it should be recognized that the demand for realism is unjustified. Comedy is an artificial thing and so only the appearance, not the reality, of naturalism is in place. The laugh must be sought for its own sake. The play-wright's aim is not now to represent life as it is (a tragic business) but to comment on it satirically and amusingly. The audience should not be allowed to ask, do such things happen? They should be content to laugh. In comedy more than ever must the playwright exact a willing suspension of disbelief. So the critics are wrong when they complain that a comedy now and then "degenerates" into farce. It has been found in practice that it is impossible to hold the attention of an audience through three acts of pure comedy. For comedy appeals to the collective mind of the audience and this grows fatigued; while farce appeals to a more robust organ, their collective belly. The great writers of comedy, Shakespeare, Molière and Bernard Shaw, have never jibbed at the farcical. It is the life blood that makes the body of comedy viable.

X L

THESE ideas floating vaguely in my mind had little by little made me increasingly dissatisfied with the theatre and at last I decided to have done with it. I have never taken very comfortably to collaboration, and as I have pointed out, a play is more than any other artistic product a matter of collective effort. I found it more and more difficult to work in harmony with my collaborators.

It is often said that good actors can get out of a play more than the author can put into it. That is not true. A good actor, bringing to a part his own talent, often gives it a value that the layman on reading the play had not seen in it, but at the utmost he can do no more than reach the ideal that the author has seen in his mind's eye. He has to be an actor of address to do this; for the most part the author has to be satisfied with an approximation to the performance he visualized. In all my plays I have been fortunate enough to have some of the parts acted as I wanted; but in none have I had all the parts so acted. This is obviously inevitable, for the actor who is suited to a certain role may very well be engaged and you have to put up with the second or the third best, because there is no help for it. In recent years, as everyone knows who has had to do with the casting of plays, the competition of New York and of the pictures both in England and America has made it more than ever difficult to get the right person for a certain part; and over and over again a manager finds himself obliged to engage an actor who he knows is mediocre because no one else can be got. Another difficulty is that of salaries. A small part often wants clever playing and so an actor of experience, but from the standpoint of the management it will only stand a certain salary and it is impracticable to engage for it the proper person. The part then is inadequately acted and the balance of the play jeopardized; a scene that has a definite value is thrown away because it is improperly played. It often happens also that the perfect actor for a part will not play it because it is too small or too unsympathetic.

In saying all this, I have no intention of minimizing my obligation to the distinguished actors and actresses to whom is due so much of the success many of my plays have had. My debt to them is great. The list of those who fulfilled all my hopes is so long that it would be tedious to give it, but there is one actor whom, since he has never reached the rank of a star and so has hardly received the recognition that he deserves, I should like to mention. This is C. V. France. He has acted in several of my plays. He has never played a part in which he has not been admirable. He has represented to the smallest particular the character that I had in my mind's eye. It would be difficult to find on the English stage a more competent, intelligent and versatile actor. On the other hand, I have had plays produced in which I was conscious that the audience were not seeing anything like what I wanted them to see. Errors of casting, especially when they occur with actors of reputation, can often not be rectified, and then the author has the mortification of being judged by something that is merely

a misrepresentation of his intent. There is no such thing as an actor-proof part. There are effective parts, and parts, often very important ones, that are the reverse, but however effective a part is, it is only fully realized when it is perfectly played. The funniest line in the world is only funny if it is said in the right way; however tender a scene is it will go for nothing if it is played without tenderness. Another pitfall that the actors prepare for the dramatist is one that is not often realized. The system of choosing actors to play themselves makes it very difficult to avoid. An author devises a character, then an actor is chosen because he has the traits the author has indicated; but the addition of his idiosyncrasies to those the author has already given his character results in an absurd exaggeration; the person of the author's invention, who was plausible and natural, is in this way turned into a grotesque. I have often sought to cast an actor contrary to his type, but I do not know that the notion has proved successful; it needs a greater adaptability than modern actors have. Probably the dramatist's best way to cope with this difficulty is to underwrite his parts, lightly sketching the characters and counting on the actors to fill them in with their own individualities. But then he must be certain of getting actors who can do this.

Exaggeration of this kind, wrong casting, inevitable sometimes, already sufficiently distort the author's intention and this is too often further distorted by the director. When I first began to write for the stage, directors took a more modest view of their functions than they have lately done. Then they confined themselves to cutting where the author had been long-winded and disguising by their ingenuity his errors of construction; they arranged the positions of the actors and helped them to get the best out of their parts. I think it must have been Reinhardt who first exacted for the director a preponderating share in the collaboration. His example was followed by directors who lacked his talent and more than once since the preposterous claim has been made that the author's script is to be looked upon merely as a vehicle for the director to express his own ideas. Instances have been known of directors who imagined that they were playwrights. Gerald du Maurier, a very good director, told me himself that he took no interest in directing a play that he could not partly rewrite. This was an extreme case. But it has certainly become very hard to find a director who is content to interpret his author's play; he has too often come to look upon it as an opportunity for an original creation of his own. The public would be surprised if they knew how often an author's purport is misrepresented by the director's stupid obstinacy and how much vulgarity and silliness for which they blame him are due to the director. The director is a man of ideas, but of few, and that is a disastrous thing. To conceive ideas is exhilarating, but it is only safe when you conceive so many that you ascribe no undue consequence to them and can take them for what they are worth. People who conceive few find it very difficult not to regard them with inordinate respect. A director who thinks of a scrap of dialogue, a bit of business or a scenic effect, will attach so much importance to it that he will cheerfully hang up the action of the play or distort its meaning in order to introduce it. Too often the director is vain, self-opinionated and unimaginative; he is some-

times so autocratic that he will force the cast to reproduce his own intonations and his own mannerisms; the actors, dependent on his good word to get parts and on their docility to gain his favour, can but slavishly do as they are told, thus taking all spontaneity from their performance. The best director is the one who does least. I have been lucky enough now and then to be given directors who were honestly anxious to do their best by the play and who have tried to fulfil my wishes; but it is very difficult to enter into somebody else's mind and the most sympathetic director can hardly do more than give an adumbration of the author's intention. I think he often gives the audience something that they like more than they would have liked what the author meant. But that is not to the author's purpose.

The remedy of course is for the author to direct his own play. Few can but those who have themselves been actors. It is not enough to be able to tell an actor that an intonation or a gesture is wrong, you must be able to show him by word and deed what is right. This is more than ever necessary now that the players of minor parts have an inadequate technique. Gerald du Maurier used often to do this by the mortifying, but efficacious, expedient of caricaturing the manner in which an actor had done something and then showing him how it should be done. He could do this only because he was a very good mimic and a very good actor. But this is a small matter. Direction is a complicated affair. It is a business, or if you like an art, of its own that has to be acquired with pains. The director deals with the mechanics of the play, the entrances and exits, the positions assigned to various characters so that their grouping may be seemly and that they may be so placed that at the proper time the attention of the audience is easily turned on them; he takes into consideration the peculiarities of individual actors and when one is asked to do something that is not within his powers by subterfuge gets over the difficulty; he is mindful also of the peculiarities of actors in general, such as that no English player can now say a speech of more than twenty lines without feeling self-conscious, and devises means of overcoming their diffidence; he directs the audience's interest to the main points of the play and lures them by ingenuity to support the necessarily dull passages of exposition and the joins, the introductions to dramatic episodes, that no play can avoid; he takes account of the facility with which their attention wanders and by the invention of "business" holds it at dangerous points; he considers the susceptibilities, the jealousy and vanity of actors and takes care that natural egoism does not disturb the balance of the play; he sees that every part is given its appropriate value and that no actor to make his own more important encroaches on somebody else's. He decides when to go quick and when to go slow; when to emphasize, when to slur; when to play up and when to play down. He deals with the sets and sees that they are suitable and practi-

cable to the action; he chooses the clothes to fit the parts and keeps a close watch on the actresses who would sooner be beautifully than aptly dressed; he concerns himself with lighting. Direction is a business, or an art, that needs technical knowledge of an elaborate order. It needs moreover tact, patience, good humour, firmness and pliability. For myself, I have been well aware that I possessed none of the knowledge and few of the qualities that are needed to direct a play. I was hampered besides by my stammer and by the unfortunate accident that after I had written a play and finally corrected the typescript I could no longer take any great interest in it. I was curious to see how it would act, but when once I had given it over to others, like a bitch who takes no more concern in her puppies when others have handled them, I could no longer look upon it any more as intimately my own. I have been blamed often for yielding too easily to directors and accepting their opinions when they were contrary to my own; the fact is that I have always been inclined to think that others knew better than I; I have never liked rows unless I was in a temper and I am seldom in a temper, and lastly, I did not very much care. What added to my growing distaste for the theatre was not that directors were sometimes incompetent, but that they were necessary at all.

XLI

A ND now the audience. It must seem ungracious that I should express anything but gratitude to the public that has given me, if not fame, at least

notoriety and a fortune that has enabled me to live in the same style as my father lived in before me. I have travelled; I live in a house with a view of the sea, silent and apart from other habitations, in the middle of a garden, with spacious rooms. I have always thought life too short to do anything for oneself that one can pay others to do for one and I have been rich enough to afford myself the luxury of only doing for myself what I alone can do. I have been able to entertain my friends and to help people whom I wanted to help. All this I owe to the favour of the public. I found myself, notwithstanding, growing more and more impatient with that section of it that makes up the theatrical audience. I have mentioned the fact that from the first I felt a singular embarrassment at witnessing one of my own plays, and this, instead of growing less with each play I produced, as I might have expected, grew greater. The feeling that a mass of people were seeing my plays became a sort of horror of distaste, so that I found myself going out of my way to avoid the street in which the theatre was situated where they were acting one of my plays.

I had long come to the conclusion that there was not much point in a play that was not successful and I thought I knew exactly how to write a successful play. I knew, that is to say, what I could expect from an audience. Without their collaboration I could do nothing and I knew how far their collaboration could go. I found myself increasingly dissatisfied with this. The dramatist must share the prepossessions of his audience, the example of Lope de Vega and Shakespeare is there to prove it, and at his boldest he can do no more than put into words what they from cowardice or laziness have been contented only to feel and not to express. I was tired of giving half a truth because that was all they were prepared to take. I

grew tired of the absurdity that admits in conversation all manner of facts that must be denied on the stage. I wearied of the necessity of fitting my theme into a certain compass, drawing it out to an unnecessary length or unduly constricting it because a play to attract had to be of a definite length. I grew bored with trying never to be boring. In fact, I did not want to conform any longer to the necessary conventions of the drama. I suspected that I was out of touch with the taste of the public and to decide the matter went to a number of plays that were drawing the town. I found them tedious. I could not laugh at the jokes that amused the delighted audience and the scenes that moved them to tears left me stone cold. That settled it.

I sighed for the liberty of fiction and I thought with pleasure of the lonely reader who was willing to listen to all I had to say and with whom I could effect an intimacy that I could never hope for in the garish publicity of the theatre. I had known too many dramatists who had survived their popularity. I had seen them pitifully writing their own plays over and over again without an inkling that the times had changed; I had seen others desperately attempting to capture the modern spirit and dismayed when their efforts were treated with derision. I had seen famous authors treated with contumely, when they offered a play to managers who had once pestered them with contracts. I had heard actors' scornful comments on them. I had seen the bewilderment, the consternation, the bitterness with which they realized at last that the public was finished with them. I had heard Arthur Pinero and Henry Arthur Jones, both celebrated in their day, say to me identically the same words, one with a grim, sardonic humour, the other with a puzzled exasperation; the words were: "They don't want me any more." I thought I would go while the going was good.

XLII

But I had several plays still in my head. Two or three of these were little more than vague schemes and I was willing enough to let them go, but there were four that were lying pigeon-holed in my fancy all ready to be written, and I knew myself well enough to be aware that they would continue to pester me till I wrote them. I had been thinking of them all for a good many years; I had done nothing about them because I did not think they would please. I have always had a dislike to managers losing money over me, due, I suppose, to my bourgeois instincts, and on the whole they have not. It is generally accepted that it is four to one against a play being profitable to a management; I do not think I am exaggerating when I say that the event has proved that with me it has been four to one on. I wrote these four plays in the order in which I expected them to be increasingly unsuccessful. I did not want to destroy my reputation with the public till I was definitely finished with it. The first two surprised me by having a considerable success. The last two had as little as I expected. I will speak but of one of them, *The Sacred Flame,* and of this only because in it I tried an experiment that some readers of this book may think interesting enough to merit a few minutes' consideration. I tried in this play to write a more formal dialogue than I had been in the habit of using. I wrote my first full-length play in 1898, my last in 1933. In that time I have seen dialogue change from the turgid, pedantic speech of Pinero, from the elegant artificiality of Oscar Wilde, to the extreme colloquialism of the present day. The demand for realism has inveigled dramatists into a naturalism ever greater and greater, a style that has been cultivated to its utmost limit, as we know, by Noel Coward. Not only is the "literary" avoided, but actuality has been so much sought after that grammar is eschewed, sentences are broken, for it is said that in ordinary life people speak ungrammatically and in short or unfinished sentences, and a vocabulary has been employed in which only the simplest and most ordinary words are allowed. This dialogue is eked out with shrugs, waves of the hand and grimaces. In thus yielding to the fashion it seems to me that dramatists have gravely handicapped themselves. For this slangy, clipped, broken speech they reproduce is only the speech of a class, the speech of the young, ill-educated well-to-do, who are described in the papers as the smart set. They are the persons who figure in the gossip columns and in the pages of illustrated weeklies. It may be a fact that the English are tongue-tied, but I do not think they are so tongue-tied as we are now asked to believe. There are a great many people, members of the various professions and cultured women, who clothe their thoughts in grammatical, well-chosen language and can say what they want to in the right words, put in the right order, with distinction. The present mode, which forces a judge or an eminent physician to express himself as inadequately as a bar-lounger, grossly misrepresents the truth. It has narrowed the range of character that the dramatist can deal with, for he can only show this by speech, and it is impossible to portray people of any subtlety of mind or intricacy of emotion when his dialogue is but a sort of spoken hieroglyph. He is insensibly led to choose as his characters persons who talk naturally in the way his audience have come to think natural and these inevitably are very simple and obvious. It has restricted his themes since it is hard to deal with the fundamental issues of human life, it is impossible to analyze the complexities of human nature (dramatic subjects both) when you confine yourself to a naturalistic dialogue. It has killed comedy, which depends on verbal wit, which in turn depends on the well-turned phrase. It has thus knocked another nail in the coffin of prose drama.

I thought then that in *The Sacred Flame* I would try to make my characters speak not the words they would actually have spoken, but in a more formal manner, using the phrases they would have used if they had been able to prepare them beforehand and had known how to put what they wanted to say in exact and well-chosen language. It may be that I did not manage it very well. During rehearsals I found that the actors, no longer used to speeches of this sort, had an uncomfortable feeling that they were delivering a recitation and I had to simplify and break up my sentences. I left enough to give the critics grounds for animadversion, and my dialogue was, in some quarters, blamed because it was "literary." I was told that people did not speak like

that. I never thought they did. But I did not insist. I was in the position of a man in a rented house, whose lease is expiring; it is not worth his while to make structural alterations. In my last two plays I reverted to the naturalistic dialogue I had hitherto used.

When for days you have been going through a mountain pass, a moment comes when you are sure that after winding round the great mass of rock in front of you, you will come upon the plain; but instead you are faced with another huge crag and the weary trail continues; surely after this you will see the plain; no; the path winds on and another mountain bars your way. And then suddenly it lies before you. Your heart exults; there it stretches wide and sunny; the oppression of the mountains is lifted from your shoulders and with exhilaration you breathe the more spacious air. You have a wonderful sense of freedom. So I felt when I had done with my last play.

I could not tell whether I was free from the theatre for good and all, for the author is the slave of what, for want of a more modest word, I am forced to call his inspiration, and I could not be certain that a theme would not some day occur to me that I could not but write in the form of a play. I hoped not. For I was possesssed of a notion which I cannot expect the reader to think other than foolishly arrogant. I had had all the experience that it seemed possible the theatre could give me. I had made as much money as I needed to live in the sort of way that pleased me and to provide for such as had claims on me. I had won a great notoriety and perhaps even a passing fame. I might have been satisfied. But there was one thing more I wanted to achieve and this it seemed to me I could not hope to reach in the drama. Perfection. I looked not at my own plays, of whose faults no one could be more irritably conscious than I, but at the plays that have come down to us from the past. Even the greatest have grave defects. You have to make excuses for them by considering the conventions of the time and the conditions of the stage for which they were written. The great Greek tragedies are so far from us and interpret a civilization that is now so strange that it is hard to judge them candidly. It has seemed to me that perhaps *Antigone* came very near perfection. In the modern drama I think no one on occasion approached it more closely than Racine. But at the cost of how many a limitation! It was a cherry stone that he carved with infinite skill. Only idolatry can refuse to see the great shortcomings in the conduct and sometimes in the characterization of Shakespeare's plays; and this is very comprehensible, since, as we know, he sacrificed everything to effective situation. All these plays were written in imperishable verse. When you come to the modern prose drama and look for perfection you will not find it. I suppose it will be admitted that Ibsen is the greatest dramatist the last hundred years have seen. For all the vast merits of his plays, how poverty-stricken was his invention, how repetitive his characters, and how silly, when you go a little below the surface, are too many of his subjects! It looks as though defects of one sort or another were inherent in the art of drama. To get one result you must sacrifice another, so that to write a play perfect in all its particulars, in the interest and significance of its theme, in the subtlety and orginality of its characterization, in the plausibility of its intrigue and in the beauty of its dialogue, is impossible. It seemed to me that in the novel and in the short story perfection had been sometimes achieved, and though I could scarcely hope to reach it, I had a notion that in those mediums I could come nearer to it than I had any chance of doing in the drama.

XLIII

THE first novel I wrote was called *Liza of Lambeth*. It was accepted by the first publisher to whom I sent it. For some time Fisher Unwin had been bringing out in what he called The Pseudonym Series a number of short novels which had attracted a good deal of attention; among them were those of John Oliver Hobbs. They were thought witty and audacious. They made the author's name and confirmed the prestige of the series. I wrote two short stories which together, I thought, would make a volume of a size suitable for this collection and sent them to Fisher Unwin. After some time he returned them, but with a letter asking me if I had not a novel I could submit to him. This was so great an encouragement that I immediately sat down and wrote one. Since I was working at the hospital all day I could only write in the evening. I used to get home soon after six, read my *Star*, which I bought at the corner of Lambeth Bridge, and as soon as the table was cleared after an early meal, set to work.

Fisher Unwin was hard on his authors. He took advantage of my youth, my inexperience, and my delight at having a book accepted, to make a contract with me whereby I was to get no royalty at all till he had sold so many copies; but he knew how to push his wares and he sent my novel to a number of influential persons. It was widely, though diversely, reviewed, and Basil Wilberforce, afterwards Archdeacon of Westminster, preached about it in the Abbey. The senior obstetric physician at St. Thomas's Hospital was sufficiently impressed by it to offer me a minor appointment under him, for soon after it appeared I passed my final examinations; but this, exaggerating its success and determined to abandon the medical profession, I unwisely refused. A second edition was called for within a month of publication and I had no doubt that I could easily earn my living as a writer. I was somewhat shaken when, a year later, on my return from Seville, I received from Fisher Unwin a cheque for my royalties. It amounted to twenty pounds. If I may judge by its continuing sales Liza of Lambeth is still readable, but any merit it may have is due to the luck I had in being, by my work as a medical student, thrown into contact with a side of life that at that time had been little exploited by novelists. Arthur Morrison with his Tales of Mean Streets and A Child of the Jago had drawn the attention of the public to what were then known as the lower classes and I profited by the interest he had aroused.

I knew nothing about writing. Though for my age I had read a good deal, I had read without discrimination, devouring one after the other books I had heard of to find out what they were about, and though I suppose I got something out of them, it was the novels and short stories of Guy de Maupassant that had most in-fluence on me when I set myself to write. I began to read them when I was sixteen. Whenever I went to Paris I spent my afternoons in the galleries of the Odéon browsing among the books there. A certain number of Maupassant's books had been reissued in little volumes at seventy-five centimes and these I bought; but the others cost three francs fifty, a sum that I could not afford, so I used to take a book out of the shelves and read what I could of it. The attendants in their pale grey smocks took no notice of me and it was often possible when none of them was looking to cut a page and continue the narrative without interruption. Thus I managed to read most of Maupassant before I was twenty. Though he does not enjoy now the reputation he did then it must be admitted that he had great merits. He was lucid and direct, he had a sense of form, and he knew how to get the utmost dramatic value out of the story he had to tell. I cannot but think that he was a better master to follow than the English novelists who at that time influenced the young. In Liza of Lambeth I described without addition or exaggeration the people I had met in the out-patients' department at the hospital and in the district during my service as an obstetric clerk, the incidents that had struck me when I went from house to house as the work called, or, when I had nothing to do, had seen on my idle saunterings. My lack of imagination (for imagination grows by exercise and contrary to common belief is more powerful in the mature than in the young) obliged me to set down quite straightforwardly what I had seen with my own eyes and heard with my own ears. Such success as the book had was due to a lucky chance. It augured nothing for my future. But this I did not know.

Fisher Unwin pressed me to write another much longer book about the slums. He told me that was what the public wanted from me and prophesied that it would have, now that I had broken the ice, a far greater success than *Liza of Lambeth*. But this was not in my ideas at all. I was ambitious. I had a feeling, I do not know where I got it, that you must not pursue a success, but fly from it; and I had learnt from the French to set no great store on the *roman régional*. I was no longer interested in the slums once I had written a book about them, and I had indeed already finished a novel of a very different sort. Fisher Unwin must have been dismayed when he received it. It was a novel set in Italy during the Renaissance and it was founded on a story I had read in Machiavelli's *History of Florence*. I wrote it because of some articles by Andrew Lang that I had read on the art of fiction. In one of them he argued, very convincingly to me, that the historical novel was the only one that the young author could hope to write with success. For he could not have sufficient experience of life to write of contemporary manners; history provided him with a story and characters and the romantic fervour of his young blood gave him the dash that was needed for this sort of composition. I know now that this was nonsense. In the first place it is not true that the young author has not sufficient knowledge to write about his contemporaries. I do not suppose one ever in after life knows people so intimately as those with whom one's childhood and early youth have been passed. One's family, the servants with whom so much of a child's life is spent,

one's masters at school, other boys and girls—the boy knows a great deal about them. He sees them with directness. Adults discover themselves, consciously and unconsciously, to the very young as they never do to other adults. And the child, the boy, is aware of his environment, the house he lives in, the countryside or the streets of the town, in a detail that he can never realize again when a multitude of past impressions has blurred his sensibilities. The historical novel calls surely for a profound experience of men to create living people out of those persons who with their different manners and different notions at first sight seem so alien to us; and to recreate the past needs not only a vast knowledge but an effort of imagination that is hardly to be expected in the young. I should have said that the truth was exactly contrary to what Andrew Lang said. The novelist should turn to the historical novel towards the end of his career, when thought and the vicissitudes of his own life have brought him knowledge of the world, and when, having for years explored the personalities of people around him, he has acquired an intuition into human nature that will enable him to understand and so to recreate the figures of a past age. I had written my first novel of what I knew, but now, seduced by this bad advice, set to work on a historical romance. I wrote it in Capri, during the long vacation, and such was my ardour that I had myself awakened every morning at six and wrote with perseverance till hunger forced me to break off and have breakfast. I had at least the sense to spend the rest of the morning in the sea.

XLIV

There is no need for me to speak of the novels I wrote during the next few years. One of them, *Mrs. Craddock*, was not unsuccessful and I have reprinted it in the collected edition of my works. Of the others two were novelizations of plays that I had failed to get produced and for long they lay on my conscience like a discreditable action; I would have given much to suppress them. But I know now that my qualms were unnecessary. Even the greatest authors have written a number of very poor books, Balzac himself left a good many out of the *Comédie Humaine,* and of those he inserted there are several that only the student troubles to read; the writer can rest assured that the books he would like to forget will be forgotten. I wrote one of these books because I had to have enough money to carry me on for the following year; the other because I was at the time much taken with a young person of extravagant tastes and the gratification of my desires was frustrated by the attentions of more opulent admirers who were able to provide the luxuries that her frivolous soul hankered after. I had nothing much to offer but a serious disposition and a sense of humour. I determined to write a book that would enable me to earn three or four hundred pounds with which I could hold my own with my rivals. For the young person was attractive. But even if you work hard it takes a long time to write a novel; you have to get it published; then publishers do not pay you till many months have elapsed. The result was that by the time I received the money the passion that I had thought would last forever was extinct and I had no longer the slightest wish to spend it in the way I had intended. I went to Egypt on it.

With these two exceptions the books I wrote during the first ten years after I became a professional writer were the exercises by which I sought to learn my business. For one of the difficulties that beset the professional writer is that he must acquire his craft at the expense of the public. He is constrained to write by the instinct within him and his brain teems with subjects. He has not the skill to cope with them. His experience is narrow. He is crude and he does not know how to make the best of such gifts as he has. And when he has finished his book he must publish it if he can, partly of course to get the money to live on; but also because he does not know what it is like till it is in print, and he can only find out his errors from the opinions of his friends and the criticisms of the reviewers. I have always heard that Guy de Maupassant submitted whatever he wrote to Flaubert and it was not till he had been writing for some years that Flaubert allowed him to publish his first story. As all the world knows it was that little masterpiece called *Boule de Suif*. But this is an exceptional case. Maupassant had a post in a government office that provided him both with a living and with sufficient leisure to write. There are few people who would have the patience to wait so long before trying their luck with the public and fewer still who can have had the good fortune to find so conscientious and great a writer as

Flaubert to direct them. For the most part writers waste in this way subjects that they could have made good use of if they had not treated them till they had a greater knowledge of life and a more intimate acquaintance with the technique of their art. I sometimes wish that I had not had the good fortune to get my first book accepted immediately, for then I should have continued with medicine; I should have got the usual hospital appointments, gone as assistant to general practitioners in various parts of the country, and done locums; I should thus have acquired a mass of valuable experience. If my books had been refused one after the other I should have come before the public at last with work less imperfect. I regret that I had no one to guide me; I might have been spared much misdirected effort. I knew a few literary people, not many, for even then I had a feeling that their company, though pleasant enough, was unprofitable to the author, and I was too shy, too arrogant and too diffident, to seek their counsel. I studied the French novelists more than the English, and having got what I was capable of getting from Maupassant, turned to Stendhal, Balzac, the Goncourts, Flaubert and Anatole France.

I tried various experiments. One of them at that time had a certain novelty. The experience of life I was forever eagerly seeking suggested to me that the novelist's method of taking two or three people, or even a group, and describing their adventures, spiritual and otherwise, as though no one else existed and nothing else was hap-

pening in the world, gave a very partial picture of reality. I was myself living in several sets that had no connection with one another, and it occurred to me that it might give a truer picture of life if one could carry on at the same time the various stories, of equal importance, that were enacted during a certain period in different circles. I took a larger number of persons than I had ever sought to cope with before and devised four or five independent stories. They were attached to one another by a very thin thread, an elderly woman who knew at least one person in each group. The book was called *The Merry-Go-Round*. It was rather absurd because owing to the influence on me of the æsthetic school of the nineties I made everyone incredibly beautiful, and it was written in a tight and affected manner. But its chief defect was that it lacked the continuous line that directs the reader's interest; the stories were not after all of equal importance and it was tiresome to divert one's attention from one set of people to another. I failed from my ignorance of the very simple device of seeing the diverse events and the characters that took part in them through the eyes of a single person. It is a device which of course the autobiographical novel has used for centuries, but which Henry James has very usefully developed. By the simple process of writing *he* for *I* and stepping down from the omniscience of an all-knowing narrator to the imperfect acquaintance of a participator he showed how to give unity and verisimilitude to a story.

XLV

I HAVE a notion that I was more slow to develop than most writers. Around the years that ended the old century and began the new one I was looked upon as a clever young writer, rather precocious, harsh and somewhat unpleasant, but worth consideration. Though I made little money out of them my books were reviewed at length and conscientiously. But when I compare my early novels with those that are written by young men now I cannot but see that theirs are vastly more accomplished. The ageing writer does well to keep in touch with what the young do and from time to time I read their novels. Girls still in their teens, youths at the university, produce books that seem to me well-written, well-composed and ripe with experience. I do not know whether the young mature sooner than they did forty years ago or whether it is that the art of fiction has in that time so much advanced that it is now as easy to write a good novel as then it was difficult to write even a mediocre one. If one takes the trouble to look through the volumes of *The Yellow Book,* which at that time seemed the last thing in sophisticated intelligence, it is startling to discover how thoroughly bad the majority of its contributions were. For all their parade these writers were no more than an eddy in a backwater and it is unlikely that the history of English literature will give them more than a passing glance. I shiver a little when I turn those musty pages and ask myself whether in another forty years the bright young things of current letters will appear as jejune as do now their maiden aunts of *The Yellow Book.*

It was fortunate for me that I suddenly achieved popularity as a dramatist and so was relieved of the necessity of writing a novel once a year to earn my living. I found plays easy to write; the notoriety they brought me was not unpleasing; and they earned for me enough money to enable me to live less straitly than I had been obliged to. I have never had the bohemian trait of being unconcerned for the morrow. I have never liked to borrow money. I have hated to be in debt. Nor has the squalid life had any attraction for me. I was not born in squalid circumstances. As soon as I could afford it I bought a house in Mayfair.

There are people who despise possessions. Of course when they say that it ill becomes the artist thus to cumber himself they may be right, but it is not a view that artists themselves have held. They have never lived from choice in the garrets in which their admirers like to see them. They have much more often ruined themselves by the extravagance with which they conducted themselves. After all they are creatures of imagination and state appeals to them, fine houses, servants to do their bidding, rich carpets, lovely pictures, and sumptuous furniture. Titian and Rubens lived like princes. Pope had his Grotto and his Quincunx and Sir Walter his Gothic Abbotsford. El Greco with his suites of rooms, his musicians to play to him while he ate, his library and his grand clothes, died bankrupt. It is unnatural for the artist to live in a semi-detached villa and eat cottage pie cooked by a maid of all work. It shows, not disinterestedness, but an arid, petty soul. For of course to the artist the luxury with which he likes to surround himself is but a diversion. His house, his grounds, his cars, his pictures, are playthings to amuse his fancy; they are visible tokens of his power; they do not penetrate to his essential aloofness. For myself I can say that, having had every good thing that money can buy, an experience like another, I could part without a pang with every possession I have. We live in uncertain times and our all may yet be taken from us. With enough plain food to satisfy my small appetite, a room to myself, books from a public library, pens and paper, I should regret nothing. I was glad to earn a great deal of money as a dramatist. It gave me liberty. I was careful with it because I did not want ever again to be in a position when for want of it I could not do anything I had really a mind to.

XLVI

I AM a writer as I might have been a doctor or a lawyer. It is so pleasant a profession that it is not surprising if a vast number of persons adopt it who have no qualifications for it. It is exciting and various. The writer is free to work in whatever place and at whatever time he chooses; he is free to idle if he feels ill or dispirited. But it is a profession that has disadvantages. One is that though the whole world, with everyone in it and all its sights and events, is your material, you yourself can only deal with what corresponds to some secret spring in your own nature. The mind is incalculably rich, but each one of us can get from it only a definite amount of ore. Thus in the midst of plenty the writer may starve to death. His material fails him and we say that he has written himself out. I think there are few writers who are not haunted by the fear of this. Another disadvantage is that the professional writer must please. Unless a sufficient number of persons can be found to read him he will starve. Sometimes the stress of circumstances is too great for him and with rage in his heart he yields to the demand of the public. One must not expect too much of human nature and an occasional pot-boiler may be accepted from him with lenity. The writers who are in independent circumstances should sympathize with, rather than sneer at, those of their brethren whom hard necessity sometimes forces to do hack work. One of the minor sages of Chelsea has remarked that the writer who wrote for money did not write for him. He has said a good many wise things (as indeed a sage should) but this was a very silly one; for the reader has nothing to do with the motive from which the author writes. He is only concerned with the result. Many writers need the spur of necessity to write at all (Samuel Johnson was one of them), but they do not write for money. It would be foolish of them if they did, for there are few avocations in which with equal ability and industry you cannot earn more money than by writing. Most of the great portraits of the world have been painted because their painters were paid to do them. In painting as in writing the excitement of the work is such that when it is once started the artist is absorbed in doing it as well as he can. But just as the painter will not get commissions unless on the whole he satisfies his patrons, so the writer's books will not be read unless on the whole they interest his readers. Yet there is in writers a feeling that the public ought to like what they write and if their books do not sell the fault is not with them but with the public. I have never met an author who admitted that people did not buy his book because it was dull. There are many instances of artists whose work for long has been little appreciated and who yet in the end achieved fame. We do not, however, hear of those whose work has continued to be ignored. Their number is far greater. Where are the votive offerings of those who perished? If it is true that talent consists in a certain facility combined with a peculiar outlook on the world it is very understandable that originality should not at first be welcomed. In this perpetually changing world people are suspicious of novelty and it takes them some time before they can accustom themselves to it. A writer with an idiosyncrasy has to find little by little the people to whom it appeals. Not only does it take him time to be himself, for the young are themselves only with timidity, but it takes him time to convince that body of persons, whom he will eventually rather pompously call his public, that he has something to give them that they want. The more individual he is the harder will he find it to achieve this and the longer will it take him to earn his living. Nor can he be sure that the result will be lasting, for it may be that with all his individuality he has but one or two things to give and then he will soon sink back into the ob-

scurity from which he with difficulty emerged.

It is easy to say that the writer should have an occupation that provides him with his bread and butter and write in such leisure as this occupation affords him. This course, indeed, was forced upon him very generally in the past, when the author, however distinguished and popular, could not earn enough money by writing to keep body and soul together. It is forced upon him still in countries with a small reading public; he must eke out his livelihood by work in an office, preferably under the government, or by journalism. But the English-speaking writer has the potentiality of such an enormous public that writing can very reasonably be adopted as a profession. It would be more overcrowded than it is if in English-speaking countries the cultivation of the arts were not slightly despised. There is a healthy feeling that to write or to paint is not a man's work, and the social force of this keeps many from entering the ranks. You have to have a very decided urge to enter a profession which exposes you to at least a small degree of moral obloquy. In France and in Germany writing is an honourable occupation, and so is adopted with the consent of parents even though its financial rewards are unsatisfactory. You can often run across a German mother who, when you ask her what her young son is going to be, will answer with complacency, a poet; and in France the family of a girl with a large *dot* will look upon her marriage with a young novelist of talent as a suitable alliance.

But the author does not only write when he is at his desk; he writes all day long, when he is thinking, when he is reading, when he is experiencing; everything he sees and feels is significant to his purpose and, consciously or unconsciously, he is forever storing and making over his impressions. He cannot give an undivided attention to any other calling. He will not follow it to his own satisfaction or that of his employers. The most common one for him to adopt is journalism, because it seems to have a closer connection with his proper work. It is the most dangerous. There is an impersonality in a newspaper that insensibly affects the writer. People who write much for the press seem to lose the faculty of seeing things for themselves; they see them from a generalized standpoint, vividly often, sometimes with hectic brightness, yet never with that idiosyncrasy which may give only a partial picture of the facts, but is suffused by the personality of the observer. The press, in fact, kills the individuality of those who write for it. Nor is reviewing less harmful; the writer has not the time to read any books but those that directly concern him, and this reading of hundreds of books haphazard, not for the spiritual advantage he may gain from them but to give a reasonably honest account of them, deadens his sensibilities and impedes the free flow of his own imagination. Writing is a whole-time job. To write must be the main object of the author's life; that is to say, he must be a professional writer. He is lucky if he has sufficient fortune to make him independent of his earnings, but that does not prevent him from being a professional writer. Swift with his deanery, Wordsworth with his sinecure, were just as much professional writers as Balzac and Dickens.

XLVII

It is acknowledged that the technique of painting and of musical composition can only be acquired by assiduous labour, and the productions of dilettantes are rightly regarded with good-humoured or exasperated contempt. We all congratulate ourselves that the radio and the gramophone have driven from our drawing-rooms the amateur pianist and the amateur singer. The technique of writing is no less difficult than that of the other arts and yet, because he can read and write a letter, there is a notion that anyone can write well enough to write a book. Writing seems now the favourite relaxation of the human race. Whole families will take to it as in happier times they entered religious houses. Women will write novels to while away their pregnancies; bored noblemen, axed officers, retired civil servants, fly to the pen as one might fly to the bottle. There is an impression abroad that everyone has it in him to write one book; but if by this is implied a good book the impression is false. It is true that the amateur may sometimes produce a work of merit. By a lucky chance he may have a natural facility for writing well, he may have had experiences that are in themselves interesting, or he may have a charming or quaint personality that his very inexpertness helps him to get down on the printed page. But let him remember that the saying asserts only that everyone has it in him to write one book; it says nothing about a second. The amateur is wise not to try his luck again. His next book is pretty sure to be worthless.

For one of the great differences between the amateur and the professional is that the latter has the capacity to progress. The literature of a country is made not by a few excellent books, I repeat, but by a great body of work, and this can only be produced by professional writers. The literature of those countries that has been produced chiefly by amateurs is thin in comparison with that of the countries in which a number of men, with difficulty trying to make their living, have followed it as a profession. A body of work, an *œuvre*, is the result of long-continued and resolute effort. The author, like other men, learns by the method of trial and error. His early works are tentative; he tries his hand at various subjects and various methods and at the same time develops his character. By a simultaneous process he discovers himself, which is what he has to give, and learns how to display this discovery to the best ad-

vantage. Then, in full possession of his faculties, he produces the best of which he is capable. Since writing is a healthy occupation, he will probably go on living long after he has done this, and since by this time writing will have become an ingrained habit he will doubtless continue to produce works of no great consequence. These the public may legitimately neglect. From the standpoint of the reader, very little that the writer produces in the whole course of his life is essential. (By essential, I mean only that small part of him which expresses his individuality, and I attach no implication of absolute value to the word.) But I think he can only give this as the result of a long apprenticeship and at the cost of a good many failures. To do it he must make literature his life's work. He must be a professional author.

XLVIII

I HAVE spoken of the disadvantages of the author's profession: now I should like to speak of its dangers.

It is evident that no professional writer can afford only to write when he feels like it. If he waits till he is in the mood, till he has the inspiration as he says, he waits indefinitely and ends by producing little or nothing. The professional writer creates the mood. He has his inspiration too, but he controls and subdues it to his bidding by setting himself regular hours of work. But in time writing becomes a habit, and like the old actor in retirement, who gets restless when the hour arrives at which he has been accustomed to go down to the theatre and make up for the evening performance, the writer itches to get to his

pens and paper at the hours at which he has been used to write. Then he writes automatically. Words come easily to him and words suggest ideas. They are old and empty ideas, but his practised hand can turn out an acceptable piece. He goes down to luncheon or goes to bed with the assurance that he has done a good day's work. Every production of an artist should be the expression of an adventure of his soul. This is a counsel of perfection and in an imperfect world a certain indulgence should be bestowed on the professional writer; but this surely is the aim he should keep before him. He does well only to write to liberate his spirit of a subject that he has so long meditated that it burdens him and if he is wise he will take care to write only for the sake of his own peace. Perhaps the simplest way to break the habit of writing is by changing the environment to one that gives no opportunity for the daily task. You cannot write well or much (and I venture the opinion that you cannot write well unless you write much) unless you form a habit; but habits in writing as in life are only useful if they are broken as soon as they cease to be advantageous.

But the greatest danger that besets the professional author is one that unfortunately only a few have to guard against. Success. It is the most difficult thing the writer has to cope with. When after a long and bitter struggle he has at last achieved it he finds that it spreads a snare to entangle and destroy him. Few of us have the determination to avoid its perils. It must be dealt with warily. The common idea that success spoils people by making them vain, egotistic and self-complacent is erroneous; on the contrary it makes them, for the most part, humble, tolerant and kind. Failure makes people bitter and cruel. Success improves the character of the man; it does not always improve the character of the author. It may very well deprive him of that force which has brought him success. His individuality has been formed by his experiences; his struggles, his frustrated hopes, his efforts to adapt himself to a hostile world; it must be very stubborn if it is not modified by the softening influences of success.

Success besides often bears within itself the seed of destruction, for it may very well cut the author off from the material that was its occasion. He enters a new world. He is made much of. He must be almost super-human if he is not captivated by the notice taken of him by the great and remains insensible to the attentions of beautiful women. He grows accustomed to another way of life, probably more luxurious than that to which he has been used, and to people who have more of the social graces than those with whom he has consorted before. They are more intellectual and their superficial brilliance is engaging. How difficult it is for him then to move freely still in the circles with which he has been familiar and which have given him his subjects! His success has changed him in the eyes of his old associates and they are no longer at home with him. They may look upon him with envy or with admiration, but no longer as one of themselves. The new world into which his success has brought him excites his imagination and he writes about it; but he sees it from the outside and can never so penetrate it as to become a part of it. No better example of this can be given than Arnold Bennett. He never knew anything intimately but the life of the Five Towns in which he had been born and bred, and it was only when he dealt with them that his work had character. When success brought him into the society of literary people, rich men and smart women, and he sought to deal with them, what he wrote was worthless. Success destroyed him.

XLIX

THE writer is wise then who is wary of success. He must look with dread on the claims that others make on him because of it, the responsibilities it

THE SUMMING UP 621

forces on him, and the hindering activities that it brings in its wake. It can only give him two good things: one, the more important by far, is the freedom to follow his own bent, and the other is confidence in himself. Notwithstanding his pretension and his susceptible vanity the author when he compares his work with what he intended it to be is never free from misgiving. There is so great a distance between what he saw in his mind's eye and the best he has been able to do that for him the result is no more than a makeshift. He may be pleased with a page here or there and regard an episode or a character with approval; I think it must be very seldom that he looks upon any work of his as a whole with complete satisfaction. At the back of his mind is the suspicion that it is not good at all and the praises of the public, even if he is inclined to doubt their value, are a heaven-sent reassurance.

That is why praise is important to him. It is a weakness that he should hanker for it; though perhaps a pardonable one. For the artist should be indifferent to praise and blame, since he is concerned with his work only in its relation to himself, and how it affects the public is a matter in which he is materially perhaps, but not spiritually, concerned. The artist produces for the liberation of his soul. It is his nature to create as it is the nature of water to run down hill. It is not for nothing that artists have called their works the children of their brains and likened the pains of production to the pains of childbirth. It is something like an organic thing that develops, not of course only in their brains, but in their heart, their nerves and their viscera, something that their creative instinct evolves out of the experiences of their soul and their body, and that at last becomes so oppressive

that they must rid themselves of it. When this happens they enjoy a sense of liberation and for one delicious moment rest in peace. But unlike human mothers, they lose interest very soon in the child that is born. It is no longer a part of them. It has given them its satisfaction and now their souls are open to a new impregnation.

In the production of his work, the author has fulfilled himself. But that is not to say that it has any value for anyone else. The reader of a book, the observer of a picture, is not concerned with the artist's feelings. The artist has sought release, but the layman seeks for a communication, and he alone can judge whether the communication is valuable to him. To the artist the communication he offers is a by-product. I am not speaking now of those who practise an art to teach; they are propagandists and with them art is a side issue. Artistic creation is a specific activity that is satisfied by its own exercise. The work created may be good art or bad art. That is a matter for the layman to decide. He forms his decision from the æsthetic value of the communication that is offered to him. If it yields escape from the reality of the world he will welcome it, but is very likely at best to describe it only as minor art; if it enriches his soul and enlarges his personality he will rightly describe it as great. But this, I insist, has nothing to do with the artist; it is human that he should be pleased if he has given others pleasure or greater strength; but he should not take it amiss if they find nothing to their purpose in the results of his production. He has already had his reward in the satisfaction of his creative instinct. Now this is no counsel of perfection; it is the only condition on which the artist can work his way towards the unattainable perfection that is his aim. If he is a novelist he uses his experience of people and places, his apprehension of himself, his love and hate, his deepest thoughts, his passing fancies, to draw in one work after another a picture of life. It can never be more than a partial one, but if he is fortunate he will succeed in the end in doing something else; he will draw a complete picture of himself.

At all events to think thus is a consolation when you cast your eye over the publishers' advertisements. When you read those long lists of books and when you discover that reviewers have extolled their wit, profundity, originality and beauty your heart sinks; what chance have you in comparison with so much genius? The publishers will tell you that the average life of a novel is ninety days. It is hard to reconcile yourself to the fact that a book into which you have put, besides your whole self, several months of anxious toil, should be read in three or four hours and after so short a period forgotten. Though it will do him no good, there is no author so small-minded as not to have a secret hope that some part at least of his work will survive him for a generation or two. The belief in posthumous fame is a harmless vanity which often reconciles the artist to the disappointments and failure of his life. How unlikely he is to attain it

we see when we look back on the writers who only twenty years ago seemed assured of immortality. Where are their readers now? And with the mass of books that are constantly produced and the ceaseless competition of those that have lived on, how small is the likelihood that work that has been once forgotten will ever be again remembered! There is one very odd, and some may think very unfair, thing about posterity; it seems to choose the works to which it gives attention from those of authors who have been popular in their lifetime. The writers who delight a clique and never reach the great public will never delight posterity, for posterity will never hear about them. It is a consolation to the popular authors who have had it impressed upon them that their popularity was sufficient proof of their worthlessness. It may be that Shakespeare, Scott and Balzac did not write for the minor sage of Chelsea, but it looks as though they did write for after ages. The writer's only safety is to find his satisfaction in his own performance. If he can realize that in the liberation of soul which his work has brought him and in the pleasure of shaping it in such a way as to satisfy to some extent at least his æsthetic sense, he is amply rewarded for his labours, he can afford to be indifferent to the outcome.

L

F o r the disadvantages and dangers of the author's calling are offset by an advantage so great as to make all its difficulties, disappointments, and maybe hardships, unimportant. It gives him spiritual freedom. To him life is a tragedy and by his gift of creation

he enjoys the catharsis, the purging of pity and terror, which Aristotle tells us is the object of art. For his sins and his follies, the unhappiness that befalls him, his unrequited love, his physical defects, illness, privation, his hopes abandoned, his griefs, humiliations, everything is transformed by his power into material and by writing it he can overcome it. Everything is grist to his mill, from the glimpse of a face in the street to a war that convulses the civilized world, from the scent of a rose to the death of a friend. Nothing befalls him that he cannot transmute into a stanza, a song or a story, and having done this be rid of it. The artist is the only free man.

Perhaps that is why the world on the whole has had the profound suspicion of him that we know. It is not sure that he can be trusted when he reacts to the common impulses of men so unaccountably. And indeed the artist, to the indignation of mankind, has never felt himself bound by ordinary standards. Why should he? With men in general the primary end of thought and action is to satisfy their needs and preserve their being; but the artist satisfies his needs and preserves his being by the pursuit of art: their pastime is his grim earnest and so his attitude to life can never be the same as theirs. He creates his own values. Men think him cynical because he does not attach importance to the virtues and is not revolted by the vices that move them. He is not cynical. But what they call virtue and what they call vice are not the sort of things that he takes any particular interest in. They are indifferent elements in the scheme of things out of which he constructs his own freedom. Of course common men are quite right to be indignant with him. But that isn't going to do him any good. He is incorrigible.

L I

WHEN, having achieved success as a dramatist, I determined to devote the rest of my life to playwriting I reckoned without my host. I was happy, I was prosperous, I was busy, my head was full of plays that I wanted to write; I do not know whether it was that success did not bring me all I had expected or whether it was a natural reaction from success: I was but just firmly established as a popular playwright when I began to be obsessed by the teeming memories of my past life. The loss of my mother and then the break-up of my home, the wretchedness of my first years at school for which my French childhood had so ill-prepared me and which my stammering made so difficult, the delight of those easy, monotonous and exciting days in Heidelberg, when I first entered upon the intellectual life, the irksomeness of my few years at the hospital and the thrill of London; it all came back to me so pressingly, in my sleep, on my walks, when I was rehearsing plays, when I was at a party, it became such a burden to me that I made up my mind that I could only regain my peace by writing it all down in the form of a novel. I knew it would be a long one and I wanted to be undisturbed, so I refused the contracts managers were anxious to give me and temporarily retired from the stage.

I had written a novel on the same themes when, after taking my medical degrees, I went to Seville. Luckily for me Fisher Unwin refused to give me the hundred pounds I wanted for it and no other publisher would have it at any price; or I should have lost a subject which I was then too young to make proper use of. The manuscript still exists, but I have not looked at it since I corrected the typescript; I have no doubt it is very immature. I was not far enough away from the events I described to see them reasonably and I had not had a number of experiences that later went to enrich the book I finally wrote. It seems to me that if the writing of this first novel did not finally repress into my subconscious the unhappy memories with which it was concerned it is because the writer is not finally disembarrassed of his subject till his work is published. When it is delivered to the public, however heedless the public be, it is his no longer and he is free from the burden that oppressed him. I called my book *Beauty from Ashes,* which is a quotation from Isaiah, but finding that this title had been recently used, I chose instead the title of one of the books in Spinoza's *Ethics* and called it *Of Human Bondage.* It is not an autobiography, but an autobiographical novel; fact and fiction are inextricably mingled; the emotions are my own, but not all the incidents are related as they happened and some of them are transferred to my hero not from my own life but from that of persons with whom I was intimate. The book did for me what I wanted, and when it was issued to the world (a world in the throes of a terrible war and too much concerned with its own sufferings to bother with the adventures of a creature of fiction) I found myself free forever from those pains and unhappy recollections. I put into it everything I then knew and having at last finished it prepared to make a fresh start.

LII

I was tired. I was tired not only of the people and thoughts that had so long occupied me; I was tired of the people I lived with and the life I was leading. I felt that I had got all that I was capable of getting out of the world in which I had been moving; my success as a playwright and the luxurious existence it had brought me; the social round, the grand dinners at the houses of the great, the brilliant balls and the week-end parties at country houses; the company of clever and brilliant people, writers, painters, actors; the love affairs I had had and the easy companionship of my friends; the comfortableness and security of life. It was stifling me and I hankered after a different mode of existence and new experiences. But I did not know where to turn for them. I thought of travelling. I was tired of the man I was, and it seemed to me that by a long journey to some far-distant country I might renew myself. Russia was very much in the thoughts of people then and I had a mind to go there for a year, learn the language of which I already knew the elements and immerse myself in the emotion and mystery of that vast country. I thought that there perhaps I might find something that would give sustenance and enrichment to my spirit. I was forty. If I meant to marry and have children it was high time I did so and for some time I had amused my imagination with pictures of myself in the married state. There was no one I particularly wanted to marry.

It was the condition that attracted me. It seemed a necessary motif in the pattern of life that I had designed, and to my ingenuous fancy (for though no longer young and thinking myself so worldly wise, I was still in many ways incredibly naïve) it offered peace; peace from the disturbance of love affairs, casual it might be in the beginning, but bringing in their train such troublesome complications (for it takes two to make a love affair and a man's meat is too often a woman's poison); peace that would enable me to write all I wanted to write without the loss of precious time or disturbance of mind; peace and a settled and dignified way of life. I sought freedom and thought I could find it in marriage. I conceived these notions when I was still at work on *Of Human Bondage,* and turning my wishes into fiction, as writers will, towards the end of it I drew a picture of the marriage I should have liked to make. Readers on the whole have found it the least satisfactory part of my book.

But my uncertainties were resolved by an event over which I had no control. The war broke out. A chapter of my life had finished. A new chapter began.

LIII

I HAD a friend who was a cabinet minister and I wrote and asked him to help me to do something, whereupon I was invited to present myself at the War Office; but fearing that I should be set to clerical work in England and anxious to get out to France at once I joined a unit of ambulance cars. Though I do not think I was less patriotic than another my patriotism was mingled with the excitement the new experience offered me and I began keeping a notebook the moment I landed in France. I kept it till the work got heavy and then at the end of the day I was too tired to do anything but go to bed. I enjoyed the new life I was thrown into and the lack of responsibility. It was a pleasure to me who had never been ordered about since I was at school to be told to do this and that and when it was done to feel that my time was my own. As a writer I had never felt that; I had felt on the contrary that I had not a minute to lose. Now with a clear conscience I wasted long hours at *estaminets* in idle chatter. I liked meeting a host of people, and, though writing no longer, I treasured their peculiarities in my memory. I was never in any particular danger. I was anxious to see how I should feel when exposed to it; I have never thought myself very courageous nor did I think there was any necessity for me to be so. The only occasion upon which I might have examined myself was when in the Grande Place at Ypres a shell blew up a wall against which I had been standing just as I had moved over to get a view of the ruined Cloth Makers' Hall from the other side; but I was too much surprised to observe my state of mind.

Later on I joined the Intelligence Department where it looked as though I could be more useful than in somewhat inadequately driving an ambulance. The work appealed both to my sense of romance and my sense of the ridiculous. The methods I was instructed to use in order to foil persons who were following me; the secret interviews with agents in unlikely places; the conveying of messages in a mysterious fashion; the reports smuggled over a frontier; it was all doubtless very necessary but so reminiscent of what was then known as the shilling shocker that for me it took most of its reality away from the war and I could not but look upon it as little more than material that might one day be of use to me. But it was so hackneyed that I doubted whether I should ever be able to profit by it. After a year in Switzerland my work there came to an end. It had entailed a good deal of exposure, the winter was bitter and I had to take journeys across the Lake of Geneva in all weathers. I was in very poor health. There seemed nothing much for me to do at the moment, so I went to America where two of my plays were about to be produced. I wanted to recover my peace of mind shattered through my own foolishness and vanity by occurrences upon which I need not dwell and so made up my mind to go to the South Seas. I had wanted to go ever since as a youth I had read *The Ebb-Tide* and *The Wrecker* and I wanted besides to get material for a novel I had long been thinking over based on the life of Paul Gauguin.

I went, looking for beauty and romance and glad to put a great ocean between me and the trouble that harassed me. I found beauty and romance, but I found also something I had never expected. I found a new self. Ever since I left St. Thomas's Hospital I had lived with people who attached value to culture. I had come to think that there was nothing in the world more important than art. I looked for a meaning in the universe and the only one I could find was the beauty that men here and there produced. On the surface my life was

varied and exciting; but beneath it was narrow. Now I entered a new world, and all the instinct in me of a novelist went out with exhilaration to absorb the novelty. It was not only the beauty of the islands that took me, Herman Melville and Pierre Loti had prepared me for that, and though it is a different beauty it is not a greater beauty than that of Greece or Southern Italy; nor was it their ramshackle, slightly adventurous, easy life; what excited me was to meet one person after another who was new to me. I was like a naturalist who comes into a country where the fauna are of an unimaginable variety. Some I recognized; they were old types that I had read of and they gave me just the same feeling of delighted surprise that I had once in the Malayan Archipelago when I saw sitting on the branch of a tree a bird that I had never seen before but in a zoo. For the first moment I thought it must have escaped from a cage. Others were strange to me and they thrilled me as Wallace was thrilled when he came upon a new species. I found them easy to get on with. They were of all sorts; indeed, the variety would have been bewildering but that my powers of observation were by now well trained and I found it possible without conscious effort to pigeon-hole each one in my awareness. Few of them had culture. They had learnt life in a different school from mine and had come to different conclusions. They led it on a different plane; I could not, with my sense of humour, go on thinking mine a higher one. It was different. Their lives too formed themselves to the discerning eye into a pattern that had order and finally coherence.

I stepped off my pedestal. It seemed to me that these men had more vitality than those I had known hitherto. They did not burn with a hard, gem-like flame, but with a hot, smoky, consuming fire. They had their own narrownesses. They had their prejudices. They were often dull and stupid. I did not care. They were different. In civilized communities men's idiosyncrasies are mitigated by the necessity of conforming to certain rules of behaviour. Culture is a mask that hides their faces. Here people showed themselves bare. These heterogeneous creatures thrown into a life that had preserved a great deal of its primitiveness had never felt the need to adapt themselves to conventional standards. Their peculiarities had been given opportunity to develop unchecked. In great cities men are like a lot of stones thrown together in a bag; their jagged corners are rubbed off till in the end they are as smooth as marbles. These men had never had their jagged corners rubbed away. They seemed to me nearer to the elementals of human nature than any of the people I had been living with for so long and my heart leapt towards them as it had done years before to the people who filed into the outpatients' room at St. Thomas's. I filled my notebook with brief descriptions of their appearance and their character, and presently, my imagination excited by these multitudinous impressions, from a hint or an incident or a happy invention, stories began to form themselves round certain of the most vivid of them.

LIV

I RETURNED to America and shortly afterwards was sent on a mission to Petrograd. I was diffident of accepting the post, which seemed to demand capacities that I did not think I possessed; but there seemed to be no one more competent available at the moment and my being a writer was very good "cover" for what I was asked to do. I was not very well. I still knew enough medicine to guess the meaning of the hæmorrhages I was having. An X-ray photograph showed clearly that I had tuberculosis of the lungs. But I could not miss the opportunity of spending certainly a considerable time in the country of Tolstoi, Dostoievski and Chekhov; I had a notion that in the intervals of the work I was being sent to do I could get something for myself that would be of value; so I set my foot hard on the loud pedal of patriotism and persuaded the physician I consulted that under the tragic circumstances of the moment I was taking no undue risk. I set off in high spirits with unlimited money at my disposal and four devoted Czechs to act as liaison officers between me and Professor Masaryk who had under his control in various parts of Russia something like sixty thousand of his compatriots. I was exhilarated by the responsibility of my position. I went as a private agent, who could be disavowed if necessary, with instructions to get in touch with parties hostile to the government and devise a scheme that would keep Russia in the war and prevent the Bolsheviks, supported by the Central Powers, from seizing power. It is not necessary for me to inform the reader that in this I failed lamentably and I do not ask him to believe me when I state that it seems to me at least possible that if I had been sent six months before I might quite well have succeeded. Three months after my arrival in Petrograd the crash came and put an end to all my plans.

I returned to England. I had had some interesting experiences and had got to know fairly well one of the most extraordinary men I have ever met. This was Boris Savinkov, the terrorist who had assassinated Trepov and the Grand Duke Sergius. But I came away disillusioned. The endless talk when action was needed, the vacillations, the apathy when apathy could only result in destruction, the high-flown protestations, the insincerity and halfheartedness that I found everywhere sickened me with Russia and the Russians. I also came back very ill indeed, for in the position I was in I could not profit by the abundant supplies that made it possible for the embassies to serve their countries on a full stomach and I was (like the Russians themselves) reduced to a meagre diet. (When I arrived in Stockholm, where I had a day to wait for the destroyer that was to take me across the North Sea, I went into a confectioner's, bought a pound of chocolates and ate them in the street.) A scheme to send me to Rumania in connection with some Polish intrigue, the details of which I now forget, fell through. I was not sorry, for I was coughing my head off and constant fever made my nights very uncomfortable. I went to see the most eminent specialist I could find in London. He packed me off to a

sanatorium in the North of Scotland, Davos and St. Moritz at that time being inconvenient to go to, and for the next two years I led an invalid life.

I had a grand time. I discovered for the first time in my life how very delightful it is to lie in bed. It is astonishing how varied life can be when you stay in bed all day and how much you find to do. I delighted in the privacy of my room with the immense window wide open to the starry winter night. It gave me a delicious sense of security, aloofness and freedom. The silence was enchanting. Infinite space seemed to enter it and my spirit, alone with the stars, seemed capable of any adventure. My imagination was never more nimble; it was like a barque under press of sail scudding before the breeze. The monotonous days, whose only excitement was the books I read and my reflections, passed with inconceivable rapidity. I left my bed with a pang.

It was a strange world that I entered when I grew well enough to mix during part of the day with my fellow-patients. In their different ways these people, some of whom had been in the sanatorium for years, were as singular as any of those I had met in the South Seas. Illness and the queer, sheltered life affected them strangely, twisting, strengthening, deteriorating their character just as in Samoa or Tahiti it was deteriorated, strengthened or twisted by the languorous climate and the alien environment. I think I learnt a good deal about human nature in that sanatorium that otherwise I should never have known.

LV

WHEN I recovered from my illness the war was over. I went to China. I went with the feelings of any traveller interested in art and curious to see what he could of the manners of a strange people whose civilization was of great antiquity; but I went also with the notion that I must surely run across men of various sorts whose acquaintance would enlarge my experience. I did. I filled notebooks with descriptions of places and persons and the stories they suggested. I became aware of the specific benefit I was capable of getting from travel; before, it had been only an instinctive feeling. This was freedom of the spirit on the one hand, and on the other, the collection of all manner of persons who might serve my purposes. After that I travelled to many countries. I journeyed over a dozen seas, in liners, in tramps, in schooners; I went by train, by car, by chair, on foot or on horseback. I kept my eyes open for character, oddness and personality. I learnt very quickly when a place promised me something and then I waited till I had got it. Otherwise I passed on. I accepted every experience that came my way. When I could I travelled as comfortably as my ample means allowed, for it seemed to me merely silly to rough it for the sake of roughing it; but I do not think I ever hesitated to do anything because it was uncomfortable or dangerous.

I have never been much of a sightseer. So much enthusiasm has been expended over the great sights of the world that I can summon up very little when I am confronted with them. I have preferred common things, a wooden house on piles nestling among fruit trees, the bend of a little bay lined with coconuts, or a group of bamboos by the wayside. My interest has been in men and the lives they led. I am shy of making acquaintance with strangers, but I was fortunate enough to have on my journeys a companion who had an inestimable social gift. He had an amiability of disposition that enabled him in a very short time to make friends with people in ships, clubs, bar-rooms and hotels, so that through him I was able to get into easy contact with an immense number of persons whom otherwise I should have known only from a distance.

I made acquaintance with them with just the degree of intimacy that suited me. It was an intimacy born on their side of ennui or loneliness, that withheld few secrets, but one that separation irrevocably broke. It was close because its limits were settled in advance. Looking back on that long procession I cannot think of anyone who had not something to tell me that I was glad to know. I seemed to myself to develop the sensitiveness of a photographic plate. It did not matter to me if the picture I formed was true; what mattered was that with the help of my imagination I could make of each person I met a plausible harmony. It was the most entrancing game in which I had ever engaged.

One reads that no one exactly resembles anyone else, and that every man is unique, and in a way this is true, but it is a truth easy to exaggerate: in practice men are very much alike. They are divided into comparatively few types. The same circumstances mould them in the same way. Certain characteristics infer certain others. You can, like the palæontologist, reconstruct the animal from a single bone. The "characters" which have been a popular form of letters since Theophrastus, and the "humours" of the seventeenth century, prove that men sort themselves into a few marked categories. Indeed this is the foundation of realism, which depends for its attractiveness on recognition. The romantic method turns its attention to the exceptional; the realistic to the usual. The slightly abnormal circumstances in which men live in the countries where life is primitive or the environment alien to them, emphasize their ordinariness so that it gains a character of its own; and when they are in themselves extraordinary, which of course they sometimes are, the want of the usual restraints permits them to develop their kinks with a freedom that in more civilized communities can be but hardly won. Then you have creatures that realism can scarcely cope with. I used to stay away till my receptivity was exhausted and I found that when I met people I had no longer the power to make the imaginative effort to give them shape and coherence; then I returned to England to sort out my impressions and rest till I felt my powers of assimilation restored. At last, after seven, I think, of these long journeys I found a certain sameness in people. I met more and more often types that I had met before. They ceased to interest me so much. I concluded that I had come to the end of my capacity for seeing with passion and individuality the people I went so far to find, for I had never doubted that it was I who gave them the idiosyncrasy that

I discovered in them, and so I decided that there was no further profit for me in travel. I had twice nearly died of fever, I had been nearly drowned, I had been shot at by bandits. I was glad to resume a more ordered way of life.

I came back from each of my journeys a little different. In my youth I had read a great deal, not because I supposed that it would benefit me, but from curiosity and the desire to learn; I travelled because it amused me, and to get material that would be of use to me: it never occurred to me that my new experiences were having an effect on me, and it was not till long afterwards that I saw how they had formed my character. In contact with all these strange people I lost the smoothness that I had acquired when, leading the humdrum life of a man of letters, I was one of the stones in a bag. I got back my jagged edges. I was at last myself. I ceased to travel because I felt that travel could give me nothing more. I was capable of no new development. I had sloughed the arrogance of culture. My mood was complete acceptance. I asked from nobody more than he could give me. I had learnt toleration. I was pleased with the goodness of my fellows; I was not distressed by their badness. I had acquired independence of spirit. I had learnt to go my own way without bothering with what others thought about it. I demanded freedom for myself and I was prepared to give freedom to others. It is easy to laugh and shrug your shoulders when people act badly to others; it is much more difficult when they act badly to you. I have not found it impossible. The conclusion I came to about men I put into the mouth of a man I met on board ship in the China Seas. "I'll give you my opinion of the human race in a nutshell, brother," I made him say. "Their heart's in the right place, but their head is a thoroughly inefficient organ."

LVI

I HAVE always liked to let things simmer in my mind for a long time before setting them down on paper, and it was not till four years after I had made my notes for it that I wrote the first of the stories I had conceived in the South Seas. I had not written short stories for many years. I began my literary career by writing them and my third book was a collection of six. They were not good. After that I tried now and then to write stories for the magazines; my agents pressed me to write humorously, but for this I had no aptitude; I was grim, indignant or satirical. My efforts to satisfy editors and thus earn a little money rarely succeeded. The first story I wrote now was called *Rain* and it looked for a while as though I should have no better luck with it than with those I had written in my youth, for editor after editor refused it; but I no longer minded and I went on. When I had written six, all of which eventually found their way into magazines, I published them in a book. The success they had was pleasant and unexpected. I liked the form. It was very agreeable to live with the personages of my fancy for two or three weeks and then be done with them. One had no time to grow sick of them as one easily may during the months one has to spend in their company when writing a novel. This sort of story, one of about twelve thousand words, gave me ample room to develop my theme, but forced upon me a concision that my practice as a dram-

atist had made grateful to me.

It was unlucky for me that I set about writing short stories seriously when the better-class writers in England and America were delivered over to the influence of Chekhov. The literary world somewhat lacks balance, and when a fancy takes it, is apt to regard it not as a passing fashion, but as Heaven's first law; and the notion prevailed that anyone who had artistic leanings and wanted to write short stories must write stories like Chekhov. Several writers transplanted Russian melancholy, Russian mysticism, Russian fecklessness, Russian despair, Russian futility, Russian infirmity of purpose, to Surrey or Michigan, Brooklyn or Clapham and made quite a reputation for themselves. It must be admitted that Chekhov is not hard to imitate. As I know to my cost there are dozens of Russian refugees who do it quite well: to my cost, because they send me their stories so that I may correct the English and then are offended with me when I cannot get vast sums of money for them from American magazines. Chekhov was a very good short story writer, but he had his limitations and he very wisely made them the basis of his art. He had no gift for devising a compact, dramatic story, such a story as you could tell with effect over the dinner-table, like *L'Héritage* or *La Parure*. As a man, he seems to have been of a cheerful and practical disposition, but as a writer, he was of a depressed melancholic nature that made him turn away with distaste from violent action or exuberance. His humour, often so painful, is the exasperated reaction of a man whose shuddering sensibilities have been rubbed the wrong way. He saw life in a monotone. His people are not sharply individualized. He does not seem to have been much interested in them as persons. Perhaps that is why he is able to give you the feeling that they are all part of one another, strange groping ectoplasms that melt into each other, the sense of the mystery of life and its futility, which give him his unique quality. It is a quality that has escaped his followers.

I do not know if I could ever have written stories in the Chekhov manner. I did not want to. I wanted to write stories that proceeded, tightly knit, in an unbroken line from the exposition to the conclusion. I saw the short story as a narrative of a single event, material or spiritual, to which by the elimination of everything that was not essential to its elucidation a dramatic unity could be given. I had no fear of what is technically known as "the point." It seemed to me that it was reprehensible only if it was not logical, and I thought that the discredit that had been attached to it was due only to the fact that it had been too often tacked on, merely for effect, without legitimate reason. In short, I preferred to end my short stories with a full-stop rather than with a straggle of dots.

It is this, I imagine, that has led to their being better appreciated in France than in England. Our great novels are shapeless and unwieldy. It has pleased the English to lose themselves in these huge, straggling, intimate works; and this laxity of construction, this haphazard conduct of a rambling story, this wandering in and out of curious characters who have nothing much to do with the theme, have given them a peculiar sense of reality. It is this, however, that has given the French an acute sense of discomfort. The sermons that Henry James preached to the English on form in the novel aroused their interest, but have little affected their practice. The fact is that they are suspicious of form. They find in it a sort of airlessness; its constraint irks them; they feel that when the author has fixed upon his material a wilful shape life has slipped through his fingers. The French critic demands that a piece of fiction should have a beginning, a middle and an end; a theme that is clearly developed to a logical conclusion; and that it should tell you all that is of moment to the point at issue. From the familiarity with Maupassant that I gained at an early age, from my training as a dramatist, and perhaps from personal idiosyncrasy, I have, it may be, acquired a sense of form that is pleasing to the French. At all events they find me neither sentimental nor verbose.

LVII

It is very seldom that life provides the writer with a ready-made story. Facts indeed are often very tiresome. They will give a suggestion that excites the imagination, but then are apt to exercise an authority that is only pernicious. The classic example of this is to be found in *Le Rouge et le Noir*.

This is a very great novel, but it is generally acknowledged that the end is unsatisfactory. The reason is not hard to find. Stendhal got the idea for it from an incident that at the time made a great stir: a young seminarist shot his mistress, was tried and guillotined. But Stendhal put into Julien Sorel, his hero, not only a great deal of himself, but much more of what he would have liked to be and was miserably conscious that he was not; he created one of the most interesting personages of fiction and for fully three quarters of his book made him behave with coherence and probability; but then he found himself forced to return to the facts that had been his inspiration. He could only do this by causing his hero to act incongruously with his character and his intelligence. The shock is so great that you no longer believe, and when you do not believe in a novel you are no longer held. The moral is that you must have the courage to throw your facts overboard if they fail to comply with the logic of your character. I do not know how Stendhal could have ended his novel; but I think it would have been hard to find a more unsatisfactory end than the one he chose.

I have been blamed because I have drawn my characters from living persons, and from criticisms that I have read one might suppose that nobody had ever done this before. That is nonsense. It is the universal custom. From the beginning of literature authors have had originals for their creations. Scholars, I believe, give a name to the rich glutton who served as a model to Petronius for his Trimalchio and Shakespearean students find an original for Mr. Justice Shallow. The very virtuous and upright Scott drew a bitter portrait of his father in one book and a pleasanter one, when the passage of years had softened his

asperity, in another. Stendhal, in one of his manuscripts, has written the names of the persons who had suggested his characters; Dickens, as we all know, portrayed his father in Mr. Micawber and Leigh Hunt in Harold Skimpole. Turgenev stated that he could not create a character at all unless as a starting point he could fix his imagination on a living person. I suspect that the writers who deny that they use actual persons deceive themselves (which is not impossible, since you can be a very good novelist without being very intelligent) or deceive us. When they tell the truth and have in fact had no particular person in mind, it will be found, I think, that they owe their characters rather to their memory than to their creative instinct. How many times have we met d'Artagnan, Mrs. Proudie, Archdeacon Grantley, Jane Eyre and Jérome Coignard with other names and in other dress! I should say that the practice of drawing characters from actual models is not only universal but necessary. I do not see why any writer should be ashamed to acknowledge it. As Turgenev said, it is only if you have a definite person in your mind that you can give vitality and idiosyncrasy to your own creation.

I insist that it is a creation. We know very little even of the persons we know most intimately; we do not know them enough to transfer them to the pages of a book and make human beings of them. People are too elusive, too shadowy, to be copied; and they are also too incoherent and contradictory. The writer does not copy his originals; he takes what he wants from them, a few traits that have caught his attention, a turn of mind that has fired his imagination, and therefrom constructs his character. He is not concerned whether it is a truthful likeness; he is concerned only to create a plausible harmony convenient for his own purposes. So different may be the finished product from the original that it must be a common experience of authors to be accused of having drawn a lifelike portrait of a certain person when they had in mind someone quite different. Further, it is just chance whether the author chooses his models from persons with whom he is intimately connected or not. It is often enough for him to have caught a glimpse of someone in a teashop or chatted with him for a quarter of an hour in a ship's smoking-room. All he needs is that tiny, fertile substratum which he can then build up by means of his experience of life, his knowledge of human nature and his native intuition.

The whole business would be plain sailing if it were not for the susceptibilities of the persons who serve as models for the author's characters. So colossal is human egotism that people who have met an author are constantly on the lookout for portraits of themselves in his works and if they can persuade themselves that such and such a character is drawn from them they are bitterly affronted if it is drawn with any imperfections. Though they will find fault with their friends freely and ridicule their absurdities, their vanity is so outrageous that they cannot reconcile themselves to the fact that they too have faults and absurdities. The matter is made worse for them by their friends who with malicious indignation offer them feigned sympathy for the outrage they have suffered. Of course there is a lot of humbug about it all. I do not suppose I am the only author who has been vilified by women who claimed that I had stayed with them and abused their hospitality by writing about them when not only

had I not stayed with them, but neither knew nor had ever heard of them. The poor drabs were so vain and their lives so empty that they deliberately identified themselves with a creature of odious character in order in some small circle to give themselves a petty notoriety.

Sometimes the author takes a very commonplace person and from him invents a character who is noble, self-controlled and courageous. He has seen in that person a significance that had escaped those he lived with. Then oddly enough the original goes unrecognized; it is only when you show somebody with faults or ridiculous foibles that a name is at once assigned. I have been forced to conclude from this that we know our friends by their defects rather than by their merits. The author seldom has the wish to give offence and he uses what means he can to protect his originals; he puts the persons of his invention in different places, gives them another means of livelihood, situates them perhaps in a different class; what he cannot so easily do is to change their appearance. The physical traits of a man influence his character and contrariwise his character is expressed, at least in the rough, in his appearance. You cannot make a tall man short and otherwise keep him the same. A man's height gives him a different outlook on his environment and so changes his character. Nor to cover your tracks can you make a little brunette into a massive blonde. You have to leave them very much as they are or you will lose what it was that moved you to draw a character from them. But no one has the right to take a character in a book and say, this is meant for me. All he may say is, I provided the suggestion for this character. If he has any common sense he will be interested rather than vexed; and the author's inventiveness and intuition may suggest to him things about himself that it is useful for him to know.

LVIII

I HAVE no illusions about my literary position. There are but two important critics in my own country who have troubled to take me seriously and when clever young men write essays about contemporary fiction they never think of considering me. I do not resent it. It is very natural. I have never been a propagandist. The reading public has enormously increased during the last thirty years and there is a large mass of ignorant people who want knowledge that can be acquired with little labour. They have thought that they were learning something when they read novels in which the characters delivered their views on the burning topics of the day. A bit of love-making thrown in here and there made the information they were given sufficiently palatable. The novel was regarded as a convenient pulpit for the dissemination of ideas and a good many novelists were willing enough to look upon themselves as leaders of thought. The novels they wrote were journalism rather than fiction. They had a news value. Their disadvantage was that after a little while they were as unreadable as last week's paper. But the demand of this great new public for knowledge has of late given rise to the production of a number of books in which subjects of common interest, science, education, social welfare and I know not what, are treated in non-technical language. Their success has been very great and has killed the propaganda novel. But it is evident that while its vogue lasted it

seemed much more significant and so offered a better subject of discourse than the novel of character or adventure.

The intelligent critics, the more serious novel readers, have since then given most of their attention to the writers who seemed to offer something new in technique, and this is very comprehensible, for the novelties they presented gave a sort of freshness to well-worn material and were a fruitful matter of discussion.

It seems strange that so much attention has been paid to these things. The method that Henry James devised and brought to a high degree of perfection of telling his story through the sensibilities of an observer who had some part in its action was an ingenious dodge that gave the dramatic effect he sought in fiction, a verisimilitude grateful to an author much influenced by the French naturalists and a means of getting round some of the difficulties of the novelist who takes up the attitude of an all-seeing and all-wise narrator. What this observer did not know could be left conveniently mysterious. It was, however, only a slight variation from the autobiographical form that has many of the same advantages, and to speak of it as though it were a great æsthetic discovery is somewhat absurd. Of the other experiments that have been made the most important is the use of the stream of thought. Writers have always been attracted by the philosophers who had an emotional value and who were not too hard to understand. They were taken in turn by Schopenhauer, Nietzsche and Bergson. It was inevitable that psychoanalysis should captivate their fancy. It had great possibilities for the novelist. He knew how much he owed to his own subconscious for the best of what he wrote and it was tempting to explore greater depths of character by an imaginative picture of the subconscious of the persons of his invention. It was a clever and amusing trick, but nothing more. When writers, instead of using it as an occasional device for a particular purpose, ironical, dramatic or explanatory, made it the basis of their work it proved tedious. I conjecture that what is useful in this and similar devices will be absorbed into the general technique of fiction, but that the works that introduced them will soon lose their interest. It seems to have escaped the attention of those who have been taken by these curious experiments that the matter treated of in the books in which they are made use of is of an extreme triviality. It almost looks as though their authors had been driven to these contrivances by an uneasy consciousness of their own emptiness. The persons they describe with all this ingenuity are intrinsically uninteresting and the subjects at issue unimportant. This might be expected. For the artist is absorbed by his technique only when his theme is of no pressing interest to him. When he is obsessed by his topic he has not much time over to think of the artfulness of his presentation. So in the seventeenth century the writers, exhausted by the mental effort of the Renaissance and prevented by the tyranny of kings and the domination of the church from occupying themselves with the great issues of life, turned their minds to gongorism, concettism and such-like toys. It may be that the interest that has been taken during recent years in every form of technical experiment in the arts points to the fact that our civilization is crumbling; the subjects that seemed important to the nineteenth century have lost their interest, and artists do not yet see what the great issues are that will affect the generation which will create the civilization that is in course of displacing our own.

LIX

I LOOK upon it as very natural then that the world of letters should have attached no great importance to my work. In the drama I have found myself at home in the traditional moulds. As a writer of fiction I go back, through innumerable generations, to the teller of tales round the fire in the cavern that sheltered neolithic men. I have had some sort of story to tell and it has interested me to tell it. To me it has been a sufficient object in itself. It has been my misfortune that for some time now a story has been despised by the intelligent. I have read a good many books on the art of fiction and all ascribe very small value to the plot. (In passing I should like to say that I cannot understand the sharp distinction some clever theorists make between story and plot. A plot is merely the pattern on which the story is arranged.) From these books you would judge that it is only a hindrance to the intelligent author and a concession that he makes to the stupid demands of the public. Indeed, sometimes you might think that the best novelist is the essayist, and that the only perfect short stories have been written by Charles Lamb and Hazlitt.

But the delight in listening to stories is as natural to human nature as the delight in looking at the dancing and miming out of which drama arose. That it exists unimpaired is shown by the vogue of the detective novel. The most intellectual persons read them, with condescension of course, but they read them, and why, if not because the psychological, the pedagogic, the psycho-analytic novels which alone their minds approve do not give them the satisfaction of this particular need? There are a number of clever writers who, with all sorts of good things in their heads to say and a gift for creating living people, do not know what on earth to do with them when they have created them. They cannot invent a plausible story. Like all writers (and in all writers there is a certain amount of humbug) they make a merit of their limitations and either tell the reader that he can imagine for himself what happens or else berate him for wanting to know. They claim that in life stories are not finished, situations are not rounded off and loose ends are left hanging. This is not always true, for at least death finishes all our stories; but even if it were it would not be a good argument.

For the novelist claims to be an artist and the artist does not copy life, he makes an arrangement out of it to suit his own purposes. Just as the painter thinks with his brush and paints the novelist thinks with his story; his view of life, though he may be unconscious of it, his personality, exist as a series of human actions. When you look back on the art of the past you can hardly fail to notice that artists have seldom attached great value to realism. On the whole they have used nature to make a formal decoration and they have only copied it directly from time to time when their imagination had taken them so far from it that a return was felt necessary. In painting and sculpture it might even be argued that a very close approximation to reality has always announced the decadence of a school. In the sculpture of Phidias you see already the dullness of the Apollo Belvedere and in Raphael's Miracle at Bolsano the vapidity of Bouguereau. Then art can only gain new vigour by forcing on nature a new convention.

But that is by the way.

It is a natural desire in the reader to want to know what happens to the people in whom his interest has been aroused and the plot is the means by which you gratify this desire. A good story is obviously a difficult thing to invent, but its difficulty is a poor reason for despising it. It should have coherence and sufficient probability for the needs of the theme; it should be of a nature to display the development of character, which is the chief concern of fiction at the present day, and it should have completeness, so that when it is finally unfolded no more questions can be asked about the persons who took part in it. It should have like Aristotle's tragedy a beginning, a middle and an end. The chief use of a plot is one that many people do not seem to have noticed. It is a line to direct the reader's interest. That is possibly the most important thing in fiction, for it is by direction of interest that the author carries the reader along from page to page and it is by direction of interest that he induces in him the mood he desires. The author always loads his dice, but he must never let the reader see that he has done so, and by the manipulation of his plot he can engage the reader's attention so that he does not perceive what violence has been done him. I am not writing a technical treatise on the novel, so I need not enumerate the various devices that novelists have used to achieve this. But how efficacious this direction of interest may be and how injurious its neglect is well shown in *Sense and Sensibility* and in *L'Educa-* *tion Sentimentale*. Jane Austen leads the reader so firmly along the line of the simple story that he does not stop to reflect that Elinor is a prig, Marianne a fool, and the three men lifeless dummies. Flaubert, aiming at a rigid objectivity, directs the reader's interest so little that he is perfectly indifferent to the fortunes of the various characters. This makes the novel very difficult to read. I cannot think of another that has so many merits and leaves so shadowy an impression.

LX

In my twenties the critics said I was brutal, in my thirties they said I was flippant, in my forties they said I was cynical, in my fifties they said I was competent, and now in my sixties they say I am superficial. I have gone my way, following the course I had mapped out for myself, and trying with my works to fill out the pattern I looked for. I think authors are unwise who do not read criticisms. It is salutary to train oneself to be no more affected by censure than by praise; for of course it is easy to shrug one's shoulders when one finds oneself described as a genius, but not so easy to be unconcerned when one is treated as a nincompoop. The history of criticism is there to show that contemporary criticism is fallible. It is a nice point to decide how far the author should consider it and how far ignore it. And such is the diversity of opinion that it is very difficult for an author to arrive at any conclusion about his merit. In England there is a natural tendency to despise the novel. The autobiography of an insignificant politician, the life of a royal courtesan will receive serious critical considera- tion, whereas half-a-dozen novels will be reviewed in a bunch by a reviewer who is concerned only too often to be amusing at their expense. The fact is simply that the English are more interested in works of information than in works of art. This makes it difficult for the novelist to get from criticisms of his work anything that will be useful to his own development.

It is a great misfortune to English letters that we have not had in this century a critic of the class, say, of Sainte-Beuve, Matthew Arnold or even Brunetière. It is true that he would not have occupied himself much with current literature, and if we may judge by the three I have mentioned, had he done so it would have been of no direct service to contemporary writers. For Sainte-Beuve, as we know, was too envious of a form of success he hankered after, but never achieved, to treat his contemporaries with fairness; and Matthew Arnold's taste was so much at fault when he dealt with French writers of his day that there is no reason to suppose it would have been any better if he had dealt with English ones. Brunetière had no tolerance; he measured writers by hard-and-fast rules and was incapable of seeing merit in those who had aims with which he did not sympathize. His force of character gave him an influence that his talents did not warrant. But notwithstanding, writers benefit by a critic who is gravely concerned with literature; even if they resent him they may be incited by antagonism to a clearer definition of their own aims. He can provoke in them an excitement that calls them to more conscious effort and his example urges them to take their art with a more intense seriousness.

In one of his dialogues Plato seemingly has tried to show the impossibility of criticism; but in fact he has only shown to what extravagance the Socratic method may sometimes lead. There is one sort of criticism that is evidently futile. This is that which is written by the critic to compensate himself for humiliations he has suffered in his early youth. Criticism affords him a means of regaining his self-esteem. Because at school, unable to adapt himself to the standards of that narrow world, he has been kicked and cuffed, he will when grown up cuff and kick in his turn in order to assuage his wounded feelings. His interest is in his reaction to the work he is considering, not in the reaction it has to him.

There can seldom have been a greater need than now of a critic of authority, for the arts are at sixes and sevens. We see composers telling stories, painters philosophizing, and novelists preaching sermons; we see poets impatient with their own harmony trying to fit with their verse the other harmony of prose, and we see the writers of prose trying to force on it the rhythms of verse. Someone is badly wanted to define once more the characters peculiar to the several arts and to point out to those who go astray that their experiments can lead only to their own confusion. It is too much to expect that anyone may be found who can speak with equal competence in all the arts; but, the demand producing the supply, we may still hope that one of these days a critic will arise to ascend the throne once occupied by Sainte-Beuve and Matthew Arnold. He could do much. I have read lately two or three books in which a claim is made to form an exact science of criticism. They have not convinced me that such a thing is possible. Criticism to my mind is a personal matter, but there is nothing against that if the critic has a great personality. It is dangerous for him to look upon his activity as creative. His business is to guide, to appraise, and to point to new avenues of creation, but if he looks upon himself as creative he will be more occupied with creation, the most enthralling of human activities, than with the functions proper to him. It is perhaps well for him to have written a play, a novel and some verse, for thus as in no other way can he acquire the technique of letters; but he cannot be a great critic unless he has realized that to create is not his affair. One of the reasons why current criticism is so useless is that it is done as a side-issue by creative writers. It is only natural that they should think the sort of thing they do the thing best worth doing. The great critic should have a sympathy as wide as his knowledge is universal. It should be grounded not on a general indifference, such as makes men tolerant of things they care nothing about, but on an active delight in diversity. He must be a psychologist and a physiologist, for he must know how the basic elements of literature are related to the minds and bodies of men; and he must be a philosopher, for from philosophy he will learn serenity, impartiality, and the transitoriness of human things. He must be familiar not only with the literature of his native land. With standards founded on the literature of the past, and studious of contemporary literature in other countries, he will see clearly the trend that literature in its evolution is pursuing and so be enabled profitably to direct that of his own countrymen. He must support himself on tradition, for tradition is the expression of the inevitable idiosyncrasies of a nation's literature, but he must do everything he can to encourage its development in its natural direction. Tradition is a guide and not a jailer. He must have patience, firmness and enthusiasm. Each book

he reads should be a new and thrilling adventure; he judges it by the universality of his knowledge and the strength of his character. In fact the great critic must be a great man. He must be great enough to recognize with good-humoured resignation that his work, though so important, can have but an ephemeral value; for his merit is that he responds to the needs of, and points the way to, his own generation. A new generation arises with other needs, a new way stretches before it; he has nothing more to say and is thrown with all his works into the dust-heap.

To spend his life to such an end can only be worth his while if he thinks literature one of the most important of human pursuits.

LXI

THAT is a claim that the author has always made and to this he has added another claim: he has asserted that he was not as other men and in consequence not amenable to their rules. Other men have received it with obloquy, derision and contempt. This he has met in different ways according to his idiosyncrasy. Sometimes he has flaunted his difference from what he was inclined to call the common herd by wilful eccentricity and to *épater le bourgeois* has paraded the red waistcoat of Théophile Gautier or, like Gérard de Nerval, led a lobster tied by a pink ribbon down the street; sometimes he has taken an ironic pleasure in pretending to be the same as every one else and with Browning has dressed the poet within him in the likeness of a prosperous banker. It may be that we are all of us a bundle of mutually contra-

dictory selves, but the writer, the artist, is deeply conscious of it. With other men, the life they lead makes one side of them predominant, so that, except perhaps in the depths of the subconscious, it ends by being the whole man. But the painter, the writer, the saint, is always looking in himself for new facets; he is bored at repeating himself and seeks, though it may be without actually knowing it, to prevent himself from becoming one-sided. He never gets the opportunity to grow into a self-consistent, coherent creature.

Other men have been outraged on discovering, as they so often have, the discrepancy between the artist's life and his work. They have not been able to reconcile Beethoven's idealism with his meanness of spirit, Wagner's heavenly rapture with his selfishness and dishonesty, Cervantes' moral obliquity with his tenderness and magnanimity. Sometimes, in their indignation, they have sought to persuade themselves that the work of such men could not possess the value they thought. When it has been brought to their knowledge that great and pure poets had left behind them a large body of obscene verse they have been horrified. They have had an uneasy feeling that the whole thing was a sham. "What arrant humbugs these people are!" they say. But the point of the writer is that he is not one man but many. It is because he is many that he can create many and the measure of his greatness is the number of selves that he comprises. When he fashions a character that does not carry conviction it is because there is in himself nothing of that person; he has had to fall back on observation, and so has only described, not begotten. The writer does not feel with; he feels in. It is not sympathy that he has, that too often results in sentimentality; he has what the psychologists call empathy. It is because Shakespeare had this to so great a degree that he was at once the most living and the least sentimental of authors. I think Goethe was the first writer to grow conscious of this multiple personality and it troubled him all his life. He was always comparing the writer that he was with the man and he could not quite reconcile the discongruity. But the end of the artist and the end of other men are different, for the end of the artist is production while the end of other men is right action. And so the artist's attitude to life is in a certain way peculiar to himself. The psychologists tell us that with the ordinary man an image is less vivid than a sensation. It is an attenuated experience that serves to give information about objects of sense and in the world of sense is a guide to

action. His day-dreams satisfy emotional needs and fulfil desires that in the world of affairs are frustrated. But they are pale shadows of real life and at the back of his mind is the awareness that the demands of the world of sense have another validity. To the writer this is not so. The images, free ideas that throng his mind, are not guides but materials for action. They have all the vividness of sensation. His day-dreams are so significant to him that it is the world of sense that is shadowy and he has to reach out for it by an effort of will. His castles in Spain are no baseless fabric, but real castles that he lives in.

The artist's egoism is outrageous: it must be; he is by nature a solipsist and the world exists only for him to exercise upon it his powers of creation. He partakes of life only with part of him and never feels the common emotions of men with his whole being, for however urgent the necessity he is an observer as well as an actor. It often makes him seem heartless. Women with their shrewd sense are on their guard against him; they are attracted by him, but instinctively feel that they can never completely dominate him, which is their desire, for they know that somehow he escapes them. Has not Goethe, that great lover, himself told us how he composed verses in the arms of his beloved and with singing fingers softly tapped the beat of his hexameters on her shapely back? The artist is ill to live with. He can be perfectly sincere in his creative emotion and yet there is someone else within him who is capable of cocking a snook at its exercise. He is not dependable.

But the gods never make any of their gifts without adding to it a drawback and this multiplicity of the writer that enables him, like the gods, to create human beings prevents him from achieving perfect truth in their creation. Realism is relative. The most realistic writer by the direction of his interests falsifies his creatures. He sees them through his own eyes. He makes them more self-conscious than they really are. He makes them more reflective and more complicated. He throws himself into them, trying to make them ordinary men, but he never quite succeeds; for the peculiarity that gives him his talent and makes him a writer forever prevents him from knowing exactly what ordinary men are. It is not truth he attains, but merely a transposition of his own personality. And the greater his talent, the more powerful his individuality, the more fantastic is the picture of life he draws. It has sometimes seemed to me that if posterity wants to know what the world of today was like it will not go to those writers whose idiosyncrasy has impressed our contemporaries, but to the mediocre ones whose ordinariness has allowed them to describe their surroundings with a greater faithfulness. I do not mention them since, even though they may be assured of the appreciation of after ages, people do not like to be labelled as mediocre. But I think it may be admitted that one gets the impression of a truer picture of life in the novels of Anthony Trollope than in those of Charles Dickens.

LXII

SOMETIMES the writer must ask himself whether what he has written has any value except to himself and the question is perhaps urgent now when the world seems, at least to us who live in it, in such a condition of unrest and wretchedness as it has not often been in before. For me the question has had a special import for I have never wished to be nothing but a writer; I have wished to live life completely. I have been uneasily conscious that it was a duty I owed myself to take some part, however small, in the business of the common weal. My natural inclination has been to keep aloof from every kind of public activity and it has been with the greatest reluctance that I have even served on committees formed to effect some aim of passing interest. Thinking that not the whole of life was long enough to learn to write well, I have been unwilling to give to other activities time that I so much needed to achieve the purpose I had in mind. I have never been able intimately to persuade myself that anything else mattered. Notwithstanding, when men in millions are living on the borderline of starvation, when freedom in great parts of the inhabited globe is dying or dead, when a terrible war has been succeeded by years during which happiness has been out of the reach of the great mass of the human race, when men are distraught because they can see no value in life and the hopes that had enabled them for so many centuries to support its misery seem illusory; it is hard not to ask oneself whether it is anything but futility to write plays and stories and novels. The only answer I can think of is that some of us are so made that there is nothing else we can do. We do not write because we want to; we write because we must. There may be other things in the world that more pressingly want doing: we must liberate our souls of the burden of creation. We must go on though Rome burns. Others may despise us because we do not lend a hand with a bucket of water; we cannot help it; we do not know how to handle a bucket. Besides, the conflagration thrills us and charges our mind with phrases.

From time to time, however, writers have engaged in politics. Its effects on them as writers has been injurious. I have not noticed that their counsel has had much influence on the conduct of affairs. The only exception I can recall is Disraeli; but in his case, it is not unfair to say, writing was not an end in itself, but a means to political advancement. At the present day, living as we do in an age of specialization, I have a notion that on the whole the cobbler does best to stick to his last.

Because I had heard that Dryden had learnt to write English from his study of Tillotson, I read certain passages of this author and I came across a piece that gave me some consolation in this matter. It ran as follows: "We ought to be glad, when those that are fit for government, and called to it, are willing to take the burden of it upon them; yea, and to be very thankful to them too, that they will be at the pains, and can have the patience, to govern and live publicly. Therefore it is happy for the world that there are some who are born and bred up to it; and that custom hath made it easy, or at least tolerable to them. . . . The advantage which men have by a more devout and retired and contemplative life, is, that they are not distracted about many things; their minds and affections are set upon one thing; and the whole stream and force of their affections run one way. All their thoughts and endeavours are united in one great end and design, which makes their life all of a piece and to be consistent with itself throughout."

LXIII

When I started this book I warned the reader that perhaps the only thing of which I was certain was that I was certain of nothing else. I was trying to put my thoughts on sundry subjects in order and I asked no one to agree with me in my opinions. On revising what I have written, I have cut out the words, I think, in a great many places because, though they came to my pen naturally, I found them tedious, but they are to be understood as qualifying my every statement. And now that I come to this last section of my book, I am constrained more anxiously than ever to repeat that what I give are my own private convictions. It may be that they are superficial. It may be that some of them are contradictory. It is unlikely that surmises that are the outcome of thoughts, feelings, and desires built up out of all sorts of haphazard experiences and coloured by a particular personality should fit with the logical precision of a proposition of Euclid. When I wrote of the drama and of fiction I wrote of what by practice I had some cognizance of, but now that I come to deal with matters of which philosophers treat I have no more special knowledge than can be acquired by any man who has lived for many years a busy and varied life.

Life also is a school of philosophy, but it is like one of those modern kindergartens in which children are left to their own devices and work only at the subjects that arouse their interest. Their attention is drawn to what seems to have a meaning for them and they take no notice of what does not immediately concern them. In psychological laboratories rats are trained to find their way through a maze and presently by trial and error they learn the path that leads to the food they seek. In the matters with which I now occupy myself I am like one of these rats scurrying along the pathways of the complicated maze, but I do not know that it has a centre where I shall find what I seek. For all I know all the alleys are blind.

I was introduced to philosophy by Kuno Fischer whose lectures I attended when I was at Heidelberg. He had a great reputation there and he was giving that winter a course of lectures on Schopenhauer. They were crowded and one had to queue up early in order to get a good seat. He was a dapper, short, stoutish man, neat in his dress, with a bullet head, white hair *en brosse* and a red face. His little eyes were quick and shining. He had a funny, flattened snub nose that looked as if it had been bashed in, and you would have been much more likely to take him for an old prize-fighter than for a philosopher. He was a humourist; he had indeed written a book on wit which I read at the time, but which I have completely forgotten, and every now and then a great guffaw broke from his audience of students as he made a joke. His voice was powerful and he was a vivid, impressive and exciting speaker. I was too young and too ignorant to understand much of what he said, but I got a very clear impression of Schopenhauer's odd and original personal-

ity and a confused feeling of the dramatic value and the romantic quality of his system. I hesitate to make any statement after so many years, but I have a notion that Kuno Fischer treated it as a work of art rather than as a serious contribution to metaphysics.

Since then I have read a great deal of philosophy. I have found it very good reading. Indeed, of the various great subjects that afford reading matter to the person for whom reading is a need and a delight it is the most varied, the most copious and the most satisfying. Ancient Greece is thrilling, but from this point of view there is not enough in it; a time comes when you have read the little that remains of its literature and all of significance that has been written about it. The Italian Renaissance is fascinating too, but the subject, comparatively, is small; the ideas that informed it were few, and you get tired of its art which has been long since drained of its creative value so that you are left only with grace, charm and symmetry (qualities of which you can have enough) and you get tired of its men, whose versatility falls into too uniform a pattern. You can go on reading about the Italian Renaissance forever, but your interest fails before the material is exhausted. The French Revolution is another subject that may well engage the attention and it has the advantage that its significance is actual. It is close to us in point of time so that with a very small effort of imagination we can put ourselves into the men who made it. They are almost contemporaries. And what they did and what they thought affect the lives we lead today; after a fashion we are all descendants of the French Revolution. And the material is abundant. The documents that relate to it are countless and the last thing has never been said about it. You can always find something fresh and interesting to read. But it does not satisfy. The art and literature it directly produced are negligible so that you are driven to the study of the men who made it, and the more you read about them the more are you dismayed by their pettiness and vulgarity. The actors in one of the greatest dramas in the world's history were pitifully inadequate to their parts. You turn away from the subject at last with a faint disgust.

But metaphysics never lets you down. You can never come to the end of it. It is as various as the soul of man. It has greatness, for it deals with nothing less than the whole of knowledge. It treats of the universe, of God and immortality, of the properties of human reason and the end and purpose of life, of the power and limitations of man; and if it cannot answer the questions that assail him on his journey through this dark and mysterious world it persuades him to support his ignorance with good humour. It teaches resignation and inculcates courage. It appeals to the imagination as well as to the intelligence; and to the amateur, much more, I suppose, than to the professional it affords matter for that reverie which is the most delicious pleasure with which man can beguile his idleness.

Since, inspired by Kuno Fischer's lectures, I began to read Schopenhauer I have read pretty well all the most important works of the great classical philosophers. Though there is in them a great deal that I did not understand, and perhaps I did not even understand as much as I thought, I have read them with passionate interest. The only one who has consistently bored me is Hegel. This is doubtless my own fault, for his influence on philosophical thought during the nineteenth century proves his

importance. I found him terribly long-winded and I could never reconcile myself to the jugglery with which it seemed to me he proved whatever he had a mind to. Perhaps I was prejudiced against him by the scorn with which Schopenhauer always spoke of him. But to the others, from Plato onwards, I surrendered myself, one after the other, with the pleasure of a traveller adventuring into an unknown country. I did not read critically, but as I might have read a novel, for the excitement and delight of it. (I have already confessed that I read a novel not for instruction, but for pleasure. I crave my reader's indulgence.) A student of character, I got an immense amount of pleasure out of the self-revelation which these various writers offered to my survey. I saw the man behind his philosophy and I was exalted by the nobility I found in some and amused by the queerness I discerned in others. I felt a wonderful exhilaration when I dizzily followed Plotinus in his flight from the alone to the alone, and though I have learnt since that Descartes drew preposterous conclusions from his effective premiss I was entranced by the lucidity of his expression. To read him was like swimming in a lake so clear that you could see the bottom; that crystalline water was wonderfully refreshing. I look upon my first reading of Spinoza as one of the signal experiences of my life. It filled me with just that feeling of majesty and exulting power that one has at the sight of a great mountain range.

And when I came to the English philosophers, with perhaps a slight prejudice, for it had been impressed upon me in Germany that, with the possible exception of Hume, they were quite negligible and Hume's only importance was that Kant had demolished him, I found that besides being philosophers they were uncommonly good writers. And though they might not be very great thinkers, of this I could not presume to judge, they were certainly very curious men. I should think that few could read Hobbes' *Leviathan* without being taken by the gruff, downright John Bullishness of his personality and surely no one could read Berkeley's *Dialogues* without being ravished by the charm of that delightful bishop. And though it may be true that Kant made hay of Hume's theories it would be impossible, I think, to write philosophy with more elegance, urbanity and clearness. They all, and Locke too for the matter of that, wrote English that the student of style could do much worse than study. Before I start writing a novel I read *Candide* over again so that I may have in the back of my mind the touchstone of that lucidity, grace and wit; I have a notion that it would not hurt the English philosophers of our

own day if before they set about a work they submitted themselves to the discipline of reading Hume's *Inquiry Concerning the Human Understanding*. For it is not invariably that they write now with distinction. It may be that their thoughts are so much more subtle than those of their predecessors that they are obliged to use a technical vocabulary of their own invention; but it is a dangerous procedure, and when they deal with matters that are of pressing concern to all reflective persons, one can only regret that they cannot make their meaning so plain that all who read may understand. They tell me that Professor Whitehead has the most ingenious brain of anyone who is now engaged in philosophic thought. It seems to me a pity then that he should not always take pains to make his sense clear. It was a good rule of Spinoza's to indicate the nature of things by words whose customary meanings should not be altogether opposed to the meanings he desired to bestow upon them.

LXIV

THERE is no reason why philosophers should not be also men of letters. But to write well does not come by instinct; it is an art that demands arduous study. The philosopher does not speak only to other philosophers and to undergraduates working for a degree; he speaks also to the men of letters, politicians and reflective persons who directly mould the ideas of the coming generation. They, naturally enough, are taken by a philosophy that is striking and not too difficultly assimilated. We all know how the philosophy of Nietzsche has affected some parts of

the world and few would assert that its influence has been other than disastrous. It has prevailed, not by such profundity of thought as it may have, but by a vivid style and an effective form. The philosopher who will not take the trouble to make himself clear shows only that he thinks his thought of no more than academic value.

It has, however, been a consolation to me to discover that sometimes even the professional philosophers do not understand one another. Bradley frequently confesses that he is at a loss to understand what someone with whom he is arguing means and Professor Whitehead in one place states that something Bradley says is beyond his comprehension. When the most eminent philosophers cannot always understand one another the layman may well feel resigned if he often does not understand them. Of course metaphysics is difficult. One must expect that. The layman walks a tightrope without a pole to balance him and he must be thankful if he can scramble somehow to safety. The feat is exciting enough to make it worth his while to risk a tumble.

I was much disconcerted by the claim that I found here and there advanced that philosophy was the province of the higher mathematicians; and though it seemed hard to me to believe that, if knowledge, as the doctrine of evolution suggests, has been developed for practical reasons in the struggle for existence, the sum total of it, something that is essential to the well-being of man in general, could be reserved only for a small body of men who are gifted by nature with a rare faculty, I might very well have been deterred from pursuing my pleasant studies in this direction, since I have no head for mathematics, if I had not luckily come across an admission of Bradley's that he knew very little of this abstruse science. And Bradley was no mean philosopher. We know that the sense of taste differs in various persons; but without it men would perish. It seems as unlikely that you may not hold reasonable theories about the universe and man's place in it, the mystery of evil and the meaning of reality, unless you are a mathematical physicist, as that you cannot enjoy a bottle of wine unless you have the trained sensibility that enables you without error to ascribe a year to twenty different clarets.

For philosophy is not a subject that has to do only with philosophers and mathematicians. It is one that concerns us all. It is true that most of us accept our opinions on the matters with which it deals at second hand and most do not know that they have any philosophy at all. But it is implicit even in the most thoughtless. The old woman who first said, "it's no good crying over spilt milk" was a philosopher in her way. For what did she mean by this except that regret was useless? A complete system of philosophy is implied. The determinist thinks that you cannot take a step in life that is not motivated by what you are at the moment; and you are not only your muscles, your nerves, your entrails and your brain; you are your habits, your opinions and your ideas. However little you may be aware of them, however contradictory, unreasonable and prejudiced they may be, they are there, influencing your actions and reactions. Even if you have never put them into words they are your philosophy. Perhaps it is well enough that most people should leave this unformulated. It is hardly thoughts they have, at least not conscious thoughts, it is a kind of vague feeling, a sort of experience like that muscular sense that the physiologists not so long ago discovered, which they have absorbed from the notions current in the society in which they live and which has been faintly modified by their own experience. They lead their ordered lives and this confused body of ideas and feelings is enough. Since it includes something of the wisdom of the ages, it is adequate for the ordinary purposes of the ordinary life. But I have sought to make a pattern of mine and from an early age tried to find out what were the elements I had to deal with. I wanted to get what knowledge I could about the general structure of the universe; I wanted to make up my mind whether I had to consider only this life or a life to come; I wanted to discover whether I was a free agent or whether my feeling that I could mould myself according to my will was an illusion; I wanted to know whether life had any meaning or whether it was I that must strive to give it one. So in a desultory way I began to read.

LXV

THE first subject that attracted my attention was religion. For it seemed to me of the greatest importance to decide whether this world I lived in was the only one I had to reckon with or whether I must look upon it as no more than a place of trial which was to prepare me for a life to come. When I wrote *Of Human Bondage* I gave a chapter to my hero's loss of the faith in which he had been brought up. The book was read in typescript by a very clever woman who at that time was good enough to be interested in me. She told me that this chapter was inadequate; I rewrote it; but I do not think I much improved it. For it described my own experience and I have no doubt that my reasons for coming to the conclusion I came to were inadequate. They were the reasons of an ignorant boy. They were of the heart rather than of the head. When my parents died I went to live with my uncle who was a clergyman. He was a childless man of fifty, and I am sure that it was a great nuisance to have the charge of a small boy thrust upon him. He read prayers morning and evening, and we went to church twice on Sundays. Sunday was the busy day. My uncle always said that he was the only man in his parish who worked seven days a week. In point of fact he was incredibly idle and left the work of his parish to his curate and his churchwardens. But I was im-

pressionable and soon became very religious. I accepted what I was taught, both in my uncle's vicarage and afterwards at school, with unquestioning trust.

There was one point that immediately affected me. I had not been long at school before I discovered, through the ridicule to which I was exposed and the humiliations I suffered, how great a misfortune it was to me that I stammered; and I had read in the Bible that if you had faith you could move mountains. My uncle assured me that it was a literal fact. One night, when I was going back to school next day, I prayed to God with all my might that he would take away my impediment; and, such was my faith, I went to sleep quite certain that when I awoke next morning I should be able to speak like everybody else. I pictured to myself the surprise of the boys (I was still at a preparatory school) when they found that I no longer stammered. I woke full of exultation and it was a real, a terrible shock, when I discovered that I stammered as badly as ever.

I grew older. I went to the King's School. The masters were clergymen; they were stupid and irascible. They were impatient of my stammering and if they did not ignore me completely, which I preferred, they bullied me. They seemed to think it was my fault that I stammered. Presently I discovered that my uncle was a selfish man who cared for nothing but his own comfort. The neighbouring clergy sometimes came to the vicarage. One of them was fined in the county court for starving his cows; another had to resign his living because he was convicted of drunkenness. I was taught that we lived in the presence of God and that the chief business of man was to save his soul. I could not help seeing that none of these clergymen practised what they preached. Fervent though my faith was, I had been terribly bored by all the church-going that was forced upon me, both at home and at school, and on going to Germany I welcomed the freedom that enabled me to stay away. But two or three times out of curiosity I went to High Mass at the Jesuit Church in Heidelberg. Though my uncle had a natural sympathy for Catholics (he was a High Churchman and at election time they painted on the garden fence, "This way to Rome"), he had no doubt that they would frizzle in hell. He believed implicitly in eternal punishment. He hated the dissenters in his parish and indeed thought it a monstrous thing that the state tolerated them. His consolation was that they too would suffer eternal damnation. Heaven was reserved for the members of the Church of England. I accepted it as a great mercy of God that I had been bred in that communion. It was as wonderful as being born an Englishman.

But when I went to Germany I discovered that the Germans were just as proud of being Germans as I was proud of being English. I heard them say that the English did not understand music and that Shakespeare was only appreciated in Germany. They spoke of the English as a nation of shopkeepers and had no doubt in their minds that as artists, men of science and philosophers they were greatly

superior. It shook me. And now at High Mass in Heidelberg I could not but notice that the students, who filled the church to its doors, seemed very devout. They had, indeed, all the appearance of believing in their religion as sincerely as I believed in mine. It was queer that they could, for of course I knew that theirs was false and mine was true. I think I can have had by nature no strong religious feeling, or else in the intolerance of my youth I must have been so shocked by the contrast of the practice with the professions of the various clergymen with whom I had to do, that I was already inclined to doubt; otherwise I can hardly think that such a simple little notion as then occurred to me could have had consequences that were to me of so much importance. It struck me that I might very well have been born in South Germany, and then I should naturally have been brought up as a Catholic. I found it very hard that thus through no fault of my own I should have been condemned to everlasting torment. My ingenuous nature revolted at the injustice. The next step was easy; I came to the conclusion that it could not matter a row of pins what one believed; God could not condemn people just because they were Spaniards or Hottentots. I might have stopped there and if I had been less ignorant adopted some form of deism like that which was current in the eighteenth century. But the beliefs that had been instilled into me hung together and when one of them came to seem outrageous the others participated in its fate. The whole horrible structure, based not on the love of God but on the fear of Hell, tumbled down like a house of cards.

With my mind at all events I ceased to believe in God; I felt the exhilaration of a new freedom. But we do not believe only with our minds; in some deep recess of my soul there lingered still the old dread of hell-fire, and for long my exultation was tempered by the shadow of that ancestral anxiety. I no longer believed in God; I still, in my bones, believed in the Devil.

LXVI

It was this fear that I sought to banish when, becoming a medical student, I entered a new world. I read a great many books. They told me that man was a machine subject to mechanical laws; and when the machine ran down that was the end of him. I saw men die at the hospital and my startled sensibilities confirmed what my books had taught me. I was satisfied to believe that religion and the idea of God were constructions that the human race had evolved as a convenience for living, and represented something that had at one time, and for all I was prepared to say still had, value for the survival of the species, but that must be historically explained and corresponded to nothing real. I called myself an agnostic, but in my blood and my bones I looked upon God as a hypothesis that a reasonable man must reject.

But if there was no God who could consign me to eternal flames and no soul that could be thus consigned, if I was the plaything of mechanical forces and the struggle for life was the impelling force, I could not see that there was any meaning in good such as I had been taught it. I began to read Ethics. I waded conscientiously through many formidable tomes. I came to the conclusion that man aimed at nothing but his own pleasure and that when he sacrificed himself for others it was only an illusion that led him to believe that he was seeking anything but his own gratification.

And since the future was uncertain it was only common sense to seize every pleasure that the moment offered. I decided that right and wrong were merely words and that the rules of conduct were no more than conventions that men had set up to serve their own selfish purposes. The free man had no reason to follow them except in so far as they suited his convenience. Having then an epigrammatic turn, and epigrams being the fashion, I put my conviction into a phrase and said to myself: follow your inclinations with due regard to the policeman round the corner. By the time I was twenty-four I had constructed a complete system of philosophy. It rested on two principles: The Relativity of Things and The Circumferentiality of Man. I have learnt since that the first of these was not a very original discovery. It may be that the other was profound, but though I have racked my brains I cannot for the life of me remember what on earth it meant.

On a certain occasion I read a little story that greatly took my fancy. It is to be found in one of the volumes of Anatole France's *La Vie Littéraire*. It is many years since I read it, but it has remained in my recollection as follows: a young king of the East, anxious on his ascent of the throne to rule his kingdom justly, sent for the wise men of his country and ordered them to gather the wisdom of the world in books so that he might read them and learn how best to conduct himself. They went away and after thirty years returned with a string of camels laden with five thousand tomes. Here, they told him, is collected everything that wise men have learnt of the history and destiny of man. But the king was immersed in affairs of state and could not read so many books, so he bade them go and condense this knowledge into a smaller number. Fifteen years later they returned and their camels carried but five hundred works. In these volumes, they told the king, you will find all the wisdom of the world. But there were still too many and the king sent them away again. Ten years passed and they came back and now they brought no more than fifty books. But the king was old and tired. He had no time now even to read so few and he ordered his wise men once more to reduce their number and in a single volume give him an epitome of human knowledge so that he might learn at last what it was so important for him to know. They went away and set to work and in five years returned. They were old men when for the last time they came and laid the result of their labours in the king's hands, but now the king was dying and he had no time any more to read even the one book they brought him.

It was some such book as this that I sought, a book that would answer once for all the questions that puzzled me, so that, everything being settled for good and all, I could pursue the pattern of my life without let or hindrance. I read and read. From the classical philosophers I turned to the moderns, thinking that among them, perhaps, I should find what I wanted. I could not discover much agreement among them. I found myself convinced by the critical parts of their works, but when I came to the constructive, though often I failed to see the flaws, I could not but be conscious that they did not compel my assent. The impression suggested itself to me that notwithstanding their learning, their logic and their classifications, philosophers embraced such-and-such beliefs not because they were led to them by their reason, but because their temperaments forced these beliefs upon them. Otherwise I could not understand 'how after all this time they differed from one another so profoundly. When I read, I do not know where, that Fichte had said that the kind of philosophy a man adopts depends on the kind of man he is, it occurred to me that perhaps I was looking for something that could not be found. It seemed to me then that if there was in philosophy no universal truth that everyone could accept, but only a truth that agreed with the personality of the individual, the only thing for me was to narrow my search and look for some philosopher whose system suited me because I was the same sort of man that he was. The answers that he would provide to the questions that puzzled me must satisfy me because they would be the only possible answers to fit my humour.

For some time I was much attracted by the pragmatists. I had not got as much profit as I expected from the metaphysical writings of the dons at the great English universities. They seemed to me too gentlemanlike to be very good philosophers and I could not resist the suspicion that sometimes they failed to pursue an argument to its logical conclusion for fear of offending the susceptibilities of colleagues with whom they were in social relations. The pragmatists had vigour. They were very much alive. The most important of them wrote well, and they gave an appearance of simplicity to problems which I had not been able to make head or tail of. But much as I should have liked to I could not bring myself to believe, as they did, that truth is fashioned by us to meet our practical needs. The sense-datum, on which I thought all knowledge was based, seemed to me something given, which had to be accepted whether it suited the convenience or not. Nor did I feel comfortable with the argument that God existed if it consoled me to believe that he did. The pragmatists ceased to interest me so much. I found Bergson good to read, but singularly unconvincing; nor did I find in Benedetto Croce anything to my purpose. On the other hand, in Bertrand Russell I discovered a writer who greatly pleased me; he was easy to understand and his English was good. I read him with admiration.

I was very willing to accept him as the guide I sought. He had worldly wisdom and common sense. He was tolerant of human weakness. But I discovered in time that he was a guide none too certain of the way. His mind was restless. He was like an architect who, when you want a house to live in, having persuaded you to build it of brick, then sets before you good reasons why it should be built of stone; but when you have agreed to this produces reasons just as good to prove that the only material to use is reinforced concrete. Meanwhile you have not a roof to your head. I was looking for a system of philosophy as coherent and self-contained as Bradley's, in which one part hung necessarily on another, so that nothing could be altered without the whole fabric falling to pieces. This Bertrand Russell could not give me.

At last I came to the conclusion that I could never find the one, complete and satisfying book I sought, because that book could only be an expression of myself. So with more courage than discretion I made up my mind that I must write it for myself. I found out what were the books set for the undergraduate to read in order to take a philosophical degree and laboriously perused them. I thought I should thus have at least a foundation for my own work. It seemed to me that with this, the knowledge of the world I had acquired during the forty years of my life (for I was forty when I conceived this idea) and the industrious study of philosophical literature to which I was prepared to devote some years, I should be competent to write such a book as I had in mind. I was aware that except to myself it could have no value beyond such a coherent portrait as it might give of the soul (for want of a more exact word) of a reflective person who had led a fuller life and been subject to more varied experiences than generally fall to the lot of professional philosophers. I knew very well that I had no gift for metaphysical speculation. I meant to take from here and there theories that satisfied not only my mind but, what I could not but think more important than my mind, the whole body of my instincts, feelings and deep-rooted prejudices, the prejudices that are so intimate a part of one that they can hardly be distinguished from instincts; and out of them make a system that would be valid for me and enable me to pursue the course of my life.

But the more I read the more complicated the subject seemed to me and the more conscious I grew of my ignorance. I was peculiarly discouraged by the philosophical magazines in which I found topics discussed at great length which were evidently of importance but which seemed to me in my darkness very trivial; and the manner in which they were handled, the logical apparatus, the care with which each point was argued and the possible objections met, the terms which each writer defined when he first used them, the authorities he quoted, proved to me that philosophy, at all events now, was a business for the experts to deal with between them. The layman could little hope to comprehend its subtleties. I should need twenty years to prepare myself to write the book I proposed and by the time it was done I might, like the king in Anatole France's story, be on my death bed and to me at least the labour I had taken would no longer be of use.

I abandoned the idea and all I have to show for my efforts now are the few desultory notes that follow. I claim no originality for them, or even for the words in which I have put them. I am like a tramp who has rigged himself up as best he could with a pair of trousers from a charitable farmer's wife, a coat off a scarecrow, odd boots out of a dustbin, and a hat that he has found in the road. They are just shreds and patches, but he has fitted himself into them pretty comfortably and, uncomely as they may be, he finds that they suit him well enough. When he passes a gentleman in a smart blue suit, a new hat and well-polished shoes, he thinks he looks very grand, but he is not so sure that in that neat and respectable attire he would be nearly so much at his ease as in his own rags and tatters.

LXVII

WHEN I read Kant I found myself obliged to abandon the materialism in which in my youth I had exulted and the physiological determinism that went with it. I did not then know the objections that have riddled Kant's system and I found an emotional satisfaction in his philosophy. It excited me to contemplate that unknowable "thing in itself" and I was content with a world that man had constructed from appearances. It gave me a peculiar sense of liberation. I jibbed at his maxim that you should so act that your action may be a universal rule. I was too much convinced of the diversity of human nature to believe that this was reasonable. I thought that what was right for one person might very well be wrong for another. For my part I chiefly wanted to be let alone, but I had discovered that not many wanted that, and if I let them alone they thought me unkind, indifferent and selfish. But one cannot study the idealistic philosophers long without coming into touch with solipsism. Idealism is always trembling on the brink of it. The philosophers shy away from it like startled fawns, but their arguments continue to lead them back to it and so far as I can judge they escape it only because they will not pursue it to the end. It is a theory that can hardly fail to allure the writer of fiction. The claims it makes are his common practice. It has a completeness and an elegance that make it infinitely attractive. Since I cannot suppose that everyone who reads this book will know all about the various philosophical systems, the instructed reader will perhaps forgive me if I state briefly what solipsism is. The solipsist believes only in himself and his experience. He creates the world as the theatre of his activity, and the world he creates consists of himself and his thoughts and feelings; and beyond that nothing has being. Everything knowable, every fact of experience, is an idea in his mind, and without his mind does not exist. There is no possibility and no necessity for him to postulate anything outside himself. For him dream and reality are one. Life is a dream in which he creates the objects that come before him, a coherent and consistent dream, and when he ceases to dream, the world, with its beauty, its pain and sorrow and unimaginable variety, ceases to be. It is a perfect theory; it has but one defect; it is unbelievable.

When I cherished the ambition of writing a book on these matters, thinking I must start at the beginning, I studied epistemology. I found none of the theories that I examined very convincing. It seemed to me that the plain man (that object of the philosopher's contempt, except when it happens that his views agree with the philosopher's, in which case quite a lot of value is attached to them) incompetent to judge of their value was perhaps entitled to choose that one which most satisfied his prepossessions. If one is unwilling to suspend one's judgment it appears to me that there is a good deal of plausibility in the theory which holds that, beyond certain fundamental data which they call the given, and the existence of other minds, which they infer, men can be sure of nothing. All the rest of their knowledge is fiction, the construction of their minds, that they have devised for the convenience of living. Having to fit themselves, in the course of evolution, to a constantly changing environment, they have made a picture from fragments that they took here and there because they suited their

purposes. This is the world of phenomena that they know. Reality is merely the hypothesis they have suggested as its occasion. It may be that they might have taken other fragments and combined them into another picture. This different world would have been as coherent and as true as the one we imagine we know.

It would be difficult to persuade an author that there was not a close interaction between the body and the mind. The experience of Flaubert when he suffered from the symptoms of arsenical poisoning while writing of Emma Bovary's suicide is but an extreme instance of what every novelist has undergone. Most writers have chills and fevers, aches and pains, nausea at times, when they are engaged in composition; and contrariwise they are aware to what morbid states of their body they owe many of their happiest inventions. Knowing that many of their deepest emotions, many of the reflections seem to come straight from heaven, may be due to want of exercise or a sluggish liver, they can hardly fail to regard their spiritual experiences with a certain irony; which is all to the good, for thus they can manage and manipulate them. For my part, of the various theories of the relations between matter and spirit that are offered by the philosophers for the consideration of the plain man that which still seems to me most satisfactory is Spinoza's conception that substance thinking and substance extended are one and the same substance. But of course today it is more convenient to call it energy. Unless I misunderstand him Bertrand Russell has expressed in his modern fashion an idea not very dissimilar when he speaks of a neutral stuff which is the raw material of the mental and physical worlds. Trying to form for myself some sort of picture of this, I have seen spirit in the likeness of a river that forces its way through the jungle of matter; but river is jungle and jungle is river, for river and jungle are one. It does not seem impossible that the biologists will in the future succeed in creating life in their laboratories and then it may be that we shall know more of these matters.

LXVIII

But the plain man's interest in philosophy is practical. He wants to know what is the value of life, how he should live and what sense he can ascribe to the universe. When philosophers stand back and refuse to give even tentative answers to these questions they shirk their responsibilities. Now, the most urgent problem that confronts the plain man is the problem of evil.

It is curious to notice that when they speak of evil, philosophers so often use toothache as their example. They point out with justice that you cannot feel my toothache. In their sheltered, easy lives it looks as though this were the only pain that had much afflicted them and one might almost conclude that with the improvement of American dentistry the whole problem could be conveniently shelved. I have sometimes thought that it would be a very good thing if before philosophers were granted the degrees that will enable them to impart their wisdom to the young, they had to spend a year in social service in the slums of a great city or earn their living by manual labour. If they had ever seen a child die of meningitis they would face some of the problems that concern them with other eyes.

If the subject were not of such pressing moment it would be difficult to read the chapter on evil in *Appearance and Reality* without ironic amusement. It is appallingly gentle-manlike. It leaves you with the impression that it is really rather bad form to attach any great importance to evil, and though its existence must be admitted it is unreasonable to make a fuss about it. In any case it is much exaggerated and it is evident that there is a lot of good in it. Bradley held that there was no pain on the whole. The Absolute is the richer for every discord and for all diversity which it embraces. Just as in a machine, he tells us, the resistance and pressure of the parts subserve an end beyond any of them, so at a much higher level it may be with the Absolute; and if this is possible it is indubitably real. Evil and error subserve a wider scheme and in this are realized. They play a part in a higher good and in this sense unknowingly are good. Evil in short is a deception of our senses and nothing more.

I have tried to find out what philosophers of other schools had to say on this question. This is not very much. It may be that there is not very much to be said about it, and philosophers quite naturally attach importance to subjects upon which they can discourse at length. And in the little they have said I can find less to satisfy me. It may be that the evils we endure educate us and so make us better; but observation does not allow us to think that this is a universal rule. It may be that courage and sympathy are excellent and that they could not come into existence without danger and suffering. It is hard to see how the Victoria Cross that rewards the soldier who has risked his life to save a blinded man is going to solace *him* for the loss of his sight. To give alms shows charity, and charity is a virtue, but does *that* good compensate for the evil of the cripple whose poverty has called it forth? Evils are there, omnipresent; pain and disease, the death of those we love, poverty, crime, sin, frustrated hope: the list is interminable. What explanations have the philosophers to offer? Some say that evil is logically necessary so that we may know good; some say that by the nature of the world there is an opposition between good and evil and that each is metaphysically necessary to the other. What explanations have the theologians to offer? Some say that God has placed evils here for our training; some say that he has sent them upon men to punish them for their sins. But *I* have seen a child die of meningitis. I have only found one explanation that appealed equally to my sensibility and to my imagination. This is the doctrine of the transmigration of souls. As everyone knows, it assumes that life does not begin at birth or end at death, but is a link in an indefinite series of lives each one of which is determined by the

acts done in previous existences. Good deeds may exalt a man to the heights of heaven and evil deeds degrade him to the depths of hell. All lives come to an end, even the life of the gods, and happiness is to be sought in release from the round of births and repose in the changeless state called Nirvana. It would be less difficult to bear the evils of one's own life if one could think that they were but the necessary outcome of one's errors in a previous existence, and the effort to do better would be less difficult too when there was the hope that in another existence a greater happiness would reward one. But if one feels one's own woes in a more forcible way than those of others (I cannot feel your toothache, as the philosophers say) it is the woes of others that arouse one's indignation. It is possible to achieve resignation in regard to one's own, but only philosophers obsessed with the perfection of the Absolute can look upon those of others, which seem so often unmerited, with an equal mind. If Karma were true one could look upon them with pity, but with fortitude. Revulsion would be out of place and life would be robbed of the meaninglessness of pain which is pessimism's unanswered argument. I can only regret that I find the doctrine as impossible to believe as the solipsism of which I spoke just now.

LXIX

But I have not done with evil yet. The problem presses when you come to consider whether God exists, and if he does, what nature must be ascribed to him. The time came when, like everybody else, I read the

engaging works of the physicists. I was seized with awe at the contemplation of the immense distances that separated the stars and the vast stretches of time that light traversed in order to come from them to us. I was staggered by the unimaginable extent of the nebulæ. If I understood aright what I read, I must suppose that at the beginning the two forces of cosmical attraction and repulsion balanced so that the universe remained for untold ages in a state of perfect equilibrium. Then at some moment this was disturbed and the universe, toppling off its balance, gave rise to the universe the astronomers tell us of and the little earth we know. But what caused the original act of creation and what upset the balance of equilibrium? I seemed inevitably drawn to the conception of a creator, and what could create this vast, this stupendous universe but a being all-powerful? But the evil of the world then forces on us the conclusion that this being cannot be all-powerful and all-good. A God who is all-powerful may be justly blamed for the evil of the world and it seems absurd to consider him with admiration or accord him worship. But mind and heart revolt against the conception of a God who is not all-good. We are forced then to accept the supposition of a God who is not all-powerful: such a God contains within himself no explanation of his own existence or of that of the universe he creates.

It is singular when you read the documents on which the great religions of the world are founded, to note how much more succeeding ages have read into them than was there. Their teaching, their example, have created an ideal greater than themselves. Most of us find it embarrassing when flowery compliments are paid to us. It is strange that the devout should think God can be pleased when they slavishly pay them to him. When I was young I had an elderly friend who used often to ask me to stay with him in the country. He was a religious man and he read prayers to the assembled household every morning. But he had crossed out in pencil all the passages in the Book of Common Prayer that praised God. He said that there was nothing so vulgar as to praise people to their faces and, himself a gentleman, he could not believe that God was so ungentlemanly as to like it. At the time it seemed to me a curious eccentricity. I think now that my friend showed very good sense.

Men are passionate, men are weak, men are stupid, men are pitiful; to bring to bear on them anything so tremendous as the wrath of God seems strangely inept. It is not very difficult to forgive other people their sins. When you put yourself into their shoes it is generally easy to see what has caused them to do things they should not have done and excuses can be found for them. There is a natural instinct to anger when some harm is done one that leads one to revengeful action, and it is hard in what concerns oneself to take up an attitude of detachment; but a little reflection enables one to look upon the situation from the outside and with practice it is no more difficult to forgive the harm that is done one than any other. It is much harder to forgive people the harm one has done them; that indeed requires a singular power of mind.

Every artist wishes to be believed in, but he is not angry with those who will not accept the communication he offers. God is not so reasonable. He craves so urgently to be believed in that you might think he needed your belief in order to reassure himself of his own existence. He promises rewards to those who believe in him and threatens with horrible punishment those who do not. For my part I cannot believe in a God who is angry with me because I do not believe in him. I cannot believe in a God who is less tolerant than I. I cannot believe in a God who has neither humour nor common sense. Plutarch long ago put the matter succinctly. "I would much rather," he writes, "have men say of me that there never was a Plutarch, nor is now, than to say that Plutarch is a man inconstant, fickle, easily moved to anger, revengeful for trifling provocations and vexed at small things."

But though men have ascribed to God imperfections that they would deplore in themselves that does not prove that God does not exist. It proves only that the religions that men have accepted are but blind alleys cut into an impenetrable jungle and none of them leads to the heart of the great mystery. Arguments have been adduced to prove the existence of God, and I will ask the reader to have patience with me while I briefly consider them. One of them assumes that man has an idea of a perfect being; and since perfection includes existence a perfect being must exist. Another maintains that every event has a cause and since the universe exists it must have a cause and this cause is the Creator. A third, the argument from design, which Kant said was the clearest, oldest and best suited to human reason, is thus stated by one of the characters in Hume's great dialogues: "the order and arrangement of nature, the curious adjustment of final causes, the plain use and intention of every part and organ; all these bespeak in the clearest language an intelligent cause or Author." But Kant showed conclusively that there was no more to be said in favour of this argument than in that of the other two. In their place he propounded another. In a few words it is to the effect that without God there is no guarantee that the sense of duty, which presupposes a free and real self, is not an illusion and therefore that it is morally necessary to believe in God. This has been generally thought more creditable to Kant's amiable nature than to his subtle intelligence. The argument which to me seems more persuasive than any of these is one that has now fallen out of favour. It is known as the proof *e consensu gentium*. It asserts that all men from the remotest origins have had some sort of belief in God and it is hard to think that a belief that has grown up with the human race, a belief that has been accepted by the wisest men, the sages of the East, the philosophers of Greece, the great Scholastics, should not have a foundation in fact. It has seemed to many instinctive and it may be (one can only say, it may be, for it is far from certain) that an instinct does not exist unless there is a possibility of its being satisfied. Experience has shown that the prevalence of a belief, no matter for how long it has been held, is no guarantee of its truth. It appears, then, that none of the arguments for the existence of God is valid. But of course you do not disprove his existence because you cannot prove it. Awe remains, man's sense of helplessness, and his desire to attain harmony between himself and the universe at large. These, rather than the worship of nature or of ancestors, magic or morality, are the sources of religion. There is no reason to believe that what you desire exists, but it is a hard saying that you have no right to believe what you cannot prove; there is no reason why you should not believe so long as you are aware that your belief lacks proof. I suppose that if your nature is such that you want comfort in your trials and a love that sustains and encourages you, you will neither ask for proofs nor have need of them. Your intuition suffices.

Mysticism is beyond proof and indeed demands no more than an indwelling conviction. It is independent of the creeds, for it finds sustenance in all of them, and it is so personal that it satisfies every idiosyncrasy. It is the feeling that the world we live in is but part of a spiritual universe and from this gains its significance; it is the sense of a present God who supports and comforts us. The mystics have narrated their experience so often, and in terms so similar, that I do not see how one can deny its reality. Indeed, I have myself had on one occasion an experience that I could only describe in the words the mystics have used to describe their ecstasy. I was sitting in one of the deserted mosques near Cairo when suddenly I felt myself rapt as Ignatius of Loyola was rapt when he sat by the river at Manresa. I had an overwhelming sense of the power and import of the universe, and an intimate, a shattering sense of communion with it. I could almost bring myself to say that I felt the presence of God. It is doubtless a common enough sensation and the mystics have been careful to ascribe value to it only if its influence was clearly seen in its results. I have a notion that it can be occasioned by other causes than the religious. The saints themselves have been willing to admit that the artists may have it, and love, as we know, can produce a state so like it that the mystics have found themselves drawn to use the phrases of lovers to express the beatific vision.

I do not know that it is more mysterious than that condition, which the psychologists have not yet explained, when you have a strong feeling that you have at some past time been through an experience that you are in the act of undergoing. The ecstasy of the mystic is real enough, but it is valid only for himself. Mystic and sceptic agree in this, that at the end of all our intellectual efforts there remains a great mystery.

Faced with this, awed by the greatness of the universe and malcontent with what the philosophers told me, and what the saints, I have sometimes gone back, beyond Mohammed, Jesus and Buddha, beyond the gods of Greece, Jehovah and Baal, to the Brahman of the Upanishads. That spirit, if spirit it may be called, self-created and independent of all other existence, though all that exists, exists in it, the sole source of life in all that lives, has at least a grandeur that satisfies the imagination. But I have been busy with words too long not to be suspicious of them, and when I look at those I have just written I cannot but see that their meaning is tenuous. In religion above all things the only thing of use is an objective truth. The only God that is of use is a being who is personal, supreme and good, and whose existence is as certain as that two and two make four. I cannot penetrate the mystery. I remain an agnostic, and the practical outcome of agnosticism is that you act as though God did not exist.

LXX

BELIEF in God is not essential to belief in immortality, but it is difficult to dissociate one from the other. Even in that shadowy form of survival which looks forward to the dissolution of human consciousness, once divorced from the body, into the general consciousness, it is only possible to refuse the name of God to this general consciousness if you deny that it has either efficacy or value. And practically, as we know, the two notions have been so inseparably connected that a life after death has always been looked upon as the most powerful instrument to God's hand in his dealings with the human race. It has offered a merciful God the happiness of rewarding the good and a revengeful one the satisfaction of punishing the wicked. The arguments for immortality are simple enough, but, if not meaningless, they have no great force unless the premiss of God's existence is accepted first. I will nevertheless enumerate them. One is based on the incompleteness of life: we have a craving to fulfil ourselves, but the force of events, and our own limitations, leave us with a sense of frustration and this a future life will counterbalance. So Goethe, though he did so much, felt that there was still more for him to do. Akin to this is the argument from desire: if we can conceive immortality and if we desire it, does not that indicate that it exists? Our immortal longings can be understood only by the possibility of their satisfaction. Another argument insists upon the indignation, the anguish and perplexity that beset men when they consider the injustice and the inequality that reign in this world. The wicked flourish like the green bay tree. Justice demands another life in which the guilty may be punished and the innocent rewarded. Evil can be condoned only if in the beyond it is compensated by good and God himself needs immortality to vindicate his ways to man. Then there is the idealistic argument: consciousness cannot be extinguished by death; for the annihilation of consciousness is incon-

ceivable, since only consciousness can conceive the annihilation of consciousness; it goes on to assert that values exist only for mind and point to a supreme mind in which they are completely realized. If God is love, men are values to him, and it cannot be believed that what is of value to God can be allowed to perish. But at this point a certain hesitation has betrayed itself. Common experience, especially the common experience of philosophers, shows that a great many men are no great shakes. Immortality is too stupendous a notion to be entertained in connection with common mortals. They are too insignificant to deserve eternal punishment or to merit eternal bliss. So philosophers have been found to suggest that such as have the possibility of spiritual fulfilment will enjoy a limited survival till they have had the opportunity of reaching the perfection of which they are capable and will then suffer a welcome extinction, while those who have no such possibility will be forthwith mercifully annihilated. But when one comes to enquire into the qualities which in this case will admit the chosen few into the blessings of this limited survival one makes the disconcerting discovery that they are those that few but philosophers possess. One cannot but wonder, however, in what manner the philosophers will pass their time when their virtue has received its due reward, for the questions that occupied them during their sojourn on earth will presumably have received their adequate replies. One can only suppose that they will take piano lessons from Beethoven or learn to paint in water colour under the guidance of Michelangelo. Unless these two great men have much changed they will find them irascible masters.

A very good test of the force of

arguments on which you accept a belief is to ask yourself whether for reasons of equal weight you would embark on a practical operation of any importance. Would you for example buy a house on hearsay without having the title examined by a lawyer and the drains tested by a surveyor? The arguments for immortality, weak when you take them one by one, are no more cogent when you take them together. They are alluring, like a house-agent's advertisement in the daily paper, but to me at least no more convincing. For my part I cannot see how consciousness can persist when its physical basis has been de-stroyed and I am too sure of the interconnection of my body and my mind to think that any survival of my consciousness apart from my body would be in any sense the survival of myself. Even if one could persuade oneself that there was any truth in the suggestion that the human consciousness survives in some general consciousness, there would be small comfort in it, and to be satisfied with the notion that one survives in such spiritual force as one has produced is merely to cheat oneself with idle words. The only survival that has any value is the complete survival of the individual.

LXXI

IF THEN one puts aside the existence of God and the possibility of survival as too doubtful to have any effect on one's behaviour, one has to make up one's mind what is the meaning and use of life. If death ends all, if I have neither to hope for good to come nor to fear evil, I must ask myself what I am here for and how in these circumstances I must conduct myself. Now the answer to one of these questions is plain, but it is so unpalatable that most men will not face it. There is no reason for life and life has no meaning. We are here, inhabitants for a little while of a small planet, revolving round a minor star which in its turn is a member of one of unnumbered galaxies. It may be that this planet alone can support life, or it may be that in other parts of the universe other planets have had the possibility of forming a suitable environment to that substance from which, we suppose, along the vast course of time the men we are have been gradually created. And if the astronomer tells us truth this planet will eventually reach a condition when living things can no longer exist upon it and at long last the universe will attain that final stage of equilibrium when nothing more can happen. Æons and æons before this man will have disappeared. Is it possible to suppose that it will matter then that he ever existed? He will have been a chapter in the history of the universe as pointless as the chapter in which is written the life stories of the strange monsters that inhabited the primæval earth.

I must ask myself then what difference all this makes to me and how I am to deal with these circumstances if I want to make the best use of my life and to get the utmost that I can out of it. Here it is not I that speak, it is the craving within me, which is in every man, to persevere in my own being; it is the egoism that we all inherit from that remote energy which in the unplumbed past first set the ball rolling; it is the need of self-assertion which is in every living thing and which keeps it alive. It is the very essence of man. Its satisfaction is the self-satisfaction which Spinoza has told us is the highest thing for which we can hope, "for no one endeavours to preserve his being for the sake of any end." We may suppose that consciousness was kindled in man as an instrument to enable him to deal with his environment and that for long ages it reached no higher development than was needed to deal with the vital problems of his practice. But it seems in course of time to have out-grown his immediate needs, and with the rise of imagination man widened his environment to include the unseen. We know with what answers he satisfied the questions that he put to himself then. The energy that flamed within him was so intense that he could admit no doubt of his significance; his egoism was so all-embracing that he could not conceive the possibility of his extinction. To many these answers are satisfactory still. They give meaning to life and comfort to human vanity.

Most people think little. They accept their presence in the world; blind slaves of the striving which is their mainspring they are driven this way and that to satisfy their natural impulses, and when it dwindles they go out like the light of a candle. Their lives are purely instinctive. It may be that theirs is the greater wisdom. But if your consciousness has so far developed that you find certain questions pressing upon you and you think the old answers wrong, what are you going to do? What answers will you give? To

at least one of these questions two of the wisest men who ever lived have given their own answers. When you come to look at them they seem to mean pretty much the same thing and I am not so sure that that is very much. Aristotle has said that the end of human activity is right action, and Goethe that the secret of life is living. I suppose that Goethe means that man makes the most of his life when he arrives at self-realization; he had small respect for a life governed by passing whims and uncontrolled instincts. But the difficulty of self-realization, that bringing to the highest perfection every faculty of which you are possessed, so that you can get from life all the pleasure, beauty, emotion and interest you can wring from it, is that the claims of other people constantly limit your activity; and moralists, taken by the reasonableness of the theory, but frightened of its consequences, have spilt much ink to prove that in sacrifice and selflessness a man most completely realizes himself. That is certainly not what Goethe meant and it does not seem to be true. That there is a singular delight in self-sacrifice few would deny, and in so far as it offers a new field for activity and the opportunity to develop a new side of the self, it has value in self-realization; but if you aim at self-realization only in so far as it interferes with no one else's attempts at the same thing you will not get very far. Such an aim demands a good deal of ruthlessness and an absorption in oneself which is offensive to others and thus often stultifies itself. As we well know many of those who came in contact with Goethe were outraged by his frigid egotism.

LXXII

IT MAY seem arrogant that I should not have been content to walk in the steps of men much wiser than myself. But much as we resemble one another we are none of us exactly alike (our finger-prints are there to show it), and I have seen no reason why I should not, so far as I could, choose my own course. I have sought to make a pattern of my life. This, I suppose, might be described as self-realization tempered by a lively sense of irony; making the best of a bad job. But a question presents itself which I shirked when, at the beginning of my book, I dealt with this subject; and now that I can avoid it no longer I cannot but draw back. I am conscious that here and there I have taken free-will for granted; I have spoken as though I had power to mould my intentions and direct my actions as the whim took me. In other places I have spoken as though I accepted determinism. Such shilly-shallying would have been deplorable had I been writing a philosophical work. I make no such pretension. But how can I, an amateur, be expected to settle a question which the philosophers have not yet ceased to argue?

It might seem only sensible to leave the matter alone, but it happens to be one in which the writer of fiction is peculiarly concerned. For as a writer he finds himself compelled by his readers to rigid determination. I pointed out earlier in these pages how unwilling an audience is to accept impulse on the stage. Now an impulse is merely an urge to action of whose motive the agent is not conscious; it is analogous to an intuition, which is

a judgment you make without being aware of its grounds. But though an impulse has its motive, an audience, because it is not obvious, will not accept it. The spectators of a play and the readers of a book insist on knowing the reasons of action and they will not admit its probability unless the reasons are cogent. Each person must behave in character; that means that he must do what from their knowledge of him they expect him to do. Cunning must be exercised in order to persuade them to accept the coincidences and accidents which in real life they swallow without a second thought. They are determinists to a man and the writer who trifles with their obstinate prejudice is lost.

But when I look back upon my own life I cannot but notice how much that vitally affected me has been due to circumstances that it is hard not to regard as pure chance. Determinism tells us that choice follows the line of least resistance or the strongest motive. I am not conscious that I have always followed the line of least resistance, and if I have followed the strongest motive that motive has been an idea of myself that I have gradually evolved. The metaphor of chess, though frayed and shop-worn, is here wonderfully apposite. The pieces were provided and I had to accept the mode of action that was characteristic of each one; I had to accept the moves of the persons I played with; but it has seemed to me that I had the power to make on my side, in accordance perhaps with my likes and dislikes and the ideal that I set before me, moves that I freely willed. It has seemed to me that I have now and then been able to put forth an effort that was not wholly determined. If it was an illusion it was an illusion that had its own efficacy. The moves I made, I know now, were often mistaken, but in one way and another they have tended to the end in view. I wish that I had not committed a great many errors, but I do not deplore them nor would I now have them undone.

I do not think it unreasonable to hold the opinion that everything in the universe combines to cause every one of our actions, and this naturally includes all our opinions and desires; but whether an action, once performed, was inevitable from all eternity can only be decided when you have made up your mind whether or no there are events, the events that Dr. Broad calls casual progenitors, which are not completely determined. Hume long ago showed that there was no intrinsic connection between cause and effect which could be perceived by the mind; and of late the Principle of Indeterminacy, by bringing to view certain events to which apparently no causes can be assigned, has cast a doubt on the universal efficacy of those laws upon which science has hitherto been based. It looks as if chance must once more be reckoned

with. But if we are not certainly bound by the law of cause and effect, then perhaps it is not an illusion that our wills are free. The bishops and the deans have snatched at this new notion as though it were the devil's tail by which they hoped to drag the old devil himself back into existence. There has been great rejoicing, if not in the courts of heaven, at all events in the palaces of the episcopacy. Perhaps the Te Deum has been sung too soon. It is well to remember that the two most eminent scientists of our day regard Heisenberg's principle with scepticism. Planck has stated his belief that further research will sweep away the anomaly, and Einstein has described the philosophical ideas that have been based upon it as "literature"; I am afraid that this is only his civil way of calling them nonsense. The physicists themselves tell us that physics is making such rapid progress that it is only possible to keep abreast of it by close study of the periodical literature. It is surely rash to found a theory on principles suggested by a science that is so unstable. Schrödinger himself has stated that a final and comprehensive judgment on the matter is at present impossible. The plain man is justified in sitting on the fence, but perhaps he is prudent to keep his legs dangling on the side of determinism.

LXXIII

THE life force is vigorous. The delight that accompanies it counter-balances all the pains and hardships that confront men. It makes life worth living, for it works from within and lights with its own bright flame each one's circumstances so that, however

intolerable, they yet seem tolerable to him. Much pessimism is caused by ascribing to others the feelings you would feel if you were in their place. It is this (among much else) that makes novels so false. The novelist constructs a public world out of his own private world and gives to the characters of his fancy a sensitiveness, a power of reflection and an emotional capacity, which are peculiar to himself. Most people have little imagination and they do not suffer from circumstances that to the imaginative would be unbearable. The lack of privacy, to take an instance, in which the very poor live seems frightful to us who value it; but it does not seem so to the very poor. They hate to be alone; it gives them a sense of security to live in company. No one who has dwelt among them can fail to have noticed how little they envy the well-to-do. The fact is that they do not want many of the things that to others of us appear essential. It is fortunate for the well-to-do. For he is blind who will not see that in the lives of the proletariat in the great cities all is misery and confusion. It is hard to reconcile oneself to the fact that men should have no work to do, that work should be so dreary, that they should live, they, their wives and their children, on the edge of starvation, and in the end have nothing to look forward to but destitution. If only revolution can remedy this, then let revolution come and come quickly. When we see the cruelty with which men even now treat one another in countries that we have been in the habit of calling civilized, it would be rash to say that they are any better than they were, but for all that it does not seem fatuous to think that the world is on the whole a better place to live in than it was in the past that history sets before us, and that the lot of the great majority, bad as it is, is less dreadful than it was then; and one may reasonably hope that with the increase of knowledge, with the discarding of many cruel superstitions and outworn conventions, with a livelier sense of loving-kindness, many of the evils

from which men suffer will be removed. But many evils must continue to exist. We are the playthings of nature. Earthquakes will continue to wreak havoc, droughts to ruin crops and unforeseen floods to destroy the prudent constructions of men. Human folly, alas, will continue to devastate the nations with war. Men will continue to be born who are not fitted for life and life will be a burden to them. So long as some are strong and some are weak, the weak will be driven to the wall. So long as men are cursed with the sense of possession, and that I presume is as long as they exist, they will wrest what they can from those who are powerless to hold it. So long as they have the instinct of self-assertion, they will exercise it at the expense of others' happiness. In short, so long as man is man he must be prepared to face all the woes that he can bear.

There is no explanation for evil. It must be looked upon as a necessary part of the order of the universe. To ignore it is childish; to bewail it senseless. Spinoza called pity womanish; the epithet has a harsh sound on the lips of that tender and austere spirit. I suppose he thought that it was but waste of emotion to feel strongly about what you could not alter.

I am not a pessimist. Indeed, it would be nonsensical of me to be so, for I have been one of the lucky ones. I have often wondered at my good fortune. I am well aware that many who were more deserving than I have not had the happy fate that has befallen me. An accident here, an accident there, might have changed everything and frustrated me as so many with talents equal to, or greater than, mine, with equal opportunities, have been frustrated. Should any of them chance to read these pages, I would ask them to believe that I do not arrogantly ascribe to my merits what has come to me, but to some concatenation of unlikely circumstances for which I can offer no explanation. With all my limitations, physical and mental, I have been glad to live. I would not live my life over again. There would be no point in that. Nor would I care to pass again through the anguish I have suffered. It is one of the faults of my nature that I have suffered more from the pains, than I have enjoyed the pleasures of my life. But without my physical imperfections, with a stronger body and a better brain, I would not mind entering upon the world afresh. The years that now stretch immediately in front of us look as if they would be interesting. The young enter upon life now with advantages that were denied to the young of my generation. They are hampered by fewer conventions and they have learnt how great is the value of youth. The world of my twenties was a middle-aged world and youth was something to be got through as quickly as possible so that maturity might be reached. The young things of the present day, at least in that middle class to which I belong, seem to me better prepared. They are taught now many things that are useful to them, whereas we had to pick them up as best we could. The relation between the sexes is more normal. Young women have learnt now to be the companions of young men. One of the difficulties that my generation had to face, the generation that saw the emancipation of women, was this: women had ceased to be the housekeepers and mothers of an earlier age, who led a life apart from men, with their own interests and particular concerns, and were trying to participate in men's affairs without the capacity to do so; they demanded the consideration that had been their

due when they were content to look upon themselves as men's inferiors and withal insisted on their right, their new-won right, to join in all the masculine activities in which they knew only enough to make a nuisance of themselves. They were no longer housewives and had not yet learnt to be good fellows. There is no more pleasant spectacle for an elderly gentleman than that of the young girl of the present day, so competent and so self-assured, who can run an office and play a hard game of tennis, who is intelligently concerned with public affairs and can appreciate the arts, and, prepared to stand on her own feet, faces life with cool, shrewd and tolerant eyes.

Far be it from me to don the prophet's mantle, but I think it is clear that these young folk who are now taking the stage must look forward to economic changes that will transform civilization. They will not know the easy, sheltered life which makes many who were at their prime before the war look upon those years as did the survivors of the French Revolution when they look back on the Ancien Régime. They will not know the *douceur de vivre*. We live now on the eve of great revolutions. I cannot doubt that the proletariat, increasingly conscious of its rights, will eventually seize power in one country after the other, and I never cease to marvel that the governing classes of today, rather than continue a vain struggle against these overwhelming forces, do not use every effort to train the masses for their future tasks so that when they are dispossessed their fate may be less cruel than that which befell them in Russia. Years ago Disraeli told them what to do. For my part I must candidly say that I hope the present state of things will last my time. But we live in an era of rapid change and I may yet see the countries of the west given over to the rule of communism. A Russian exile of my acquaintance told me that when he lost his estates and his wealth, he was overcome with despair; but at the end of a fortnight he regained his serenity and never since gave a thought to what he had been deprived of. I do not think I have such an attachment to my various possessions as to regret their loss for long. If such a condition of things came to pass in my world I should make an attempt to adapt myself and then, if I found life intolerable, I think I should not lack the courage to quit a stage on which I could no longer play my part to my own satisfaction. I wonder why so many people turn with horror from the thought of suicide. To speak of it as cowardly is nonsense. I can only approve the man who makes an end of himself of his own will when life has nothing to offer him but pain and misfortune. Did not Pliny say that the power of dying when you please is the best thing that God has given to man amid all the sufferings of life? Putting aside those who regard suicide as sinful because it breaks a divine law, I think the reason of the indignation which it seems to arouse in so many is that the suicide flouts the life-force, and by setting at nought the strongest instinct of human beings casts a terrifying doubt on its power to preserve them.

With this book I shall have completed in sufficient outline the pattern I set myself to make. If I live I shall write other books, for my amusement and I hope for the amusement of my readers, but I do not think they will add anything essential to my design. The house is built. There will be additions, a terrace from which one has a pretty view, or an arbour in which to meditate in the heat of summer; but should death prevent me from producing them, the house, though the housebreakers may set to work on it the day after I am buried in an obituary notice, will have been built.

I look forward to old age without dismay. When Lawrence of Arabia was killed I read in an article contributed by a friend that it was his habit to ride his motor-bicycle at an excessive speed with the notion that an accident would end his life while he was still in full possession of his powers and so spare him the indignity of old age. If this is true it was a great weakness in that strange and somewhat theatrical character. It showed want of sense. For the complete life, the perfect pattern, includes old age as well as youth and maturity. The beauty of the morning and the radiance of noon are good, but it would be a very silly person who drew the curtains and turned on the light in order to shut out the tranquillity of the evening. Old age has its pleasures, which, though different, are not less than the pleasures of youth. The philosophers have always told us that we are the slaves of our passions, and is it so small a thing to be liberated from their sway? The fool's old age will be foolish, but so was his youth. The young man turns away from it with horror because he thinks that when he reaches it, he will still yearn for the things that give variety and gusto to his youth. He is mistaken. It is true that the old man will no longer be able to climb an Alp or tumble a pretty girl on a bed; it is true that he can no longer arouse the concupiscence of others. It is something to be free from the pangs of unrequited love and the torment of jealousy. It is something that envy, which so often poisons youth, should be assuaged by the extinction of desire. But these are negative compensations; old age has positive compensations also. Paradoxical as it may sound it has more time. When I was young I was amazed at Plutarch's statement that the elder Cato began at the age of eighty to learn Greek. I am amazed no longer. Old age is ready to undertake tasks that youth shirked because they would take too long. In old age the taste improves and it is possible to enjoy art and literature without the personal bias that in youth warps the judgment. It has the satisfaction of its own fulfillment. It is liberated from the trammels of human egoism; free at last, the soul delights in the passing moment, but does not bid it stay. It has completed the pattern. Goethe asked for survival after death so that he might realize those sides of himself which he felt that in his life he had not had time to develop. But did he not say that he who would accomplish anything must learn to limit himself? When you read his life you cannot but be struck by the way in which he wasted time in trivial pursuits. Perhaps if he had limited himself more carefully he would have developed everything that properly belonged to his special individuality and so found no need of a future life.

LXXIV

Spinoza says that a free man thinks of nothing less than of death. It is unnecessary to dwell upon it, but it is foolish, as so many do, to shrink from all consideration of it. It is well to make up one's mind about it. It is impossible to know till death is there facing one whether one will fear it. I have often tried to imagine what my feelings would be if a doctor told me I had a fatal disease and had no more than a little time to live. I have put them into the mouths of various characters of my invention, but I am aware that thus I dramatized them and I cannot tell whether they would be those I should actually feel. I do not think I have a very strong instinctive hold on life. I have had a good many serious illnesses, but have only once known myself to be within measurable distance of death; then I was so tired that I could not fear, I only wanted to be done with the struggle. Death is inevitable and it does not much matter how one meets it. I do not think one can be blamed if one hopes that one will not be aware of its imminence and be fortunate enough to undergo it without pain.

I have always lived so much in the future that now, though the future is so short, I cannot get out of the habit and my mind looks forward with a certain complacency to the completion within an indefinite number of years of the pattern that I have tried to make. There are moments when I have so palpitating an eagerness for death that I could fly to it as to the arms of a lover. It gives me the same passionate thrill as years ago was given me by life. I am drunk with the thought of it. It seems to me then to offer me the final and absolute freedom. Notwithstanding, I am willing enough to go on living so long as the doctors can keep me in tolerable health; I enjoy the spectacle of the world and it interests me to see what is going to happen. The consummation of many lives that have run their course parallel with my own gives me continual food for reflection and sometimes for the confirmation of theories that I formed long ago. I shall be sorry to part from my friends. I cannot be indifferent to the welfare of some whom I have guided and protected, but it is well that after depending on me so long they should enjoy their liberty whithersoever it leads them. Having held a certain place in the world for a long time I am content that others soon should occupy it. After all the point of a pattern is that it should be completed. When nothing can be added without spoiling the design the artist leaves it.

But now if anyone should ask me what is the use or sense of this pattern I should have to answer, none. It is merely something I have imposed on the senselessness of life because I am a novelist. For my own satisfaction, for my amusement and to gratify what feels to me like an organic need, I have shaped my life in accordance with a certain design, with a beginning, a middle and an end, as from people I have met here and there I have constructed a play, a novel or a short story. We are the product of our natures and our environment. I have not made the pattern I thought best, or even the pattern I should have liked to make, but merely that which seemed feasible. There are better patterns than mine. I do not believe that I am influenced only by an illusion natural to the man of letters to think that the best pattern of all is the husbandman's, who ploughs his land and reaps his crop, who enjoys his toil and enjoys his leisure, loves, marries, begets children and dies. When I have observed the peasantry in those favoured lands in which the earth produces her plenty without excessive labour, where the pleasures and pains of the individual are those incidental to the human race, it has seemed to me that there the perfect life was perfectly realized. There life, like a good story, pursues its way from beginning to end in a firm and unbroken line.

LXXV

THE egoism of man makes him unwilling to accept the meaninglessness of life and when he has unhappily found himself no longer able to believe in a higher power whose ends he could flatter himself that he subserved he has sought to give it significance by constructing certain values beyond those that seem to further his immediate welfare. The wisdom of the ages has chosen three of these as most worthy. To aim at them for their own sake has seemed to give life some kind of sense. Though it can hardly be doubted that they too have a biologic utility, they have superficially an appearance of disinterestedness which gives man the illusion that through them he escapes from human bondage. Their nobility strengthens his wavering sense of his spiritual significance and, whatever the result, the pursuit of them appears to justify his efforts. Oases in the vast desert of existence, since he knows no other end to his journey, man persuades himself that they at all event are worth reaching and that there he will find rest and the answer to his question. These three values are Truth, Beauty and Goodness.

I have a notion that Truth finds a place in this list for rhetorical reasons. Man invests it with ethical qualities, such as courage, honour and independence of spirit, which indeed are often shown by his insistence on truth, but which in effect have nothing whatever to do with it. Finding in it so great an occasion for his own self-assertion he will be indifferent to any sacrifice that it entails. But then his interest is in himself and not in the truth. If truth is a value it is because it is true and not because it is brave to speak it. But truth is a character of judgments and so one would suppose that its value lay in the judgments it characterizes rather than in itself. A bridge that joined two great cities would be more important than a bridge that led from one barren field to another. And if truth is one of the ultimate values, it seems strange that no one seems quite to know what it is. Philosophers still quarrel about its meaning and the upholders of rival doctrines say many sarcastic things of one another. In these circumstances the plain man must leave them to it and content himself with the plain man's truth. This is a very modest affair and merely asserts something about particular existents. It is a bare statement of the facts. If this is a value one must admit that none is more neglected. The books on ethics give long list of occasions on which it may be legitimately withheld; their authors might have saved themselves the trouble. The wisdom of the ages has long since decided that *toutes vérités ne sont pas bonnes à dire*. Man has always sacrificed truth to his vanity, comfort and advantage. He lives not by truth but by make-believe, and his idealism, it has sometimes seemed to me, is merely his effort to attach the prestige of truth to the fictions he has invented to satisfy his self-conceit.

LXXVI

B E A U T Y stands in a better case. For many years I thought that it was beauty alone that gave significance to life and that the only purpose that could be assigned to the teeming generations that succeed one another on the face of the earth was to produce now and then an artist. The work of art, I decided, was the crowning product of human activity, and the final justification for all the misery, the endless toil and the frustrated strivings of humanity. So that Michelangelo might paint certain figures on the ceiling of the Sistine Chapel, so that Shakespeare might write certain speeches and Keats his odes, it seemed to me worth while that untold millions should have lived and suffered and died. And though I modified this extravagance later by including the beautiful life among the works of art that alone gave a meaning to life, it was still beauty that I valued. All these notions I have long since abandoned.

In the first place I discovered that beauty was a full stop. When I considered beautiful things I found that there was nothing for me to do but to gaze and admire. The emotion they gave me was exquisite, but I could not preserve it, nor could I indefinitely repeat it; the most beautiful things in the world finished by boring me. I noticed that I got a more lasting satisfaction from works of a more tentative character. Because they had not achieved complete success they gave more scope for the activity of my imagination. In the greatest of all works of art everything had been realized, I could give nothing, and my restless mind tired of passive contemplation. It seemed to me that beauty was like the summit of a mountain peak; when you had reached it there was nothing to do but to come down again. Perfection is a trifle dull. It is not the least of life's ironies that this, which we all aim at, is better not quite achieved.

I suppose that we mean by beauty that object, spiritual or material, more often material, which satisfies our æsthetic sense. That, however, tells you just about as much as you would know about water if you were told that it was wet. I have read a good many books to discover what the authorities had to say that made the matter a little plainer. I have known intimately a great many persons who were absorbed in the arts. I am afraid that neither from them nor from books have I learnt much that greatly profited me. One of the most curious things that has forced itself on my notice is that there is no permanence in the judgment of beauty. The museums are full of objects which the most cultivated taste of a period considered beautiful, but which seem to us now worthless; and in my own lifetime I have seen the beauty evaporate from poems and pictures, exquisite not so long ago, like hoar frost before the morning sun. Vain as we may be we can hardly think our own judgment ultimate; what we think beautiful will doubtless be scorned in another generation, and what we have despised may be raised to honour. The only conclusion is that beauty is relative to the needs of a particular generation, and that to examine the things we consider beautiful for qualities of absolute beauty is futile. If beauty is one of the values that give

life significance it is something that is constantly changing and thus cannot be analyzed, for we can as little feel the beauty our ancestors felt as we can smell the roses they smelt.

I have tried to find out from the writers on æsthetics what it is in human nature that makes it possible for us to get the emotion of beauty and what exactly this emotion is. It is usual enough to talk of the æsthetic instinct: the term seems to give it a place among the mainsprings of the human being, like hunger and scx, and at the same time to endow it with a specific quality that flatters the philosophic craving for unity. So æsthetics have been derived from an instinct of expression, an exuberance of vitality, a mystical sense of the absolute and I know not what. For my part I should have said it was not an instinct at all, but a state of the body-mind, founded in part on certain powerful instincts, but combined with human characteristics, which are the result of the evolutionary process, and with the common circumstances of life. That it has a great deal to do with the sexual instinct seems to be shown by the fact, commonly admitted, that those who possess an æsthetic sense of unusual delicacy diverge sexually from the norm to an extreme and often pathological degree. There may be in the constitution of the body-mind something that renders certain tones, certain rhythms and certain colours peculiarly attractive to man, so that there may be a physiological reason for the elements of what we consider beautiful. But we also find things beautiful because they remind us of objects, people or places, that we have loved or to which the passage of time has lent a sentimental value. We find things beautiful because we recognize them and contrariwise we find things beautiful because their novelty surprises us. All this means that association, by likeness or contrast, enters largely into the æsthetic emotion. It is only association that can explain the æsthetic value of the ugly. I do not know that anyone has studied the effect of time on the creation of beauty. It is not only that we grow to see the beauty of things as we know them better; it is rather that the delight that succeeding ages take in them somehow adds to their beauty. That, I suppose, is why certain works whose beauty now seems manifest should, when first given to the world, have attracted no great attention. I have a notion that the odes of Keats are more beautiful than when he wrote them. They are enriched by the emotion of all who have found solace and strength in their loveliness. Far then from thinking the æsthetic emotion a specific, simple affair, I think it is a very complicated one, which is made up of various, often discordant elements. It is no good for the æstheticians to say that you ought not to be moved by a picture or a symphony because it fills you with erotic excitement or melts you to tears by reminding you of some long-forgotten scene, or through its associations exalts you to mystic rapture. It does; and these sides of it are just as much part and parcel of the æsthetic emotion as the disinterested satisfaction in balance and composition.

What exactly is one's reaction to a great work of art? What does one feel when for instance one looks at Titian's Entombment in the Louvre or listens to the quintet in the *Meistersinger*? I know what mine is. It is an excitement that gives me a sense of exhilaration, intellectual but suffused with sensuality, a feeling of well-being in which I seem to discern a sense of power and of liberation from human ties; at the same time I feel in myself a tenderness which is rich with human sympathy; I feel rested, at peace and yet spiritually aloof. Indeed on occasion, looking at certain pictures or statues, listening to certain music, I have had an emotion so strong that I could only describe it in the same words as those the mystics use to describe the union with God. That is why I have thought that this sense of communion with a larger reality is not only the privilege of the religious, but may be reached by other paths than prayer and fasting. But I have asked myself what was the use of this emotion. Of course it is delightful and pleasure in itself is good, but what is there in it that makes it superior to any other pleasure, so superior that to speak of it as pleasure at all seems to depreciate it? Was Jeremy Bentham so foolish after all when he said that one sort of happiness was as good as another, and if the amount of pleasure was equal pushpin as good as poetry? The answer the mystics gave to this question was unequivocal. They said that rapture was worthless unless it strengthened the character and rendered man more capable of right action. The value of it lay in works.

It has been my lot to live much among persons of æsthetic sensibility. I am not speaking now of the creators: to my mind there is a great difference between those who create art and those who enjoy it; the creators produce because of that urge within them that forces them to exteriorize their personality. It is an accident if what they produce has beauty; that is seldom their special aim. Their aim is to disembarrass their souls of the burdens that oppress them and they use the means, their pen, their paints or their clay, for which they have by nature a facility. I am speaking now of those to whom the contemplation and appreciation of art is the main business of life. I have found little to admire in them. They are vain and self-complacent. Inapt for the practical affairs of life, they disdain those who with humility perform the modest offices to which their destiny has constrained them. Because they have read a great many books or seen a great many pictures they think themselves superior to other men. They use art to escape the realities of life and in their imbecile contempt for common things deny value to the essential activities of humanity. They are no better really than drug-fiends; worse rather, for the drug-fiend at all events does not set himself on a pedestal from which to look down on his fellowmen. The value of art, like the value of the Mystic Way, lies in its effects. If it can only give pleasure, however spiritual that pleasure may be, it is of no great consequence or at least of no more consequence than a dozen oysters and a pint of Montrachet. If it is a solace, that is well enough; the world is full of inevitable evils and it is good that man should have some hermitage to which from time to time he may withdraw himself; but not to escape them, rather to gather fresh strength to face them. For art, if it is to be reckoned as one of the great values of life, must teach men humility, tolerance, wisdom and magnanimity. The value of art is not beauty, but right action.

If beauty is one of the great values of life, then it seems hard to believe that the æsthetic sense which enables men to appreciate it should be the privilege only of a class. It is not possible to maintain that a form of sensibility that is shared but by the elect can be a necessity of human life. Yet that is what the æsthetics

claim. I must confess that in my foolish youth when I considered that art (in which I included the beauties of nature, for I was very much of opinion, as indeed I still am, that their beauty was constructed by men as definitely as they constructed pictures or symphonies) was the crown of human endeavour and the justification of man's existence, it gave me a peculiar satisfaction to think that it could be appreciated only by the chosen few. But this notion has long stuck in my gizzard. I cannot believe that beauty is the appanage of a set and I am inclined to think that a manifestation of art that has a meaning only to persons who have undergone a peculiar training is as inconsiderable as the set to which it appeals. An art is only great and significant if it is one that all may enjoy. The art of a clique is but a plaything. I do not know why distinctions are made between ancient art and modern art. There is nothing but art. Art is living. To attempt to give an object of art life by dwelling on its historical, cultural, or archæological associations is senseless. It does not matter whether a statue was hewn by an archaic Greek or a modern Frenchman. Its only importance is that it should give us here and now the æsthetic thrill and that this æsthetic thrill should move us to works. If it is to be anything more than a self-indulgence and an occasion of self-complacency, it must strengthen your character and make it more fitted for right action. And little as I like the deduction, I cannot but accept it; and this is that the work of art must be judged by its fruits, and if these are not good it is valueless. It is an odd fact, which must be accepted as in the nature of things and for which I know no explanation, that the artist achieves this effect only when he does not intend it. His sermon is most efficacious if he has no notion that he is preaching one. The bee produces wax for her own purposes and is unaware that man will put it to diverse uses.

LXXVII

IT APPEARS then impossible to say that either truth or beauty has intrinsic value. What about goodness? But before I speak of goodness I would speak of love; for there are philosophers who, thinking that it embraced every other, have accepted it as the highest of human values. Platonism and Christianity have combined to give it a mystical significance. The associations of the word lend it an emotion that makes it more exciting than plain goodness. Goodness in comparison is a trifle dull. But love has two meanings, love pure and simple, sexual love, namely; and loving-kindness. I do not think that even Plato distinguished them with exactness. He seems to me to ascribe the exultation, the sense of power, the feeling of heightened vitality which accompany sexual love to that other love which he calls the heavenly love and which I should prefer to call loving-kindness; and by doing so infects it with the ineradicable vice of earthly love. For love passes. Love dies. The great tragedy of life is not that men perish, but that they cease to love. Not the least of the evils of life, and one for which there is small help, is that someone whom you love no longer loves you; when La Rochefoucauld discovered that between two lovers there is one who loves and one who lets himself be loved he put in an epigram the discord that must ever prevent men from achieving in love perfect happiness. However much people may resent the fact and however angrily deny it, there can surely be no doubt that love depends on certain secretions of the sexual glands. In the immense majority these do not continue indefinitely to be excited by the same object and with advancing years they atrophy. People are very hypocritical in this matter and will not face the truth. They so deceive themselves that they can accept it with complacency when their love dwindles into what they describe as a solid and enduring affection. As if affection had anything to do with love! Affection is created by habit, community of interests, convenience and the desire of companionship. It is a comfort rather than an exhilaration. We are creatures of change, change is the atmosphere we breathe, and is it likely that the strongest but one of all our instincts should be free from the law? We are not the same persons this year as last; nor are those we love. It is a happy chance if we, changing, continue to love a changed person. Mostly, different ourselves, we make a desperate, pathetic effort to love in a different person the person we once loved. It is only because the power of love when it seizes us seems so mighty that we persuade ourselves that it will last forever. When it subsides we are ashamed, and, duped, blame ourselves for our weakness, whereas we should accept our change of heart as a natural effect of our humanity. The experience of mankind has led them to regard love with mingled feelings. They have been suspicious of it. They have as often cursed as praised it. The soul of man, struggling to be free, has except for brief moments looked upon the self-surrender that it claims as a fall from grace. The happiness it brings may be the greatest of which man is capable, but it is seldom, seldom unalloyed. It writes a story that generally has a sad ending. Many have resented its power and angrily prayed to be delivered from its burden. They have hugged their chains, but knowing they were chains hated them too. Love is not always blind and there are few things that cause greater wretchedness than to love with all your heart someone who you know is unworthy of love.

But loving-kindness is not coloured with that transitoriness which is the irremediable defect of love. It is true that it is not entirely devoid of the sexual element. It is like dancing; one dances for the pleasure of the rhythmic movement, and it is not necessary that one should wish to go to bed with one's partner; but it is a pleasant exercise only if to do so would not be disgusting. In loving-kindness the sexual instinct is sublimated, but it lends the emotion something of its own warm and vitalizing energy. Loving-kindness is the better part of goodness. It lends grace to the sterner qualities of which this consists and makes it a little less difficult to practice those minor virtues of self-control and self-restraint, patience, discipline and tolerance, which are the passive and not very exhilarating elements of goodness. Goodness is the only value that seems in this world of appearances to have any claim to be an end in itself. Virtue is its own reward. I am ashamed to have reached so commonplace a conclusion. With my in-

stinct for effect I should have liked to end my book with some startling and paradoxical announcement or with a cynicism that my readers would have recognized with a chuckle as characteristic. It seems I have little more to say than can be read in any copybook or heard from any pulpit. I have gone a long way round to discover what everyone knew already.

I have little sense of reverence. There is a great deal too much of it in the world. It is claimed for many objects that do not deserve it. It is often no more than the conventional homage we pay to things in which we are not willing to take an active interest. The best homage we can pay to the great figures of the past, Dante, Titian, Shakespeare, Spinoza, is to treat them not with reverence, but with the familiarity we should exercise if they were our contemporaries. Thus we pay them the highest compliment we can; our familiarity acknowledges that they are alive for us. But when now and then I have come across real goodness I have found reverence rise naturally in my heart. It has not seemed to matter then that its rare possessors were perhaps sometimes a trifle less intelligent than I should have liked them to be. When I was a small boy and unhappy I used to dream night after night that my life at school was all a dream and that I should wake to find myself at home again with my mother. Her death was a wound that fifty years have not entirely healed. I have long ceased to have that dream; but I have never quite lost the sense that my living life was a mirage in which I did this and that because that was how it fell out, but which, even while I was playing my part in it, I could look at from a distance and know for the mirage it was. When I look back on my life, with its successes and its failures, its endless errors, its deceptions and its fulfilments, its joys and miseries, it seems to me strangely lacking in reality. It is shadowy and unsubstantial. It may be that my heart, having found rest nowhere, had some deep ancestral craving for God and immortality which my reason would have no truck with. In default of anything better it has seemed to me sometimes that I might pretend to myself that the goodness I have not so seldom after all come across in many of those I have encountered on my way had reality. It may be that in goodness we may see, not a reason for life nor an explanation of it, but an extenuation. In this indifferent universe, with its inevitable evils that surround us from the cradle to the grave, it may serve, not as a challenge or a reply, but as an affirmation of our own independence. It is the retort that humour makes to the tragic absurdity of fate. Unlike beauty, it can be perfect without being tedious, and, greater than love, time does not wither its delight. But goodness is shown in right action and who can tell in this meaningless world what right action is? It is not action that aims at happiness; it is a happy chance if happiness results. Plato, as we know, enjoined upon his wise man to abandon the serene life of contemplation for the turmoil of practical affairs and thereby set the claim of duty above the desire for happiness; and we have all of us, I suppose, on occasion adopted a course because we thought it right though we well knew that it could bring us happiness neither then nor in the future. What then is right action? For my own part the best answer I know is that given by Fray Luis de Leon. To follow it does not look so difficult that human weakness quails before it as beyond its strength. With it I can end my

book. The beauty of life, he says, is nothing but this, that each should act in conformity with his nature and his business.

With these words nearly twenty years ago I finished *The Summing Up*. I never read again any of my old books if I can help it and it was only lately that I re-read this one because I was told that in the printing of several new editions a number of misprints had crept in. I found that on the whole I had not much changed my mind on those great subjects of human meditation, the existence of God, immortality and the meaning and worth of life, of which Dr. Johnson said that there was nothing true to be said about them that was new and nothing new to be said that was true. In *The Summing Up* I tried to review for my own comfort what I had learnt of life and literature, what I had done and what satisfaction it had brought me. Time passed and at the age of seventy I wrote the reflections that occurred to me on reaching that stage of my life and inserted the piece I wrote at the end of a book called *A Writer's Notebook,* in which I had given a selection of the notes I had made from a very early age, which I thought might be useful to me in my profession as a writer. I have just read the piece again and in this postcript I shall ask the reader's indulgence if I repeat something of what I said in it. It was natural that I should deal with the matter of old age which many people look forward to with dismay. The greatest compensation of old age, I said, is its freedom of spirit and now, ten years older, I realize how wonderful a compensation that is. Old age liberates you from envy, hatred and malice. I do not believe that I envy anyone. I have made the most I could of such gifts as nature provided me with; I do not envy the greater gifts of others; I have had a great deal of success; I do not envy the success of others. I am quite willing to vacate the little niche I have occupied so long and let another step into it. I no longer mind what people think of me. They can take me or leave me. I am mildly pleased when they appear to like me and undisturbed when they appear not to. I have long known that there is something in me that antagonizes certain persons; I think it very natural, no one can like everyone; and their ill-will interests rather than discomposes me. I am only curious to know what it is in me that is disagreeable to them. Nor do I mind what they think of me as a writer. On the whole I have done what I set out to do and the rest does not concern me. I have never much cared for the notoriety which surrounds the successful author and which many of us are simple enough to mistake for fame, and I have often wished that I had written under an assumed name so that I might have passed through the world unnoticed.

There is one distress incident to old age, however, for which I know no remedy. I have had a great many acquaintances, but few, though devoted, friends. One by one, during the last few years, they have died. One of them had been my companion for many years on my travels round about the world and without his gift for easy comradeship with all and sundry (a gift I have never had) I would never have got the material which enabled me to write the stories on which, it may be, my reputation, if any, will rest. His death bitterly grieved me. But time is a great healer. The pain that seemed so cruel is assuaged, and now though I miss him, I can look back on him with affection and regret, with gratitude for all he did for me and for the happiness he brought me, without repining. So it is with other of my friends, and so I would wish the friends I still have to look back on me when in what must now be a very short time I leave them. Unlike old Omar, I would not even have them turn down an empty glass when "among the guests star-scattered on the grass," where I made one, they pass.

I have been asked on occasion whether I would be willing to live my life over again. On the whole it has been a pretty good one, perhaps better than that of most people, but I should see no point in repeating it. It would be as idle as to read again a detective story that you have read before. But supposing there were such a thing as reincarnation, belief in which is held by three quarters of the human race, and one could choose whether or no to enter upon a new life on earth, I have in the past sometimes thought that I would be willing to try the experiment on the chance that I might enjoy experiences which circumstances and my own idiosyncrasies, spiritual and corporeal, have prevented me from enjoying and learn the many things that I have not had the time or the opportunity to learn. But now I should refuse. I have had enough. There are indeed days when I feel that I have done everything too often, known too many people, read too many books, seen too many pictures, statues, churches and fine houses, and listened to too much music. I neither believe in immortality nor desire it. I should like to die quietly and painlessly, and I am content to be assured that with my last breath, my soul, with its aspirations and its weaknesses, will dissolve into nothingness.

Thus I wrote in *A Writer's Notebook*. We were still engaged in a war that has proved almost as disastrous for the victors as for the vanquished. I did not realize that peace would bring us not a return to the old life we had known before, but a future of anxiety and apprehension. The state is assuming ever greater power over the individual and it seems inevitable that his liberty will continue to be encroached upon. For my part I rejoice that I shall not have to cope with the regimented life that I see approaching. The survivors of the French Revolution claimed that only those who had known the world before that event knew *la douceur de vivre*. We who were in the full vigour of our youth before the First World War may not unreasonably claim that we too knew the sweetness of life. Of course I welcome the relief that has been afforded in my country to the underprivileged so that they may profit by an education that before was within reach only of the well-to-do; it is not only all to the good, but common justice, that they should be able in sickness to be cared for and after a lifetime of labour be decently provided for. To be old and poor is bad; to be dependent on charity for a roof over one's head and for bread to eat is not to be borne.

In Tolstoi's book *My Confession* he asks himself whether there is any meaning in life that can overcome the inevitable death that awaits us all, and because man is subject to illness, because he grows old, because he dies, he arrives at the conclusion that life has no meaning. I do not think that is reasonable. The human body is a mechanism and there is no more sense in supposing that it will not get out of order than to expect your car or your watch never to fail you, never to need repair, never to wear out. I have had numerous illnesses, but I have recovered from them and I do not know that they have done me harm. From some indeed I have spiritually profited. Tolstoi dreaded old age. It seems not to have occurred to him that in old age one no longer has the desires of youth. One no longer wants to do the things that make youth, with its passions, its ambitions, its curiosity, so exciting and delightful. That is not a fact. It is true that old age is accompanied by a certain indifference to things to which men in their prime attach importance. The old enjoyments remain, music, art and literature, but one enjoys them differently. If one's pleasures are not so vivid, one's pains have lost their sting. Tolstoi was obsessed by the fear of death. He might with advantage have read what Epicurus wrote to a correspondent: "Become accustomed to the belief that death is nothing to us. For all good and evil consists in sensation, but death is deprivation of sensation. And therefore a right understanding that death is nothing to us makes the mortality of life enjoyable, not because it adds to it an infinite space of time, but because it takes away the craving for immortality. For there is nothing terrible in life for the man who has truly comprehended that there is nothing terrible in not living." Tolstoi found comfort at last in the recovery of the faith he had had as a child and lost. The meaning of life, he came to believe, was to do God's will in the assurance of immortality. That surely is to admit that life in itself has no meaning. But is there any sense in asking what is the meaning of life? I should have said not more than in asking what is the meaning of Beethoven's *Eroica* or Cézanne's Mont Ste. Victoire in the Metropolitan.

I look forward to death with no apprehension. Not long ago I had a very serious illness and one morning I was so weak that I felt I had only to grow a little weaker to die. I said to myself that if dying was so easy as that I was all for it. It irked me a trifle that I should not be able to finish the book I was then engaged in writing, but then I thought it did not matter because in any case it would have been forgotten in a year or two.

I do not know whether God exists or not. None of the arguments that have been adduced to prove his existence carries conviction, and belief must rest, as Epicurus put it long ago, on immediate apprehension. That immediate apprehension I have never had. Nor has anyone satisfactorily explained the compatibility of evil with an all-powerful and all-good God. For a while I was attracted to the Hindu conception of that mysterious neuter which is existence, knowledge and bliss, without beginning, without end, and I should be more inclined to believe in that than in any other god that human wishes, and fears, have devised. But I think it no more than an impressive fantasy. When I consider the vastness of the universe, with its innumerable stars and its spaces measured by thousands upon thousands of light years, I am overwhelmed with awe, but my imagination cannot conceive a creator of it. I am willing enough to accept the existence of the universe as an enigma the wit of man cannot hope to solve. So far as the existence of life is concerned I am not disinclined to believe that there is a psychophysical stuff in which is the germ of life and that the psychic side of this is the source of the complex business of evolution. But what the object of it all is, if any, what the meaning of it all is, if any, is as dark to me as it ever was. All I know is that nothing philosophers, theologians or mystics have said about it persuades me. Of late I have read some of the works of Kierkegaard and having read them I turned back to Pascal. It seemed to me that there was little of real importance in Kierkegaard that Pascal had not already said. Both ask you to accept the premiss of a vengeful and irascible God. That is something I could never bring myself to believe. Spinoza, that God-intoxicated man, said that God has infinite attributes. Surely among them must be humour and common sense. If God exists and he concerns himself with the affairs of humanity, then surely he will take a lenient view, as lenient a view as a sensible man takes, of the weakness of human beings.

EXTRACTS FROM
"A WRITER'S NOTEBOOK"

1944

BY WAY of postscript. Yesterday I was seventy years old. As one enters upon each succeeding decade it is natural, though perhaps irrational, to look upon it as a significant event. When I was thirty my brother said to me: "Now you are a boy no longer, you are a man and you must be a man." When I was forty I said to myself: "That is the end of youth." On my fiftieth birthday I said: "It's no good fooling myself, this is middle age and I may just as well accept it." At sixty I said: "Now it's time to put my affairs in order, for this is the threshold of old age and I must settle my accounts." I decided to withdraw from the theatre and I wrote *The Summing Up*, in which I tried to review for my own comfort what I had learnt of life and literature, what I had done and what satisfaction it had brought me. But of all anniversaries I think the seventieth is the most momentous. One has reached the three score years and ten which one is accustomed to accept as the allotted span of man, and one can but look upon such years as remain to one as uncertain contingencies stolen while old Time with his scythe has his head turned the other way. At seventy one is no longer on the threshold of old age. One is just an old man.

On the continent of Europe they have an amiable custom when a man who has achieved some distinction reaches that age. His friends, his colleagues, his disciples (if he has any) join together to write a volume of essays in his honour. In England we give our eminent men no such flattering mark of our esteem. At the utmost we give a dinner, and we don't do that unless he is very eminent indeed. Such a dinner I attended when H. G. Wells attained his seventieth year. Hundreds of people came to it. Bernard Shaw, a magnificent figure with his height, his white beard and white hair, his clean skin and bright eyes, made a speech. He stood very erect, his arms crossed, and with his puckish humour said many things highly embarrassing to the guest of the evening and to sundry of his hearers. It was a most amusing discourse delivered in a resonant voice with admirable elocution, and his Irish brogue pointed and at the same time mitigated his malice. H. G., his nose in the manuscript, read his speech in a high-pitched voice. He spoke peevishly of his advanced age, and not without a natural querulousness protested against the notion any of those present might have that the anniversary, with the attendant banquet, indicated any willingness on his part to set a term to his activities. He protested that he was as ready as ever to set the world to rights.

My own birthday passed without ceremony. I worked as usual in the morning and in the afternoon went for a walk in the solitary woods behind my house. I have never been able to discover what it is that gives these woods their mysterious attractiveness. They are like no woods I have ever known. Their silence seems more intense than any other silence. The live oaks with their massive foliage are festooned with the grey of the Spanish moss as if with a ragged shroud, the gum trees at this season are bare of leaf and the clustered berries of the wild China tree are dried and yellow; here and there tall pines, their rich green flaming, tower over the lower trees. There is a strangeness about these bedraggled, abandoned woods, and though you walk alone you do not feel alone, for you have an eerie feeling that unseen beings, neither human nor inhuman, flutter about you. A shadowy something seems to slink from behind a tree trunk and watch you silently as you pass. There is a sense of suspense as though all about you there were a lying in wait for something to come.

I went back to my house, made myself a cup of tea and read till dinner time. After dinner I read again, played two or three games of patience, listened to the news on the radio and took a detective story to bed with me. I finished it and went to sleep. Except for a few words to my coloured maids I had not spoken to a soul all day.

So I passed my seventieth birthday and so I would have wished to pass it. I mused.

Two or three years ago I was walking with Liza and she spoke, I don't know why, of the horror with which the thought of old age filled her.

"Don't forget," I told her, "that when you're old you won't have the desire to do various things that make life pleasant to you now. Old age has its compensations."

"What?" she asked.

"Well, you need hardly ever do anything you don't want to. You can enjoy music, art and literature, differently from when you were young, but in that different way as keenly. You can get a good deal of fun out of observing the course of events in which you are no longer intimately concerned. If your pleasures are not so vivid your pains also have lost their sting."

My best book is generally supposed to be *Of Human Bondage*. Its sales prove that it is still widely read, and it was published thirty years ago. That is a long life for a novel. But posterity is little inclined to occupy itself with works of great length, and I take it that with the passing of the present generation, which very much to my own surprise has found it significant, it will be forgotten along with many other better books. I think that one or two of my comedies may retain for some time a kind of pale life, for they are written in the tradition of English comedy and on that account may find a place in the long line that began with the Restoration dramatists and in the plays of Noel Coward continues to please. It may be that they will secure me a line or two in the histories of the English theatre. I think a few of my best stories will find their way into anthologies for a good many years to come if only because some of them deal with circumstances and places to which the passage of time and the growth of civilisation will give a romantic glamour. This is slender baggage, two or three plays and a dozen short stories, with which to set out on a journey to the future, but it is better than nothing. And if I am mistaken and I am forgotten a month after my death I shall know nothing about it.

Ten years ago I made my final bow on the stage (metaphorically speaking, for after my first plays I refused to expose myself to the indignity of this proceeding); the Press and my friends thought I did not mean it and in a year or so would emerge from my retirement; but I never have, nor have I had any inclination to do so. Some years ago I decided to write four more novels and then have done with fiction also. One I have written. (I do not count a war novel that I wrote as part of the war work I was asked to do in America and which I found a weariness to do), but I think it unlikely now that I shall write the other three. One was to be a miracle story set in sixteenth-century Spain; the second, a story of Machiavelli's stay with Cesare Borgia in the Romagna, which gave him the best of his material for *The Prince*, and I proposed to interweave with their conversations the material on which he founded his play *Mandragola*. Knowing how often the author makes up his fiction from incidents of his own experience, trifling perhaps and made interesting or dramatic only by his power of creation, I thought it would be amusing to reverse the process and from the play guess at the events that may have occasioned it. I meant to end up with a novel about a working-class family in the slums of Bermondsey. I thought it would form a pleasing termination to my career to finish with the same sort of story of the shiftless poor of London as I had begun with fifty years before. But I am content now to keep these three novels as an amusement for my idle reveries. That is how the author gets most delight out of his books; when once he has written them they are his no longer and he can no more entertain himself with the conversations and actions of the persons of his fancy. Nor do I think I am likely at the age of seventy or over to write anything of any great

value. Incentive fails, energy fails, invention fails. The histories of literature with pitying sympathy sometimes, but more often with a curt indifference, dismiss the works of even the greatest writers' old age, and I have myself sadly witnessed the lamentable falling off of talented authors among my friends who went on writing when their powers were but a shadow of what they had been. The best of the communications an author has to make is to his own generation, and he is wise to let the generation that succeeds his choose its own exponents. They will do it whether he lets them or not. His language will be Greek to them. I do not think I can write anything more that will add to the pattern I have sought to make of my life and its activities. I have fulfilled myself and I am very willing to call it a day.

One sign that calls my attention to the notion that I am wise to do so is that whereas I have always lived more in the future than in the present, I have for some time now found myself more and more occupied with the past. Perhaps it is but natural when the future must inevitably be so short and the past is so long. I have always made plans ahead and generally carried them out; but who can make plans now? Who can tell what next year or the year after will bring, what one's circumstances will be and if it will be possible to live as one lived before? The sailing-boat in which I used to like to lounge about on the blue waters of the Mediterranean has been seized by the Germans, my car has been taken by the Italians, my house has been occupied by the Italians and now by the Germans, and my furniture, books and pictures, if they have not been looted, are scattered here and there. But no one can be more indifferent to all this than I.

I have enjoyed every luxury that man can desire, and a couple of rooms to myself, three meals a day and access to a good library will sufficiently satisfy my wants.

My reveries tend often to be concerned with my long past youth. I have done various things I regret, but I make an effort not to let them fret me; I say to myself that it is not I who did them, but the different I that I was then. I injured some, but since I could not repair the injuries I had done I have tried to make amends by benefiting others. At times I reflect somewhat ruefully on the opportunities for sexual congress that I missed when I was of an age to enjoy them; but I know that I couldn't help missing them, for I was always squeamish, and when it came to the point a physical repulsion often prevented me from entering upon an adventure that beforehand had fired my imagination with desire. I have been more chaste than I wished to be. Most people talk too much and old age is loquacious. Though I have always been more disposed to listen than to talk, it has seemed to me of late that I was falling into the defect of garrulity, and I no sooner noticed it than I took care to correct it. For the old man is on sufferance and he must walk warily. He should try not to make a nuisance of himself. He is indiscreet to force his company on the young, for he puts them under a constraint, they cannot be quite themselves with him, and he must be obtuse if he does not detect that his departure will be a relief to them. If he has made some stir in the world they will on occasion seek his society, but he is foolish should he fail to see that it is not for its own sake, but that they may go and prattle about it afterward with friends of their own age. To them he is a mountain you have climbed not for the fun of the ascent or for the view you may get from the top, but so that you may recount your exploit when you have come down again. The old man is well advised to frequent the society of his contemporaries, and he is lucky if he can get any amusement out of that. It is certainly depressing to be bidden to a party where there is no one but has one foot in the grave. Fools don't become less foolish when they grow old, and an old fool is infinitely more tiresome than a young one. I don't know which are more intolerable, the old people who have refused to surrender to the assault of time and behave with a nauseous frivolity, or those fast-rooted in times gone by who have no patience with a world that has refused to stand still with them. These things being so, it might seem a poor lookout for the old man, when the young do not want his company and he finds that of his contemporaries tedious. Nothing remains to him then but his own, and I look upon it as singularly fortunate that none has ever been so enduringly satisfactory to me as mine. I have never liked large gatherings of my fellow creatures, and I regard it as not the least of the compensations of old age that I can make it an excuse either to refuse to go to parties or slink away quietly when they have ceased to entertain me. Now that solitude is more and more forced upon me I am more and more content with it. Last year I spent some weeks by myself in a little house on the banks of the Combahee river, seeing no one, and I was neither lonely nor bored. It was indeed with reluctance that I returned to New York when the heat and the anopheles obliged me to abandon my retreat.

It is strange how long it can take one to become aware of the benefits a kindly nature has bestowed on one. It is only recently that it occurred to me how lucky I was never to have suffered from head-aches, stomach-aches or tooth-aches. I read the other day that Cardan in his autobiography, written when he was approaching eighty, congratulated himself on still having fifteen teeth. I have just counted mine and find that I have twenty-six. I have had many severe illnesses, tuberculosis, dysentery, malaria and I know not what, but I have neither drunk too much nor eaten too much, and I am sound in wind and limb. It is evident that one cannot expect to get much satisfaction out of old age unless one has fairly good health; nor unless one has an adequate income. It need not be a large one, for one's wants are few. Vice is expensive, and in old age it is easy to be virtuous. But to be poor and old is bad; to be dependent on others for the necessities of life is worse: I am grateful for the favour of the public which enables me not only to live in comfort, but to gratify my whims and to provide for those who have claims upon me. Old men are inclined to be avaricious. They are prone to use their money to retain their power over those dependent on them. I do not find in myself any impulse to succumb to these infirmities. I have a good memory, except for names and faces, and I do not forget what I have read. The disadvantage of this is that having read all the great novels of the world two or three times I can no longer read them with relish. There are few modern novels that excite my interest, and I do not know what I should do for relaxation were it not for the innumerable detective stories that so engagingly pass the time and once read pass straight out of one's mind. I have never cared to read books on subjects that were in no way my concern, and I still cannot bring myself to read books of entertainment or instruction about people or places that mean nothing to me. I do not want to know the history of Siam or the manners and customs of the Esquimaux, I do not want to read a life of Manzoni, and my curiosity about stout Cortez is satisfied with the fact that he stood upon a peak in Darien. I can still read with pleasure the poets that I read in my youth and with interest the poets of today. I am glad to have lived long enough to read the later poems of Yeats and Eliot. I can read everything that pertains to Dr. Johnson and almost everything that pertains to Coleridge, Byron and Shelley. Old age robs one of the thrill one had when first one read the great masterpieces of the world; that one can never recapture. It is sad, indeed, to reread something that at one time had made one feel like Keats's Watcher of the Skies and be forced to the conclusion that after all it's not so much. But there is one subject with which I can still occupy myself with my old excitement, and that is philosophy, not the philosophy that is disputatious and aridly technical—"Vain is the word of a philosopher which does not heal any suffering of man"—but the philosophy that treats the problems that confront us all. Plato, Aristotle (who they say is dry, but in whom if you have a sense of humour you can find quite a lot to amuse you), Plotinus and Spinoza, with sundry moderns, among whom Bradley and Whitehead, never cease to entertain me and incite me to reflection. After all, they and the Greek tragedians deal with the only things that are important to man. They exalt and tranquillise. To read them is to sail with a gentle breeze in an inland sea studded with a thousand isles.

Ten years ago I set down haltingly

in *The Summing Up* such impressions and thoughts as experience, reading and my meditations had occasioned in me concerning God, immortality and the meaning and worth of life, and I do not know that on these matters I have since then found cause to change my mind. If I had to write it over again I should try to deal a little less superficially with the pressing subject of values and perhaps find something less haphazard to say about intuition, a subject upon which certain philosophers have reared an imposing edifice of surmise, but which seems to me to offer as insecure a foundation for any structure more substantial than a Castle in Spain as a ping-pong ball wavering on a jet of water in a shooting-gallery.

Now that I am ten years nearer to death I look forward to it with no more apprehension than I did then. There are indeed days when I feel that I have done everything too often, known too many people, read too many books, seen too many pictures, statues, churches and fine houses, and listened to too much music.

And what of the soul? The Hindus call it the Atman, and they think it has existed from eternity and will continue to exist to eternity. It is easier to believe that than that it is created with the conception or birth of the individual. They think it is of the nature of Absolute Reality, and having emanated from that will at long last return to it. It is a pleasing fancy; no one can know that it is anything more. It entails the belief in transmigration, which in turn offers the only plausible explanation for the existence of evil that human ingenuity has conceived, for it supposes that evil is the retribution for past error. It does not explain why an all-wise and all-good creator should have been willing or even able to produce error.

But what is the soul? From Plato onwards many answers have been given to this question, and most of them are but modifications of his conjectures. We use the word constantly, and it must be presumed that we mean something by it. Christianity has accepted it as an article of faith that the soul is a simple spiritual substance created by God and immortal. One may not believe that and yet attach some signification to the word. When I ask myself what I mean by it I can only answer that I mean by it my consciousness of myself, the I in me, the personality which is me; and that personality is compounded of my thoughts, my feelings, my experiences and the accidents of my body. I think many people shrink from the notion that the accidents of the body can have an effect on the constitution of the soul. There is nothing of which for my own part I am more assured. My soul would have been quite different if I had not stammered or if I had been four or five inches taller; I am slightly prognathous; in my childhood they did not know that this could be remedied by a gold band worn while the jaw is still malleable; if they had, my countenance would have borne a different cast, the reaction toward me of my fellows would have been different and therefore my disposition, my attitude to them, would have been different too. But what sort of thing is this soul that can be modified by a dental apparatus? We all know how greatly changed our lives would have been if we had not by what seems mere chance met such and such a person or if we had not been at a particular moment at a particular place; and so our character, and so our soul, would have been other than they are.

For whether the soul is a conglomeration of qualities, affections, idiosyncrasies, I know not what, or a simple spiritual substance, character is its sensible manifestation. I suppose everyone would agree that suffering, mental or physical, has its effect on the character. I have known men who when poor and unrecognised were envious, harsh and mean, but on achieving success became kindly and magnanimous. Is it not strange that a bit of money in the bank and a taste of fame should give them greatness of soul? Contrariwise I have known men who were decent and honourable, in illness or penury become lying, deceitful, querulous and malevolent. I find it then impossible to believe that the soul thus contingent on the accidents of the body can exist in separation from it. When you see the dead it can hardly fail to occur to you that they do look awfully dead.

It is five years since I wrote the above piece. I have not altered it, though I have since written three of the four novels of which I spoke; the fourth I shall leave unwritten. When I came back to England after my long sojourn in the United States and revisited the part of London in which I proposed to situate my story and renewed my acquaintance with the people some of whom were to serve as models for my characters I found that great changes had taken place. Bermondsey was no longer the Bermondsey I had known. The war had destroyed much; there had been grave loss of life; but there was no longer the unemployment the fear of which had hung, a black cloud, over the lives of my friends, and they dwelt no longer in bug-ridden tenements, but in neat and tidy council flats. They had a radio and a piano and went to the movies twice a week. They were no longer members of the proletariat, but of the petty bourgeoisie. But these changes, all to the good, were not the only ones I found. The spirit of the people was different. Whereas in the bad old days, notwithstanding the hardships and privation they endured, they were gay and friendly, now their lives were sadly embittered by envy, hatred and malice. They had not been discontented with their lot; now they were filled with resentment against those who enjoyed advantages of which they were deprived. They were sullen and dissatisfied. The mother of a family, a charwoman by occupation, whom I had known for many years, told me: "They've cleaned up the slums and the dirt, and all the happiness and joy has gone with it." I entered upon a world that was strange to me. I have no doubt that it still offers ample material for a novel, but that which I had in mind was a picture of conditions that have ceased to exist, and I see no point in writing it.

During the last five years I have perhaps learnt a little more than I knew before. Through a chance encounter with an eminent biologist I was led to make myself at least superficially acquainted with the philosophy of organism. It is an instructive and absorbing subject. It liberates the spirit. Men of science seem to be agreed that at some remote period this earth of ours will cease to support even the most elementary forms of life; but long before this state is reached the human race will have become extinct, as have so many species of living creatures which could not adapt themselves to a changing environment. The conclusion can hardly escape one that then all this business of evolution will have been singularly futile and, indeed, that the process that led to the creation of man was a stupendous absurdity on the part of nature, stupendous in the sense that the volcano at Kilauea in eruption or the Mississippi in flood is stupendous, but an absurdity all the same. For no sensible person can deny that throughout the history of the world the sum of unhappiness has been far, far greater than the sum of happiness. Only in brief periods has man lived save in continual fear and danger of violent death, and it is not only in the savage state, as Hobbes asserted, that his life has been solitary, poor, nasty, brutish and short. Throughout the ages many have found in the belief in a life to come an adequate compensation for the troubles of their brief sojourn in a world of sorrow. They are the lucky ones. Faith, to those who have it, solves difficulties which reason finds insoluble. Some have ascribed to art a value which is its own justification and persuaded themselves that the wretched lot of the common run of men was not too high a price to pay for the radiant productions of painter and poet.

I look askance at such an attitude. It seems to me that the philosophers were right who claimed that the value of art lies in its effects and from this drew the corollary that its value lies not in beauty, but in right action. For an effect is idle unless it is effective. If art is no more than a pleasure, no matter how spiritual, it is of no great consequence: it is like the sculptures on the capitals of columns that support a mighty arch; they delight the eye by their grace and variety, but serve no functional purpose. Art, unless it leads to right action, is no more than the opium of an intelligentsia.

It is not in art then that one may hope to find some assuagement to the pessimism that long ago found immortal expression in the Book of Ecclesiastes. I think there is in the heroic courage with which man confronts the irrationality of the world a beauty greater than the beauty of art. I find it in the defiant gesture of Paddy Finucane when, plunging to his death, he transmitted the message to the airmen in his squadron: "This is it, chaps." I find it in the cool determination of Captain Oates when he went out to his death in the arctic night rather than be a burden to his comrades. I find it in the loyalty of Helen Vagliano, a woman not very young, not very pretty, not very intelligent, who suffered hellish torture and accepted death, for a country not her own, rather than betray her friends. In a famous passage Pascal wrote: *"L'homme n'est qu'un roseau, le plus foible de la nature, mais c'est un roseau pensant. Il ne faut pas que l'univers entier s'arme pour l'écraser. Une vapeur, une goutte d'eau, suffit pour le tuer. Mais quand l'univers l'écraseroit, l'homme seroit encore plus noble que ce qui le tue, parce qu'il meurt; et l'avantage que l'univers a sur lui, l'univers n'en sait rien. Toute notre dignité consiste donc en la pensée."* Is that true? Surely not. I think there is some disparagement to-day in the notion of dignity, and I believe that the French word is better translated into English by nobility. There is a nobility which does not proceed from thought. It is more elemental. It depends neither on culture nor breeding. It has its roots among the most primitive instincts of the human being. Faced with it, God, if he had created man, might hide his head in shame. It may be that in the knowledge that man for all his weakness and sin is capable on occasion of such splendour of spirit, one may find some refuge from despair.

But these are grave subjects for which, even if I had the capacity to deal with them, this is not the place. For I am like a passenger waiting for his ship at a war-time port. I do not know on which day it will sail, but I am ready to embark at a moment's notice. I leave the sights of the city unvisited. I do not want to see the fine new speedway along which I shall never drive, nor the grand new theatre, with all its modern appliances, in which I shall never sit. I read the papers and flip the pages of a magazine, but when someone offers to lend me a book I refuse because I may not have time to finish it, and in any case with this journey before me I am not of a mind to interest myself in it. I strike up acquaintances at the bar or the card-table, but I do not try to make friends with people from whom I shall so soon be parted. I am on the wing.